Atlas of Polymer and Plastics Analysis

HUMMEL/SCHOLL

Atlas of Polymer and Plastics Analysis

Second, completely revised edition

Vol. 1 Polymers: Structures and Spectra

By Prof. Dr. Dieter O. Hummel, Cologne

Vol. 2 Plastics, Fibres, Rubbers, Resins

Spectra and Methods of Identification

By Prof. Dr. Dieter O. Hummel, Cologne

Vol. 3 Additives and Processing Aids

Spectra and Methods of Identification

By Dr. Friedrich Scholl, Stuttgart

Carl Hanser Verlag · Munich · Vienna
VCH Verlagsgesellschaft · Weinheim
VCH Publishers · Deerfield Beach, Florida

HUMMEL/SCHOLL

Atlas of Polymer and Plastics Analysis

Second, completely revised edition

Vol. 1
Polymers: Structures and Spectra

By Prof. Dr. Dieter O. Hummel, Cologne

Carl Hanser Verlag · Munich · Vienna
VCH Verlagsgesellschaft · Weinheim
VCH Publishers · Deerfield Beach, Florida

Prof. Dr. Dieter O. Hummel
Institut für Physikalische Chemie der Universität Köln
Luxemburger Straße 116
D-5000 Köln 41, Germany

2nd, completely revised Edition 1978
1st Reprint 1985, of the 2nd, completely revised Edition 1978

Editorial Director: Dr. Hans F. Ebel

This book contains 1903 spectra

Deutsche Bibliothek, Cataloguing – in – Publication Data

Atlas of polymer and plastics analysis / Hummel; Scholl. – Munich;
Vienna: Hanser; Weinheim; Deerfield Beach, Fl.: VCH
   Dt. Ausg. u. d. T.: Atlas der Polymer- und Kunststoffanalyse

NE: Hummel, Dieter O. [Mitverf.]; Scholl, Friedrich [Mitverf.]

Vol. 1. Polymers: structures and spectra / by Dieter O. Hummel. –
1. reprint of the 2., completely rev. ed. – 1985.

   ISBN 3-446-12590-6 (Hanser);
   ISBN 3-527-25801-9 (VCH, Weinheim ...)
   ISBN 0-89573-001-4 (VCH, Deerfield Beach, Fl. ...)

Composition: Hans Richarz, D-5205 St. Augustin. Printing: Zechner-
sche Buchdruckerei, D-6720 Speyer. Bookbinding: Buchbinderei Josef
Spinner, D-7583 Ottersweier. Process engraving: Georg Gehringer
GmbH, D-6750 Kaiserslautern
Printed in the Federal Republic of Germany

Preface to the Second Edition

Ten years have passed since the first edition of "Atlas der Kunststoff-Analyse" was published, and twenty since the publication of the first – and only – edition of "Kunststoff-, Lack- und Gummi-Analyse". That is a long time and it moves us to quote from Goethe's "Faust":

Oh dear! Art lasts a long time
But life is short.

The "art", *i.e.* the infra-red-spectroscopic analysis of polymers, has proved to be long-lived and it will always assume an important position among physical methods of analyzing macromolecular systems. It has changed, however, the better we learned to understand it, even in competition with other analytical techniques. It has disappeared from certain areas, *e.g.* the field of stereo-regularity, where high-resolution nuclear resonance spectroscopy has celebrated its greatest triumphs. In other fields the technique was able to become more firmly established, *e.g.* in the identification of structural units in complex macromolecular systems and in the vibrational analysis of highly ordered polymer systems.

One special challenge was the unique activity in the synthesis field during the past fifteen years or so. Satellites and spaceships made most unusual demands on the materials of which they and their equipment were made, *e.g.* resistance to heat, cold, radiation and light. But new products were required also for applications here on earth, and fundamental research brought forth interesting new polymers which could be used – or are already being used – as ion exchangers, redox resins, semi-conductors, carriers for pharmaceutical preparations, or enzymes. Thus, dozens of new polymeric compound groups, including exotic ones like polycarboranes or organo-metallic polymers, have been developed and modified and combined in so many different ways that we are now able to name and describe thousands of chemically different polymers.

What this meant to the analyst and, especially, the IR spectroscopist, was already clear when the first edition of the "Atlas" was published: an attempt had to be made to produce a systematically arranged collection of IR spectra of defined polymers described in the literature. This is more easily said than done, but the result was a veritable avalanche of letters which descended upon thousands of authors all over the world. Many – indeed very many – replied, sent reprints of articles and samples as well as giving important additional information about the synthesis and structure of the polymers. This success gave me courage and filled me with gratitude. It is impossible to name the many people who helped me, in this preface – but their names can be found in the captions to the various spectra and in the author index. My heartfelt thanks to all of them, for the great patience with which they dealt with my enquiries. But not only individuals gave me assistance – public institutions, research institutes of the US Air Force, the Academy of Sciences of the GDR and the Soviet Union, NASA, the Bulgarian, Polish and Romanian People's Republics all helped and supplied me with new polymers. Perhaps I can take this opportunity to ask all colleagues working in the field of synthetics to make available for the next edition any defined polymers not to be found in this Atlas.

The decision as to which polymers to select was determined first and foremost by the cooperation of the authors in making samples available, as well as by the inevitable limitation of literature searches in the publications available to us. Quite a few spectra are therefore missing, despite the fact that the polymers on which these are based are important and interesting. On the other hand, a great deal of space has been given to certain polymer groups (aliphatic polyethers and polyesters, modified polyurethanes) because the possibility of systematic comparison of the spectra of homologous series (also in different states) or systematically altered copolymers seemed to justify it. We also hope that a certain amount of duplication or even triplication will be forgiven: polyvinyl chloride, polyphenylacetylene and many such designations only give an approximation of a particular structure so that it was thought right to reproduce the spectra of polymers bearing the same name but coming from different laboratories, especially in those cases where the polymers had been synthesized by different methods. Finally, the observant reader will notice that there are occasional discrepancies between a spectrum and the indicated structure. Here we were dealing with syntheses which resulted in poorly defined products. The authors concerned (or I myself) wanted at least to indicate one of the possible structures, however.

When determining the various spectra we were extremely careful about the method of sample preparation and the condition of the spectrometer. Many spectra were determined twice or three times before they were included. Nonetheless, it was quite often necessary to compromise in order to keep the time and effort expended within reasonable limits. We avoided the use of specialized techniques (ATR, FMIR) – with a few exceptions – in order to maintain the possibility of direct comparison. Conversion of the entire assembly of data to linear wavelength abscissae was inevitable because prism instruments had been replaced by grating-type instruments so that, at the beginning of the seventies, the majority of spectroscopic laboratories was equipped with wavelength-linear instruments. Most of the spectra in this volume were scanned with the Beckman Spectrophotometer IR-12, a smaller number (especially those at low and high temperatures) with models 125 and 325 made by Bodenseewerk Perkin-Elmer.

I had to forgo a detailed discussion of the spectra now available or even a discussion of the spectral characteristics of the most important groups of compounds, however important I considered them to be: they would have delayed the publication of this volume by several years and thus have done considerable harm to its actuality. Instead, as much information about the structure, synthesis and literature relating to a particular polymer as could be accomodated and reasonably expected, has been given in the captions. Since there is a wealth of literature[*] on the fundamentals of infra-red spectroscopy, the correlation of IR spectra with organic structures, and finally on the chemical and spectroscopic techniques of polymer analysis, the above-mentioned gaps are not, perhaps, so serious. I hope those of my colleagues whose books I have not mentioned in the footnote will forgive me: their works will be found in the bibliography.

One major problem was the systematic arrangement of the spectral material according to chemical points of view and the creation of additional principles which not only would enable the spectra of certain groups of compounds to be found, but also the spectra of defined, individual polymers, however complex their structure. First of all, a "linear" decimal classification was produced according to element composition and chemical structure, after which the spectra were arranged, and which serves above all to find certain groups of substances. Then, the chemical names of the polymers were arranged alphabetically, using not only the former nomenclature (*e.g.* "polymethyl methacrylate") but also the new names recommended by a nomenclature commission of the IUPAC[**], *e.g.* {poly[1-(methoxycarbonyl)-1-methyl ethylene]} (insofar as these could be used without much difficulty). It was, however, found that the usefulness of this kind of alphabetical list, according to the first letter of a frequently un-

---

[*] N. B. COLTHUP, L. H. DALY and S. E. WIBERLEY: Introduction to Infrared and Raman Spectroscopy, 2nd ed. Academic Press, New York 1975.

J. DECHANT, R. DANZ, W. KIMMER and R. SCHMOLKE: Ultrarotspektroskopische Untersuchungen an Polymeren. Akademie-Verlag, Berlin 1972.

J. HASLAM, H. A. WILLIS and D. C. M. SQUIRRELL: Identification and Analysis of Plastics, 2nd ed. Iliffe Books, London 1972.

M. HOFMANN, H. KRÖMER and R. KUHN: Polymeranalytik (2 vols.). G. Thieme, Stuttgart 1977.

D. O. HUMMEL (ed.): Polymer Spectroscopy. Verlag Chemie, Weinheim 1974.

K. J. IVIN (ed.): Structural Studies of Macromolecules by Spectroscopic Methods. John Wiley, London–New York 1976.

[**] International Union of Pure and Applied Chemistry, IUPAC Macromolecular Division; Tentative Nomenclature of Regular Single-Strand Organic Polymers, J. Polymer Sci., Polym. Lett. Ed. **11** (1973), pp. 389–414.

V

important structural characteristic, is limited. We therefore decided to produce an additional index of empirical formulae giving the elementary constitution of one or more repeating structural units. The others can be easily found with the help of the empirical formula.

Most of the spectra were measured by ELSBETH ZOSCHKE and ILSE VIERLING. The manuscript was typed by ANGELIKA RÖMER and HELGA GRAFF. W. STACH and K. VAN WERDEN helped in the difficult task of selecting the right decimal figures. They also helped (together with H. GRAFF) in the proof reading and the production of the index. I extend my thanks to all these colleagues – and to all others who have not been mentioned – for their diligence, stamina and patience (not least with the author).

What of the future? The "Atlas" — as is clear from the new title — has been extended by another volume, this present one. The second volume, like volume I of the first edition, will deal with the analysis of plastics, fibres, rubbers, and resins in the widest possible sense. A third and final volume will be written by F. SCHOLL (like volume II of the first edition) and deal with the analysis of auxiliary substances.

One more word of thanks, addressed to all the many users of the "Atlas" who wrote to me or who talked to me, who pointed out errors or suggested improvements, and who encouraged me to proceed with my labours; please do continue to help us in the future.

Cologne, Summer 1978   *D. O. Hummel*

Preface to the First Edition

Ten years ago, "Kunststoff-, Lack- und Gummi-Analyse" was published. It was a small edition, and stocks were soon exhausted. The purpose of the book was to show that macromolecular systems can be quickly and reliably identified by a combination of chemical and infra-red spectroscopic techniques. This has by now become an accepted fact and need no longer be proved. What new ideas have then determined the form of the present Atlas?

One of the conditions underlying the Atlas was that it should contain all the technically important information on the subject and as many scientifically interesting examples as possible. On the other hand, duplication had to be avoided. The industrial polymers and resins were not selected on the basis of "who makes what?" but rather on the principle of "what can be achieved?". Finally, the arrangement had to be so systematic that any particular group of substances would be easy to find. The result was a collection of around 1700 spectra and a three-digit decimal classification, i.e. one decimal place more than 10 years ago.

The question that had to be resolved was whether to reproduce the spectra linearly in wavelengths or as wave numbers. Without doubt, a linear frequency scale over the entire IR range i.e. from $10,000 \, cm^{-1}$ (NIR) to about $40 \, cm^{-1}$ (FIR) would be ideal. There are, indeed, spectrographs on the market today with which one can almost achieve this objective. Anyone owning such an instrument and not put off by the considerable technical difficulties in preparing samples for analysis in the near and far infra-red range, could obtain a wealth of material for scientific discussion. For the practical analyst, however, it is the middle IR from $4000 \, cm^{-1}$ to $400 \, cm^{-1}$ which continues to provide the greatest amount of information. The materials considered show about ten times as many bands as the following decimal group ($400 \ldots 40 \, cm^{-1}$) and this range has been far better investigated than the near infra-red.

The reason why the spectral material (in contrast to the spectra of Part II by F. Scholl) has been reproduced here mainly on a linear wavelength scale is essentially historical. When we began compiling the spectral data we had at our disposal the Leitz Spectrograph III ($2 \ldots 15 \, \mu$), which we were able to exchange a little later for the Grating Spectrograph III G. At that time (1963) more than 90% of all IR spectrographs sold were calibrated linearly in wavelengths so that most industrial analysts had become used to wavelength-linear spectra. Moreover, we felt that the spectrograph used offered a good compromise between spectroscopic quality (resolution, measuring range, signal-to-noise ratio and variability) on the one hand and rugged construction on the other.

The past decade has seen the publication of a number of outstanding books on the analytical chemistry of polymers and resins. There was justification, therefore, for giving only a relatively brief account in this book of the methods of chemical analysis. Another question under discussion was whether simple physical constants should be incorporated in tabular form and briefly discussed. Since properties such as thermal behaviour, density, refractive index and solubility contain valuable analytical information, the decision was positive. The same applies to a number of physico-chemical techniques (gas, paper and thin-layer chromatography, pyrolysis mass spectrometry) which are ideally suited for backing up and supplementing spectroscopic results. It was essential therefore to include these techniques.

Several excellent books have also been published on the IR spectroscopic identification and analysis of high polymers and resins, notably those by Haslam and Willis, Henniker and Zbinden. In these books, the main or exclusive emphasis was placed on the text, so that we were able to use another approach, i.e. to reserve the greater part of the work for spectral details laying less emphasis on descriptions of fundamentals and techniques of IR spectroscopy.

I should like to thank the reviewers of "Kunststoff-, Lack- und Gummi-Analyse" for numerous suggestions and welcome criticism. As a result of their comments, more attention has now been paid to copolymers than before (C. E. Schildknecht, H. Schlenk), tables of physical constants have been added (R. Reichherzer), a complete chapter on gas chromatography has been added (G. Salomon, H. Luther) and the decimal classification of the substances discussed has been expanded and freed of major discrepancies (J. Derkosch, H. Schlenk). Following a suggestion by J. Haslam, the bibliography was expanded and arranged systematically. I should like to thank H. Luther for drawing my attention to a few serious and several inadvertent errors; this time we paid even more attention to solvent residues in our preparations.

Much still remains to be desired. What the reader will miss most of all is accurate quantitative data, e.g. a table giving the maximum and integral extinction coefficients of analytical bands for specially important constituents of paint and varnish resins. Those who are familiar with these problems will understand why we have restricted ourselves in this respect. An enormous amount of effort is needed here in order to work out really reliable data and specifications – and this we could not afford, despite the extremely attractive and stimulating nature of the subject.

In producing this work I have often unduly taxed the patience and forbearance of many friends in both industry and universities, without whose unfailing help and advice I should have achieved but little. My special thanks are due to the following: K. Hultzsch, Chemische Werke Albert, E. Knappe, Glasurit-Werke, I. O. Salyer, Monsanto Research Corp., C. E. Schildknecht, Gettysburgh College, Pa., Paul Schneider, Farbenfabriken Bayer, Leverkusen, R. C. Schulz, Universität Mainz, and R. Seidler, Firma Herberts. I am equally indebted to Burgunde Hirzinger, Ute Morlock and Elsbeth Zoschke, who carried out the spectroscopic work and also did the corrections. My colleagues E. Lünebach, U. Pohl, R. Schürmann and F. Winther helped with difficult preparations, the solution of spectroscopic problems and in compiling the bibliography. My very special thanks are due to the Fachgruppe "Kunststoffe und Kautschuk" of the Gesellschaft Deutscher Chemiker, for giving our work financial support. The scientific programme "Copolymers" was generously supported by the Deutsche Forschungsgemeinschaft. Agfa-Gevaert kindly supplied photographic paper for our spectrum card index. Last but not least, I should like to thank all those firms which helped us by supplying samples and very often also giving valuable advice.

D. O. Hummel

Contents

Contents

Arrangement of Spectra

The substances described in "Atlas of Polymer and Plastics Analysis" are divided into three large groups:

Volume 1: Defined polymers.

Volume 2: Macromolecular substances for technical applications, low molecular raw materials and auxiliaries.

Volume 3: Additives and processing aids.

The large number of chemical structures in polymers produced through fundamental research and technology, coupled with the necessity of classifying these polymers according to their chemical constitution so as to leave as little doubt as possible, led to the development of a new decimal classification system. This was intended to show difficult-to-connect properties:

Completeness as regards the structures to be classified.

Limited demand for decimal places in view of the system's use in electronic data processing.

Absolute clarity as a condition for the quick decimalization of spectra according to the structure of the polymer concerned.

Use of technical characteristics (Volume 2) in addition to structural characteristics.

It is easy to see that, with so many different requirements, a compromise has had to be made which relativized each of these requirements. The system undoubtedly does not contain all the structures encountered in polymers, although (for homopolymers) it can generally manage with ten decimal places. This, again, is such a far-reaching classification that the demand for clarity was probably the one that was least respected. It was possible to maintain clarity in the simpler structures, but in the case of more complex ones and those which are not explicitly contained in the system, there may be problems which, however, can usually be overcome by dispensing with a few decimal places. The combination of technical and chemical characteristics was the easiest to realize.

The fundamental principle underlying the division according to chemical points of view was the constitution according to elements, given in alphabetical order. The halogens were given the common symbol Hal, but have been listed in the order of increasing atomic number rather than alphabetically. The number of different elements in the structural unit (repeating structure) also gave the first digit in the numerical sequence for the chemical structure. Since there are but few elements which are capable of forming macromolecules on their own (C, S), the number 1 was reserved for the group "macromolecular substances for technical applications, low molecular raw materials and auxiliaries" (Volume 2). This group was then further sub-divided according to application features: plastics and fibres, rubbers, resins, adhesives, vegetable oils and waxes, hardeners, surfactants, low-molecular raw materials and degradation products, commonly used solvents. Following this, substances were classified according to chemical considerations, this classification closely following that of defined polymers.

In the case of defined polymers, a maximum of 6 different elements in the structural unit was taken into account. This resulted in the following decimal numbers together with the appropriate element symbols:

2 Polymers made up of 2 elements
  2.1 CH
  2.2 CHal
    2.2.1 CF
    2.2.2 CCl
    2.2.3 CBr
    2.2.4 CI
  2.3 CN

3 Polymers made up of 3 elements
  3.1 CHHal
    3.1.1 CHF
    3.1.2 CHCl
    3.1.3 CHBr
    3.1.4 CHI
  3.2 CHN
  3.3 CHO
  3.4 CHS
  3.5 CHalX (X ≠ H)
    3.5.1 CHalHal'
      3.5.1.1 CFCl
      3.5.1.2 CFBr
      3.5.1.3 CFI
      3.5.1.4 CClBr
      3.5.1.5 CClI
      3.5.1.6 CBrI
    3.5.2 CHalN (sub-division as for **3.1**)
    3.5.3 CHalO (sub-division as for **3.1**)
    3.5.4 CHalS (sub-division as for **3.1**)
  3.6 CNO
  3.7 CNS

4 Polymers made up of 4 elements
  4.1 CHHalX
    4.1.1 CHHalHal' (sub-division as for **3.5.1**)
    4.1.2 CHHalN (sub-division as for **3.1**)
    4.1.3 CHHalO (sub-division as for **3.1**)
    4.1.4 CHHalS (sub-division as for **3.1**)
  4.2 CHNX
    4.2.1 CHNO
    4.2.2 CHNS
  4.3 CHOS
  4.4 CHalNX
    4.4.1 CHalNO (sub-division as for **3.1**)
    4.4.2 CHalNS (sub-division as for **3.1**)

5 Polymers made up of 5 elements
  5.1 CHHalXY
    5.1.1 CHHalHal' (sub-division as for **3.5.1**)
    5.1.2 CHHalNO (sub-division as for **3.1**)
    5.1.3 CHHalOS (sub-division as for **3.1**)
  5.2 CHNOS

6 Polymers made up of 6 elements
  6.1 CHHalHal'NO (sub-division as for **3.5.1**)
  6.2 CHHalHal'NS (sub-division as for **3.5.1**)
  6.3 CHHalNOS (sub-division as for **3.1**)

The first digits 7 to 9 no longer stand for the number of different elements in the structural unit of the polymer. In order to make spectroscopically or chemically/analytically important, correlated groups easier to find, the following divisions and sub-divisions were made:

7 Deuterated polymers
  7.1 D—C(X, Y, Z ...)
    7.1.1 D—C
    7.1.2 D—CX
      7.1.2.1 D—CHal (sub-division as for **3.1**)
      7.1.2.2 D—CN
      7.1.2.3 D—CO
      7.1.2.4 D—CS
    7.1.3 D—CXY
      7.1.3.1 D—CHalX
        7.1.3.1.1 D—CHalHal' (sub-division as for **4.1.1**)
        7.1.3.1.2 D—CHalN (sub-division as for **4.1.2**)
        7.1.3.1.3 D—CHalO (sub-division as for **4.1.3**)
        7.1.3.1.4 D—CHalS (sub-division as for **4.1.4**)
      7.1.3.2 D—CNX
      7.1.3.3 D—COS
    7.1.4 D—CXYZ

Metal ions (in salts of polymeric acids) and *halogen ions* (in salts of polymeric bases) are not included with their symbols in the series of the other elements, but attached to the element symbol with a hyphen, *e.g.* CHO-Na (Na polyacrylate), CHN-Cl (polyvinyl pyridinium chloride).

Copolymers are characterized by linking both decimal figures and element symbols of the different components. In the first position there is always the component of which there is the greatest molar amount in the copolymer. This is followed by the other constituents in accordance with the size of their molar fractions. In cases where the composition was not known, it was guessed. Ethene-propene copolymers, for example, are not only listed under **21111-2111211**, but also under **21111211-21111** — depending on whether ethylene or propylene units predominate in the copolymer. (Ethene and propene we take to be the monomers, ethylene and propylene the appropriate monomer units in the copolymer.)

In the case of copolymers with units in groups 7 to 9, these were put in first place, irrespective of the molar fraction.

In the decimal figure which characterizes a particular polymer, the numerical sequence for the element symbol is printed in semi-bold type, that for the linkage of these elements (chemical structure)*[)] in normal type. Decimal points have been omitted, e.g.

4212211 polyacrylamide, poly(1-aminocarbonyl ethylene).

The numerical sequence at the top left of each spectrum stands for the polymer in question, the *element symbol* is in the centre, above the spectrum, and the *serial number* at top right.

The arrangement of the various chemical structures in the decimal classification was carried out "hierarchically".

For *hydrocarbon structures* the following applies:
  saturated
    unsaturated
      aliphatic-aromatic
        aromatic.

In the case of chains, the following applies:
  linear
    branched
      cyclic.

As far as the position of characteristic *hetero functions* is concerned, (*e.g.* O, CONH *etc.*), the following applies:
  main chain
    side chain.

---

* *c.f.* the structure code to follow for polyacrylamide; see also p. XXII.

The chains themselves have been characterized as follows:
  vinyl chain
    vinylidene chain
      other chains.

In the case of polymers made up of *ring systems* linked by acyclic groups, the ring system has been characterized first, followed by the bridge:
  polyimides
    aliphatic ring
      aromatic ring
        CH bridge
          CHN bridge
            CHO bridge
              CHS bridge
                CHNO bridge.

This system was condensed in cases where there was no point in having so many groups.

Where the structural unit had been produced through *modification* of a simpler unit (polyurethane — polyether urethane), a special decimal figure was created, which was then sub-divided:
  modified polyurethanes
    with CHN
      with CHO
        with CHS

Here, too, the system was condensed wherever possible.

The other principles of sub-division — some of them arbitrary — are easy to understand.

The decimal classification created for this work cannot, of course, be claimed to be absolutely perfect. Nor is it strictly logical. To achieve this degree of perfection would have made it even more extensive — perhaps to such a degree as to make it unusable. The system does, however, enable polymers with almost any structure to be reliably classified and traced.

The following three examples may serve to illustrate the access to defined information in this spectrum atlas.

First example: The reader is interested in polymeric imides containing the succinimide structure. He looks at the following structural possibilities:

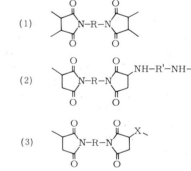

(1) is produced, for example, by the thermal polymerization of bis-maleimides. R can be an aliphatic radical, C_nH_{2n} or an aromatic bridge, *e.g.* phenylene-oxyphenylene.

(2) is formed, for example, by a kind of Michael addition of a diamine to a bis-maleimide. For this, aliphatic as well as aromatic diamines can be used.

(3) may be regarded as the result of a simplification of the reaction which leads to (2). X is a divalent heteroelement, *e.g.* O or S. A polythioether imide of the type shown in formula (3) is produced, for example, by the polyaddition of H_2S to a bis-maleimide.

(1) and (2) belong to the group CHNO. The decimal classification system enables one to quickly find group **4.2.1.**5, polyimides. The imide ring in our example is aliphatic. The polymerization process occurred *via* C=C linkages, so that N does not form part of the chain. Consequently, (1) and (2) belong to group **4.2.1.**5.1.1.4, "imide ring in the C main chain, rings linked through bridges between imide-nitrogen". In this group there are 14 substances, which is a reasonable number.

In the case of (3) X = S, so that the element symbol of this polymer is CHNOS (**5.2**). It is reasonable to take the imide rings to be units which are linked to S. (3) thus belongs to the group **5.2.**4.2.1. There is, indeed a substance representing that group.

Second example: One is looking for a derivative of isophthalic hydrazide chelated with Ni and having the following formula:

$+ 7{,}8\%$ Ni

The group **4.2.1.**2.2.5 (amides of hydrazine and its derivatives) has numerous members, the polymer has a long chemical name and is not familiar to everybody. The empirical formula of the polymer is $C_{13}H_{14}N_8O_2 + Ni$ and is represented only once. The number of the spectrum (p. 426, first spectrum) may be easily found by referring to the empirical formula index.

Third example: The reader is interested in polymeric azo compounds, looks under CHN, **3.2.**2.3.4 and finds a number of examples. He forgets to also look under **4.2.1.**8, polymeric azo compounds with O functions, but obtains information about more recent work carried out by Barbro Löfgren. He then looks up the author index and finds the missing information.

The Decimal Classification System

1 Macromolecular substances for technical applications, low molecular raw materials and auxiliaries*)

1.1 Plastics, natural and synthetic fibres
- **1.1.1** one single element (graphite materials)
- **1.1.2** two elements
  - **1.1.2.1** CH
  - **1.1.2.2** CHal
  - **1.1.2.3** CN
- **1.1.3** three elements
  - **1.1.3.1** CHHal
    - **1.1.3.1.1** CHF
    - **1.1.3.1.2** CHCl
    - **1.1.3.1.3** CHBr
    - **1.1.3.1.4** CHI
  - **1.1.3.2** CHN
  - **1.1.3.3** CHO
  - **1.1.3.4** CHS
  - **1.1.3.5** CHalX
    - **1.1.3.5.1** CHalHal′
      - **1.1.3.5.1.1** CFCl
      - **1.1.3.5.1.2** CFBr
      - **1.1.3.5.1.3** CFI
      - **1.1.3.5.1.4** CClBr
      - **1.1.3.5.1.5** CClI
      - **1.1.3.5.1.6** CBrI
    - **1.1.3.5.2** CHalN
      - **1.1.3.5.2.1** CFN
      - **1.1.3.5.2.2** CClN
      - **1.1.3.5.2.3** CBrN
      - **1.1.3.5.2.4** ClN
    - **1.1.3.5.3** CHalO
    - **1.1.3.5.4** CHalS
  - **1.1.3.6** CNO
  - **1.1.3.7** CNS

1.2 Natural and synthetic rubbers
(sub-division as for **1.1**)

1.3 Resins (natural and synthetic resins, impregnating resins, dispersions)
(sub-division as for **1.1**)

1.4 Adhesives and related materials (sealants and fillers)
(sub-division as for **1.1**)

1.5 Vegetable oils, waxes
(sub-division as for **1.1**)

1.6 Hardeners
(sub-division as for **1.1**)

1.7 Surfactants
- **1.7.1** cationic surfactants
- **1.7.2** anionic surfactants
- **1.7.3** non-ionic surfactants

1.8 Low molecular raw materials and degradation products
- **1.8.1** monomers
  (sub-division as for **1.1**)
- **1.8.2** amines and their salts
- **1.8.3** alcohols and phenols
- **1.8.4** epoxides
- **1.8.5** acids and their salts
- **1.8.6** anhydrides
- **1.8.7** isocyanates, uretdiones, urethanes
- **1.8.8** other raw materials and degradation products

1.9 Common solvents

* The first two digits stand for classification according to application. Further sub-division is according to the number and type of elements which form the substance in question. If a further sub-division, according to structural characteristics, is necessary or required, this occurs after **2**...**9** (defined polymers).

2 Polymers made up of 2 elements*)

2.1 CH

1 aliphatic
- 1.1 saturated
  - 1.1.1 unbranched (polymethylene)
  - 1.1.2 branched (acyclic)
    - 1.1.2.1 poly(alkylethylene)s with linear side chain
      - 1.1.2.1.1 poly(1-methylethylene), polypropylenes
      - 1.1.2.1.2 poly(1-ethylethylene), poly(1-butene)
      - 1.1.2.1.3 poly(1-propylethylene), poly(1-pentene)
      - 1.1.2.1.4 higher poly(*n*-alkylethylene)s
    - 1.1.2.2 poly(alkylethylene)s with branched side chain
    - 1.1.2.3 higher poly[1-alkyl(polymethylene)]s
      - 1.1.2.3.1 linear side chain
      - 1.1.2.3.2 branched side chain
    - 1.1.2.4 saturated aliphatic polyhydrocarbons with quaternary C atoms in the main chain (poly-1,1-dimethylethylene)
    - 1.1.2.5 other defined-branched saturated aliphatic polyhydrocarbons
    - 1.1.2.6 saturated aliphatic polyhydrocarbons with undefined long and short chain branching (low density polyethylene)
  - 1.1.3 cyclic
    - 1.1.3.1 rings in the main chain
    - 1.1.3.2 rings in the side chain
- 1.2 unsaturated
  - 1.2.1 one C=C bond per monomer unit
    - 1.2.1.1 unbranched
      - 1.2.1.1.1 C_2 (polyvinylene, polyethenylene)
      - 1.2.1.1.2 C_3 (polypropenylene)
      - 1.2.1.1.3 C_4 (polybutenylene)
      - 1.2.1.1.4 C_5 (polypentenylene)
      - 1.2.1.1.5 C_6 (polyhexenylene)
      - 1.2.1.1.6 C_7 (polyheptenylene)
      - 1.2.1.1.7 C_8 (polyoctenylene)
      - 1.2.1.1.8 higher polyalkenylenes with 1 double bond per monomer unit
    - 1.2.1.2 branched
    - 1.2.1.3 cyclic
  - 1.2.2 one C≡C bond per monomer unit
    - 1.2.2.1 unbranched
    - 1.2.2.2 branched
    - 1.2.2.3 cyclic
  - 1.2.3 several multiple bonds per monomer unit

2 aliphatic-aromatic
- 2.1 aromatic grouping in the main chain
  - 2.1.1 saturated aliphatic groups
    - 2.1.1.1 poly(phenylene polymethylene)s of the type $-\Phi-(CH_2)_n-$
    - 2.1.1.2 nucleus-substituted poly(phenylene polymethylene)s
    - 2.1.1.3 branched alkyl bridge
    - 2.1.1.4 cycloparaffin bridge
  - 2.1.2 unsaturated aliphatic groups

* In the main groups **2**...**6**, bold figures characterize the element composition and meager ones the chemical structure.

(**2.1** CH, *continued*)

2.2 aromatic grouping in the side chain
    2.2.1 saturated aliphatic groups
        2.2.1.1 polymers of mono-vinyl-substituted aromatic compounds
            2.2.1.1.1 unsubstituted phenyl residue (polystyrene)
            2.2.1.1.2 alkyl-substituted phenyl residue
            2.2.1.1.3 aryl-substituted phenyl residue
            2.2.1.1.4 polymers of mono-vinyl-substituted condensed aromatic compounds
        2.2.1.2 polymers of multi-vinyl-substituted aromatic compounds
        2.2.1.3 polymers of vinylidene-substituted aromatic compounds (sub-division as for 2.2.1.1)
        2.2.1.4 polymers of multi-vinylidene-substituted aromatic compounds
        2.2.1.5 polymers with other, aryl- and alkyl-substituted chains
        2.2.1.6 polymers of cyclo-olefinically-substituted or anellated aromatic compounds
    2.2.2 unsaturated aliphatic groups
        2.2.2.1 multiple linkages in the main chain
        2.2.2.2 multiple linkages in the side chain
2.3 polymeric condensed aromatic compounds (polyanthracene, polyphenanthrene)
3 aromatic (polyphenylenes)
    3.1 unsubstituted
    3.2 (aryl) substituted

2.2 CHal
2.2.1 CF

1 aliphatic
    1.1 saturated
        1.1.1 unbranched (polytetrafluoroethylene)
        1.1.2 branched
    1.2 unsaturated
        1.2.1 unbranched
        1.2.2 branched
2 aliphatic-aromatic
    2.1 aromatic group in the main chain
    2.2 aromatic group in the side chain
3 aromatic (perfluorinated polyphenylenes)

2.2.2 CCl
2.2.3 CBr
2.2.4 CI

2.3 CN

3 Polymers made up of 3 elements
3.1 CHHal
3.1.1 CHF

1 aliphatic
    1.1 saturated
        1.1.1 unbranched
            1.1.1.1 one Hal per monomer unit
            1.1.1.2 several Hal per monomer unit
        1.1.2 branched
            1.1.2.1 one Hal per monomer unit
            1.1.2.2 several Hal per monomer unit

        1.1.3 cyclic
            1.1.3.1 one Hal per monomer unit
            1.1.3.2 several Hal per monomer unit
    1.2 unsaturated (sub-division as for 1.1)
2 aliphatic-aromatic
    2.1 aromatic group in the main chain
        2.1.1 Hal on aliphatic group
            2.1.1.1 one Hal attached to aliphatic group
            2.1.1.2 several Hal attached to aliphatic group
        2.1.2 Hal attached to aromatic system
            2.1.2.1 one Hal attached to aromatic system
            2.1.2.2 several Hal attached to aromatic system
        2.1.3 Hal attached to aliphatic group and to aromatic system
    2.2 aromatic group in the side chain
        2.2.1 Hal attached to aliphatic group
            2.2.1.1 one Hal attached to aliphatic group
            2.2.1.2 several Hal attached to aliphatic group
        2.2.2 Hal attached to aromatic system
            2.2.2.1 one Hal attached to aromatic system
            2.2.2.2 several Hal attached to aromatic system
        2.2.3 Hal attached to aliphatic group and to aromatic system
    2.3 aromatic group in the main and side chains
3 aromatic
    3.1 one Hal attached to aromatic system
    3.2 several Hal attached to aromatic system

3.1.2 CHCl
(sub-division as for **3.1.1**)
3.1.3 CHBr
(sub-division as for **3.1.1**)
3.1.4 CHI
(sub-division as for **3.1.1**)

3.2 CHN

1 N in the main chain (without heterocycles)
    1.1 aliphatic
        1.1.1 acyclic
            1.1.1.1 polyalkylene imines
            1.1.1.2 derivatives of hydrazine
            1.1.1.3 polymeric Schiff bases of the type $-\mathrm{N}{=}\overset{|}{\mathrm{C}}-$
            1.1.1.4 polymeric azo compounds
        1.1.2 carbocyclic
    1.2 aliphatic-aromatic
        1.2.1 polyimines of the type $-\mathrm{NH-R-Ar-}$, $-\mathrm{NR-Ar-}$ or $-\mathrm{NAr-R-}$
        1.2.2 derivatives of hydrazine
        1.2.3 aromatically substituted Schiff bases
        1.2.4 polymeric azo compounds
    1.3 aromatic
        1.3.1 polyimines of the type $-\mathrm{NH-Ar}$ or $-\overset{\overset{\textstyle Ar}{|}}{\mathrm{N}}-$
        1.3.2 derivatives of hydrazine
        1.3.3 Schiff bases of the type $-\mathrm{N}{=}\overset{\mathrm{C}-\mathrm{Ar}-}{\underset{\overset{|}{\textstyle Ar}}{}}$
        1.3.4 polymeric azo compounds
2 N in the side chain (without heterocycles)
    2.1 aliphatic
        2.1.1 amines
            2.1.1.1 acyclic (polyvinyl-, polyallylamine)
            2.1.1.2 carbocyclic (derivatives of cyclohexylamine)
        2.1.2 derivatives of hydrazine
        2.1.3 Schiff bases

(3.3 CHO, *continued*)

---

[*] Mono-linked O atoms next to carbonyl functions: see the latter.

4 Polymers made up of 4 elements

4.1 CHHalX

4.1.1 CHHalHal'
4.1.1.1 CHFCl
1 aliphatic
2 aliphatic-aromatic
3 aromatic

4.1.1.2 CHFBr ⎫
4.1.1.3 CHFI ⎪
4.1.1.4 CHClBr ⎬ sub-division as for **4.1.1.1**
4.1.1.5 CHClI ⎪
4.1.1.6 CHBrI ⎭

4.1.2 CHHalN
4.1.2.1 CHFN
1 aliphatic
2 aliphatic-aromatic
3 aliphatic-heterocyclic
4 aromatic
5 heterocyclic

4.1.2.2 CHClN ⎫
4.1.2.3 CHBrN ⎬ sub-division as for **4.1.2.1**
4.1.2.4 CHIN ⎭

4.1.3 CHHalO
4.1.3.1 CHFO
1 Alcohols
2 Phenols
3 Ethers, peroxides
4 Various single-bonded O atoms in the structural unit
5 Aldehydes, ketones
6 Carboxylic acids and their salts
7 Esters
8 Anhydrides
9 Acid halogenides, other CHFO polymers
(further sub-division according to the relevant section in **3.3**, CHO)

4.1.3.2 CHClO
(sub-division according to **4.1.3.1**, further sub-division according to **3.3**)

4.1.3.3 CHBrO
(sub-division according to **4.1.3.1**, further sub-division according to **3.3**)

4.1.3.4 CHIO
1 Iodized CHO polymers
2 Polyesters of iodic acids

4.1.4 CHHalS
4.1.4.1 CHFS
4.1.4.2 CHClS
4.1.4.3 CHBrS
4.1.4.4 CHIS

4.2 CHNX

4.2.1 CHNO
1 Polymeric NO compounds (O linked directly to N)
1.1 aminoxides
1.1.1 aliphatic
1.1.2 aliphatic-aromatic
1.1.3 alicyclic-aromatic
1.1.4 heterocyclic
1.2 hydroxamic acids

1.2.1 type —X—CO—N— (with OH)
(sub-division as for 1.1)
1.2.2 type —N—X—N—CO—X'—CO— (with OH, OH)
(sub-division as for 1.1)

1.3 oximes and O-substituted oximes
(sub-division as for 1.1)
1.4 nitroso compounds
1.4.1 C-nitroso compounds
1.4.1.1 —NO attached to the aliphatic residue
1.4.1.2 —NO attached to the aromatic residue
1.4.2 N-nitrosocompounds (nitrosamines)
1.5 nitroso compounds
1.5.1 —NO$_2$ attached to the aliphatic residue
1.5.1.1 no further hetero functions
1.5.1.2 with CHO function(s)
1.5.1.3 with CHN function(s)
1.5.1.4 with CHNO function(s)
1.5.1.5 with various additional hetero functions
1.5.2 —NO$_2$ attached to the aromatic residue
(sub-division as for 1.5.1)
1.6 nitrates (nitric acid esters)
1.6.1 —ONO$_2$ attached to the aliphatic residue
(sub-division as for 1.5.1)
1.6.2 —ONO$_2$ attached to the aromatic residue
(sub-division as for 1.5.1)

2 Polyamides (characteristic grouping —R—C(=O)—N<)
2.1 amido group in the main chain
2.1.1 polyamides made from aminocarboxylic acids (formally)
2.1.1.1 aliphatic, saturated
2.1.1.1.1 unbranched C chain
2.1.1.1.2 branched C chain
2.1.1.1.3 carbocyclic C chain, spiropolyamides
2.1.1.1.4 tertiary (N-substituted) amides
2.1.1.2 olefinic
2.1.1.2.1 secondary amides
2.1.1.2.2 tertiary amides
2.1.1.3 aliphatic-aromatic
2.1.1.3.1 aromatic system not directly attached to the amido group
2.1.1.3.2 —Ar—CONH—R— or —R—CONH—Ar—
2.1.1.3.3 —Ar—CONH—Ar— with aliphatic substituents
2.1.1.3.4 tertiary amides
2.1.1.4 aromatic
2.1.1.4.1 uncondensed
2.1.1.4.2 condensed
2.1.1.5 polyamides of type 2.1.1 with additional hetero functions
2.1.1.5.1 aliphatic
2.1.1.5.1.1 with CHN functions
2.1.1.5.1.2 with CHO functions
2.1.1.5.1.2.1 amidoalcohols (-phenols)
2.1.1.5.1.2.2 amidoethers
2.1.1.5.1.2.3 amide + ketone
2.1.1.5.1.2.4 amide + COOH
2.1.1.5.1.2.5 amide + ester
2.1.1.5.1.3 with CHNO functions
2.1.1.5.2 aliphatic-aromatic
(sub-division as for 2.1.1.5.1)
2.1.1.5.3 aromatic, uncondensed
(sub-division as for 2.1.1.5.1)
2.1.1.5.4 aromatic, condensed
(sub-division as for 2.1.1.5.1)
2.1.2 polyamides made from diamines and dicarboxylic acids **XXIII**
2.1.2.1 aliphatic, saturated
2.1.2.1.1 unbranched
2.1.2.1.1.1 PA-2x, 2y (x, y = 1, 2, 3 ...)

4.2.2 CHNS*)

* The CHN decimal figure (without the prefix **3.2**) for the rest of the structural unit is attached to the decimal figure indicating the type of sulfur linkage, provided S and N do not represent common constituents of a grouping (—CS—NH—, heterocycle and the like)

(**4.2.2** CHNS, *continued*)

5.2 2 S in the ring
  5.2.1 5-ring
  5.2.2 6-ring
  5.2.3 higher rings
5.3 3 and more S in the ring
6 Only S in the condensed heterocycle
  6.1 1 S in the condensed heterocycle
    6.1.1 two-ring system
    6.1.2 three-ring system
    6.1.3 higher ring systems
  6.2 2 S in the condensed heterocycle
    6.2.1 two-ring system
    6.2.2 three-ring system
    6.2.3 higher ring systems
  6.3 3 and more S in the ring system
7 S and N in the unconndensed heterocycle
  7.1 1 S and 1 N in the unconndensed heterocycle
    7.1.1 5-ring
      7.1.1.1 directly linked rings
      7.1.1.2 aliphatic bridge
      7.1.1.3 aliphatic-aromatic bridge
      7.1.1.4 unconndensed-aromatic bridge
      7.1.1.5 condensed-aromatic bridge
      7.1.1.6 heterocyclic bridge
    7.1.2 6-ring
    (sub-division as for 7.1.1)
    7.1.3 higher rings
    (sub-division as for 7.1.1)
  7.2 1 S and 2 N in the unconndensed heterocycle
    7.2.1 5-ring
    (sub-division as for 7.1.1)
    7.2.2 6-ring
    (sub-division as for 7.1.1)
    7.2.3 higher rings
    (sub-division as for 7.1.1)
  7.3 other representatives of type 7
8 S and N in the condensed heterocycle
  8.1 1 S and 1 N in the condensed heterocycle
    8.1.1 two-ring systems
    8.1.2 three-ring systems
    8.1.3 higher ring systems
  8.2 more than 2 S + N in the condensed heterocycle
  (sub-division as for 8.1)
9 S and N in other joint groupings
  9.1 thioamides, —CS—NX— (X = H, R, Ar *etc.*)
    9.1.1 aliphatic
    9.1.2 aliphatic-aromatic
    9.1.3 aromatic
  9.2 thiourethanes, $>$N—CS—S—
  (sub-division as for 9.1)
  9.3 thioureas
  (sub-division as for 9.1)

4.3 CHOS*)

1 Oxygen-free S functions, linked with (CH)O functions.

The decimal figure for this type of polymer is produced through linking the sequence for the CHS function (3.4) with the sequence for the CHO function (3.3). Sequence **4.3.1** is put in front of the CHS

sequence instead of **3.4**. The sequence for the CHO function is attached, although without the prefixes **3.3**.

2 S and O attached to the same C atom
  2.1 thioesters of the type $-\overset{\displaystyle O}{\overset{\|}{C}}-S-$
    2.1.1 aliphatic
      2.1.1.1 unbranched
      2.1.1.2 branched
      2.1.1.3 cyclic
        2.1.1.3.1 carbocyclic
        2.1.1.3.2 thioester group in the ring (thiolactones)
    2.1.2 aliphatic-aromatic
    2.1.3 aromatic
  2.2 thioesters of the type $-\overset{\displaystyle S}{\overset{\|}{C}}-O-$
  (sub-division as for 2.1)
  2.3 thiocarbonic acid esters
3 Sulfoxides
  3.1 aliphatic
    3.1.1 $-\overset{\displaystyle O}{\overset{\|}{S}}-$ in the main chain
    3.1.2 $-\overset{\displaystyle O}{\overset{\|}{S}}-$ in the side chain
  3.2 aliphatic-aromatic
  3.3 aromatic
4 Sulfones*)
  4.1 aliphatic
    4.1.1 unbranched
    4.1.2 branched
      4.1.2.1 $-SO_2-$ in the main chain
      4.1.2.2 $-SO_2-$ in the side chain
      4.1.2.3 $-SO_2-$ in the main and side chains
    4.1.3 cyclic
      4.1.3.1 carbocyclic
      4.1.3.2 $-SO_2-$ in the ring
  4.2 aliphatic-aromatic
    4.2.1 $-SO_2-$ in the main chain
      4.2.1.1 $-R-SO_2-R-$
      4.2.1.2 $-R-SO_2-Ar-$
      4.2.1.3 $-Ar-SO_2-Ar-$
    4.2.2 $-SO_2-$ in the side chain
    (sub-division as for 4.2.1)
    4.2.3 $-SO_2-$ in the main and side chains
  4.3 aromatic
5 Sulfonic acids*)
  5.1 aliphatic
    5.1.1 vinyl chain
    5.1.2 vinylidene chain
    5.1.3 other chains
  5.2 aliphatic-aromatic
    5.2.1 R—SO$_2$OH
    5.2.2 Ar—SO$_2$OH
  5.3 aromatic
6 Salts of sulfonic acids*)
  (sub-division as 5; $-SO_3^{\ominus}$ replaces $-SO_2OH$)
7 Sulfonic acid esters*)
  7.1 $-SO_2-O-$ in the main chain
    7.1.1 aliphatic
      7.1.1.1 sulfonic acid esters of the type $+R-SO_2-O+_n$
      7.1.1.2 sulfonic acid esters of the type
        $+O-R-O-SO_2-R'-SO_2+_n$

---

* This combination of elements can be formed either through the linkage of O-free S functions with O functions, or through the linkage of SO(C) functions with CH functions. Finally, polymers with SO(C) functions can contain further (CH)O functions. The presence of further (CH)O functions is expressed by the use of the decimal number for CHO.

---

* Polysulfones (polysulfonic acids, their salts and esters) with additional O functions are first classified according to **4.3.4** (5, 6, 7). This is followed by the number sequence which characterizes additional CHO functions, this being put after **3.3** (without these figures *c.f.* **4.3.**1)

If a sub-division is necessary, the following procedure is adopted: first of all, the C(H)Hal part of the structure is defined according to **3.1.X** (no matter whether this structural component contains H or not). This is followed by defining the CHNO part according to **4.2.1**. (When defining the CHNO number sequence, Hal can be assumed to be H.) The decimal figure of the entire structure is then obtained by attaching 3 figures from the CHHal and the CHNO classification (omitting the prefixes **3.1.X** and **4.2.1**) to the CHHalNO index number. If specification to three figures is

not required, or not possible, zero is put for every missing digit.

(sub-division as for **5.1.2.**) Further sub-division, if necessary, is effected according to the following scheme: type of linkage of the Hal according to **3.1**, of the O according to **3.3**, of the S according to **3.4** and 3 places in this sequence, omitting the prefixes for the element symbol. If specification to three figures is not required, or not possible, zero is put for every missing digit. If the structure contains SO functions, the sequence 000 after the Hal triad indicates that the CHO and CHS triads have been omitted. Then there only follows the CHOS triad according to **4.3.1**, and no additional CHO functions can be given. Finally, if Hal is attached directly to the S (sulfonyl halogenides *etc.*), the sequence 000 after the number sequence for the element symbol (*e.g.* **5.1.3.2** for CHClOS) indicates the presence of such a grouping. Then, if necessary, only the CHO triad is added.

5.2 CHNOS

1 Sulfinamides, $-SO-N{<}$
(Sub-division as for amides, SO is equivalent to CO. The decimal number is composed of the sequence for sulfinamides, **5.2.**1 and the sequence following **4.2.1.**2, which characterises the rest of the structure. If the structural unit contains other hetero groupings, these are characterized by their own decimal figure. For this purpose, the $-SO-NX-$ function is regarded as non-existent. To differentiate between copolymers, the decimal figure of the structural components of one and the same repetitive unit is linked by a plus sign. The same applies to the element symbols.)

2 Sulfonamides, $-SO_2-N{<}$
(Sub-division as for amides, SO_2 is regarded as equivalent to CO. As far as the decimal figure is concerned, the remarks made in section 1 above apply.)

3 Sulfamides, ${>}N-SO_2-N{<}$
(Sub-division as for ureas, SO_2 is regarded as equivalent to CO. As far as the decimal figure is concerned, the remarks made in section 1 above apply.)

4 Structures linked to simple S(O) functions
  4.1 CHN$-$SO*)
    4.1.1 CHN sulfoxide
    4.1.2 CHN sulfone
    4.1.3 CHN sulfonic acid esters
    4.1.4 CHN sulfuric acid esters
  4.2 CHNO$-$S**)
    4.2.1 CHN thioethers
    4.2.1 CHNO dithioethers and polythioethers
  4.3 CHNO$-$SO**)
    4.3.1 CHNO sulfoxide

---

* The number sequence characterizing the CHN structure is appended to the CHNOS number, but without the prefix **3.2**.

** The number sequence characterizing the CHNO structure is appended to the CHNOS number, but without the prefix **4.2.1**.

---

* The number sequence characterizing the CHN structure is appended to the CHNOS number, but without the prefix **3.2**.
** The number sequence characterizing the CHNO structure is appended to the CHNOS number, but without the prefix **4.2.1**.

(7 D-Polymers, *continued*)

7.2.6.2 D—CHHalN
(sub-division as for **4.1.2**)

7.2.6.3 D—CHHalO
(sub-division as for **4.1.3**)

7.2.6.4 D—CHHalS
(sub-division as for **4.1.4**)

7.2.7 D—CHNX

7.2.7.1 D—CHNO
(sub-division as for **4.2.1**)

7.2.7.2 D—CHNS
(sub-division as for **4.2.2**)

7.2.8 D—CHOS
(sub-division as for **4.3**)

7.2.9 D—CHXYZ
(sub-division as for **5**)

7.3 Deuterated polymers with additional non-metals or semi-metals (with or without Hal, N, O, S)

7.3.1 proton-free deuterated polymers

7.3.1.1 D—CB(X,Y,Z ...)

7.3.1.2 D—CSi(X,Y,Z ...)

7.3.1.3 D—CGe(X,Y,Z ...)

7.3.1.4 D—CP(X,Y,Z ...)

7.3.2 proton-containing deuterated polymers

7.3.2.1 D—CHB

7.3.2.2 D—CHSi

7.3.2.3 D—CHGe

7.3.2.4 D—CHP

8 Polymers with heteroelements (non-metals and semi-metals in addition to Hal, N, O, S)

8.1 Boron compounds*[)]

1 Derivatives of boric and metaboric acid

1.1 —B—O— in the main chain (metaboric acid derivatives)
   |
   OX

1.2 BO function in the side chain

2 other polymers with BO groupings

3 polymers with B—C linkages

3.1 polycarboranes (derivatives of decaborane)

3.1.1 *o*-carborane

3.1.2 *m*-carborane

3.1.3 *p*-carborane

3.2 polyboranes of the type —B—
                              |
                              R

3.2.1 aliphatic

3.2.2 aromatic

4 other polymeric boron compounds

8.2 silicon compounds**[)]

8.2.1 Si linked only to C (SiC_4)

8.2.1.1 only aliphatic substituents attached to the Si; SiR_4

8.2.1.2 three aliphatic and one aromatic substituent attached to the Si; R_3SiAr

8.2.1.3 R_2SiAr_2

8.2.1.4 $RSiAr_3$

8.2.1.5 $SiAr_4$

8.2.2 Si linked only to O (SiO_4)

8.2.3 Si linked only to another heteroelement (SiX_4, $X \neq C$ or O)

8.2.4 2 different elements attached to Si (SiX_mY_n, $m+n=4$)

8.2.4.1 CSiX

8.2.4.1.1 $X = H$

8.2.4.1.2 $X = N$

8.2.4.1.3 $X = O$

8.2.4.1.4 $X = S$

8.2.4.2 HSiX ($X \neq C$)

8.2.4.3 NSiX ($X \neq C$ or H)

8.2.4.4 OSiS

8.2.5 3 different elements attached to Si ($SiX_mY_nZ_o$, $m+n+o=4$)

8.2.5.1 HSiXY

8.2.5.1.1 $X = C$

8.2.5.1.1.1 $Y = N$

8.2.5.1.1.2 $Y = O$

8.2.5.1.1.3 $Y = S$

8.2.5.1.2 $X = N$ ($\neq C$), $Y = O, S$

8.2.5.1.3 $X = O$, $Y = S$

8.2.5.2 CSiXY ($X, Y \neq H$)

8.2.5.2.1 $X = N$, $Y = O$

8.2.5.2.2 $X = N$, $Y = S$

8.2.5.2.3 $X = O$, $Y = S$

8.2.5.3 NSiOS

8.2.6 4 different elements attached to Si (SiXYZU)

8.2.7 coordinatively linked Si (polymeric Si complexes)

8.3 germanium compounds
(sub-division as for **8.2**)

8.4 phosphorus compounds*[)]

8.4.1 exclusively the same elements attached to P

8.4.1.1 4 identical elements attached to P

8.4.1.1.1 PN_4

8.4.1.1.1.1 P in the main chain

8.4.1.1.1.2 P in the side chain

8.4.1.1.1.3 P in the ring

8.4.1.1.2 PO_4**[)]

8.4.1.2 3 identical elements attached to P

8.4.1.2.1 PC_3

8.4.1.2.2 PN_3

8.4.1.2.3 PO_3

8.4.2 2 different elements attached to P

8.4.2.1 C + X

8.4.2.1.1 C + N

---

* If further sub-division proves to be necessary, the number sequence characterizing the rest of the repetitive unit is attached to the prefix characterizing the boron linkage. Example: boric acid ester of a Novolak. Element symbol: BO_3—CHO. Decimal number: **8.1**.1.2.**3.3**.2.1.1.1. If the boron polymer can be regarded as a copolymer, especially when several other structural components must be characterized, the copolymer classification system is used.

** If further sub-division proves to be necessary, the number sequence characterizing the rest of the repetitive unit is attached to the prefix characterizing the silicon linkage. This is done as follows: first of all, Si is regarded as C, and then the main group is determined according to which the entire structural unit can be characterized. The prefix in question is then attached to the Si number and to this, in turn, one attaches the rest of the number sequence. If this results in the necessity of regarding the structural unit as a copolymer, the entire number sequence of the second structural unit is attached, as in the case of the copolymers.

---

* For further sub-division, the remarks in the footnote to **8.1** apply. Atoms or groupings which link the P function to the rest of the repetitive unit are taken into consideration both when characterizing the linkage of the P as well as in characterizing the rest of the repetitive unit. If the main chain is composed exclusively of P functions (*e.g.* in the case of polyphosphates or polyphosphazenes) only the element symbol of the side chains (without further sub-division) is appended to the number sequence characterizing the P function.

** Sub-division as for **8.4.1.1.1**.

(**8** Polymers with heteroelements, *continued*)

8.4.2.1.1.1 $PC_3N^{**)}$

8.4.2.1.1.2 $PC_2N_2^{**)}$

8.4.2.1.1.3 $PCN_3^{**)}$

8.4.2.1.2 C + O

8.4.2.1.2.1 $PC_3O^{**)}$

8.4.2.1.2.2 $PC_2O_2^{**)}$

8.4.2.1.2.3 $PCO_3^{**)}$

8.4.2.2 H + N**)

8.4.2.3 H + O**)

8.4.2.4 Hal + X

8.4.2.4.1 F + N**)

8.4.2.4.2 Cl + N**)

8.4.2.5 N + O**)

8.4.3 3 different elements attached to P

8.4.3.1 C + N + O**)

8.4.3.2 Hal + N + O

8.4.3.2.1 F + N + O**)

8.4.3.2.2 Cl + N + O**)

8.5 polymers with two different heteroelements of group 8*)

8.5.1 B + X

8.5.1.1 B + Si

8.5.1.2 B + Ge

8.5.1.3 B + P

8.5.2 Si + X

8.5.2.1 Si + Ge

8.5.2.2 Si + P

8.5.3 Ge + P

8.6 polymers with heteroelement and metal***)

8.6.1 B + Mt

8.6.2 Si + Mt

8.6.3 Ge + Mt

8.6.4 P + Mt

9 Polymers with non-ionic metal (coordinative or main valency bond)*)

9.1 Group I of the periodic system

9.1.1 main group I: alkali metals

9.1.2 sub-group I**): Cu, Ag, Au

9.2 Group II of the periodic system

9.2.1 main group II: alkaline earth metals

9.2.2 sub-group II**): Zn, Cd, Hg

9.3 Group III of the periodic system

9.3.1 main group III: earth metals, lanthanides, actinides (Al, Sc, Y; La, Ac)

9.3.2 sub-group III**): Ga, In, Tl

9.4 Group IV of the periodic system

9.4.1 main group IV: Sn, Pb

9.4.2 sub-group IV**): Ti, Zr, Hf

9.5 Group V of the periodic system

9.5.1 main group V: As, Sb, Bi

9.5.2 sub-group V**): V, Nb, Ta

9.6 Group VI of the periodic system

9.6.1 main group VI: Se, Te, Po

9.6.2 sub-group VI**): Cr, Mo, W

9.7 sub-group VII**): Mn, Re

9.8 sub-group VIII**)

9.8.1 ferrous metals: Fe, Co, Ni

9.8.2 light platinum metals: Ru, Rh, Pd

9.8.3 heavy platinum metals: Os, Ir, Pt

9.9 various metals in the polymer

---

* The organic part of the polymer is characterized only according to the element composition. Example: SiP—CHO polymer, **8.5.2.2.3.3.**

** Sub-division as for **8.4.1.1.1.**

*** The number sequence after **9** (omitting the **9**) is appended to the number sequence **8.6.x** to characterize the heavy metal. Example: P—Sn—CHO polymer, **8.6.4.4.1.3.3.**

---

* For practical reasons, the heavy elements of the main groups V and VI have also been included, although they are not, strictly speaking, metals (As, Sb, Bi; Se, Te).

The organic constituent of the polymer is characterized only according to the element composition, *e.g.* Sn polyester, Sn—CHO, **9.4.1.3.3.**

** Transition elements.

21111 C_2H_4 1

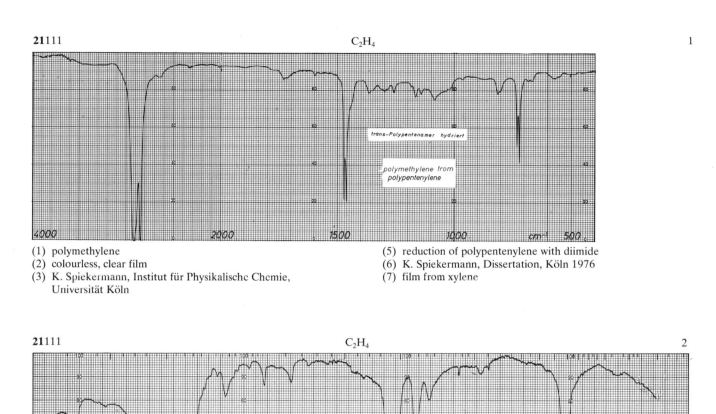

trans-Polypentenamer hydriert

polymethylene from polypentenylene

(1) polymethylene
(2) colourless, clear film
(3) K. Spiekermann, Institut für Physikalische Chemie, Universität Köln
(5) reduction of polypentenylene with diimide
(6) K. Spiekermann, Dissertation, Köln 1976
(7) film from xylene

21111 C_2H_4 2

Vestolen A 6012

(1) linear poly(ethylene)
(2) glassy-turbid granules
(3) Chemische Werke Hüls AG, Marl
(4) high density, high molecular weight, small molecular weight distribution
(7) recrystallized melting film between CsI, thin film (a few μm)
(8) commercial product „Vestolen A 6012"

21111 C_2H_4 3

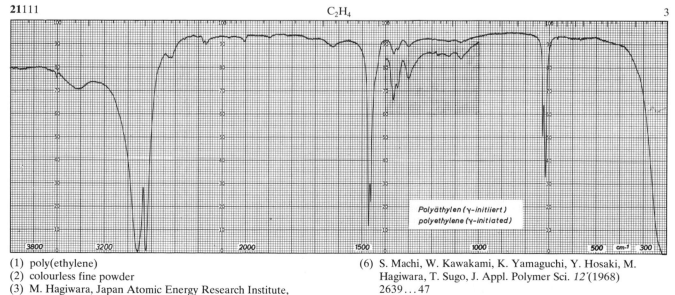

Polyäthylen (γ-initiiert)
polyethylene (γ-initiated)

(1) poly(ethylene)
(2) colourless fine powder
(3) M. Hagiwara, Japan Atomic Energy Research Institute, Takasaki
(4) crystalline, low branching
(5) γ-initiated heterogenous polymerization
(6) S. Machi, W. Kawakami, K. Yamaguchi, Y. Hosaki, M. Hagiwara, T. Sugo, J. Appl. Polymer Sci. *12*′(1968) 2639...47
(7) KBr (8/1000)
(8) increase of absorption beyond 400 cm^{-1} is due to KBr

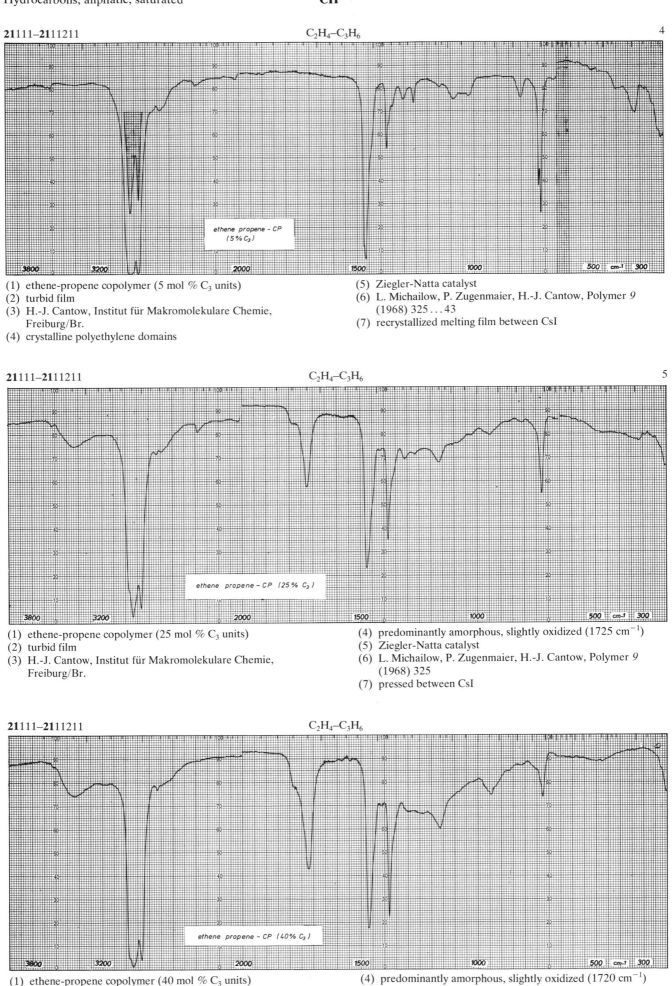

ethene propene – CP (5% C$_3$)

(1) ethene-propene copolymer (5 mol % C$_3$ units)
(2) turbid film
(3) H.-J. Cantow, Institut für Makromolekulare Chemie, Freiburg/Br.
(4) crystalline polyethylene domains

(5) Ziegler-Natta catalyst
(6) L. Michailow, P. Zugenmaier, H.-J. Cantow, Polymer *9* (1968) 325...43
(7) recrystallized melting film between CsI

ethene propene – CP (25% C$_3$)

(1) ethene-propene copolymer (25 mol % C$_3$ units)
(2) turbid film
(3) H.-J. Cantow, Institut für Makromolekulare Chemie, Freiburg/Br.

(4) predominantly amorphous, slightly oxidized (1725 cm^{-1})
(5) Ziegler-Natta catalyst
(6) L. Michailow, P. Zugenmaier, H.-J. Cantow, Polymer *9* (1968) 325
(7) pressed between CsI

ethene propene – CP (40% C$_3$)

(1) ethene-propene copolymer (40 mol % C$_3$ units)
(2) viscous yellowish material
(3) H.-J. Cantow, Institut für Makromolekulare Chemie, Freiburg/Br.

(4) predominantly amorphous, slightly oxidized (1720 cm^{-1})
(5) Ziegler-Natta catalyst
(6) L. Michailow, P. Zugenmaier, H.-J. Cantow, Polymer *9* (1968) 325
(7) film between CsI

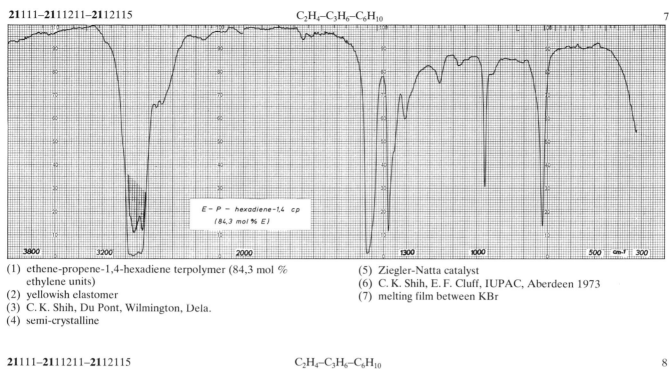

E – P – hexadiene-1,4 cp (84,3 mol % E)

(1) ethene-propene-1,4-hexadiene terpolymer (84,3 mol % ethylene units)
(2) yellowish elastomer
(3) C. K. Shih, Du Pont, Wilmington, Dela.
(4) semi-crystalline
(5) Ziegler-Natta catalyst
(6) C. K. Shih, E. F. Cluff, IUPAC, Aberdeen 1973
(7) melting film between KBr

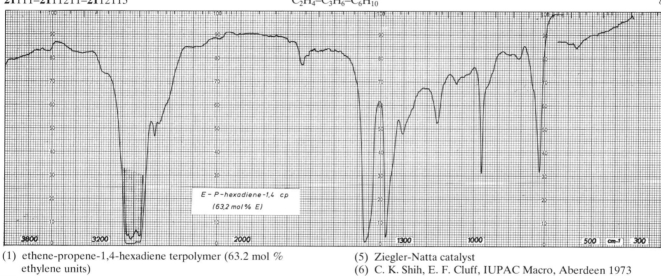

E – P-hexadiene-1,4 cp (63,2 mol % E)

(1) ethene-propene-1,4-hexadiene terpolymer (63.2 mol % ethylene units)
(2) yellowish elastomer
(3) C. K. Shih, Du Pont, Wilmington, Dela.
(4) semi-crystalline
(5) Ziegler-Natta catalyst
(6) C. K. Shih, E. F. Cluff, IUPAC Macro, Aberdeen 1973
(7) melting film between KBr

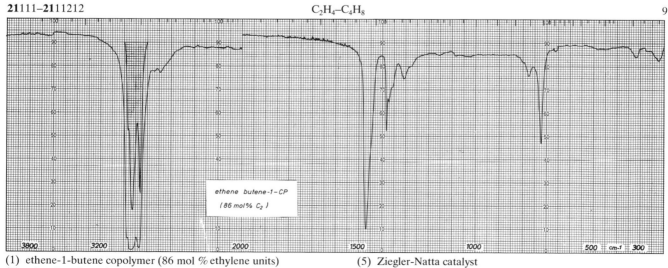

ethene butene-1–CP (86 mol% C_2)

(1) ethene-1-butene copolymer (86 mol % ethylene units)
(2) colourless clear elastomer
(3) A. Zambelli, Istituto di Chimica Industriale del Polytecnico, Milano
(4) semi-crystalline
(5) Ziegler-Natta catalyst
(6) A. Zambelli, A. Léty, C. Tosi, I. Pasquon, Makromol. Chem. *115* (1968) 73...88
(7) pressed film

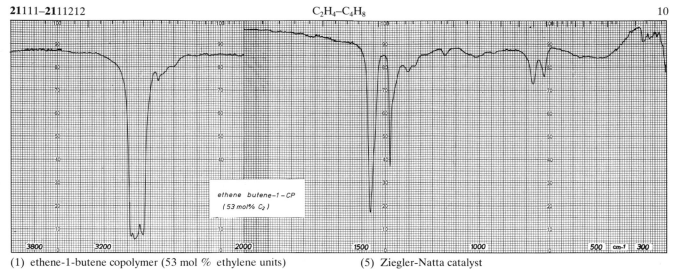

(1) ethene-1-butene copolymer (53 mol % ethylene units)
(2) viscous colourless material
(3) A. Zambelli, Istituto di Chimica Industriale del Polytecnico, Milano
(4) amorphous
(5) Ziegler-Natta catalyst
(6) A. Zambelli, A. Léty, C. Tosi, I. Pasquon, Makromol. Chem. *115* (1968) 73...88
(7) film between KBr

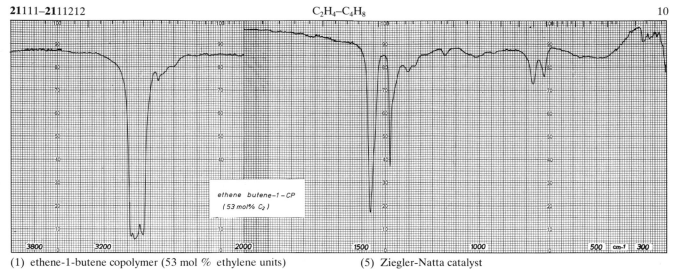

(1) ethene-4-methylpent-1-ene copolymer (76.8 wt.-% C$_2$)
(2) colourless material
(3) C. Tosi, Centro di Ricerche di Milano, Montecatini Edison, Milano
(5) Ziegler-Natta catalyst
(6) C. Tosi, Maria P. Lachi, A. Pinto, Makromol. Chem. *120* (1968) 225...30
(7) pressed film between CsI

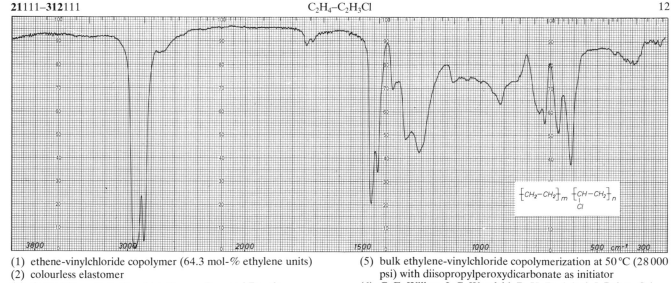

(1) ethene-vinylchloride copolymer (64.3 mol-% ethylene units)
(2) colourless elastomer
(3) C. E. Wilkes, B. F. Goodrich Comp., Res. and Develop. Center, Brecksville, Ohio
(4) m ≈ 2 n
(5) bulk ethylene-vinylchloride copolymerization at 50 °C (28 000 psi) with diisopropylperoxydicarbonate as initiator
(6) C. E. Wilkes, J. C. Westfahl, R. H. Backderf, J. Polym. Sci. A-1 *7* (1969) 23...33
(7) film from CHCl$_3$ on CsI

21111–3121111   C₂H₄–C₂H₃Cl   13

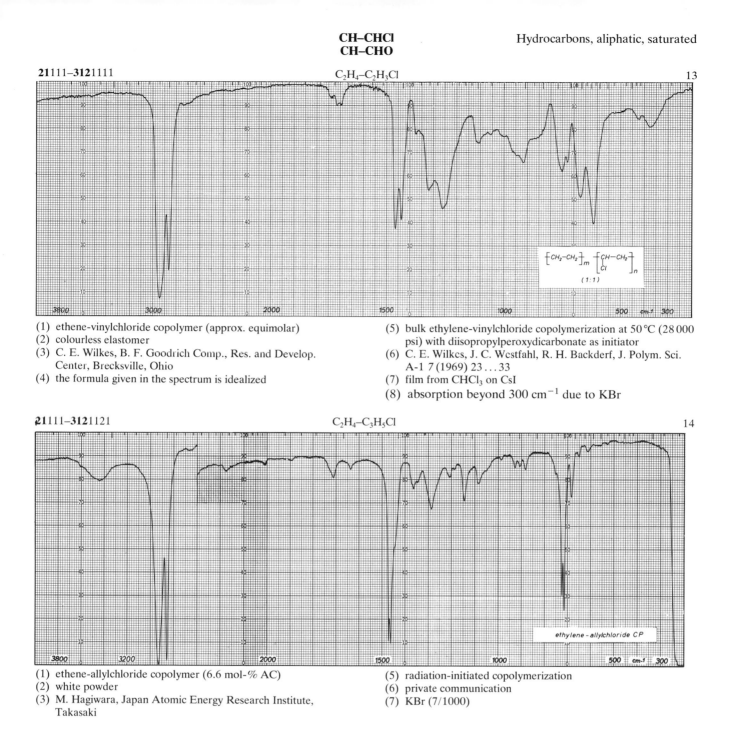

(1) ethene-vinylchloride copolymer (approx. equimolar)
(2) colourless elastomer
(3) C. E. Wilkes, B. F. Goodrich Comp., Res. and Develop. Center, Brecksville, Ohio
(4) the formula given in the spectrum is idealized

(5) bulk ethylene-vinylchloride copolymerization at 50 °C (28 000 psi) with diisopropylperoxydicarbonate as initiator
(6) C. E. Wilkes, J. C. Westfahl, R. H. Backderf, J. Polym. Sci. A-1 7 (1969) 23 . . . 33
(7) film from CHCl₃ on CsI
(8) absorption beyond 300 cm⁻¹ due to KBr

21111–3121121   C₂H₄–C₃H₅Cl   14

ethylene - allylchloride CP

(1) ethene-allylchloride copolymer (6.6 mol-% AC)
(2) white powder
(3) M. Hagiwara, Japan Atomic Energy Research Institute, Takasaki

(5) radiation-initiated copolymerization
(6) private communication
(7) KBr (7/1000)

21111–33611   C₂H₄–C₃H₄O₂   15

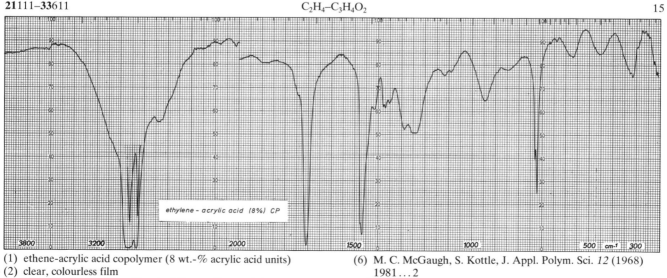

ethylene - acrylic acid (8%) CP

(1) ethene-acrylic acid copolymer (8 wt.-% acrylic acid units)
(2) clear, colourless film
(3) M. C. McGaugh, Dow Chemical Comp., Texas Division, Free Port, Tex.

(6) M. C. McGaugh, S. Kottle, J. Appl. Polym. Sci. 12 (1968) 1981 . . . 2
(7) film (35 μm, thin film from benzene on KBr)
(8) interferences in the long-wavelength region

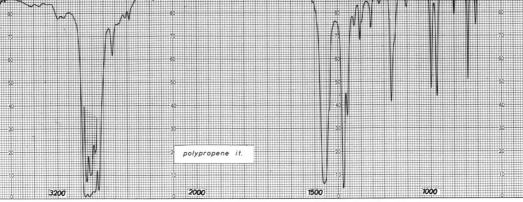

polypropene it.

(1) poly(propylene), isotactic
(2) slightly turbid, colourless film
(3) Chem. Werke Hüls AG, Marl (laboratory preparation)
(4) high degree of crystallinity

(5) Ziegler-Natta catalyst
(6) private communication
(7) original material melted between CsI, slowly cooled to room temp.; 20 μm

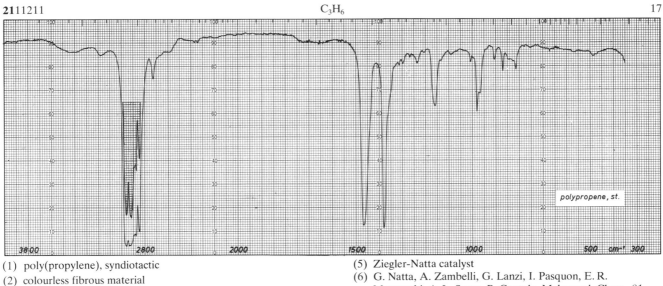

polypropene, st.

(1) poly(propylene), syndiotactic
(2) colourless fibrous material
(3) C. Tosi, Montecatini Edison, Bollate
(4) crystalline

(5) Ziegler-Natta catalyst
(6) G. Natta, A. Zambelli, G. Lanzi, I. Pasquon, E. R. Mognaschi, A. L. Segre, P. Centola, Makromol. Chem. *81* (1965) 161...72
(7) recrystallized melting film, stretched thin film (a few μm)

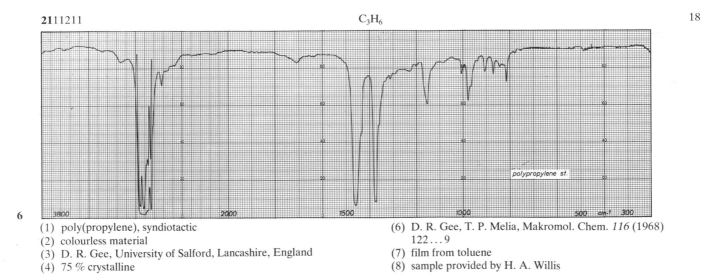

polypropylene st.

(1) poly(propylene), syndiotactic
(2) colourless material
(3) D. R. Gee, University of Salford, Lancashire, England
(4) 75 % crystalline

(6) D. R. Gee, T. P. Melia, Makromol. Chem. *116* (1968) 122...9
(7) film from toluene
(8) sample provided by H. A. Willis

2111211 C_3H_6 19

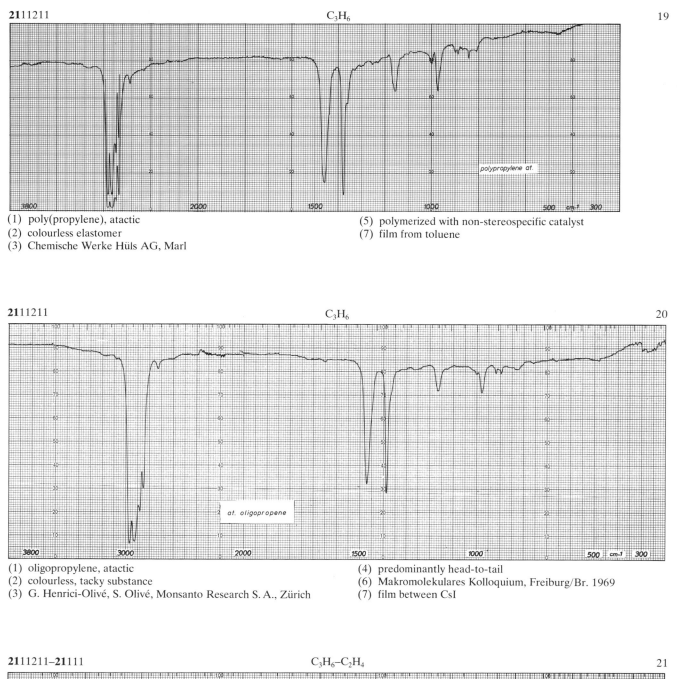

polypropylene at.

(1) poly(propylene), atactic
(2) colourless elastomer
(3) Chemische Werke Hüls AG, Marl

(5) polymerized with non-stereospecific catalyst
(7) film from toluene

2111211 C_3H_6 20

at. oligopropene

(1) oligopropylene, atactic
(2) colourless, tacky substance
(3) G. Henrici-Olivé, S. Olivé, Monsanto Research S. A., Zürich

(4) predominantly head-to-tail
(6) Makromolekulares Kolloquium, Freiburg/Br. 1969
(7) film between CsI

2111211–**21**111 C_3H_6–C_2H_4 21

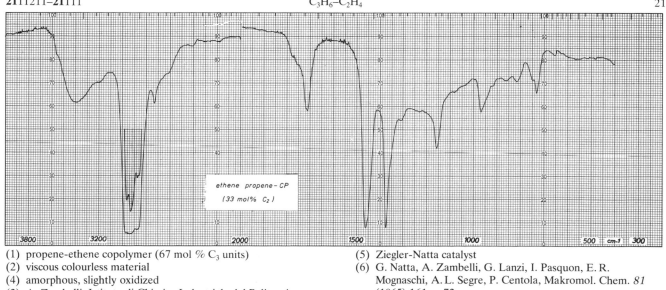

ethene propene – CP
(33 mol% C_2)

(1) propene-ethene copolymer (67 mol % C_3 units)
(2) viscous colourless material
(4) amorphous, slightly oxidized
(3) A. Zambelli, Istituto di Chimica Industriale del Politecnico, Milano

(5) Ziegler-Natta catalyst
(6) G. Natta, A. Zambelli, G. Lanzi, I. Pasquon, E. R. Mognaschi, A. L. Segre, P. Centola, Makromol. Chem. *81* (1965) 161...72
(7) film between KBr

2111211–**21**111 C_3H_6–C_2H_4 22

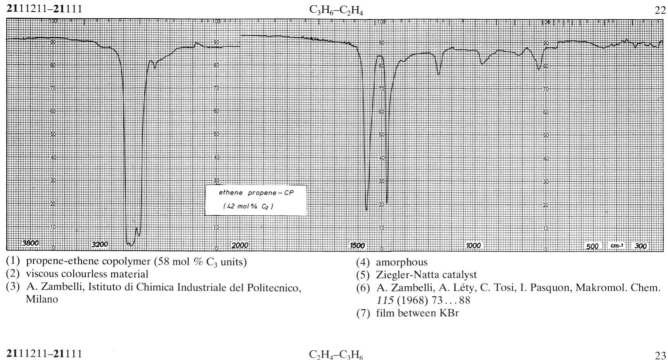

ethene propene – CP
(42 mol% C₂)

(1) propene-ethene copolymer (58 mol % C_3 units)
(2) viscous colourless material
(3) A. Zambelli, Istituto di Chimica Industriale del Politecnico, Milano
(4) amorphous
(5) Ziegler-Natta catalyst
(6) A. Zambelli, A. Léty, C. Tosi, I. Pasquon, Makromol. Chem. *115* (1968) 73...88
(7) film between KBr

2111211–**21**111 C_2H_4–C_3H_6 23

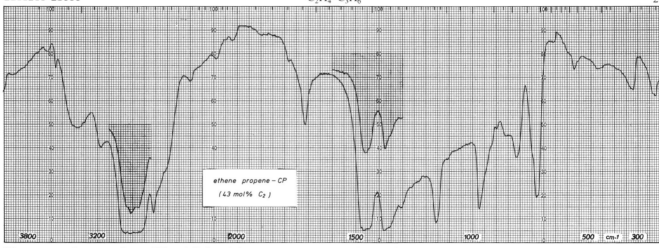

ethene propene – CP
(43 mol% C₂)

(1) propene-ethene copolymer (57 mol % C_3 units)
(2) colourless tacky material
(3) A. Zambelli, Istituto di Chim. Industr. del Politecnico, Milano
(4) amorphous, short homo-sequences
(5) VCl_4-$Al(C_2H_5)_2Cl$ at $-78\,°C$
(6) A. Zambelli, A. Léty, C. Tosi, I. Pasquon, Makromol. Chem. *115* (1968) 73...88
(7) film between CsI

2111211–**21**11212 C_3H_6–C_4H_8 24

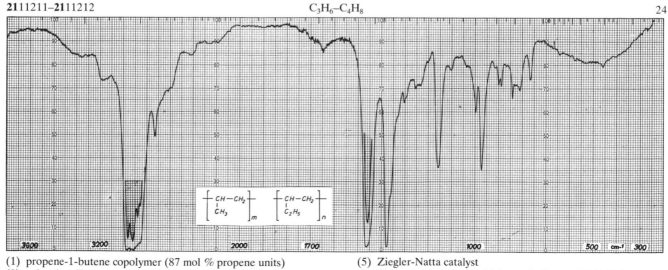

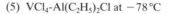

(1) propene-1-butene copolymer (87 mol % propene units)
(2) colourless fibrous material
(3) R. Laputte, Institut de Recherche sur la Catalyse, Villeurbanne
(4) partly crystalline
(5) Ziegler-Natta catalyst
(6) R. Laputte, A. Guyot, Makromol. Chem. *129* (1969) 234...49
(7) film from benzene on CsI

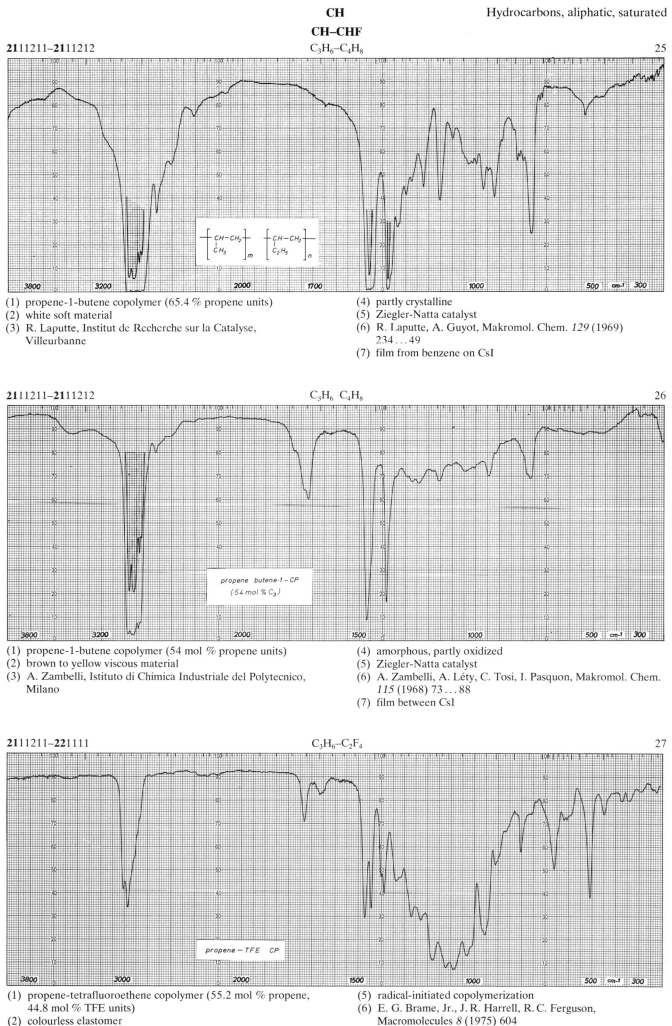

(1) propene-1-butene copolymer (65.4 % propene units)
(2) white soft material
(3) R. Laputte, Institut de Recherche sur la Catalyse, Villeurbanne

(4) partly crystalline
(5) Ziegler-Natta catalyst
(6) R. Laputte, A. Guyot, Makromol. Chem. *129* (1969) 234...49
(7) film from benzene on CsI

propene butene-1 - CP
(54 mol % C₃)

(1) propene-1-butene copolymer (54 mol % propene units)
(2) brown to yellow viscous material
(3) A. Zambelli, Istituto di Chimica Industriale del Polytecnico, Milano

(4) amorphous, partly oxidized
(5) Ziegler-Natta catalyst
(6) A. Zambelli, A. Léty, C. Tosi, I. Pasquon, Makromol. Chem. *115* (1968) 73...88
(7) film between CsI

propene – TFE   CP

(1) propene-tetrafluoroethene copolymer (55.2 mol % propene, 44.8 mol % TFE units)
(2) colourless elastomer
(3) E. G. Brame, Jr., Du Pont, Wilmington, Dela.

(5) radical-initiated copolymerization
(6) E. G. Brame, Jr., J. R. Harrell, R. C. Ferguson, Macromolecules *8* (1975) 604
(7) film from Cl₃C–CH₃ on CsI

C_3H_6–C_2H_3Cl

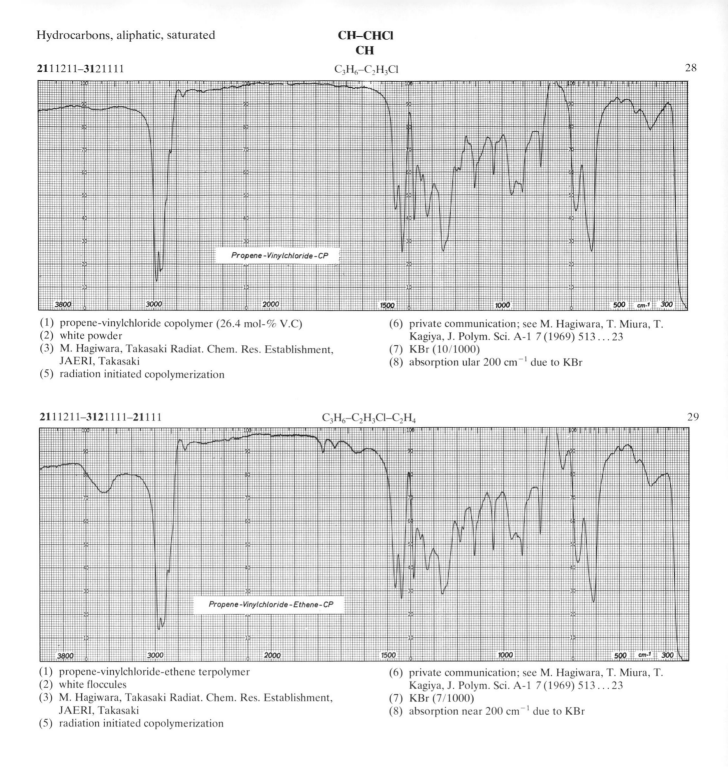

Propene-Vinylchloride-CP

(1) propene-vinylchloride copolymer (26.4 mol-% V.C)
(2) white powder
(3) M. Hagiwara, Takasaki Radiat. Chem. Res. Establishment, JAERI, Takasaki
(5) radiation initiated copolymerization

(6) private communication; see M. Hagiwara, T. Miura, T. Kagiya, J. Polym. Sci. A-1 7 (1969) 513...23
(7) KBr (10/1000)
(8) absorption ular 200 cm^{-1} due to KBr

C_3H_6–C_2H_3Cl–C_2H_4

Propene-Vinylchloride-Ethene-CP

(1) propene-vinylchloride-ethene terpolymer
(2) white floccules
(3) M. Hagiwara, Takasaki Radiat. Chem. Res. Establishment, JAERI, Takasaki
(5) radiation initiated copolymerization

(6) private communication; see M. Hagiwara, T. Miura, T. Kagiya, J. Polym. Sci. A-1 7 (1969) 513...23
(7) KBr (7/1000)
(8) absorption near 200 cm^{-1} due to KBr

C_4H_8

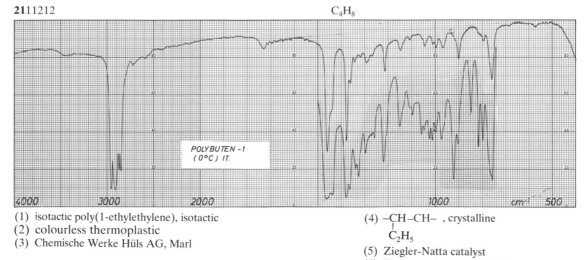

POLYBUTEN-1
(0°C) IT.

(1) isotactic poly(1-ethylethylene), isotactic
(2) colourless thermoplastic
(3) Chemische Werke Hüls AG, Marl

(4) –CH–CH– , crystalline
    C_2H_5
(5) Ziegler-Natta catalyst
(7) film from the melt (273 K)

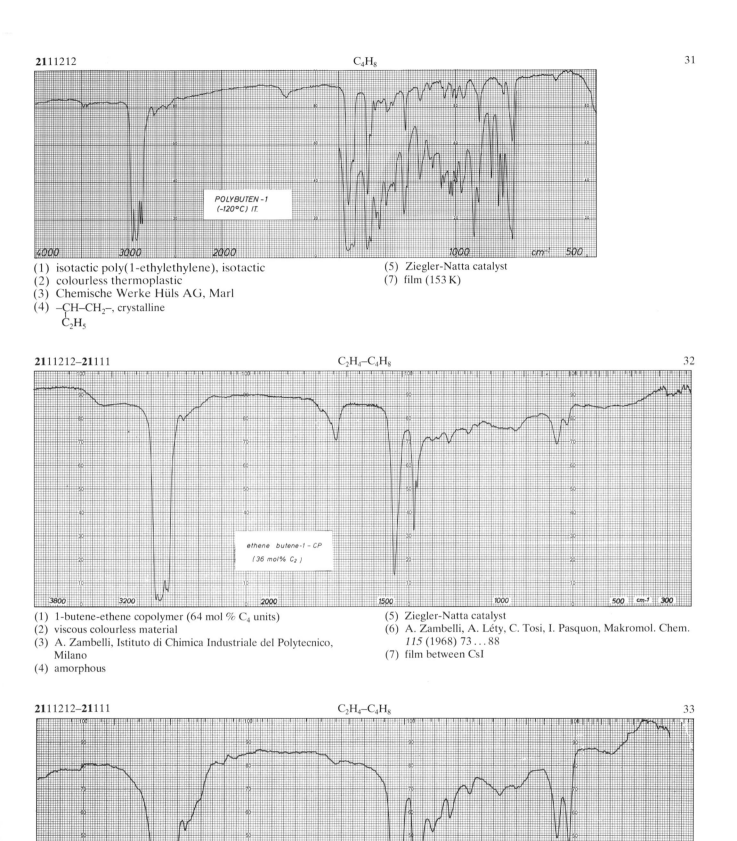

2111212 C_4H_8 31

POLYBUTEN-1
(-120°C) IT.

(1) isotactic poly(1-ethylethylene), isotactic
(2) colourless thermoplastic
(3) Chemische Werke Hüls AG, Marl
(4) –CH–CH$_2$–, crystalline
     |
     C$_2$H$_5$

(5) Ziegler-Natta catalyst
(7) film (153 K)

2111212–**21111** C_2H_4–C_4H_8 32

ethene butene-1 - CP
(36 mol% C$_2$)

(1) 1-butene-ethene copolymer (64 mol % C$_4$ units)
(2) viscous colourless material
(3) A. Zambelli, Istituto di Chimica Industriale del Polytecnico, Milano
(4) amorphous

(5) Ziegler-Natta catalyst
(6) A. Zambelli, A. Léty, C. Tosi, I. Pasquon, Makromol. Chem. *115* (1968) 73 … 88
(7) film between CsI

2111212–**21111** C_2H_4–C_4H_8 33

ethylene-butene-1 CP

(1) 1-butene-ethene copolymer (42.5 wt.-% C$_2$)
(2) colourless, soft material
(3) C. Tosi, Centro di Recerche di Milano, Montecatini Edison, Milano

(5) Ziegler-Natta catalyst
(6) C. Tosi, Maria P. Lachi, A. Pinto, Makromol. Chem. *120* (1968) 225 … 30
(7) melting film between CsI

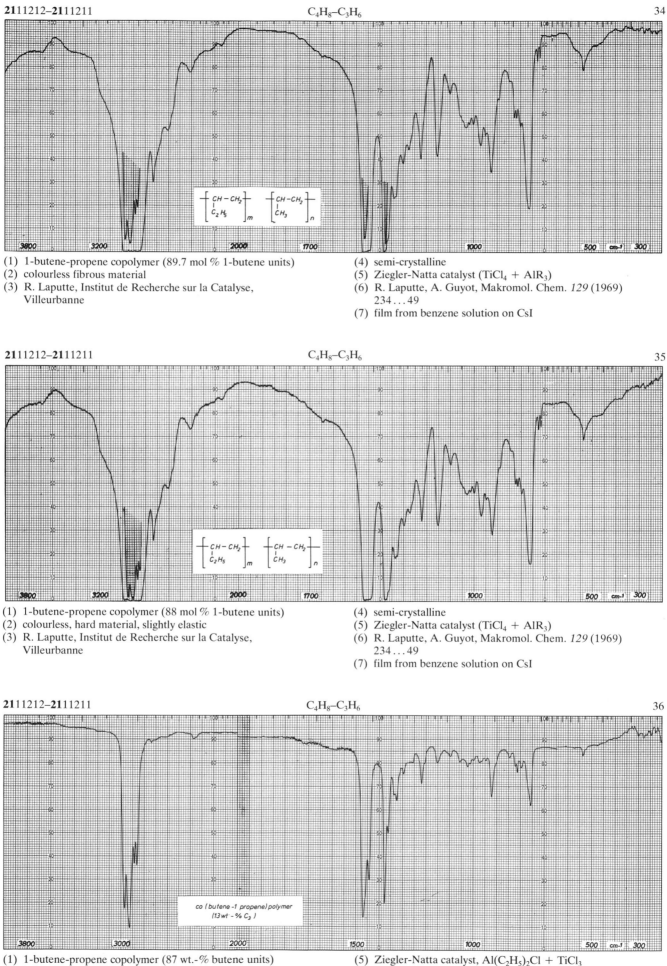

(1) 1-butene-propene copolymer (89.7 mol % 1-butene units)
(2) colourless fibrous material
(3) R. Laputte, Institut de Recherche sur la Catalyse, Villeurbanne
(4) semi-crystalline
(5) Ziegler-Natta catalyst (TiCl₄ + AlR₃)
(6) R. Laputte, A. Guyot, Makromol. Chem. *129* (1969) 234...49
(7) film from benzene solution on CsI

(1) 1-butene-propene copolymer (88 mol % 1-butene units)
(2) colourless, hard material, slightly elastic
(3) R. Laputte, Institut de Recherche sur la Catalyse, Villeurbanne
(4) semi-crystalline
(5) Ziegler-Natta catalyst (TiCl₄ + AlR₃)
(6) R. Laputte, A. Guyot, Makromol. Chem. *129* (1969) 234...49
(7) film from benzene solution on CsI

co (butene -1 propene) polymer
(13 wt - % C₃)

(1) 1-butene-propene copolymer (87 wt.-% butene units)
(2) colourless material
(3) G. Gianotti, Centro Ricerche Milano, Montecatini Edison S.p.A., Milano
(4) semi-crystalline
(5) Ziegler-Natta catalyst, Al(C₂H₅)₂Cl + TiCl₃
(6) G. Gianotti, A. Capizzi, Makromol. Chem. *124* (1969) 152...9
(7) film from decalin on CsI

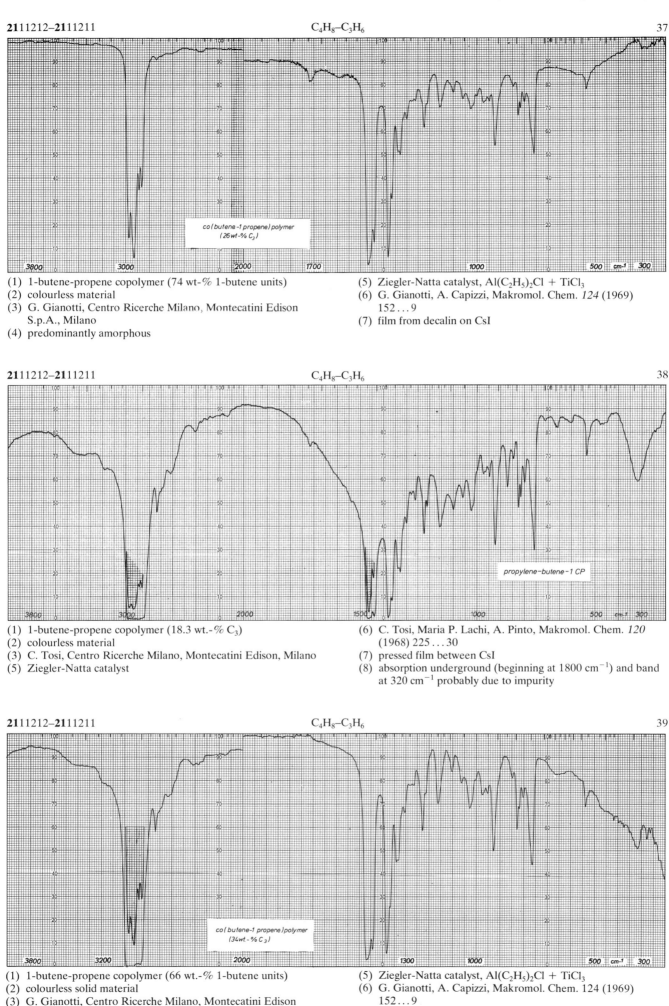

co(butene-1 propene) polymer
(26 wt-% C₃)

(1) 1-butene-propene copolymer (74 wt-% 1-butene units)
(2) colourless material
(3) G. Gianotti, Centro Ricerche Milano, Montecatini Edison
     S.p.A., Milano
(4) predominantly amorphous

(5) Ziegler-Natta catalyst, Al(C₂H₅)₂Cl + TiCl₃
(6) G. Gianotti, A. Capizzi, Makromol. Chem. *124* (1969)
     152 ... 9
(7) film from decalin on CsI

propylene–butene-1 CP

(1) 1-butene-propene copolymer (18.3 wt.-% C₃)
(2) colourless material
(3) C. Tosi, Centro Ricerche Milano, Montecatini Edison, Milano
(5) Ziegler-Natta catalyst

(6) C. Tosi, Maria P. Lachi, A. Pinto, Makromol. Chem. *120*
     (1968) 225 ... 30
(7) pressed film between CsI
(8) absorption underground (beginning at 1800 cm⁻¹) and band
     at 320 cm⁻¹ probably due to impurity

co(butene-1 propene)polymer
(34wt.-% C₃)

(1) 1-butene-propene copolymer (66 wt.-% 1-butene units)
(2) colourless solid material
(3) G. Gianotti, Centro Ricerche Milano, Montecatini Edison
     S.p.A., Milano
(4) predominantly amorphous

(5) Ziegler-Natta catalyst, Al(C₂H₅)₂Cl + TiCl₃
(6) G. Gianotti, A. Capizzi, Makromol. Chem. 124 (1969)
     152 ... 9
(7) film from decalin on CsI
(8) absorption bands beyond 400 cm⁻¹ probably not true

2111212–**35111**   C$_4$H$_8$–C$_2$F$_3$Cl   40

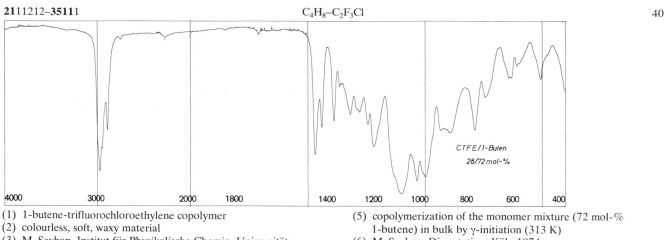

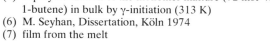

(1) 1-butene-trifluorochloroethylene copolymer
(2) colourless, soft, waxy material
(3) M. Seyhan, Institut für Physikalische Chemie, Universität Köln
(4) 65.8 mol-% 1-butene unit; the product has probably alternating structure with alkyl endgroups
(5) copolymerization of the monomer mixture (72 mol-% 1-butene) in bulk by γ-initiation (313 K)
(6) M. Seyhan, Dissertation, Köln 1974
(7) film from the melt

2111212–**35111**   C$_4$H$_8$–C$_2$F$_3$Cl   41

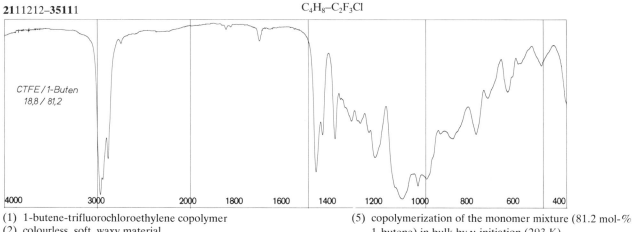

(1) 1-butene-trifluorochloroethylene copolymer
(2) colourless, soft, waxy material
(3) M. Seyhan, Institut für Physikalische Chemie, Universität Köln
(4) 61.7 mol-% 1-butene; probably alternating structure with alkyl endgroups
(5) copolymerization of the monomer mixture (81.2 mol-% 1-butene) in bulk by γ-initiation (293 K)
(6) M. Seyhan, Dissertation, Köln 1974
(7) film from the melt

2111213   C$_5$H$_{10}$ 42

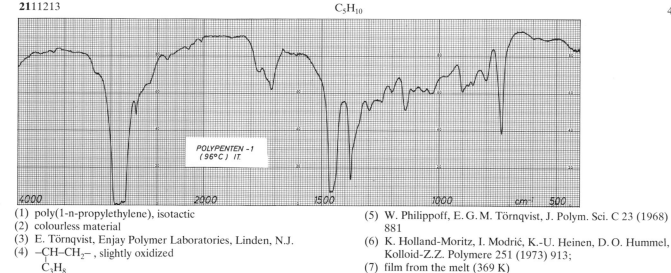

(1) poly(1-n-propylethylene), isotactic
(2) colourless material
(3) E. Törnqvist, Enjay Polymer Laboratories, Linden, N.J.
(4) –CH–CH$_2$– , slightly oxidized
　　　|
　　C$_3$H$_8$
(5) W. Philippoff, E. G. M. Törnqvist, J. Polym. Sci. C 23 (1968) 881
(6) K. Holland-Moritz, I. Modrić, K.-U. Heinen, D. O. Hummel, Kolloid-Z.Z. Polymere 251 (1973) 913;
(7) film from the melt (369 K)
(8) slightly oxidized

2111213   C₅H₁₀   43

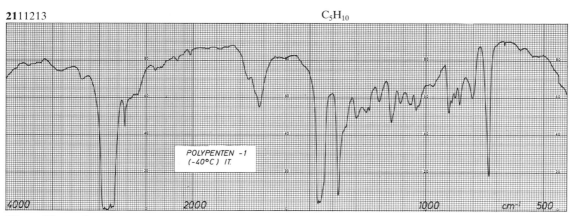

POLYPENTEN -1
(-40°C) IT.

(1) ....(6) see above
(7) recrystallized film (233 K)
(8) slightly oxidized

2111214   C₆H₁₂   44

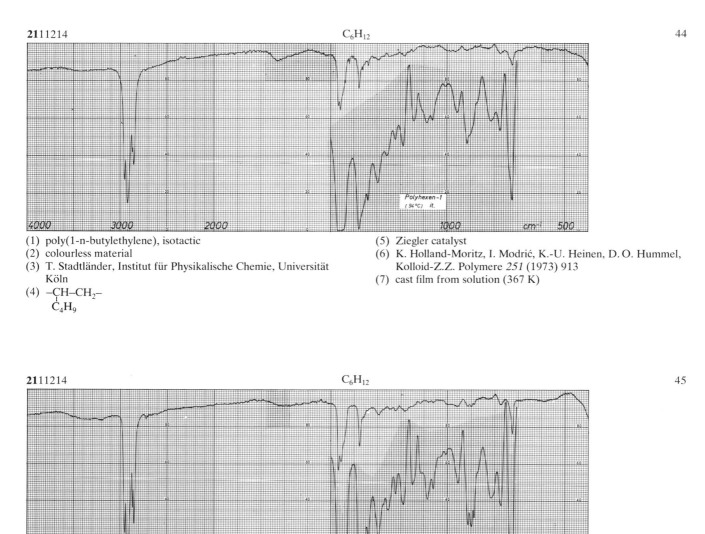

Polyhexen-1
(94°C) it.

(1) poly(1-n-butylethylene), isotactic
(2) colourless material
(3) T. Stadtländer, Institut für Physikalische Chemie, Universität Köln
(4) –CH–CH₂–
        │
       C₄H₉

(5) Ziegler catalyst
(6) K. Holland-Moritz, I. Modrić, K.-U. Heinen, D. O. Hummel, Kolloid-Z.Z. Polymere *251* (1973) 913
(7) cast film from solution (367 K)

2111214   C₆H₁₂   45

Polyhexen-1
(-113°C) it.

(1) ...(6) see above
(7) cast film from solution, partly crystallized (160 K)

2111214 C_7H_{14} 46

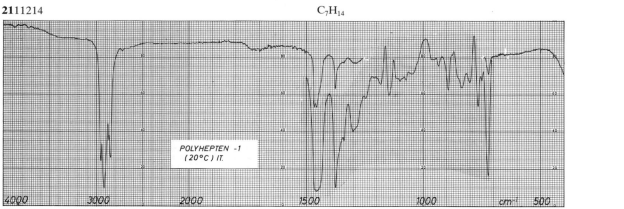

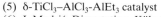

(1) poly(1-n-pentylethylene), amorphous, isotactic
(2) colourless material
(3) E. Törnqvist, Enjay Polymer Laboratories, Linden, N.J.
(4) –CH–CH$_2$–
    C_5H_{11}

(5) δ-TiCl$_3$–AlCl$_3$-AlEt$_3$ catalyst
(6) I. Modrić, Dissertation, Köln 1974; E. G. M. Törnqvist, Ann. New York Acad. Sci. *155* (1969) 447
(7) cast film from solution (293 K)

2111214 C_7H_{14} 47

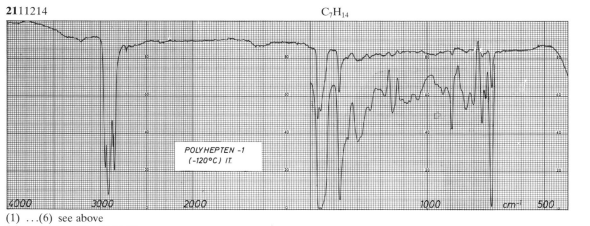

(1) ...(6) see above
(7) amorphous film (153 K)

2111214 C_8H_{16} 48

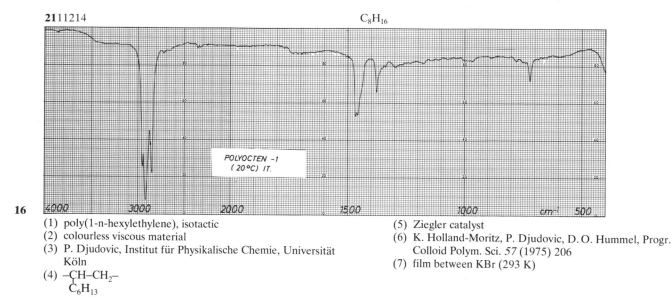

16

(1) poly(1-n-hexylethylene), isotactic
(2) colourless viscous material
(3) P. Djudovic, Institut für Physikalische Chemie, Universität Köln
(4) –CH–CH$_2$–
    C_6H_{13}

(5) Ziegler catalyst
(6) K. Holland-Moritz, P. Djudovic, D. O. Hummel, Progr. Colloid Polym. Sci. *57* (1975) 206
(7) film between KBr (293 K)

2111214 C_8H_{16} 49

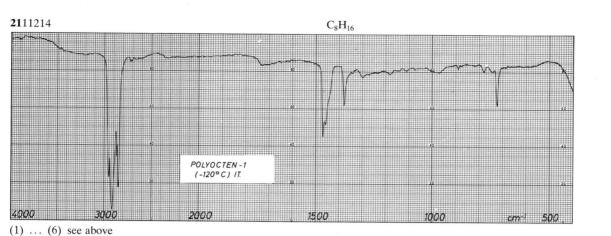

POLYOCTEN - 1
(-120°C) I.T.

(1) ... (6) see above
(7) amorphous film (153 K)

2111214 $C_{10}H_{20}$ 50

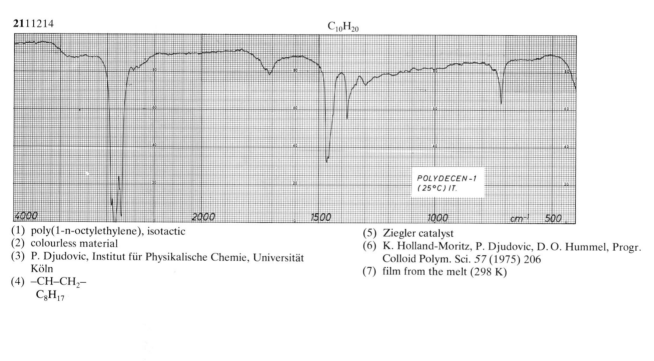

POLYDECEN - 1
(25°C) I.T.

(1) poly(1-n-octylethylene), isotactic
(2) colourless material
(3) P. Djudovic, Institut für Physikalische Chemie, Universität Köln
(4) –CH–CH$_2$–
   C_8H_{17}

(5) Ziegler catalyst
(6) K. Holland-Moritz, P. Djudovic, D. O. Hummel, Progr. Colloid Polym. Sci. *57* (1975) 206
(7) film from the melt (298 K)

2111214 $C_{10}H_{20}$ 51

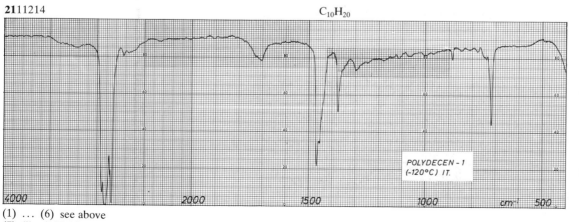

POLYDECEN - 1
(-120°C) I.T.

(1) ... (6) see above
(7) film (153 K)

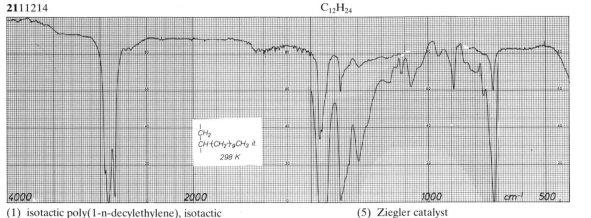

(1) isotactic poly(1-n-decylethylene), isotactic
(2) colourless material
(3) T. Stadtländer, Institut für Physikalische Chemie, Universität Köln
(4) amorphous

(5) Ziegler catalyst
(6) K. Holland-Moritz, Colloid Polym. Sci. *253* (1975) 922
(7) film (298 K)

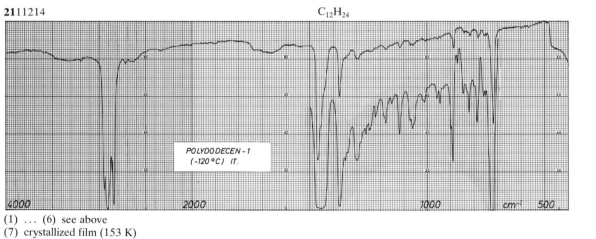

POLYDODECEN-1
(-120 °C) IT.

(1) ... (6) see above
(7) crystallized film (153 K)

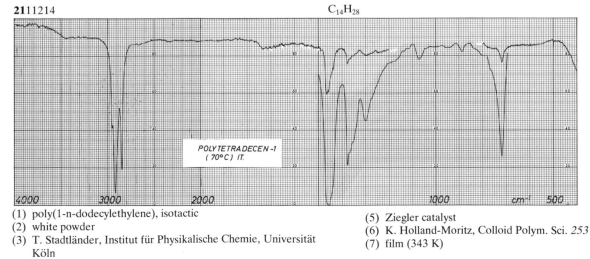

POLYTETRADECEN-1
(70 °C) IT.

(1) poly(1-n-dodecylethylene), isotactic
(2) white powder
(3) T. Stadtländer, Institut für Physikalische Chemie, Universität Köln
(4) –CH–CH$_2$– , amorphous
    $C_{12}H_{25}$

(5) Ziegler catalyst
(6) K. Holland-Moritz, Colloid Polym. Sci. *253* (1975) 922
(7) film (343 K)

2111214 $C_{14}H_{28}$ 55

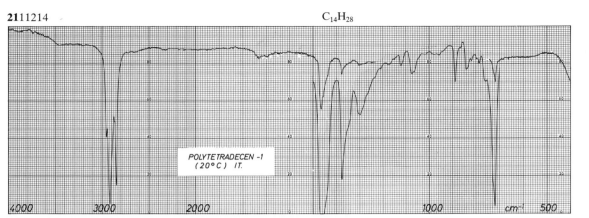

POLYTETRADECEN -1
(20°C) I.T.

(1) ... (6) see above
(7) partly crystallized film from the melt (293 K)

2111214 $C_{14}H_{28}$ 56

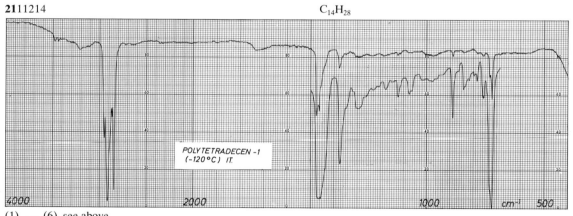

POLYTETRADECEN -1
(-120°C) I.T.

(1) ... (6) see above
(7) crystallized film from the melt (153 K)

2111214 $C_{16}H_{32}$ 57

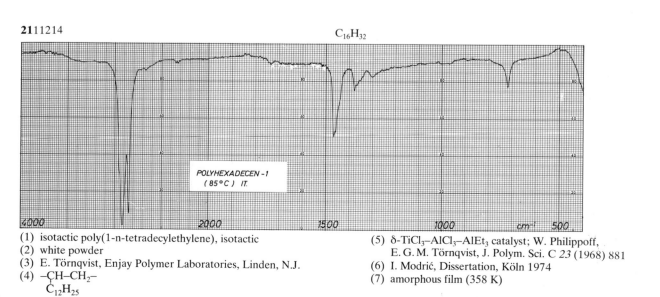

POLYHEXADECEN -1
(85°C) I.T.

(1) isotactic poly(1-n-tetradecylethylene), isotactic
(2) white powder
(3) E. Törnqvist, Enjay Polymer Laboratories, Linden, N.J.
(4) $-CH-CH_2-$
       $C_{12}H_{25}$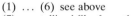

(5) δ-$TiCl_3$–$AlCl_3$–$AlEt_3$ catalyst; W. Philippoff,
     E. G. M. Törnqvist, J. Polym. Sci. C *23* (1968) 881
(6) I. Modrić, Dissertation, Köln 1974
(7) amorphous film (358 K)

2111214 $C_{16}H_{32}$ 58

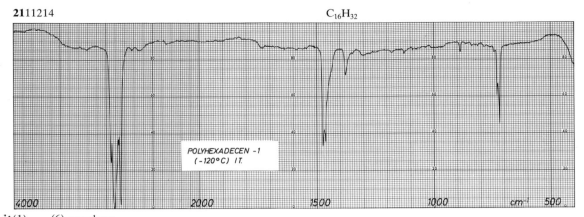

POLYHEXADECEN -1
(-120°C) I.T.

∴ (1) ... (6) see above
(7) crystallized film (153 K)

2111214 $C_{18}H_{36}$ 59

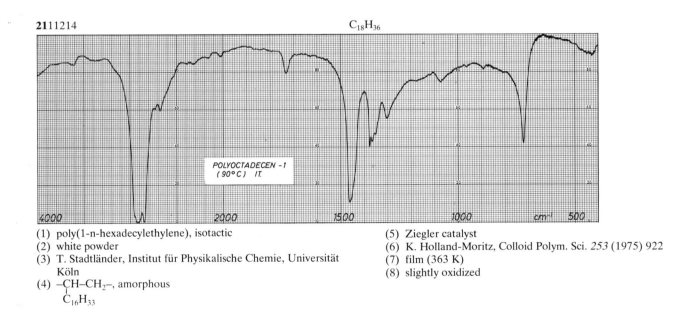

POLYOCTADECEN -1
(90°C) I.T.

(1) poly(1-n-hexadecylethylene), isotactic
(2) white powder
(3) T. Stadtländer, Institut für Physikalische Chemie, Universität Köln
(4) –CH–CH$_2$–, amorphous
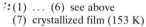
   $\overset{|}{C}_{16}H_{33}$

(5) Ziegler catalyst
(6) K. Holland-Moritz, Colloid Polym. Sci. *253* (1975) 922
(7) film (363 K)
(8) slightly oxidized

2111214 $C_{18}H_{36}$ 60

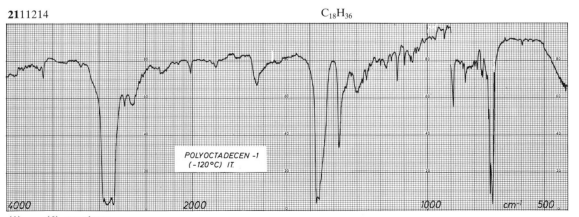

POLYOCTADECEN -1
(-120°C) I.T.

(1) ... (6) see above
(7) crystallized film from the melt (153 K)
(8) slightly oxidized

2111214 $C_{18}H_{36}$ 61

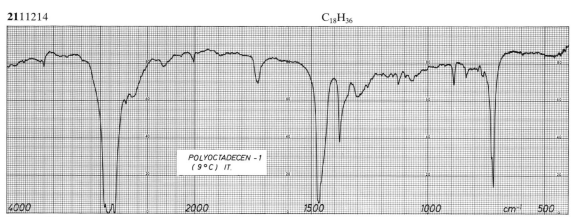

POLYOCTADECEN - 1
(9 °C) IT.

(1) ... (6) see above
(7) partly crystallized film from the melt (282 K)
(8) slightly oxidized

211122 C_6H_{12} 62

-CH-CH₂-
* CHCH₃   it.,o.a.
CH₂-CH₃

(1) poly[(S)-3-methylpent-1-ene]
(3) F. Ciardelli, Istituto di Chimica Organica Industriale,
    Universitá di Pisa
(4) optically active, (partially) isotactic

(5) polymerization with stereospecific catalyst (by C. Carlini,
    F. Ciardelli, O. Pieroni)
(6) private communication
(7) film from solution (spectrum by E. Benedetti and
    P. Vergamini)

211122 C_6H_{12} 63

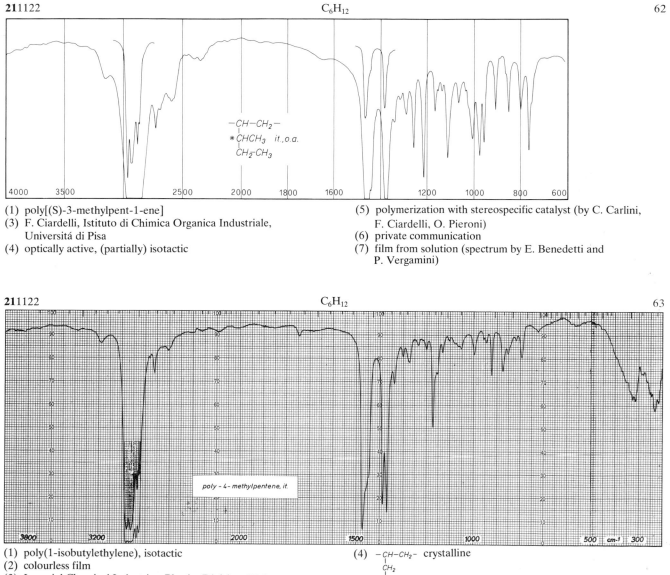

poly - 4- methylpentene, it.

(1) poly(1-isobutylethylene), isotactic
(2) colourless film
(3) Imperial Chemical Industries, Plastics Division, Welwyn
    Garden City, Herts.

(4) –CH–CH₂- crystalline
       |
      CH₂
       |
  CH₃–CH–CH₃

(7) film (40 μm, KBr 2/350)

211122 C_7H_{14} 64

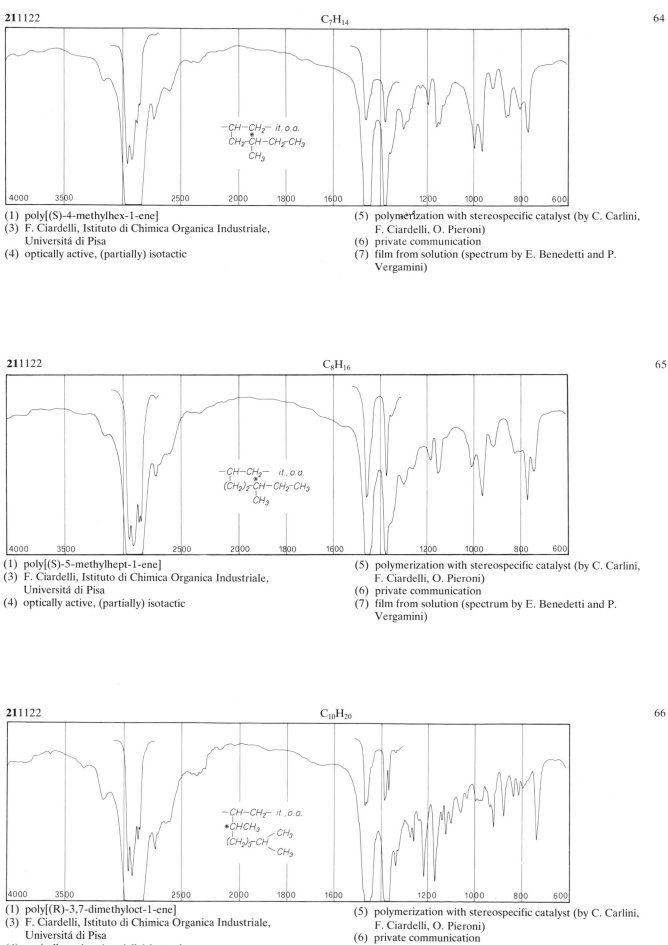

(1) poly[(S)-4-methylhex-1-ene]
(3) F. Ciardelli, Istituto di Chimica Organica Industriale, Universitá di Pisa
(4) optically active, (partially) isotactic
(5) polymerization with stereospecific catalyst (by C. Carlini, F. Ciardelli, O. Pieroni)
(6) private communication
(7) film from solution (spectrum by E. Benedetti and P. Vergamini)

211122 C_8H_{16} 65

(1) poly[(S)-5-methylhept-1-ene]
(3) F. Ciardelli, Istituto di Chimica Organica Industriale, Universitá di Pisa
(4) optically active, (partially) isotactic
(5) polymerization with stereospecific catalyst (by C. Carlini, F. Ciardelli, O. Pieroni)
(6) private communication
(7) film from solution (spectrum by E. Benedetti and P. Vergamini)

211122 $C_{10}H_{20}$ 66

22

(1) poly[(R)-3,7-dimethyloct-1-ene]
(3) F. Ciardelli, Istituto di Chimica Organica Industriale, Universitá di Pisa
(4) optically active, (partially) isotactic
(5) polymerization with stereospecific catalyst (by C. Carlini, F. Ciardelli, O. Pieroni)
(6) private communication
(7) film from solution (spectrum by E. Benedetti and P. Vergamini)

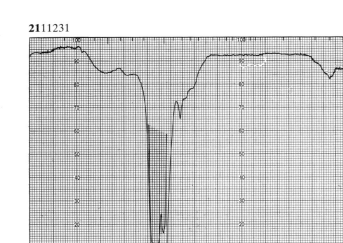
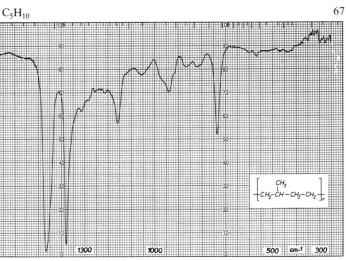

(1) polyisoprene, hydrogenated; poly(1-methyltetramethylene)
(2) colourless elastomer
(3) E. C. Gregg, B. F. Goodrich Research Center, Brecksville, O.
(4) amorphous

(5) Ameripol SN, hydrogenated with H_2 in the presence of Raney nickel
(6) E. C. Gregg, jr., J. Polymer Sci. Pt. C *24* (1968) 295...302
(7) film from benzene on CsI

2111231 C_6H_{12} 68

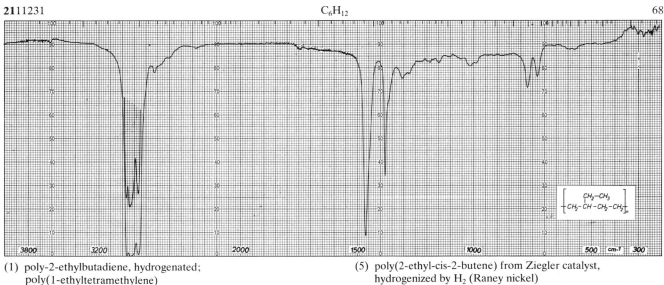

(1) poly-2-ethylbutadiene, hydrogenated;
    poly(1-ethyltetramethylene)
(2) colourless elastomer
(3) E. C. Gregg, B. F. Goodrich Research Center, Brecksville, O.
(4) amorphous

(5) poly(2-ethyl-cis-2-butene) from Ziegler catalyst, hydrogenized by H_2 (Raney nickel)
(6) E. C. Gregg, jr., J. Polymer Sci. Pt. C *24* (1968) 295...302
(7) film from benzene on CsI

2111231 C_7H_{14} 69

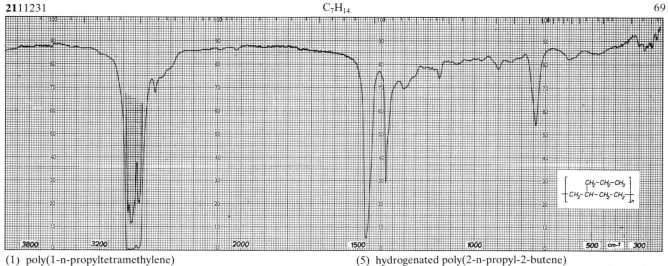

(1) poly(1-n-propyltetramethylene)
(2) tacky colourless elastomer
(3) E. C. Gregg, B. F. Goodrich Research Center, Brecksville, O.
(4) amorphous

(5) hydrogenated poly(2-n-propyl-2-butene)
(6) E. C. Gregg, jr., J. Polymer Sci. Pt. C *24* (1968) 295...302
(7) film from benzene on CsI

2111231 C$_9$H$_{18}$ 70

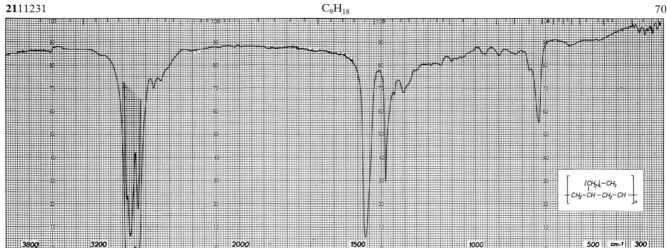

(1) poly(1-n-pentyl-tetramethylene)
(2) colourless tacky elastomer
(3) E. C. Gregg, B. F. Goodrich Research Center, Brecksville, O.
(4) amorphous

(5) hydrogenated poly(2-pentyl-2-butene)
(6) E. C. Gregg, jr., J. Polymer Sci. Pt. C 24 (1968) 295 ... 302
(7) film from benzene on CsI

2111231 C$_8$H$_{16}$ 71

Poly-1-methylheptamethylen
313 K

(1) poly(1-methylheptamethylene)
(2) colourless material
(3) K. Spiekermann, Institut für Physikalische Chemie, Universität Köln

(5) ring opening polymerization of 3-methylcycloheptene with WCl$_4$(OC$_2$H$_4$Cl)$_2$/Al(C$_2$H$_5$)$_2$Cl (toluene, 273 K), followed by reduction with diimide.
(6) K. Spiekermann, Dissertation, Köln 1976
(7) film from toluene (313 K)

2111231 C$_8$H$_{16}$ 72

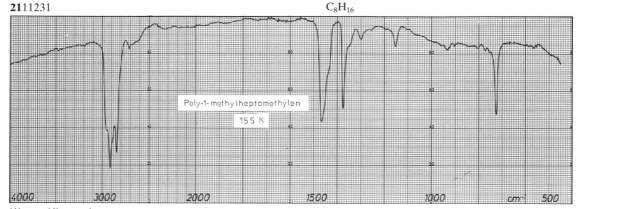

Poly-1-methylheptamethylen
155 K

(1) ... (6) see above
(7) film from toluene (155 K)

2111231 C_9H_{18} 73

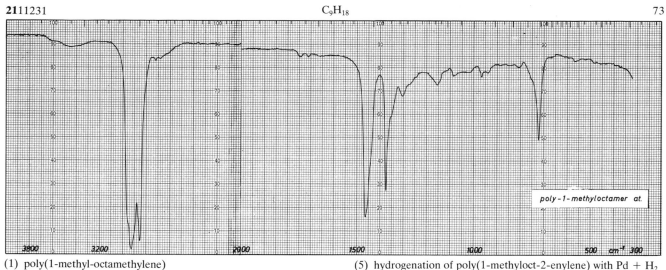

poly-1-methyloctamer at.

(1) poly(1-methyl-octamethylene)
(2) clear brownish elastomer
(3) G. Dall'Asta, Centro Ricerche Milano, Montecatini Edison S.p.A., Milano
(4) amorphous
(5) hydrogenation of poly(1-methyloct-2-enylene) with Pd + H_2
(6) G. Gianotti, G. Dall'Asta, A. Valvassori, V. Zamboni, Makromol. Chem. 149 (1971) 117
(7) film from benzene on KBr

2111232 C_9H_{18} 74

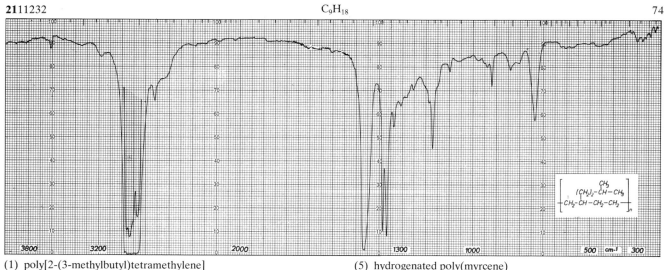

(1) poly[2-(3-methylbutyl)tetramethylene]
(2) soft colourless elastomer
(3) E. C. Gregg, B. F. Goodrich Research Center, Brecksville, O.
(4) amorphous
(5) hydrogenated poly(myrcene)
(6) E. C. Gregg, jr., J. Polymer Sci. Pt. C *24* (1968) 295...302
(7) film from benzene on CsI

211124 C_4H_8 75

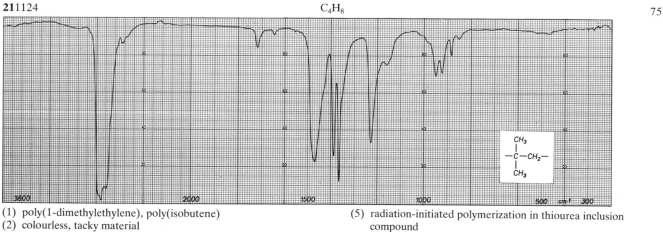

(1) poly(1-dimethylethylene), poly(isobutene)
(2) colourless, tacky material
(3) H.-P. Bohlmann, Institut für Physikalische Chemie, Universität Köln
(4)
(5) radiation-initiated polymerization in thiourea inclusion compound
(6) H.-P. Bohlmann, Diplomarbeit, Köln 1975
(7) film from n-hexane on CsI

25

211126 C_2H_4 76

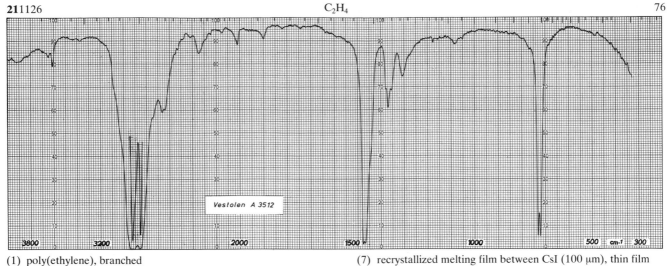

Vestolen A 3512

(1) poly(ethylene), branched
(2) glassy-turbid granules
(3) Chemische Werke Hüls AG, Marl
(4) low density, high molecular weight, small molecular weight distribution

(7) recrystallized melting film between CsI (100 μm), thin film (a few μm)
(8) commercial product „Vestolen A 3512"

211126 C_2H_4 77

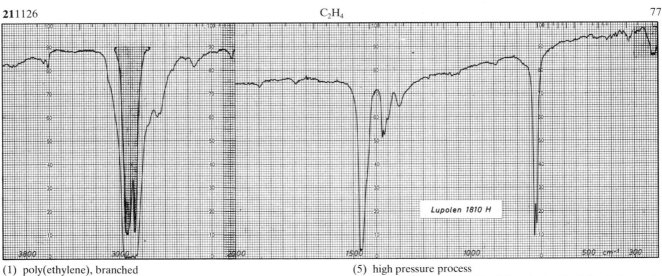

Lupolen 1810 H

(1) poly(ethylene), branched
(2) white granules
(3) BASF AG

(5) high pressure process
(7) recrystallized melting film (70 μm), stretched film (a few μm)
(8) commercial product „Lupolen 1810 H"

211126 C_3H_6 78

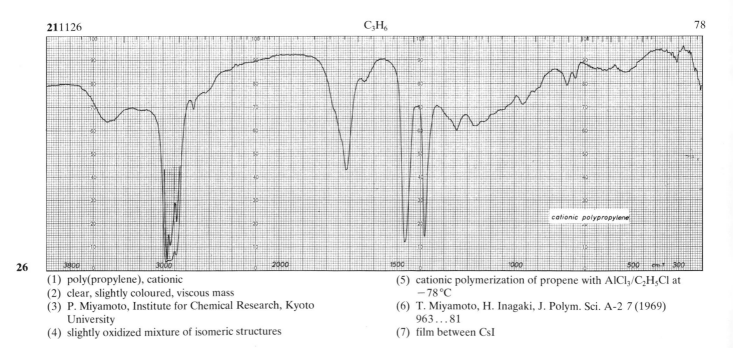

cationic polypropylene

(1) poly(propylene), cationic
(2) clear, slightly coloured, viscous mass
(3) P. Miyamoto, Institute for Chemical Research, Kyoto University
(4) slightly oxidized mixture of isomeric structures

(5) cationic polymerization of propene with $AlCl_3/C_2H_5Cl$ at −78 °C
(6) T. Miyamoto, H. Inagaki, J. Polym. Sci. A-2 7 (1969) 963...81
(7) film between CsI

211132   C$_8$H$_{12}$ 79

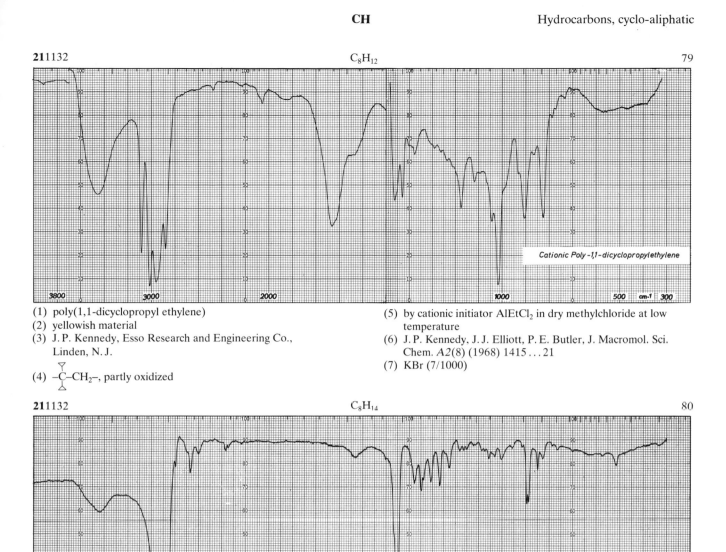

Cationic Poly -1,1-dicyclopropylethylene

(1) poly(1,1-dicyclopropyl ethylene)
(2) yellowish material
(3) J. P. Kennedy, Esso Research and Engineering Co., Linden, N. J.
(4) –C–CH$_2$–, partly oxidized

(5) by cationic initiator AlEtCl$_2$ in dry methylchloride at low temperature
(6) J. P. Kennedy, J. J. Elliott, P. E. Butler, J. Macromol. Sci. Chem. *A2*(8) (1968) 1415...21
(7) KBr (7/1000)

211132   C$_8$H$_{14}$ 80

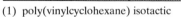

(1) poly(vinylcyclohexane) isotactic
(2) colourless (white) light powder
(3) A. Abe, Central Research Lab., Showa Denko K.K., Tokyo
(4) crystalline

(5) from vinylcyclohexane by stereospecific polymerization
(6) A. Abe, T. Hama, Polymer Letters *7* (1969) 427...35
(7) KBr (2/300)

211132   C$_8$H$_{14}$ 81

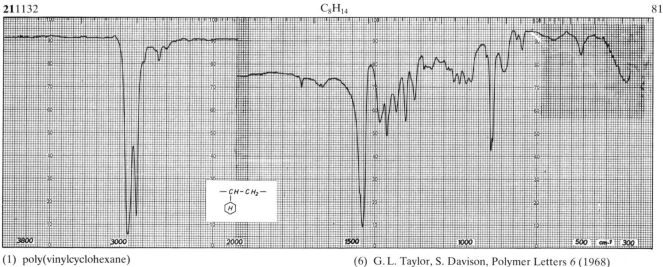

(1) poly(vinylcyclohexane)
(2) colourless (white) powder
(3) G. L. Taylor, Synthetic Rubber Technical Center, Shell Chemical Company, Torrance, Calif.
(5) from anionic polystyrene (60 °C) by hydrogenation (activated nickel catalyst)

(6) G. L. Taylor, S. Davison, Polymer Letters *6* (1968) 699...705
(7) brittle film from CHCl$_3$ (4000...2000 cm^{-1}), KBr (2000...300 cm^{-1})

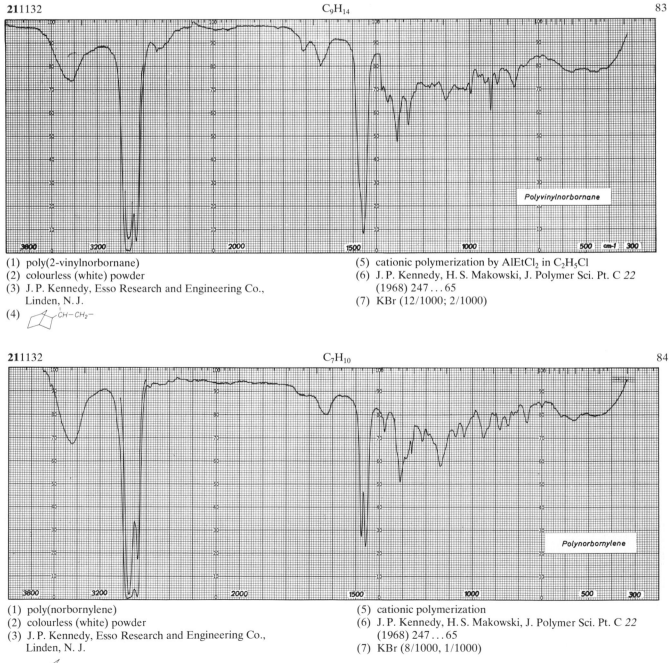

211132 C_8H_{14} 82

*polyvinylcyclohexane it.
(3% styrene units)*

(1) poly(vinylcyclohexane), isotactic, with 3 % styrene units
(2) colourless clear film
(3) A. Abe, Central Research Lab., Showa Denko K.K., Tokyo
(5) by hydrogenation of isotactic polystyrene
(6) Abe, T. Hama, Polymer Letters 7 (1969) 427 ... 35
(7) KBr (2/300)

211132 C_9H_{14} 83

Polyvinylnorbornane

(1) poly(2-vinylnorbornane)
(2) colourless (white) powder
(3) J. P. Kennedy, Esso Research and Engineering Co.,
     Linden, N. J.
(4) $\overset{|}{CH}-CH_2-$
(5) cationic polymerization by AlEtCl$_2$ in C$_2$H$_5$Cl
(6) J. P. Kennedy, H. S. Makowski, J. Polymer Sci. Pt. C *22*
     (1968) 247 ... 65
(7) KBr (12/1000; 2/1000)

211132 C_7H_{10} 84

Polynorbornylene

(1) poly(norbornylene)
(2) colourless (white) powder
(3) J. P. Kennedy, Esso Research and Engineering Co.,
     Linden, N. J.
(5) cationic polymerization
(6) J. P. Kennedy, H. S. Makowski, J. Polymer Sci. Pt. C *22*
     (1968) 247 ... 65
(7) KBr (8/1000, 1/1000)

2112113 C_4H_6 85

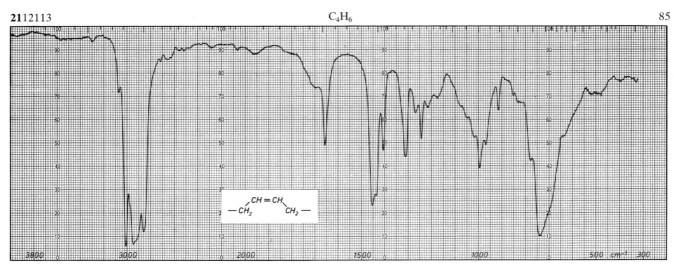

(1) poly(cis-2-butenylene)
(2) almost colourless elastomer
(3) Chemische Werke Hüls AG (laboratory preparation)

(6) private communication
(7) film from CCl_4 solution on KBr

2112113 C_4H_6 86

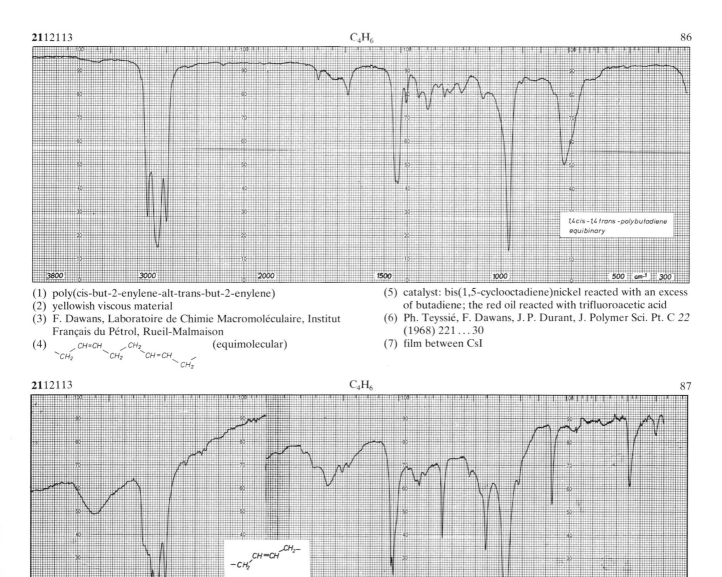

1,4 cis - 1,4 trans - polybutadiene
equibinary

(1) poly(cis-but-2-enylene-alt-trans-but-2-enylene)
(2) yellowish viscous material
(3) F. Dawans, Laboratoire de Chimie Macromoléculaire, Institut Français du Pétrol, Rueil-Malmaison
(4) 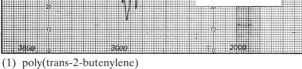 (equimolecular)

(5) catalyst: bis(1,5-cyclooctadiene)nickel reacted with an excess of butadiene; the red oil reacted with trifluoroacetic acid
(6) Ph. Teyssié, F. Dawans, J. P. Durant, J. Polymer Sci. Pt. C 22 (1968) 221...30
(7) film between CsI

2112113 C_4H_6 87

(1) poly(trans-2-butenylene)
(2) yellowish material
(3) C. Tosi, Montecatini Edison S.p.A., Milano

(4) crystalline
(6) private communication
(7) KBr (6/300)

2112113 C_4H_6 88

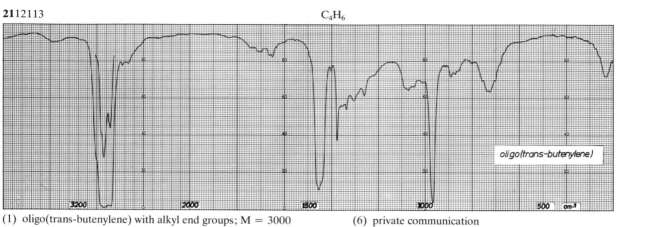

oligo(trans-butenylene)

(1) oligo(trans-butenylene) with alkyl end groups; M = 3000
(2) colourless viscous material
(3) W. Ast, R. Kerber, Institut für Technische Chemie,
    TU München
(5) depolymerization of poly(cis-butenylene) by a metathesis
    catalyst $WCl_6 + Sn(CH_3)_4$ in the presence of trans-4-octene

(6) private communication
(7) film between thin KBr wafers
(8) part of the 4-octene forms the end-groups

2112113–**21**1212 C_4H_6 89

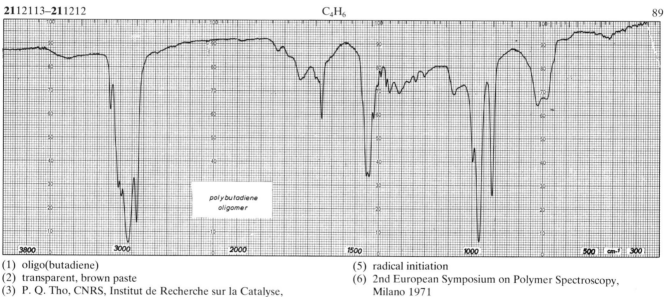

polybutadiene oligomer

(1) oligo(butadiene)
(2) transparent, brown paste
(3) P. Q. Tho, CNRS, Institut de Recherche sur la Catalyse,
    Villeurbanne
(4) mixture of isomers

(5) radical initiation
(6) 2nd European Symposium on Polymer Spectroscopy,
    Milano 1971
(7) film between CsI

2112113–**21**1212–**31**21211 $C_4H_6–C_4H_5Cl$ 90

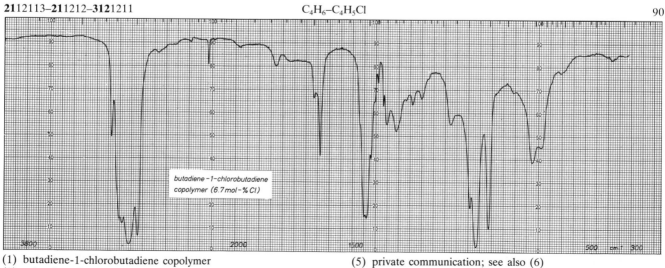

butadiene–1-chlorobutadiene copolymer (6.7 mol-% Cl)

(1) butadiene-1-chlorobutadiene copolymer
(2) colourless elastomer
(3) S. Yamashita, Department of Chemistry, Kyoto Institute of
    Technology, Kyoto
(4) bulk copolymer with 6.7 mol-% Cl and some CN

(5) private communication; see also (6)
(6) S. Yamashita, S. Kohjiya, S. Atomori, A. Yamada, Angew.
    Makromol. Chem. *56* (1976) 65 . . . 75; private communication
(7) film from toluene on CsI

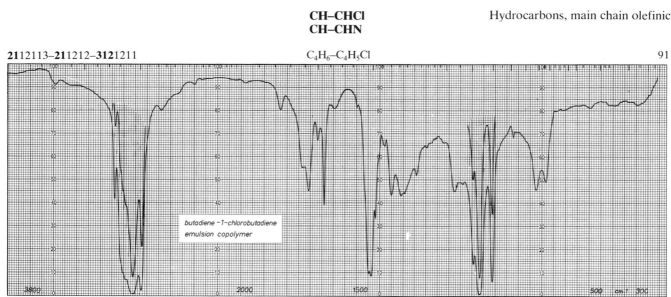

butadiene –1-chlorobutadiene emulsion copolymer

(1) butadiene-1-chlorobutadiene copolymer, partly hydrolyzed
(2) colourless elastomer
(3) S. Yamashita, Department of Chemistry, Kyoto Institute of Technology, Kyoto
(4) the copolymer originally contained 3.17 mol-% Cl-BD units; after partial hydrolysis 1.94 mol-% Cl, 1.23 mol-% OH

(5) low-temperature emulsion copolymerization (5 °C, redox-type initiator)
(6) S. Yamashita, S. Kohjiya, S. Atomori, A. Yamada, Angew. Makromol. Chem. *56* (1976) 65 . . . 75; private communication
(7) film from toluene on CsI

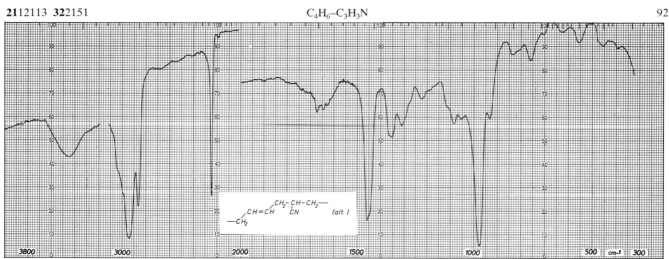

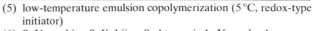

(1) alternating butadiene-acrylonitrile copolymer
(2) greyish-brown elastomer
(3) W. Kuran, Institute of Organic Chemistry and Technology, TU Warszawa
(4) the butadiene units have predominantly 1,4-trans structure

(5) reaction of an AN → AlRCl₂ complex with butadiene; see W. Kuran, S. Pasynkiewicz, Z. Florjanczyk, Makromol. Chem. *162* (1972) 53
(6) W. Kuran, S. Pasynkiewicz, Z. Florjańczyk, ibid. *174* (1973) 73 . . . 80
(7) swollen in CHCl₃, ground with KBr, dried and pressed

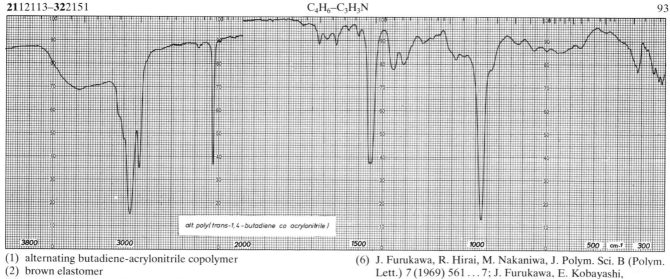

alt. poly(trans-1,4 – butadiene co acrylonitrile)

(1) alternating butadiene-acrylonitrile copolymer
(2) brown elastomer
(3) J. Furukawa, Kyoto University, Yoshida
(4) predominantly 1,4-trans configuration of the BD units
(5) copolymerization of the monomers with EtAlCl₂-VOCl₃-initiator

(6) J. Furukawa, R. Hirai, M. Nakaniwa, J. Polym. Sci. B (Polym. Lett.) *7* (1969) 561 . . . 7; J. Furukawa, E. Kobayashi, Y. Iseda, Polym. J. *1* (1970) 155. . .63
(7) film from CHCl₃ on CsI

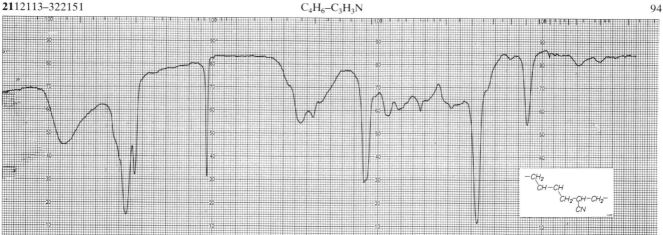

(1) butadiene-acrylonitrile copolymer
(2) brown resinous material
(3) M. Taniguchi, Maruzen Petochem. Comp., Ichihara. Chibá
(4) alternating, BD-units predominantly trans
(5) copolymerization of monomers in equimolar amounts with a CrO_2Cl_2/$AlEt_3$ catalyst at 35 °C

(6) M. Taniguchi, A. Kawasaki, J. Furukawa, Polym. Lett. *7* (1969) 411 ... 7
(7) ground with KBr (3/350) and $CHCl_3$, dried and pressed
(8) bands at 1220 and 760 cm^{-1} due to residual $CHCl_3$

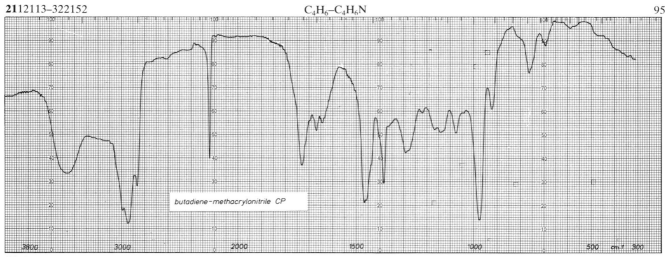

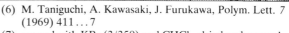

butadiene-methacrylonitrile CP

(1) butadiene-methacrylonitrile copolymer
(2) yellowish elastomer
(3) K.-F. Elgert, Institut für Makromolekulare Chemie, Universität Freiburg i. Br.
(4) alternating structure; BD units: 58 % 1,4-trans, 22 % 1,4-cis, 20 % 1,2

(5) J. Furukawa, E. Kobayashi, Y. Iseda, Y. Arai, Polymer. J. *1* (1970) 442; J. Furukawa, Y. Iseda, K. Haga, N. Kataoka, J. Polym. Sci. A-1 *8* (1970) 1147
(6) K.-F. Elgert. B. Stützel, I. Forgó, Polymer *16* (1975) 761 ... 3
(7) swollen in $CHCl_3$, ground with KBr, dried and pressed
(8) partly oxidized

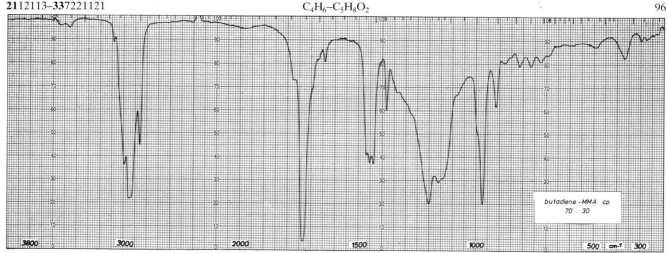

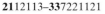

butadiene-MMA cp
70 : 30

(1) butadiene-methylmethacrylate copolymer (30 mol-% MMA units in the copolymer)
(2) colourless, tough material
(3) H. J. Harwood, N. W. Johnston, University of Akron, O.
(4) predominantly trans-1,4 units, less 1,2 units, only small amount of cis-1,4

(5) radical copolymerization
(6) private communication
(7) film from $CHCl_3$ on CsI

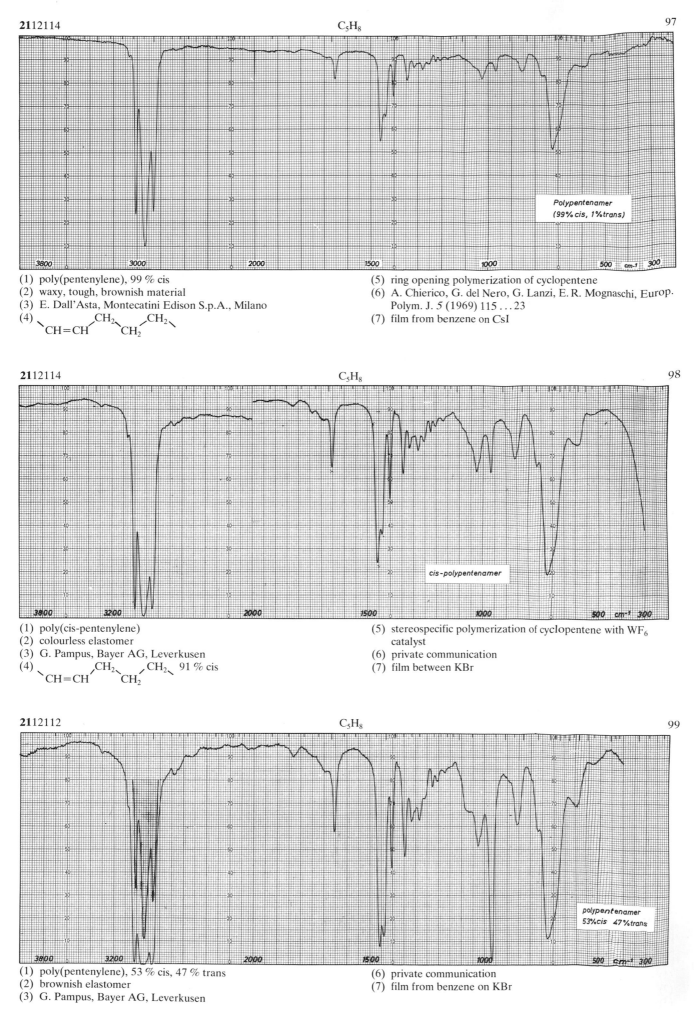

2112114 C_5H_8 97

Polypentenamer (99% cis, 1% trans)

(1) poly(pentenylene), 99 % cis
(2) waxy, tough, brownish material
(3) E. Dall'Asta, Montecatini Edison S.p.A., Milano
(4) $\backslash CH=CH \diagup CH_2 \diagdown CH_2 \diagup CH_2 \backslash$
(5) ring opening polymerization of cyclopentene
(6) A. Chierico, G. del Nero, G. Lanzi, E. R. Mognaschi, Europ. Polym. J. *5* (1969) 115 ... 23
(7) film from benzene on CsI

2112114 C_5H_8 98

cis-polypentenamer

(1) poly(cis-pentenylene)
(2) colourless elastomer
(3) G. Pampus, Bayer AG, Leverkusen
(4) $\backslash CH=CH \diagup CH_2 \diagdown CH_2 \diagup CH_2 \backslash$ 91 % cis
(5) stereospecific polymerization of cyclopentene with WF_6 catalyst
(6) private communication
(7) film between KBr

2112112 C_5H_8 99

polypentenamer 53% cis 47% trans

(1) poly(pentenylene), 53 % cis, 47 % trans
(2) brownish elastomer
(3) G. Pampus, Bayer AG, Leverkusen
(6) private communication
(7) film from benzene on KBr

2112114   C$_5$H$_8$ 100

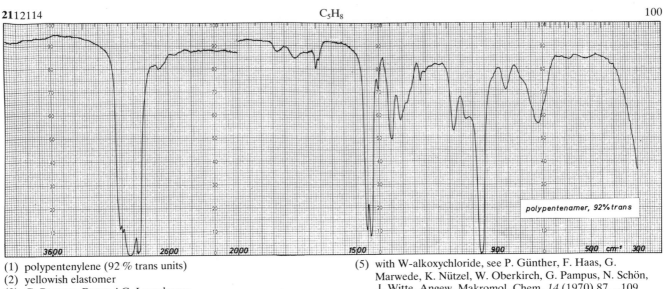

polypentenamer, 92% trans

(1) polypentenylene (92 % trans units)
(2) yellowish elastomer
(3) G. Pampus, Bayer AG, Leverkusen

(5) with W-alkoxychloride, see P. Günther, F. Haas, G.
     Marwede, K. Nützel, W. Oberkirch, G. Pampus, N. Schön,
     J. Witte, Angew. Makromol. Chem. *14* (1970) 87...109
(7) film from benzene on KBr

2112114   C$_5$H$_8$ 101

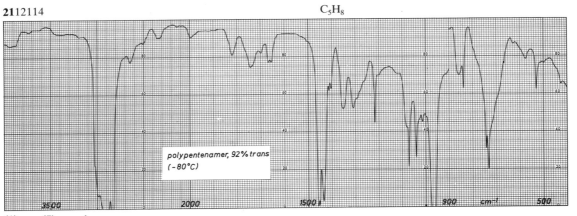

polypentenamer, 92% trans
(-80°C)

(1) ... (7) see above
(8) film measured at 193 K

2112114   C$_5$H$_8$ 102

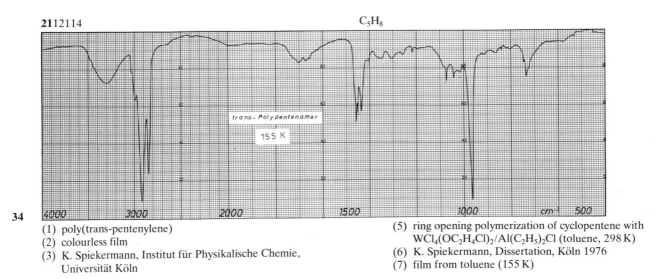
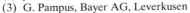

trans-Polypentenamer

155 K

(1) poly(trans-pentenylene)
(2) colourless film
(3) K. Spiekermann, Institut für Physikalische Chemie,
     Universität Köln

(5) ring opening polymerization of cyclopentene with
     WCl$_4$(OC$_2$H$_4$Cl)$_2$/Al(C$_2$H$_5$)$_2$Cl (toluene, 298 K)
(6) K. Spiekermann, Dissertation, Köln 1976
(7) film from toluene (155 K)

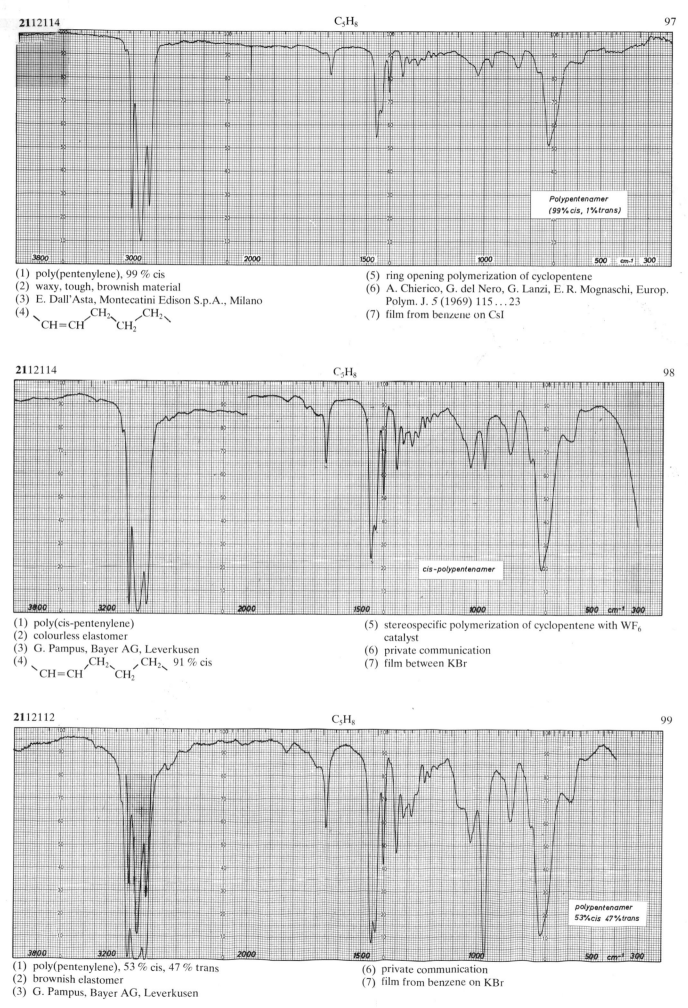

*Polypentenamer
(99% cis, 1% trans)*

(1) poly(pentenylene), 99 % cis
(2) waxy, tough, brownish material
(3) E. Dall'Asta, Montecatini Edison S.p.A., Milano
(4) CH=CH—CH₂—CH₂—CH₂—

(5) ring opening polymerization of cyclopentene
(6) A. Chierico, G. del Nero, G. Lanzi, E. R. Mognaschi, Europ. Polym. J. *5* (1969) 115...23
(7) film from benzene on CsI

cis-polypentenamer

(1) poly(cis-pentenylene)
(2) colourless elastomer
(3) G. Pampus, Bayer AG, Leverkusen
(4) CH=CH—CH₂—CH₂—CH₂— 91 % cis

(5) stereospecific polymerization of cyclopentene with WF_6 catalyst
(6) private communication
(7) film between KBr

*polypentenamer
53% cis 47% trans*

(1) poly(pentenylene), 53 % cis, 47 % trans
(2) brownish elastomer
(3) G. Pampus, Bayer AG, Leverkusen

(6) private communication
(7) film from benzene on KBr

2112114   C$_5$H$_8$ 100

polypentenamer, 92% trans

(1) polypentenylene (92 % trans units)
(2) yellowish elastomer
(3) G. Pampus, Bayer AG, Leverkusen

(5) with W-alkoxychloride, see P. Günther, F. Haas, G.
    Marwede, K. Nützel, W. Oberkirch, G. Pampus, N. Schön,
    J. Witte, Angew. Makromol. Chem. *14* (1970) 87...109
(7) film from benzene on KBr

2112114   C$_5$H$_8$ 101

polypentenamer, 92% trans
(-80°C)

(1) ... (7) see above
(8) film measured at 193 K

2112114   C$_5$H$_8$ 102

trans-Polypentenamer

155 K

(1) poly(trans-pentenylene)
(2) colourless film
(3) K. Spiekermann, Institut für Physikalische Chemie,
    Universität Köln

(5) ring opening polymerization of cyclopentene with
    WCl$_4$(OC$_2$H$_4$Cl)$_2$/Al(C$_2$H$_5$)$_2$Cl (toluene, 298 K)
(6) K. Spiekermann, Dissertation, Köln 1976
(7) film from toluene (155 K)

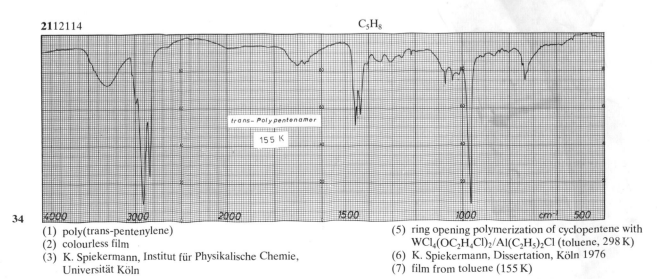

2112116   C₇H₁₂   103

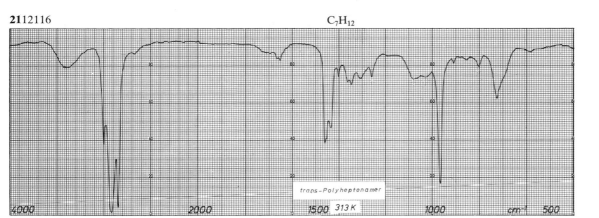

(1) poly(trans-heptenylene)
(2) colourless film
(3) K. Spiekermann, Institut für Physikalische Chemie,
Universität Köln

(5) ring opening polymerization of cycloheptene with
WCl₄(OC₂H₄Cl)₂/Al(C₂H₅)₂Cl (toluene, 273 K)
(6) K. Spiekermann, Dissertation, Köln 1976
(7) film from toluene (313 K)

2112116   C₇H₁₂   104

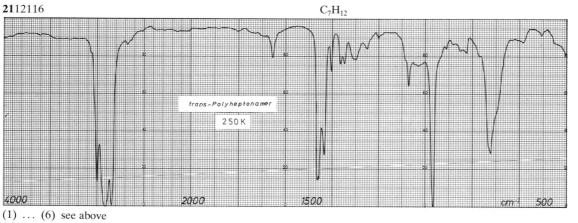

(1) ... (6) see above
(7) film from toluene (250 K)
(8) partly crystalline

2112116   C₇H₁₂   105

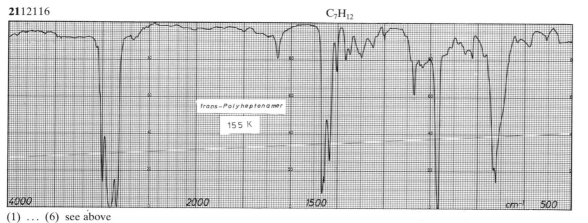

(1) ... (6) see above
(7) film from toluene (155 K)
(8) partly crystalline

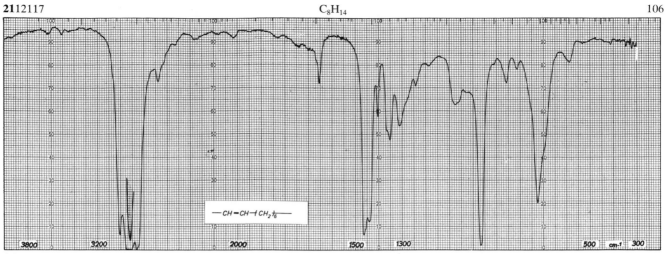

(1) poly(octenylene) (predominantly trans-units)
(2) yellowish elastomer
(3) Chemische Werke Hüls AG (by W. Glenz)

(5) with W catalyst, see, e. g., N. Calderon, E. A. Ofstead, W. A. Judy, J. Polym. Sci. *A-1* (1976) 2209; G. Natta, G. Dall'Asta, I. W. Bassi, G. Carella, Makromol. Chem. *91* (1966) 87
(7) film from $CHCl_3$ on CsI

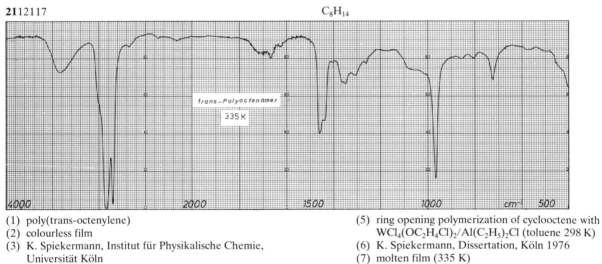

(1) poly(trans-octenylene)
(2) colourless film
(3) K. Spiekermann, Institut für Physikalische Chemie, Universität Köln

(5) ring opening polymerization of cyclooctene with $WCl_4(OC_2H_4Cl)_2/Al(C_2H_5)_2Cl$ (toluene 298 K)
(6) K. Spiekermann, Dissertation, Köln 1976
(7) molten film (335 K)

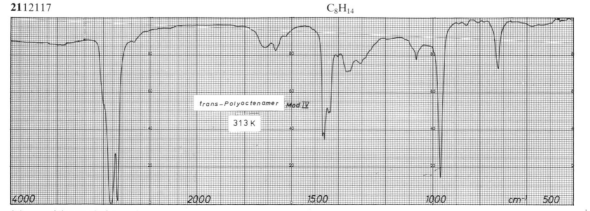

(1) . . . (6) see above
(7) film from toluene (313 K); partly recrystallized (modification IV)

2112117   C₈H₁₄   109

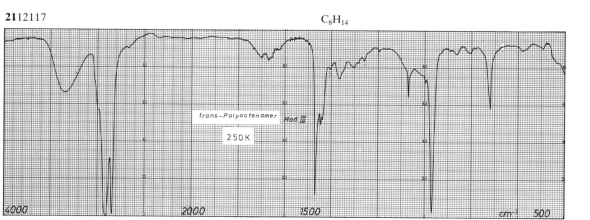

(1) ... (6) see above
(7) film from toluene (250 K); partly crystallized (modification
III)

2112117   C₈H₁₄   110

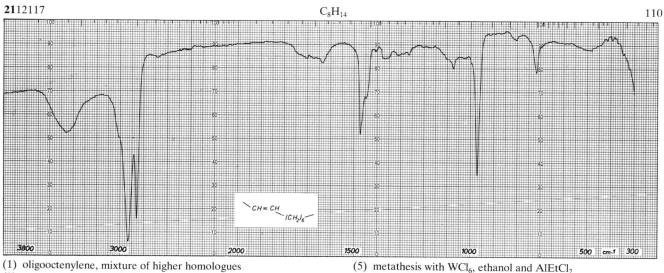

(1) oligooctenylene, mixture of higher homologues
(2) colourless, lumpy material
(3) H. Höcker, Institut für Organische Chemie, Universität Mainz
(4) cyclic oligomers with 2...12 trans-octenylene units

(5) metathesis with WCl₆, ethanol and AlEtCl₂
(6) H. Höcker, R. Musch, Makromol. Chem. 175 (1974)
1395...1409
(7) KBr (3/350)

2112118   C₁₀H₁₈   111

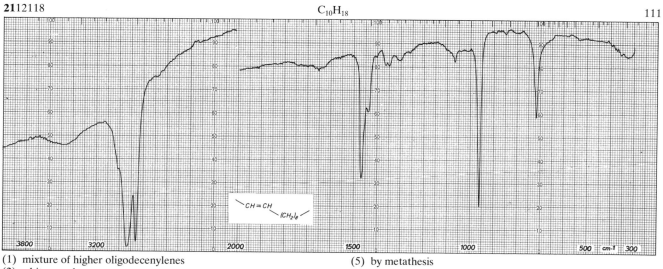

(1) mixture of higher oligodecenylenes
(2) white powder
(3) H. Höcker, Organisch-Chemisches Institut, Universität Mainz
(4) almost exclusively trans units

(5) by metathesis
(6) H. Höcker, F. R. Jones, Makromol. Chem. 161 (1972) 251
(7) KBr (2/350)

2112118 $C_{12}H_{22}$ 112

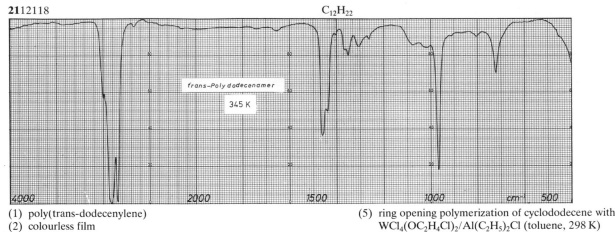

trans-Polydodecenamer

345 K

(1) poly(trans-dodecenylene)
(2) colourless film
(3) K. Spiekermann, Institut für Physikalische Chemie,
Universität Köln

(5) ring opening polymerization of cyclododecene with
$WCl_4(OC_2H_4Cl)_2/Al(C_2H_5)_2Cl$ (toluene, 298 K)
(6) K. Spiekermann, Dissertation, Köln 1976
(7) molten film (345 K)

2112118 $C_{12}H_{22}$ 113

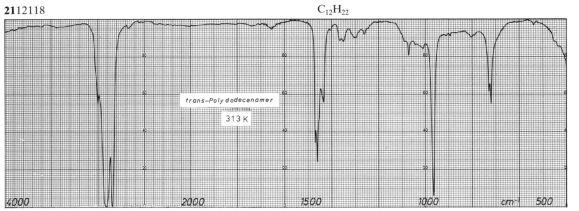

trans-Polydodecenamer

313 K

(1) ... (6) see above
(7) partly recrystallized melting film (313 K)

2112118 $C_{12}H_{22}$ 114

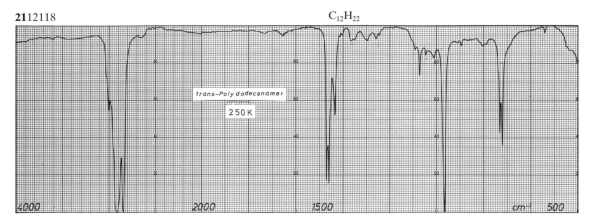

trans-Polydodecenamer

250 K

(1) ... (6) see above
(7) recrystallized melting film (250 K)

211212 C_3H_4 115

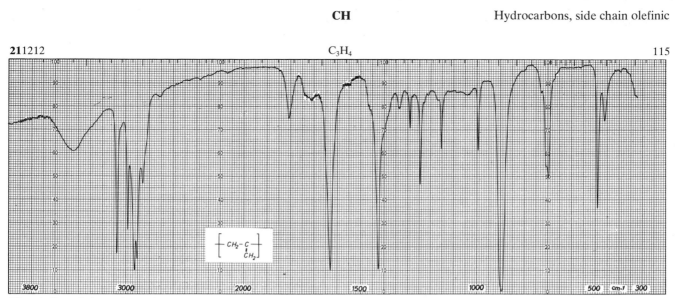

(1) poly(1-methylene ethylene), polyallene
(2) white coarse powder
(3) R. Havinga, Central Lab. TNO, Delft
(4) the polymer is highly crystalline; it possibly contains small amounts of $-CH=CH_2$ (994 cm^{-1}) and cis-vinylene (700 cm^{-1})

(5) Ziegler type catalyst with $VOCl_3$, Al-t-Bu$_3$ + $VOCl_3$, Al: V = 9
(6) R. Havinga, A. Schors, J. Macromol. Sci. Chem. *A2*(1) (1968) 1...20; ibid. 31...42
(7) swollen in toluene, ground with KBr, dried and pressed

211212 C_4H_6 116

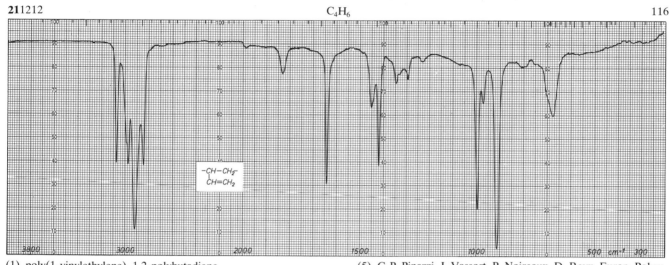

(1) poly(1-vinylethylene), 1,2-polybutadiene
(2) colourless, highly viscous material
(3) C. P. Pinazzi, Laboratoire de Chimie et Physico-Chimie Organique Macromoléculaire, Centre Universitaire, Le Mans
(4) 87 % 1,2-structures, 13 % 1,4-structures

(5) C. P. Pinazzi, J. Vassort, P. Noireaux, D. Reyx, Europ. Polym. J. *12* (1976) 83
(6) C. P. Pinazzi, J. Vassort, V. Jean, D. Reyx, Makromol. Chem. *177* (1976) 3119...37
(7) film on CsI

211212–**21**12113 C_4H_6 117

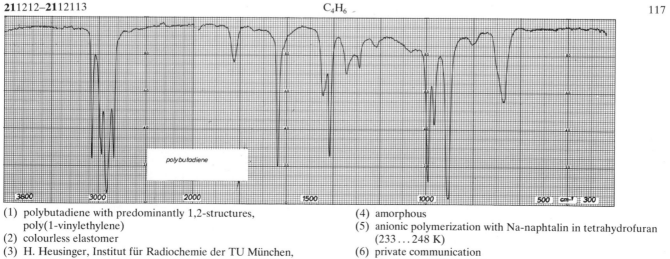

(1) polybutadiene with predominantly 1,2-structures, poly(1-vinylethylene)
(2) colourless elastomer
(3) H. Heusinger, Institut für Radiochemie der TU München, Garching

(4) amorphous
(5) anionic polymerization with Na-naphtalin in tetrahydrofuran (233...248 K)
(6) private communication
(7) film from CHCl$_3$ on CsI

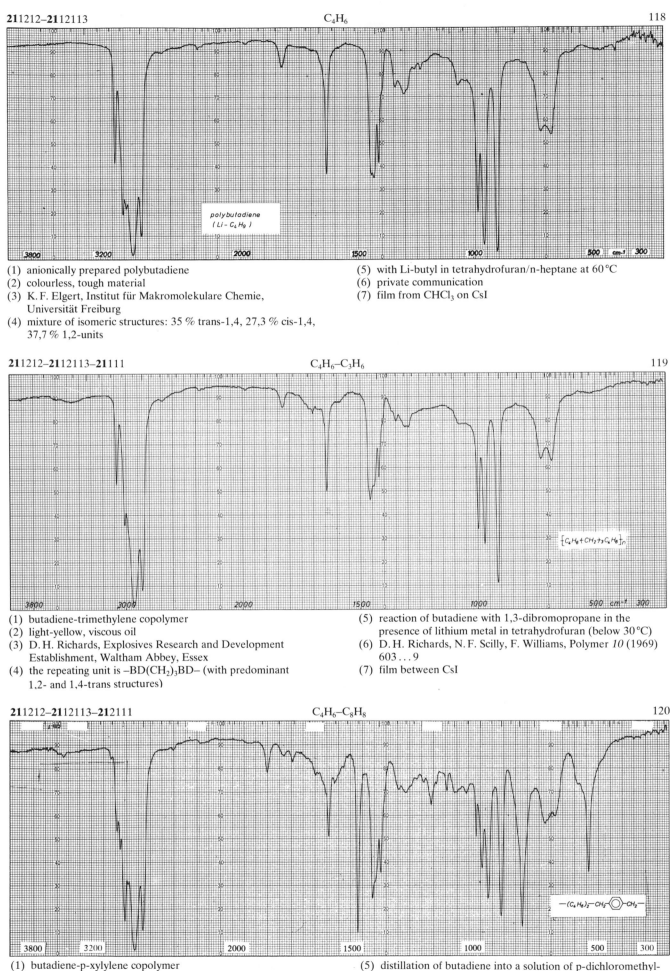

211212–2112113 C_4H_6 118

polybutadiene (Li – C_4H_9)

(1) anionically prepared polybutadiene
(2) colourless, tough material
(3) K. F. Elgert, Institut für Makromolekulare Chemie, Universität Freiburg
(4) mixture of isomeric structures: 35 % trans-1,4, 27,3 % cis-1,4, 37,7 % 1,2-units

(5) with Li-butyl in tetrahydrofuran/n-heptane at 60 °C
(6) private communication
(7) film from $CHCl_3$ on CsI

211212–2112113–21111 C_4H_6–C_3H_6 119

$[C_4H_6 + CH_2 +_3 C_4H_6]_n$

(1) butadiene-trimethylene copolymer
(2) light-yellow, viscous oil
(3) D. H. Richards, Explosives Research and Development Establishment, Waltham Abbey, Essex
(4) the repeating unit is –BD$(CH_2)_3$BD– (with predominant 1,2- and 1,4-trans structures)

(5) reaction of butadiene with 1,3-dibromopropane in the presence of lithium metal in tetrahydrofuran (below 30 °C)
(6) D. H. Richards, N. F. Scilly, F. Williams, Polymer *10* (1969) 603 ... 9
(7) film between CsI

211212–2112113–212111 C_4H_6–C_8H_8 120

$-(C_4H_6)_2-CH_2-\bigcirc-CH_2-$

(1) butadiene-p-xylylene copolymer
(2) yellowish, coarse, porous material
(3) D. H. Richards, Explosives Research and Development Establishment, Waltham Abbey, Essex
(4) alternating structure –BD–CH_2–C_6H_4–CH_2–BD– (with predominantly 1,2- and 1,4-trans structures in the butadiene units)

(5) distillation of butadiene into a solution of p-dichloromethyl-benzene in tetrahydrofuran in the presence of lithium metal
(6) D. H. Richards, N. F. Scilly, F. Williams, Polymer *10* (1969) 603 ... 9
(7) film from $CHCl_3$ on CsI

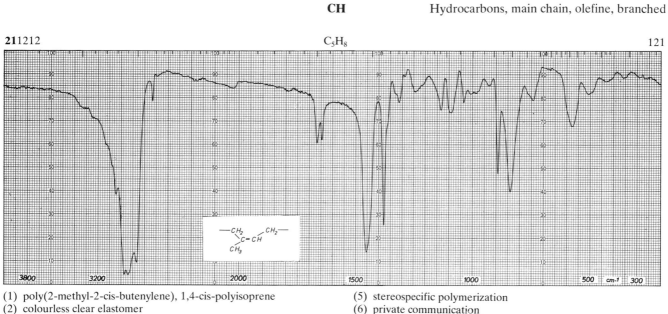

(1) poly(2-methyl-2-cis-butenylene), 1,4-cis-polyisoprene
(2) colourless clear elastomer
(3) H. Willersinn, BASF, Ludwigshafen

(5) stereospecific polymerization
(6) private communication
(7) film from $CHCl_4$ on CsI

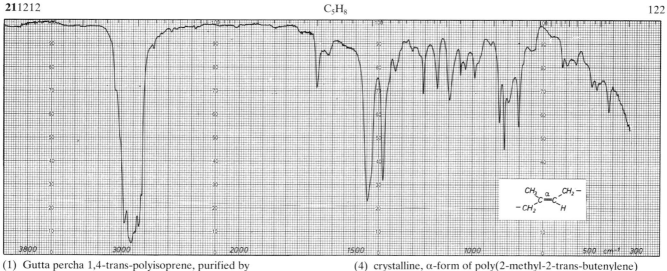

(1) Gutta percha 1,4-trans-polyisoprene, purified by
    reprecipitation
(2) brownish hard elastomer
(3) university's drugstore

(4) crystalline, α-form of poly(2-methyl-2-trans-butenylene)
(7) film from benzene solution

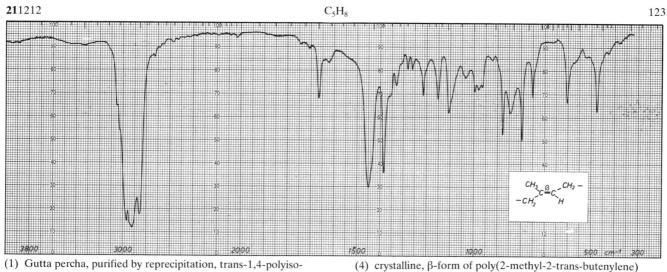

(1) Gutta percha, purified by reprecipitation, trans-1,4-polyiso-
    prene
(2) brownish hard elastomer
(3) university's drugstore

(4) crystalline, β-form of poly(2-methyl-2-trans-butenylene)
(7) film from benzene solution
(8) film with α-form heated to 100 °C (several h), quenched
    between cold metal plates

211212 C_5H_8–C_5H_8 124

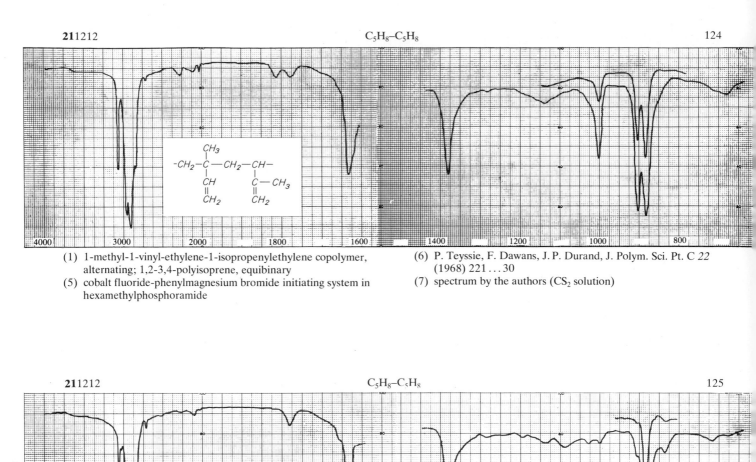

(1) 1-methyl-1-vinyl-ethylene-1-isopropenylethylene copolymer,
     alternating; 1,2-3,4-polyisoprene, equibinary
(5) cobalt fluoride-phenylmagnesium bromide initiating system in
     hexamethylphosphoramide

(6) P. Teyssie, F. Dawans, J. P. Durand, J. Polym. Sci. Pt. C *22*
     (1968) 221 ... 30
(7) spectrum by the authors (CS$_2$ solution)

211212 C_5H_8–C_5H_8 125

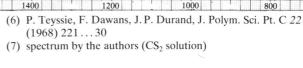
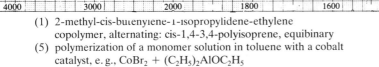

(1) 2-methyl-cis-butenylene-1-isopropylidene-ethylene
     copolymer, alternating: cis-1,4-3,4-polyisoprene, equibinary
(5) polymerization of a monomer solution in toluene with a cobalt
     catalyst, e. g., CoBr$_2$ + (C$_2$H$_5$)$_2$AlOC$_2$H$_5$

(6) P. Teyssie, F. Dawans, J. P. Durand, J. Polym. Sci. Pt. C *22*
     (1968) 221 ... 30
(7) spectrum by the authors (CS$_2$ solution)

211212 C_5H_8 126

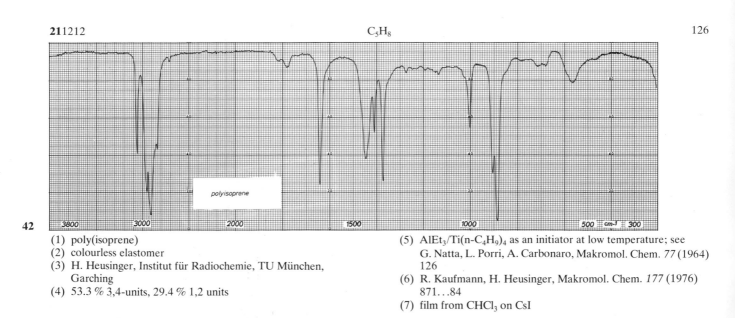

polyisoprene

42

(1) poly(isoprene)
(2) colourless elastomer
(3) H. Heusinger, Institut für Radiochemie, TU München,
     Garching
(4) 53.3 % 3,4-units, 29.4 % 1,2 units

(5) AlEt$_3$/Ti(n-C$_4$H$_9$)$_4$ as an initiator at low temperature; see
     G. Natta, L. Porri, A. Carbonaro, Makromol. Chem. *77* (1964)
     126
(6) R. Kaufmann, H. Heusinger, Makromol. Chem. *177* (1976)
     871 ... 84
(7) film from CHCl$_3$ on CsI

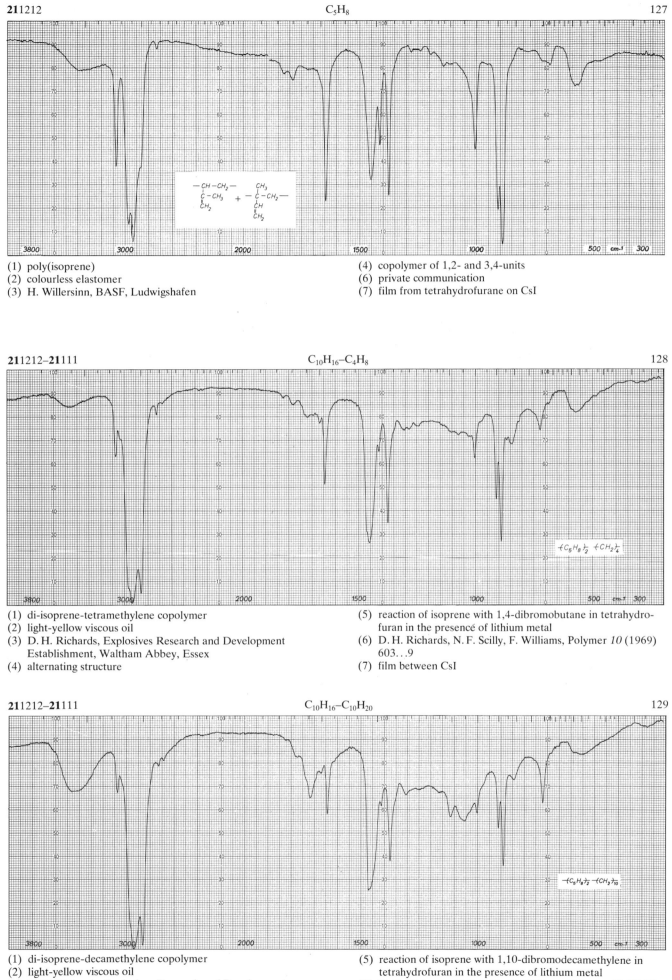

2111212 C₅H₈ 127

(1) poly(isoprene)
(2) colourless elastomer
(3) H. Willersinn, BASF, Ludwigshafen

(4) copolymer of 1,2- and 3,4-units
(6) private communication
(7) film from tetrahydrofurane on CsI

2111212–**21**111 C₁₀H₁₆–C₄H₈ 128

(1) di-isoprene-tetramethylene copolymer
(2) light-yellow viscous oil
(3) D. H. Richards, Explosives Research and Development Establishment, Waltham Abbey, Essex
(4) alternating structure

(5) reaction of isoprene with 1,4-dibromobutane in tetrahydrofuran in the presencé of lithium metal
(6) D. H. Richards, N. F. Scilly, F. Williams, Polymer *10* (1969) 603…9
(7) film between CsI

2111212–**21**111 C₁₀H₁₆–C₁₀H₂₀ 129

(1) di-isoprene-decamethylene copolymer
(2) light-yellow viscous oil
(3) D. H. Richards, Explosives Research and Development Establishment, Waltham Abbey, Essex
(4) alternating structure

(5) reaction of isoprene with 1,10-dibromodecamethylene in tetrahydrofuran in the presence of lithium metal
(6) D. H. Richards, N. F. Scilly, F. Williams, Polymer *10* (1969) 603…9
(7) film between CsI

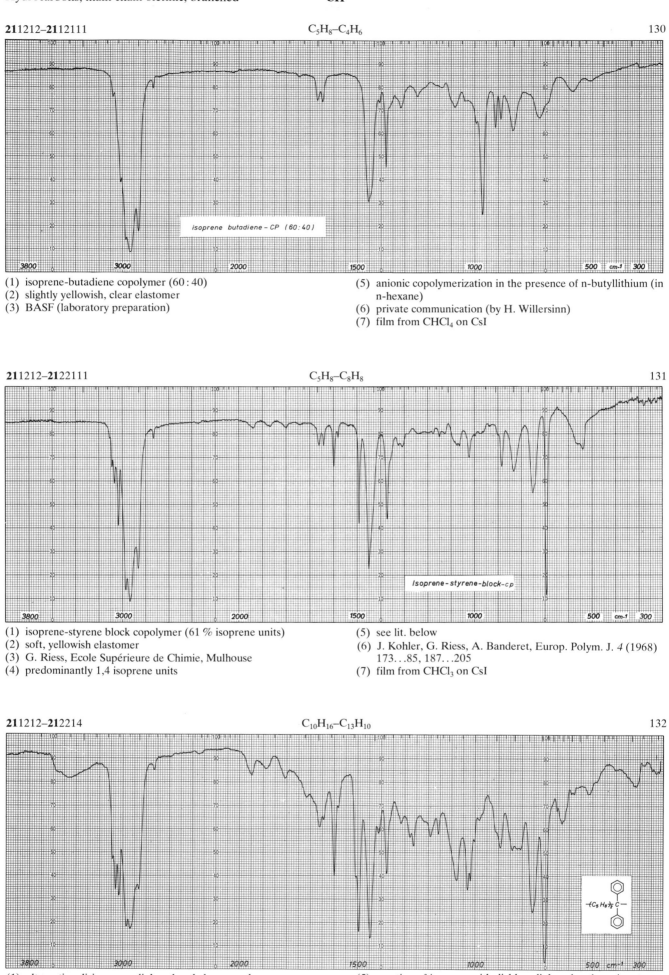

isoprene butadiene – CP (60:40)

(1) isoprene-butadiene copolymer (60 : 40)
(2) slightly yellowish, clear elastomer
(3) BASF (laboratory preparation)
(5) anionic copolymerization in the presence of n-butyllithium (in n-hexane)
(6) private communication (by H. Willersinn)
(7) film from $CHCl_4$ on CsI

Isoprene-styrene-block-cp

(1) isoprene-styrene block copolymer (61 % isoprene units)
(2) soft, yellowish elastomer
(3) G. Riess, Ecole Supérieure de Chimie, Mulhouse
(4) predominantly 1,4 isoprene units
(5) see lit. below
(6) J. Kohler, G. Riess, A. Banderet, Europ. Polym. J. *4* (1968) 173…85, 187…205
(7) film from $CHCl_3$ on CsI

$-(C_5H_8)_2 C-$

(1) alternating di-isoprene-diphenylmethylene copolymer
(2) light-yellow powder
(3) D. H. Richards, Explosives Research and Development Establishment, Waltham Abbey, Essex
(4) predominantly 1,4-isoprene units
(5) reaction of isoprene with dichlorodiphenylmethane in tetrahydrofuran in the presence of lithium metal
(6) D. H. Richards, N. F. Scilly, F. Williams, Polymer *10* (1969) 603…9
(7) film from $CHCl_3$ on CsI

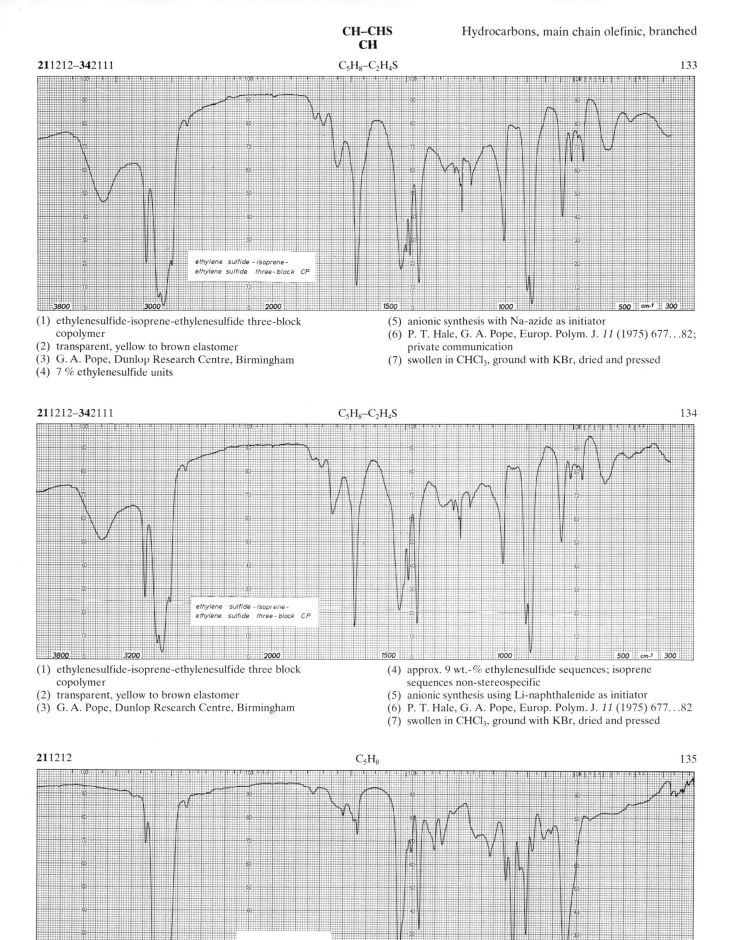

ethylene sulfide - isoprene -
ethylene sulfide three-block CP

(1) ethylenesulfide-isoprene-ethylenesulfide three-block
    copolymer
(2) transparent, yellow to brown elastomer
(3) G. A. Pope, Dunlop Research Centre, Birmingham
(4) 7 % ethylenesulfide units

(5) anionic synthesis with Na-azide as initiator
(6) P. T. Hale, G. A. Pope, Europ. Polym. J. *11* (1975) 677...82;
    private communication
(7) swollen in CHCl₃, ground with KBr, dried and pressed

ethylene sulfide - isoprene -
ethylene sulfide three-block CP

(1) ethylenesulfide-isoprene-ethylenesulfide three block
    copolymer
(2) transparent, yellow to brown elastomer
(3) G. A. Pope, Dunlop Research Centre, Birmingham

(4) approx. 9 wt.-% ethylenesulfide sequences; isoprene
    sequences non-stereospecific
(5) anionic synthesis using Li-naphthalenide as initiator
(6) P. T. Hale, G. A. Pope, Europ. Polym. J. *11* (1975) 677...82
(7) swollen in CHCl₃, ground with KBr, dried and pressed

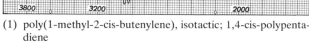

(1) poly(1-methyl-2-cis-butenylene), isotactic; 1,4-cis-polypenta-
    diene
(2) colourless elastomer
(3) G. Costa, Istituto di Chim. Macromol., Milano
(4) 71,5 % cis, 17,5 % trans, 11 % vinyl; optically active (+)
(5) asymmetric polymerization of pentadiene with Ti–C–Al

catalyst from Ti-tetrabenzyl and Al-tribenzyl with (−)-men-
thol; see V. Zucchini, E. Albizzati, U. Giannini,
J. Organometal. Chem. *26* (1971) 357
(6) G. Costa, P. Locatelli, A. Zambelli, Macromolecules *6* (1973)
    653
(7) film from CHCl₃ on CsI

211212 C_5H_8 136

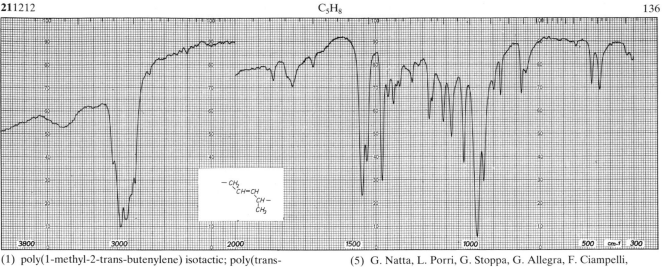

(1) poly(1-methyl-2-trans-butenylene) isotactic; poly(trans-1,4-penta-1,3-diene)
(2) colourless material
(3) G. Allegra, Montecatini Edison, Milano
(4) crystalline
(5) G. Natta, L. Porri, G. Stoppa, G. Allegra, F. Ciampelli, J. Polym. Sci. B *1* (1963) 67
(6) J. W. Bassi, G. Allegra, R. Scordamaglia, Macromolecules *4* (1971) 575...9, 579...84
(7) ground with KBr (5/300) and dimethylacetamide, dried and pressed

211212 C_8H_{14} 137

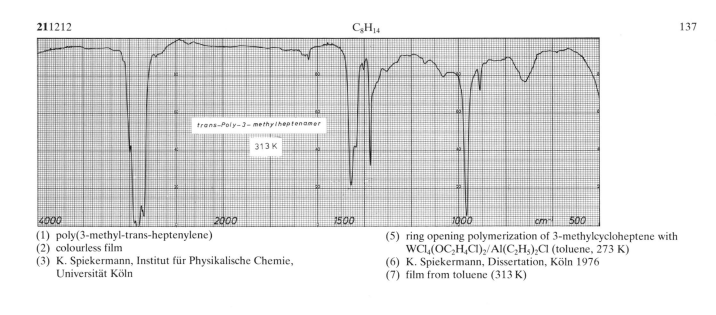

trans-Poly-3-methylheptenamer

313 K

(1) poly(3-methyl-trans-heptenylene)
(2) colourless film
(3) K. Spiekermann, Institut für Physikalische Chemie, Universität Köln
(5) ring opening polymerization of 3-methylcycloheptene with $WCl_4(OC_2H_4Cl)_2/Al(C_2H_5)_2Cl$ (toluene, 273 K)
(6) K. Spiekermann, Dissertation, Köln 1976
(7) film from toluene (313 K)

211212 $C_{13}H_{24}$ 138

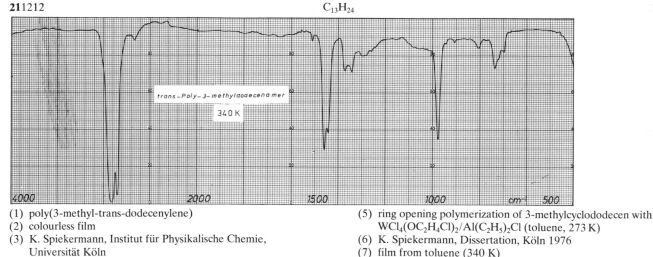

trans-Poly-3-methyldodecenamer

340 K

(1) poly(3-methyl-trans-dodecenylene)
(2) colourless film
(3) K. Spiekermann, Institut für Physikalische Chemie, Universität Köln
(5) ring opening polymerization of 3-methylcyclododecen with $WCl_4(OC_2H_4Cl)_2/Al(C_2H_5)_2Cl$ (toluene, 273 K)
(6) K. Spiekermann, Dissertation, Köln 1976
(7) film from toluene (340 K)

211212 $C_{13}H_{24}$ 139

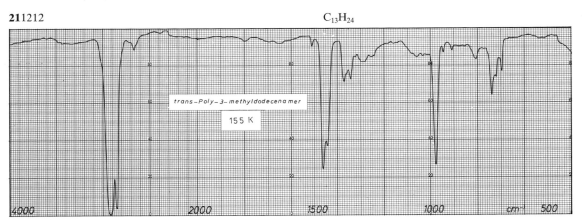

trans-Poly-3-methyldodecenamer

155 K

(1) ... (6) see above
(7) film from toluene (155 K); the sample did not crystallize

211212 C_6H_{10} 140

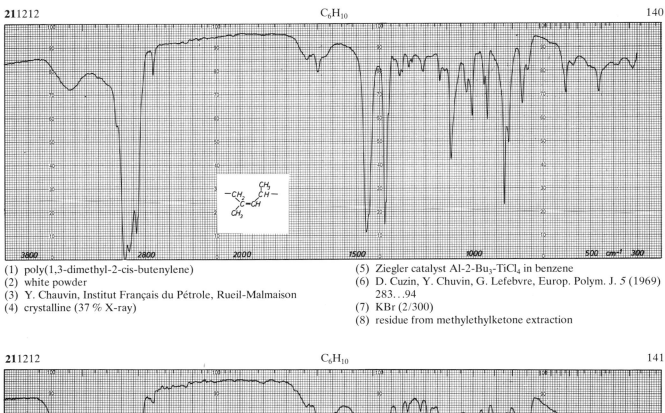

(1) poly(1,3-dimethyl-2-cis-butenylene)
(2) white powder
(3) Y. Chauvin, Institut Français du Pétrole, Rueil-Malmaison
(4) crystalline (37 % X-ray)

(5) Ziegler catalyst Al-2-Bu$_3$-TiCl$_4$ in benzene
(6) D. Cuzin, Y. Chuvin, G. Lefebvre, Europ. Polym. J. 5 (1969) 283...94
(7) KBr (2/300)
(8) residue from methylethylketone extraction

211212 C_6H_{10} 141

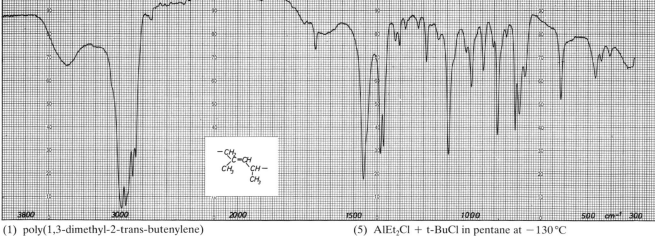

(1) poly(1,3-dimethyl-2-trans-butenylene)
(2) white powder
(3) Y. Chauvin, Institut Français du Pétrole, Rueil-Malmaison
(4) amorphous

(5) AlEt$_2$Cl + t-BuCl in pentane at −130 °C
(6) D. Cuzin, Y. Chauvin, G. Lefebvre, Europ. Polym. J. 5 (1969) 283...94
(7) KBr (2/300)

211213 C_7H_{10} 142

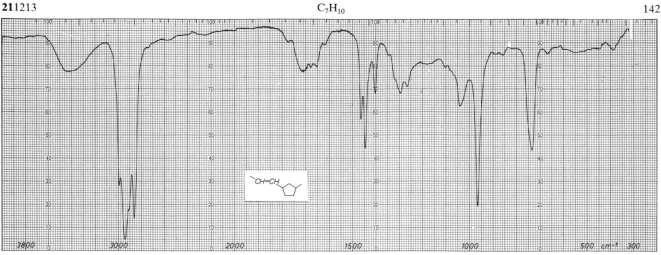

(1) poly(1,3-cyclopentanediyl-1-trans-vinylene), poly(nor-bornene)
(2) eggshell-coloured material
(3) R. Rossi, Istituto di Chimia Organica Industriale, Università di Pisa
(4) predominantly trans
(5) ruthenium catalyst, e. g., dichloro(2,7-dimethylocta-2,6-di-ene-1,8-diyl)ruthenium
(6) L. Porri, R. Rossi, P. Diversi, A. Lucherini, Makromol. Chem. *175* (1974) 3097...115

211213 C_7H_{10} 143

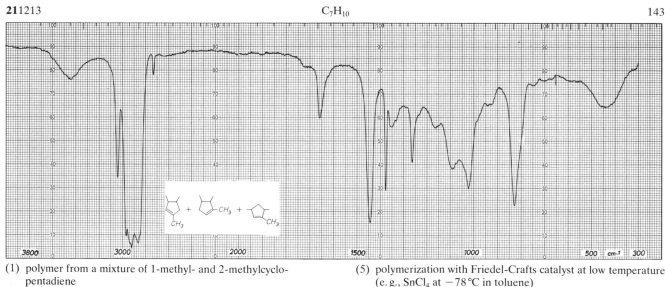

(1) polymer from a mixture of 1-methyl- and 2-methylcyclo-pentadiene
(2) white powder
(3) C. Aso, Department of Organic Synthesis, Faculty of Engineering, Kyushu University, Fukuoka
(5) polymerization with Friedel-Crafts catalyst at low temperature (e. g., $SnCl_4$ at $-78\,°C$ in toluene)
(6) C. Aso, O. Ohara, Makromol. Chem. *109* (1967) 161...75, ibid. *127* (1969) 78...93
(7) KBr (2/300)

211213 C_7H_{10} 144

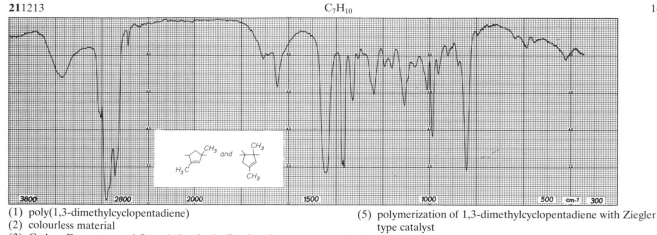

(1) poly(1,3-dimethylcyclopentadiene)
(2) colourless material
(3) C. Aso, Department of Organic Synthesis, Faculty of Engineering, Kyushu University, Fukuoka
(5) polymerization of 1,3-dimethylcyclopentadiene with Ziegler type catalyst
(6) C. Aso, O. Ohara, Makromol. Chem. *127* (1969) 78...93
(7) KBr (2/300)

212111   C$_7$H$_6$ 145

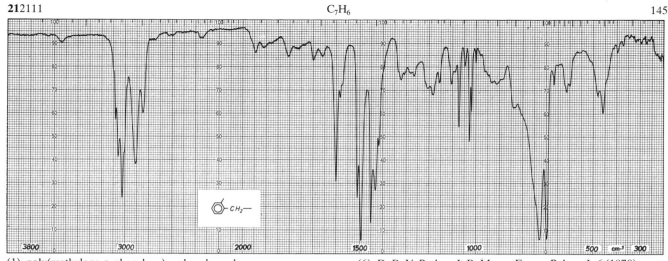

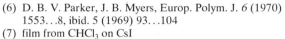

(1) poly(methylene-o-phenylene), poly-o-benzyl
(2) sand-coloured powder
(3) D. Parker, Department Polymer Science and Technology, Brunel University, London
(5) polycondensation of benzyl chloride with SnCl$_4$; L. Valentine, R. W. Winter, J. Chem. Soc. (Lond.) *1956*, 4768
(6) D. B. V. Parker, J. B. Myers, Europ. Polym. J. *6* (1970) 1553...8, ibid. 5 (1969) 93...104
(7) film from CHCl$_3$ on CsI

212111   C$_7$H$_6$ 146

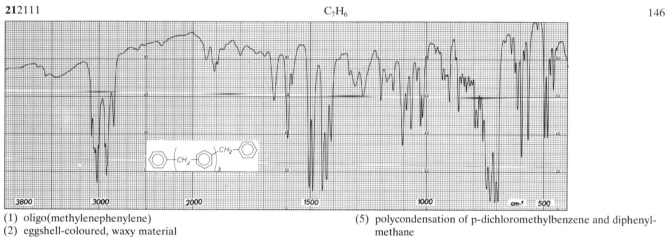

(1) oligo(methylenephenylene)
(2) eggshell-coloured, waxy material
(3) J. G. Meldrum, University of Glasgow, Scotland
(4) linear molecule consisting of 5 benzene rings, linked together by methylene groups
(5) polycondensation of p-dichloromethylbenzene and diphenyl-methane
(6) J. G. Meldrum, IUPAC Macro, Toronto 1968
(7) film between KBr

212111   C$_7$H$_6$ 147

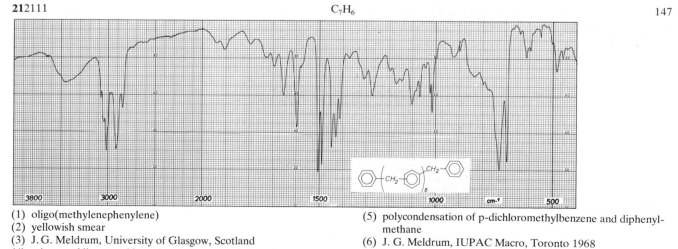

(1) oligo(methylenephenylene)
(2) yellowish smear
(3) J. G. Meldrum, University of Glasgow, Scotland
(4) mixture of linear and branched isomers consisting of 8 benzene rings linked together by methylene groups
(5) polycondensation of p-dichloromethylbenzene and diphenyl-methane
(6) J. G. Meldrum, IUPAC Macro, Toronto 1968
(7) film between KBr

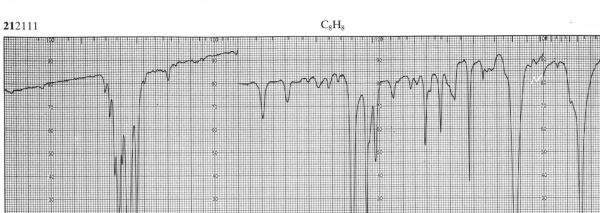

Parylene N

(1) poly(dimethylene-1,4-phenylene), poly(p-xylylene)
(2) colourless clear film
(3) Union Carbide Corp., Bound Brook, N.J. (by B. L. Joesten)
(4) $-CH_2-\bigcirc-CH_2-$

(5) thermal polycondensation of p-xylene
(6) B.L. Joesten, Polymer Preprints *13/2* (1972) 1948
(7) ground film, 28 μm
(8) commercial product „Parylene N"

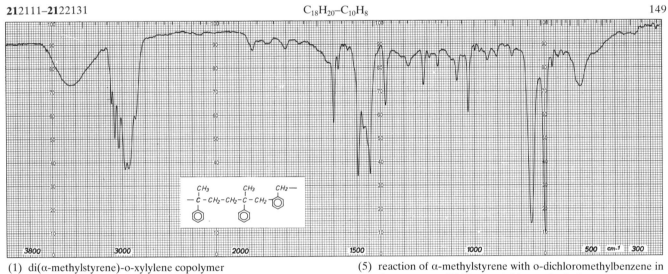

$-\overset{CH_3}{\underset{\bigcirc}{C}}-CH_2-CH_2-\overset{CH_3}{\underset{\bigcirc}{C}}-CH_2-\overset{CH_2-}{\bigcirc}$

(1) di(α-methylstyrene)-o-xylylene copolymer
(2) colourless material
(3) D. H. Richards, Explosives Research and Development
Establishment, Waltham Abbey, Essex
(4) alternating structure (α-methylstyrene units in head-to-head
arrangement)

(5) reaction of α-methylstyrene with o-dichloromethylbenzene in
the presence of lithium metal in tetrahydrofuran
(6) D. H. Richards, N. F. Scilly, F. Williams, Polymer *10* (1969)
603...9
(7) film between CsI

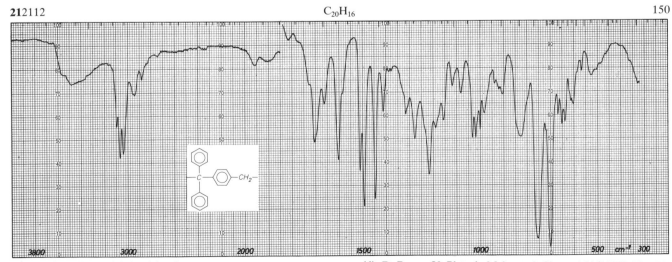

$\underset{\bigcirc}{\overset{\bigcirc}{C}}-\bigcirc-CH_2-$

(1) poly(α,α-diphenyl-1,4-xylylene)
(2) yellow powder
(3) D. Braun, Deutsches Kunststoffinstitut, Darmstadt
(5) by polycondensation of 4-methyltriphenylmethylbromide in
pyridine at 95 °C

(6) D. Braun, U. Platzek, Makromol. Chem. *164* (1973) 41...53,
ibid. 55...9
(7) film from CHCl₃ on KBr

212112   C$_{72}$H$_{56}$ 151

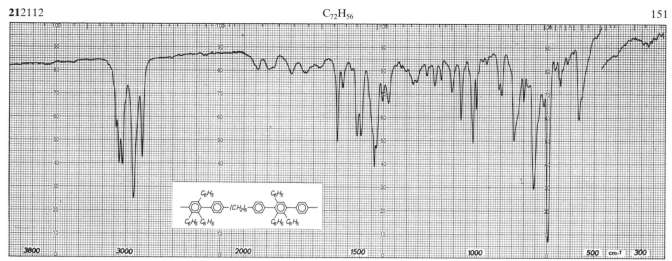

(1) phenyl-substituted poly(hexamethylene-pentaphenylene), phenyl-substituted
(2) eggshell-coloured powder
(3) J. K. Stille, Department of Chemistry, University of Iowa, Io.
(5) reaction of bis-tetracyclones with p-diethynylbenzene in toluene at 225 °C (24 h); see J. K. Stille, F. W. Harris, R. O.

Rakutis, H. Mukamal, J. Polym. Sci. *B4* (1966) 791;
H. Mukamal, F.W. Harris, J.K. Stille, J. Polym. Sci. A-1 *5* (1967) 2721
(6) J. K. Stille, J. Macromol. Sci.-Chem. A3 *6* (1969) 1043...65
(7) film from CHCl$_3$ on CsI

212112   C$_8$H$_6$ 152

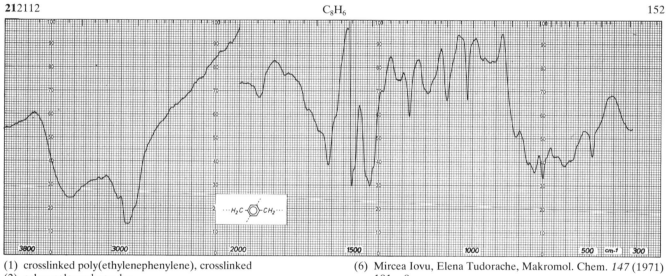

(1) crosslinked poly(ethylenephenylene), crosslinked
(2) ochre-coloured powder
(3) Mircea Iovu, Univ. Bucuresti, Catedra de Chimie
(5) polycondensation of 1,4-dichloromethylbenzene with AlCl$_3$ in CS$_2$

(6) Mircea Iovu, Elena Tudorache, Makromol. Chem. *147* (1971) 101...9
(7) KBr (10/350)

212112   C$_{10}$H$_{10}$ 153

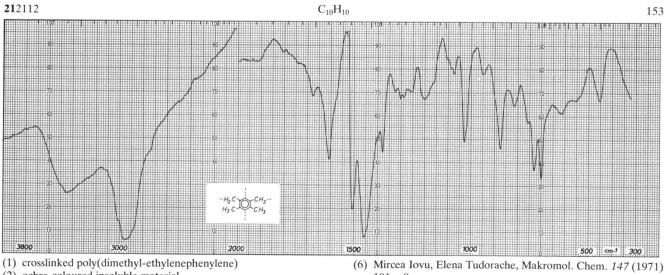
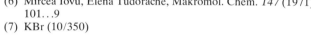

(1) crosslinked poly(dimethyl-ethylenephenylene)
(2) ochre-coloured insoluble material
(3) Mircea Iovu, Univ. Bucuresti, Catedra de Chimie
(5) polycondensation of 1,3-dichloromethyl-4,6-dimethylbenzene in CS$_2$ in the presence of AlCl$_3$

(6) Mircea Iovu, Elena Tudorache, Makromol. Chem. *147* (1971) 101...9
(7) KBr (10/350)

212112 $C_{10}H_{10}$ 154

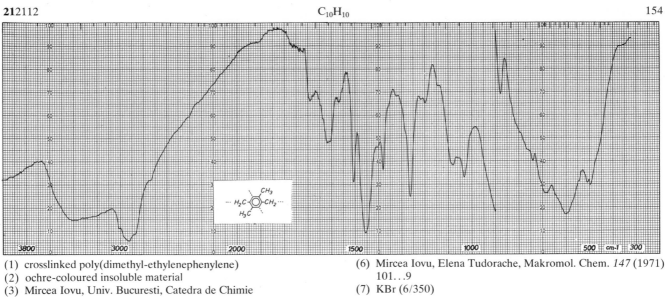
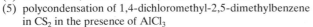

(1) crosslinked poly(dimethyl-ethylenephenylene)
(2) ochre-coloured insoluble material
(3) Mircea Iovu, Univ. Bucuresti, Catedra de Chimie
(5) polycondensation of 1,4-dichloromethyl-2,5-dimethylbenzene
     in CS_2 in the presence of $AlCl_3$

(6) Mircea Iovu, Elena Tudorache, Makromol. Chem. *147* (1971)
     101...9
(7) KBr (6/350)

2122111 C_8H_8 155

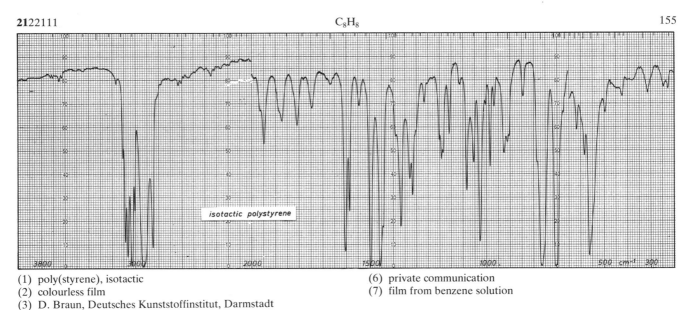

isotactic polystyrene

(1) poly(styrene), isotactic
(2) colourless film
(3) D. Braun, Deutsches Kunststoffinstitut, Darmstadt

(6) private communication
(7) film from benzene solution

2122111 C_8H_8 156

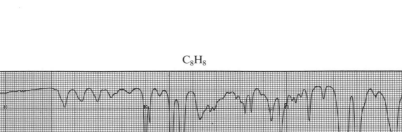

atactic polystyrene

(1) poly(styrene), atactic
(2) colourless thermoplastic
(3) Chemische Werke Hüls AG, Marl

(7) film from $CHCl_3$ solution
(8) commercial material „Vestyron N"

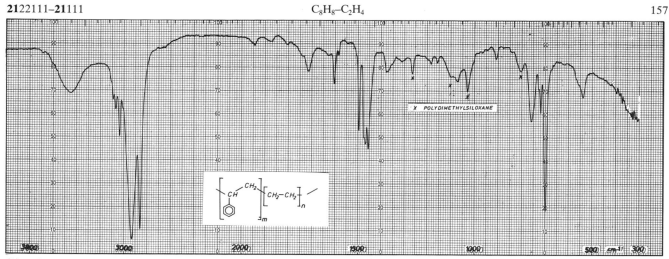

(1) polystyrene-polyethylene-polystyrene block copolymer
(2) white powder
(3) H. Höcker, Institut für Organische Chemie, Universität Mainz
(5) hydrogenation of styrene-butadiene (1,4) block copolymer
    with Co-2-ethylhexane carboxylic acid, AlEt₃ and H₂
    (4,3 atm) in benzene at 80 °C

(6) H. Höcker, M. Sondergeld, IUPAC Macro, Madrid 1974
(7) KBr (2/350)
(8) slightly contaminated with polydimethylsiloxane

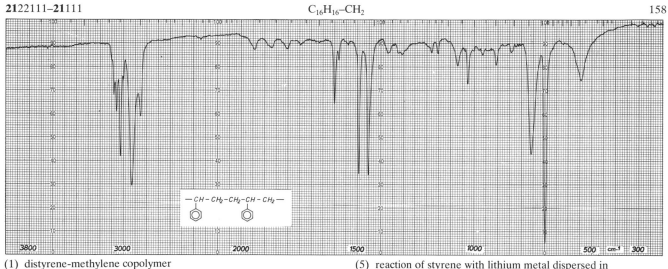

(1) distyrene-methylene copolymer
(2) white material
(3) D. H. Richards, Explosives Research and Development
    Establishment, Waltham Abbey, Essex
(4) alternating structure (styrene units head-to-head)

(5) reaction of styrene with lithium metal dispersed in
    tetrahydrofuran and methylene dibromide
(6) D. H. Richards, N. F. Scilly, F. Williams, Polymer 10 (1969)
    603...9
(7) film from CHCl₃ on CsI

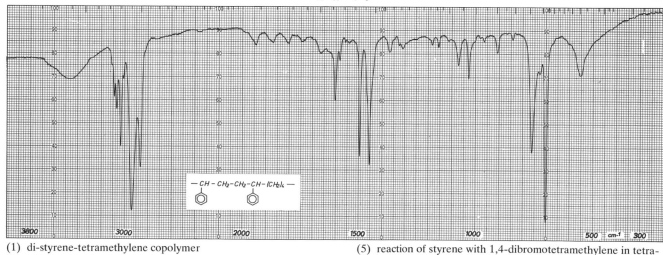

(1) di-styrene-tetramethylene copolymer
(2) white material
(3) D. H. Richards, Explosives Research and Development
    Establishment, Waltham Abbey, Essex
(4) alternating structure (styrene units head-to-head)

(5) reaction of styrene with 1,4-dibromotetramethylene in tetra-
    hydrofuran in the presence of lithium metal
(6) D. H. Richards, N. F. Scilly, F. Williams, Polymer 10 (1969)
    603...9
(7) film from CHCl₃ on CsI

2122111–**21**111 $C_{16}H_{16}$–$C_{10}H_{20}$ 160

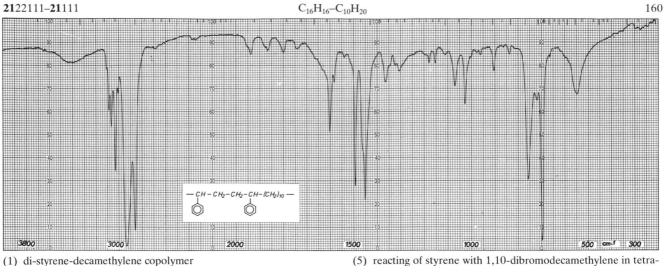

(1) di-styrene-decamethylene copolymer
(2) glassy, soft material
(3) D. H. Richards, Explosives Research and Development Establishment, Waltham Abbey, Essex
(4) alternating structure (styrene units head-to-head)
(5) reacting of styrene with 1,10-dibromodecamethylene in tetrahydrofuran in the presence of lithium metal
(6) D. H. Richards, N. F. Scilly, F. Williams, Polymer *10* (1969) 603...9
(7) film from $CHCl_3$ on CsI

2122111–**21**1124 C_8H_8–C_4H_8 161

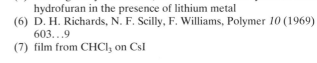

(1) isobutene-styrene block copolymer (74 % styrene sequences, MW $7,3 \cdot 10^4$
(2) white flocky material
(3) J. Jozefonvicz, Laboratoire de Chimie-Physique, Faculté des Sciences, Orsay
(5) radiation chemical method; J. Jozefonvicz, Thesis, Paris 1967
(6) J. Jozefonvicz, J. Danon, IUPAC Macro, Toronto 1968
(7) film from $CHCl_3$ on CsI

2122111–**21**1124 C_8H_8–C_4H_8 162

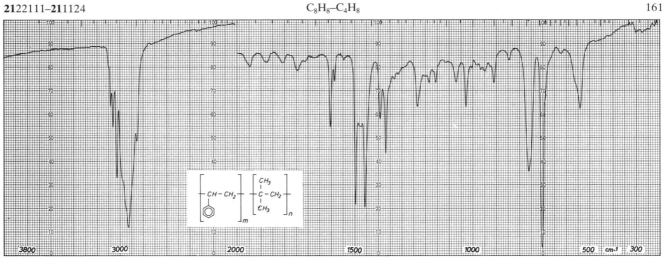

(1) isobutene-styrene block copolymer
(2) white flocky material
(3) J. Jozefonvicz, Laboratoire de Chimie-Physique, Faculté des Sciences, Orsay
(4) 54 % styrene sequences, $M = 2.11 \cdot 10^5$
(5) radiation chemical method; J. Jozefonvicz, Thesis, Paris 1967
(6) J. Jozefonvicz, J. Danon, IUPAC Macro, Toronto 1968
(7) film from $CHCl_3$ on CsI

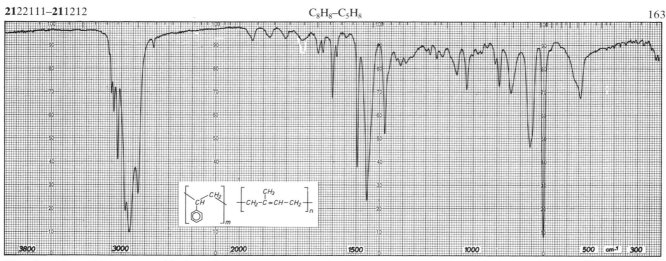

(1) polystyrene-polyisoprene two-block copolymer
(2) white, fibrous material
(3) J. Prud'Homme, Département de Chimie, Université de Montréal
(5) anionic copolymerization with sec-butyllithium in benzene; see J. Prud'Homme, J. E. L. Roovers, S. Bywater, Europ.

Polym. J. *8* (1972) 901; J. Prud'Homme, S. Bywater, in Block Polymers, ed. S. L. Aggarwal, Plenum Press, New York 1970; p. 11
(6) J. P. Plante, Nga Ho-Duc, J. Prud'Homme, Europ. Polym. J. *9* (1973) 77...83
(7) film from $CHCl_3$ on CsI

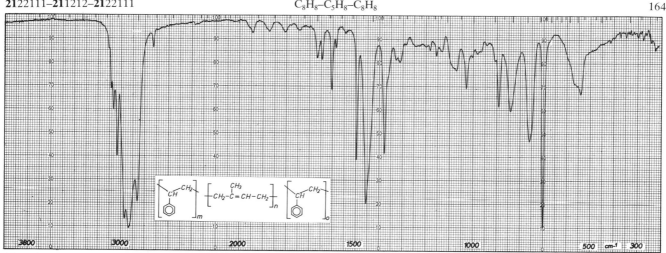

(1) polystyrene-polyisoprene-polystyrene three-block copolymer
(2) white, fibrous material
(3) J. Prud'Homme, Département de Chimie, Université de Montréal
(5) anionic copolymerization with sec-butyllithium in benzene; with the addition of styrene, 1 % tetrahydrofuran is added;

see J. Prud'Homme, J. E. L. Roovers, S. Bywater, Europ. Polym. J. *8* (1972) 901; J. Prud'Homme, S. Bywater, in Block Polymers, ed. S. L. Aggarwal, Plenum Press, New York 1970; p. 11
(6) J. P. Plante, Nga Ho-Duc, J. Prud'Homme, Europ. Polym. J. *9* (1973) 77...83
(7) film from $CHCl_3$ on CsI

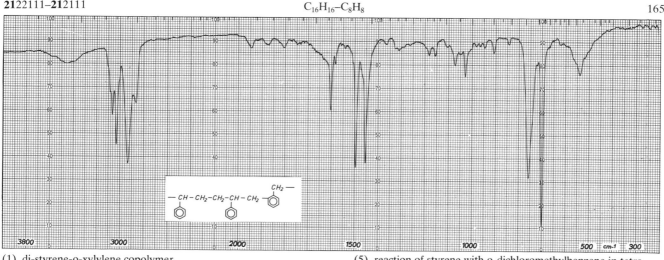

(1) di-styrene-o-xylylene copolymer
(2) white powder
(3) D. H. Richards, Explosives Research and Development Establishment, Waltham Abbey, Essex
(4) alternating structure (di-styrene units in head-to-head arrangement)

(5) reaction of styrene with o-dichloromethylbenzene in tetrahydrofuran in the presence of lithium metal
(6) D. H. Richards, N. F. Scilly, F. Williams, Polymer *10* (1969) 603...9
(7) film from $CHCl_3$ on CsI

C.H
CH–CHCl

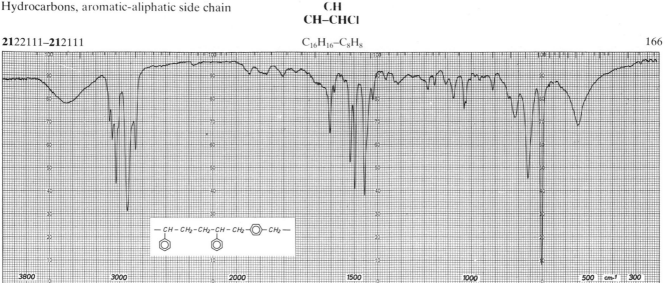

(1) distyrene-p-xylylene copolymer
(2) white powder
(3) D. H. Richards, Explosives Research and Development Establishment, Waltham Abbey, Essex
(4) alternating structure (distyrene units in head-to-head arrangement)

(5) reaction of styrene with p-dichloromethylbenzene in tetra-hydrofuran in the presence of lithium metal
(6) D. H. Richards, N. F. Scilly, F. Williams, Polymer *10* (1969) 603...9
(7) film from CHCl₃ on CsI

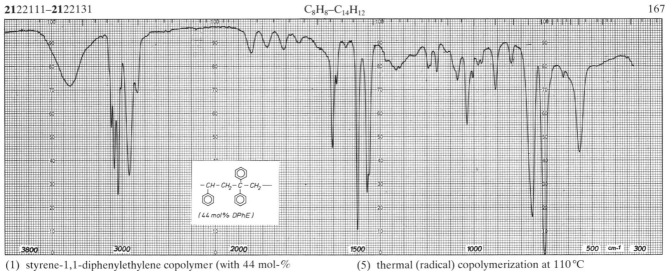

(1) styrene-1,1-diphenylethylene copolymer (with 44 mol-% DPhE units)
(2) white powder
(3) J. P. Fischer, Hoechst AG, Frankfurt/M.

(5) thermal (radical) copolymerization at 110 °C
(6) J. P. Fischer, Makromol. Chem. *155* (1972) 227...38; J. P. Fischer, W. Lüders. ibid., 239...57
(7) KBr (2/350)

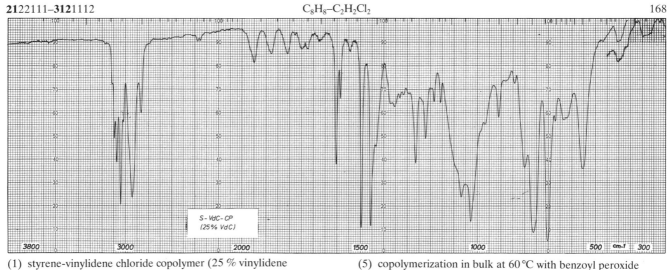

(1) styrene-vinylidene chloride copolymer (25 % vinylidene chloride units)
(2) white powder
(3) J. N. Hay, Chemistry Department, The University, Birmingham

(5) copolymerization in bulk at 60 °C with benzoyl peroxide
(6) G. M. Burnet, R. A. Haldon, J. N. Hay, Europ. Polym. J. *4* (1968) 83...92
(7) film from CHCl₃ on CsI

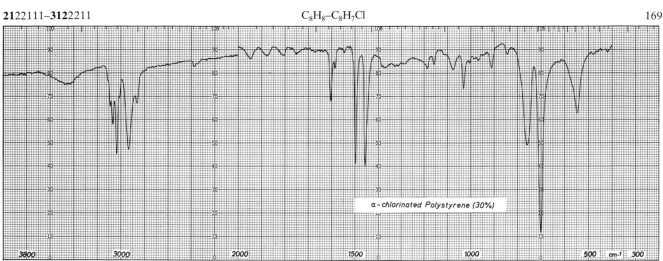

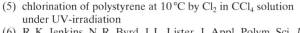

α - chlorinated Polystyrene (30%)

(1) polystyrene α-chlorinated (30 mol-% α-chlorinated units); styrene-α-chlorostyrene copolymer
(2) white powder
(3) R. K. Jenkins, McDonnell Astronautics Comp., Newport Beach, Ca.
(5) chlorination of polystyrene at 10 °C by Cl_2 in CCl_4 solution under UV-irradiation
(6) R. K. Jenkins, N. R. Byrd, J. L. Lister, J. Appl. Polym. Sci. *12* (1968) 2059...66
(7) KBr (3/1000)

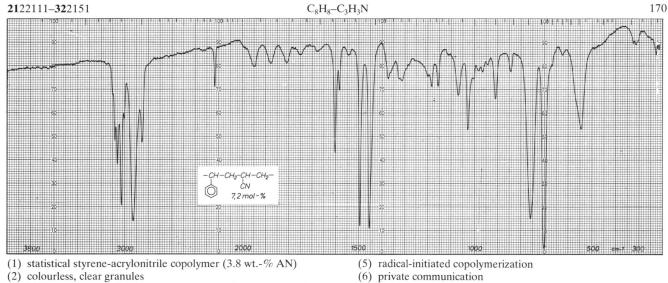

–CH–CH₂–CH–CH₂–
CN
7,2 mol-%

(1) statistical styrene-acrylonitrile copolymer (3.8 wt.-% AN)
(2) colourless, clear granules
(3) BASF AG, Kunststofflabor, Ludwigshafen (by B. J. Schmitt)
(5) radical-initiated copolymerization
(6) private communication
(7) film from $CHCl_3$ on CsI

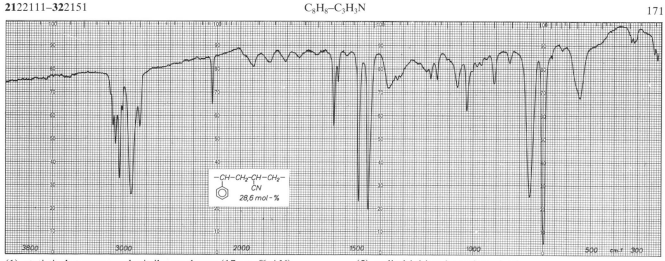

–CH–CH₂–CH–CH₂–
CN
28,6 mol-%

(1) statistical styrene-acrylonitrile copolymer (17 wt.-% AN)
(2) colourless, clear granules
(3) BASF AG, Kunststofflabor, Ludwigshafen (by B. J. Schmitt)
(5) radical-initiated copolymerization
(6) private communication
(7) film from $CHCl_3$ on CsI

2122111–**322212/32224** C$_8$H$_8$–C$_{10}$H$_{13}$N 172

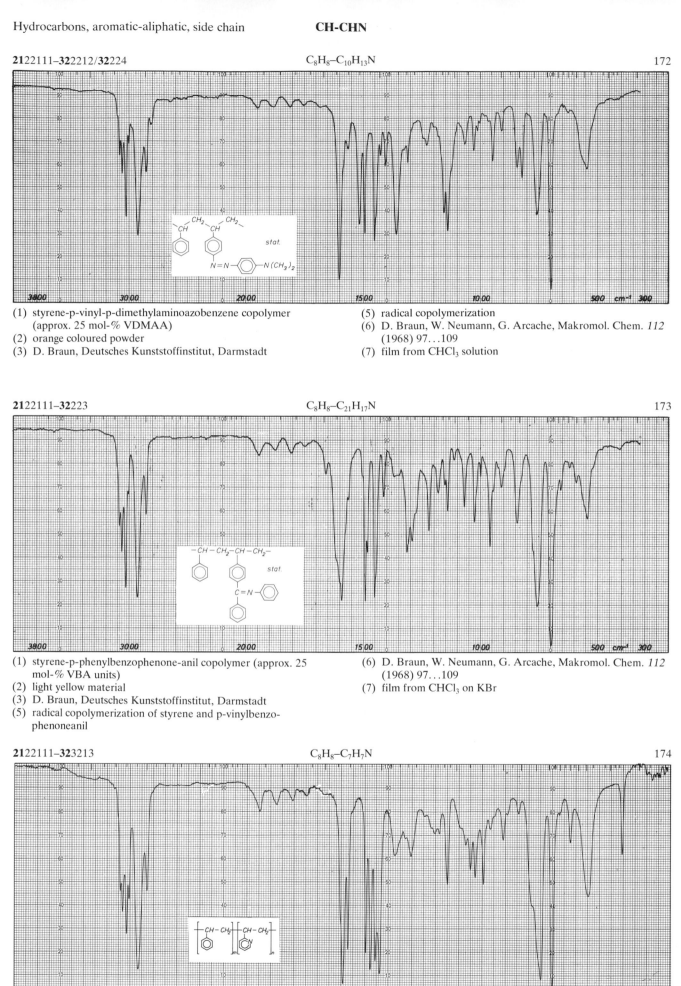

(1) styrene-p-vinyl-p-dimethylaminoazobenzene copolymer
(approx. 25 mol-% VDMAA)
(2) orange coloured powder
(3) D. Braun, Deutsches Kunststoffinstitut, Darmstadt

(5) radical copolymerization
(6) D. Braun, W. Neumann, G. Arcache, Makromol. Chem. *112*
(1968) 97...109
(7) film from CHCl$_3$ solution

2122111–**32223** C$_8$H$_8$–C$_{21}$H$_{17}$N 173

(1) styrene-p-phenylbenzophenone-anil copolymer (approx. 25
mol-% VBA units)
(2) light yellow material
(3) D. Braun, Deutsches Kunststoffinstitut, Darmstadt
(5) radical copolymerization of styrene and p-vinylbenzo-
phenoneanil

(6) D. Braun, W. Neumann, G. Arcache, Makromol. Chem. *112*
(1968) 97...109
(7) film from CHCl$_3$ on KBr

2122111–**323213** C$_8$H$_8$–C$_7$H$_7$N 174

(1) styrene-vinyl-2-pyridine block copolymer
(2) white powder
(3) P. Grosius, Centre National de la Recherche Scientifique,
Strasbourg
(4) M-PS = 18500, M-PV2P = 21500

(5) anionic block copolymerization in tetrahydrofuran with
cumyl-potassium
(6) P. Grosius, Y. Gallot, A. Skoulios, Makromol. Chem. *127*
(1969) 94...112; see also ibid. *132* (1970) 35...55
(7) film from CHCl$_3$ on CsI

2122111–**323213**   C₈H₈–C₇H₇N   175

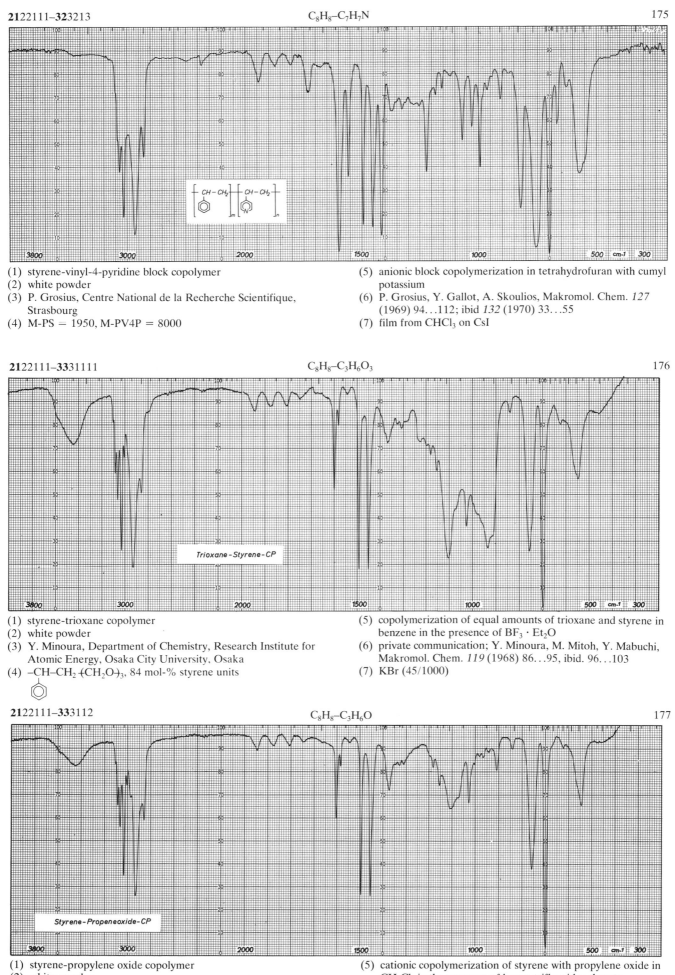

(1) styrene-vinyl-4-pyridine block copolymer
(2) white powder
(3) P. Grosius, Centre National de la Recherche Scientifique, Strasbourg
(4) M-PS = 1950, M-PV4P = 8000

(5) anionic block copolymerization in tetrahydrofuran with cumyl potassium
(6) P. Grosius, Y. Gallot, A. Skoulios, Makromol. Chem. *127* (1969) 94...112; ibid *132* (1970) 33...55
(7) film from CHCl₃ on CsI

2122111–**3331111**   C₈H₈–C₃H₆O₃   176

Trioxane-Styrene-CP

(1) styrene-trioxane copolymer
(2) white powder
(3) Y. Minoura, Department of Chemistry, Research Institute for Atomic Energy, Osaka City University, Osaka
(4) –CH–CH₂ +(CH₂O)₃, 84 mol-% styrene units

(5) copolymerization of equal amounts of trioxane and styrene in benzene in the presence of BF₃ · Et₂O
(6) private communication; Y. Minoura, M. Mitoh, Y. Mabuchi, Makromol. Chem. *119* (1968) 86...95, ibid. 96...103
(7) KBr (45/1000)

2122111–**333112**   C₈H₈–C₃H₆O   177

Styrene-Propeneoxide-CP

(1) styrene-propylene oxide copolymer
(2) white powder
(3) Y. Minoura, Research Institute for Atomic Energy, Osaka City University
(4) +(CH–CH₂)ₙ CH–CH₂–O–
         ⌀   CH₃

(5) cationic copolymerization of styrene with propylene oxide in CH₂Cl₂ in the presence of boron trifluoride etherate
(6) Y. Minoura, M. Mitoh, Makromol. Chem. *124* (1969) 241...8
(7) KBr (3,5/1000)

2122111+**333213** $C_8H_8 + C_8H_9O$ 178

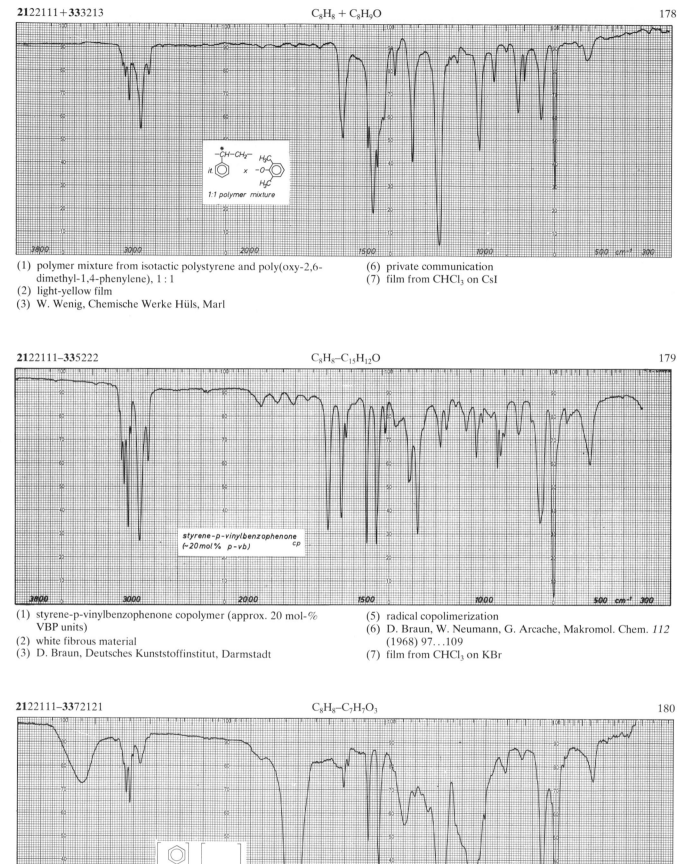

(1) polymer mixture from isotactic polystyrene and poly(oxy-2,6-dimethyl-1,4-phenylene), 1:1
(2) light-yellow film
(3) W. Wenig, Chemische Werke Hüls, Marl

(6) private communication
(7) film from CHCl₃ on CsI

2122111–**335222** C_8H_8–$C_{15}H_{12}O$ 179

(1) styrene-p-vinylbenzophenone copolymer (approx. 20 mol-% VBP units)
(2) white fibrous material
(3) D. Braun, Deutsches Kunststoffinstitut, Darmstadt

(5) radical copolimerization
(6) D. Braun, W. Neumann, G. Arcache, Makromol. Chem. *112* (1968) 97...109
(7) film from CHCl₃ on KBr

2122111–**3372121** C_8H_8–$C_7H_7O_3$ 180

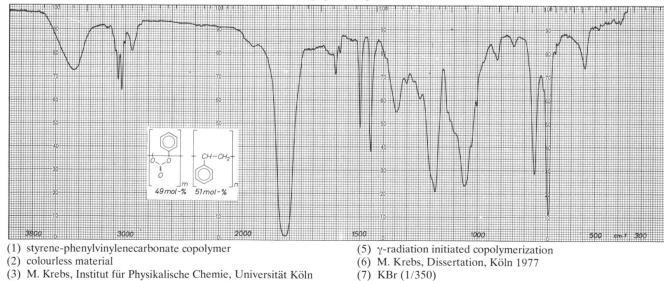

(1) styrene-phenylvinylenecarbonate copolymer
(2) colourless material
(3) M. Krebs, Institut für Physikalische Chemie, Universität Köln
(4) almost equimolar composition

(5) γ-radiation initiated copolymerization
(6) M. Krebs, Dissertation, Köln 1977
(7) KBr (1/350)

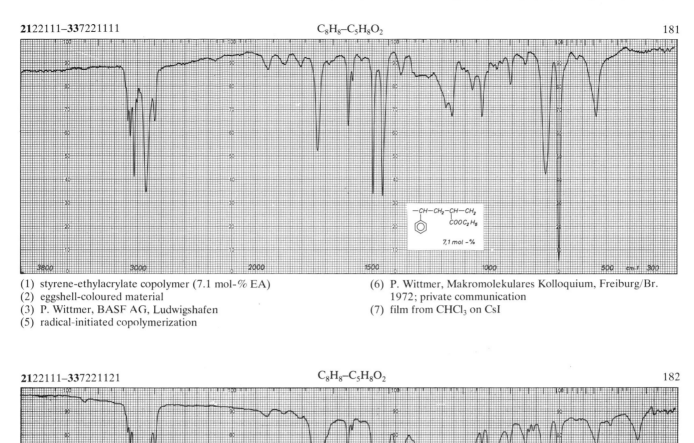

7,1 mol -%

(1) styrene-ethylacrylate copolymer (7.1 mol-% EA)
(2) eggshell-coloured material
(3) P. Wittmer, BASF AG, Ludwigshafen
(5) radical-initiated copolymerization

(6) P. Wittmer, Makromolekulares Kolloquium, Freiburg/Br. 1972; private communication
(7) film from $CHCl_3$ on CsI

S–MMA block CP

(1) styrene-methylmethacrylate block copolymer
(2) white material
(3) T. Kotaka, Institute for Chemical Research, Kyoto University
(5) anionic copolymerization with sodiumbiphenyl and tetra-hydrofuran; M. Szwarc, A. Rembaum, J. Polym. Sci. *22*

(1956) 189; M. Szwarc, Adv. Polym. Sci. *2* (1960) 275; J. R. Urwin, J. M. Stearn, Makromol. Chem. *78* (1964) 194...206
(6) T. Kotaka, T. Tanaka, H. Ohnuma, Y. Murakami, H. I. H. I. Nagaki, Polymer J. *1* (1970) 245...59
(7) film from ethylacetate on CsI

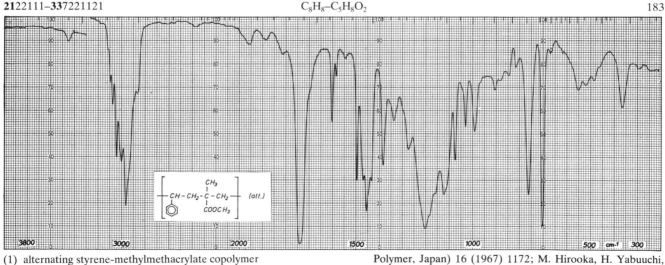

(1) alternating styrene-methylmethacrylate copolymer
(2) white material
(3) T. Kotaka, Institute for Chemical Research, Kyoto University
(5) copolymerization of MMA-ethylaluminum sesquichloride with styrene in toluene at −78 °C; M. Hirooka, Kobunshi (High

Polymer, Japan) 16 (1967) 1172; M. Hirooka, H. Yabuuchi, J. Iseki, Y. Nakai, J. Polym. Sci. A1 6 (1968) 1381
(6) T. Kotaka, T. Tanaka, H. Ohnuma, Y. Murakami, H. I. Nagaki, Polymer J. *1* (1970) 245...59
(7) film from ethylacetate on CsI

2122111–**337**221121   C$_8$H$_8$–C$_5$H$_8$O$_2$ 184

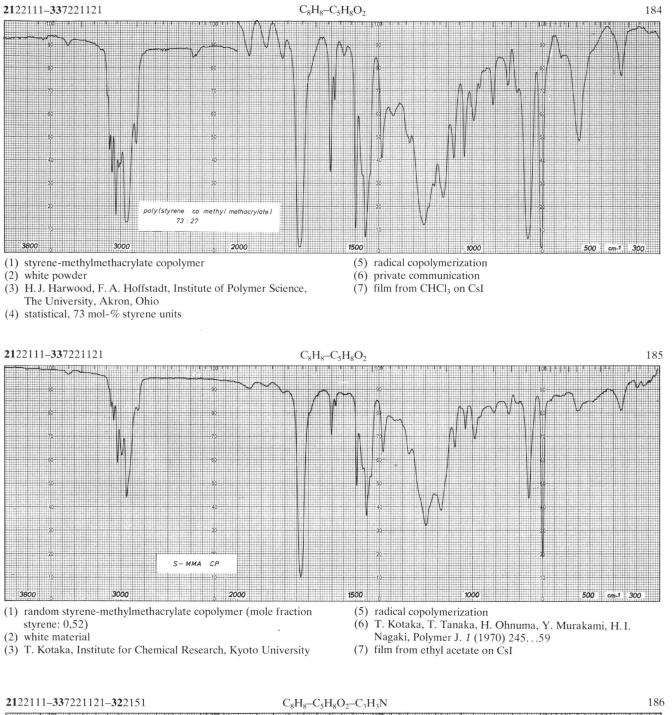

poly(styrene   co methyl methacrylate)
73 : 27

(1) styrene-methylmethacrylate copolymer
(2) white powder
(3) H. J. Harwood, F. A. Hoffstadt, Institute of Polymer Science, The University, Akron, Ohio
(4) statistical, 73 mol-% styrene units
(5) radical copolymerization
(6) private communication
(7) film from CHCl$_3$ on CsI

2122111–**337**221121   C$_8$H$_8$–C$_5$H$_8$O$_2$ 185

S – MMA CP

(1) random styrene-methylmethacrylate copolymer (mole fraction styrene: 0,52)
(2) white material
(3) T. Kotaka, Institute for Chemical Research, Kyoto University
(5) radical copolymerization
(6) T. Kotaka, T. Tanaka, H. Ohnuma, Y. Murakami, H. I. Nagaki, Polymer J. *1* (1970) 245...59
(7) film from ethyl acetate on CsI

2122111–**337**221121–**322**151   C$_8$H$_8$–C$_5$H$_8$O$_2$–C$_3$H$_3$N   186

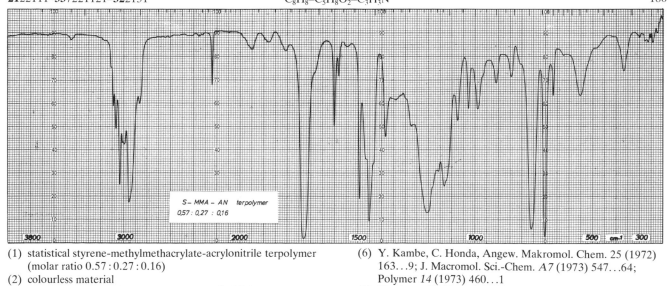

S – MMA – AN   terpolymer
0,57 : 0,27 : 0,16

(1) statistical styrene-methylmethacrylate-acrylonitrile terpolymer (molar ratio 0.57 : 0.27 : 0.16)
(2) colourless material
(3) Y. Kambe, Showa College of Pharmaceutical Sciences, Tsurumaki, Setagaya, Tokyo
(5) radical copolymerization in DMF with α,α′-azobisisobutyro-nitrile
(6) Y. Kambe, C. Honda, Angew. Makromol. Chem. 25 (1972) 163...9; J. Macromol. Sci.-Chem. *A7* (1973) 547...64; Polymer *14* (1973) 460...1
(7) film from CHCl$_3$ on CsI

2122111–**33**811 $C_8H_8–C_4H_2O_3$ 187

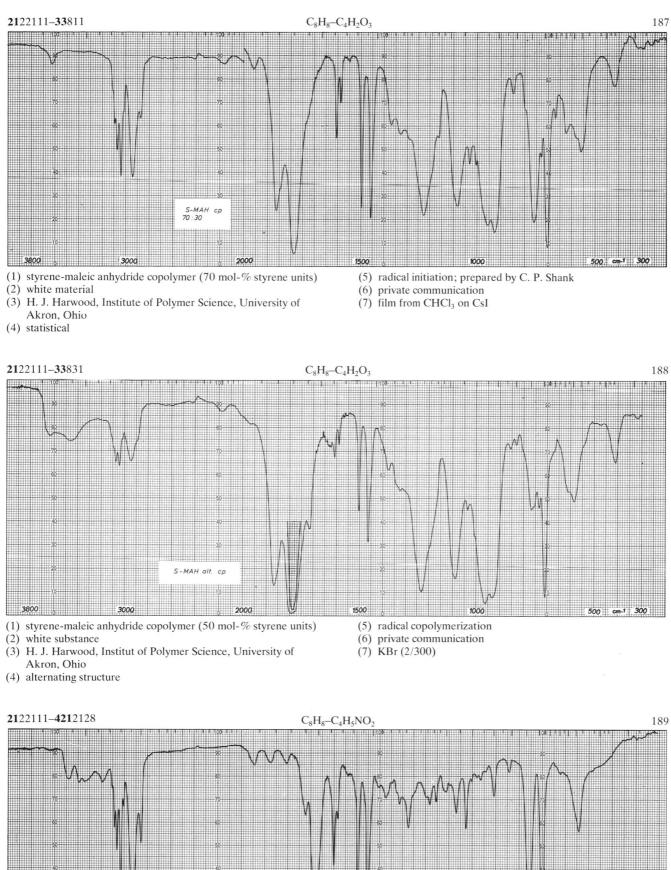

(1) styrene-maleic anhydride copolymer (70 mol-% styrene units)
(2) white material
(3) H. J. Harwood, Institute of Polymer Science, University of Akron, Ohio
(4) statistical
(5) radical initiation; prepared by C. P. Shank
(6) private communication
(7) film from CHCl₃ on CsI

2122111–**33**831 $C_8H_8–C_4H_2O_3$ 188

(1) styrene-maleic anhydride copolymer (50 mol-% styrene units)
(2) white substance
(3) H. J. Harwood, Institut of Polymer Science, University of Akron, Ohio
(4) alternating structure
(5) radical copolymerization
(6) private communication
(7) KBr (2/300)

2122111–**42**12128 $C_8H_8–C_4H_5NO_2$ 189

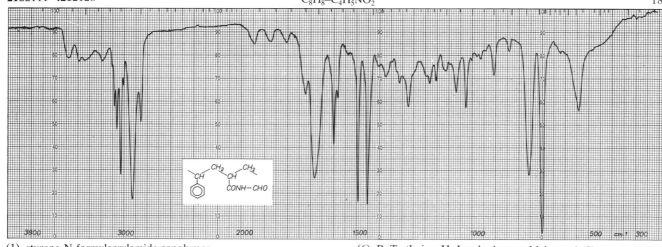

(1) styrene-N-formylacrylamide copolymer
(2) white powder
(3) B. Trathnigg, Abteilung für Organische Chemie I, Universität Graz
(5) copolymerization of styrene and N-formylacrylamide in methanol with dibenzoylperoxide
(6) B. Trathnigg, H. Junek, Angew. Makromol. Chem. *53* (1976) 81...91
(7) film from styrene on CsI

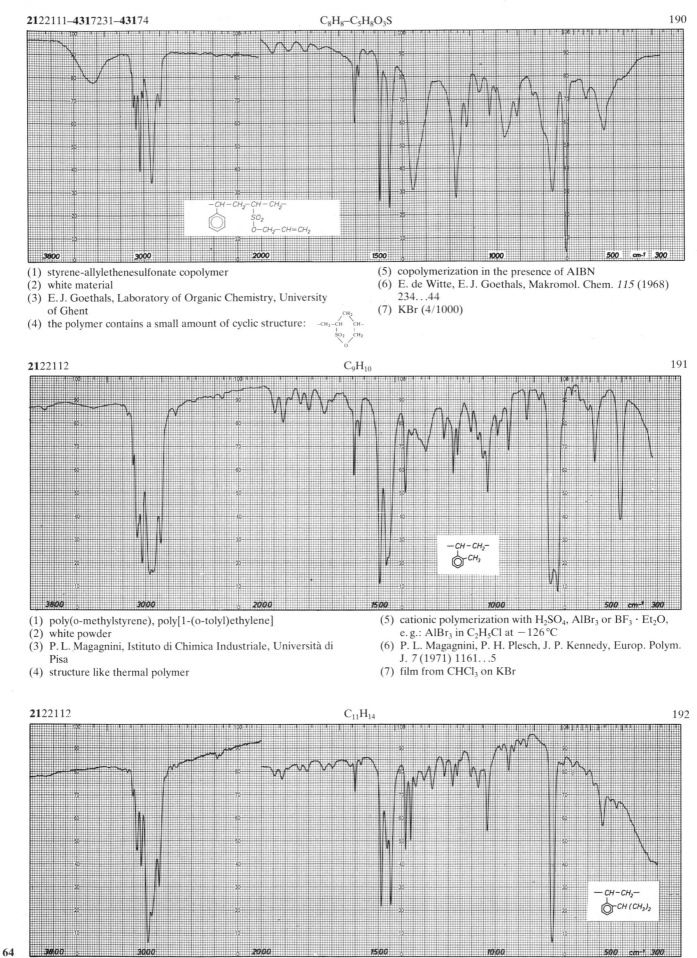

2122111–4317231–43174   C₈H₈–C₅H₈O₃S   190

(1) styrene-allylethenesulfonate copolymer
(2) white material
(3) E. J. Goethals, Laboratory of Organic Chemistry, University of Ghent
(4) the polymer contains a small amount of cyclic structure:

(5) copolymerization in the presence of AIBN
(6) E. de Witte, E. J. Goethals, Makromol. Chem. *115* (1968) 234...44
(7) KBr (4/1000)

2122112   C₉H₁₀   191

(1) poly(o-methylstyrene), poly[1-(o-tolyl)ethylene]
(2) white powder
(3) P. L. Magagnini, Istituto di Chimica Industriale, Università di Pisa
(4) structure like thermal polymer

(5) cationic polymerization with H₂SO₄, AlBr₃ or BF₃ · Et₂O, e. g.: AlBr₃ in C₂H₅Cl at −126 °C
(6) P. L. Magagnini, P. H. Plesch, J. P. Kennedy, Europ. Polym. J. 7 (1971) 1161...5
(7) film from CHCl₃ on KBr

2122112   C₁₁H₁₄   192

(1) poly(o-isopropylstyrene), poly[1-(o-isopropylbenzene)ethyl-ene]
(2) white coarse powder
(3) P. L. Magagnini, Istituto di Chimica Industriale, Università di Pisa
(4) structure like thermal polymer

(5) cationic polymerization
(6) private communication, see also P. L. Magagnini, P. H. Plesch, J. P. Kennedy, Europ. Polym. J. 7 (1971) 1161...5
(7) film from CHCl₃ on KBr

2122112 C_9H_{10} 193

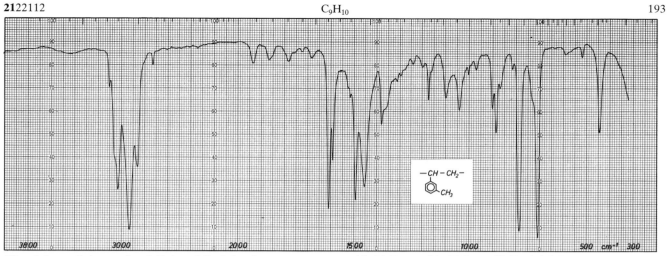

(1) poly(m-methylstyrene), poly[1-(m-tolyl)ethylene]
(2) white powder
(3) P. L. Magagnini, Istituto di Chimica Industriale, Università di Pisa
(5) V. Frosini, P. L. Magagnini, Europ. Polym. J. *2* (1966) 129; P. L. Magagnini, V. Frosini, ibid. 139
(6) M. Baccaredda, E. Butta, V. Frosini, P. L. Magagnini, J. Polym. Sci. A2, *4* (1966) 789
(7) film from $CHCl_3$ on KBr

2122112 $C_{10}H_{12}$ 194

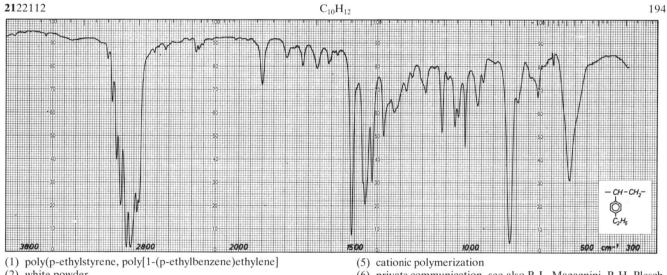

(1) poly(p-ethylstyrene, poly[1-(p-ethylbenzene)ethylene]
(2) white powder
(3) P. L. Magagnini, Istituto di Chimica Industriale, Università di Pisa
(5) cationic polymerization
(6) private communication, see also P. L. Magagnini, P. H. Plesch, J. P. Kennedy, Europ. Polym. J. *7* (1971) 1161...5
(7) film from $CHCl_3$ on KBr

2122112–**21**111 $C_{18}H_{20}$–C_4H_8 195

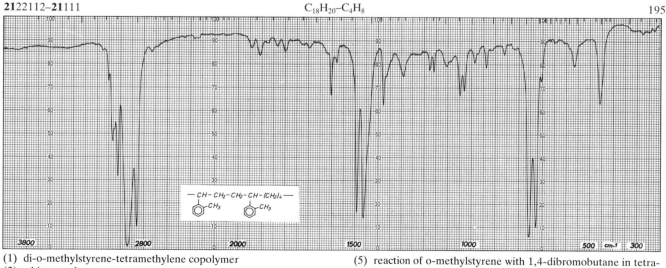

(1) di-o-methylstyrene-tetramethylene copolymer
(2) white powder
(3) D. H. Richards, Explosives Research and Development Establishment, Waltham Abbey, Essex
(4) alternating structure (o-methylstyrene units in head-to-head arrangement)
(5) reaction of o-methylstyrene with 1,4-dibromobutane in tetrahydrofuran in the presence of lithium metal
(6) D. H. Richards, N. F. Scilly, F. Williams, Polymer *10* (1969) 603...9
(7) film from $CHCl_3$ on CsI

2122112–**21**111 $C_{18}H_{20}$–C_4H_8 196

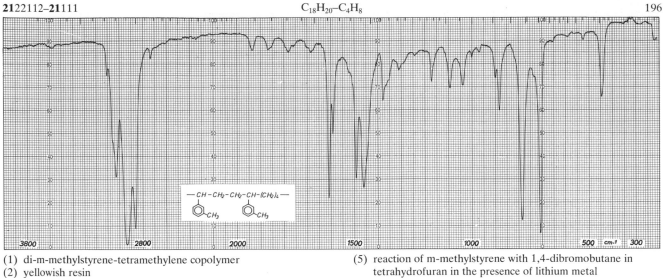

(1) di-m-methylstyrene-tetramethylene copolymer
(2) yellowish resin
(3) D. H. Richards, Explosives Research and Development
    Establishment, Waltham Abbey, Essex
(4) alternating structure (m-methylstyrene units in head-to-head
    arrangement)

(5) reaction of m-methylstyrene with 1,4-dibromobutane in
    tetrahydrofuran in the presence of lithium metal
(6) D. H. Richards, N. F. Scilly, F. Williams, Polymer *10* (1969)
    603...9
(7) film from $CHCl_3$ on CsI

2122112–**21**111 $C_{18}H_{20}$–C_4H_8 197

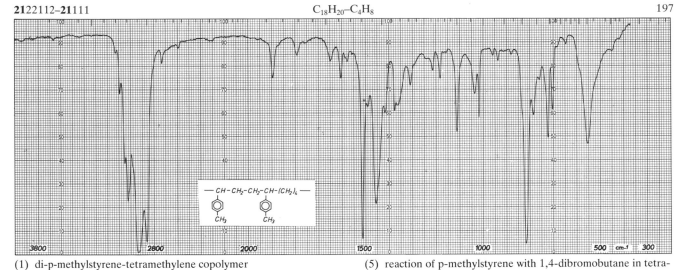

(1) di-p-methylstyrene-tetramethylene copolymer
(2) white powder
(3) D. H. Richards, Explosives Research and Development
    Establishment, Waltham Abbey, Essex
(4) alternating structure (p-methylstyrene units in head-to-head
    arrangement)

(5) reaction of p-methylstyrene with 1,4-dibromobutane in tetra-
    hydrofuran in the presence of lithium metal
(6) D. H. Richards, N. F. Scilly, F. Williams, Polymer *10* (1969)
    603...9
(7) film from $CHCl_3$ on CsI

2122113–**21**111 $C_{28}H_{24}$–C_4H_8 198

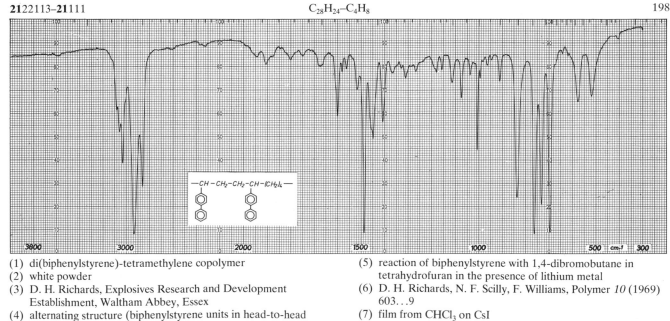

(1) di(biphenylstyrene)-tetramethylene copolymer
(2) white powder
(3) D. H. Richards, Explosives Research and Development
    Establishment, Waltham Abbey, Essex
(4) alternating structure (biphenylstyrene units in head-to-head
    arrangement)

(5) reaction of biphenylstyrene with 1,4-dibromobutane in
    tetrahydrofuran in the presence of lithium metal
(6) D. H. Richards, N. F. Scilly, F. Williams, Polymer *10* (1969)
    603...9
(7) film from $CHCl_3$ on CsI

2122114   C₁₂H₁₀   199

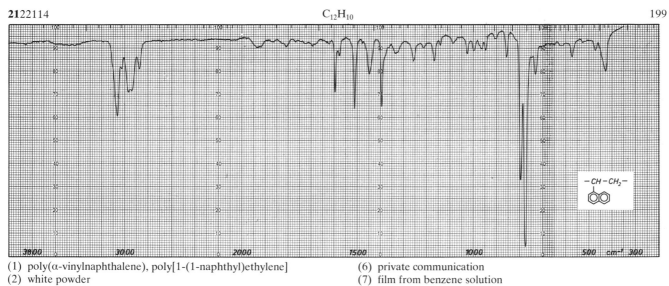

(1) poly(α-vinylnaphthalene), poly[1-(1-naphthyl)ethylene]
(2) white powder
(3) P. L. Magagnini, Istituto di Chimica Industriale, Università di Pisa

(6) private communication
(7) film from benzene solution

2122114   C₂₀H₁₂   200

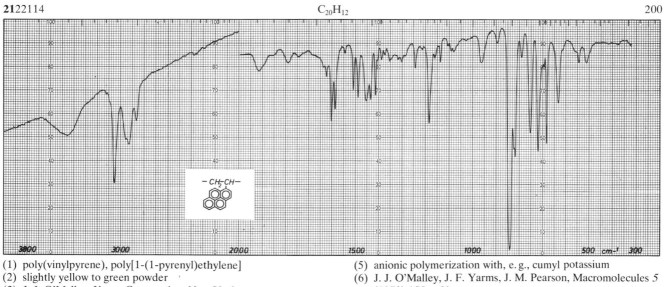

(1) poly(vinylpyrene), poly[1-(1-pyrenyl)ethylene]
(2) slightly yellow to green powder
(3) J. J. O'Malley, Xerox Corporation, New York

(5) anionic polymerization with, e. g., cumyl potassium
(6) J. J. O'Malley, J. F. Yarms, J. M. Pearson, Macromolecules *5* (1972) 158...61
(7) KBr (1,8/350)

2122114   C₂₀H₁₂   201

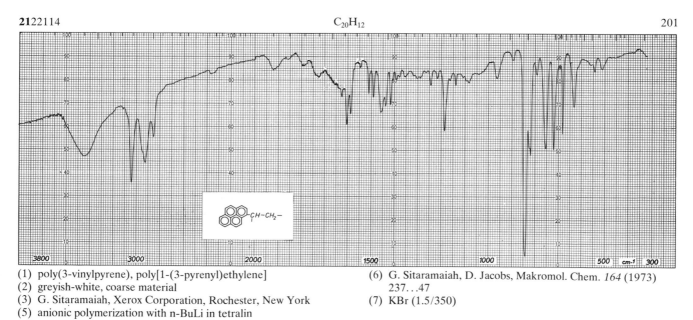

(1) poly(3-vinylpyrene), poly[1-(3-pyrenyl)ethylene]
(2) greyish-white, coarse material
(3) G. Sitaramaiah, Xerox Corporation, Rochester, New York
(5) anionic polymerization with n-BuLi in tetralin

(6) G. Sitaramaiah, D. Jacobs, Makromol. Chem. *164* (1973) 237...47
(7) KBr (1.5/350)

212212 $C_{13}H_{16}$ 202

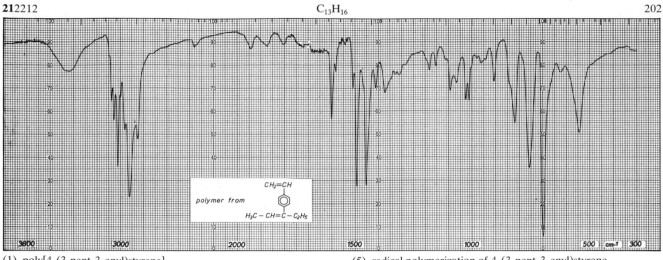

(1) poly[4-(3-pent-3-enyl)styrene]
(2) white coarse powder
(3) G. Greber, Institut für Makromolekulare Chemie, Universität Freiburg
(5) radical polymerization of 4-(3-pent-3-enyl)styrene
(6) private communication; Makromolekulares Colloquium, Freiburg/Br. 1969
(7) KBr (2/300)

212212 $C_{10}H_{10} + C_{10}H_{10}$ 203

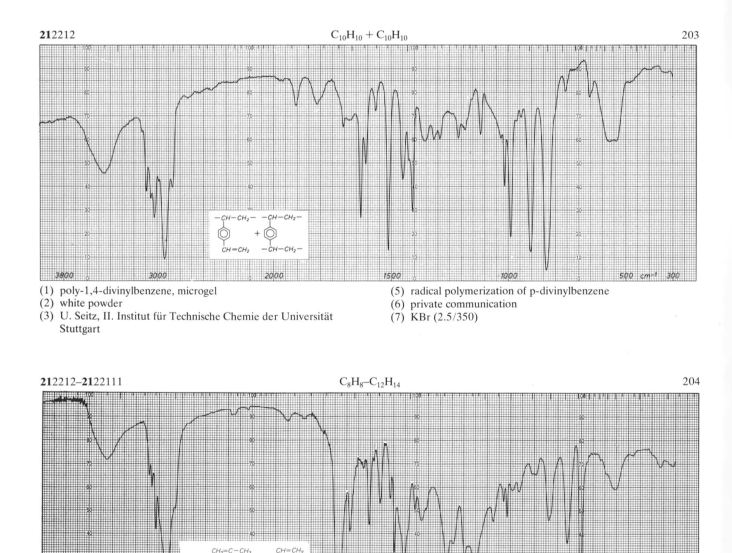

(1) poly-1,4-divinylbenzene, microgel
(2) white powder
(3) U. Seitz, II. Institut für Technische Chemie der Universität Stuttgart
(5) radical polymerization of p-divinylbenzene
(6) private communication
(7) KBr (2.5/350)

212212–**21**22111 C_8H_8–$C_{12}H_{14}$ 204

(1) copolymer from 1,4-di-α-methylstyrene and styrene (1 : 2.3), grafted with methylmethacrylate
(2) yellowish, coarse material
(3) G. Greber, Institut für Makromolekulare Chemie, Universität Freiburg/Br.
(6) private communication
(7) KBr (2.5/300)

2122131 C_9H_{10} 205

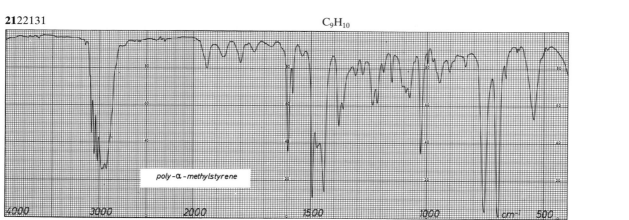

poly-α-methylstyrene

(1) poly-α-methylstyrene, poly(1-methyl-1-phenyl-ethylene)
(2) clear, colourless material
(3) Dow Chemical Company, Midland, Mich.

(7) film from $CHCl_3$ solution
(8) commercial product

2122131–**21**111 $C_{28}H_{24}$–C_3H_6 206

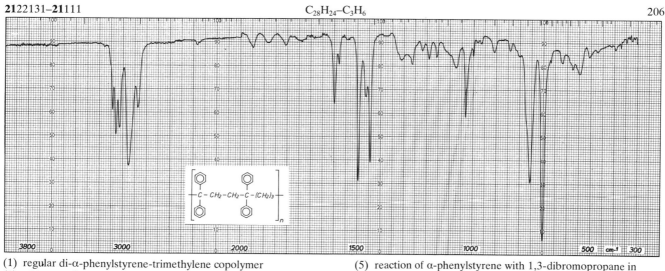

(1) regular di-α-phenylstyrene-trimethylene copolymer
(2) white powder
(3) D. H. Richards, Explosives Research and Development
     Establishment, Waltham Abbey, Essex
(4) alternating structure, α-phenylstyrene units head-to-head

(5) reaction of α-phenylstyrene with 1,3-dibromopropane in
     tetrahydrofuran in the presence of lithium metal; see
     D. H. Richards, N. F. Scilly, F. Williams, Polymer *10* (1969) 603
(6) D. H. Richards, N. F. Scilly, S. M. Hutchinson, ibid. 611...20
(7) film from $CHCl_3$ on CsI

2122131–**21**111 $C_{18}H_{20}$–C_4H_8 207

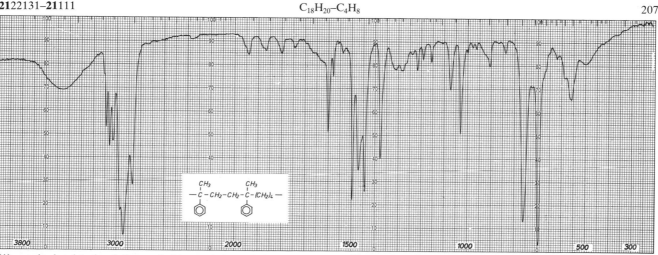

(1) regular head-to-head di-α-methylstyrene-tetramethylene
     copolymer
(2) white powder
(3) D. H. Richards, Explosives Research and Development
     Establishment, Waltham Abbey, Essex

(5) reaction of α-methylstyrene with an alkali metal in
     tetrahydrofuran in the presence of tetramethylene dibromide;
     see D. H. Richards, N. F. Scilly, F. Williams, Polymer *10*
     (1969) 603
(6) D. H. Richards, N. F. Scilly, S. M. Hutchinson, ibid. 611...20
(7) film from $CHCl_3$ on CsI

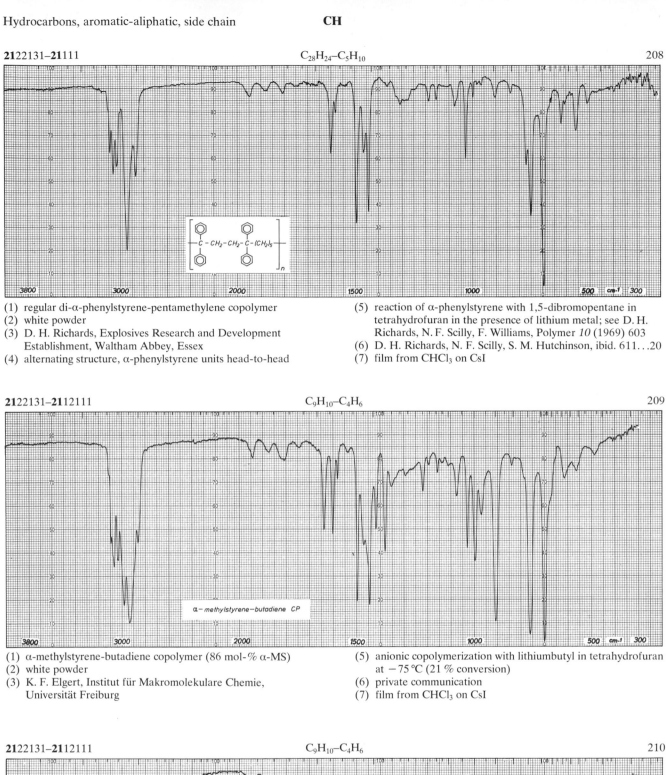

(1) regular di-α-phenylstyrene-pentamethylene copolymer
(2) white powder
(3) D. H. Richards, Explosives Research and Development Establishment, Waltham Abbey, Essex
(4) alternating structure, α-phenylstyrene units head-to-head
(5) reaction of α-phenylstyrene with 1,5-dibromopentane in tetrahydrofuran in the presence of lithium metal; see D. H. Richards, N. F. Scilly, F. Williams, Polymer 10 (1969) 603
(6) D. H. Richards, N. F. Scilly, S. M. Hutchinson, ibid. 611...20
(7) film from CHCl₃ on CsI

α–methylstyrene–butadiene CP

(1) α-methylstyrene-butadiene copolymer (86 mol-% α-MS)
(2) white powder
(3) K. F. Elgert, Institut für Makromolekulare Chemie, Universität Freiburg
(5) anionic copolymerization with lithiumbutyl in tetrahydrofuran at −75 °C (21 % conversion)
(6) private communication
(7) film from CHCl₃ on CsI

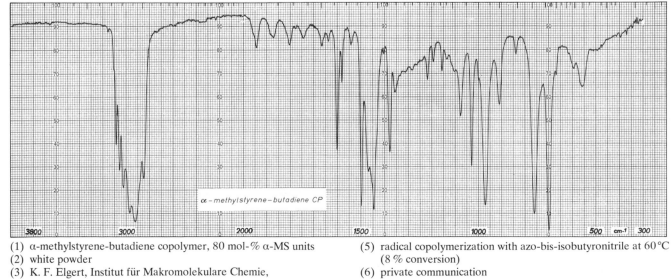

α – methylstyrene – butadiene CP

(1) α-methylstyrene-butadiene copolymer, 80 mol-% α-MS units
(2) white powder
(3) K. F. Elgert, Institut für Makromolekulare Chemie, Universität Freiburg
(5) radical copolymerization with azo-bis-isobutyronitrile at 60 °C (8 % conversion)
(6) private communication
(7) film from CHCl₃ on CsI

2122131–212111 $C_{18}H_{20}–C_8H_8$ 211

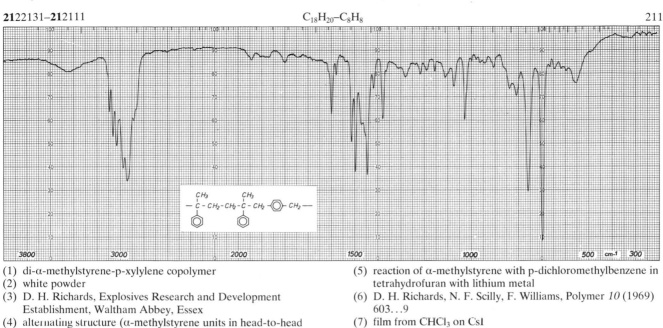

(1) di-α-methylstyrene-p-xylylene copolymer
(2) white powder
(3) D. H. Richards, Explosives Research and Development Establishment, Waltham Abbey, Essex
(4) alternating structure (α-methylstyrene units in head-to-head arrangement)
(5) reaction of α-methylstyrene with p-dichloromethylbenzene in tetrahydrofuran with lithium metal
(6) D. H. Richards, N. F. Scilly, F. Williams, Polymer *10* (1969) 603...9
(7) film from CHCl₃ on CsI

2122131–212215 $C_9H_{10}–CH_2-C_9H_{10}$ 212

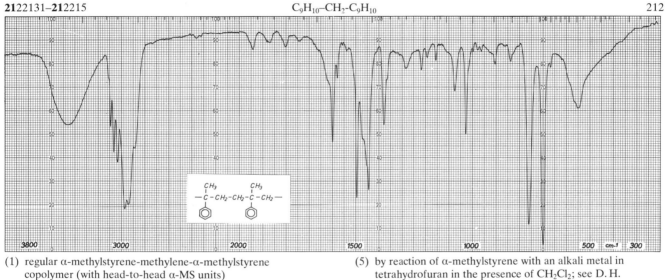

(1) regular α-methylstyrene-methylene-α-methylstyrene copolymer (with head-to-head α-MS units)
(2) white powder
(3) D. H. Richards, Explosives Research and Development Establishment, Waltham Abbey, Essex
(5) by reaction of α-methylstyrene with an alkali metal in tetrahydrofuran in the presence of CH₂Cl₂; see D. H. Richards, N. F. Scilly, F. Williams, Polymer *10* (1969) 603
(6) D. H. Richards, N. F. Scilly, S. M. Hutchinson, ibid. 611...20
(7) film from CHCl₃ on CsI

2122131–322151 $C_9H_{10}–C_3H_3N$ 213

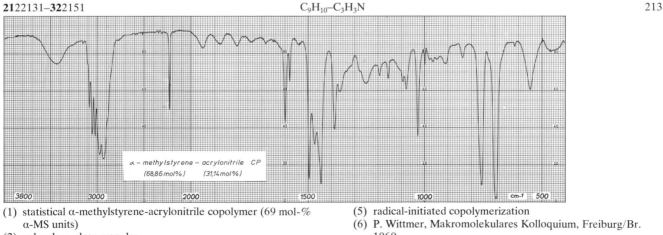

α – methylstyrene – acrylonitrile   CP
(68,86 mol%)   (31,14 mol%)

(1) statistical α-methylstyrene-acrylonitrile copolymer (69 mol-% α-MS units)
(2) colourless, clear granules
(3) BASF AG, Kunststofflaboratorium, Ludwigshafen (by P. Wittmer)
(5) radical-initiated copolymerization
(6) P. Wittmer, Makromolekulares Kolloquium, Freiburg/Br. 1969
(7) KBr (6.6/1000)

2122131–**3**22151 C_9H_{10}–C_3H_3N 214

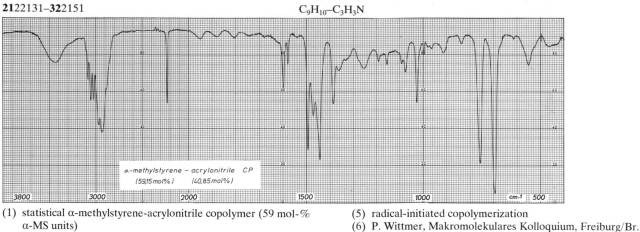

α-methylstyrene – acrylonitrile   CP
(59,15 mol%)   (40,85 mol%)

(1) statistical α-methylstyrene-acrylonitrile copolymer (59 mol-%
    α-MS units)
(2) colourless, clear granules
(3) BASF AG, Kunststofflaboratorium, Ludwigshafen
    (by P. Wittmer)

(5) radical-initiated copolymerization
(6) P. Wittmer, Makromolekulares Kolloquium, Freiburg/Br.
    1969
(7) KBr (5.5/1000)

2122131–**3**22151 C_9H_{10}–C_3H_3N 215

α-methylstyrene – acrylonitrile   CP
(50,55 mol%)   (49,45 mol%)

(1) statistical α-methylstyrene-acrylonitrile copolymer (almost
    equimolar)
(2) colourless, clear granules
(3) BASF AG, Kunststofflaboratorium, Ludwigshafen
    (by P. Wittmer)

(5) radical-initiated copolymerization
(6) P. Wittmer, Makromolekulares Kolloquium, Freiburg/Br.
    1969
(7) KBr (7/1000)

2122131–**33**72121 C_9H_{10}–$C_9H_6O_3$ 216

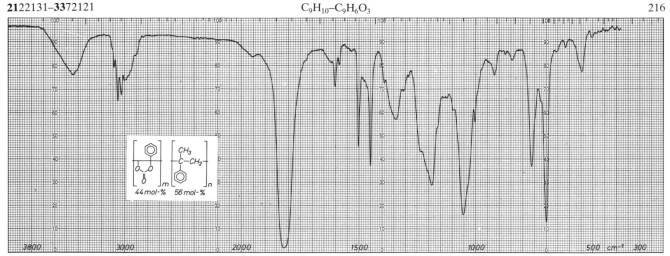

44 mol-%   56 mol-%

(1) α-methylstyrene-phenylvinylenecarbonate copolymer
(2) colourless material
(3) M. Krebs, Institut für Physikalische Chemie, Universität Köln
(4) 56 mol-% α-methylstyrene units

(5) γ-radiation initiated copolymerization
(6) M. Krebs, Dissertation, Köln 1977
(7) KBr (1/350)

2122132 $C_{10}H_{12}$ 217

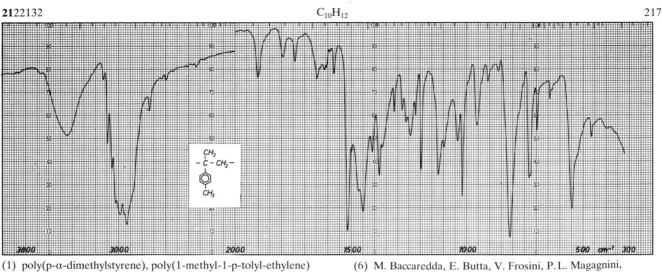

(1) poly(p-α-dimethylstyrene), poly(1-methyl-1-p-tolyl-ethylene)
(2) white material
(3) P. L. Magagnini, Istituto di Chimica Industriale, Universita di Pisa
(5) cationic polymerization, see V. Frosini, P. L. Magagnini, Europ. Polym. J. *2* (1966) 129, ibid. 139

(6) M. Baccaredda, E. Butta, V. Frosini, P. L. Magagnini, J. Polym. Sci. A-2, *4* (1966) 789; see also P. L. Magagnini, P. H. Plesch, J. P. Kennedy, Europ. Polym. J. *7* (1971) 1161...5
(7) KBr (5/350)
(8) insoluble in $CHCl_3$

212215 $C_{18}H_{20}-C_4H_8$ 218

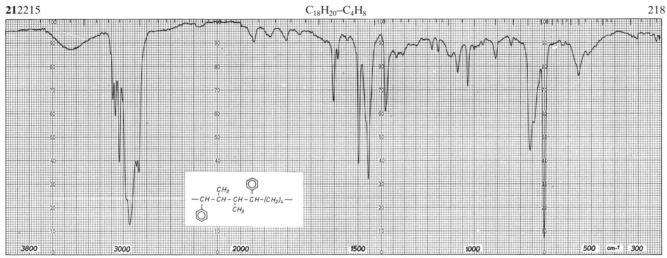

(1) alternating head-to-head di-β-methylstyrene-tetramethylene copolymer
(2) white powder
(3) D. H. Richards, Explosives Research and Development Establishment, Waltham Abbey, Essex

(5) dimerisation of β-methylstyrene in a suspension of lithium metal in tetrahydrofuran followed by polycondensation with 1,4-dibromobutane
(6) D. H. Richards, N. S. Scilly, F. Williams, Polymer *10* (1969) 603...9
(7) film from $CHCl_3$ on CsI

212216 C_9H_8 219

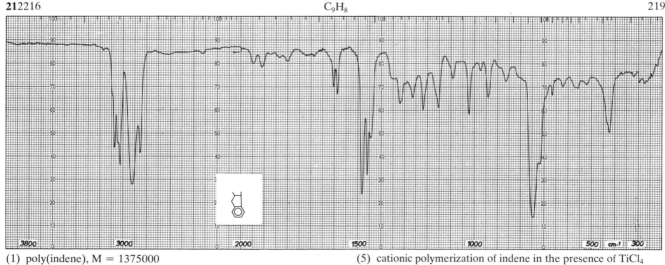

(1) poly(indene), M = 1375000
(2) white material
(3) N. A. Hung, Université de Paris

(5) cationic polymerization of indene in the presence of $TiCl_4$
(6) N. A. Hung, H. Cheradame, P. Sigwalt, Europ. Polym. J. *9* (1973) 385...97
(7) film from $CHCl_3$ solution

212216 $C_{10}H_{10}$ 220

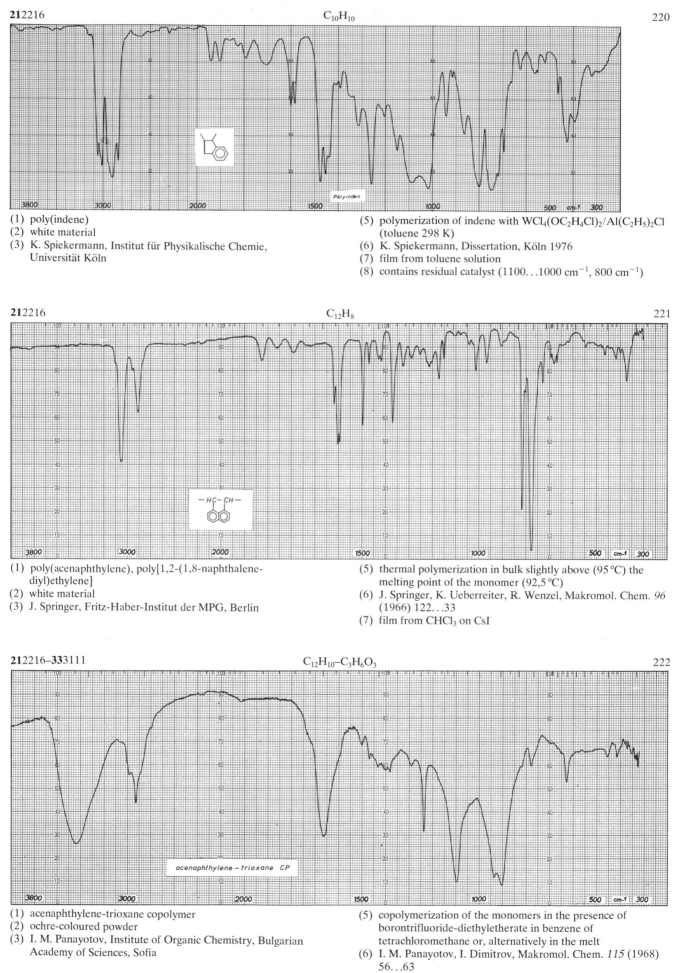

(1) poly(indene)
(2) white material
(3) K. Spiekermann, Institut für Physikalische Chemie,
Universität Köln

(5) polymerization of indene with $WCl_4(OC_2H_4Cl)_2/Al(C_2H_5)_2Cl$
(toluene 298 K)
(6) K. Spiekermann, Dissertation, Köln 1976
(7) film from toluene solution
(8) contains residual catalyst (1100...1000 cm^{-1}, 800 cm^{-1})

212216 $C_{12}H_8$ 221

(1) poly(acenaphthylene), poly[1,2-(1,8-naphthalene-
diyl)ethylene]
(2) white material
(3) J. Springer, Fritz-Haber-Institut der MPG, Berlin

(5) thermal polymerization in bulk slightly above (95 °C) the
melting point of the monomer (92,5 °C)
(6) J. Springer, K. Ueberreiter, R. Wenzel, Makromol. Chem. *96*
(1966) 122...33
(7) film from CHCl$_3$ on CsI

212216–**333**111 $C_{12}H_{10}$–$C_3H_6O_3$ 222

(1) acenaphthylene-trioxane copolymer
(2) ochre-coloured powder
(3) I. M. Panayotov, Institute of Organic Chemistry, Bulgarian
Academy of Sciences, Sofia

(5) copolymerization of the monomers in the presence of
borontrifluoride-diethyletherate in benzene of
tetrachloromethane or, alternatively in the melt
(6) I. M. Panayotov, I. Dimitrov, Makromol. Chem. *115* (1968)
56...63
(7) KBr (1.2/300)

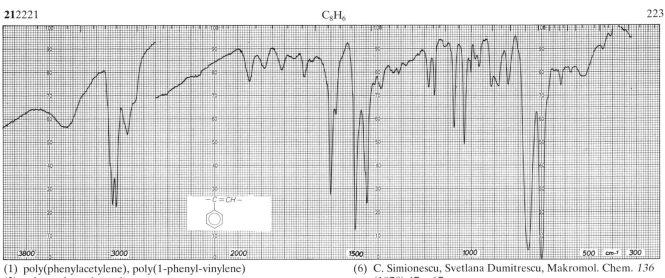

(1) poly(phenylacetylene), poly(1-phenyl-vinylene)
(2) ochre-coloured powder
(3) C. Simionescu, Institutul Politehnic, Iaşi
(5) thermal polymerization of phenylacetylene

(6) C. Simionescu, Svetlana Dumitrescu, Makromol. Chem. *136* (1970) 47...67
(7) KBr (4/350)

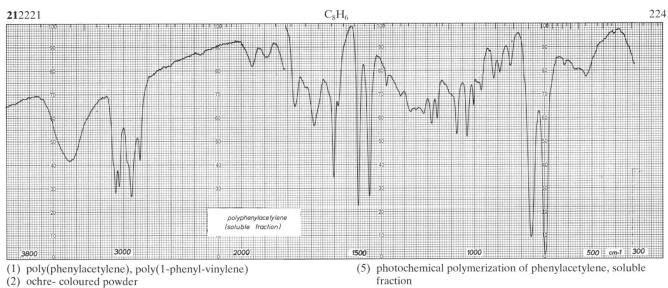

polyphenylacetylene
(soluble fraction)

(1) poly(phenylacetylene), poly(1-phenyl-vinylene)
(2) ochre- coloured powder
(3) C. Simionescu, Institutul Politehnic, Iaşi

(5) photochemical polymerization of phenylacetylene, soluble fraction
(6) C. Simionescu, Svetlana Dumitrescu, Makromol. Chem. *136* (1970) 47...67
(7) KBr (4/350)

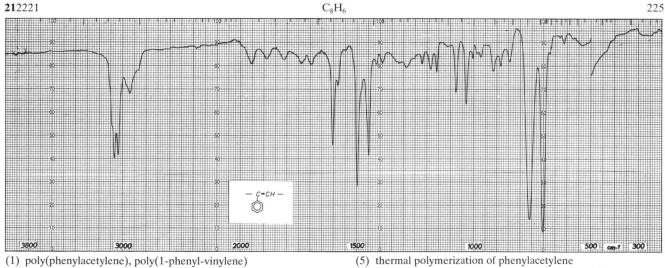

(1) poly(phenylacetylene), poly(1-phenyl-vinylene)
(2) yellow powder
(3) R. J. Kern, Monsanto Comp., St. Louis, Mo.

(5) thermal polymerization of phenylacetylene
(6) R. J. Kern, J. Polym. Sci. A-1 7 (1969) 621...31
(7) film from CHCl$_3$ on CsI

212221   C$_8$H$_6$ 226

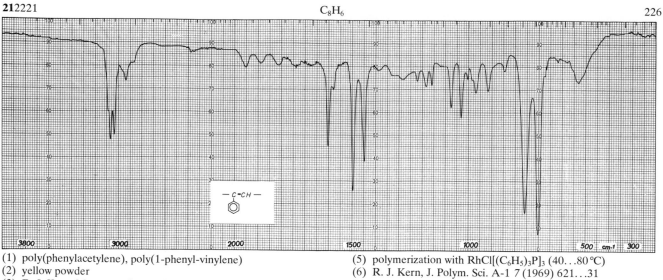

(1) poly(phenylacetylene), poly(1-phenyl-vinylene)
(2) yellow powder
(3) R. J. Kern, Monsanto Comp., St. Louis, Mo.

(5) polymerization with RhCl[(C$_6$H$_5$)$_3$P]$_3$ (40...80 °C)
(6) R. J. Kern, J. Polym. Sci. A-1 7 (1969) 621...31
(7) film from CHCl$_3$ on CsI

212221   C$_8$H$_6$ 227

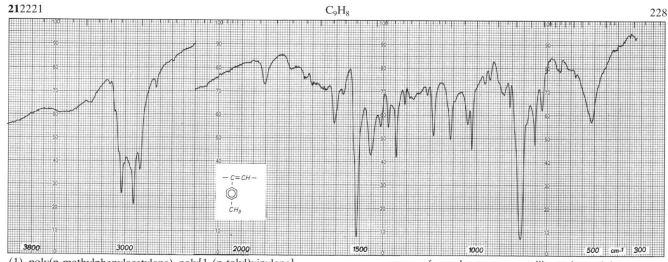

(1) poly(phenylacetylene), poly(1-phenyl-vinylene)
(2) brick-red powder
(3) P. Ehrlich, State University of New York at Buffalo, N.Y.
(5) from phenylacetylene, polymerized in the presence of ferric acetylacetonate and aluminum triethyl; M. Biyany, A. J.

Campagna, D. Daruvalla, C. M. Srivastava, P. Ehrlich, J. Macromol. Sci., Chem. 9 (1975) 327
(6) S. H. C. Chang, E. C. Mertzlufft, P. Ehrlich, R. D. Allendörfer, Macromolecules 8 (1975) 642...4
(7) KBr (1.5/350)

212221   C$_9$H$_8$ 228

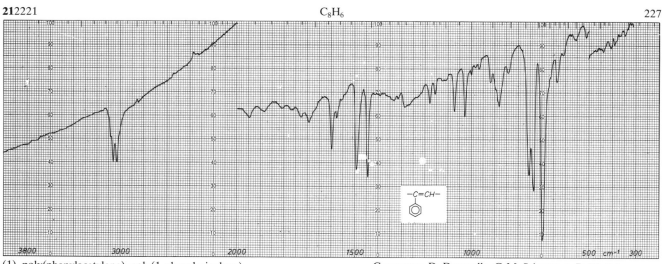

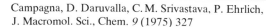

(1) poly(p-methylphenylacetylene), poly[1-(p-tolyl)vinylene]
(2) orange powder
(3) C. Simionescu, Acad. Republicii Socialiste România, Jaşi
(5) ionic polymerization of p-methylphenylacetylene in the

presence of complex organo-metallic catalysts of the type Al(C$_2$H$_5$)$_3$/Ti(OC$_4$H$_9$)$_4$, Al(C$_2$H$_5$)$_3$/VO(C$_5$H$_7$O$_2$)$_2$ or others
(6) C. Simionescu, Svetlana Dumitrescu, Makromol. Chem. 136 (1970) 47...64

212221   C$_{16}$H$_{10}$ 229

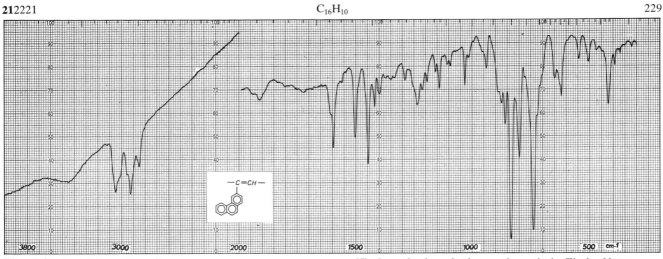

(1) poly(3-ethynylphenanthrene),
   poly[1-(3-phenanthrenyl)vinylene]
(2) orange powder
(3) C. Simionescu, Institutul de Chimie Macromoleculare,
   Academia R. S. Romania, Iaşy

(5) thermal polymerization or, alternatively, Ziegler-Natta
   initiators of the type AlEt$_3$/TiCl$_4$ or others
(6) C. Simionescu, Svetlana Dumitrescu, M. Grigoras, IUPAC
   Macro, Madrid 1974, preprints vol. 1, 336
(7) ground with KBr (2.2/350) and CHCl$_3$, dried and pressed

212222   C$_{29}$H$_{20}$ 230

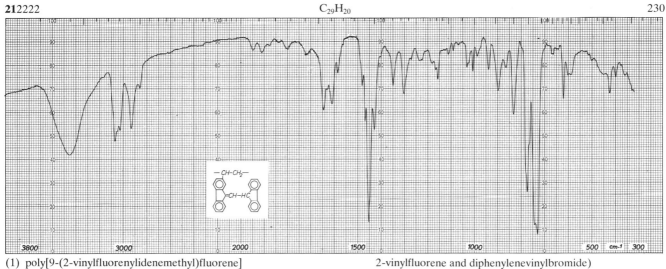

(1) poly[9-(2-vinylfluorenylidenemethyl)fluorene]
(2) white-yellow powder
(3) H. J. Förster, Institut für Organische Chemie, FU Berlin
(5) cationic (with BF$_3$-etherate in toluene at −70 °C) or radial
   (with AIBN) polymerization of the monomer (from

2-vinylfluorene and diphenylenevinylbromide)
(6) H. J. Förster, G. Manecke, Makromol. Chem. *133* (1970)
   53...60
(7) KBr (1.8/350)

212221   C$_{12}$H$_{6}$ 231

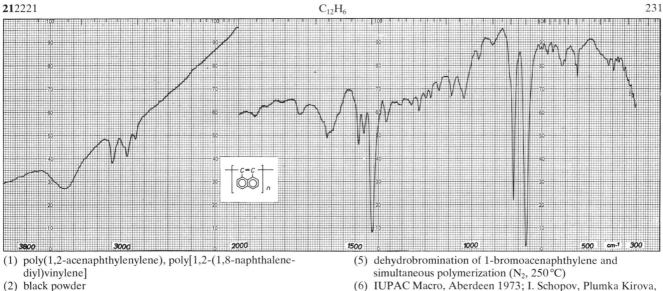

(1) poly(1,2-acenaphthylenylene), poly[1,2-(1,8-naphthalene-
   diyl)vinylene]
(2) black powder
(3) I. Schopov, Bulgarische Akademie der Wissenschaften,
   Zentrallaboratorium für Polymere, Sofia

(5) dehydrobromination of 1-bromoacenaphthylene and
   simultaneous polymerization (N$_2$, 250 °C)
(6) IUPAC Macro, Aberdeen 1973; I. Schopov, Plumka Kirova,
   Makromol. Chem. *176* (1975) 511...4
(7) KBr (3/350) (ordinate expansion between 2000 and 300
   cm^{-1})

212221 $C_{12}H_6$ 232

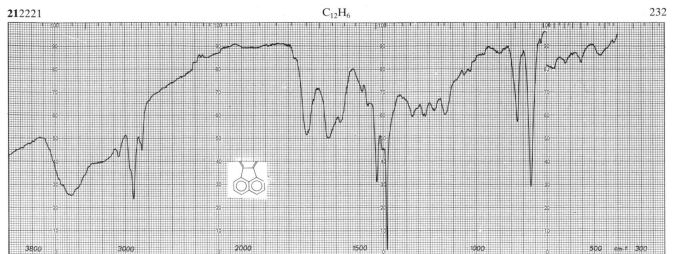

(1) poly(1,2-acenaphthene-diylidene)
(2) black powder
(3) I. Schopov, Central Laboratory for Polymer, Bulgarian
    Academy of Science, Sofia
(5) I. Schopov, Plumka Kirova, Makromol. Chem. *177* (1976)
    1653…63

(6) polycondensation of acenaphthenone in polyphosphoric acid
    at 150 °C (N_2)
(7) KBr (2/350)
(8) ordinate expanded

2123 $C_{14}H_8$ 233

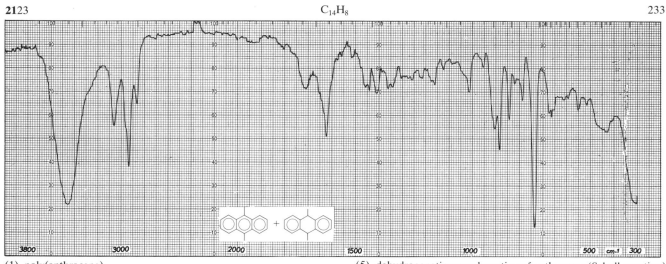
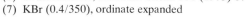

(1) poly(anthracene)
(2) yellowish-green powder
(3) O. Hinterhofer, Österreichisches Kunststoffinstitut, Wien
(4) structures according to the author

(5) dehydrogenation-condensation of anthracene (Scholl-reaction)
(6) O. Hinterhofer, Monatsh. Chem. *106* (1975) 67
(7) KBr (0.4/350), ordinate expanded

2123–33831 $C_{14}H_{10}-C_4H_2O_3$ 234

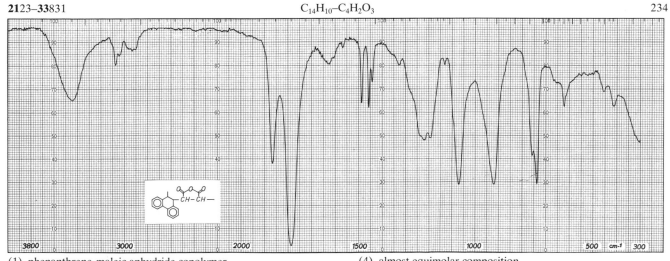

(1) phenanthrene-maleic anhydride copolymer
(2) white, hard powder
(3) Y. Nakayama, Department of Polymer Chemistry, Kyoto
    University, Kyoto

(4) almost equimolar composition
(5) radical copolymerization with AIBN
(6) Y. Nakayama, K. Hayashi, S. Okamura, J. Polym. Sci. A-1 *6*
    (1968) 2418…20

2131 C_6H_4 235

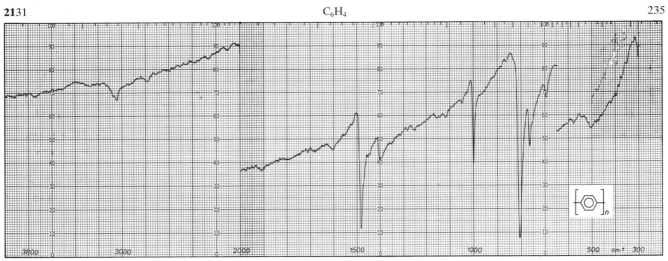

(1) poly-1,4-phenylene
(2) brown powder
(3) G. F. L. Ehlers, Wright-Patterson AFB, Ohio
(4) the polymer contained 6,2 % Cl and 1,6 % ash (Fe_2O_3); the summary formula was $C_6 (H + Cl)_{3,5}$. This corresponds to a polyphenylene with 1 Cl every 7th ring and 1 crosslink at every 2nd ring.

(5) polycondensation of 2 mol benzene with 1 mol $FeCl_3$ and 1 mol H_2O; P. Kovacic et al., J. Polym. Sci *47* (1960) 45, ibid. *A2* (1964) 1193; J. Org. Chem. *28* (1963) 1864
(6) G. F. L. Ehlers, K. R. Fisch, W. R. Powell, J. Polym. Sci. A-1 *7* (1969) 2931...53
(7) KBr (1.6/300)

2132 $C_{66}H_{44}$ 236

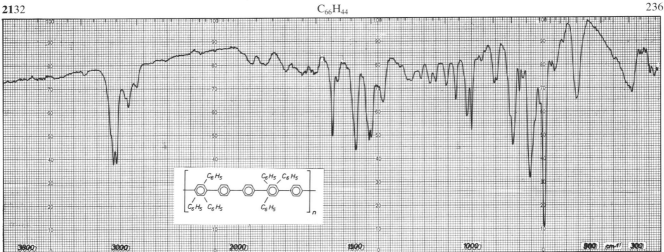

(1) poly(p-pentaphenylene), phenylsubstituted
(2) ochre-coloured, coarse powder
(3) J. K. Stille, Department of Chemistry, University of Iowa, Io.
(5) reaction of bis-tetracyclones with p-diethynylbenzene in toluene at 225 °C (24 h); see J. K. Stille, F. W. Harris, R. O.

Racutis, H. Mukamal, J. Polym. Sci. *B 4* (1966) 791, H. Mukamal, F. W. Harris, J. K. Stille, ibid. A-1 5 (1967) 2721
(6) J. K. Stille, J. Macromol. Sci.-Chem. A-3 *6* (1969) 1043...65
(7) film from $CHCl_3$ on CsI
(8) toluene-soluble fraction

2132 $C_{66}H_{44}$ 237

(1) poly(p-pentaphenylene), phenylsubstituted
(2) brown, tough material
(3) J. K. Stille, Department of Chemistry, University of Iowa, Io.
(5) reaction of bis-tetracyclones with p-diethynylbenzene in toluene at 225 °C (24 h); see J. K. Stille, F. W. Harris, R. O.

Racutis, H. Mukamal, J. Polym. Sci. *B 4* (1966) 791;
H. Mukamal, F. W. Harris, J. K. Stille, ibid. A-1 *5* (1967) 2721
(6) J. K. Stille, J. Macromol. Sci.-Chem. A-3 *6* (1969) 1043...65
(7) ground with KBr and $CHCl_3$, dried and pressed
(8) xylene-insoluble fraction

221111 C₂F₄ 238

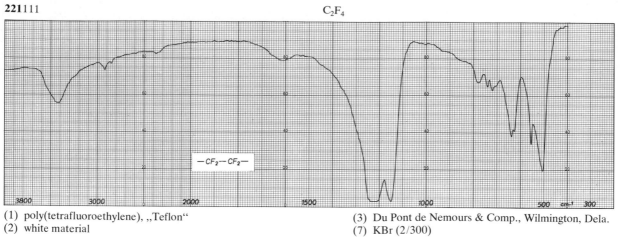

(1) poly(tetrafluoroethylene), „Teflon"
(2) white material

(3) Du Pont de Nemours & Comp., Wilmington, Dela.
(7) KBr (2/300)

221111–**21**111 C₂F₄-C₂H₄ 239

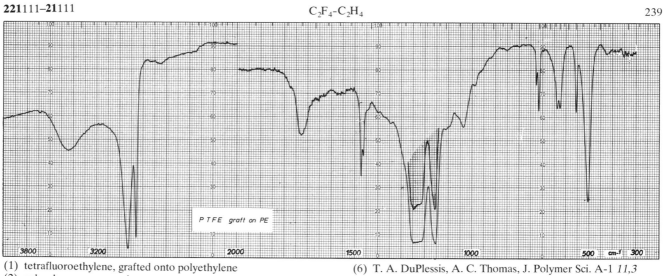

(1) tetrafluoroethylene, grafted onto polyethylene
(2) colourless coarse powder
(3) T. A. DuPlessis, Atomic Energy Board, Pretoria, Republic of South Africa
(5) pre-irradiation of polyethylene by ⁶⁰Co γ-radiation, treatment with TFE

(6) T. A. DuPlessis, A. C. Thomas, J. Polymer Sci. A-1 *11,3* (1973) 2681
(7) KBr + THF (2/350)

221111–**21**111 C₂F₄–C₂H₄ 240

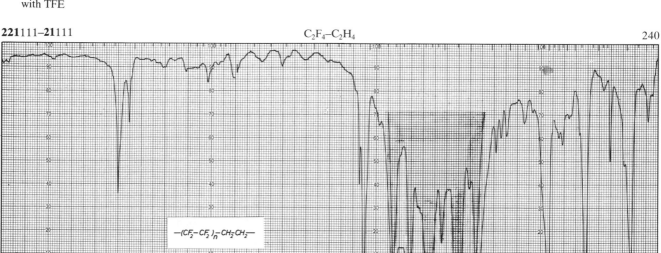

(1) tetrafluoroethylene-ethylene copolymer
(2) colourless film

(3) laboratory preparation, Hoechst AG, Frankfurt/M.-Höchst
(7) film (35 μm), milled film (a few μm)

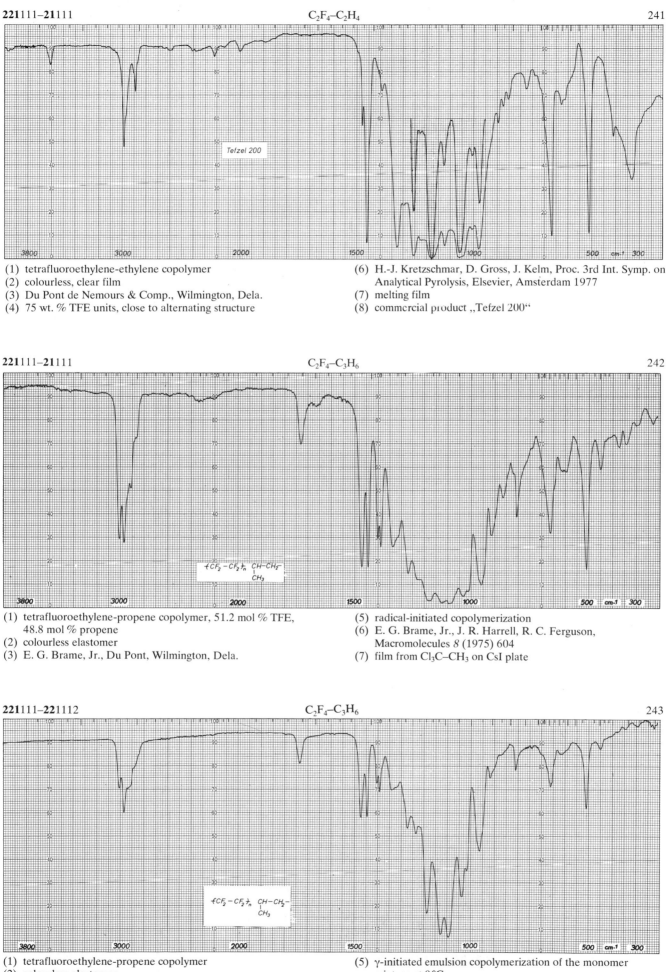

221111–21111 C_2F_4–C_2H_4 241

Tefzel 200

(1) tetrafluoroethylene-ethylene copolymer
(2) colourless, clear film
(3) Du Pont de Nemours & Comp., Wilmington, Dela.
(4) 75 wt. % TFE units, close to alternating structure

(6) H.-J. Kretzschmar, D. Gross, J. Kelm, Proc. 3rd Int. Symp. on Analytical Pyrolysis, Elsevier, Amsterdam 1977
(7) melting film
(8) commercial product ,,Tefzel 200"

221111–21111 C_2F_4–C_3H_6 242

$+CF_2-CF_2+_n$ $CH-CH_2^-$
                        |
                        CH_3

(1) tetrafluoroethylene-propene copolymer, 51.2 mol % TFE, 48.8 mol % propene
(2) colourless elastomer
(3) E. G. Brame, Jr., Du Pont, Wilmington, Dela.

(5) radical-initiated copolymerization
(6) E. G. Brame, Jr., J. R. Harrell, R. C. Ferguson, Macromolecules *8* (1975) 604
(7) film from Cl_3C–CH_3 on CsI plate

221111–221112 C_2F_4–C_3H_6 243

$+CF_2-CF_2+_n$ $CH-CH_2^-$
                        |
                        CH_3

(1) tetrafluoroethylene-propene copolymer
(2) colourless elastomer
(3) K. Ishigure, Dept. of Nuclear Engineering, University of Tokyo, Tokyo
(4) equimolar, alternating structure

(5) γ-initiated emulsion copolymerization of the monomer mixture at 0 °C
(6) private communication; see also O. Matsuda, J. Okamoto, M. Suzuki, M. Ito, Y. Tabata, J. Macromol. Sci. Chem. *A8* (4) 775...91
(7) film from Cl_3C–CH_3 on CsI

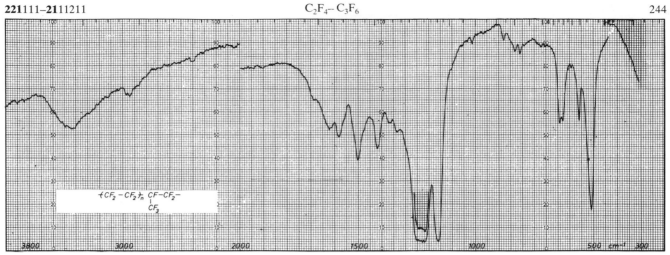

(1) tetrafluoroethylene-hexafluoropropene copolymer
(2) colourless powder
(3) Hoechst AG, Frankfurt/M.-Höchst

(4) poly(tetrafluoroethylene) with approx. 1 % copolymerized
hexafluoropropene
(7) KBr (2/350)
(8) commercial product „Hostaflon TF 23"

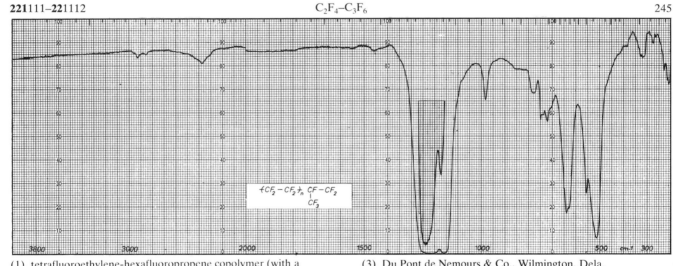

(1) tetrafluoroethylene-hexafluoropropene copolymer (with a
small amount of HFP units)
(2) colourless, clear film

(3) Du Pont de Nemours & Co., Wilmington, Dela.
(7) film (approx. 10 µm), KBr
(8) commercial product „Teflon FEP" (type Λ)

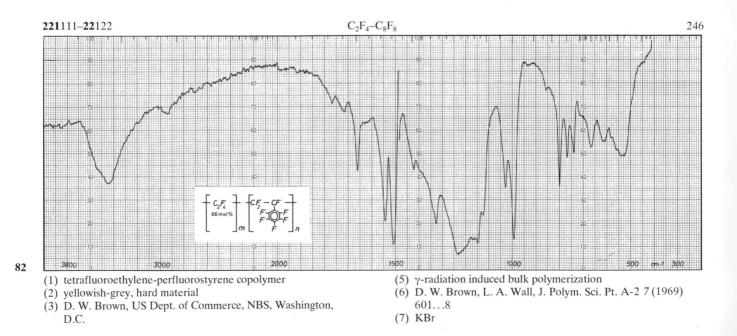

(1) tetrafluoroethylene-perfluorostyrene copolymer
(2) yellowish-grey, hard material
(3) D. W. Brown, US Dept. of Commerce, NBS, Washington,
D.C.

(5) γ-radiation induced bulk polymerization
(6) D. W. Brown, L. A. Wall, J. Polym. Sci. Pt. A-2 7 (1969)
601…8
(7) KBr

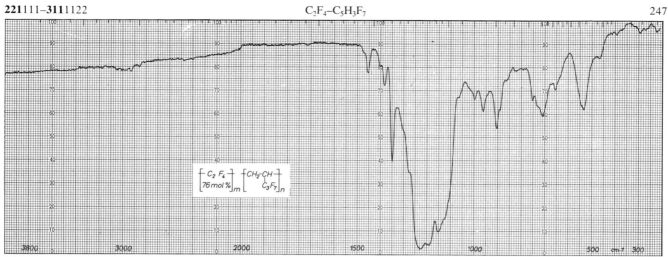

(1) tetrafluoroethylene-1-perfluoropropyl-ethylene copolymer (76 mol-% TFE)
(2) colourless elastomer
(3) D. W. Brown, National Bureau of Standards, Washington, D.C.
(5) γ-radiation initiated copolymerization
(6) D. W. Brown, L. A. Wall, J. Polym. Sci. A-1 *6* (1968) 1367...79
(7) film from C₆F₆ on CsI

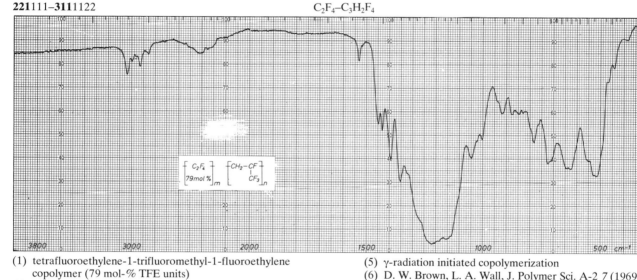

(1) tetrafluoroethylene-1-trifluoromethyl-1-fluoroethylene copolymer (79 mol-% TFE units)
(2) colourless, clear film
(3) D. W. Brown, National Bureau of Standards, Washington, D.C.
(5) γ-radiation initiated copolymerization
(6) D. W. Brown, L. A. Wall, J. Polymer Sci. A-2 *7* (1969) 601...8
(7) film from C₆F₆

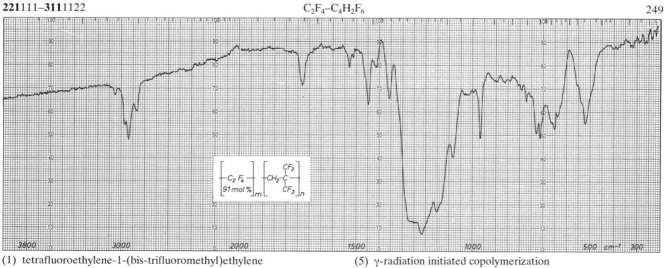

(1) tetrafluoroethylene-1-(bis-trifluoromethyl)ethylene copolymer (91 mol-% TFE units)
(2) colourless, turbid film
(3) D. W. Brown, National Bureau of Standards, Washington, D.C.
(5) γ-radiation initiated copolymerization
(6) D. W. Brown, L. A. Wall, J. Polym. Sci. A-2 *7* (1969) 601...8
(7) film from C₆F₆

221111–3111122 C_2F_4–$C_4H_2F_6$ 250

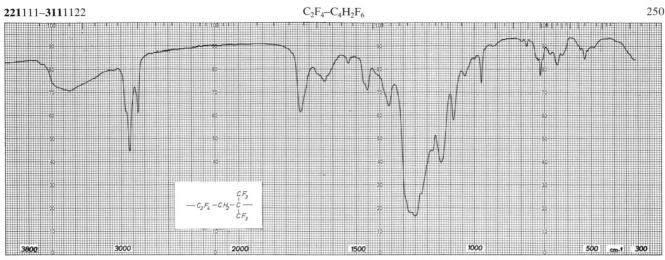

(1) tetrafluoroethylene-1-(bis-trifluoromethyl)ethylene
    copolymer (59 mol-% TFE units)
(2) colourless elastomer
(3) D. W. Brown, National Bureau of Standards, Washington,
    D.C.

(5) γ-radiation initiated copolymerization
(6) D. W. Brown, L. A. Wall, J. Polym. Sci. A-2 7 (1969)
    601...8
(7) ground with KBr and C_6F_6, dried and pressed; ordinate
    expanded

221111–353131211 C_2F_4–C_3F_6O 251

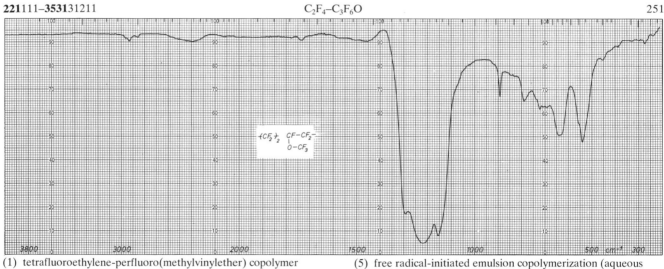

(1) tetrafluoroethylene-perfluoro(methylvinylether) copolymer
    with 65 mol-% TFE units
(2) colourless, hard elastomer
(3) A. L. Barney, Research Laboratory, Elastomer Chemicals
    Department, E. I. Du Pont de Nemours & Comp.,
    Wilmington, Dela.

(5) free radical-initiated emulsion copolymerization (aqueous
    system)
(6) A. L. Barney, W. J. Keller, N. M. van Gulick, J. Polym. Sci.
    A-1 8 (1970) 1091...8
(7) film from C_6F_6 on CsI

221111–353131211 C_2F_4–C_3F_6O 252

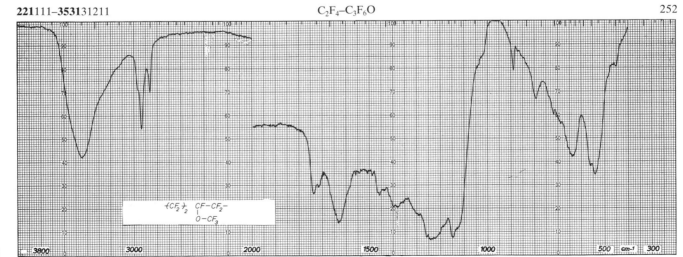

(1) tetrafluoroethylene-perfluoro(methylvinylether) copolymer
    with 65 mol-% TFE units
(2) colourless, hard elastomer
(3) A. L. Barney, Research Laboratory, Elastomer Chemicals
    Department, E. I. Du Pont De Nemours & Co., Wilmington,
    Dela.

(5) free-radical initiated copolymerization in aqueous emulsion
    systems
(6) A. L. Barney, W. J. Keller, N. M. van Gulick, J. Polym. Sci.
    A-1 8 (1970) 1091...8
(7) KBr

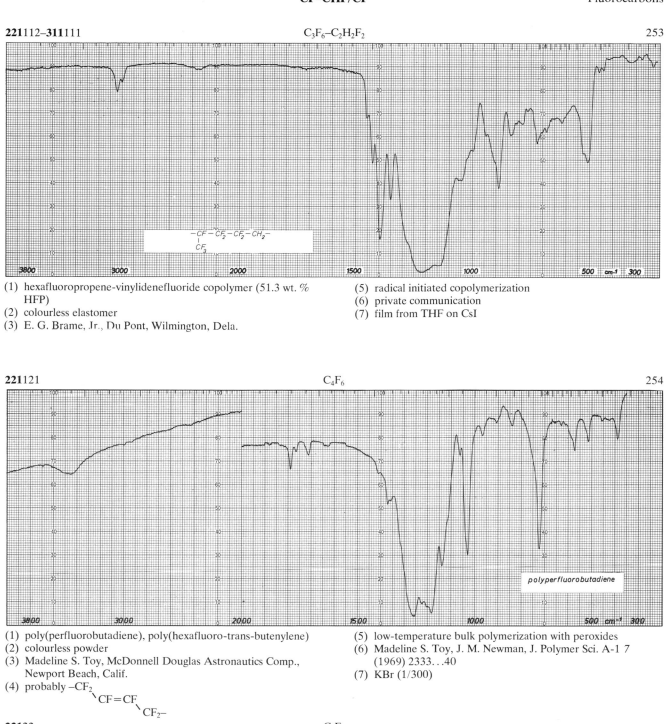

(1) hexafluoropropene-vinylidenefluoride copolymer (51.3 wt. % HFP)
(2) colourless elastomer
(3) E. G. Brame, Jr., Du Pont, Wilmington, Dela.

(5) radical initiated copolymerization
(6) private communication
(7) film from THF on CsI

(1) poly(perfluorobutadiene), poly(hexafluoro-trans-butenylene)
(2) colourless powder
(3) Madeline S. Toy, McDonnell Douglas Astronautics Comp., Newport Beach, Calif.
(4) probably –CF_2
$\quad\quad\quad\quad$ \CF=CF\
$\quad\quad\quad\quad\quad\quad\quad$ CF_2–

(5) low-temperature bulk polymerization with peroxides
(6) Madeline S. Toy, J. M. Newman, J. Polymer Sci. A-1 7 (1969) 2333...40
(7) KBr (1/300)

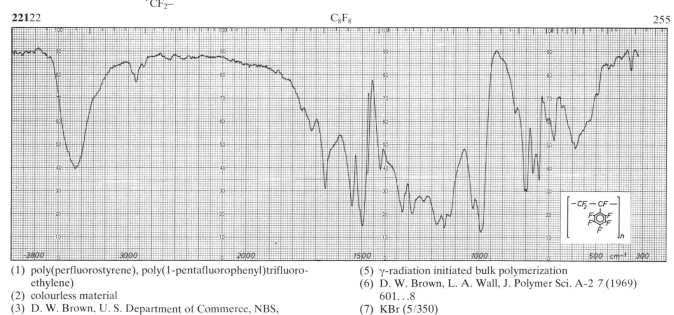

(1) poly(perfluorostyrene), poly(1-pentafluorophenyl)trifluoro-ethylene)
(2) colourless material
(3) D. W. Brown, U. S. Department of Commerce, NBS, Washington, D. C.

(5) γ-radiation initiated bulk polymerization
(6) D. W. Brown, L. A. Wall, J. Polymer Sci. A-2 7 (1969) 601...8
(7) KBr (5/350)

3111111 C_2H_3F 256

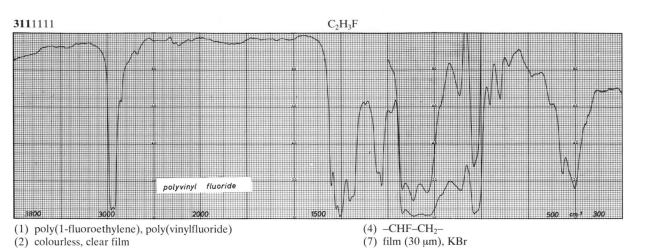

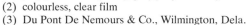

polyvinyl fluoride

(1) poly(1-fluoroethylene), poly(vinylfluoride)
(2) colourless, clear film
(3) Du Pont De Nemours & Co., Wilmington, Dela.

(4) $-CHF-CH_2-$
(7) film (30 μm), KBr
(8) ,,Tedlar" (Du Pont)

3111111 C_2H_3F 257

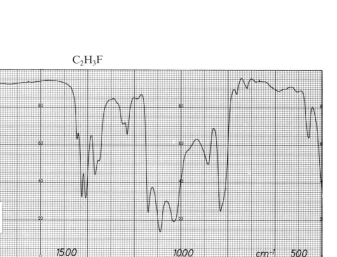

$-CHF-CH_2-$
$T_p = 273\,K$

(1) poly(1-fluoroethylene), poly(vinylfluoride)
(2) colourless film
(3) D. Vierkotten, Institut für Physikalische Chemie, Universität zu Köln

(5) γ-radiation initiated polymerization
(6) Diplomarbeit D. Vierkotten, Köln 1976
(7) film from dimethylformamide (15...20 μm)

3111111–**311**1112 $C_2H_3F–C_2H_2F_2$ 258

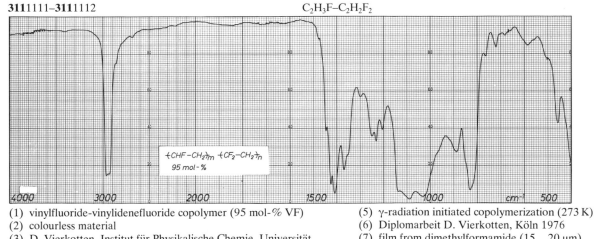

$+CHF-CH_2+_m +CF_2-CH_2+_n$
95 mol-%

(1) vinylfluoride-vinylidenefluoride copolymer (95 mol-% VF)
(2) colourless material
(3) D. Vierkotten, Institut für Physikalische Chemie, Universität zu Köln

(5) γ-radiation initiated copolymerization (273 K)
(6) Diplomarbeit D. Vierkotten, Köln 1976
(7) film from dimethylformamide (15...20 μm)

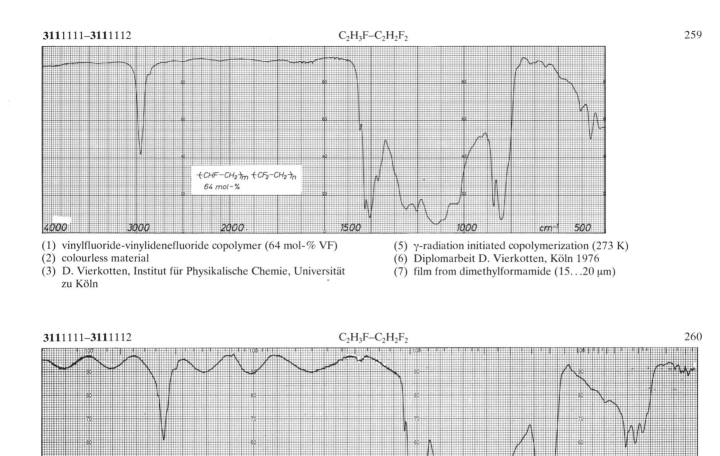

$+CHF-CH_2+_m$ $+CF_2-CH_2+_n$
64 mol-%

(1) vinylfluoride-vinylidenefluoride copolymer (64 mol-% VF)
(2) colourless material
(3) D. Vierkotten, Institut für Physikalische Chemie, Universität zu Köln

(5) γ-radiation initiated copolymerization (273 K)
(6) Diplomarbeit D. Vierkotten, Köln 1976
(7) film from dimethylformamide (15...20 μm)

$-CHF-CH_2-CF_2-CH_2-$

(1) vinylfluoride-vinylidene fluoride copolymer (approx. equimolar)
(2) colourless film
(3) D. Vierkotten, Institut für Physikalische Chemie, Universität Köln

(5) γ-radiation initiated copolymerization (273 K)
(6) Diplomarbeit D. Vierkotten, Köln 1976
(7) film from dimethylformamide (15...20 μm)
(8) interferences at 3800, 3400, 2600, 2200, 1850 cm^{-1}

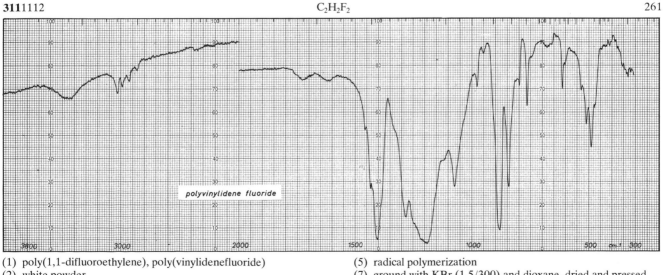

polyvinylidene fluoride

(1) poly(1,1-difluoroethylene), poly(vinylidenefluoride)
(2) white powder
(3) Pennsalt Chemicals Corp., Philadelphia, Pa.
(4) –CH$_2$–CF$_2$–

(5) radical polymerization
(7) ground with KBr (1.5/300) and dioxane, dried and pressed
(8) „Kynar 401" (Pennsalt)

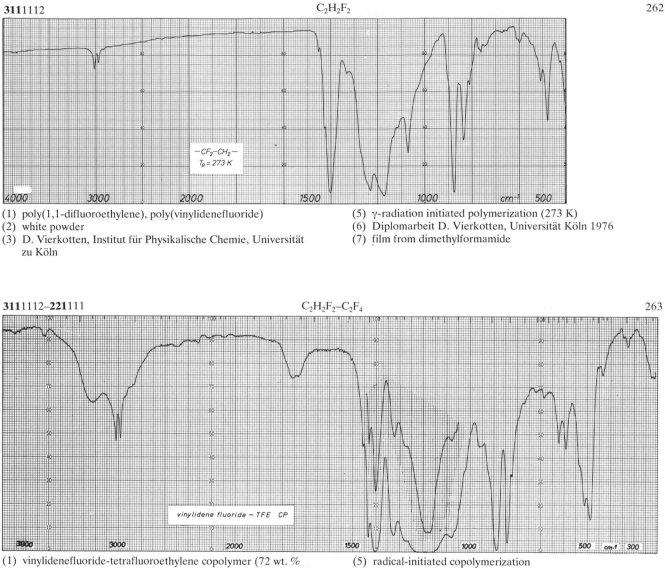

3111112 $C_2H_2F_2$ 262

$-CF_2-CH_2-$
$T_p = 273\ K$

(1) poly(1,1-difluoroethylene), poly(vinylidenefluoride)
(2) white powder
(3) D. Vierkotten, Institut für Physikalische Chemie, Universität zu Köln

(5) γ-radiation initiated polymerization (273 K)
(6) Diplomarbeit D. Vierkotten, Universität Köln 1976
(7) film from dimethylformamide

3111112–**221**111 $C_2H_2F_2$–C_2F_4 263

vinylidene fluoride – TFE CP

(1) vinylidenefluoride-tetrafluoroethylene copolymer (72 wt. % VF$_2$ units)
(2) yellowish-white, coarse material
(3) E. G. Brame, Du Pont de Nemours & Comp., Wilmington, Dela.

(5) radical-initiated copolymerization
(6) private communication
(7) film from tetrahydrofuran on CsI

3111112–**221**112 $C_2H_2F_2$–C_3F_6 264

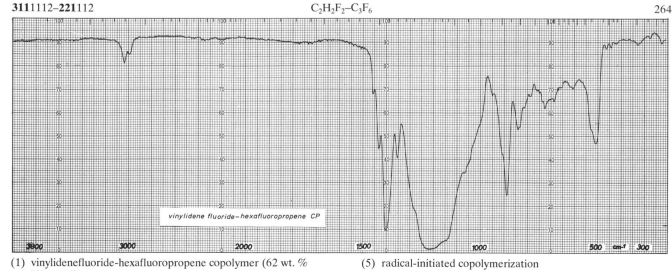

vinylidene fluoride – hexafluoropropene CP

(1) vinylidenefluoride-hexafluoropropene copolymer (62 wt. % VF$_2$ units)
(2) colourless elastomer
(3) E. G. Brame, Du Pont de Nemours & Comp., Wilmington, Dela.

(5) radical-initiated copolymerization
(6) private communication
(7) film from tetrahydrofuran on CsI

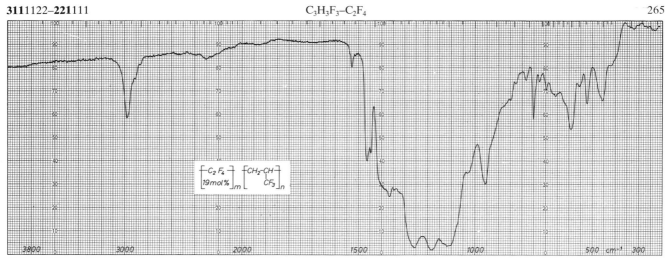

(1) 3,3,3-trifluoropropene-tetrafluoroethylene copolymer (19 mol-% TFE units)
(2) colourless film
(3) D. W. Brown, National Bureau of Standards, Washington, D.C.
(5) radiation-initiated copolymerization of the monomers
(6) D. W. Brown, L. A. Wall, J. Polym. Sci. A-1 6 (1968) 1367...79
(7) KBr

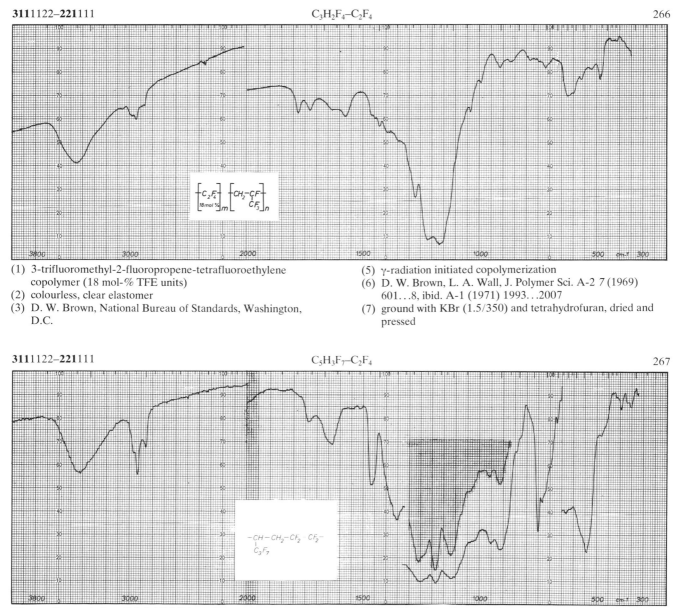

(1) 3-trifluoromethyl-2-fluoropropene-tetrafluoroethylene copolymer (18 mol-% TFE units)
(2) colourless, clear elastomer
(3) D. W. Brown, National Bureau of Standards, Washington, D.C.
(5) γ-radiation initiated copolymerization
(6) D. W. Brown, L. A. Wall, J. Polymer Sci. A-2 7 (1969) 601...8, ibid. A-1 (1971) 1993...2007
(7) ground with KBr (1.5/350) and tetrahydrofuran, dried and pressed

(1) tetrafluoroethylene-3,3,4,4,5,5,5-heptafluoropentene copolymer (21 mol-% TFE units)
(2) white, turbid elastomer
(3) D. W. Brown, National Bureau of Standards, Washington, D.C.
(5) γ-initiated copolymerization of the monomers
(6) D. W. Brown, R. E. Lowry, L. A. Wall, J. Polym. Sci. A-1 8 (1970) 2441...52
(7) KBr (2/350; 1/350)

3111122–221111 $C_5H_3F_7$–C_2F_4 268

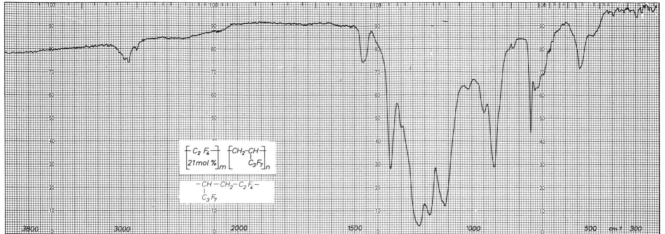

(1) 3,3,4,4,5,5,5-heptafluoropentene-tetrafluoroethylene copolymer
(2) colourless elastomer
(3) D. W. Brown, National Bureau of Standards, Washington, D.C.

(5) γ-initiated copolymerization of the monomers
(6) D. W. Brown, R. E. Lowry, L. A. Wall, J. Polym. Sci. A-1 *8* (1970) 2441...52
(7) film from C_6F_6 on CsI

3111122–221111 $C_5H_3F_7$–C_2F_4 269

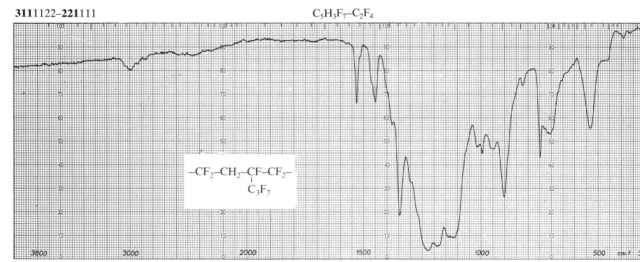

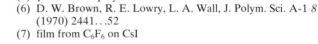

(1) tetrafluoroethylene-3,3,4,4,5,5,5-heptafluoropentene copolymer (48 mol-% TFE units)
(2) white, turbid elastomer
(3) D. W. Brown, National Bureau of Standards, Washington, D.C.

(5) γ-initiated copolymerization of the monomers
(6) D. W. Brown, R. E. Lowry, L. A. Wall, J. Polym. Sci. A-1 *8* (1970) 2441...52
(7) film from hexafluorobenzene on CsI
(8) film from C_6F_6 on CsI

3111112–221112 $C_2H_2F_2$–C_3F_6 270

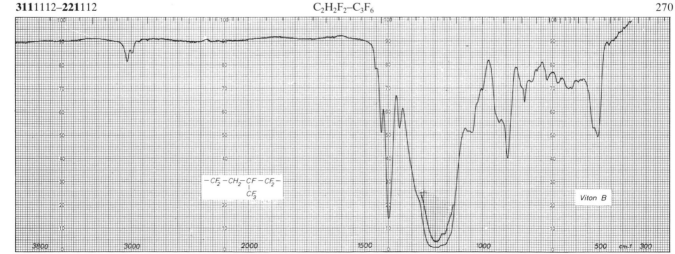

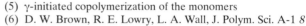

(1) vinylidene fluoride-hexafluoropropene copolymer
(2) colourless elastomer
(3) Du Pont de Nemours & Comp., Wilmington, Dela.

(7) film from acetone on CsI
(8) commercial product „Viton B"

3111122   C$_3$H$_3$F$_3$ 271

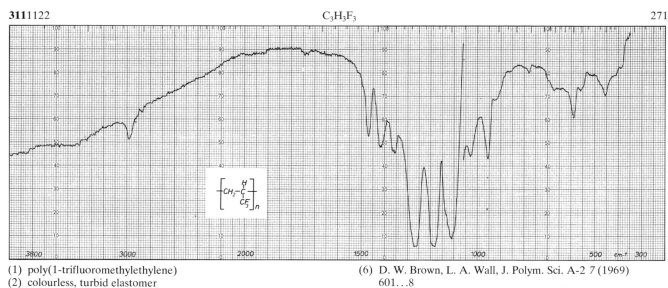
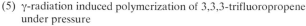

(1) poly(1-trifluoromethylethylene)
(2) colourless, turbid elastomer
(3) D. W. Brown, National Bureau of Standards, Washington, D.C.
(5) γ-radiation induced polymerization of 3,3,3-trifluoropropene under pressure

(6) D. W. Brown, L. A. Wall, J. Polym. Sci. A-2 7 (1969) 601...8
(7) ground with KBr (2/350) and tetrahydrofuran, dried and pressed

3111122   C$_3$H$_2$F$_4$ 272

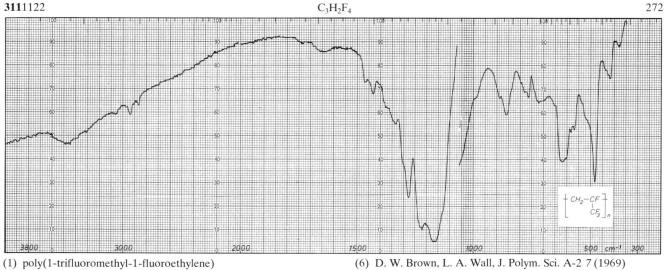
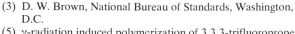

(1) poly(1-trifluoromethyl-1-fluoroethylene)
(2) colourless, turbid elastomer
(3) D. W. Brown, National Bureau of Standards, Washington, D.C.
(5) γ-radiation induced polymerization of 2-fluoro-3,3,3-tri-fluoro-propene

(6) D. W. Brown, L. A. Wall, J. Polym. Sci. A-2 7 (1969) 601...8
(7) ground with KBr (3/350; 1.5/350) and tetrahydrofuran, dried and pressed

3111122   C$_4$H$_3$F$_5$ 273

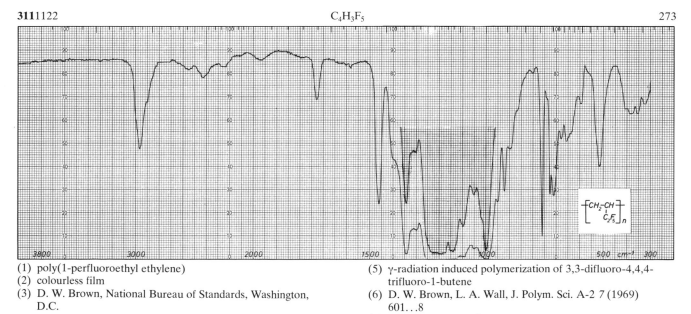
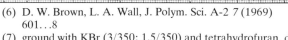

(1) poly(1-perfluoroethyl ethylene)
(2) colourless film
(3) D. W. Brown, National Bureau of Standards, Washington, D.C.

(5) γ-radiation induced polymerization of 3,3-difluoro-4,4,4-trifluoro-1-butene
(6) D. W. Brown, L. A. Wall, J. Polym. Sci. A-2 7 (1969) 601...8
(7) film (25 µm, 13 µm)

3111122 $C_5H_3F_7$ 274

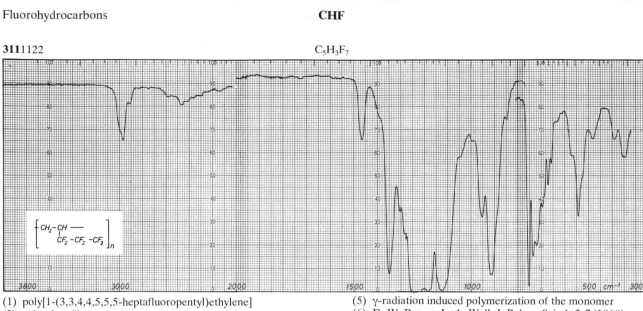

(1) poly[1-(3,3,4,4,5,5,5-heptafluoropentyl)ethylene]
(2) colourless film
(3) D. W. Brown, National Bureau of Standards, Washington, D.C.
(5) γ-radiation induced polymerization of the monomer
(6) D. W. Brown, L. A. Wall, J. Polym. Sci. A-2 7 (1969) 601...8
(7) film (25 μm, 15 μm)

3111122 $C_4H_2F_6$ 275

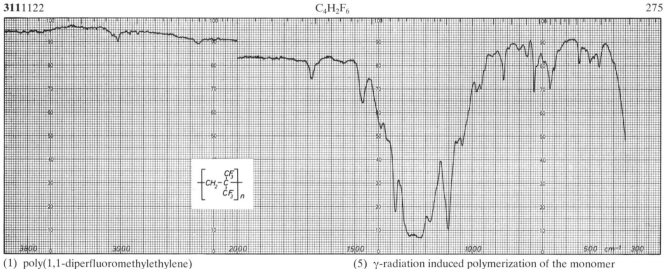

(1) poly(1,1-diperfluoromethylethylene)
(2) colourless oil
(3) D. W. Brown, National Bureau of Standards, Washington, D.C.
(5) γ-radiation induced polymerization of the monomer
(6) D. W. Brown, L. A. Wall, J. Polym. Sci. A-2 7 (1969) 601...8
(7) capillary film between KBr

3112221 C_8H_7F 276

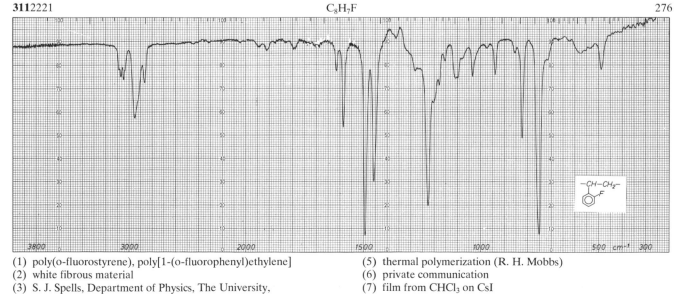

(1) poly(o-fluorostyrene), poly[1-(o-fluorophenyl)ethylene]
(2) white fibrous material
(3) S. J. Spells, Department of Physics, The University, Manchester
(5) thermal polymerization (R. H. Mobbs)
(6) private communication
(7) film from $CHCl_3$ on CsI

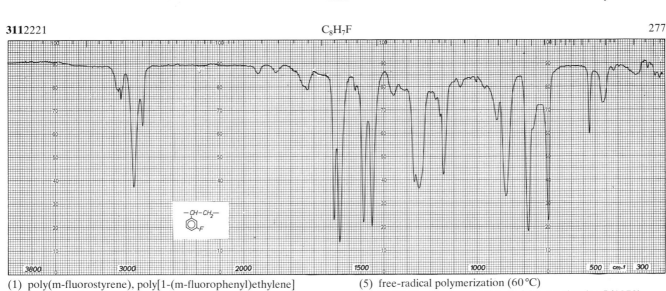

(1) poly(m-fluorostyrene), poly[1-(m-fluorophenyl)ethylene]
(2) white powder
(3) W. H. Stockmayer, Department of Chemistry, Darmouth College, Hanover, N.H.

(5) free-radical polymerization (60 °C)
(6) W. H. Stockmayer, J. Matsuo, Macromolecules *5* (1972) 766...70
(7) film from $CHCl_3$ on CsI

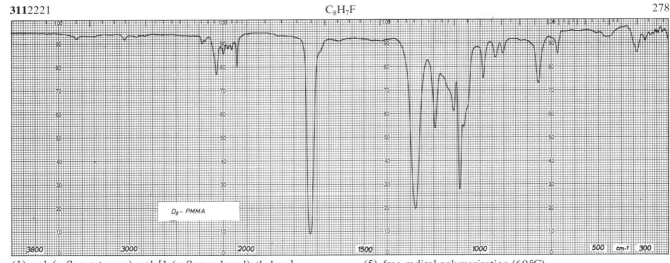

(1) poly(p-fluorostyrene), poly[1-(p-fluorophenyl)ethylene]
(2) white powder
(3) W. H. Stockmayer, Department of Chemistry, Dartmouth College, Hanover, N.H.

(5) free-radical polymerization (60 °C)
(6) W. H. Stockmayer, K. Matsuo, Macromolecules *5* (1972) 766...70
(7) film from $CHCl_3$ on CsI

(1) poly(p-fluoro-α-methylstyrene), poly[1-methyl-1-(p-fluoro-phenyl)ethylene]
(2) white powder
(3) W. Regel, Institut für Makromolekulare Chemie, Universität Freiburg

(4) 83 % syndiotactic and 17 % heterotactic triads
(5) modified Ziegler-Natta catalyst (prepared by L. Westfelt)
(6) Makromolekulares Kolloquium, Freiburg/Br. 1973; private communication
(7) film from $CHCl_3$

3112221 C₉H₉F 280

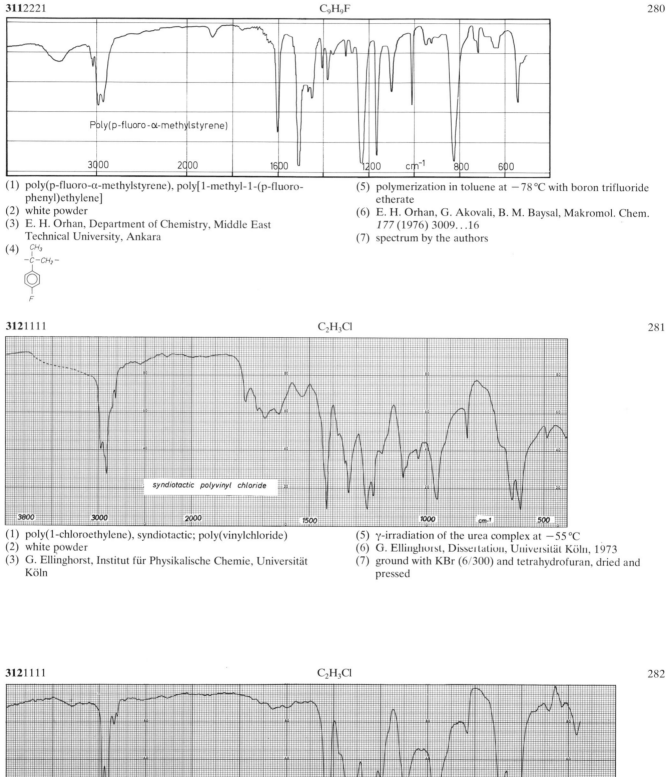

Poly(p-fluoro-α-methylstyrene)

3000 2000 1600 1200 cm⁻¹ 800 600

(1) poly(p-fluoro-α-methylstyrene), poly[1-methyl-1-(p-fluoro-phenyl)ethylene]
(2) white powder
(3) E. H. Orhan, Department of Chemistry, Middle East Technical University, Ankara
(4)
$$-\overset{\overset{\displaystyle CH_3}{|}}{\underset{}{C}}-CH_2-$$
(5) polymerization in toluene at −78 °C with boron trifluoride etherate
(6) E. H. Orhan, G. Akovali, B. M. Baysal, Makromol. Chem. *177* (1976) 3009...16
(7) spectrum by the authors

3121111 C₂H₃Cl 281

syndiotactic polyvinyl chloride

3800 3000 2000 1500 1000 cm⁻¹ 500

(1) poly(1-chloroethylene), syndiotactic; poly(vinylchloride)
(2) white powder
(3) G. Ellinghorst, Institut für Physikalische Chemie, Universität Köln
(5) γ-irradiation of the urea complex at −55 °C
(6) G. Ellinghorst, Dissertation, Universität Köln, 1973
(7) ground with KBr (6/300) and tetrahydrofuran, dried and pressed

3121111 C₂H₃Cl 282

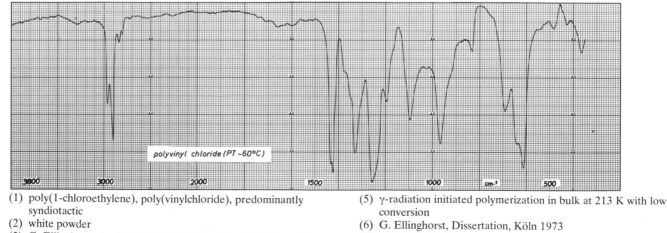

polyvinyl chloride (PT −60°C)

3800 3000 2000 1500 1000 cm⁻¹ 500

(1) poly(1-chloroethylene), poly(vinylchloride), predominantly syndiotactic
(2) white powder
(3) G. Ellinghorst, Institut für Physikalische Chemie, Universität Köln
(5) γ-radiation initiated polymerization in bulk at 213 K with low conversion
(6) G. Ellinghorst, Dissertation, Köln 1973
(7) KBr (4/300)

3121111   C₂H₃Cl   283

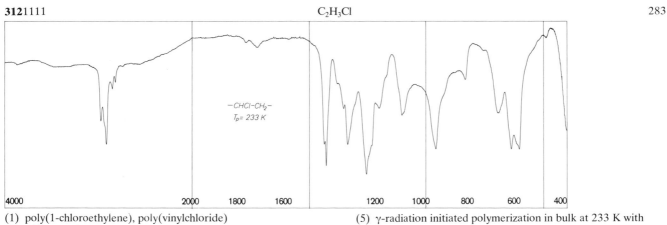

$-CHCl-CH_2-$
$T_p = 233\ K$

(1) poly(1-chloroethylene), poly(vinylchloride)
(2) white powder
(3) G. Ellinghorst, Institut für Physikalische Chemie, Universität Köln

(5) γ-radiation initiated polymerization in bulk at 233 K with 9.5 % conversion
(6) G. Ellinghorst, Dissertation, Köln 1973
(7) film from tetrahydrofuran (10...15 μm)

3121111   C₂H₃Cl   284

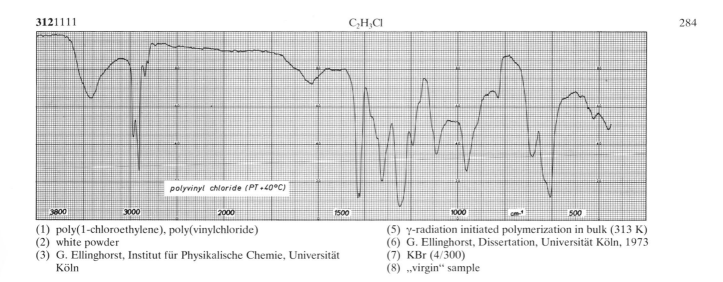

polyvinyl chloride (PT +40°C)

(1) poly(1-chloroethylene), poly(vinylchloride)
(2) white powder
(3) G. Ellinghorst, Institut für Physikalische Chemie, Universität Köln

(5) γ-radiation initiated polymerization in bulk (313 K)
(6) G. Ellinghorst, Dissertation, Universität Köln, 1973
(7) KBr (4/300)
(8) „virgin" sample

3121111   C₂H₃Cl   285

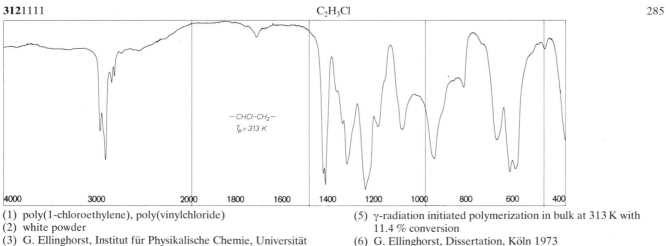

$-CHCl-CH_2-$
$T_p = 313\ K$

(1) poly(1-chloroethylene), poly(vinylchloride)
(2) white powder
(3) G. Ellinghorst, Institut für Physikalische Chemie, Universität Köln

(5) γ-radiation initiated polymerization in bulk at 313 K with 11.4 % conversion
(6) G. Ellinghorst, Dissertation, Köln 1973
(7) film from tetrahydrofuran (10...15 μm)
(8) the differences between this and the preceding sample are due to the preparation

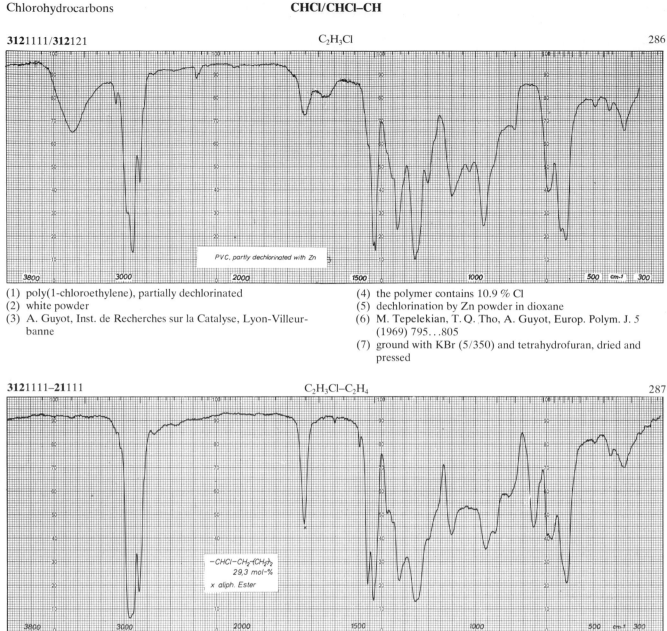

(1) poly(1-chloroethylene), partially dechlorinated
(2) white powder
(3) A. Guyot, Inst. de Recherches sur la Catalyse, Lyon-Villeur-banne

(4) the polymer contains 10.9 % Cl
(5) dechlorination by Zn powder in dioxane
(6) M. Tepelekian, T. Q. Tho, A. Guyot, Europ. Polym. J. 5 (1969) 795...805
(7) ground with KBr (5/350) and tetrahydrofuran, dried and pressed

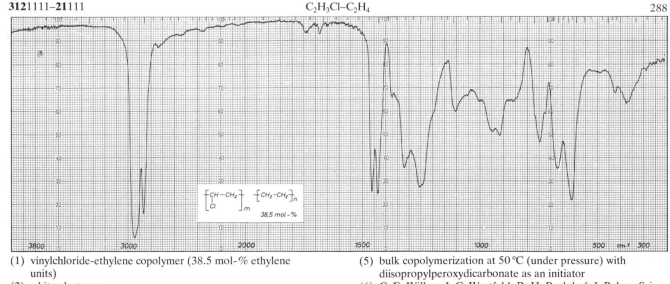

(1) vinylchloride-ethylene copolymer (29.3 mol-% ethylene units)
(2) white, fibrous material
(3) C. E. Wilkes, B. F. Goodrich Comp., Research Center, Brecksville, O.

(5) high pressure copolymerization of the monomers at 50 °C with diisopropylperoxydicarbonate as an initiator
(6) C. E. Wilkes, J. C. Westfahl, R. H. Backderf, J. Polym. Sci. A-1 7 (1969) 23...33
(7) film from CHCl₃ on CsI

(1) vinylchloride-ethylene copolymer (38.5 mol-% ethylene units)
(2) white elastomer
(3) C. E. Wilkes, B. F. Goodrich Co., Research Center, Brecksville, O.

(5) bulk copolymerization at 50 °C (under pressure) with diisopropylperoxydicarbonate as an initiator
(6) C. E. Wilkes, J. C. Westfahl, R. H. Beckderf, J. Polym. Sci. A-1 7 (1969) 23...33
(7) film from CHCl₃ on CsI

3121111–2111211–21111   C₂H₃Cl–C₃H₆–C₂H₄   289

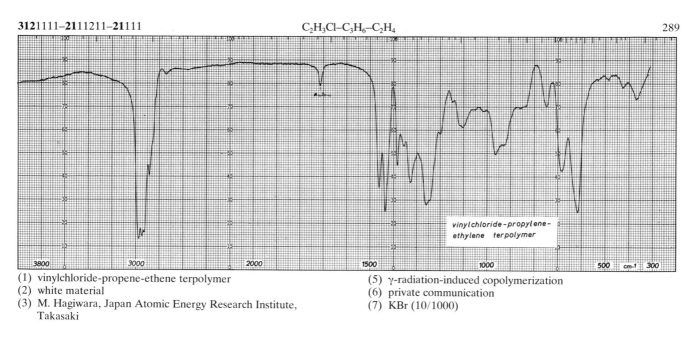

vinylchloride-propylene-
ethylene terpolymer

(1) vinylchloride-propene-ethene terpolymer
(2) white material
(3) M. Hagiwara, Japan Atomic Energy Research Institute,
     Takasaki

(5) γ-radiation-induced copolymerization
(6) private communication
(7) KBr (10/1000)

3121111–211124   C₂H₃Cl–C₄H₈   290

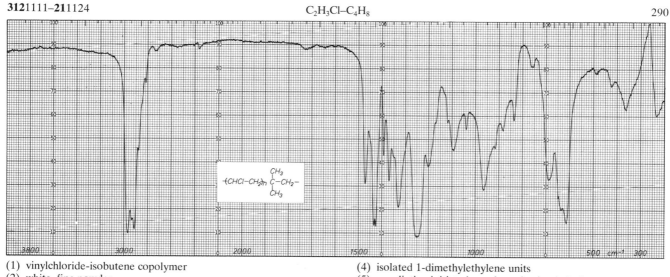

$$+(CHCl-CH_2)_n \begin{array}{c} CH_3 \\ | \\ C-CH_2- \\ | \\ CH_3 \end{array}$$

(1) vinylchloride-isobutene copolymer
(2) white, fine powder
(3) J. Denaxas, Institut für Physikalische Chemie, Universität
     Köln

(4) isolated 1-dimethylethylene units
(5) γ-radiation initiated copolymerization in bulk
(6) J. Denaxas, Dissertation, Köln 1968
(7) KBr

3121111–2122111   C₂H₃Cl–C₈H₈   291

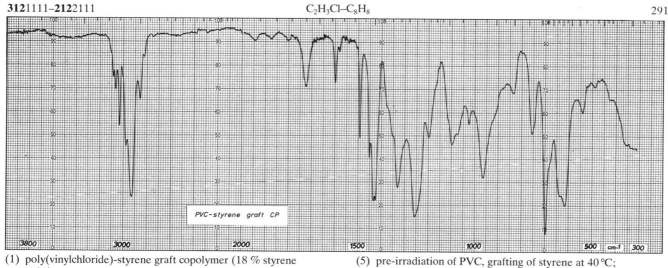

PVC-styrene graft CP

(1) poly(vinylchloride)-styrene graft copolymer (18 % styrene
     units)
(2) white lumps
(3) H. Langner, Institut für Metallphysik und Reinstmetalle, Abt.
     Strahlenchemie, Dresden

(5) pre-irradiation of PVC, grafting of styrene at 40 °C;
     fractionated
(6) H. Langner, Makromol. Chem. 119 (1968) 37...49
(7) KBr (5/350)

3121111–3121211 C$_2$H$_3$Cl–C$_4$H$_5$Cl 292

vinylchloride-2-chlorobutadiene CP

(1) vinylchloride-2-chlorobutadiene copolymer (39 mol-% 2-chlorobutadiene
(2) white powder
(3) D. Braun, Deutsches Kunststoffinstitut, Darmstadt
(5) radical-initiated copolymerization at 25 °C, with acetylcyclohexanesulfonylperoxide
(6) D. Braun, F. Weiss, Angew. Makromol. Chem. *13* (1970) 55...66
(7) film from CCl$_4$ on KBr

3121111–337211111 C$_2$H$_3$Cl–C$_{22}$H$_{35}$O$_2$ 293

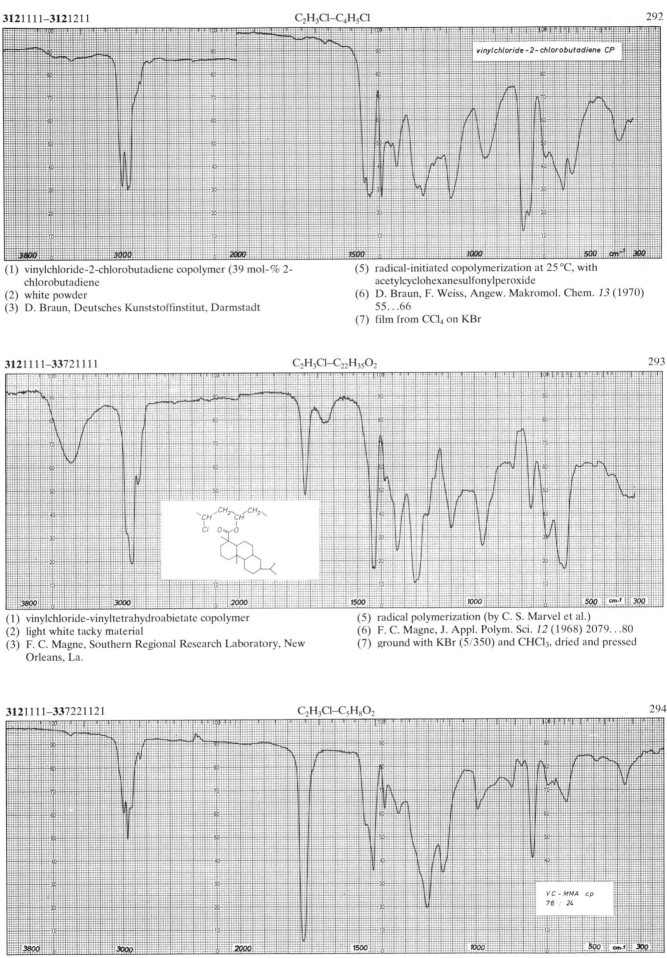

(1) vinylchloride-vinyltetrahydroabietate copolymer
(2) light white tacky material
(3) F. C. Magne, Southern Regional Research Laboratory, New Orleans, La.
(5) radical polymerization (by C. S. Marvel et al.)
(6) F. C. Magne, J. Appl. Polym. Sci. *12* (1968) 2079...80
(7) ground with KBr (5/350) and CHCl$_3$, dried and pressed

3121111–337221121 C$_2$H$_3$Cl–C$_5$H$_8$O$_2$ 294

VC-MMA cp
76 : 24

(1) vinylchloride-methylmethacrylate copolymer (76 mol-% VC units)
(2) white powder
(3) H. J. Harwood, Institute of Polymer Science, University of Akron, O.
(5) radical copolymerization (by N. W. Johnston)
(6) private communication; see also ACS polymer preprints, Spring 1968
(7) film from CHCl$_3$ on CsI

3121111–337621　　　　　　$C_2H_3Cl–C_{26}H_{34}O_5$　　　　　295

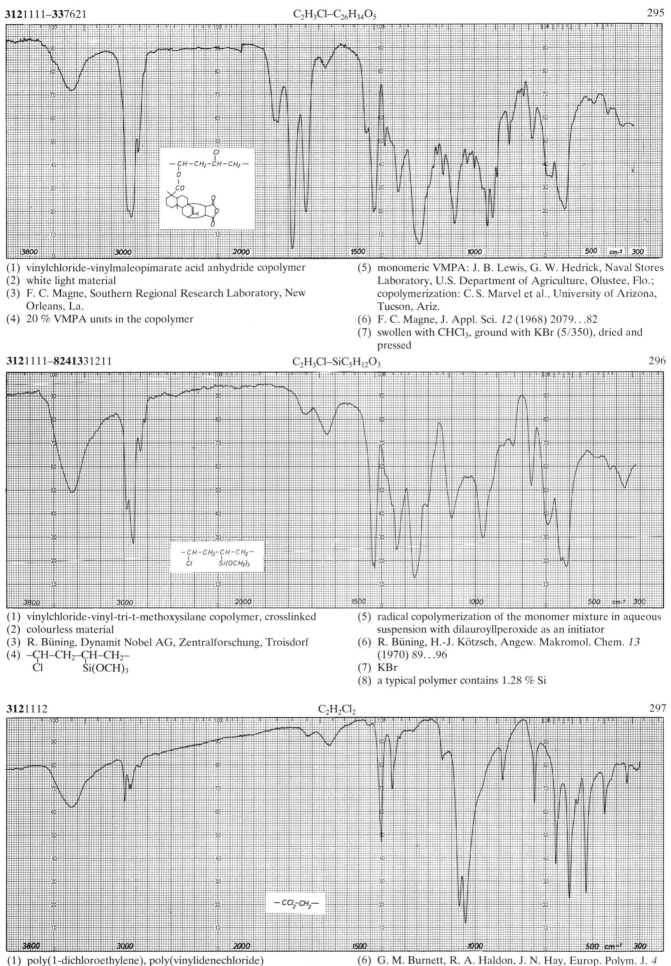

(1) vinylchloride-vinylmaleopimarate acid anhydride copolymer
(2) white light material
(3) F. C. Magne, Southern Regional Research Laboratory, New Orleans, La.
(4) 20 % VMPA units in the copolymer

(5) monomeric VMPA: J. B. Lewis, G. W. Hedrick, Naval Stores Laboratory, U.S. Department of Agriculture, Olustee, Flo.; copolymerization: C. S. Marvel et al., University of Arizona, Tucson, Ariz.
(6) F. C. Magne, J. Appl. Sci. *12* (1968) 2079...82
(7) swollen with $CHCl_3$, ground with KBr (5/350), dried and pressed

3121111–8241331211　　　　　$C_2H_3Cl–SiC_5H_{12}O_3$　　　　　296

(1) vinylchloride-vinyl-tri-t-methoxysilane copolymer, crosslinked
(2) colourless material
(3) R. Büning, Dynamit Nobel AG, Zentralforschung, Troisdorf
(4) –CH–CH₂–CH–CH₂–
　　Cl　　　　Si(OCH)₃

(5) radical copolymerization of the monomer mixture in aqueous suspension with dilauroyllperoxide as an initiator
(6) R. Büning, H.-J. Kötzsch, Angew. Makromol. Chem. *13* (1970) 89...96
(7) KBr
(8) a typical polymer contains 1.28 % Si

3121112　　　　　　　　　　$C_2H_2Cl_2$　　　　　　　　　　297

(1) poly(1-dichloroethylene), poly(vinylidenechloride)
(2) white powder
(3) G. M. Burnett, University of Aberdeen, Old Aberdeen
(5) radical polymerization; see G. M. Burnett, R. A. Haldon, J. N. Hay, Europ. Polym. J. *3* (1967) 449

(6) G. M. Burnett, R. A. Haldon, J. N. Hay, Europ. Polym. J. *4* (1968) 83...92
(7) KBr (2/300)

3121112 $C_2H_2Cl_2$ 298

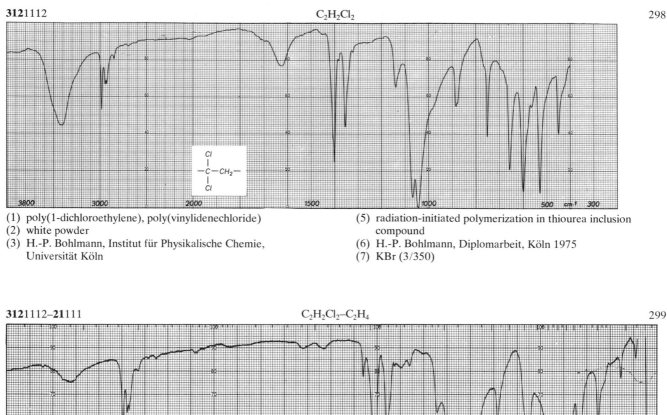

(1) poly(1-dichloroethylene), poly(vinylidenechloride)
(2) white powder
(3) H.-P. Bohlmann, Institut für Physikalische Chemie,
    Universität Köln

(5) radiation-initiated polymerization in thiourea inclusion
    compound
(6) H.-P. Bohlmann, Diplomarbeit, Köln 1975
(7) KBr (3/350)

3121112–**21**111 $C_2H_2Cl_2$–C_2H_4 299

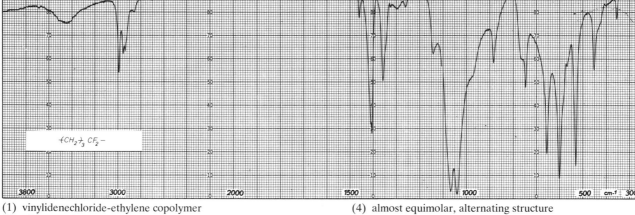

(1) vinylidenechloride-ethylene copolymer
(2) white powder
(3) M. Hagiwara, Japan Atomic Energy Research Establishment,
    Takasaki

(4) almost equimolar, alternating structure
(5) γ-radiation initiated copolymerization
(6) private communication
(7) KBr (10/1000)

3121112–**211**124 $C_2H_2Cl_2$–C_4H_8 300

(1) vinylidenechloride-isobutene copolymer
(2) light-brown material
(3) H.-P. Bohlmann, Institut für Physikalische Chemie,
    Universität Köln
(4) 76 % VdC units

(5) radiation-initiated copolymerization in thiourea inclusion
    compound
(6) H.-P. Bohlmann, Diplomarbeit, Köln 1975
(7) film from tetrahydrofuran on CsI

$$- CH_2 - CCl_2 - CH - CH_2 -$$

(1) vinylidenechloride-styrene copolymer (68 % VdC units)
(2) white powder
(3) J. N. Hay, Department of Chemistry, University of
    Birmingham

(5) radical copolymerization
(6) G. M. Burnett, R. A. Haldon, J. N. Hay, Europ. Polym. J. *4*
    (1968) 83...92
(7) film from $CHCl_3$ on CsI

(1) vinylidenechloride-methacrylonitrile copolymer (77 mol-%
    VdC units)
(2) white powder
(3) J. N. Hay, University of Birmingham, England

(5) radical copolymerization; see G. M. Burnett, R. A. Haldon,
    J. N. Hay, Europ. Polym. J. *3* (1967) 449
(6) G. M. Burnett, R. A. Haldon, J. N. Hay, Europ. Polym. J. *4*
    (1968) 83...92
(7) KBr (2/350)

(1) vinylidenechloride-methylmethacrylate copolymer (86 mol-%
    VdC units)
(2) white powder
(3) J. N. Hay, University of Birmingham, England

(5) radical copolymerization; see G. M. Burnett, R. A. Haldon,
    J. N. Hay, Europ. Polym. J. *3* (1967) 449
(6) G. M. Burnett, R. A. Haldon, J. N. Hay, Europ. Polym. J. *4*
    (1968) 83...92
(7) film from $CHCl_3$ on CsI

3121112 C$_2$HCl$_3$ 304

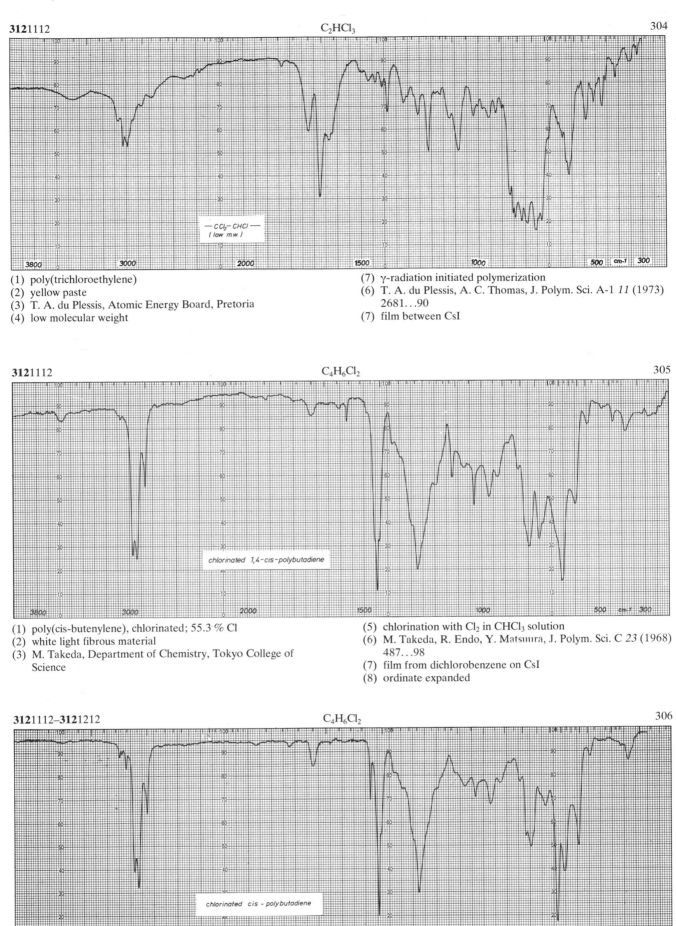

— CCl$_2$– CHCl —
(low m.w.)

(1) poly(trichloroethylene)
(2) yellow paste
(3) T. A. du Plessis, Atomic Energy Board, Pretoria
(4) low molecular weight

(7) γ-radiation initiated polymerization
(6) T. A. du Plessis, A. C. Thomas, J. Polym. Sci. A-1 *11* (1973) 2681...90
(7) film between CsI

3121112 C$_4$H$_6$Cl$_2$ 305

chlorinated 1,4-cis-polybutadiene

(1) poly(cis-butenylene), chlorinated; 55.3 % Cl
(2) white light fibrous material
(3) M. Takeda, Department of Chemistry, Tokyo College of Science

(5) chlorination with Cl$_2$ in CHCl$_3$ solution
(6) M. Takeda, R. Endo, Y. Matsuura, J. Polym. Sci. C *23* (1968) 487...98
(7) film from dichlorobenzene on CsI
(8) ordinate expanded

3121112–3121212 C$_4$H$_6$Cl$_2$ 306

chlorinated cis - polybutadiene

(1) poly(cis-butenylene), chlorinated
(2) white flocky material
(3) G. Dall'Asta, Montecatini Edison, Milano
(4) –(CHCl)$_2$(CH$_2$)$_2$–

(5) chlorination in CH$_2$Cl$_2$ solution
(6) G. Dall'Asta, P. Meneghini, U. Genaro, Makromol. Chem. *154* (1972) 279...90, ibid. 291...302

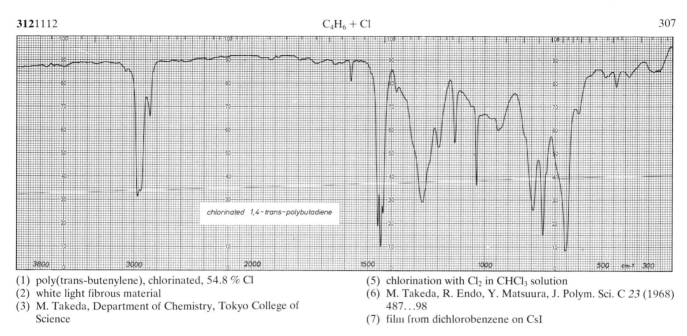

chlorinated 1,4-trans-polybutadiene

(1) poly(trans-butenylene), chlorinated, 54.8 % Cl
(2) white light fibrous material
(3) M. Takeda, Department of Chemistry, Tokyo College of
     Science

(5) chlorination with Cl_2 in $CHCl_3$ solution
(6) M. Takeda, R. Endo, Y. Matsuura, J. Polym. Sci. C *23* (1968)
     487...98
(7) film from dichlorobenzene on CsI

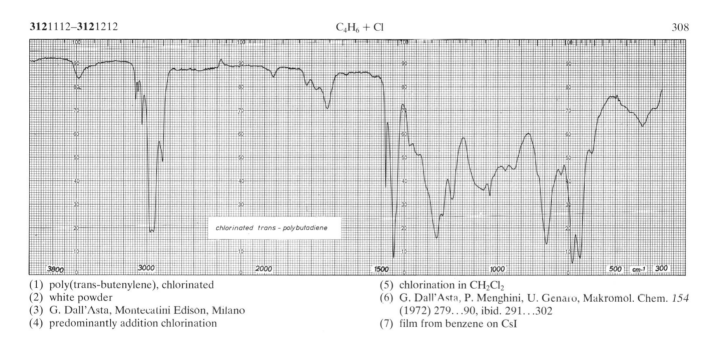

chlorinated trans-polybutadiene

(1) poly(trans-butenylene), chlorinated
(2) white powder
(3) G. Dall'Asta, Montecatini Edison, Milano
(4) predominantly addition chlorination

(5) chlorination in CH_2Cl_2
(6) G. Dall'Asta, P. Menghini, U. Genaro, Makromol. Chem. *154*
     (1972) 279...90, ibid. 291...302
(7) film from benzene on CsI

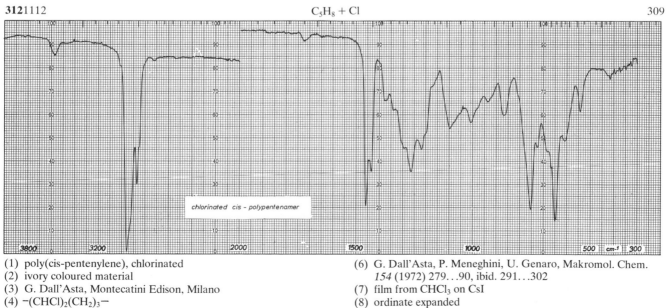

chlorinated cis-polypentenamer

(1) poly(cis-pentenylene), chlorinated
(2) ivory coloured material
(3) G. Dall'Asta, Montecatini Edison, Milano
(4) −(CHCl)$_2$(CH$_2$)$_3$−
(5) chlorination in CH_2Cl_2

(6) G. Dall'Asta, P. Meneghini, U. Genaro, Makromol. Chem.
     154 (1972) 279...90, ibid. 291...302
(7) film from $CHCl_3$ on CsI
(8) ordinate expanded

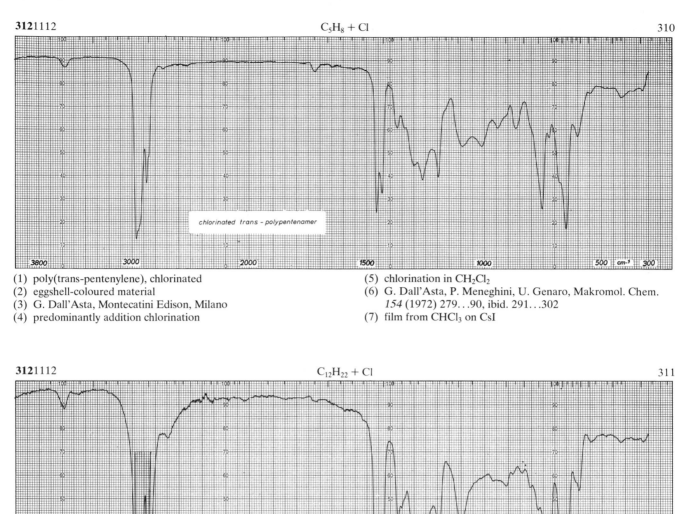

chlorinated trans - polypentenamer

(1) poly(trans-pentenylene), chlorinated
(2) eggshell-coloured material
(3) G. Dall'Asta, Montecatini Edison, Milano
(4) predominantly addition chlorination

(5) chlorination in CH_2Cl_2
(6) G. Dall'Asta, P. Meneghini, U. Genaro, Makromol. Chem.
    154 (1972) 279...90, ibid. 291...302
(7) film from $CHCl_3$ on CsI

chlorinated trans - polydodecenamer

(1) poly(trans-dodecenylene), chlorinated
(2) white material
(3) G. Dall'Asta, Montecatini Edison, Milano
(4) approx. $(CHCl)_2(CH_2)_{10}$

(5) chlorination in CH_2Cl_2
(6) G. Dall'Asta, P. Meneghini, U. Genaro, Makromol. Chem.
    154 (1972) 279...90, ibid. 291...302
(7) film from benzene on CsI

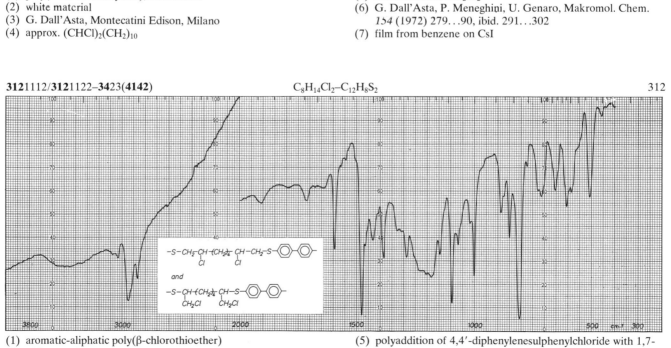

(1) aromatic-aliphatic poly(β-chlorothioether)
(2) white powder
(3) G. G. Cameron, Department of Chemistry, University of
    Aberdeen, Old Aberdeen

(5) polyaddition of 4,4′-diphenylenesulphenylchloride with 1,7-
    octadiene
(6) G. G. Cameron, D. R. Hogg, S. A. Stachowiak, Makromol.
    Chem. *176* (1975) 9...21
(7) KBr (4/350)

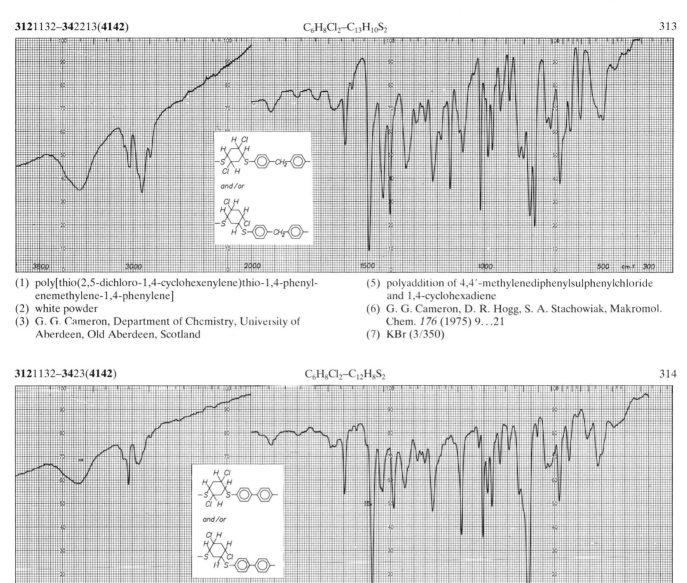

(1) poly[thio(2,5-dichloro-1,4-cyclohexenylene)thio-1,4-phenyl-enemethylene-1,4-phenylene]
(2) white powder
(3) G. G. Cameron, Department of Chemistry, University of Aberdeen, Old Aberdeen, Scotland

(5) polyaddition of 4,4′-methylenediphenylsulphenylchloride and 1,4-cyclohexadiene
(6) G. G. Cameron, D. R. Hogg, S. A. Stachowiak, Makromol. Chem. *176* (1975) 9...21
(7) KBr (3/350)

(1) poly[thio(2,5-dichloro-1,4-cyclohexenylene)thio-1,4-di-phenylene]
(2) white powder
(3) G. G. Cameron, Department of Chemistry, University of Aberdeen, Old Aberdeen, Scotland

(5) polyaddition of diphenyl-4,4′-sulphenylchloride and 1,4-cyclohexadiene
(6) G. G. Cameron, D. R. Hogg, S. A. Stachowiak, Makromol. Chem. *176* (1975) 9...21
(7) KBr (2/350)

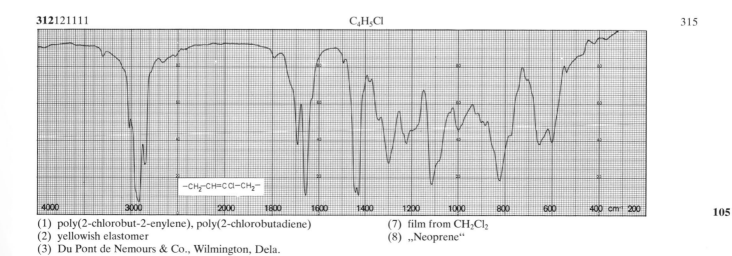

$-CH_2-CH=CCl-CH_2-$

(1) poly(2-chlorobut-2-enylene), poly(2-chlorobutadiene)
(2) yellowish elastomer
(3) Du Pont de Nemours & Co., Wilmington, Dela.

(7) film from CH_2Cl_2
(8) „Neoprene"

3121212 $C_4H_4Cl_2$ 316

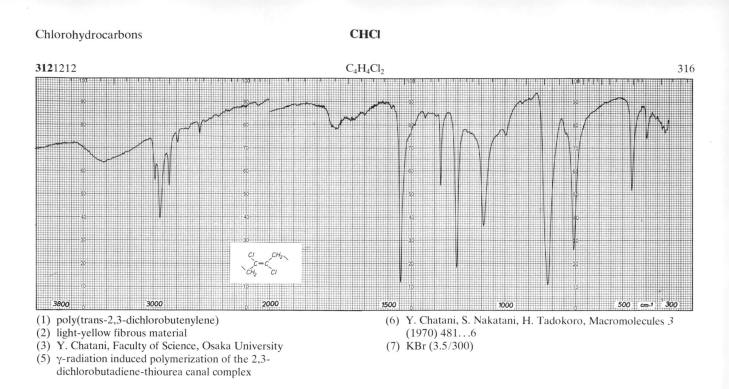

(1) poly(trans-2,3-dichlorobutenylene)
(2) light-yellow fibrous material
(3) Y. Chatani, Faculty of Science, Osaka University
(5) γ-radiation induced polymerization of the 2,3-
      dichlorobutadiene-thiourea canal complex

(6) Y. Chatani, S. Nakatani, H. Tadokoro, Macromolecules *3*
      (1970) 481...6
(7) KBr (3.5/300)

3121212 $C_4H_4Cl_2$ 317

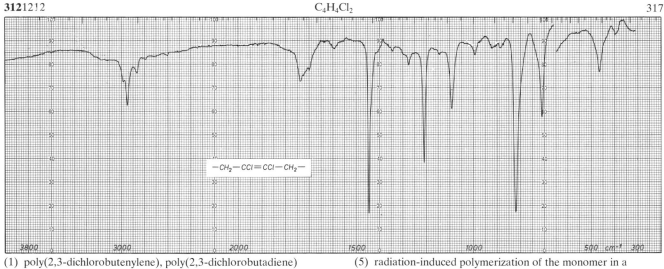

(1) poly(2,3-dichlorobutenylene), poly(2,3-dichlorobutadiene)
(2) white, fibrous material
(3) K. Takemoto, Faculty of Engineering, Osaka University, Suita
(4) crystalline, probably trans-configuration

(5) radiation-induced polymerization of the monomer in a
      deoxycholic acid canal complex
(6) M. Miyata, K. Takemoto, Angew. Makromol. Chem. *55*
      (1976) 191...202
(7) melting film between KBr, ordinate expanded

3122121 C_8H_7Cl 318

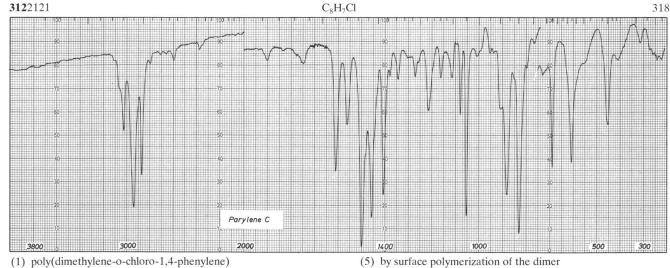

(1) poly(dimethylene-o-chloro-1,4-phenylene)
(3) B. L. Joesten, Union Carbide Corp., Bound Brook, N.J.

(5) by surface polymerization of the dimer
(6) B. L. Joesten, ACS Polym. Prepr. *13*, 2 (1972) 1048
(7) film (28 μm)

3122122 C$_8$H$_6$Cl$_2$ 319

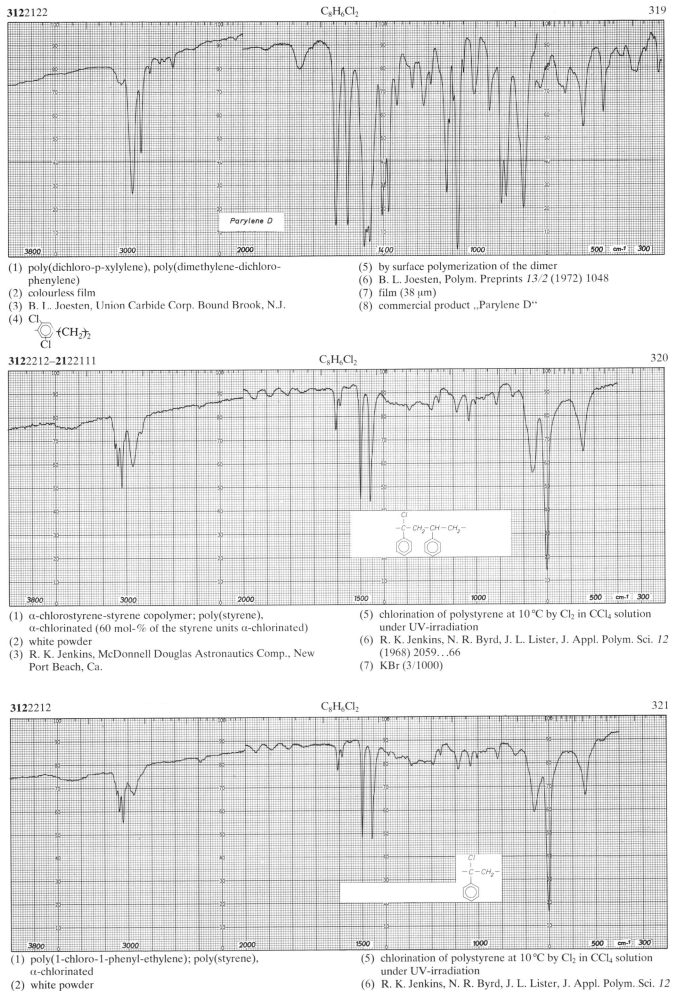

Parylene D

(1) poly(dichloro-p-xylylene), poly(dimethylene-dichloro-
phenylene)
(2) colourless film
(3) B. L. Joesten, Union Carbide Corp. Bound Brook, N.J.
(4)

(5) by surface polymerization of the dimer
(6) B. L. Joesten, Polym. Preprints *13/2* (1972) 1048
(7) film (38 μm)
(8) commercial product „Parylene D"

3122212–2122111 C$_8$H$_6$Cl$_2$ 320

(1) α-chlorostyrene-styrene copolymer; poly(styrene),
α-chlorinated (60 mol-% of the styrene units α-chlorinated)
(2) white powder
(3) R. K. Jenkins, McDonnell Douglas Astronautics Comp., New
Port Beach, Ca.

(5) chlorination of polystyrene at 10 °C by Cl$_2$ in CCl$_4$ solution
under UV-irradiation
(6) R. K. Jenkins, N. R. Byrd, J. L. Lister, J. Appl. Polym. Sci. *12*
(1968) 2059...66
(7) KBr (3/1000)

3122212 C$_8$H$_6$Cl$_2$ 321

(1) poly(1-chloro-1-phenyl-ethylene); poly(styrene),
α-chlorinated
(2) white powder
(3) R. K. Jenkins, McDonnell Douglas Astronautics Comp., New
Port Beach, Ca.

(5) chlorination of polystyrene at 10 °C by Cl$_2$ in CCl$_4$ solution
under UV-irradiation
(6) R. K. Jenkins, N. R. Byrd, J. L. Lister, J. Appl. Polym. Sci. *12*
(1968) 2059...66
(7) KBr (3/1000)

3122221 C_8H_7Cl 322

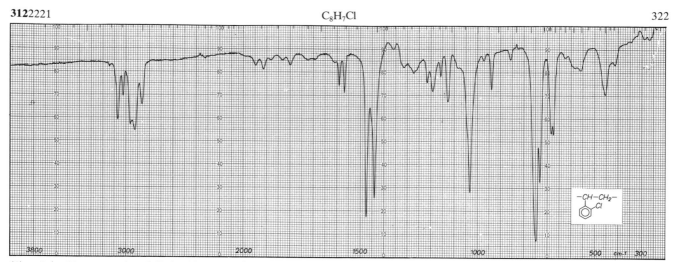

(1) poly(o-chlorostyrene), poly[1-(o-chlorophenyl)ethylene]
(2) white fibrous material
(3) S. J. Spells, Department of Physics, University of Manchester
(5) thermal polymerization of the monomer (by R. H. Mobbs)
(6) private communication; 4th Europ. Symp. on Polymer Spectroscopy
(7) film from $CHCl_3$ on CsI

3122221 C_8H_7Cl 323

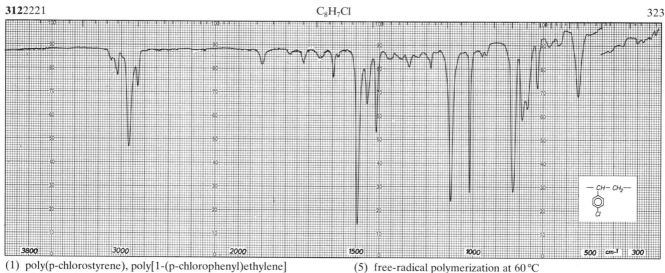

(1) poly(p-chlorostyrene), poly[1-(p-chlorophenyl)ethylene]
(2) white powder
(3) W. H. Stockmayer, Dartmouth College, Hanover, N.H.
(5) free-radical polymerization at 60 °C
(6) W. H. Stockmayer, K. Matsuo, Macromolecules 5 (1972) 766

3122221 C_8H_7Cl 324

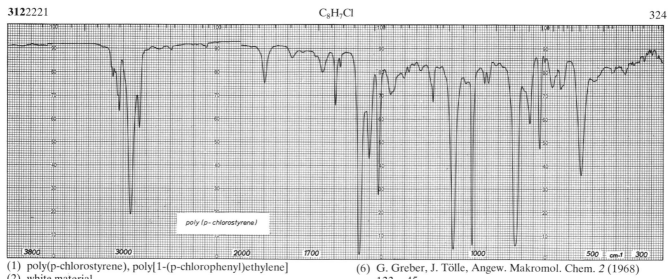

poly (p- chlorostyrene)

(1) poly(p-chlorostyrene), poly[1-(p-chlorophenyl)ethylene]
(2) white material
(3) G. Greber, Institut für Makromol. Chemie, Universität Freiburg i.Br.
(6) G. Greber, J. Tölle, Angew. Makromol. Chem. 2 (1968) 133...45

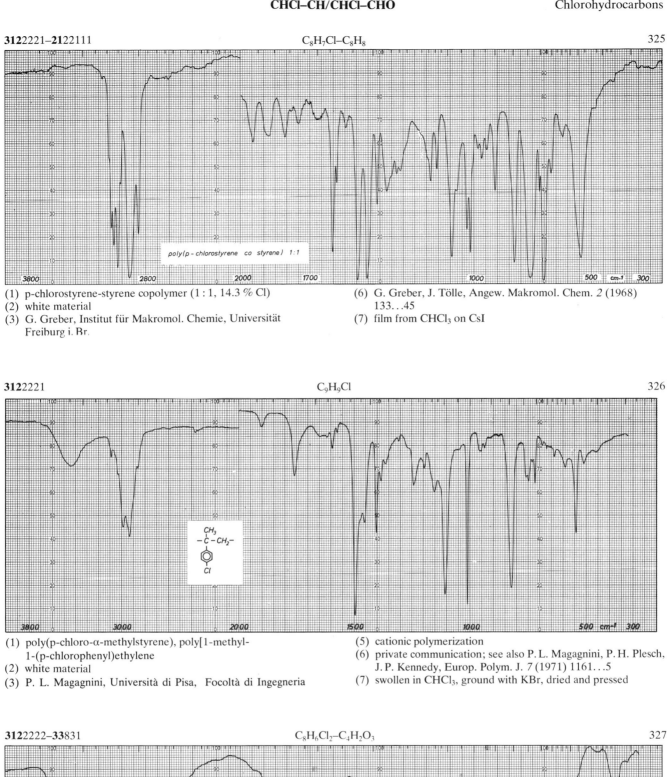

poly(p - chlorostyrene co styrene) 1:1

(1) p-chlorostyrene-styrene copolymer (1 : 1, 14.3 % Cl)
(2) white material
(3) G. Greber, Institut für Makromol. Chemie, Universität Freiburg i. Br.
(6) G. Greber, J. Tölle, Angew. Makromol. Chem. *2* (1968) 133...45
(7) film from CHCl$_3$ on CsI

(1) poly(p-chloro-α-methylstyrene), poly[1-methyl-1-(p-chlorophenyl)ethylene]
(2) white material
(3) P. L. Magagnini, Università di Pisa, Focoltà di Ingegneria
(5) cationic polymerization
(6) private communication; see also P. L. Magagnini, P. H. Plesch, J. P. Kennedy, Europ. Polym. J. 7 (1971) 1161...5
(7) swollen in CHCl$_3$, ground with KBr, dried and pressed

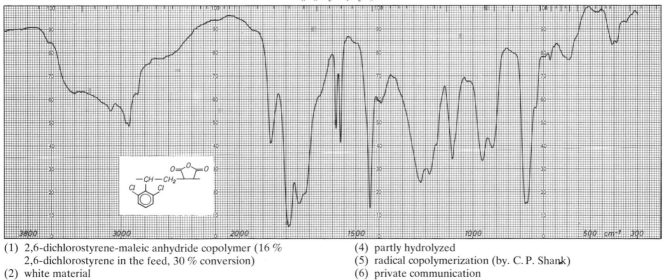

(1) 2,6-dichlorostyrene-maleic anhydride copolymer (16 % 2,6-dichlorostyrene in the feed, 30 % conversion)
(2) white material
(3) H. J. Harwood, Institute of Polymer Science, University of Akron, O.
(4) partly hydrolyzed
(5) radical copolymerization (by. C. P. Shank)
(6) private communication
(7) ground with KBr (2/350) and CHCl$_3$ under dry conditions, dried and pressed

3132221 C_8H_7Br 328

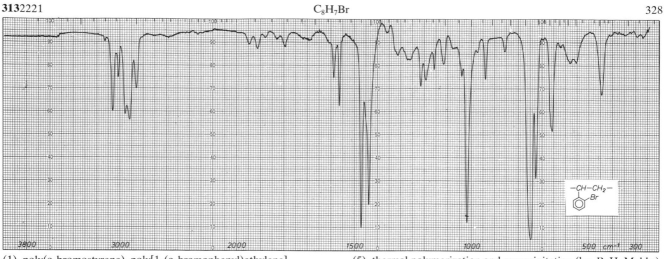

(1) poly(o-bromostyrene), poly[1-(o-bromophenyl)ethylene]
(2) light white fibrous material
(3) S. J. Spells, Department of Physics, University of Manchester

(5) thermal polymerization and reprecipitation (by. R. H. Mobbs)
(6) private communication
(7) film from $CHCl_3$ on CsI

321111 C_2H_5N 329

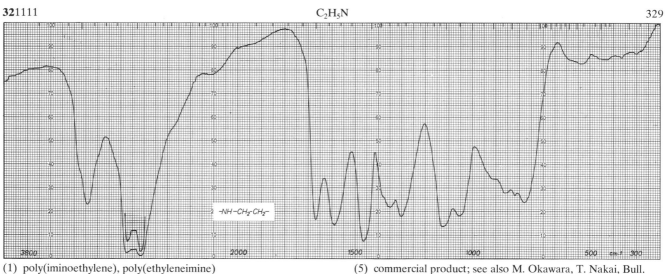

(1) poly(iminoethylene), poly(ethyleneimine)
(2) colourless, soft-waxy material
(3) G. Esslemont, Department of Chemistry, University of Reading, Whiteknights

(5) commercial product; see also M. Okawara, T. Nakai, Bull. Tokyo Inst. Technol. *78* (1966) (1)
(6) J. H. Barnes, G. F. Esslemont, Makromol. Chem. *177* (1976) 307...10
(7) film on CsI

321111 C_2H_6ClN 330

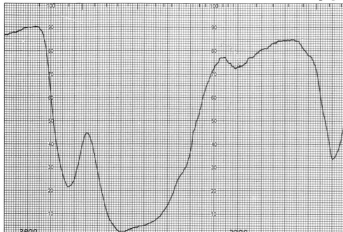
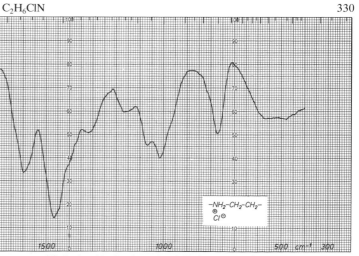

(1) poly(ethylene ammonium chloride), poly(iminoethylene hydrochloride)
(2) white powder
(3) K. Spiekermann, Institut für Physikalische Chemie, Universität Köln

(5) hydrochlorination of poly(iminoethylene)
(7) KBr (2.5/350)

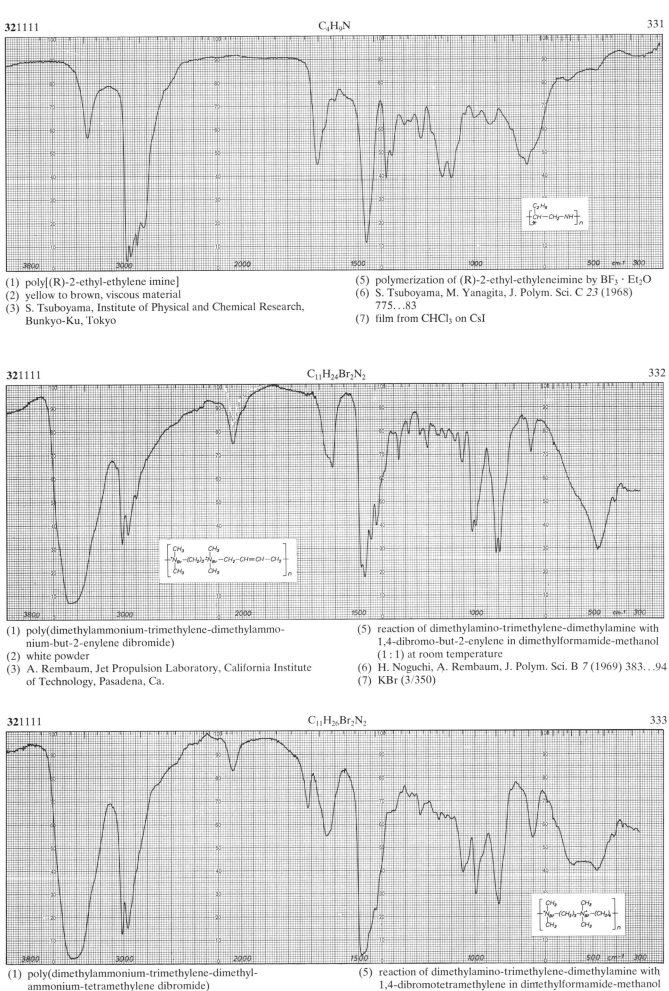

(1) poly[(R)-2-ethyl-ethylene imine]
(2) yellow to brown, viscous material
(3) S. Tsuboyama, Institute of Physical and Chemical Research, Bunkyo-Ku, Tokyo
(5) polymerization of (R)-2-ethyl-ethyleneimine by $BF_3 \cdot Et_2O$
(6) S. Tsuboyama, M. Yanagita, J. Polym. Sci. C *23* (1968) 775...83
(7) film from $CHCl_3$ on CsI

(1) poly(dimethylammonium-trimethylene-dimethylammonium-but-2-enylene dibromide)
(2) white powder
(3) A. Rembaum, Jet Propulsion Laboratory, California Institute of Technology, Pasadena, Ca.
(5) reaction of dimethylamino-trimethylene-dimethylamine with 1,4-dibromo-but-2-enylene in dimethylformamide-methanol (1 : 1) at room temperature
(6) H. Noguchi, A. Rembaum, J. Polym. Sci. B *7* (1969) 383...94
(7) KBr (3/350)

(1) poly(dimethylammonium-trimethylene-dimethylammonium-tetramethylene dibromide)
(2) white powder
(3) A. Rembaum, Jet Propulsion Laboratory, California Institute of Technology, Pasadena, Ca.
(5) reaction of dimethylamino-trimethylene-dimethylamine with 1,4-dibromotetramethylene in dimethylformamide-methanol (1 : 1) at room temperature
(6) A. Rembaum, J. Polym. Sci. B *7* (1969) 383...94
(7) ground with KBr (3/350) and CH_3OH, dried and pressed

321113 $C_4H_2N_2$ 334

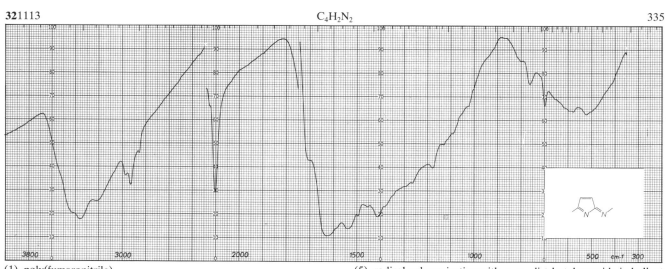

(1) poly(maleonitrile)
(2) very hard, coarse powder
(3) R. Liepins, Camille Dreyfus Laboratory, Research Triangle Institute, North Carolina
(4) the structure shown in the spectrum (given by the authors) is probably idealized
(5) radical polymerization
(6) R. Liepins, D. Campbell, C. Walker, J. Polym. Sci. A-1 *6* (1968) 3059...73
(7) ground with KBr (6/1000) and tetrahydrofuran, dried and pressed

321113 $C_4H_2N_2$ 335

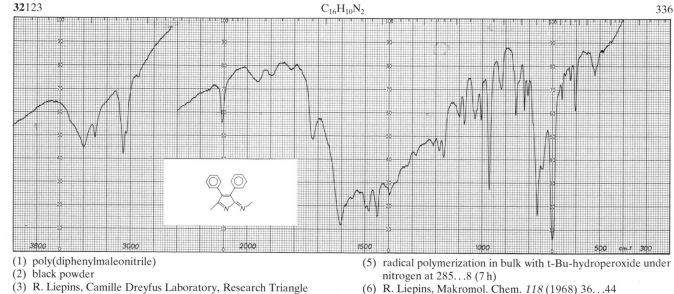

(1) poly(fumaronitrile)
(2) very hard, coarse powder
(3) R. Liepins, Camille Dreyfus Laboratory, Research Triangle Institute, North Carolina
(4) the structure shown in the spectrum (given by the authors) is probably idealized
(5) radical polymerization with, e. g., di-t-butylperoxide in bulk at 160 °C
(6) R. Liepins, D. Campbell, C. Walker, J. Polym. Sci. A-1 *6* (1968) 3059...73
(7) KBr (3/1000)

32123 $C_{16}H_{10}N_2$ 336

(1) poly(diphenylmaleonitrile)
(2) black powder
(3) R. Liepins, Camille Dreyfus Laboratory, Research Triangle Institute, North Carolina
(4) the structure in the spectrum (according to the authors) is probably idealized; the material contains a small amount of residual nitrile groups
(5) radical polymerization in bulk with t-Bu-hydroperoxide under nitrogen at 285...8 (7 h)
(6) R. Liepins, Makromol. Chem. *118* (1968) 36...44
(7) ground with KBr (3.5/300) and CHCl$_3$, dried and pressed

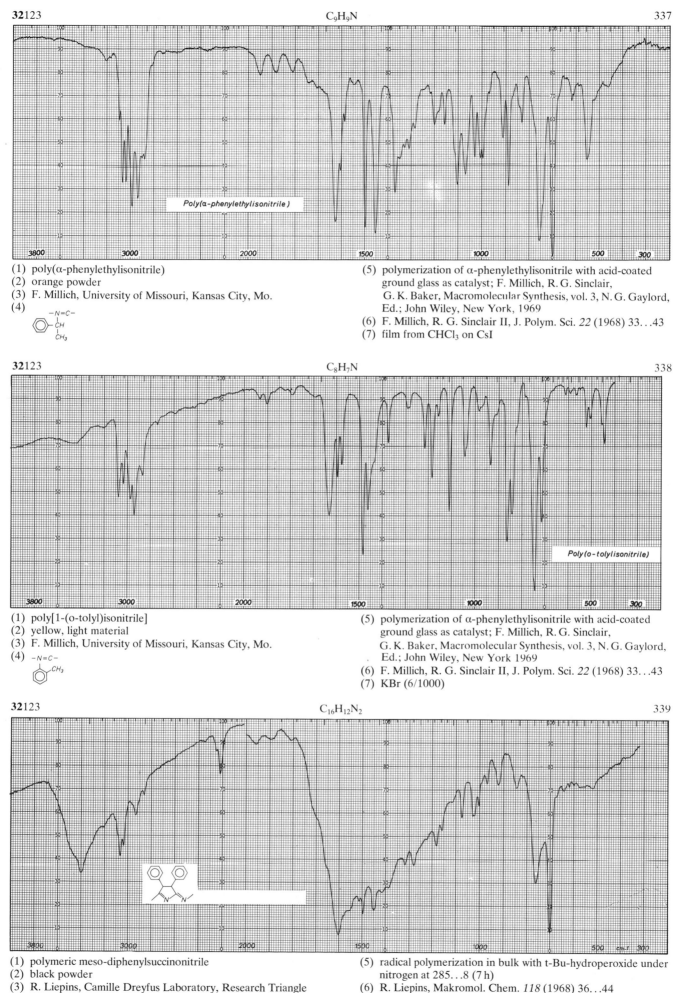

Poly(α-phenylethylisonitrile)

(1) poly(α-phenylethylisonitrile)
(2) orange powder
(3) F. Millich, University of Missouri, Kansas City, Mo.
(4)

(5) polymerization of α-phenylethylisonitrile with acid-coated
    ground glass as catalyst; F. Millich, R. G. Sinclair,
    G. K. Baker, Macromolecular Synthesis, vol. 3, N. G. Gaylord,
    Ed.; John Wiley, New York, 1969
(6) F. Millich, R. G. Sinclair II, J. Polym. Sci. *22* (1968) 33...43
(7) film from CHCl₃ on CsI

Poly(o-tolylisonitrile)

(1) poly[1-(o-tolyl)isonitrile]
(2) yellow, light material
(3) F. Millich, University of Missouri, Kansas City, Mo.
(4)

(5) polymerization of α-phenylethylisonitrile with acid-coated
    ground glass as catalyst; F. Millich, R. G. Sinclair,
    G. K. Baker, Macromolecular Synthesis, vol. 3, N. G. Gaylord,
    Ed.; John Wiley, New York 1969
(6) F. Millich, R. G. Sinclair II, J. Polym. Sci. *22* (1968) 33...43
(7) KBr (6/1000)

(1) polymeric meso-diphenylsuccinonitrile
(2) black powder
(3) R. Liepins, Camille Dreyfus Laboratory, Research Triangle
    Institute, North Carolina
(4) the structure in the spectrum (according to the authors) is
    idealized; the material contains a small amount of residual
    nitrile groups

(5) radical polymerization in bulk with t-Bu-hydroperoxide under
    nitrogen at 285...8 (7 h)
(6) R. Liepins, Makromol. Chem. *118* (1968) 36...44
(7) ground with KBr (3/300) and CHCl₃, dried and pressed

32123 $C_4H_2N_2-C_{16}H_{10}N_2$ 340

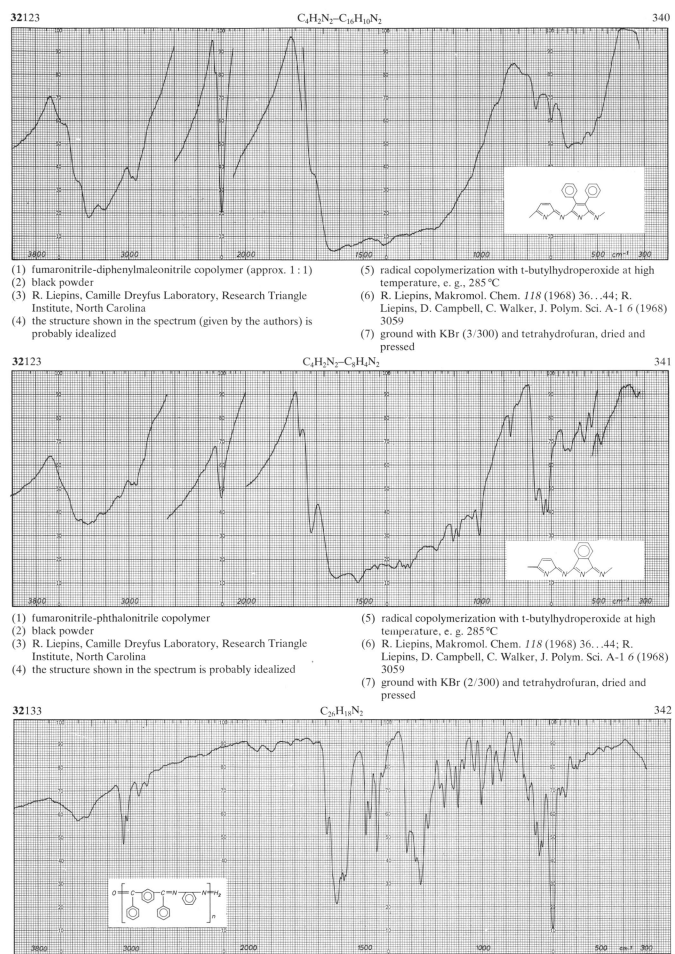

(1) fumaronitrile-diphenylmaleonitrile copolymer (approx. 1 : 1)
(2) black powder
(3) R. Liepins, Camille Dreyfus Laboratory, Research Triangle Institute, North Carolina
(4) the structure shown in the spectrum (given by the authors) is probably idealized
(5) radical copolymerization with t-butylhydroperoxide at high temperature, e. g., 285 °C
(6) R. Liepins, Makromol. Chem. *118* (1968) 36...44; R. Liepins, D. Campbell, C. Walker, J. Polym. Sci. A-1 *6* (1968) 3059
(7) ground with KBr (3/300) and tetrahydrofuran, dried and pressed

32123 $C_4H_2N_2-C_8H_4N_2$ 341

(1) fumaronitrile-phthalonitrile copolymer
(2) black powder
(3) R. Liepins, Camille Dreyfus Laboratory, Research Triangle Institute, North Carolina
(4) the structure shown in the spectrum is probably idealized
(5) radical copolymerization with t-butylhydroperoxide at high temperature, e. g. 285 °C
(6) R. Liepins, Makromol. Chem. *118* (1968) 36...44; R. Liepins, D. Campbell, C. Walker, J. Polym. Sci. A-1 *6* (1968) 3059
(7) ground with KBr (2/300) and tetrahydrofuran, dried and pressed

32133 $C_{26}H_{18}N_2$ 342

(1) polymeric Schiff-base, aromatic
(2) yellow powder
(3) A. A. Volpe, Department of Chemistry and Chemical Engineering, Stevens Institute of Technology, Hoboken, N.J.
(5) polycondensation of m-dibenzoylbenzene with o-phenylenediamine in the presence of p-toluene sulfonic acid monohydrate in dry decahydronaphthalene (24 h)
(6) A. A. Volpe, L. G. Kaufman, R. G. Dondero, J. Macromol. Sci.-Chem. *A 3* (6) (1969) 1087...1103
(7) KBr (1.5/350)

32133 $C_{26}H_{18}N_2$ 343

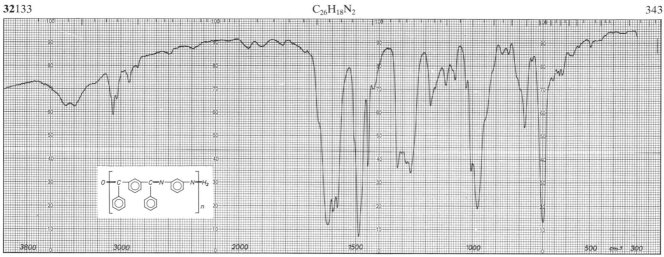

(1) polymeric Schiff-base, aromatic
(2) yellow powder
(3) A. A. Volpe, Department of Chemistry and Chemical
    Engineering, Stevens Institute of Technology, Hoboken, N.J.
(5) polycondensation of m-dibenzoylbenzene with m-phenyl-
    enediamine in the presence of p-toluene sulfonic acid

monohydrate in dry decahydronaphthalene (24 h)
(6) A. A. Volpe, L. G. Kaufman, R. G. Dondero, J. Macromol.
    Sci.-Chem. *A3* (6) (1969) 1087...1103
(7) KBr (1.5/350)

32133 $C_{26}H_{18}N_2$ 344

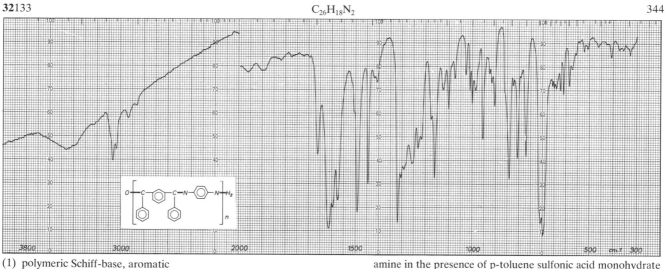

(1) polymeric Schiff-base, aromatic
(2) greyish-yellow powder
(3) A. A. Volpe, Department of Chemistry and Chemical
    Engineering, Stevens Institute of Technology, Hoboken, N.J.
(5) polycondensation of m-dibenzoylbenzene with p-phenylenedi-

amine in the presence of p-toluene sulfonic acid monohydrate
in dry decahydronaphthalene (24 h)
(6) A. A. Volpe, L. G. Kaufman, R. G. Dondero, J. Macromol.
    Sci.-Chem. *A3* (6) (1969) 1087...1103
(7) KBr (1.5/350)

32133 $C_{26}H_{18}N_2$ 345

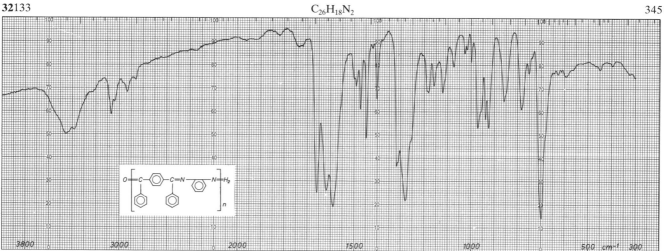

(1) polymeric Schiff-base, aromatic
(2) yellowish-green powder
(3) A. A. Volpe, Department of Chemistry and Chemical
    Engineering, Stevens Institute of Technology, Hoboken, N.J.
(5) polycondensation of p-dibenzoylbenzene with o-phenylenedi-

amine in the presence of p-toluene sulfonic acid monohydrate
in dry decahydronaphthalene (24 h)
(6) A. A. Volpe, L. G. Kaufman, R. G. Dondero, J. Macromol.
    Sci.-Chem. *A3* (6) (1969) 1087...1103
(7) KBr (1.5/350)

32133   C₂₆H₁₈N₂   346

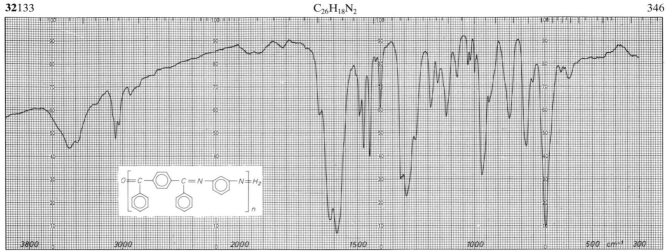

(1) polymeric Schiff-base, aromatic
(2) yellow powder
(3) A. A. Volpe, Department of Chemistry and Chemical
    Engineering, Stevens Institute of Technology, Hoboken, N.J.
(5) polycondensation of p-dibenzoylbenzene with

m-phenylenediamine in the presence of p-toluene acid
monohydrate in dry decahydronaphthalene (24 h)
(6) A. A. Volpe, L. G. Kaufman, R. G. Dondero, J. Macromol.
    Sci.-Chem. *A3* (6) (1969) 1087...1103
(7) KBr (1.5/350)

32133   C₂₆H₁₈N₂   347

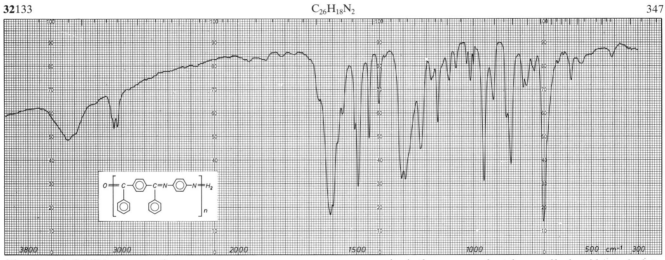

(1) polymeric Schiff-base, aromatic
(2) ochre-coloured powder
(3) A. A. Volpe, Department of Chemistry and Chemical
    Engineering, Stevens Institute of Technology, Hoboken, N.J.
(5) polycondensation of p-dibenzoylbenzene with p-phenylenedi-

amine in the presence of p-toluene sulfonic acid monohydrate
in dry decahydronaphthalene (24 h)
(6) A. A. Volpe, L. G. Kaufman, R. G. Dondero, J. Macromol.
    Sci.-Chem. *A3* (6) (1969) 1087...1103
(7) KBr (1.5/350)

322111   C₂H₅N   348

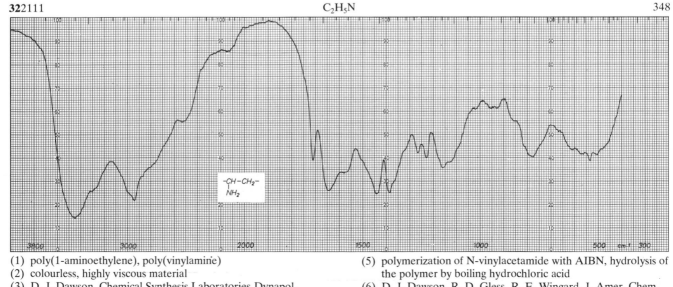

(1) poly(1-aminoethylene), poly(vinylamine)
(2) colourless, highly viscous material
(3) D. J. Dawson, Chemical Synthesis Laboratories Dynapol,
    Palo Alto, Calif.

(5) polymerization of N-vinylacetamide with AIBN, hydrolysis of
    the polymer by boiling hydrochloric acid
(6) D. J. Dawson, R. D. Gless, R. E. Wingard, J. Amer. Chem.
    Soc. *98* (1976) 5996...6000
(7) KBr (3/350)

322111 C_2H_6ClN 349

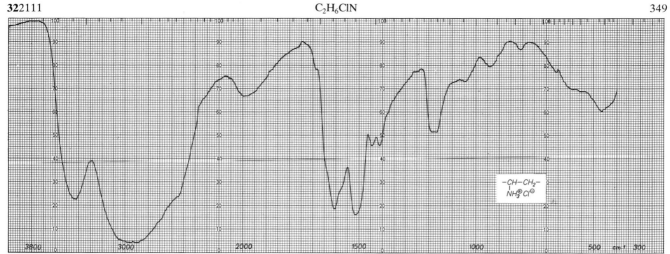

(1) poly(1-aminoethylene hydrochloride),
  poly(vinylammoniumchloride)
(2) white powder
(3) D. J. Dawson, Chemical Synthesis Laboratories Dynapol,
  Palo Alto, Calif.

(5) polymerization of N-vinylacetamide with AIBN, hydrolysis of
  the polymer by boiling hydrochloric acid
(6) D. J. Dawson, R. D. Gless, R. E. Wingard, ACS Polym.
  Preprints *17*/2 (1976) 779; J. Amer. Chem. Soc. *98* (1976)
  5996...6000
 (7) KBr (2/350)

322151 C_3H_3N 350

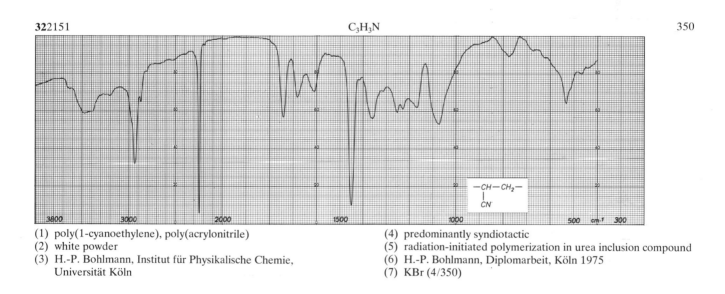

(1) poly(1-cyanoethylene), poly(acrylonitrile)
(2) white powder
(3) H.-P. Bohlmann, Institut für Physikalische Chemie,
  Universität Köln

(4) predominantly syndiotactic
(5) radiation-initiated polymerization in urea inclusion compound
(6) H.-P. Bohlmann, Diplomarbeit, Köln 1975
(7) KBr (4/350)

322151 C_3H_3N 351

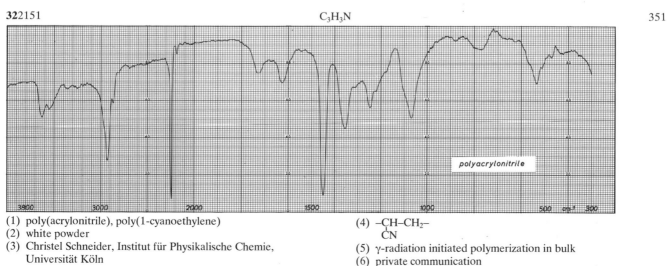

(1) poly(acrylonitrile), poly(1-cyanoethylene)
(2) white powder
(3) Christel Schneider, Institut für Physikalische Chemie,
  Universität Köln

(4) –CH–CH$_2$–
   CN
(5) γ-radiation initiated polymerization in bulk
(6) private communication
(7) KBr (5/300)

322151–**21**11211 C_3H_3N–C_3H_6 352

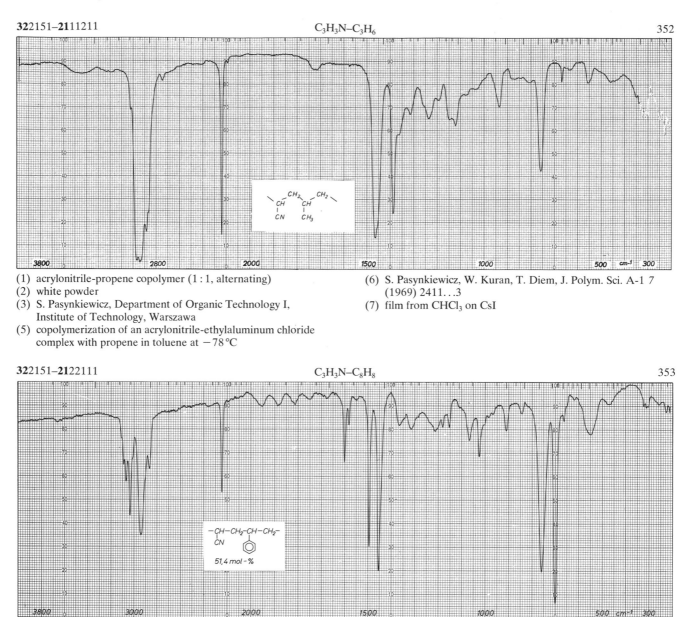

(1) acrylonitrile-propene copolymer (1 : 1, alternating)
(2) white powder
(3) S. Pasynkiewicz, Department of Organic Technology I,
Institute of Technology, Warszawa
(5) copolymerization of an acrylonitrile-ethylaluminum chloride
complex with propene in toluene at −78 °C

(6) S. Pasynkiewicz, W. Kuran, T. Diem, J. Polym. Sci. A-1 7
(1969) 2411...3
(7) film from $CHCl_3$ on CsI

322151–**21**22111 C_3H_3N–C_8H_8 353

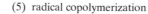

(1) acrylonitrile-styrene copolymer
(2) colourless granules
(3) BASF AG (by B. J. Schmitt)
(4) almost equimolar, statistical distribution

(5) radical copolymerization
(6) private communication; Makromolekulares Kolloquium,
Freiburg i. Br. 1976
(7) film from $CHCl_3$ on CsI

322151–**21**22131 C_3H_3N–C_9H_{10} 354

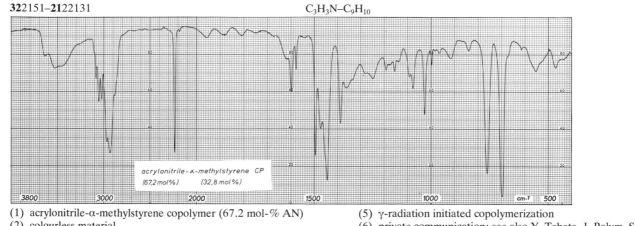

acrylonitrile-α-methylstyrene CP
(67,2 mol%)   (32,8 mol%)

(1) acrylonitrile-α-methylstyrene copolymer (67.2 mol-% AN)
(2) colourless material
(3) Y. Tabata, Department of Nuclear Engineering, University of
Tokyo

(5) γ-radiation initiated copolymerization
(6) private communication; see also Y. Tabata, J. Polym. Sci. A 2
(1964) 3649...55
(7) KBr (8/1000)

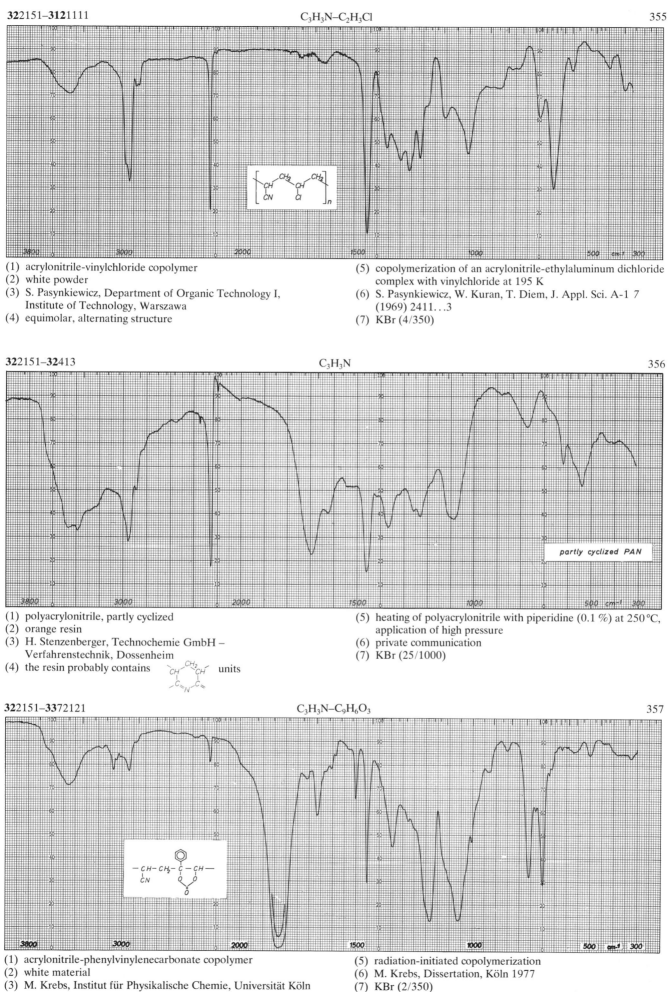

(1) acrylonitrile-vinylchloride copolymer
(2) white powder
(3) S. Pasynkiewicz, Department of Organic Technology I, Institute of Technology, Warszawa
(4) equimolar, alternating structure
(5) copolymerization of an acrylonitrile-ethylaluminum dichloride complex with vinylchloride at 195 K
(6) S. Pasynkiewicz, W. Kuran, T. Diem, J. Appl. Sci. A-1 7 (1969) 2411...3
(7) KBr (4/350)

322151–32413　　　　　　　　C$_3$H$_3$N　　　　　　　　　356

partly cyclized PAN

(1) polyacrylonitrile, partly cyclized
(2) orange resin
(3) H. Stenzenberger, Technochemie GmbH – Verfahrenstechnik, Dossenheim
(4) the resin probably contains　　units
(5) heating of polyacrylonitrile with piperidine (0.1 %) at 250°C, application of high pressure
(6) private communication
(7) KBr (25/1000)

322151–3372121　　　　　　　C$_3$H$_3$N–C$_9$H$_6$O$_3$　　　　　　357

(1) acrylonitrile-phenylvinylenecarbonate copolymer
(2) white material
(3) M. Krebs, Institut für Physikalische Chemie, Universität Köln
(4) 52 mol-% acrylonitrile
(5) radiation-initiated copolymerization
(6) M. Krebs, Dissertation, Köln 1977
(7) KBr (2/350)

322151–3311121   C₆H₉N–C₄H₈O   358

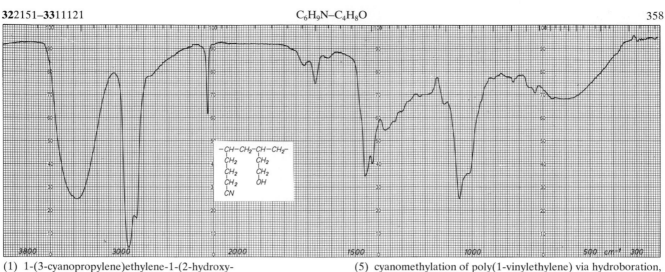

(1) 1-(3-cyanopropylene)ethylene-1-(2-hydroxy-
ethylene)ethylene copolymer
(2) colourless, very tough material
(3) C. Pinazzi, Laboratoire de Chimie et Physico-Chimie
Organique et Macromoléculaire, Centre Universitaire, Le
Mans

(5) cyanomethylation of poly(1-vinylethylene) via hydroboration,
partial cleavage of the hydroborated material by alkaline
oxidation
(6) C. Pinazzi, J. Vassort, F. Jean, D. Reyx, Makromol. Chem.
177 (1976) 3119…37
(7) film on CsI

322152–2122131–2112113   C₄H₅N–C₉H₁₀–C₄H₆   359

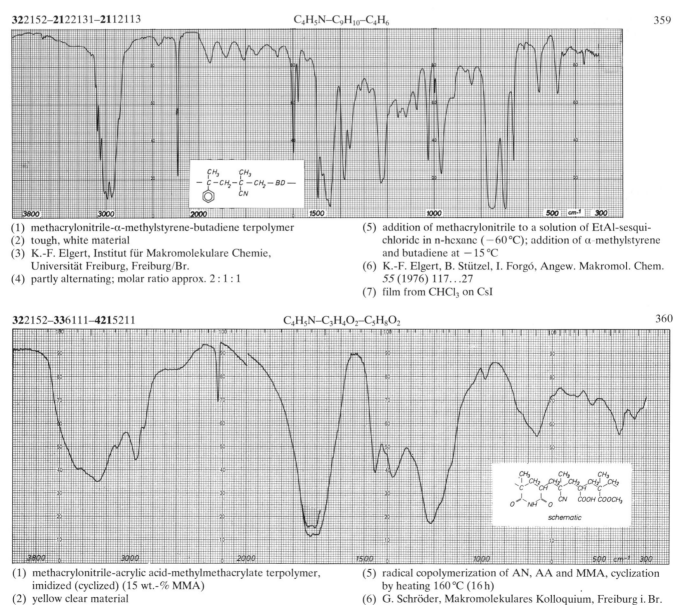

(1) methacrylonitrile-α-methylstyrene-butadiene terpolymer
(2) tough, white material
(3) K.-F. Elgert, Institut für Makromolekulare Chemie,
Universität Freiburg, Freiburg/Br.
(4) partly alternating; molar ratio approx. 2 : 1 : 1

(5) addition of methacrylonitrile to a solution of EtAl-sesqui-
chloride in n-hexane (−60 °C); addition of α-methylstyrene
and butadiene at −15 °C
(6) K.-F. Elgert, B. Stützel, I. Forgó, Angew. Makromol. Chem.
55 (1976) 117…27
(7) film from CHCl₃ on CsI

322152–336111–4215211   C₄H₅N–C₃H₄O₂–C₅H₈O₂   360

(1) methacrylonitrile-acrylic acid-methylmethacrylate terpolymer,
imidized (cyclized) (15 wt.-% MMA)
(2) yellow clear material
(3) G. Schröder, Röhm GmbH, Darmstadt

(5) radical copolymerization of AN, AA and MMA, cyclization
by heating 160 °C (16 h)
(6) G. Schröder, Makromolekulares Kolloquium, Freiburg i. Br.
1970
(7) KBr (3/350)

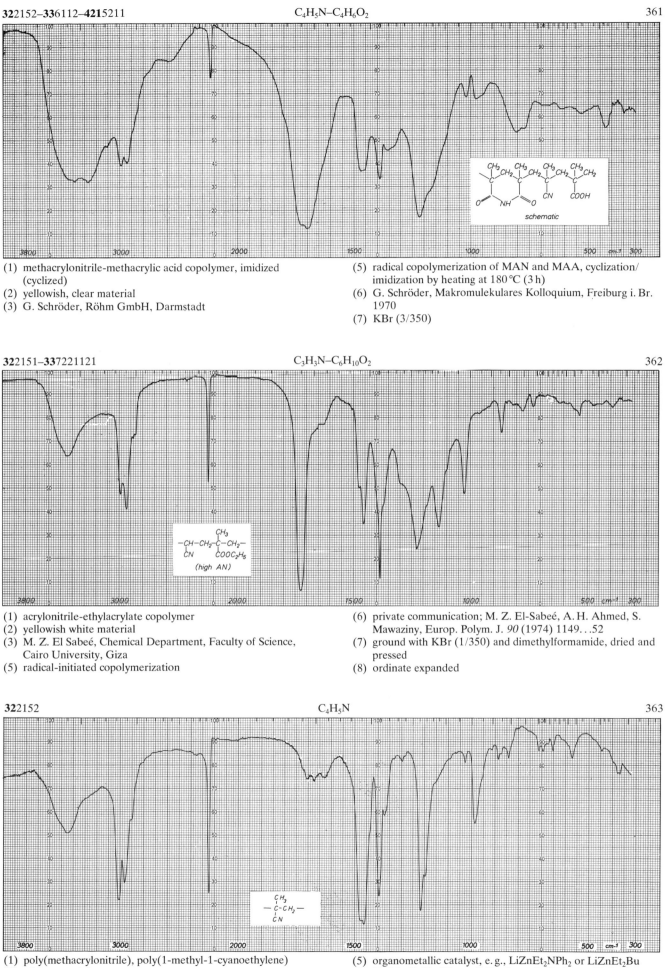

(1) methacrylonitrile-methacrylic acid copolymer, imidized (cyclized)
(2) yellowish, clear material
(3) G. Schröder, Röhm GmbH, Darmstadt
(5) radical copolymerization of MAN and MAA, cyclization/imidization by heating at 180 °C (3 h)
(6) G. Schröder, Makromulekulares Kolloquium, Freiburg i. Br. 1970
(7) KBr (3/350)

(1) acrylonitrile-ethylacrylate copolymer
(2) yellowish white material
(3) M. Z. El Sabeé, Chemical Department, Faculty of Science, Cairo University, Giza
(5) radical-initiated copolymerization
(6) private communication; M. Z. El-Sabeé, A. H. Ahmed, S. Mawaziny, Europ. Polym. J. *90* (1974) 1149...52
(7) ground with KBr (1/350) and dimethylformamide, dried and pressed
(8) ordinate expanded

(1) poly(methacrylonitrile), poly(1-methyl-1-cyanoethylene)
(2) white material
(3) Y. Joh, Mitsubishi Rayon Co., Otake City, Hiroshima
(4) stereoregular (isotactic), partly crystalline (approximately 30 %)
(5) organometallic catalyst, e. g., LiZnEt$_2$NPh$_2$ or LiZnEt$_2$Bu
(6) Y. Joh, T. Yoshihara, S. Kurihara, J. Tsukuma, Y. Imai, Macromol. Chem. *119* (1968) 239...43
(7) KBr (4.5/350)

322152 C_4H_5N 364

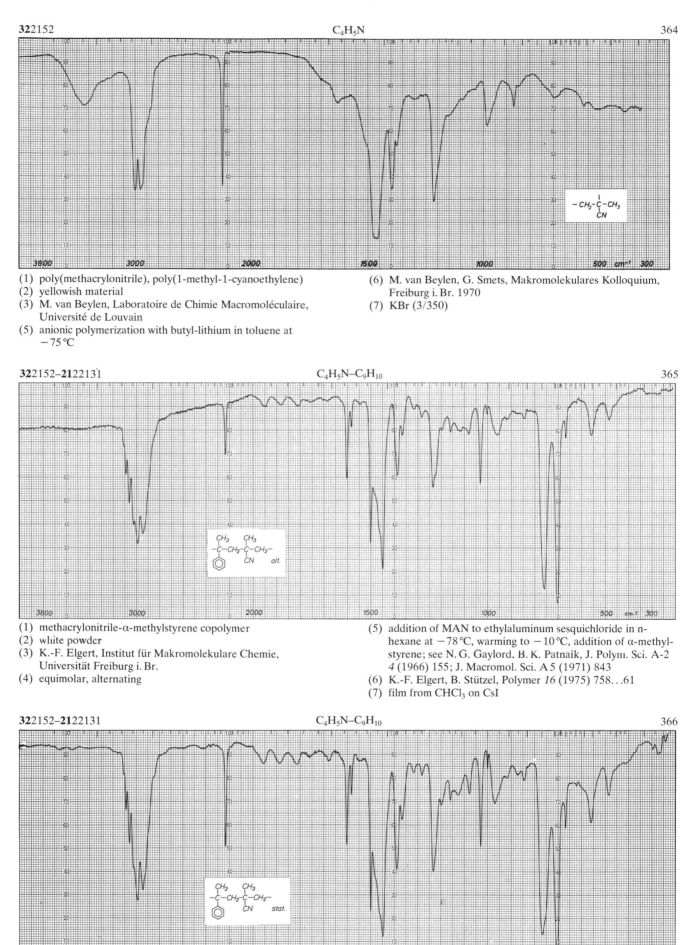

(1) poly(methacrylonitrile), poly(1-methyl-1-cyanoethylene)
(2) yellowish material
(3) M. van Beylen, Laboratoire de Chimie Macromoléculaire, Université de Louvain
(5) anionic polymerization with butyl-lithium in toluene at −75 °C

(6) M. van Beylen, G. Smets, Makromolekulares Kolloquium, Freiburg i. Br. 1970
(7) KBr (3/350)

322152–**2122**131 $C_4H_5N–C_9H_{10}$ 365

(1) methacrylonitrile-α-methylstyrene copolymer
(2) white powder
(3) K.-F. Elgert, Institut für Makromolekulare Chemie, Universität Freiburg i. Br.
(4) equimolar, alternating

(5) addition of MAN to ethylaluminum sesquichloride in n-hexane at −78 °C, warming to −10 °C, addition of α-methyl-styrene; see N. G. Gaylord, B. K. Patnaik, J. Polym. Sci. A-2 4 (1966) 155; J. Macromol. Sci. A 5 (1971) 843
(6) K.-F. Elgert, B. Stützel, Polymer 16 (1975) 758...61
(7) film from CHCl₃ on CsI

322152–**2122**131 $C_4H_5N–C_9H_{10}$ 366

(1) methacrylonitrile-α-methylstyrene copolymer
(2) white powder
(3) K.-F. Elgert, Institut für Makromolekulare Chemie, Universität Freiburg i. Br.

(4) statistical; 55 mol-% MAN
(5) radical copolymerization
(6) K.-F. Elgert, B. Stützel, Polymer 16 (1975) 758...61
(7) film from CHCl₃ on CsI

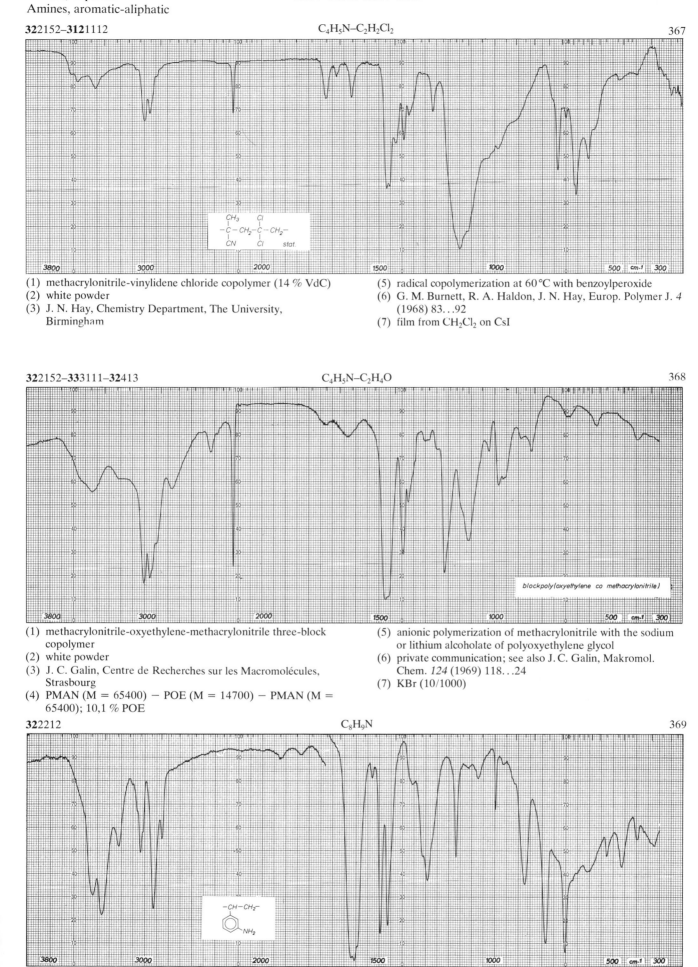

(1) methacrylonitrile-vinylidene chloride copolymer (14 % VdC)
(2) white powder
(3) J. N. Hay, Chemistry Department, The University, Birmingham

(5) radical copolymerization at 60 °C with benzoylperoxide
(6) G. M. Burnett, R. A. Haldon, J. N. Hay, Europ. Polymer J. *4* (1968) 83...92
(7) film from CH_2Cl_2 on CsI

blockpoly(oxyethylene co methacrylonitrile)

(1) methacrylonitrile-oxyethylene-methacrylonitrile three-block copolymer
(2) white powder
(3) J. C. Galin, Centre de Recherches sur les Macromolécules, Strasbourg
(4) PMAN (M = 65400) − POE (M = 14700) − PMAN (M = 65400); 10,1 % POE

(5) anionic polymerization of methacrylonitrile with the sodium or lithium alcoholate of polyoxyethylene glycol
(6) private communication; see also J. C. Galin, Makromol. Chem. *124* (1969) 118...24
(7) KBr (10/1000)

(1) poly(m-aminostyrene), poly[1-(m-aminophenyl)ethylene]
(2) eggshell-coloured powder
(3) R. H. Still, Department of Chemical Sciences, The Hatfield Polytechnic, Hatfield, Herts.

(5) R. H. Still, C. J. Keattch, J. Appl. Polymer Sci. *10* (1966) 193
(6) R. H. Still, P. B. Jones, J. Appl. Polymer Sci. *13* (1969) 1555...67
(7) KBr (2/350)

322212 $C_{10}H_{13}N$ 370

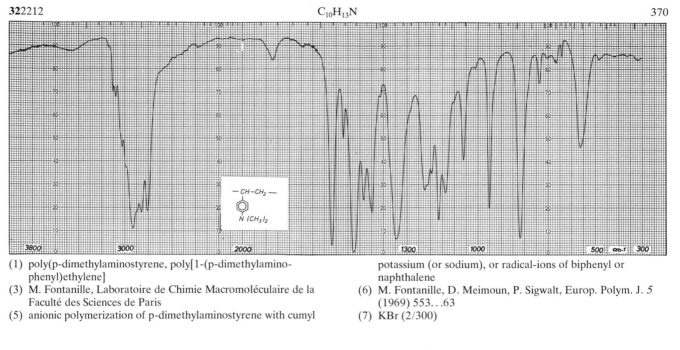

(1) poly(p-dimethylaminostyrene, poly[1-(p-dimethylamino-phenyl)ethylene]
(3) M. Fontanille, Laboratoire de Chimie Macromoléculaire de la Faculté des Sciences de Paris
(5) anionic polymerization of p-dimethylaminostyrene with cumyl

potassium (or sodium), or radical-ions of biphenyl or naphthalene
(6) M. Fontanille, D. Meimoun, P. Sigwalt, Europ. Polym. J. *5* (1969) 553...63
(7) KBr (2/300)

322251 C_9H_6N 371

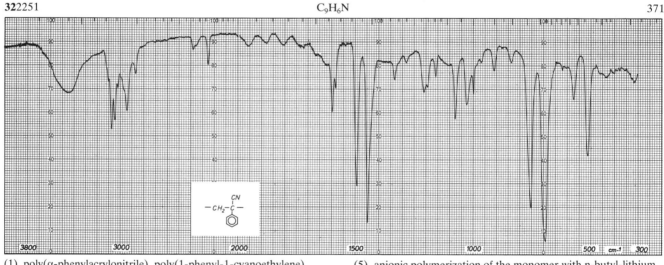

(1) poly(α-phenylacrylonitrile), poly(1-phenyl-1-cyanoethylene)
(2) white powder
(3) W. Funke, Forschungsinstitut für Pigmente und Lacke, Universität Stuttgart

(5) anionic polymerization of the monomer with n-butyl-lithium in dimethylformamide at −45 °C
(6) M. Sonntag, W. Funke, Makromol. Chem. *137* (1970) 23...8
(7) KBr (2/350)

322253 $C_{10}H_6N_2$ 372

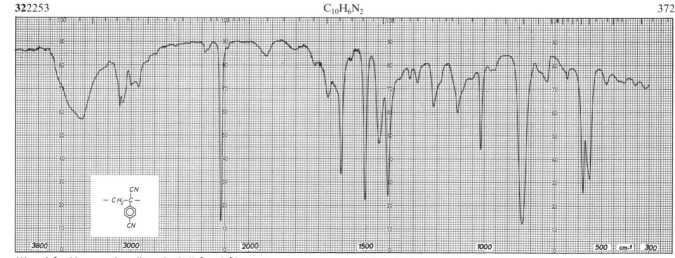

(1) poly[α-(4-cyanophenyl)acrylonitrile], poly[1-cyano-1-(p-cyanophenyl)ethylene]
(2) white powder
(3) W. Funke, Forschungsinstitut für Pigmente und Lacke, Universität Stuttgart

(5) anionic polymerization of the monomer with n-butyl-lithium in dimethylformamide at −45 °C
(6) M. Sonntag, W. Funke, Makromol. Chem. *137* (1970) 23...8
(7) KBr (2/350)

323112   C$_8$H$_{16}$ClN   373

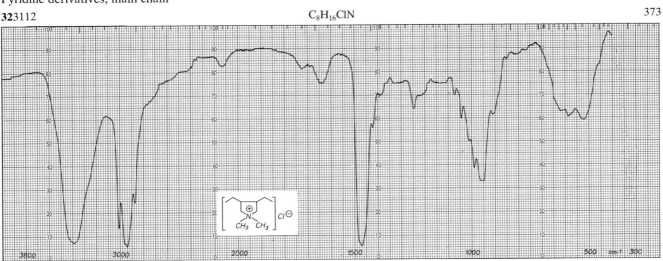

(1) poly(diallyldimethylammoniumchloride),
    poly(3,4-dimethylen-N-dimethyl-pyrrolidiniumchloride)
(2) colourless material
(3) R. C. Slagel, Calgon Center, Pittsburgh, Pa.
(5) radical-induced cyclopolymerization of diallyldimethylammo-
    niumchloride; see J. E. Boothe, H. G. Flock, M. F. Hoover, J.
    Macromol. Sci. A4 (6) (1970) 1419

(6) J. E. Lancaster, L. Baccei, H. P. Panzer, Polym. Lett. *14*
    (1976) 549...54
(7) film from n-butanol
(8) the material is highly hygroscopic: water bands at 3400 cm^{-1}
    and 1640 cm^{-1}

323113   C$_7$H$_8$BrN   374

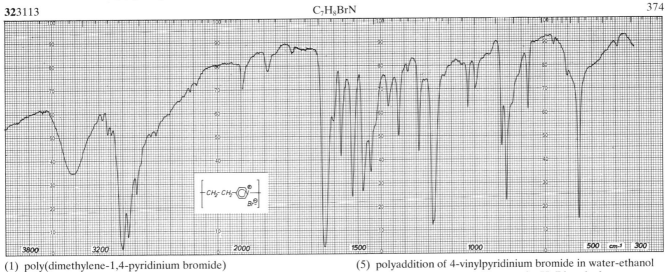

(1) poly(dimethylene-1,4-pyridinium bromide)
(2) eggshell-coloured powder
(3) V. Martin, Organisch-Chemisches Institut, Universität Mainz
(4) polymerization degree: 13

(5) polyaddition of 4-vinylpyridinium bromide in water-ethanol
(6) private communication; V. Martin, H. Ringsdorf,
    Makromolekulares Kolloquium, Freiburg i. Br. 1973
(7) KBr (2/350)

323113   C$_7$H$_8$ClNO$_4$ 375

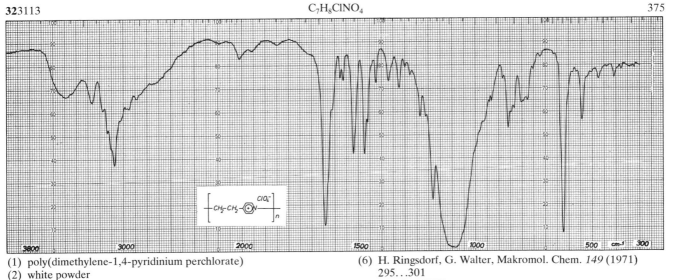

(1) poly(dimethylene-1,4-pyridinium perchlorate)
(2) white powder
(3) G. Walter, Institut für Organische Chemie der Universität
    Mainz
(5) anionic polymerization of 4-vinylpyridine (private
    communication); see also I. Mielke, H. Ringsdorf, J. Polym.
    Sci. C 31 (1970) 107, ibid. B-1 *9* (1971) 1

(6) H. Ringsdorf, G. Walter, Makromol. Chem. *149* (1971)
    295...301
(7) KBr (1.5/350)

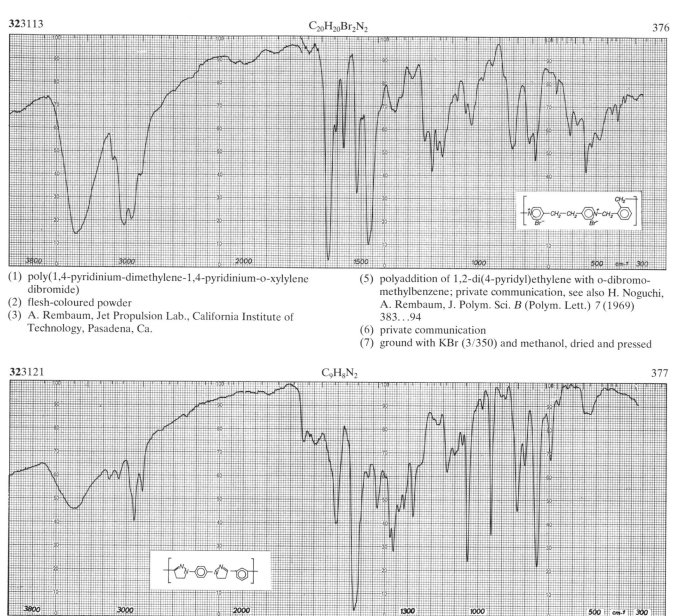

323113 $C_{20}H_{20}Br_2N_2$ 376

(1) poly(1,4-pyridinium-dimethylene-1,4-pyridinium-o-xylylene dibromide)
(2) flesh-coloured powder
(3) A. Rembaum, Jet Propulsion Lab., California Institute of Technology, Pasadena, Ca.

(5) polyaddition of 1,2-di(4-pyridyl)ethylene with o-dibromo-methylbenzene; private communication, see also H. Noguchi, A. Rembaum, J. Polym. Sci. *B* (Polym. Lett.) 7 (1969) 383...94
(6) private communication
(7) ground with KBr (3/350) and methanol, dried and pressed

323121 $C_9H_8N_2$ 377

(1) polymeric pyrazol with aromatic bridges
(2) yellowish to ochre powder
(3) J. K. Stille, Department of Chemistry, University of Iowa, Iowa City, Io.
(5) polycondensation of p-phenylene-3,3′-disydnone with m-diethynylbenzene

(6) J. K. Stille, M. A. Bedford, J. Polym. Sci. A 1 6 (1968) 2331
(7) ground with KBr (1.5/350) and dimethylacetamide, dried and pressed

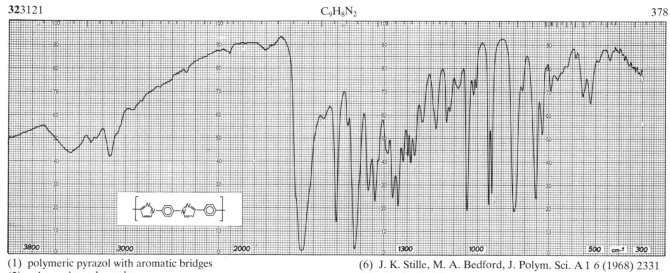

323121 $C_9H_8N_2$ 378

(1) polymeric pyrazol with aromatic bridges
(2) ochre-coloured powder
(3) J. K. Stille, Department of Chemistry, University of Iowa, Iowa City, Io.
(5) polycondensation of p-phenylene-3,3′-disydnone with p-diethynylbenzene

(6) J. K. Stille, M. A. Bedford, J. Polym. Sci. A 1 6 (1968) 2331
(7) KBr (1.5/350)
(8) the reaction probably has not been completed: absorption of the $-N\overset{N\pm O}{\underset{CH-C=O}{}}$ ring at 1750 cm^{-1}

323121 $C_{16}H_{16}N_4$ 379

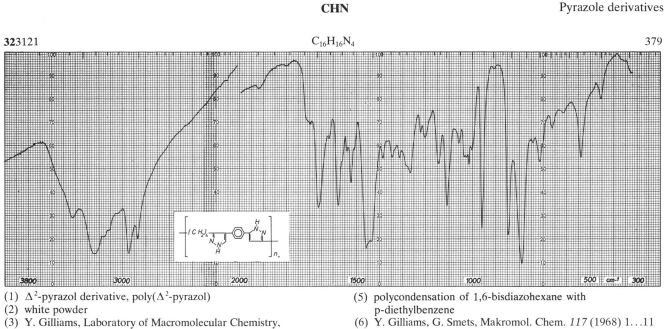

(1) Δ^2-pyrazol derivative, poly(Δ^2-pyrazol)
(2) white powder
(3) Y. Gilliams, Laboratory of Macromolecular Chemistry, University of Louvain

(5) polycondensation of 1,6-bisdiazohexane with p-diethylbenzene
(6) Y. Gilliams, G. Smets, Makromol. Chem. *117* (1968) 1...11
(7) KBr (2.5/350)

323121 $C_{15}H_{10}N_2$ 380

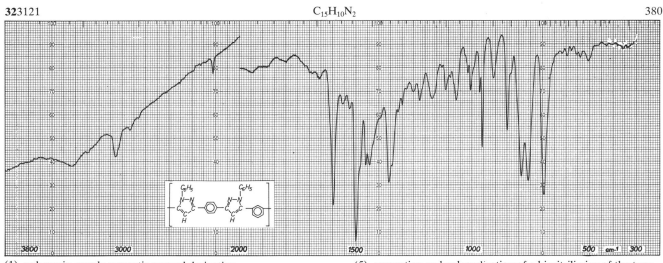

(1) polymeric, purely aromatic pyrazol derivative
(2) yellow to brown powder
(3) J. K. Stille, Department of Chemistry, University of Iowa, Iowa City, Io.

(5) generation and polycyclization of a bisnitrilimine of the type
$C_6H_5-\overset{\ominus}{N}-N\overset{\oplus}{=}C$ Ar$-\overset{\oplus}{C}=N-\overset{\ominus}{N}-C_6H_5$ in situ by the action of a tertiary amine base in the presence of m-divinylbenzene
(6) J. K. Stille, J. Macromol. Sci.-Chem. A 3 *6* (1969) 1043...65
(7) ground with KBr (2/350) and CHCl₃, dried and pressed

323121 $C_{15}H_{10}N_2$ 381

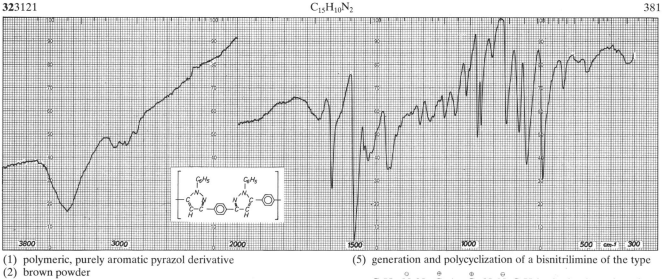

(1) polymeric, purely aromatic pyrazol derivative
(2) brown powder
(3) J. K. Stille, Department of Chemistry, University of Iowa, Iowa City, Io.

(5) generation and polycyclization of a bisnitrilimine of the type
$C_6H_5-\overset{\ominus}{N}-N\overset{\oplus}{=}C-Ar-\overset{\oplus}{C}=N-\overset{\ominus}{N}-C_6H_5$ in situ by the action of a tertiary amine base in the presence of p-diethynylbenzene
(6) J. K. Stille, J. Macromol. Sci.-Chem. A 3 *6* (1969) 1043...65
(7) KBr

323131 $C_{14}H_{14}N_6$ 382

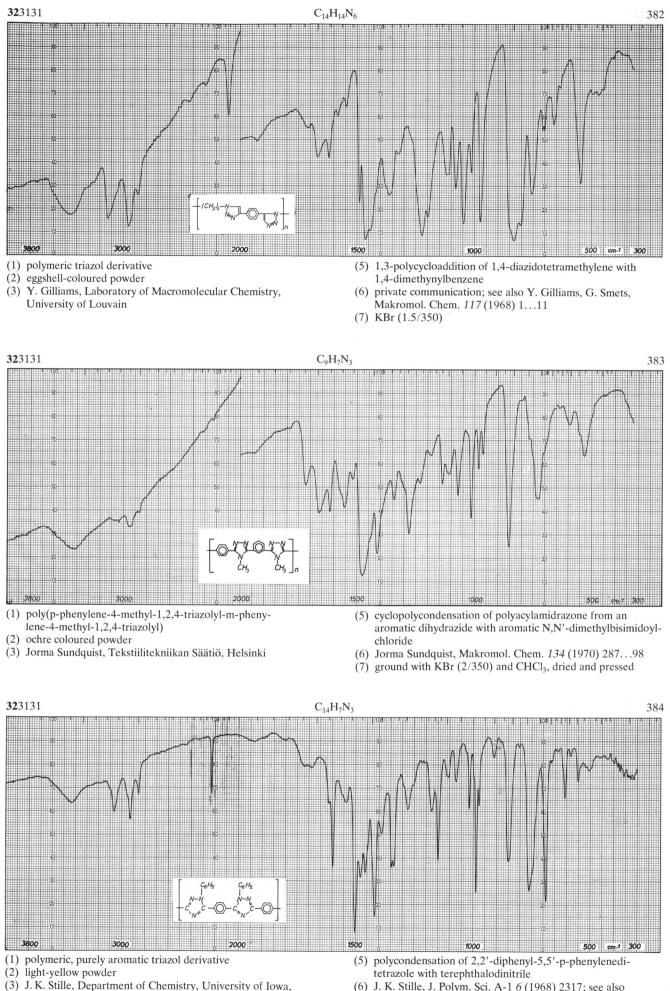

(1) polymeric triazol derivative
(2) eggshell-coloured powder
(3) Y. Gilliams, Laboratory of Macromolecular Chemistry, University of Louvain

(5) 1,3-polycycloaddition of 1,4-diazidotetramethylene with 1,4-dimethynylbenzene
(6) private communication; see also Y. Gilliams, G. Smets, Makromol. Chem. *117* (1968) 1...11
(7) KBr (1.5/350)

323131 $C_9H_7N_3$ 383

(1) poly(p-phenylene-4-methyl-1,2,4-triazolyl-m-pheny-lene-4-methyl-1,2,4-triazolyl)
(2) ochre coloured powder
(3) Jorma Sundquist, Tekstiilitekniikan Säätiö, Helsinki

(5) cyclopolycondensation of polyacylamidrazone from an aromatic dihydrazide with aromatic N,N′-dimethylbisimidoyl-chloride
(6) Jorma Sundquist, Makromol. Chem. *134* (1970) 287...98
(7) ground with KBr (2/350) and CHCl₃, dried and pressed

323131 $C_{14}H_7N_3$ 384

(1) polymeric, purely aromatic triazol derivative
(2) light-yellow powder
(3) J. K. Stille, Department of Chemistry, University of Iowa, Iowa City, Io.

(5) polycondensation of 2,2′-diphenyl-5,5′-p-phenylenedi-tetrazole with terephthalodinitrile
(6) J. K. Stille, J. Polym. Sci. A-1 *6* (1968) 2317; see also J. K. Stille, J. Macromol. Sci.-Chem. A-3 *6* (1969) 1043...65
(7) ground with KBr (2/350) and CHCl₃, dried and pressed
(8) the product still contains some nitrile groups

323131–3241121   C₄₀H₂₅N₇   385

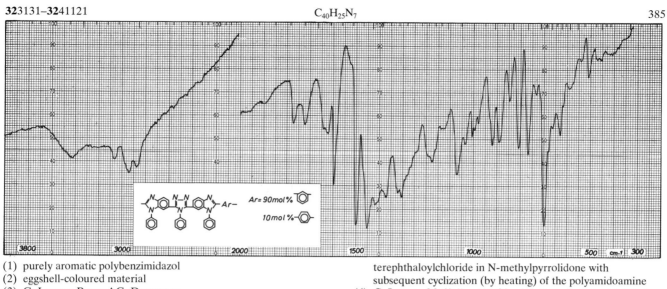

(1) purely aromatic polybenzimidazol
(2) eggshell-coloured material
(3) G. Lorenz, Bayer AG, Dormagen
(5) polycondensation of 3,5-bis(4-arylamino-3-amino-phenyl)-4-aryl-1,2,4-triazole and a mixture of iso- and

terephthaloylchloride in N-methylpyrrolidone with subsequent cyclization (by heating) of the polyamidoamine
(6) G. Lorenz, M. Gallus, W. Giessler, F. Bodesheim, H. Wieder, G. E. Nischk, Makromol. Chem. *130* (1969) 65...89
(7) ground with KBr (4/350) and tetrahydrofuran, dried and pressed

323132   C₁₀H₇N₃   386

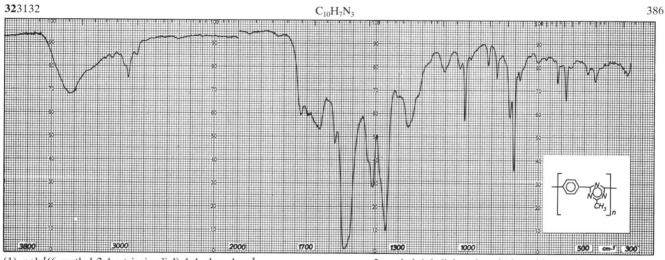

(1) poly[(6-methyl-2,4-s-triazinediyl)-1,4-phenylene]
(2) ivory-coloured powder
(3) H. G. Elias, TH Zürich/Midland Macromolecular Institute
(5) condensation of benzamidine hydrochloride with acetanhydride, polycondensation of the resulting

2-methyl-4,6-diphenyl-s-triazine with terephthaldiamidine dihydrochloride
(6) E. Greth, H. G. Elias, Makromol. Chem. *125* (1969) 24...32
(7) KBr (0.5/350)

323132   C₁₉H₁₃N₃   387

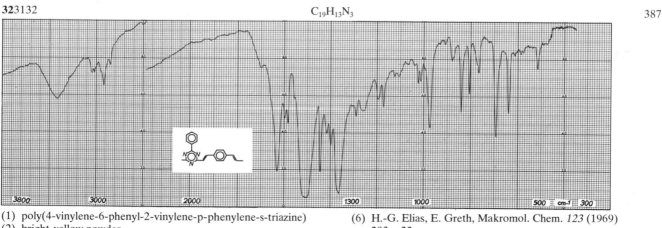

(1) poly(4-vinylene-6-phenyl-2-vinylene-p-phenylene-s-triazine)
(2) bright-yellow powder
(3) H.-G. Elias, TH Zürich/Midland Macromolecular Institute
(5) polycondensation of 2,4-dimethyl-6-phenyl-s-triazine with terephthalic dialdehyde

(6) H.-G. Elias, E. Greth, Makromol. Chem. *123* (1969) 203...22
(7) ground with KBr (0.75/300) and dimethylacetamide, dried and pressed

323132 $C_{23}H_{16}N_3$ 388

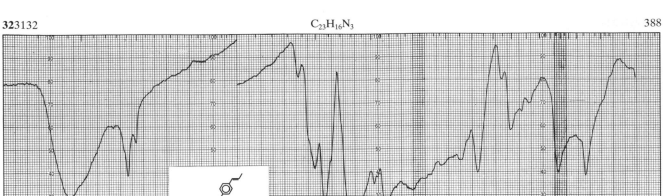

(1) poly[di(vinylene-1,4-phenylenevinylene)2,4-6-s-triazinetriyl]
(2) yellow to brown material
(3) H.-G. Elias, TH Zürich/Midland Macromolecular Institute
(5) polycondensation of 2,4,6-trimethyltriazine with terephthalic dialdehyde in sulfuric acid

(6) H.-G. Elias, E. Greth, Makromol. Chem. *123* (1969) 203…22
(7) ground with KBr (4/300) and CHCl$_3$, dried and pressed

323132 $C_{33}H_{18}N_3$ 389

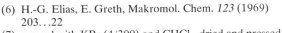

(1) polymer with triazine-type structure
(2) black powder
(3) G. Manecke, Fritz-Haber-Institut der Max-Planck-Gesellschaft, Berlin-Dahlem
(4) the structure in the spectrum is idealized

(5) polyaddition of 1,4-bis(2,2-dicyanovinyl)benzene in quinoline
(6) G. Manecke, D. Wöhrle, Makromol. Chem. *120* (1968) 176…91
(7) KBr (2/350)

323132 $C_{15}H_9N_3$ 390

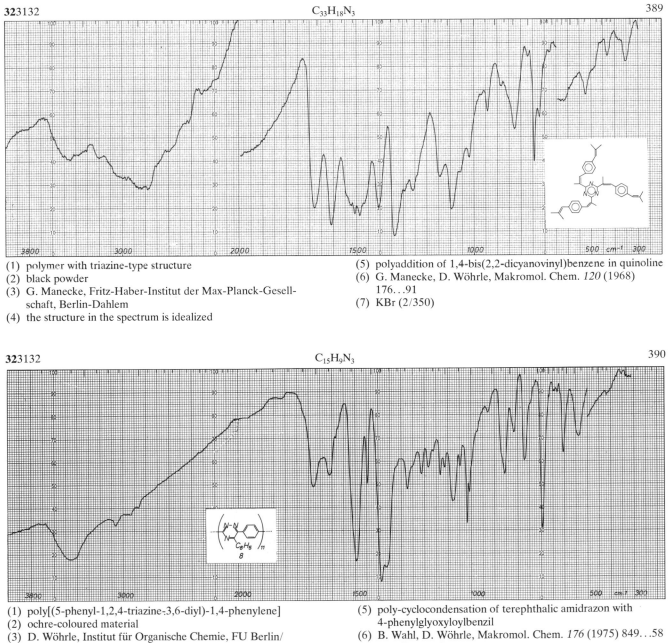

(1) poly[(5-phenyl-1,2,4-triazine-3,6-diyl)-1,4-phenylene]
(2) ochre-coloured material
(3) D. Wöhrle, Institut für Organische Chemie, FU Berlin/ Universität Bremen

(5) poly-cyclocondensation of terephthalic amidrazon with 4-phenylglyoxyloylbenzil
(6) B. Wahl, D. Wöhrle, Makromol. Chem. *176* (1975) 849…58
(7) KBr (1.8/350)

323132 C₁₅H₉N₃ 391

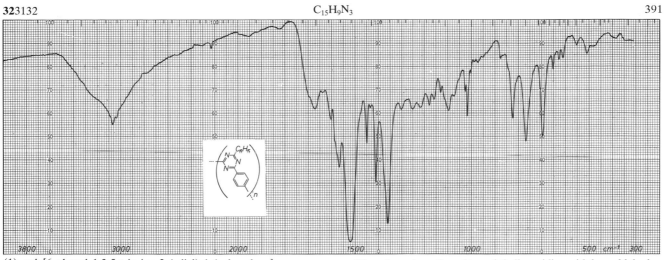

(1) poly[6-phenyl-1,3,5-triazine-2,4-diyl)-1,4-phenylene]
(2) ochre-coloured powder
(3) D. Wöhrle, Institut für Organische Chemie, FU Berlin/ Universität Bremen
(5) polycondensation of terephthalic amidine with benzaldehyde
(6) B. Wahl, D. Wöhrle, Makromol. Chem. *176* (1975) 849...58
(7) ground with KBr (1.5/350) and CHCl₃, dried and pressed

323132 C₁₅H₉N₃ 392

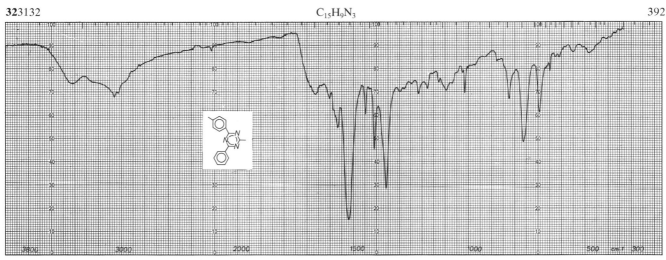

(1) poly[(6-phenyl-1,3,5-triazine-2,4-diyl)-1,4-phenylene]
(2) ochre-coloured powder
(3) D. Wöhrle, Institut für Organische Chemie, FU Berlin/ Universität Bremen
(5) poly-cyclocondensation of terephthalic amidine with benzaldehyde
(6) B. Wahl, D. Wöhrle, Makromol. Chem. *176* (1975) 849...58
(7) KBr (1.5/350)

323132 C₂₁H₆N₃ 393

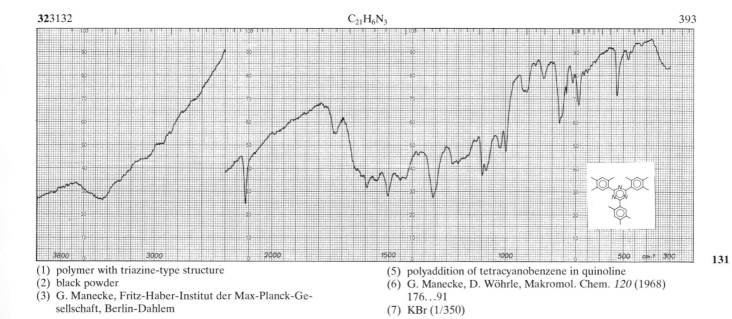

(1) polymer with triazine-type structure
(2) black powder
(3) G. Manecke, Fritz-Haber-Institut der Max-Planck-Gesellschaft, Berlin-Dahlem
(5) polyaddition of tetracyanobenzene in quinoline
(6) G. Manecke, D. Wöhrle, Makromol. Chem. *120* (1968) 176...91
(7) KBr (1/350)

323212 C_7H_8NCl 394

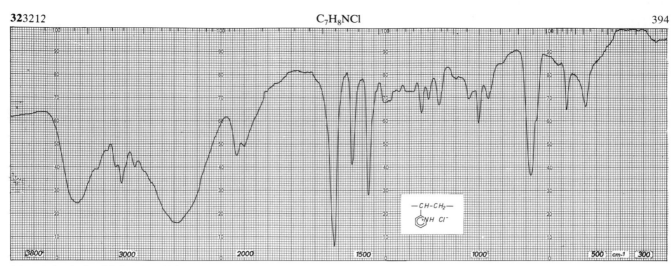

(1) poly(2-vinylpyridiniumchloride)
(2) white, hard material
(3) A. Dondos, Centre de Recherches sur les Macromolécules, Strasbourg; Elsbeth Zoschke, Institut für Physikalische Chemie, Universität Köln

(5) reaction of poly(2-vinylpyridine) in methanolic solution with HCl
(7) film from H_2O on KRS–5 (thallium bromide iodide)

323213 C_7H_7N 395

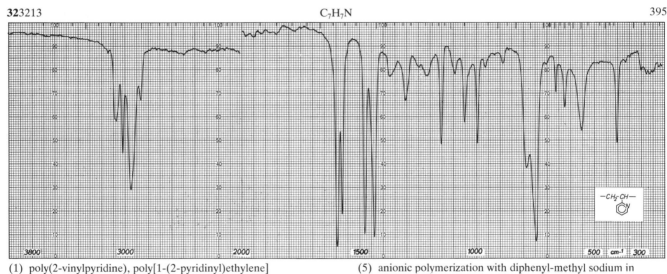

(1) poly(2-vinylpyridine), poly[1-(2-pyridinyl)ethylene]
(2) white powder
(3) A. Dondos, Centre de Recherches sur les Macromolécules, Strasbourg

(5) anionic polymerization with diphenyl-methyl sodium in tetrahydrofuran at low temperature
(6) A. Dondos, Makromol. Chem. *135* (1970) 181...94
(7) film from $CHCl_3$ on CsI

323213 $C_7H_7N–C_7H_7N$ 396

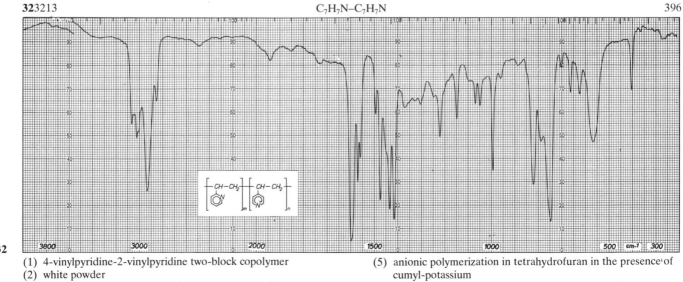

(1) 4-vinylpyridine-2-vinylpyridine two-block copolymer
(2) white powder
(3) Y. Gallot, Centre de Recherche sur les Macromolécules, Strasbourg,
(4) M(2-PVP): 15000, M(4-PVP): 8000

(5) anionic polymerization in tetrahydrofuran in the presence of cumyl-potassium
(6) P. Grosius, Y. Gallot, A. Skoulios, Makromol. Chem. *136* (1970) 191...200; private communication
(7) film from $CHCl_3$ on CsI

Triazine derivatives
Pyridine derivatives, side chain

CHN

323213–**21**22111
C₇H₇N–C₈H₈
397

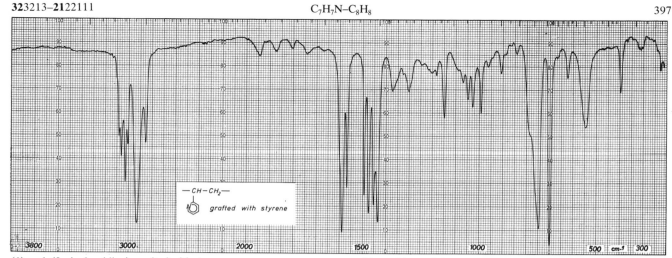

(1) poly(2-vinylpyridine), grafted with styrene
(2) white material
(3) V. T. Stannett, Camille Dreyfus Lab., Research Triangle Institute, N.C.: North Carolina State University, School of Engineering

(5) grafting of living polystyrene onto polyvinylpyridine according to Szwarc's method (private communication)
(6) J. A. Gervasi, A. B. Gosnell, V. Stannett, J. Polym. Sci. C *24* (1968) 207...18
(7) film from CHCl₃ on CsI

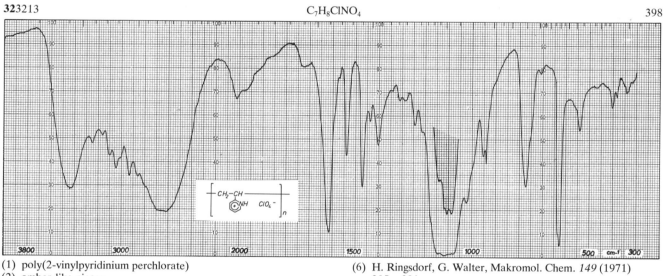

(1) poly(2-vinylpyridinium perchlorate)
(2) amber-like pieces
(3) H. Ringsdorf, Institut für Organische Chemie, Universität Mainz
(5) heating of a solution of monomeric 2-vinylpyridinium perchlorate in acetonitrile (until dryness)

(6) H. Ringsdorf, G. Walter, Makromol. Chem. *149* (1971) 295...301
(7) ground with KBr (3/350) and dimethylsulfoxide, dried and pressed

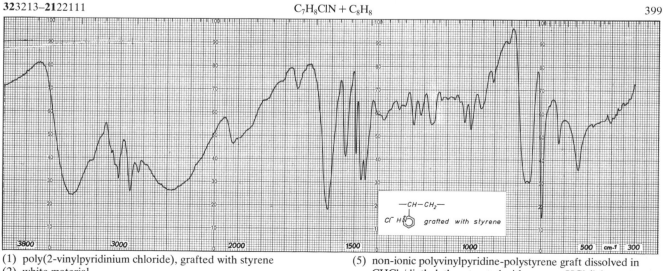

(1) poly(2-vinylpyridinium chloride), grafted with styrene
(2) white material
(3) V. T. Stannett, Camille Dreyfus Lab., Research Triangle Institute, N.N.; North Carolina State University, School of Engineering

(5) non-ionic polyvinylpyridine-polystyrene graft dissolved in CHCl₃/diethylether, treated with gaseous HCl (laboratory preparation by E. Zoschke)
(6) J. A. Gervasi, A. B. Gosnell, V. Stannett, J. Polym. Sci. C *24* (1968) 207...18
(7) KBr (4/350)

323213   C$_7$H$_7$N   400

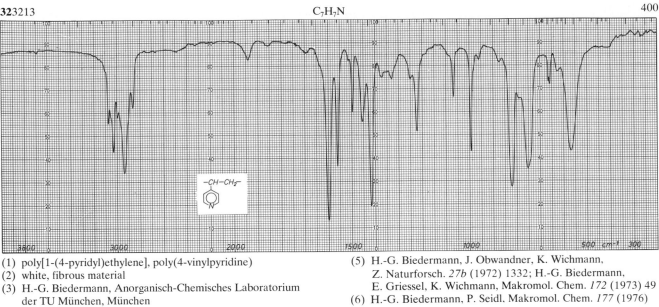

(1) poly[1-(4-pyridyl)ethylene], poly(4-vinylpyridine)
(2) white, fibrous material
(3) H.-G. Biedermann, Anorganisch-Chemisches Laboratorium der TU München, München

(5) H.-G. Biedermann, J. Obwandner, K. Wichmann, Z. Naturforsch. *27b* (1972) 1332; H.-G. Biedermann, E. Griessel, K. Wichmann, Makromol. Chem. *172* (1973) 49
(6) H.-G. Biedermann, P. Seidl, Makromol. Chem. *177* (1976) 631...43
(7) film from CHCl$_3$ on CsI

323213   C$_7$H$_7$N   401

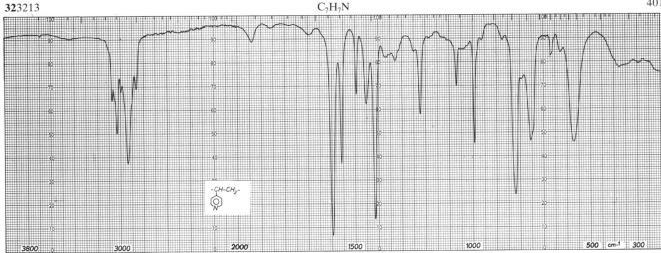

(1) poly[1-(4-pyridyl)ethylene], poly(4-vinylpyridine)
(2) white, fibrous material
(3) H. Ringsdorf, Institut für Organische Chemie, Universität Mainz

(5) bulk polymerization with 0.05 % AIBN
(6) private communication; see also V. Martin, W. Sutter, H. Ringsdorf, Makromol. Chem. *177* (1976) 89...99
(7) film from CHCl$_3$ on CsI

323213   C$_7$H$_7$N–C$_7$M$_7$N   402

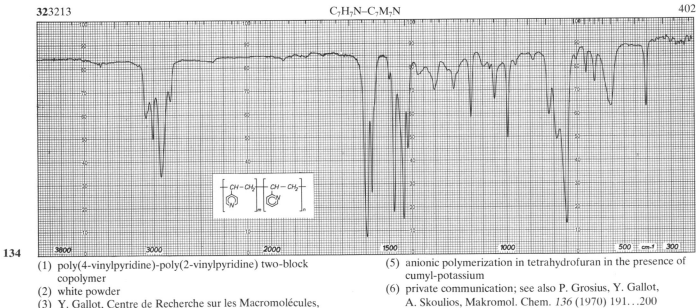
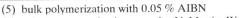

(1) poly(4-vinylpyridine)-poly(2-vinylpyridine) two-block copolymer
(2) white powder
(3) Y. Gallot, Centre de Recherche sur les Macromolécules, Strasbourg
(4) M(2-PVP): 11500, M(4-PVP): 4500

(5) anionic polymerization in tetrahydrofuran in the presence of cumyl-potassium
(6) private communication; see also P. Grosius, Y. Gallot, A. Skoulios, Makromol. Chem. *136* (1970) 191...200
(7) film from CHCl$_3$ on CsI

323213   C$_7$H$_8$BrN   403

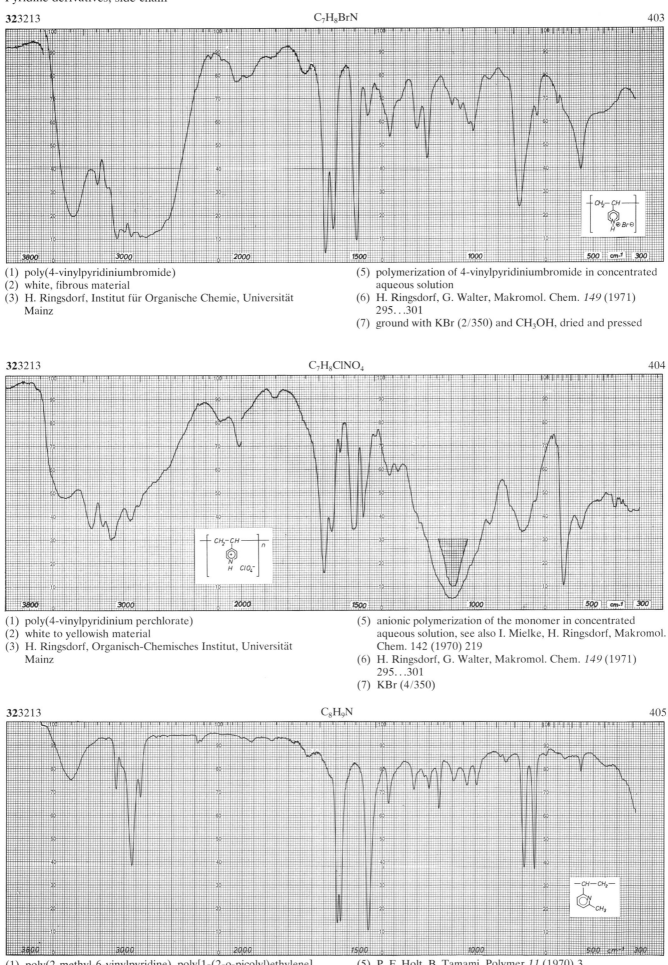

(1) poly(4-vinylpyridiniumbromide)
(2) white, fibrous material
(3) H. Ringsdorf, Institut für Organische Chemie, Universität
    Mainz

(5) polymerization of 4-vinylpyridiniumbromide in concentrated
    aqueous solution
(6) H. Ringsdorf, G. Walter, Makromol. Chem. *149* (1971)
    295...301
(7) ground with KBr (2/350) and CH$_3$OH, dried and pressed

323213   C$_7$H$_8$ClNO$_4$ 404

(1) poly(4-vinylpyridinium perchlorate)
(2) white to yellowish material
(3) H. Ringsdorf, Organisch-Chemisches Institut, Universität
    Mainz

(5) anionic polymerization of the monomer in concentrated
    aqueous solution, see also I. Mielke, H. Ringsdorf, Makromol.
    Chem. 142 (1970) 219
(6) H. Ringsdorf, G. Walter, Makromol. Chem. *149* (1971)
    295...301
(7) KBr (4/350)

323213   C$_8$H$_9$N   405

(1) poly(2-methyl-6-vinylpyridine), poly[1-(2-o-picolyl)ethylene]
(2) white powder
(3) P. Holt, Department of Chemistry, University of Reading,
    Berks.

(5) P. F. Holt, B. Tamami, Polymer *11* (1970) 3
(7) KBr (1/350)

135

323213 $C_8H_{10}IN$ 406

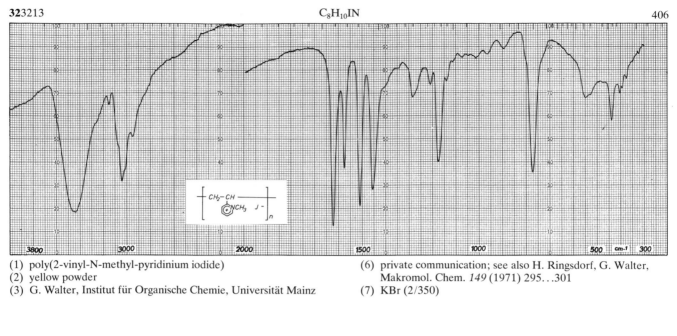

(1) poly(2-vinyl-N-methyl-pyridinium iodide)
(2) yellow powder
(3) G. Walter, Institut für Organische Chemie, Universität Mainz

(6) private communication; see also H. Ringsdorf, G. Walter, Makromol. Chem. *149* (1971) 295...301
(7) KBr (2/350)

323213 $C_{10}H_{15}NO_4S$ 407

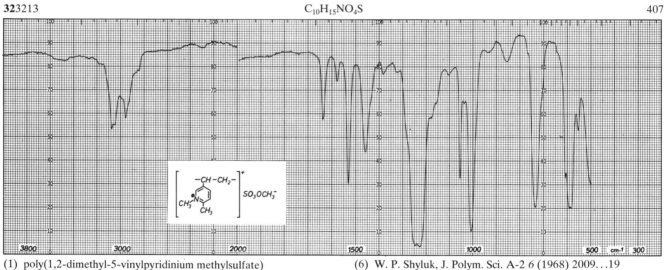

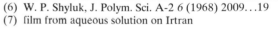

(1) poly(1,2-dimethyl-5-vinylpyridinium methylsulfate)
(2) colourless material
(3) W. P. Shyluk, Hercules Inc., Wilmington, Dela.

(6) W. P. Shyluk, J. Polym. Sci. A-2 *6* (1968) 2009...19
(7) film from aqueous solution on Irtran

323213 $C_{11}H_{17}BrN$ 408

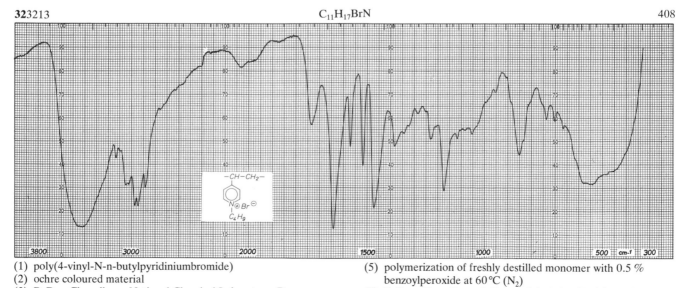

(1) poly(4-vinyl-N-n-butylpyridiniumbromide)
(2) ochre coloured material
(3) P. Roy-Chowdhury, National Chemical Laboratory, Poona

(5) polymerization of freshly destilled monomer with 0.5 % benzoylperoxide at 60 °C (N_2)
(6) P. Roy-Chowdhury, J. Polym. Sci. A-2 *7* (1969) 1451...9
(7) ground with KBr (4/350) and acetone, dried and pressed

323213　　　　　　　　　　　　　　　C_8H_9N　　　　　　　　　　　　　409

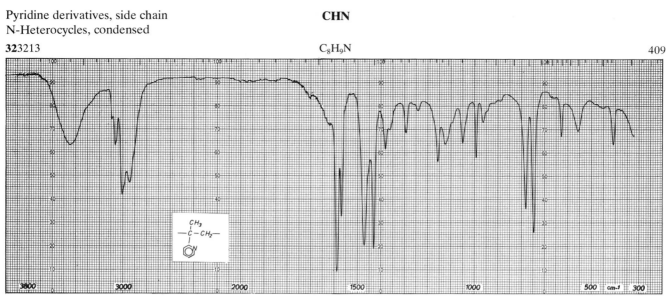

(1) poly(2-isopropenylpyridine), poly[1-methyl-1
　　1-(2-pyridyl)ethylene]
(2) eggshell-coloured powder
(3) P. F. Holt, Department of Chemistry, University of Reading,
　　Berks.

(5) P. F. Holt, B. Tamami, Polymer *11* (1970) 3
(7) KBr (1.5/350)

3241111　　　　　　　　　　　　　$C_{17}H_{14}N_4$　　　　　　　　　　410

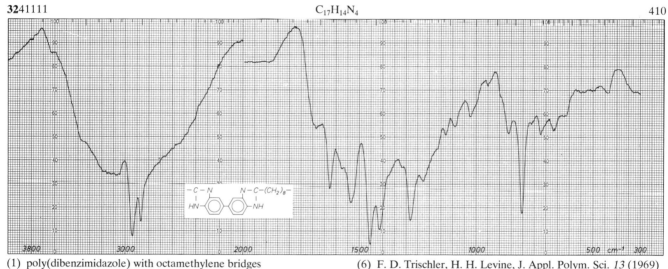

(1) poly(dibenzimidazole) with octamethylene bridges
(2) dark-brown brittle material
(3) F. D. Trischler, Narmco Research & Development Division,
　　Whittaker Corp., Santiago, Ca.
(5) F. D. Trischler, K. J. Kyoller, H. H. Levine, J. Appl. Polym.
　　Sci. *11* (1967) 1325

(6) F. D. Trischler, H. H. Levine, J. Appl. Polym. Sci. *13* (1969)
　　101...6
(7) KBr (2/350), ordinate expanded
(8) partly hydrolyzed

3241111　　　　　　　　　　　　　$C_{20}H_{12}N_4$　　　　　　　　　　411

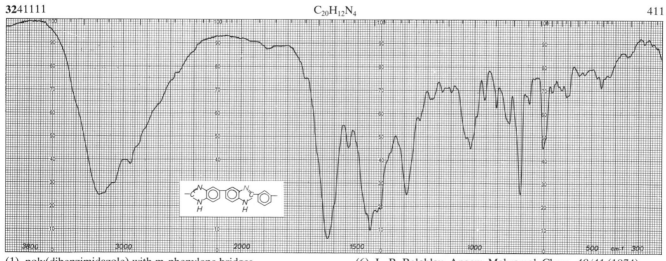

(1) poly(dibenzimidazole) with m-phenylene bridges
(2) brown, glassy fiber
(3) L. R. Belohlav, Celanese Research Comp., Summit, N. J.
(5) polycondensation of isophthalic diphenylester with
　　3,4,3′,4′-tetraaminodiphenyl; see H. A. Vogel, C. S. Marvel,
　　J. Polym. Sci. *50* (1961) 511

(6) L. R. Belohlav, Angew. Makromol. Chem. *40/41* (1974)
　　465...83
(7) film from dimethylacetamide solution of the fiber on CsI

3241112   C_{34}H_{20}N_4   412

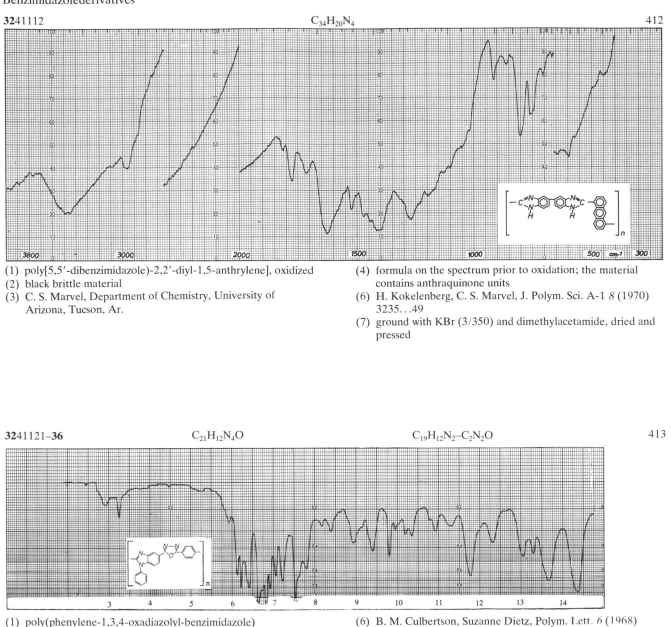

(1) poly[5,5'-dibenzimidazole)-2,2'-diyl-1,5-anthrylene], oxidized
(2) black brittle material
(3) C. S. Marvel, Department of Chemistry, University of Arizona, Tucson, Ar.

(4) formula on the spectrum prior to oxidation; the material contains anthraquinone units
(6) H. Kokelenberg, C. S. Marvel, J. Polym. Sci. A-1 *8* (1970) 3235...49
(7) ground with KBr (3/350) and dimethylacetamide, dried and pressed

---

3241121–**36**   C_{21}H_{12}N_4O   C_{19}H_{12}N_2–C_2N_2O   413

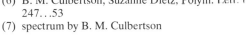

(1) poly(phenylene-1,3,4-oxadiazolyl-benzimidazole)
(3) B. M. Culbertson, Ashland Chemical Comp., Minneapolis Research Center, Minneapolis, Minn.
(5) polycondensation of 3-amino-4-anilinobenzoyl hydrazide with terephthaloyl chloride, cyclization of the polyhydrazide by heating at 300 °C i. v. (2 h)

(6) B. M. Culbertson, Suzanne Dietz, Polym. Lett. *6* (1968) 247...53
(7) spectrum by B. M. Culbertson

3241121   C_{28}H_{16}N_4   414

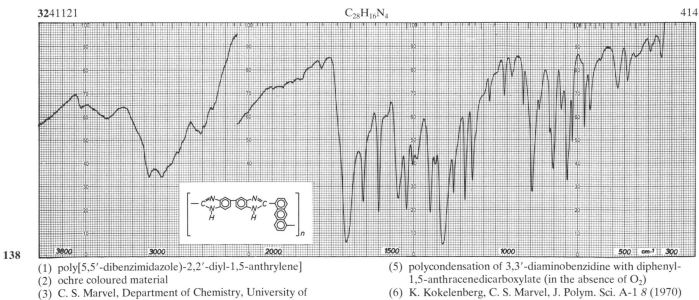

(1) poly[5,5'-dibenzimidazole)-2,2'-diyl-1,5-anthrylene]
(2) ochre coloured material
(3) C. S. Marvel, Department of Chemistry, University of Arizona, Tucson, Ar.

(5) polycondensation of 3,3'-diaminobenzidine with diphenyl-1,5-anthracenedicarboxylate (in the absence of O_2)
(6) K. Kokelenberg, C. S. Marvel, J. Polym. Sci. A-1 *8* (1970) 3235...49
(7) KBr (1.5/350)

$C_{28}H_{16}N_4$
415

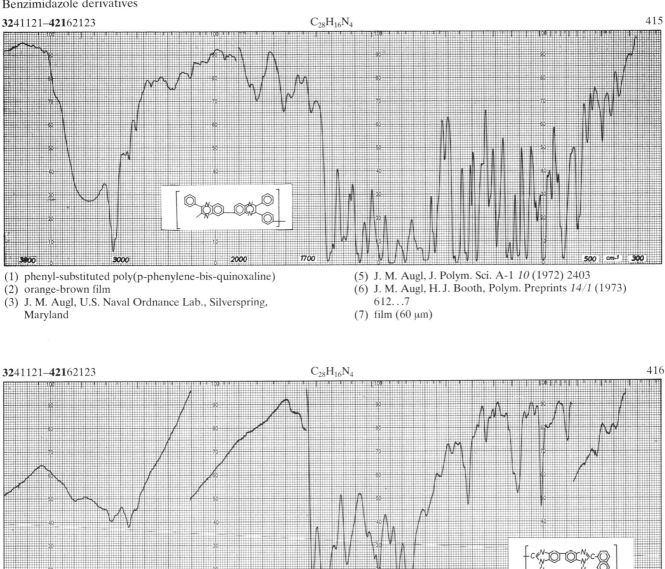

(1) phenyl-substituted poly(p-phenylene-bis-quinoxaline)
(2) orange-brown film
(3) J. M. Augl, U.S. Naval Ordnance Lab., Silverspring, Maryland

(5) J. M. Augl, J. Polym. Sci. A-1 *10* (1972) 2403
(6) J. M. Augl, H. J. Booth, Polym. Preprints *14/1* (1973) 612...7
(7) film (60 μm)

$C_{28}H_{16}N_4$
416

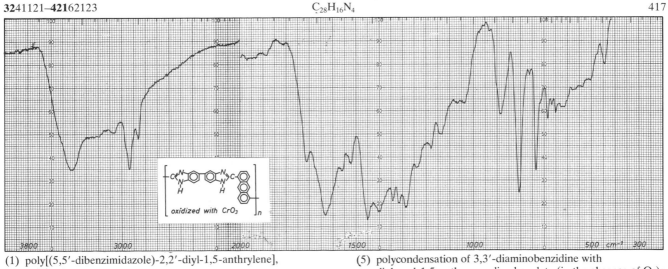

(1) poly[(5,5'-dibenzimidazole)-2,2'-diyl-1,5-anthrylene], oxidized and partly nitrated with HNO_3
(2) black coarse material
(3) C. S. Marvel, Department of Chemistry, University of Arizona, Tucson, Ar.
(4) formula in the spectrum prior to oxidation

(5) polycondensation of 3,3'-diaminobenzidine with diphenyl-1,5-anthracenedicarboxylate (in the absence of O_2); oxidized with HNO_3
(6) H. Kokelenberg, C. S. Marvel, J. Polym Sci. A-1 *8* (1970) 3235...49
(7) ground with KBr (3/350) and dimethylacetamide, dried and pressed

$C_{28}H_{16}N_4$
417

(1) poly[(5,5'-dibenzimidazole)-2,2'-diyl-1,5-anthrylene], oxidized
(2) brown coarse material
(3) C. S. Marvel, Department of Chemistry, University of Arizona, Tucson, Ar.
(4) the material contains anthraquinone units; formula in the ... to oxidation

(5) polycondensation of 3,3'-diaminobenzidine with diphenyl-1,5-anthracenedicarboxylate (in the absence of O_2); oxidized with CrO_3
(6) H. Kokelenberg, C. S. Marvel, J. Polym. Sci. A-1 *8* (1970) 3235...49
(7) ground with KBr (3/400, 5/400) and dimethylacetamide, dried and pressed

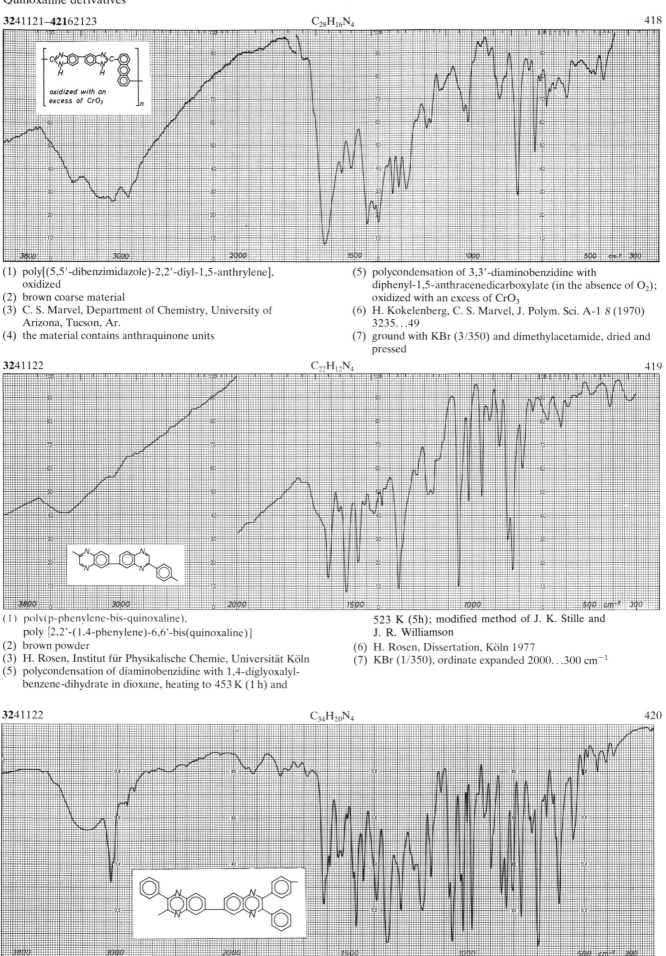

3241121–42162123   C$_{28}$H$_{16}$N$_4$ 418

(1) poly[(5,5'-dibenzimidazole)-2,2'-diyl-1,5-anthrylene], oxidized
(2) brown coarse material
(3) C. S. Marvel, Department of Chemistry, University of Arizona, Tucson, Ar.
(4) the material contains anthraquinone units

(5) polycondensation of 3,3'-diaminobenzidine with diphenyl-1,5-anthracenedicarboxylate (in the absence of O$_2$); oxidized with an excess of CrO$_3$
(6) H. Kokelenberg, C. S. Marvel, J. Polym. Sci. A-1 *8* (1970) 3235...49
(7) ground with KBr (3/350) and dimethylacetamide, dried and pressed

3241122   C$_{22}$H$_{12}$N$_4$ 419

(1) poly(p-phenylene-bis-quinoxaline),
 poly [2,2'-(1,4-phenylene)-6,6'-bis(quinoxaline)]
(2) brown powder
(3) H. Rosen, Institut für Physikalische Chemie, Universität Köln
(5) polycondensation of diaminobenzidine with 1,4-diglyoxalyl-benzene-dihydrate in dioxane, heating to 453 K (1 h) and

523 K (5h); modified method of J. K. Stille and J. R. Williamson
(6) H. Rosen, Dissertation, Köln 1977
(7) KBr (1/350), ordinate expanded 2000...300 cm^{-1}

3241122   C$_{34}$H$_{20}$N$_4$ 420

(1) poly[bis(phenylquinoxalyl)1,4-phenylene];
 poly(phenylquinoxaline)
(2) orange to brown film
(3) J. M. Augl, US Naval Ordnance Laboratory, Silver Spring, Maryland

(5) J. M. Augl, J. Polym. Sci. A-1 *10* (1972) 2403
(6) J. M. Augl, H. J. Booth, ACS Polymer Preprints *14/1* (1973) 612...7
(7) free film, thinned by scraping

32413 $C_{24}H_{10}N_6$ 421

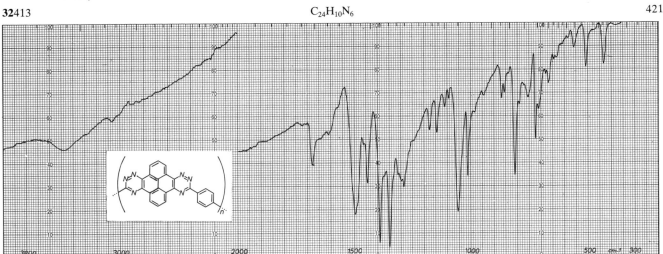

(1) poly(1,2,4-triazino[8′,9′:5,6]pyreno[4,5-e]1,2,4-tri-
     azine-3,9-diyl-1,4-phenylene)
(2) brown powder
(3) D. Wöhrle, Institut für Organische Chemie der FU Berlin/
     Universität Bremen

(5) polycyclocondensation of terephthalamidrazon with
     1,2,6,7-pyrenediquinone in, e. g., polyphosphoric acid
(6) B. Wahl, D. Wöhrle, Makromol. Chem. 176 (1975) 849...58
(7) ground with KBr (0.8/350) and CHCl₃, dried and pressed;
     ordinate expanded

3242211 $C_{14}H_{11}N$ 422

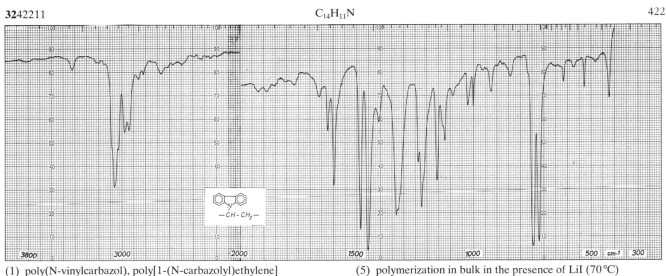

(1) poly(N-vinylcarbazol), poly[1-(N-carbazolyl)ethylene]
(2) white powder
(3) L. P. Ellinger, BP Chemicals Ltd., Epsom Division, Polymer
     Branch; Epsom, Surrey

(5) polymerization in bulk in the presence of LiI (70 °C)
(6) L. P. Ellinger, Polymer 10 (1969) 531...8

3242211 $C_{14}H_{11}N$ 423

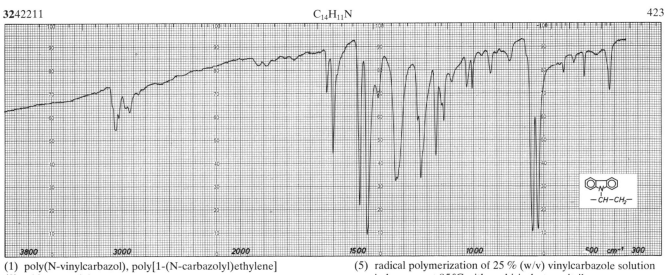

(1) poly(N-vinylcarbazol), poly[1-(N-carbazolyl)ethylene]
(2) white material
(3) G. Sitaramaiah, Research Laboratories Department, Xerox
     Corp., Rochester, N.Y.

(5) radical polymerization of 25 % (w/v) vinylcarbazole solution
     in benzene at 85 °C with azobisisobutyronitrile
(6) G. Sitaramaiah, D. Jacobs, Polymer 11 (1970) 165...76
(7) KBr (1/300)

3242211 $C_{14}H_9N$ 424

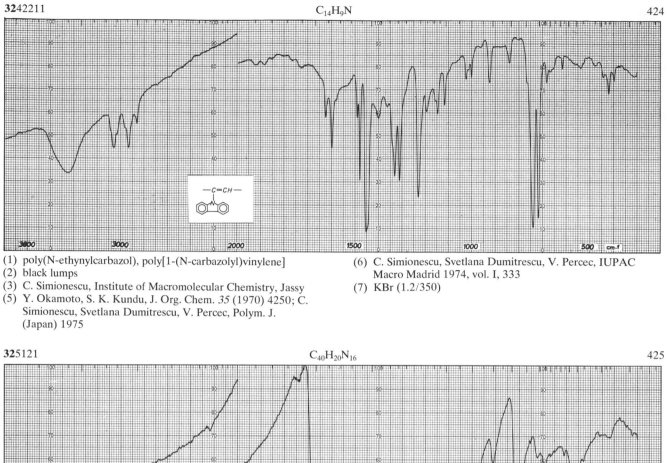

(1) poly(N-ethynylcarbazol), poly[1-(N-carbazolyl)vinylene]
(2) black lumps
(3) C. Simionescu, Institute of Macromolecular Chemistry, Jassy
(5) Y. Okamoto, S. K. Kundu, J. Org. Chem. 35 (1970) 4250; C. Simionescu, Svetlana Dumitrescu, V. Percec, Polym. J. (Japan) 1975
(6) C. Simionescu, Svetlana Dumitrescu, V. Percec, IUPAC Macro Madrid 1974, vol. I, 333
(7) KBr (1.2/350)

325121 $C_{40}H_{20}N_{16}$ 425

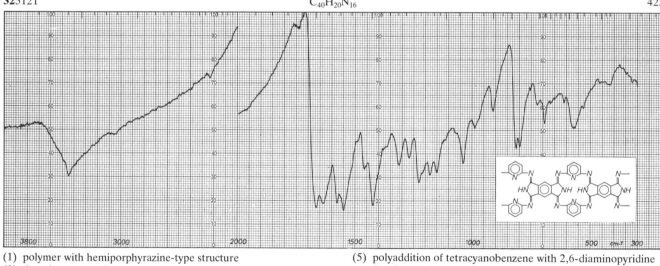

(1) polymer with hemiporphyrazine-type structure
(2) deep-brown powder
(3) G. Manecke, Fritz-Haber-Institut der Max-Planck-Gesellschaft, Berlin-Dahlem
(5) polyaddition of tetracyanobenzene with 2,6-diaminopyridine (1:2) in trichlorobenzene
(6) G. Manecke, D. Wöhrle, Makromol. Chem. 120 (1968) 192...209
(7) KBr (2/350)

331111 C_2H_4O 426

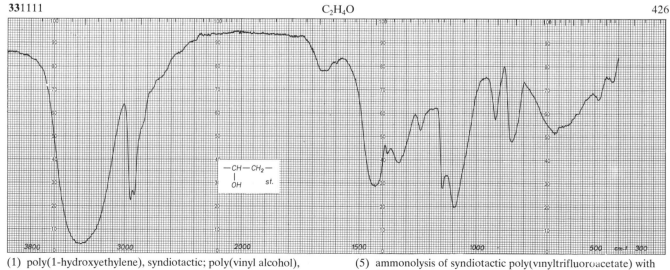

(1) poly(1-hydroxyethylene), syndiotactic; poly(vinyl alcohol), syndiotactic
(2) white, fibrous material
(3) S. Matsuzawa, Faculty of Textile Science and Technology, Shinshu University, Ueda
(5) ammonolysis of syndiotactic poly(vinyltrifluoroacetate) with diethylenetriamine
(6) private communication
(7) KBr (2/350)

331111 C_2H_4O 427

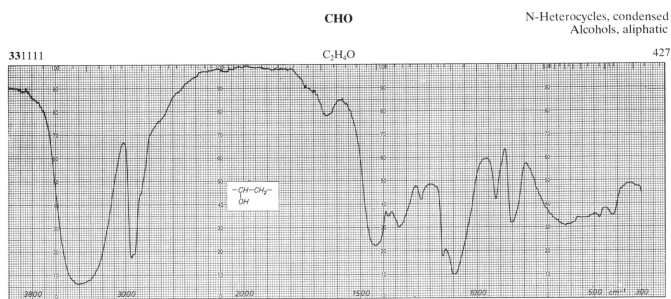

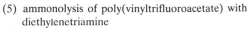

(1) poly(1-hydroxyethylene); poly(vinyl alcohol), 61%
     syndiotactic dyads
(2) white fibrous material
(3) S. Matsuzawa, Faculty of Textile Science and Technology,
     Shinshu University, Ueda

(5) ammonolysis of poly(vinyltrifluoroacetate) with
     diethylenetriamine
(6) private communication
(7) KBr (2/300)

331111 C_2H_4O 428

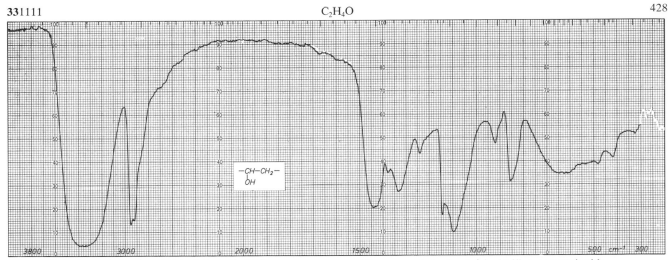

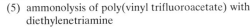

(1) poly(1-hydroxyethylene); poly(vinyl alcohol), 51%
     syndiotactic dyads
(2) white, fibrous material
(3) S. Matsuzawa, Faculty of Textile Science and Technology,
     Shinshu University, Ueda

(5) ammonolysis of poly(vinyl trifluoroacetate) with
     diethylenetriamine
(6) private communication
(7) film from H_2O

3311122 C_4H_8O 429

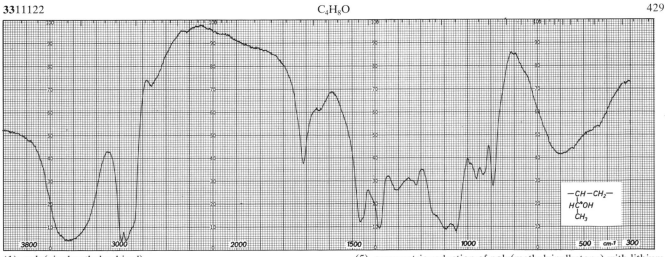

(1) poly(vinylmethylcarbinol)
(2) brown, brittle material
(3) Y. Minoura, Research Institute for Atomic Energy, Osaka
     City University, Osaka
(4) the structure on the spectrum is idealized; the material
     contains carbonyl groups

(5) asymmetric reduction of poly(methylvinylketone) with lithium
     borneoxyl aluminohydride
(6) Y. Minoura, H. Yamaguchi, J. Polym. Sci. A-1 6 (1968)
     2013...22

3311221 C_4H_8O 430

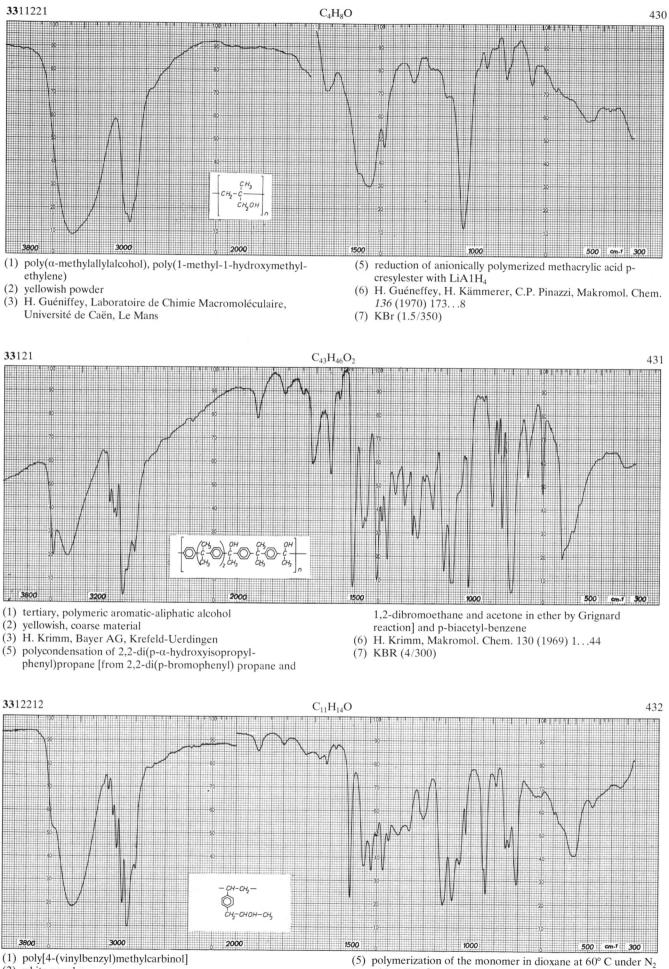

(1) poly(α-methylallylalcohol), poly(1-methyl-1-hydroxymethyl-ethylene)
(2) yellowish powder
(3) H. Guéniffey, Laboratoire de Chimie Macromoléculaire, Université de Caën, Le Mans

(5) reduction of anionically polymerized methacrylic acid p-cresylester with $LiAlH_4$
(6) H. Guéneffey, H. Kämmerer, C.P. Pinazzi, Makromol. Chem. *136* (1970) 173...8
(7) KBr (1.5/350)

33121 $C_{43}H_{46}O_2$ 431

(1) tertiary, polymeric aromatic-aliphatic alcohol
(2) yellowish, coarse material
(3) H. Krimm, Bayer AG, Krefeld-Uerdingen
(5) polycondensation of 2,2-di(p-α-hydroxyisopropyl-phenyl)propane [from 2,2-di(p-bromophenyl) propane and

1,2-dibromoethane and acetone in ether by Grignard reaction] and p-biacetyl-benzene
(6) H. Krimm, Makromol. Chem. 130 (1969) 1...44
(7) KBR (4/300)

3312212 $C_{11}H_{14}O$ 432

(1) poly[4-(vinylbenzyl)methylcarbinol]
(2) white powder
(3) K. Anda, Tokyo Metropolitan Industrial Research Institute, Tokyo

(5) polymerization of the monomer in dioxane at 60° C under N_2 with AIBN [K. Kunitomo, S. Tanimoto, R. Oda, Kogyo Kagaku Zasshi *68* (1965) 1967]
(6) K. Anda. S. Iwai, J. Polym. Sci. A-1 7 (1969) 2414...6
(7) KBr (2/300)

3312212 $C_{12}H_{16}O$ 433

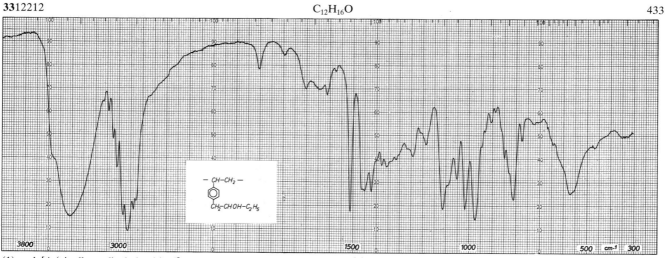

(1) poly[4-(vinylbenzyl)ethylcarbinol]
(2) white material
(3) K. Anda, Tokyo Metropolitan Industrial Research Institute, Tokyo

(5) polymerization of the monomer in dioxane at 60° C under N_2 with AIBN [K. Kunimoto, S. Tanimoto, R. Oda, Kogyo Kagaku Zasshi *68* (1965) 1967]
(6) K. Anda, S. Iwai, J. Polym. Sci. A-1 7 (1969) 2414...6
(7) KBr (3/300)

3312212–3122221 $C_{11}H_{14}O$-C_8H_7Cl 434

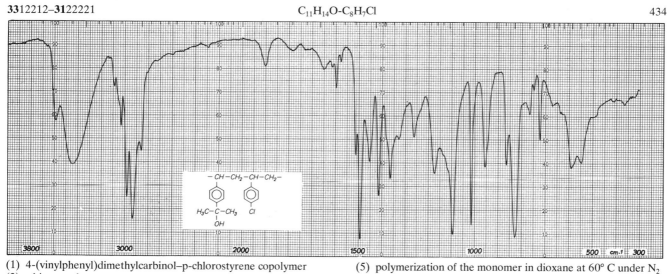

(1) 4-(vinylphenyl)dimethylcarbinol–p-chlorostyrene copolymer
(2) white powder
(3) K. Anda, Tokyo Metropolitan Industrial Research Institute, Tokyo

(5) polymerization of the monomer in dioxane at 60° C under N_2 with AIBN [K. Kunimoto, S. Tanimoto, R. Oda, Kogyo Kagaku Zasshi *68* (1965) 1967]
(6) K. Anda, S. Iwai, J. Polym. Sci. A-1 7 (1969) 2414...6
(7) KBr (3/350)

33212 C_6H_4O 435

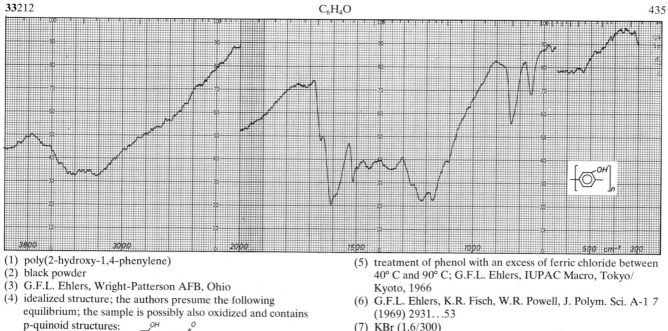

(1) poly(2-hydroxy-1,4-phenylene)
(2) black powder
(3) G.F.L. Ehlers, Wright-Patterson AFB, Ohio
(4) idealized structure; the authors presume the following equilibrium; the sample is possibly also oxidized and contains p-quinoid structures:

(5) treatment of phenol with an excess of ferric chloride between 40° C and 90° C; G.F.L. Ehlers, IUPAC Macro, Tokyo/Kyoto, 1966
(6) G.F.L. Ehlers, K.R. Fisch, W.R. Powell, J. Polym. Sci. A-1 7 (1969) 2931...53
(7) KBr (1.6/300)

33221 C$_8$H$_8$O 436

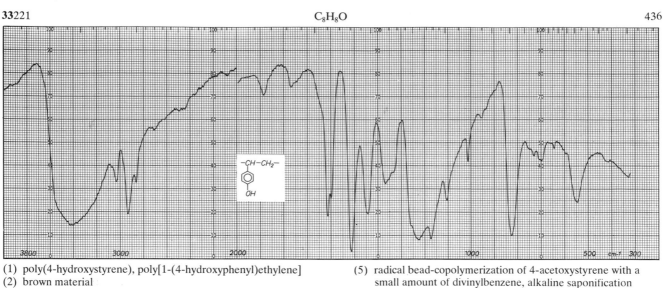

(1) poly(4-hydroxystyrene), poly[1-(4-hydroxyphenyl)ethylene]
(2) brown material
(3) E. Blasius, Institut für Analytische Chemie und Radiochemie, Universität des Saarlandes, Saarbrücken
(4) crosslinked

(5) radical bead-copolymerization of 4-acetoxystyrene with a small amount of divinylbenzene, alkaline saponification
(6) E. Blasius, W. Vallot-Burghardt, Angew. Makromol. Chem. *12* (1970) 167...74
(7) KBr (5/350)

3331111 CH$_2$O 437

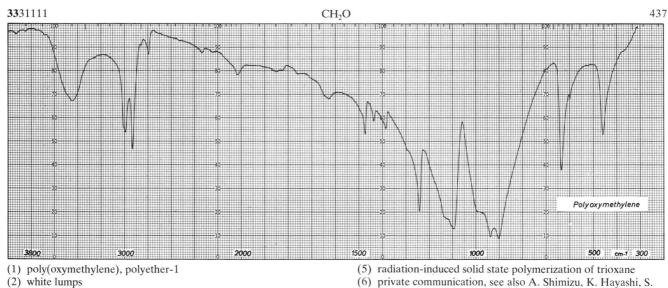

Polyoxymethylene

(1) poly(oxymethylene), polyether-1
(2) white lumps
(3) K. Hayashi, Faculty of Engineering, Hokkaido University, Sapporo
(4) –CH$_2$–O–, crystalline

(5) radiation-induced solid state polymerization of trioxane
(6) private communication, see also A. Shimizu, K. Hayashi, S. Okamura, J. Macromol. Sci., *A 1* (1967) 569...79
(7) KBr (4/1000)

3331111 CH$_2$O 438

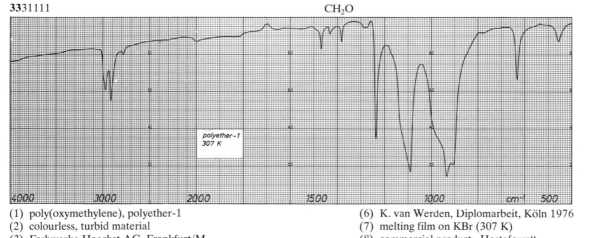

*polyether-1
307 K*

(1) poly(oxymethylene), polyether-1
(2) colourless, turbid material
(3) Farbwerke Hoechst AG, Frankfurt/M.

(6) K. van Werden, Diplomarbeit, Köln 1976
(7) melting film on KBr (307 K)
(8) commercial product „Hostaform"

3331111 CH_2O 439

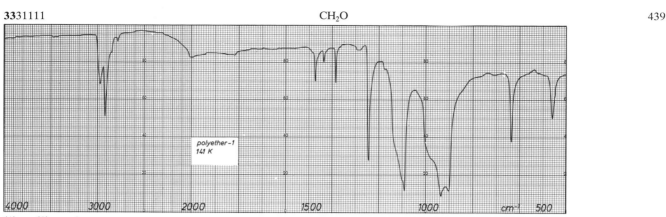

polyether-1
141 K

(1) ...(3) see above
(7) melting film on KBr (141 K)

3331111 $CH_2O-C_2H_4O$ 440

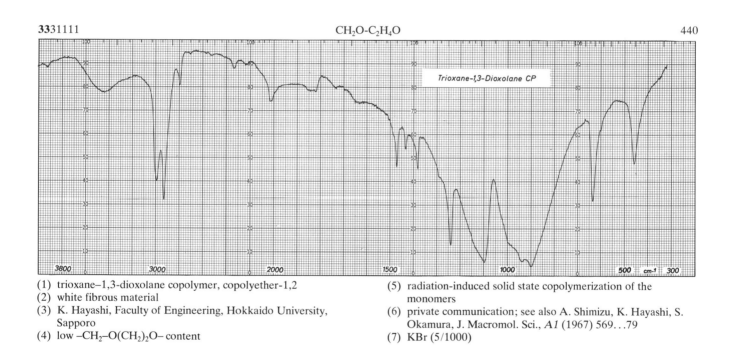

Trioxane-1,3-Dioxolane CP

(1) trioxane–1,3-dioxolane copolymer, copolyether-1,2
(2) white fibrous material
(3) K. Hayashi, Faculty of Engineering, Hokkaido University, Sapporo
(4) low –CH_2–$O(CH_2)_2O$– content

(5) radiation-induced solid state copolymerization of the monomers
(6) private communication; see also A. Shimizu, K. Hayashi, S. Okamura, J. Macromol. Sci., *A1* (1967) 569...79
(7) KBr (5/1000)

3331111 $CH_2O–C_2H_4O$ 441

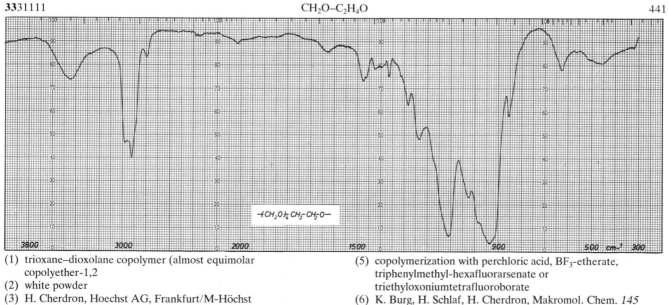

–$(CH_2O)_x$ CH_2–CH_2–O–

(1) trioxane–dioxolane copolymer (almost equimolar copolyether-1,2
(2) white powder
(3) H. Cherdron, Hoechst AG, Frankfurt/M-Höchst

(5) copolymerization with perchloric acid, BF_3-etherate, triphenylmethyl-hexafluorarsenate or triethyloxoniumtetrafluoroborate
(6) K. Burg, H. Schlaf, H. Cherdron, Makromol. Chem. *145* (1971) 247...58
(7) KBr (1/300)

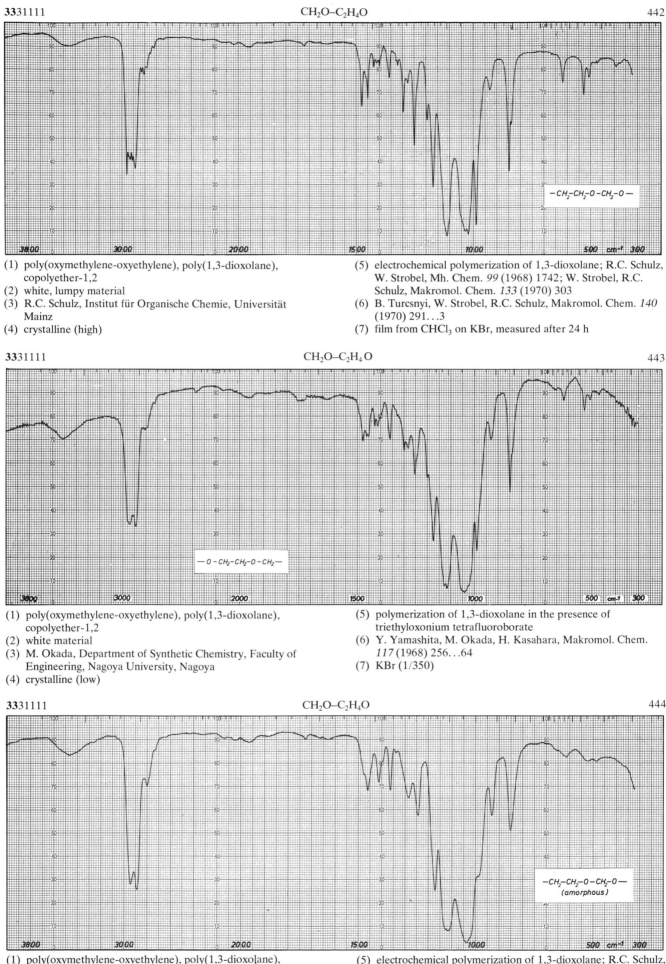

$-CH_2-CH_2-O-CH_2-O-$

(1) poly(oxymethylene-oxyethylene), poly(1,3-dioxolane), copolyether-1,2
(2) white, lumpy material
(3) R.C. Schulz, Institut für Organische Chemie, Universität Mainz
(4) crystalline (high)

(5) electrochemical polymerization of 1,3-dioxolane; R.C. Schulz, W. Strobel, Mh. Chem. *99* (1968) 1742; W. Strobel, R.C. Schulz, Makromol. Chem. *133* (1970) 303
(6) B. Turcsnyi, W. Strobel, R.C. Schulz, Makromol. Chem. *140* (1970) 291...3
(7) film from CHCl₃ on KBr, measured after 24 h

$-O-CH_2-CH_2-O-CH_2-$

(1) poly(oxymethylene-oxyethylene), poly(1,3-dioxolane), copolyether-1,2
(2) white material
(3) M. Okada, Department of Synthetic Chemistry, Faculty of Engineering, Nagoya University, Nagoya
(4) crystalline (low)

(5) polymerization of 1,3-dioxolane in the presence of triethyloxonium tetrafluoroborate
(6) Y. Yamashita, M. Okada, H. Kasahara, Makromol. Chem. *117* (1968) 256...64
(7) KBr (1/350)

$-CH_2-CH_2-O-CH_2-O-$
(amorphous)

(1) poly(oxymethylene-oxyethylene), poly(1,3-dioxolane), copolyether-1,2
(2) white, lumpy material
(3) R.C. Schulz, Institut für Organische Chemie, Universität Mainz
(4) amorphous

(5) electrochemical polymerization of 1,3-dioxolane; R.C. Schulz, W. Strobel, Monatsh. der Chem. *99* (1968) 1742; W. Strobel, R.C. Schulz, Makromol. Chem. *133* (1970) 303
(6) B. Turcsányi, W. Strobel, R.C. Schulz, Makromol. Chem. *140* (1970) 291...3
(7) film from CHCl₃ on KBr, measured immediately after removal of CHCl₃

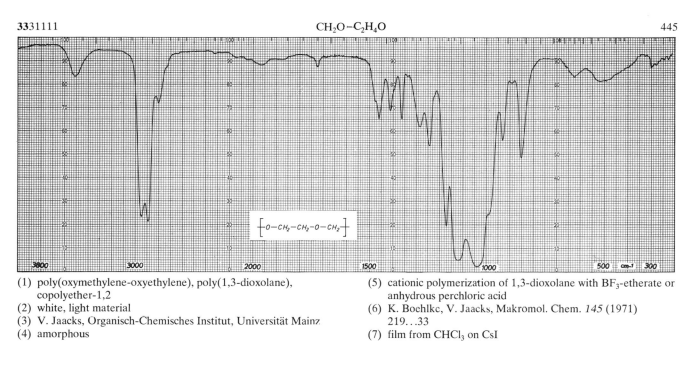

$$\left[-O-CH_2-CH_2-O-CH_2-\right]$$

(1) poly(oxymethylene-oxyethylene), poly(1,3-dioxolane), copolyether-1,2
(2) white, light material
(3) V. Jaacks, Organisch-Chemisches Institut, Universität Mainz
(4) amorphous

(5) cationic polymerization of 1,3-dioxolane with BF₃-etherate or anhydrous perchloric acid
(6) K. Boehlke, V. Jaacks, Makromol. Chem. *145* (1971) 219...33
(7) film from CHCl₃ on CsI

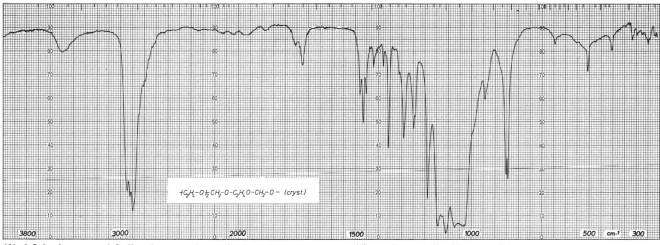

$$\left(C_2H_4-O\right)_2\, CH_2-O-C_2H_4\, O-CH_2-O-\ (cryst.)$$

(1) 1,3,6-trioxocane–1,3-dioxolane copolymer (with 67.3 mol % monomer units from trioxocane); copolyether-1,2
(2) white lumps
(3) R.C. Schulz, Institut für Organische Chemie, Universität Mainz

(4) partly crystallized by annealing
(5) electrochemical copolymerization (under N₂); R.C. Schulz, W. Strobel, Monatsh. Chem. *99* (1968) 1742
(6) D. Fleischer, R.C. Schulz, Makromol. Chem. *162* (1972) 103...11
(7) film from CHCl₃ on CsI

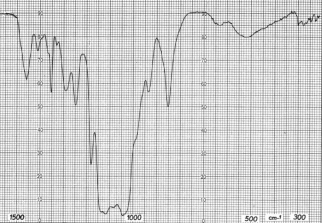

$$\left(C_2H_4-O\right)_2\, CH_2-O-C_2H_4\, O-CH_2-O-\ (amorphous)$$

(1) 1,3,6-trioxocane–1,3-dioxolane copolymer (with 67.3 mol % monomer units from trioxocane); copolyether-1,2
(2) white lumps
(3) R.C. Schulz, Institut für Organische Chemie, Universität Mainz
(4) almost statistical distribution of the sequences from the two monomers; amorphous

(5) electrochemical copolymerization (under N₂); R.C. Schulz, W. Strobel, Monatsh. Chem. *99* (1968) 1742
(6) D. Fleischer, R.C. Schulz, Makromol. Chem. *162* (1972) 103...11
(7) film from CHCl₃ on CsI

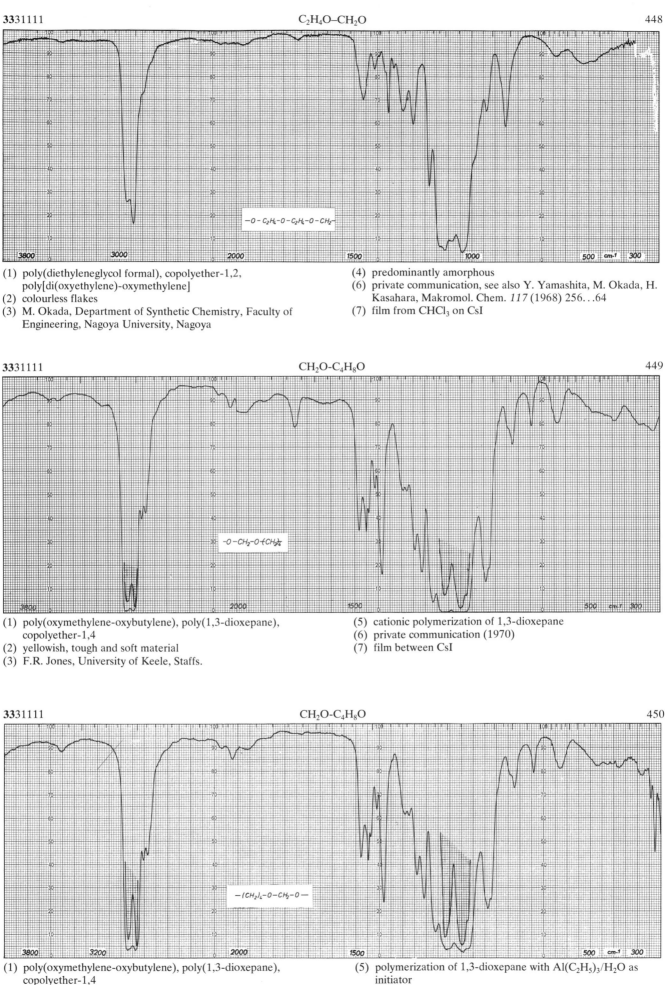

3331111 C₂H₄O–CH₂O 448

$-O-C_2H_4-O-C_2H_4-O-CH_2-$

(1) poly(diethyleneglycol formal), copolyether-1,2,
poly[di(oxyethylene)-oxymethylene]
(2) colourless flakes
(3) M. Okada, Department of Synthetic Chemistry, Faculty of
Engineering, Nagoya University, Nagoya

(4) predominantly amorphous
(6) private communication, see also Y. Yamashita, M. Okada, H.
Kasahara, Makromol. Chem. *117* (1968) 256...64
(7) film from CHCl₃ on CsI

3331111 CH₂O-C₄H₈O 449

$-O-CH_2-O-(CH_2)_4-$

(1) poly(oxymethylene-oxybutylene), poly(1,3-dioxepane),
copolyether-1,4
(2) yellowish, tough and soft material
(3) F.R. Jones, University of Keele, Staffs.

(5) cationic polymerization of 1,3-dioxepane
(6) private communication (1970)
(7) film between CsI

3331111 CH₂O-C₄H₈O 450

$-(CH_2)_4-O-CH_2-O-$

(1) poly(oxymethylene-oxybutylene), poly(1,3-dioxepane),
copolyether-1,4
(2) colourless, transparent, soft material
(3) D. Donescu, Institute of Macromolecular Chemistry,
Bukuresti

(5) polymerization of 1,3-dioxepane with Al(C₂H₅)₃/H₂O as
initiator
(6) D. Donescu, Makromol. Chem. *175* (1974) 2355...63
(7) film between CsI
(8) absorptions between 250 and 200 cm⁻¹ due to water vapor

3331112 C_2H_4O 451

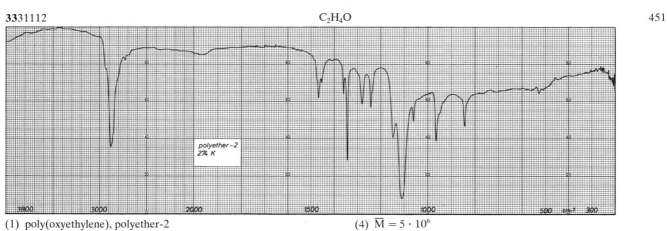

(1) poly(oxyethylene), polyether-2
(2) colourless material
(3) commercial product; BDM Chemicals Ltd., Pool, Engl.

(4) $\overline{M} = 5 \cdot 10^6$
(6) K. van Werden, Diplomarbeit, Köln 1976
(7) recrystallized melting film on KBr (274 K)

3331112 C_2H_4O 452

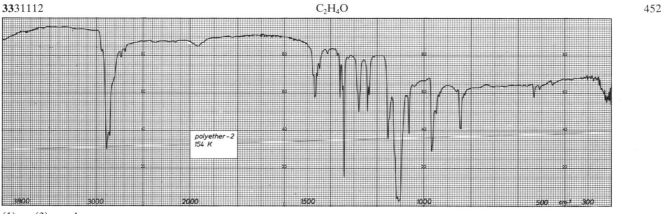

(1) ...(3) see above
(7) recrystallized melting film (154 K)

3331112 C_2H_4O 453

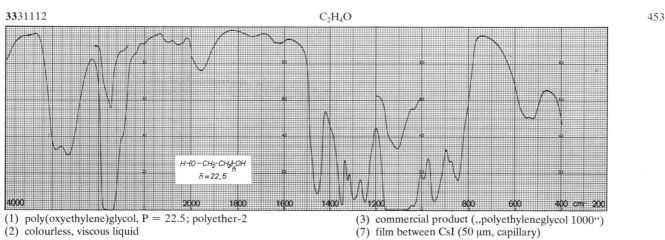

(1) poly(oxyethylene)glycol, P = 22.5; polyether-2
(2) colourless, viscous liquid

(3) commercial product (,,polyethyleneglycol 1000")
(7) film between CsI (50 μm, capillary)

3331112–2122131   C$_2$H$_4$O-C$_9$H$_{10}$ 454

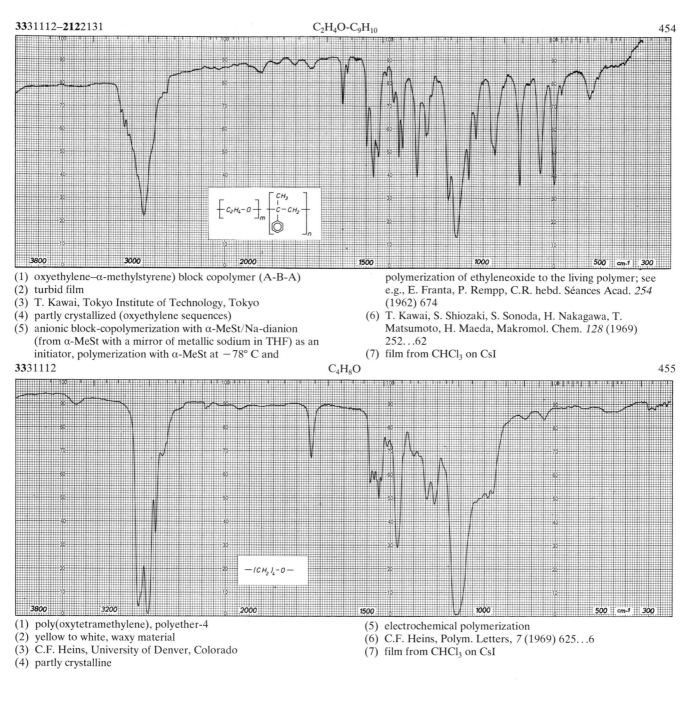

(1) oxyethylene–α-methylstyrene) block copolymer (A-B-A)
(2) turbid film
(3) T. Kawai, Tokyo Institute of Technology, Tokyo
(4) partly crystallized (oxyethylene sequences)
(5) anionic block-copolymerization with α-MeSt/Na-dianion (from α-MeSt with a mirror of metallic sodium in THF) as an initiator, polymerization with α-MeSt at −78° C and

polymerization of ethyleneoxide to the living polymer; see e.g., E. Franta, P. Rempp, C.R. hebd. Séances Acad. *254* (1962) 674
(6) T. Kawai, S. Shiozaki, S. Sonoda, H. Nakagawa, T. Matsumoto, H. Maeda, Makromol. Chem. *128* (1969) 252...62
(7) film from CHCl$_3$ on CsI

3331112   C$_4$H$_8$O   455

(1) poly(oxytetramethylene), polyether-4
(2) yellow to white, waxy material
(3) C.F. Heins, University of Denver, Colorado
(4) partly crystalline

(5) electrochemical polymerization
(6) C.F. Heins, Polym. Letters, *7* (1969) 625...6
(7) film from CHCl$_3$ on CsI

3331112   C$_4$H$_8$O   456

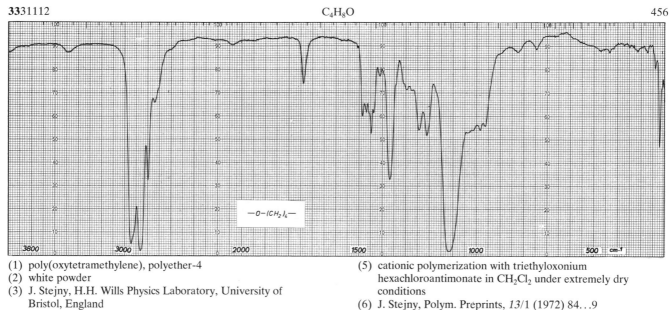

(1) poly(oxytetramethylene), polyether-4
(2) white powder
(3) J. Stejny, H.H. Wills Physics Laboratory, University of Bristol, England
(4) partly crystalline

(5) cationic polymerization with triethyloxonium hexachloroantimonate in CH$_2$Cl$_2$ under extremely dry conditions
(6) J. Stejny, Polym. Preprints, *13/1* (1972) 84...9
(7) film from CHCl$_3$ on CsI
(8) the absorptions between 250 and 200 cm^{-1} are due to H$_2$O

3331112 C_4H_8O 457

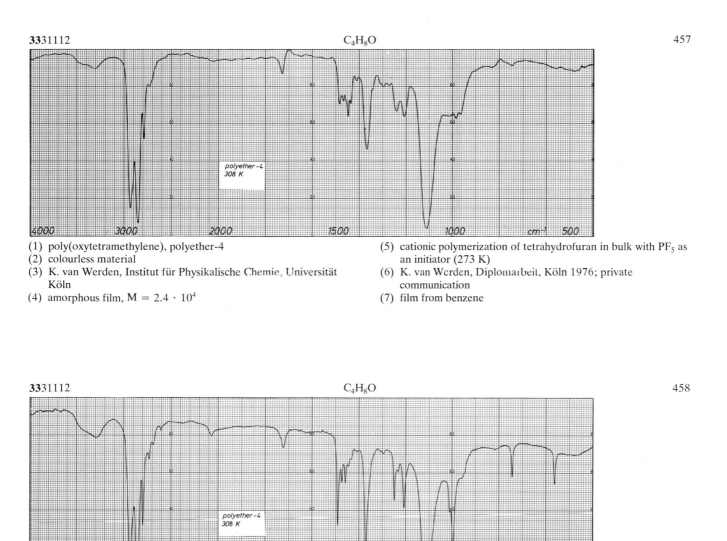

(1) poly(oxytetramethylene), polyether-4
(2) colourless material
(3) K. van Werden, Institut für Physikalische Chemie, Universität Köln
(4) amorphous film, M = 2.4 · 10^4

(5) cationic polymerization of tetrahydrofuran in bulk with PF_5 as an initiator (273 K)
(6) K. van Werden, Diplomarbeit, Köln 1976; private communication
(7) film from benzene

3331112 C_4H_8O 458

(1) ...(3) see above
(4) partly crystallized
(5) ...(7) see above

3331112 C_4H_8O 459

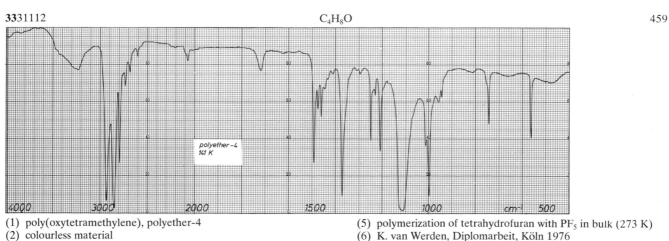

(1) poly(oxytetramethylene), polyether-4
(2) colourless material
(3) K. van Werden, Institut für Physikalische Chemie, Universität Köln

(5) polymerization of tetrahydrofuran with PF_5 in bulk (273 K)
(6) K. van Werden, Diplomarbeit, Köln 1976
(7) recrystallized melting film on KBr (141 K)

3331112 C_4H_8O 460

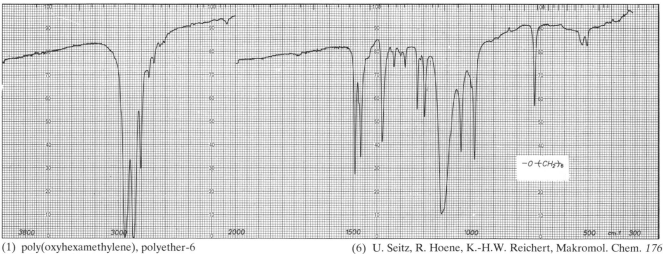

$$H{-}[O{-}(CH_2)_4]_{\bar{n}}{-}OH$$
$$\bar{n} \approx 13,6$$

(1) poly(oxytetramethylene)glycol, polyether-4
(2) colourless liquid
(3) commercial product (,,polytetramethyleneglycol 1000")
(7) film (50 μm, capillary)

3331112–**337**123 C_4H_8O-$C_{23}H_{18}O_4$ 461

(1) block copolymer from bisphenol-A-terephthalate and poly(tetramethylene oxide), approx 65% PTMO
(2) almost colourless material
(3) K. Riches, Woodstock Agric. Res. Centre, Sittingbourne, Kent
(5) end-tipping of one of the base units (alcoholic endgroups) with phosgene (thus forming bischloroformates), followed by reaction with the second block
(6) K. Riches, R.N. Haward, Polymer *9* (1968) 103...11
(7) film from $CHCl_3$ on CsI

3331112 $C_6H_{12}O$ 462

$-O{-}(CH_2)_6$

(1) poly(oxyhexamethylene), polyether-6
(2) white powder
(3) U. Seitz, Institut für Technische Chemie, Universität Stuttgart
(5) ring-opening cationic polymerization of oxepane in the presence of diethoxycarbenium-hexachloroantimonate or ethylhexamethyleneoxonium-hexachloroantimonate
(6) U. Seitz, R. Hoene, K.-H.W. Reichert, Makromol. Chem. *176* (1975) 1689...1701
(7) film from $CHCl_3$ on CsI

3331112 $C_6H_{12}O$ 463

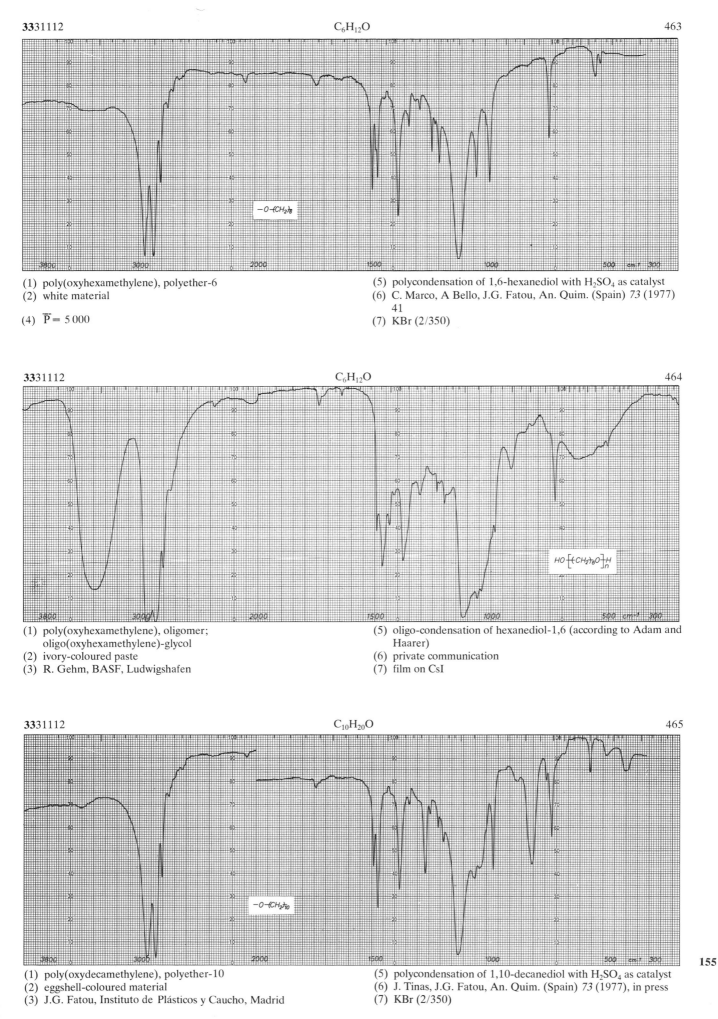

(1) poly(oxyhexamethylene), polyether-6
(2) white material

(4) $\overline{P} = 5\,000$

(5) polycondensation of 1,6-hexanediol with H_2SO_4 as catalyst
(6) C. Marco, A Bello, J.G. Fatou, An. Quim. (Spain) *73* (1977) 41
(7) KBr (2/350)

3331112 $C_6H_{12}O$ 464

(1) poly(oxyhexamethylene), oligomer; oligo(oxyhexamethylene)-glycol
(2) ivory-coloured paste
(3) R. Gehm, BASF, Ludwigshafen

(5) oligo-condensation of hexanediol-1,6 (according to Adam and Haarer)
(6) private communication
(7) film on CsI

3331112 $C_{10}H_{20}O$ 465

(1) poly(oxydecamethylene), polyether-10
(2) eggshell-coloured material
(3) J.G. Fatou, Instituto de Plásticos y Caucho, Madrid

(5) polycondensation of 1,10-decanediol with H_2SO_4 as catalyst
(6) J. Tinas, J.G. Fatou, An. Quim. (Spain) *73* (1977), in press
(7) KBr (2/350)

155

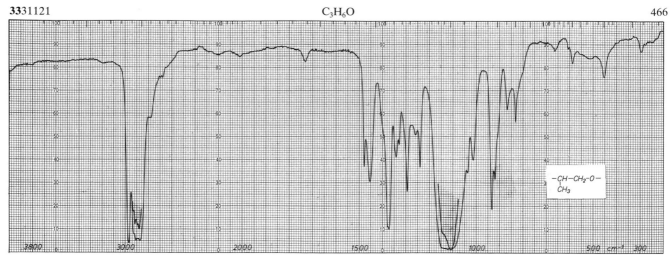

(1) poly(oxypropylene), isotactic, poly[oxy(1-methylethylene)]
(2) white material
(3) R.J. Valles, Polymer Research Branch, Picatinny Arsenal, Dover, N.J.
(5) polymerization of propylene oxide with an aluminum isopropoxide-zinc chloride catalyst system (70...80° C)
(6) R.J. Valles, Makromol. Chem. *113* (1968) 147...54
(7) film from CHCl₄ on CsI

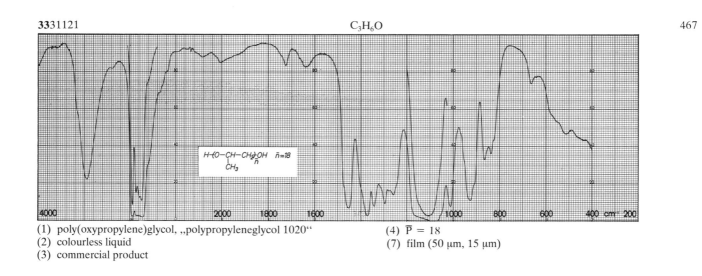

(1) poly(oxypropylene)glycol, „polypropyleneglycol 1020"
(2) colourless liquid
(3) commercial product
(4) $\overline{P} = 18$
(7) film (50 µm, 15 µm)

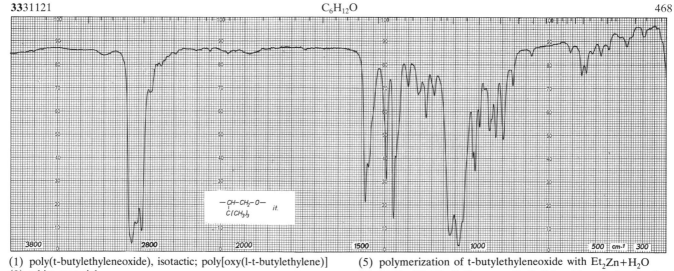

(1) poly(t-butylethyleneoxide), isotactic; poly[oxy(l-t-butylethylene)]
(2) white material
(3) N. Doddi, University of Pennsylvania, Philadelphia, Pa.
(4) crystalline
(5) polymerization of t-butylethyleneoxide with Et₂Zn+H₂O
(6) N. Doddi, W. C. Forsman, C. C. Price, Macromolecules *4* (1971) 648
(7) film from CHCl₃ on CsI

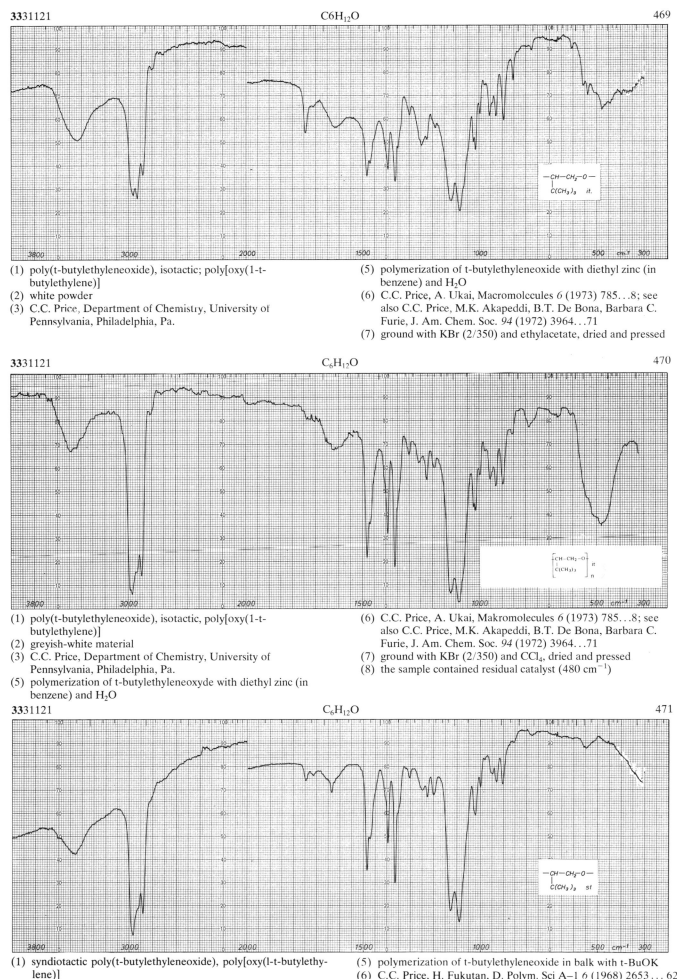

(1) poly(t-butylethyleneoxide), isotactic; poly[oxy(1-t-butylethylene)]
(2) white powder
(3) C.C. Price, Department of Chemistry, University of Pennsylvania, Philadelphia, Pa.
(5) polymerization of t-butylethyleneoxide with diethyl zinc (in benzene) and H_2O
(6) C.C. Price, A. Ukai, Macromolccules 6 (1973) 785...8; see also C.C. Price, M.K. Akapeddi, B.T. De Bona, Barbara C. Furie, J. Am. Chem. Soc. 94 (1972) 3964...71
(7) ground with KBr (2/350) and ethylacetate, dried and pressed

(1) poly(t-butylethyleneoxide), isotactic, poly[oxy(1-t-butylethylene)]
(2) greyish-white material
(3) C.C. Price, Department of Chemistry, University of Pennsylvania, Philadelphia, Pa.
(5) polymerization of t-butylethyleneoxyde with diethyl zinc (in benzene) and H_2O
(6) C.C. Price, A. Ukai, Makromolecules 6 (1973) 785...8; see also C.C. Price, M.K. Akapeddi, B.T. De Bona, Barbara C. Furie, J. Am. Chem. Soc. 94 (1972) 3964...71
(7) ground with KBr (2/350) and CCl_4, dried and pressed
(8) the sample contained residual catalyst (480 cm^{-1})

(1) syndiotactic poly(t-butylethyleneoxide), poly[oxy(l-t-butylethylene)]
(2) white powder
(3) C. C. Price, Department of Chemistry, University of Pensylvania, Philadelphia, Pa.
(5) polymerization of t-butylethyleneoxide in balk with t-BuOK
(6) C.C. Price, H. Fukutan, D. Polym. Sci A–1 6 (1968) 2653...62
(7) KBr (13/350)

3331121 $C_6H_{12}O$ 472

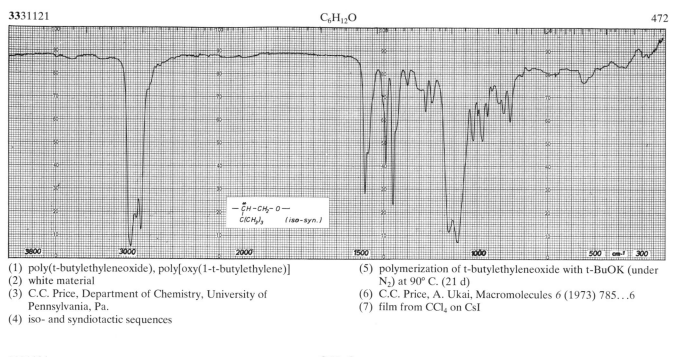

(1) poly(t-butylethyleneoxide), poly[oxy(1-t-butylethylene)]
(2) white material
(3) C.C. Price, Department of Chemistry, University of Pennsylvania, Pa.
(4) iso- and syndiotactic sequences
(5) polymerization of t-butylethyleneoxide with t-BuOK (under N_2) at 90° C. (21 d)
(6) C.C. Price, A. Ukai, Macromolecules *6* (1973) 785...6
(7) film from CCl_4 on CsI

3331121 $C_6H_{12}O$ 473

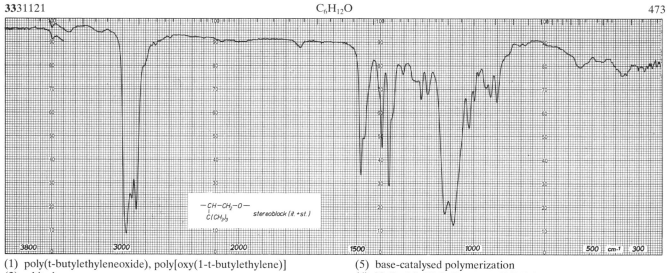

(1) poly(t-butylethyleneoxide), poly[oxy(1-t-butylethylene)]
(2) white lumps
(3) N. Doddi, University of Pennsylvania, Philadelphia, Pa.
(4) stereoblock copolymer (isotactic and syndiotactic blocks), partly crystalline
(5) base-catalysed polymerization
(6) N. Doddi, W.C. Forsman, C.C. Price, Macromolecules *4* (1971) 648
(7) film from $CHCl_3$ on CsI

3331121 C_4H_8O 474

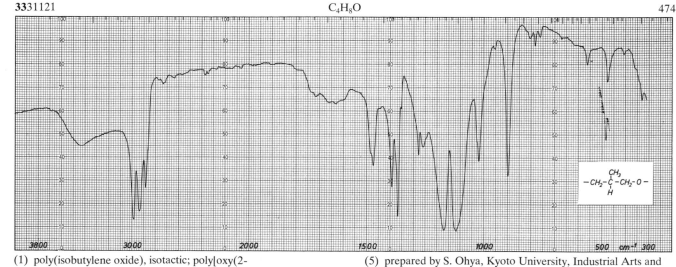

(1) poly(isobutylene oxide), isotactic; poly[oxy(2-methyl-trimethylene)]
(2) light yellow film
(3) J. Sakurada, Department of Polymer Chemistry, Kyoto University, Kyoto
(4) partly crystalline
(5) prepared by S. Ohya, Kyoto University, Industrial Arts and Textile Fibres, Kyoto
(6) K. Kaji, I. Sakurada, Makromol. Chem. *148* (1971) 261...9
(7) KBr

3331121 C_5H_{10}O 475

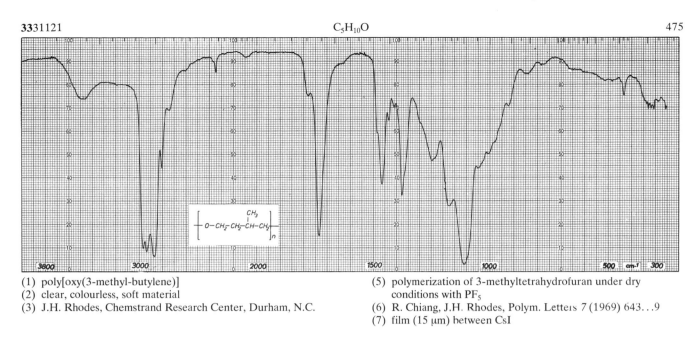

(1) poly[oxy(3-methyl-butylene)]
(2) clear, colourless, soft material
(3) J.H. Rhodes, Chemstrand Research Center, Durham, N.C.

(5) polymerization of 3-methyltetrahydrofuran under dry conditions with PF_5
(6) R. Chiang, J.H. Rhodes, Polym. Letters 7 (1969) 643...9
(7) film (15 μm) between CsI

3331121 C_4H_8O 476

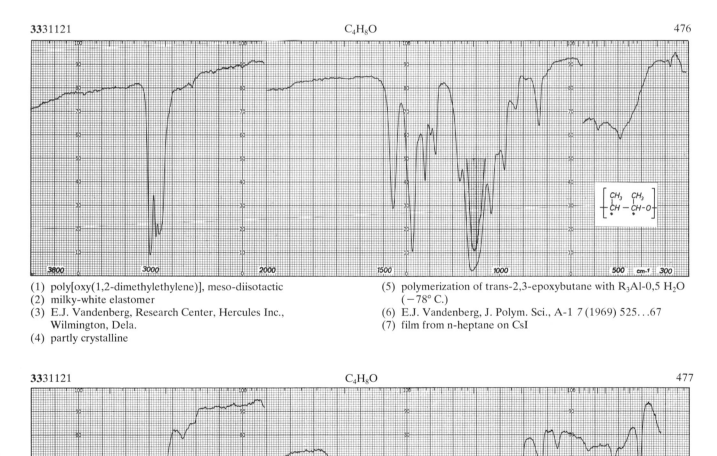

(1) poly[oxy(1,2-dimethylethylene)], meso-diisotactic
(2) milky-white elastomer
(3) E.J. Vandenberg, Research Center, Hercules Inc., Wilmington, Dela.
(4) partly crystalline

(5) polymerization of trans-2,3-epoxybutane with $R_3Al-0,5\ H_2O$ (−78° C.)
(6) E.J. Vandenberg, J. Polym. Sci., A-1 7 (1969) 525...67
(7) film from n-heptane on CsI

3331121 C_4H_8O 477

(1) poly[oxy(1,2-dimethylethylene)], racemic diisotactic
(2) white elastomer
(3) E.J. Vandenberg, Research Center, Hercules Inc., Wilmington, Dela.
(4) partly crystalline

(5) polymerization of cis-2,3-epoxybutane with $R_3Al-0,5\ H_2O-0,5$ acetylacetone (65° C.)
(6) E.J. Vandenberg, J. Polym. Sci., A-1 7 (1969) 525...67
(7) material swollen in $CHCl_3$, ground with KBr, dried and pressed

3331121 $C_8H_{16}O_2$ 478

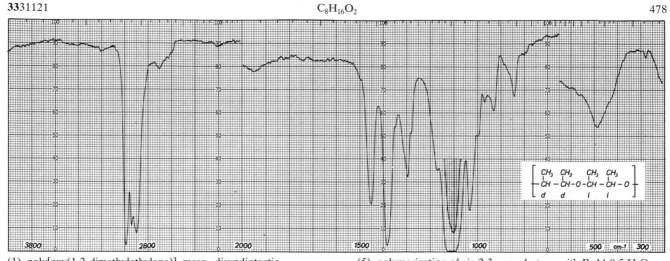

(1) poly[oxy(1,2-dimethylethylene)], meso$_2$-disyndiotactic
(2) very though, almost colourless elastomer
(3) E.J. Vandenberg, Research Center, Hercules Inc., Wilmington, Dela.
(4) predominantly amorphous
(5) polymerization of cis-2,3-epoxybutane with R$_3$Al-0.5 H$_2$O (−78 °C)
(6) E.J. Vandenberg, J. Polym. Sci., A-1 *7* (1969) 525...67
(7) film from CHCl$_3$ on CsI

3331122 $C_4H_8O_2$ 479

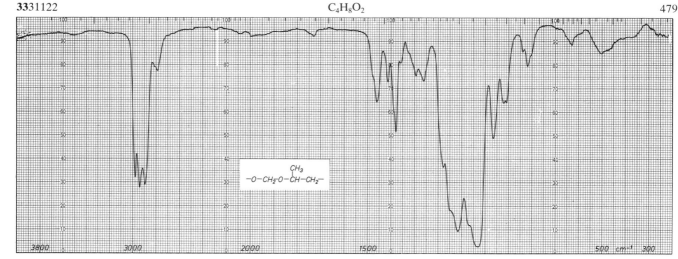

(1) poly(4-methyl-1,3-dioxapentamethylene)
(2) yellowish paste
(3) P.H. Plesch, Department of Chemistry, University of Keele, Staffs.
(5) polymerization of 4-methyl-1,3-dioxolane by anhydrous perchloric acid in methylene dichloride solution
(6) Y. Firat, P.H. Plesch, Makromol. Chem. *176* (1975) 1179...86
(7) layer between CsI

3331131 C_6H_9O 480

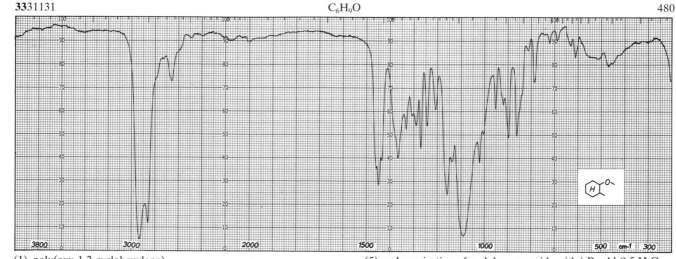

(1) poly(oxy-1,2-cyclohexylene)
(2) white material
(3) E.J. Vandenberg, Research Center, Hercules Inc., Wilmington, Dela.
(5) polymerization of cyclohexene oxide with i-Bu$_3$Al-0,5 H$_2$O
(6) E.J. Vandenberg, J. Polym. Sci., A-1 *7* (1969) 525...67
(7) film from heptane on CsI

3331131   C₆H₁₀O   481

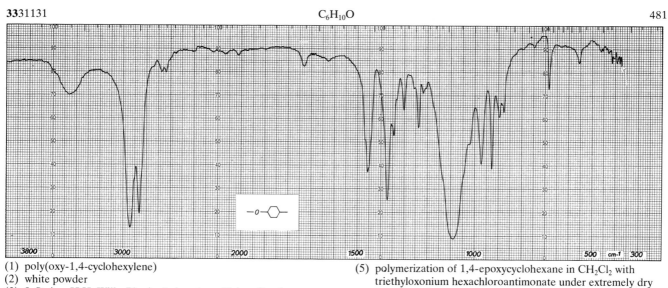

(1) poly(oxy-1,4-cyclohexylene)
(2) white powder
(3) J. Stejny, H.H. Wills, Physics Laboratory, University of
    Bristol, England
(4) crystalline

(5) polymerization of 1,4-epoxycyclohexane in CH₂Cl₂ with
    triethyloxonium hexachloroantimonate under extremely dry
    conditions (at low temperatures, e.g. −15° C.)
(6) J. Stejny, J. Macromol. Sci.-Chem. A-7 (1973) 1435...54
(7) KBr (1.8/350)

3331131   C₇H₁₂O   482

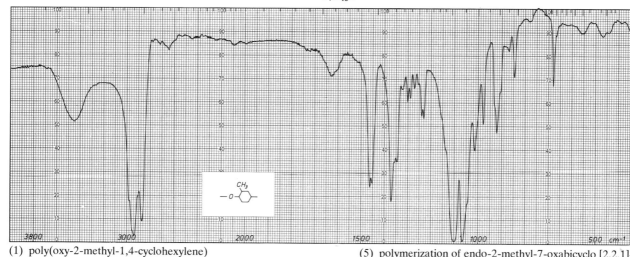

(1) poly(oxy-2-methyl-1,4-cyclohexylene)
(2) white powder
(3) F. Andruzzi, Istituto di Chimica Industriale ed Applicata,
    Università di Pisa, Pisa

(5) polymerization of endo-2-methyl-7-oxabicyclo [2.2.1]-
    heptane in CH₂Cl₂ with PF₅
(6) F. Andruzzi, D.S. Barnes, P.H. Plesch, Makromol. Chem. 176
    (1975) 2053...7
(7) KBr (2/350)

3331131   C₈H₁₄P₂   483

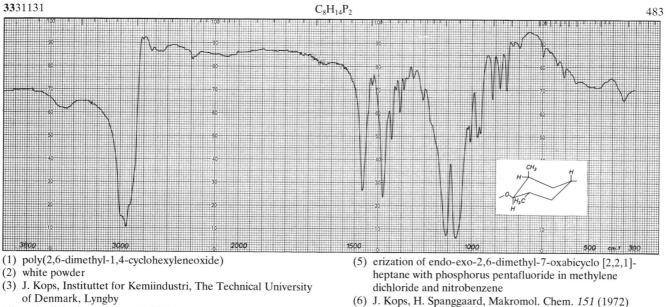

(1) poly(2,6-dimethyl-1,4-cyclohexyleneoxide)
(2) white powder
(3) J. Kops, Instituttet for Kemiindustri, The Technical University
    of Denmark, Lyngby
(4) cycloaliphatic analogue of „PPO"

(5) erization of endo-exo-2,6-dimethyl-7-oxabicyclo [2,2,1]-
    heptane with phosphorus pentafluoride in methylene
    dichloride and nitrobenzene
(6) J. Kops, H. Spanggaard, Makromol. Chem. 151 (1972)
    21...32
(7) KBr (4/1000)

3331131 $C_8H_{14}O$ 484

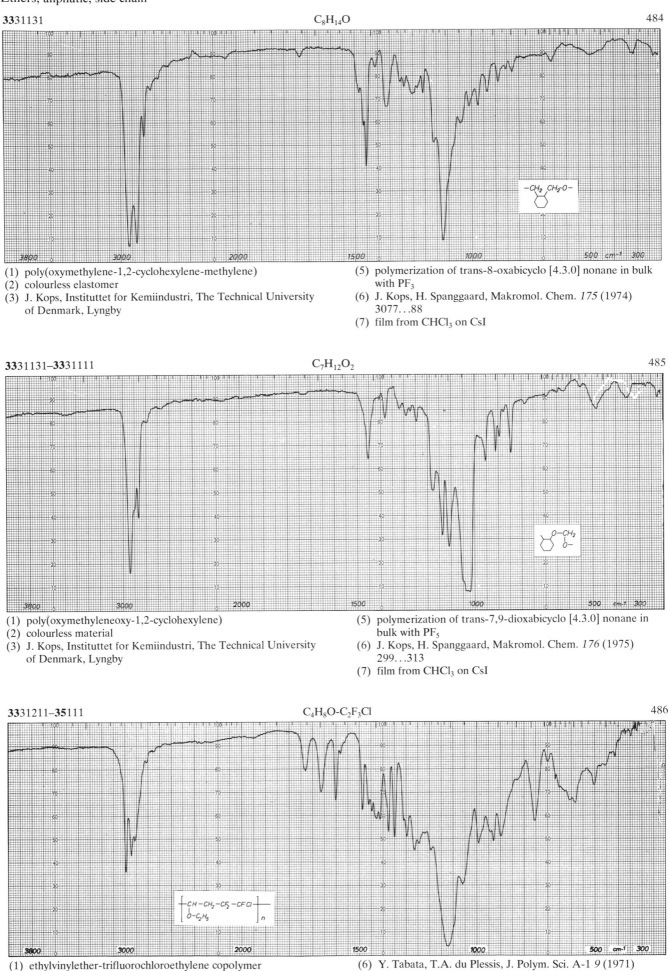

(1) poly(oxymethylene-1,2-cyclohexylene-methylene)
(2) colourless elastomer
(3) J. Kops, Instituttet for Kemiindustri, The Technical University of Denmark, Lyngby
(5) polymerization of trans-8-oxabicyclo [4.3.0] nonane in bulk with PF_3
(6) J. Kops, H. Spanggaard, Makromol. Chem. *175* (1974) 3077...88
(7) film from $CHCl_3$ on CsI

3331131–3331111 $C_7H_{12}O_2$ 485

(1) poly(oxymethyleneoxy-1,2-cyclohexylene)
(2) colourless material
(3) J. Kops, Instituttet for Kemiindustri, The Technical University of Denmark, Lyngby
(5) polymerization of trans-7,9-dioxabicyclo [4.3.0] nonane in bulk with PF_5
(6) J. Kops, H. Spanggaard, Makromol. Chem. *176* (1975) 299...313
(7) film from $CHCl_3$ on CsI

3331211–35111 C_4H_8O-C_2F_3Cl 486

(1) ethylvinylether-trifluorochloroethylene copolymer
(2) colourless elastomer
(3) T.A. du Plessis, Atomic Energy Board, Pretoria
(5) γ-radiation initiated copolymerization
(6) Y. Tabata, T.A. du Plessis, J. Polym. Sci. A-1 *9* (1971) 3425...35; see also T.A. du Plessis, A.C. Thomas, J. Polym. Sci.-Polym. Chem. Ed. *11* (1973) 2681...90
(7) film from $CHCl_3$ on CsI

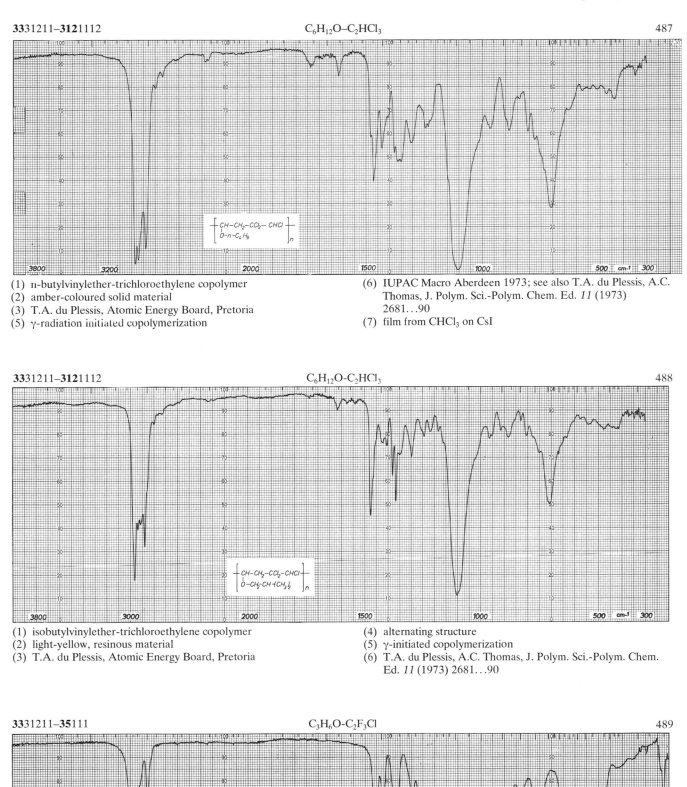

3331211–3121112 $C_6H_{12}O–C_2HCl_3$ 487

(1) n-butylvinylether-trichloroethylene copolymer
(2) amber-coloured solid material
(3) T.A. du Plessis, Atomic Energy Board, Pretoria
(5) γ-radiation initiated copolymerization
(6) IUPAC Macro Aberdeen 1973; see also T.A. du Plessis, A.C. Thomas, J. Polym. Sci.-Polym. Chem. Ed. *11* (1973) 2681...90
(7) film from $CHCl_3$ on CsI

3331211–3121112 $C_6H_{12}O–C_2HCl_3$ 488

(1) isobutylvinylether-trichloroethylene copolymer
(2) light-yellow, resinous material
(3) T.A. du Plessis, Atomic Energy Board, Pretoria
(4) alternating structure
(5) γ-initiated copolymerization
(6) T.A. du Plessis, A.C. Thomas, J. Polym. Sci.-Polym. Chem. Ed. *11* (1973) 2681...90

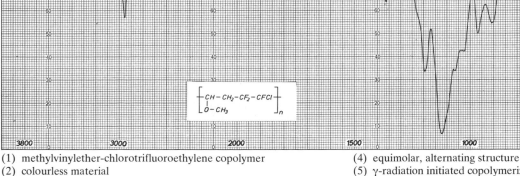

3331211–35111 $C_3H_6O-C_2F_3Cl$ 489

(1) methylvinylether-chlorotrifluoroethylene copolymer
(2) colourless material
(3) R. Klipper, Institut für Physikalische Chemie, Universität Köln
(4) equimolar, alternating structure
(5) γ-radiation initiated copolymerization at 259 K
(6) R. Klipper, Diplomarbeit, Köln 1974
(7) film from $CHCl_3$ on CsI

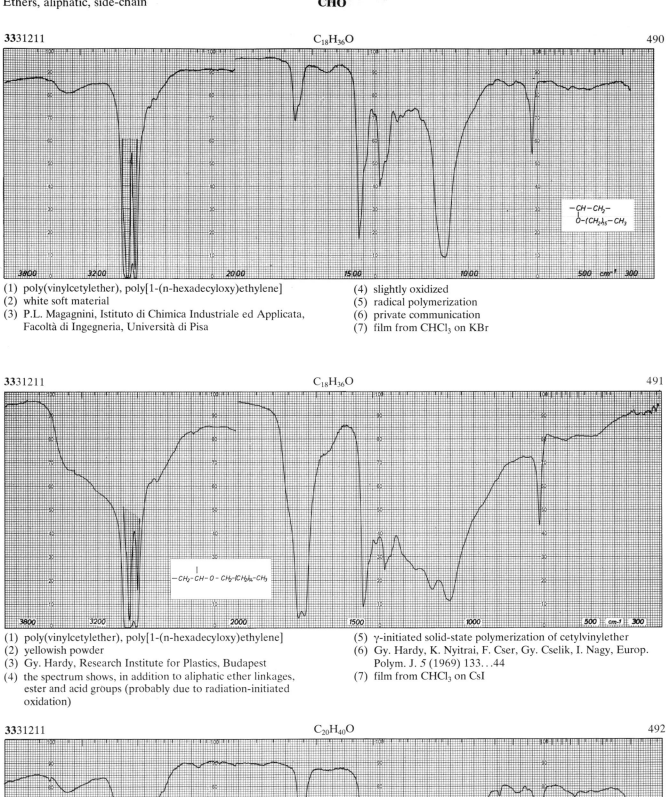

3331211　　　　　　　　　　$C_{18}H_{36}O$　　　　　　　　　　490

Structure label on spectrum:
$$-CH-CH_2-$$
$$O-(CH_2)_{15}-CH_3$$

(1) poly(vinylcetylether), poly[1-(n-hexadecyloxy)ethylene]
(2) white soft material
(3) P.L. Magagnini, Istituto di Chimica Industriale ed Applicata, Facoltà di Ingegneria, Università di Pisa
(4) slightly oxidized
(5) radical polymerization
(6) private communication
(7) film from $CHCl_3$ on KBr

3331211　　　　　　　　　　$C_{18}H_{36}O$　　　　　　　　　　491

Structure label on spectrum:
$$-CH_2-CH-O-CH_2-(CH_2)_{14}-CH_3$$

(1) poly(vinylcetylether), poly[1-(n-hexadecyloxy)ethylene]
(2) yellowish powder
(3) Gy. Hardy, Research Institute for Plastics, Budapest
(4) the spectrum shows, in addition to aliphatic ether linkages, ester and acid groups (probably due to radiation-initiated oxidation)
(5) γ-initiated solid-state polymerization of cetylvinylether
(6) Gy. Hardy, K. Nyitrai, F. Cser, Gy. Cselik, I. Nagy, Europ. Polym. J. 5 (1969) 133...44
(7) film from $CHCl_3$ on CsI

3331211　　　　　　　　　　$C_{20}H_{40}O$　　　　　　　　　　492

Structure label on spectrum:
$$-CH-CH_2-$$
$$O-(CH_2)_{17}-CH_3$$

(1) poly(vinylstearylether), poly[1-(n-octadecyloxy)ethylene]
(2) white material
(3) P.L. Magagnini, Istituto di Chimica Industriale ed Applicata, Facoltà di Ingegneria, Università di Pisa
(4) slightly oxidized
(6) private communication
(7) film from $CHCl_3$ on KBr

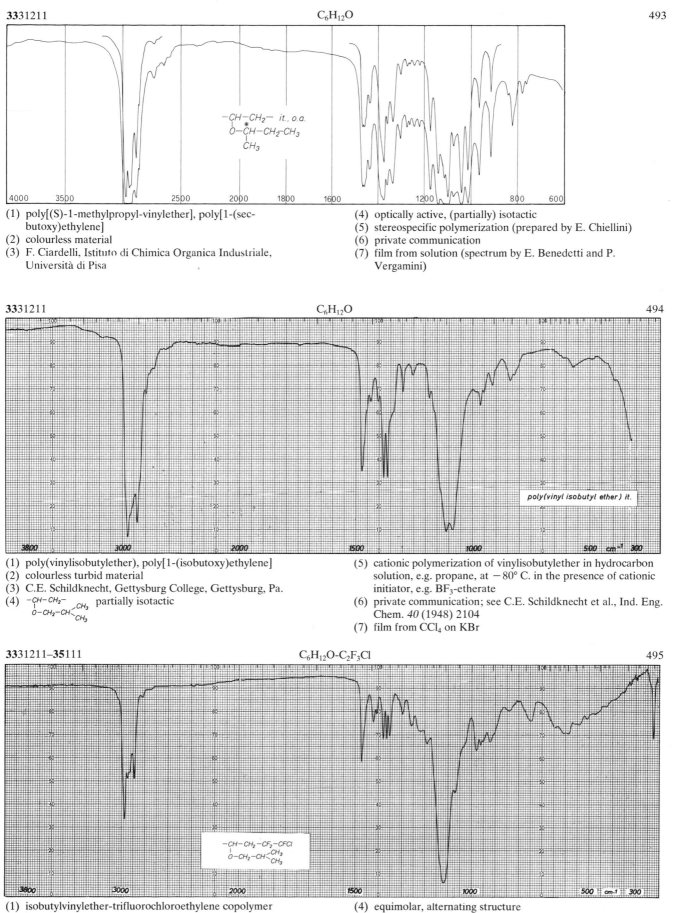

3331211   C₆H₁₂O   493

(1) poly[(S)-1-methylpropyl-vinylether], poly[1-(sec-butoxy)ethylene]
(2) colourless material
(3) F. Ciardelli, Istituto di Chimica Organica Industriale, Università di Pisa
(4) optically active, (partially) isotactic
(5) stereospecific polymerization (prepared by E. Chiellini)
(6) private communication
(7) film from solution (spectrum by E. Benedetti and P. Vergamini)

3331211   C₆H₁₂O   494

poly(vinyl isobutyl ether) it.

(1) poly(vinylisobutylether), poly[1-(isobutoxy)ethylene]
(2) colourless turbid material
(3) C.E. Schildknecht, Gettysburg College, Gettysburg, Pa.
(4) partially isotactic
(5) cationic polymerization of vinylisobutylether in hydrocarbon solution, e.g. propane, at −80° C. in the presence of cationic initiator, e.g. BF₃-etherate
(6) private communication; see C.E. Schildknecht et al., Ind. Eng. Chem. *40* (1948) 2104
(7) film from CCl₄ on KBr

3331211–35111   C₆H₁₂O-C₂F₃Cl   495

(1) isobutylvinylether-trifluorochloroethylene copolymer
(2) colourless, clear film
(3) R. Klipper, Institut für Physikalische Chemie, Universität Köln
(4) equimolar, alternating structure
(5) γ-radiation initiated copolymerization at 301 K
(6) R. Klipper, Diplomarbeit, Köln 1974
(7) film

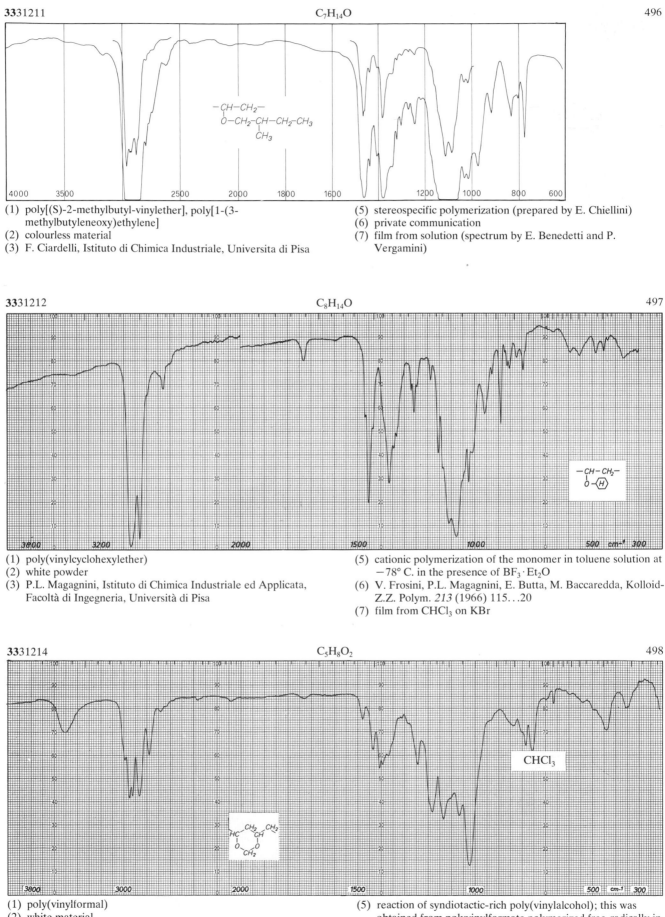

3331211 $C_7H_{14}O$ 496

$$-CH-CH_2-$$
$$O-CH_2-CH-CH_2-CH_3$$
$$CH_3$$

(1) poly[(S)-2-methylbutyl-vinylether], poly[1-(3-methylbutyleneoxy)ethylene]
(2) colourless material
(3) F. Ciardelli, Istituto di Chimica Industriale, Universita di Pisa

(5) stereospecific polymerization (prepared by E. Chiellini)
(6) private communication
(7) film from solution (spectrum by E. Benedetti and P. Vergamini)

3331212 $C_8H_{14}O$ 497

$$-CH-CH_2-$$
$$O-\boxed{H}$$

(1) poly(vinylcyclohexylether)
(2) white powder
(3) P.L. Magagnini, Istituto di Chimica Industriale ed Applicata, Facoltà di Ingegneria, Università di Pisa

(5) cationic polymerization of the monomer in toluene solution at $-78°$ C. in the presence of $BF_3 \cdot Et_2O$
(6) V. Frosini, P.L. Magagnini, E. Butta, M. Baccaredda, Kolloid-Z.Z. Polym. *213* (1966) 115...20
(7) film from $CHCl_3$ on KBr

3331214 $C_5H_8O_2$ 498

$CHCl_3$

$$CH_2\ \ CH_2$$
$$HC\ \ \ \ \ \ CH$$
$$O\ \ \ \ \ \ O$$
$$CH_2$$

(1) poly(vinylformal)
(2) white material
(3) K. Fujii, Central Research Laboratories, Kuraray Co., Okayama
(4) 50 mol-% cis-formal rings and 37 mol-% trans-formal rings

(5) reaction of syndiotactic-rich poly(vinylalcohol); this was obtained from polyvinylformate polymerized free-radically in methylformate at $-78°$ C.
(6) private communication
(7) swollen in $CHCl_3$, spread on CsI and dried (14 d i.v.)

3331214 $C_5H_8O_2$ 499

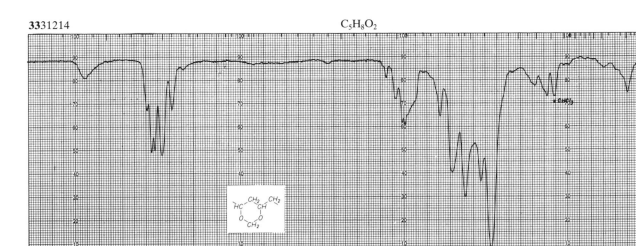

(1) poly(vinylformal)
(2) white material
(3) K. Fujii, Central Research Laboratory, Kuraray Co., Okayama
(4) 70% cis formal rings and 14 mol-% trans formal rings (crosslinked)

(5) obtained by reaction of isotactic-rich polyvinylalcohol with formaldehyde (obtained from polyvinyl-t-butyl ether polymerized with $BF_3 \cdot Et_2O$ in toluene at $-78°$ C)
(6) private communication
(7) swollen in $CHCl_3$, spread on CsI and dried (14 d i. v.)

3331231 C_4H_8O 500

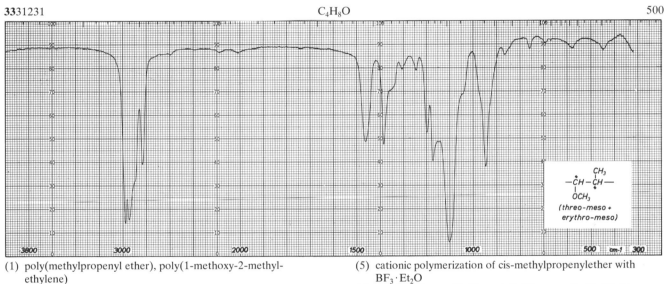

(1) poly(methylpropenyl ether), poly(1-methoxy-2-methyl-ethylene)
(2) white material
(3) T. Higashimura, Department of Polymer Chemistry, Kyoto University, yoto
(4) threo-meso together with erythro-meso units

(5) cationic polymerization of cis-methylpropenylether with $BF_3 \cdot Et_2O$
(6) T. Higashimura, Y. Ohsumi, S. Okamura, R. Chûjô, T. Kuroda, Makromol. Chem. *126* (1969) 87...98
(7) film from $CHCl_3$ on KBr

3331231 C_4H_8O 501

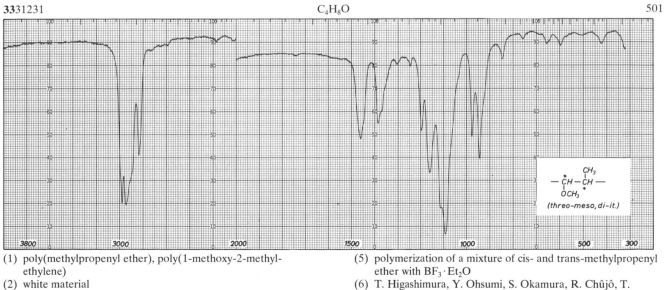

(1) poly(methylpropenyl ether), poly(1-methoxy-2-methyl-ethylene)
(2) white material
(3) T. Higashimura, Department of Polymer Chemistry, Kyoto University, Kyoto
(4) diisotactic polymer with threo-meso units

(5) polymerization of a mixture of cis- and trans-methylpropenyl ether with $BF_3 \cdot Et_2O$
(6) T. Higashimura, Y. Ohsumi, S. Okamura, R. Chûjô, T. Kuroda, Makromol. Chem. *126* (1969) 87...98
(7) film from $CHCl_3$ on KBr

167

3331231 $C_5H_{10}O$ 502

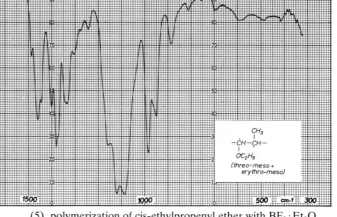

(1) poly(ethylpropenyl ether), poly(1-ethoxy-2-methyl-ethylene)
(2) white material
(3) T. Higashimura, Department of Polymer Chemistry, Kyoto University, Kyoto
(4) threo-meso together with erythro-meso units; crystalline

(5) polymerization of cis-ethylpropenyl ether with $BF_3 \cdot Et_2O$
(6) T. Higashimura, Y. Ohsumi, S. Okamura, R. Chûjô, T. Kuroda, Makromol. Chem. *126* (1969) 87...98
(7) film from CH_2Cl_2 on KBr

3331231 $C_5H_{10}O$ 503

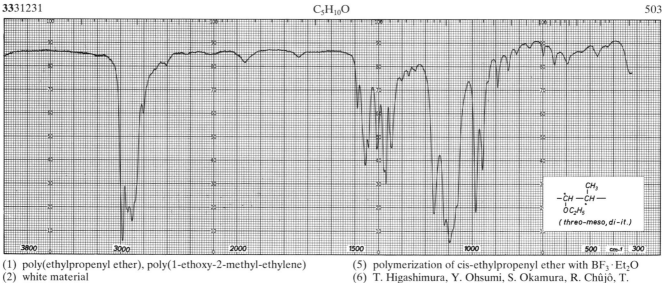

(1) poly(ethylpropenyl ether), poly(1-ethoxy-2-methyl-ethylene)
(2) white material
(3) T. Higashimura, Department of Polymer Chemistry, Kyoto University, Kyoto
(4) diisotactic material with threo-meso units; crystalline

(5) polymerization of cis-ethylpropenyl ether with $BF_3 \cdot Et_2O$
(6) T. Higashimura, Y. Ohsumi, S. Okamura, R. Chûjô, T. Kuroda, Makromol. Chem. *126* (1969) 87...98
(7) film from $CHCl_3$ on KBr

333211 C_8H_8O 504

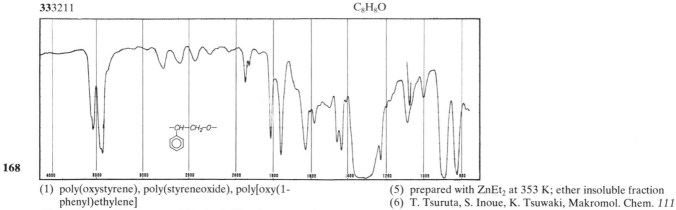

(1) poly(oxystyrene), poly(styreneoxide), poly[oxy(1-phenyl)ethylene]
(3) T. Tsuruta, Department of Synthetic Chemistry, Faculty of Engineering, University of Tokyo

(5) prepared with $ZnEt_2$ at 353 K; ether insoluble fraction
(6) T. Tsuruta, S. Inoue, K. Tsuwaki, Makromol. Chem. *111* (1968) 236...46; private communication
(7) film from $CHCl_3$ (spectrum by K. Tsuruta)

333211   C$_8$H$_8$O   505

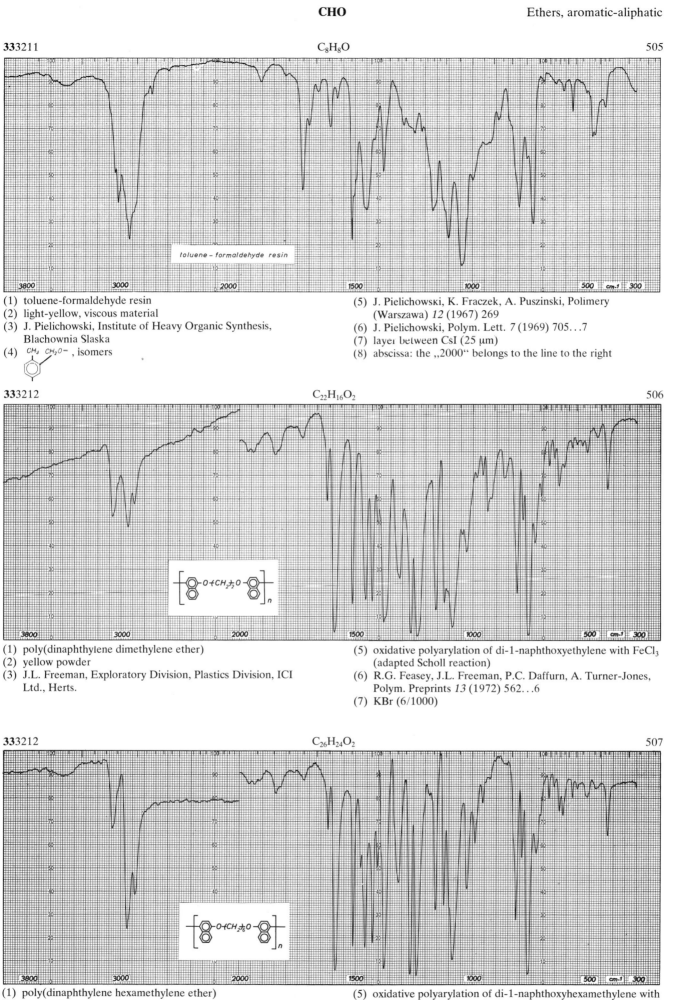

toluene – formaldehyde resin

(1) toluene-formaldehyde resin
(2) light-yellow, viscous material
(3) J. Pielichowski, Institute of Heavy Organic Synthesis, Blachownia Slaska
(4) CH$_3$ CH$_2$O$-$, isomers

(5) J. Pielichowski, K. Fraczek, A. Puszinski, Polimery (Warszawa) *12* (1967) 269
(6) J. Pielichowski, Polym. Lett. *7* (1969) 705...7
(7) layer between CsI (25 μm)
(8) abscissa: the „2000" belongs to the line to the right

333212   C$_{22}$H$_{16}$O$_2$ 506

$\left[O\!-\!(CH_2)_2\!-\!O \right]_n$

(1) poly(dinaphthylene dimethylene ether)
(2) yellow powder
(3) J.L. Freeman, Exploratory Division, Plastics Division, ICI Ltd., Herts.

(5) oxidative polyarylation of di-1-naphthoxyethylene with FeCl$_3$ (adapted Scholl reaction)
(6) R.G. Feasey, J.L. Freeman, P.C. Daffurn, A. Turner-Jones, Polym. Preprints *13* (1972) 562...6
(7) KBr (6/1000)

333212   C$_{26}$H$_{24}$O$_2$ 507

$\left[O\!-\!(CH_2)_6\!-\!O \right]_n$

(1) poly(dinaphthylene hexamethylene ether)
(2) ivory-coloured powder
(3) J.L. Freeman, Exploratory Division, Plastics Division, ICI Ltd., Herts.

(5) oxidative polyarylation of di-1-naphthoxyhexamethylene with FeCl$_3$ (adapted Scholl reaction)
(6) R.G. Feasey, J.L. Freeman, P.C. Daffurn, A. Turner-Jones, Polym. Preprints *13* (1972) 562...6
(7) KBr (5/1000)

333212 $C_8H_{12}O$ 508

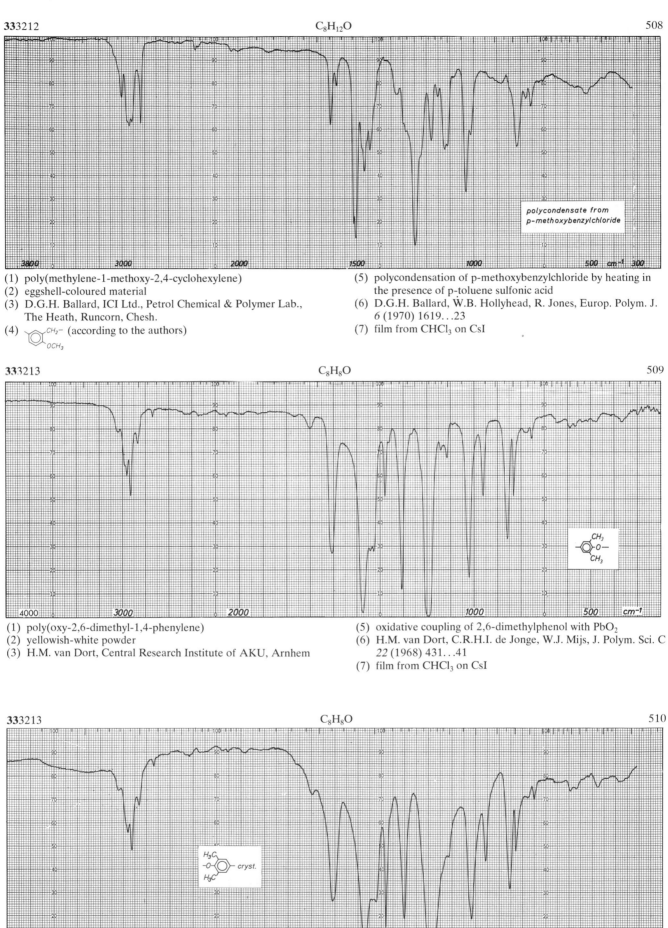

polycondensate from
p-methoxybenzylchloride

(1) poly(methylene-1-methoxy-2,4-cyclohexylene)
(2) eggshell-coloured material
(3) D.G.H. Ballard, ICI Ltd., Petrol Chemical & Polymer Lab., The Heath, Runcorn, Chesh.
(4) (according to the authors)

(5) polycondensation of p-methoxybenzylchloride by heating in the presence of p-toluene sulfonic acid
(6) D.G.H. Ballard, W.B. Hollyhead, R. Jones, Europ. Polym. J. *6* (1970) 1619...23
(7) film from $CHCl_3$ on CsI

333213 C_8H_8O 509

(1) poly(oxy-2,6-dimethyl-1,4-phenylene)
(2) yellowish-white powder
(3) H.M. van Dort, Central Research Institute of AKU, Arnhem

(5) oxidative coupling of 2,6-dimethylphenol with PbO_2
(6) H.M. van Dort, C.R.H.I. de Jonge, W.J. Mijs, J. Polym. Sci. C *22* (1968) 431...41
(7) film from $CHCl_3$ on CsI

333213 C_8H_8O 510

(1) poly(oxy-2,6-dimethyl-1,4-phenylene)
(2) light-brown film
(3) W. Wenig, Chemische Werke Hüls AG, Marl

(4) crystalline (approx. 30%)
(6) W. Wenig, Makromolekulares Kolloquium, Freiburg/Br. 1976; private communication
(7) KBr

333213 C_8H_8O 511

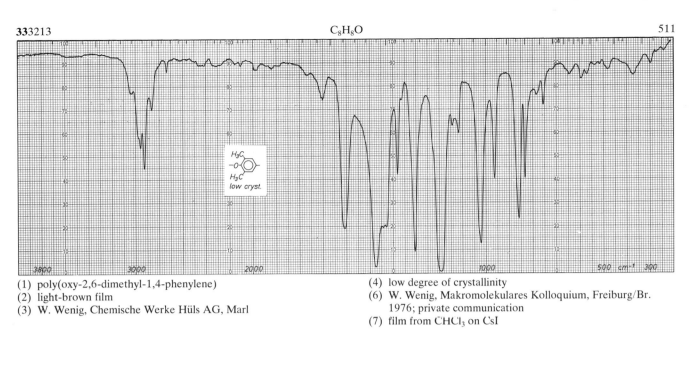

(1) poly(oxy-2,6-dimethyl-1,4-phenylene)
(2) light-brown film
(3) W. Wenig, Chemische Werke Hüls AG, Marl

(4) low degree of crystallinity
(6) W. Wenig, Makromolekulares Kolloquium, Freiburg/Br.
    1976; private communication
(7) film from $CHCl_3$ on CsI

333213 $C_{13}H_{10}O$ 512

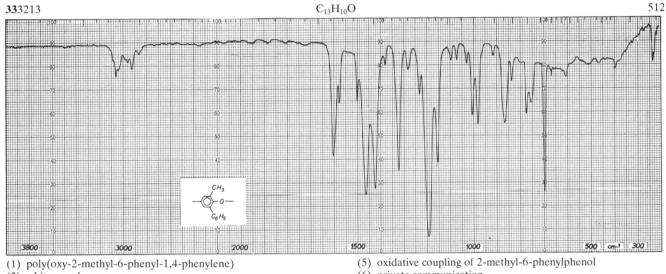

(1) poly(oxy-2-methyl-6-phenyl-1,4-phenylene)
(2) white powder
(3) A.R. Schulz, General Electric Comp., Research and
    Development Center, Schenectady, N.Y.

(5) oxidative coupling of 2-methyl-6-phenylphenol
(6) private communication
(7) film from $CHCl_3$ on CsI
(8) absorption near 240 cm^{-1} due to H_2O

333213 $C_{13}H_{10}O$ 513

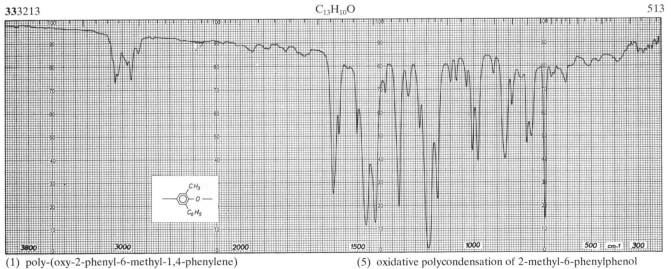

(1) poly-(oxy-2-phenyl-6-methyl-1,4-phenylene)
(2) eggshell-coloured, fibrous material
(3) A.S. Hay, General Electric Research and Development
    Center, Schenectady, N.Y.

(5) oxidative polycondensation of 2-methyl-6-phenylphenol
    (with, e.g., Ag_2O in benzene)
(6) A.S. Hay, R.F. Clark, Macromolecules 3 (1970) 533...5
(7) film from $CHCl_3$ on CsI

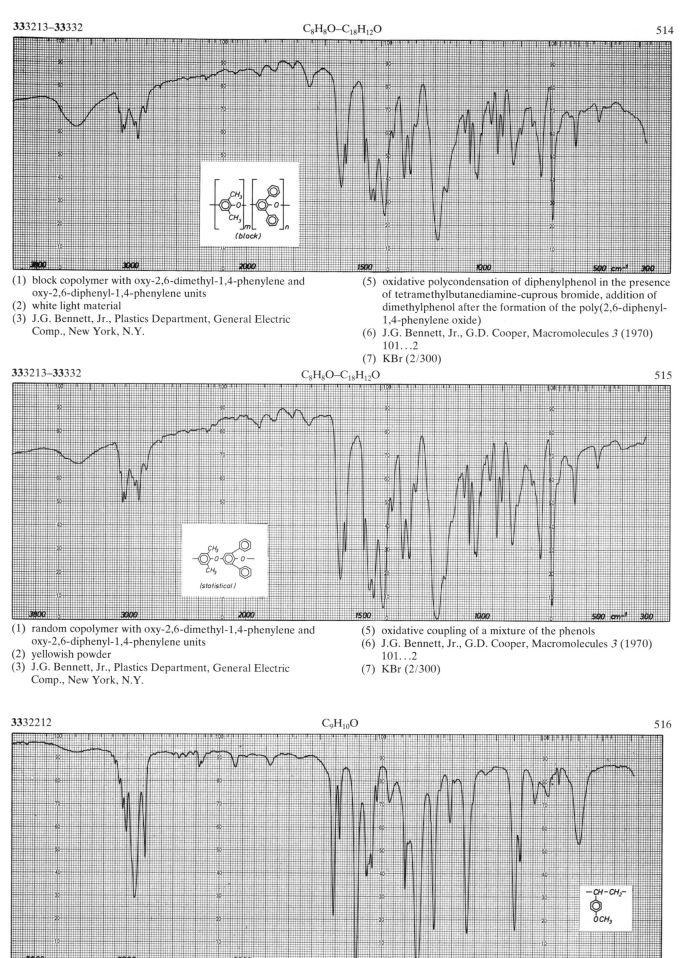

(block)

(1) block copolymer with oxy-2,6-dimethyl-1,4-phenylene and oxy-2,6-diphenyl-1,4-phenylene units
(2) white light material
(3) J.G. Bennett, Jr., Plastics Department, General Electric Comp., New York, N.Y.
(5) oxidative polycondensation of diphenylphenol in the presence of tetramethylbutanediamine-cuprous bromide, addition of dimethylphenol after the formation of the poly(2,6-diphenyl-1,4-phenylene oxide)
(6) J.G. Bennett, Jr., G.D. Cooper, Macromolecules 3 (1970) 101...2
(7) KBr (2/300)

(statistical)

(1) random copolymer with oxy-2,6-dimethyl-1,4-phenylene and oxy-2,6-diphenyl-1,4-phenylene units
(2) yellowish powder
(3) J.G. Bennett, Jr., Plastics Department, General Electric Comp., New York, N.Y.
(5) oxidative coupling of a mixture of the phenols
(6) J.G. Bennett, Jr., G.D. Cooper, Macromolecules 3 (1970) 101...2
(7) KBr (2/300)

(1) poly(p-methoxystyrene), poly[1-(p-methoxyphenyl)ethylene]
(2) white powder
(3) P.L. Magagnini, Istituto di Chimica Industriale ed Applicata, Facultà di Ingegneria, Università di Pisa
(5) V. Frosini, P.L. Magagnini, Europ. Polym. J. 2 (1966) 129; P.L. Magagnini, V. Frosini, ibid. 139
(6) M. Baccaredda, E. Butta, V. Frosini, P.L. Magnini, J. Polym. Sci. A-2 4 (1966) 789...96
(7) film from CHCl₃ on KBr

3332212/1   C$_{16}$H$_{22}$O$_5$ 517

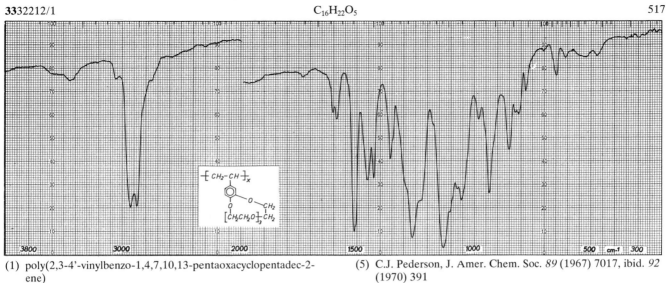

(1) poly(2,3-4'-vinylbenzo-1,4,7,10,13-pentaoxacyclopentadec-2-ene)
(2) white powder
(3) J. Smid, Department of Chemistry, College of Forestry, State University of New York, Syracuse, N.Y.

(5) C.J. Pederson, J. Amer. Chem. Soc. *89* (1967) 7017, ibid. *92* (1970) 391
(6) S. Kopolow, T.E. Hogen Esch, J. Smid, Macromolecules *4* (1971) 359...60
(7) film from CHCl$_3$ on CsI

3332212/1   C$_{18}$H$_{26}$O$_6$ 518

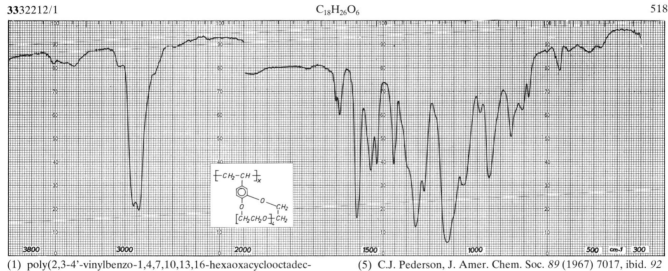

(1) poly(2,3-4'-vinylbenzo-1,4,7,10,13,16-hexaoxacyclooctadec-2-ene)
(2) white powder
(3) J. Smid, Department of Chemistry, College of Forestry, State University of New York, Syracuse, N.Y.

(5) C.J. Pederson, J. Amer. Chem. Soc. *89* (1967) 7017, ibid. *92* (1970) 391
(6) S. Kopolow, T.E. Hogen Esch, J. Smid, Macromolecules *4* (1971) 359...60
(7) film from CHCl$_3$ on CsI

3332213   C$_{14}$H$_{10}$O   519

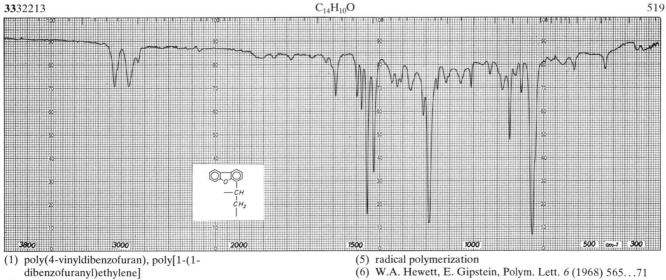

(1) poly(4-vinyldibenzofuran), poly[1-(1-dibenzofuranyl)ethylene]
(2) white lumps
(3) W.H. Hewett, IBM Research Laboratory, San Jose, Ca.

(5) radical polymerization
(6) W.A. Hewett, E. Gipstein, Polym. Lett. *6* (1968) 565...71
(7) film from CHCl$_3$ on CsI

3332321 $C_{27}H_{30}O_6$ 520

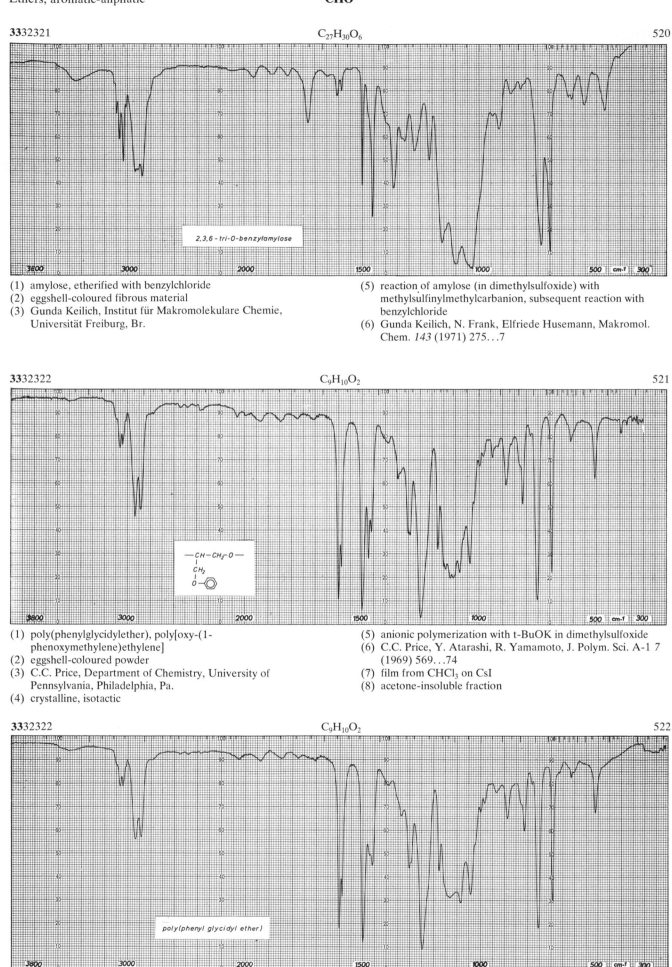

2,3,6 - tri-O-benzylamylose

(1) amylose, etherified with benzylchloride
(2) eggshell-coloured fibrous material
(3) Gunda Keilich, Institut für Makromolekulare Chemie, Universität Freiburg, Br.

(5) reaction of amylose (in dimethylsulfoxide) with methylsulfinylmethylcarbanion, subsequent reaction with benzylchloride
(6) Gunda Keilich, N. Frank, Elfriede Husemann, Makromol. Chem. *143* (1971) 275...7

3332322 $C_9H_{10}O_2$ 521

$-CH-CH_2-O-$
$\quad |$
$\quad CH_2$
$\quad |$
$\quad O-\hexagon$

(1) poly(phenylglycidylether), poly[oxy-(1-phenoxymethylene)ethylene]
(2) eggshell-coloured powder
(3) C.C. Price, Department of Chemistry, University of Pennsylvania, Philadelphia, Pa.
(4) crystalline, isotactic

(5) anionic polymerization with t-BuOK in dimethylsulfoxide
(6) C.C. Price, Y. Atarashi, R. Yamamoto, J. Polym. Sci. A-1 7 (1969) 569...74
(7) film from $CHCl_3$ on CsI
(8) acetone-insoluble fraction

3332322 $C_9H_{10}O_2$ 522

poly(phenyl glycidyl ether)

(1) poly(phenylglycidylether), poly[oxy-(1-phenoxymethylene)ethylene]
(2) glassy-clear, colourless material
(3) Z. Jedliński, Department of Polymer Technology, Silesian Institute of Technology, Gliwice
(4) amorphous

(5) base-catalysed polymerization of phenylglycidylether (e.g., with KOH)
(6) Z. Jedliński, A. Stolarzewicz, Europ. Polym. J. *5* (1969) 515...9
(7) film from $CHCl_3$ on CsI
(8) acetone-insoluble fraction

3332322 $C_9H_{10}O_2$ 523

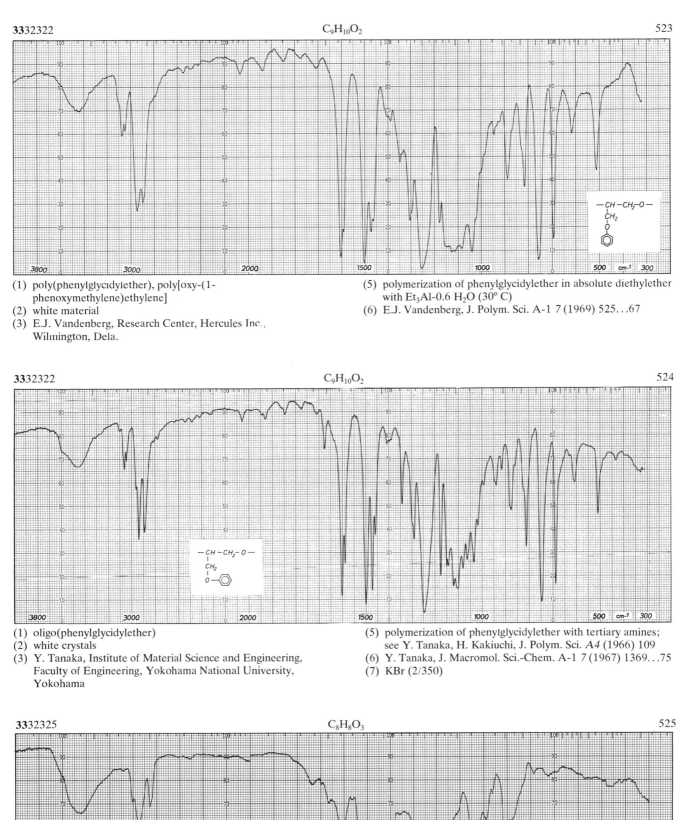

(1) poly(phenylglycidylether), poly[oxy-(1-phenoxymethylene)ethylene]
(2) white material
(3) E.J. Vandenberg, Research Center, Hercules Inc., Wilmington, Dela.

(5) polymerization of phenylglycidylether in absolute diethylether with Et₃Al-0.6 H₂O (30° C)
(6) E.J. Vandenberg, J. Polym. Sci. A-1 7 (1969) 525...67

3332322 $C_9H_{10}O_2$ 524

(1) oligo(phenylglycidylether)
(2) white crystals
(3) Y. Tanaka, Institute of Material Science and Engineering, Faculty of Engineering, Yokohama National University, Yokohama

(5) polymerization of phenylglycidylether with tertiary amines; see Y. Tanaka, H. Kakiuchi, J. Polym. Sci. *A4* (1966) 109
(6) Y. Tanaka, J. Macromol. Sci.-Chem. A-1 7 (1967) 1369...75
(7) KBr (2/350)

3332325 $C_8H_8O_3$ 525

(1) poly(oxy-2,5-dimethoxy-1,4-phenylene)
(2) yellow to brown powder
(3) G.F.L. Ehlers, Wright-Patterson AFB, Ohio
(5) oxidative polycondensation, see N.P. Loire, AFML-TR-65-377 (1965)

(6) G.F.L. Ehlers, R.C. Evers, K.R. Fisch, J. Polym. Sci. A-1 7 (1969) 3413...5; G.F.L. Ehlers, K.R. Fisch, W.R. Powell, ibid. 2931...53
(7) KBr (1/300)

33331   C$_6$H$_4$O   526

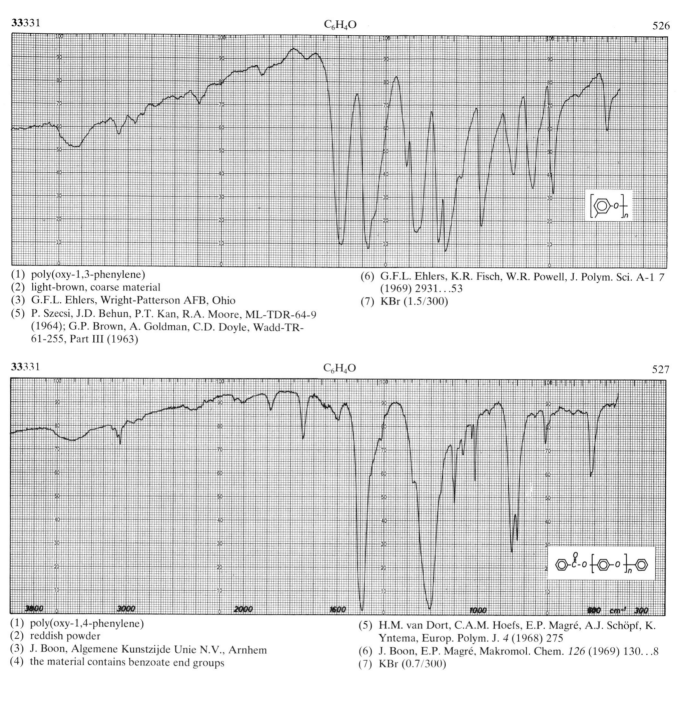

(1) poly(oxy-1,3-phenylene)
(2) light-brown, coarse material
(3) G.F.L. Ehlers, Wright-Patterson AFB, Ohio
(5) P. Szecsi, J.D. Behun, P.T. Kan, R.A. Moore, ML-TDR-64-9 (1964); G.P. Brown, A. Goldman, C.D. Doyle, Wadd-TR-61-255, Part III (1963)

(6) G.F.L. Ehlers, K.R. Fisch, W.R. Powell, J. Polym. Sci. A-1 7 (1969) 2931...53
(7) KBr (1.5/300)

33331   C$_6$H$_4$O   527

(1) poly(oxy-1,4-phenylene)
(2) reddish powder
(3) J. Boon, Algemene Kunstzijde Unie N.V., Arnhem
(4) the material contains benzoate end groups

(5) H.M. van Dort, C.A.M. Hoefs, E.P. Magré, A.J. Schöpf, K. Yntema, Europ. Polym. J. 4 (1968) 275
(6) J. Boon, E.P. Magré, Makromol. Chem. 126 (1969) 130...8
(7) KBr (0.7/300)

33331–**33**5213–**43**143–**42**14312   C$_{12}$H$_8$O$_2$–C$_8$H$_4$O$_2$–C$_6$H$_4$O$_4$S$_2$–C$_9$H$_3$NO$_2$ 528

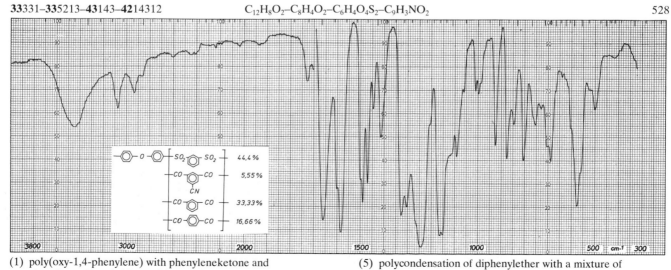

(1) poly(oxy-1,4-phenylene) with phenyleneketone and phenylenesulfone bridges, with a small amount of carbimino crosslinks
(2) white powder
(3) C.S. Marvel, Department of Chemistry, University of Arizona, Tucson, Ariz.

(5) polycondensation of diphenylether with a mixture of diacidchlorides
(6) C.S. Marvel, IUPAC Macro, Aberdeen 1973; private communication
(7) ground with KBr (2/350) and dimethylacetamide, dried and pressed

33331–**33**5213–**43**143–**42**14312 $C_{12}H_8O_2$–$C_8H_4O_2$–$C_6H_4O_4S_2$–$C_9H_3NO_2$ 529

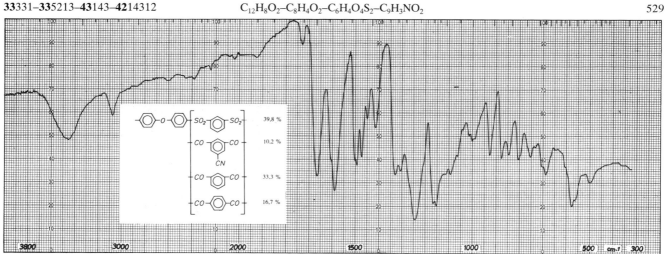

(1) poly(oxy-1,4-phenylene) with phenyleneketone and phenylenesulfone bridges, with a small amount of carbimino crosslinks
(2) white powder
(3) C.S. Marvel, Department of Chemistry, University of Arizona, Tucson, Ariz.

(5) polycondensation of diphenylether with a mixture of diacidchlorides
(6) C.S. Marvel, IUPAC Macro, Aberdeen 1973; private communication
(7) KBr (3/350)

33331–**33**5213–**43**143–**42**14312 $C_{12}H_8O_2$–$C_8H_4O_2$–$C_6H_4O_4S_2$–$C_9H_3NO_2$ 530

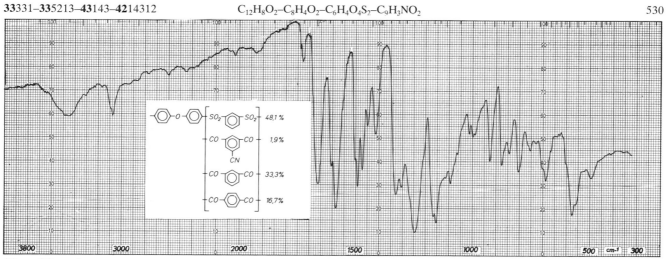

(1) ... (7) see above

33332 $C_{18}H_{12}O$ 531

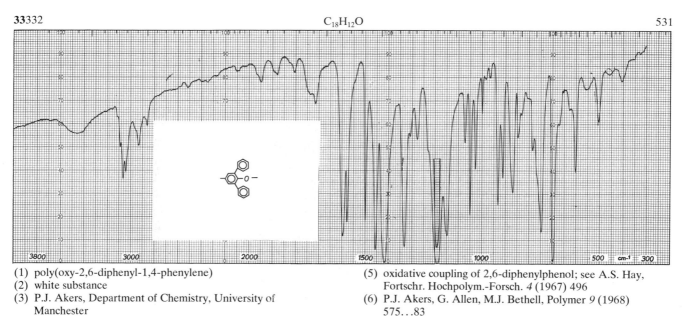

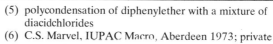

(1) poly(oxy-2,6-diphenyl-1,4-phenylene)
(2) white substance
(3) P.J. Akers, Department of Chemistry, University of Manchester

(5) oxidative coupling of 2,6-diphenylphenol; see A.S. Hay, Fortschr. Hochpolym.-Forsch. *4* (1967) 496
(6) P.J. Akers, G. Allen, M.J. Bethell, Polymer *9* (1968) 575...83
(7) ground with KBr (2/300) and acetone+CHCl₃, dried and pressed

33332 $C_{18}H_{12}O$ 532

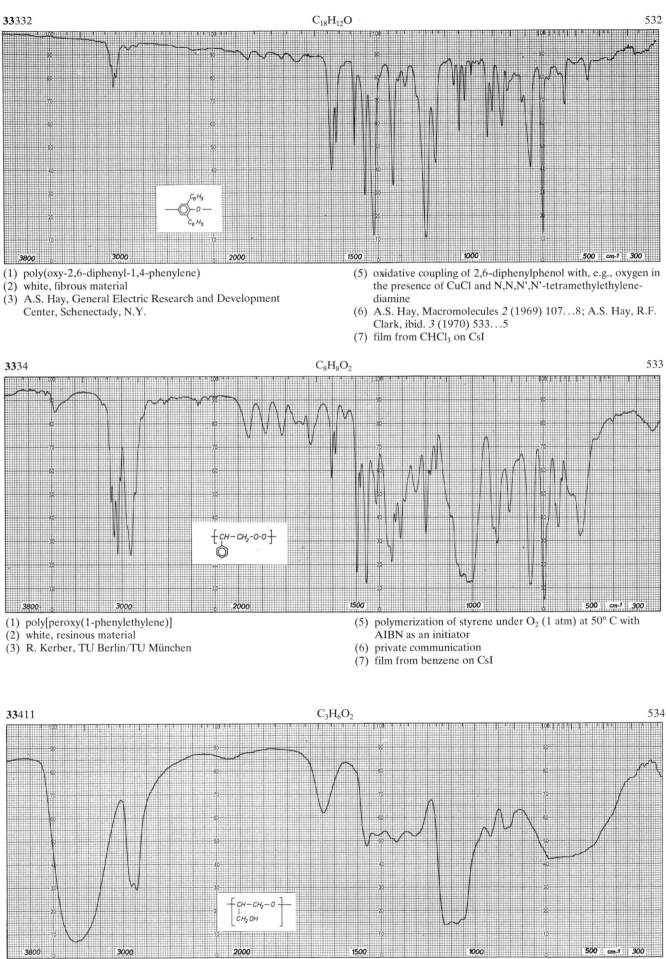

(1) poly(oxy-2,6-diphenyl-1,4-phenylene)
(2) white, fibrous material
(3) A.S. Hay, General Electric Research and Development
    Center, Schenectady, N.Y.

(5) oxidative coupling of 2,6-diphenylphenol with, e.g., oxygen in
    the presence of CuCl and N,N,N',N'-tetramethylethylene-
    diamine
(6) A.S. Hay, Macromolecules *2* (1969) 107...8; A.S. Hay, R.F.
    Clark, ibid. *3* (1970) 533...5
(7) film from CHCl₃ on CsI

3334 $C_8H_8O_2$ 533

(1) poly[peroxy(1-phenylethylene)]
(2) white, resinous material
(3) R. Kerber, TU Berlin/TU München

(5) polymerization of styrene under O_2 (1 atm) at 50° C with
    AIBN as an initiator
(6) private communication
(7) film from benzene on CsI

33411 $C_3H_6O_2$ 534

(1) poly[oxy(1-hydroxymethylene)ethylene]
(2) colourless viscous material
(3) E. Krejcar, Research Institute for Synthetic Resins and
    Lacquers, Pardubice

(5) saponification of crosslinked diglycidylester of
    hexahydrophthalic acid; crosslinking agent: BF₃-amine adduct
(6) S. Luňak, E. Krejcar, Angew. Makromol. Chem. *10* (1970)
    109...14
(7) film between CsI (12.5 μm)

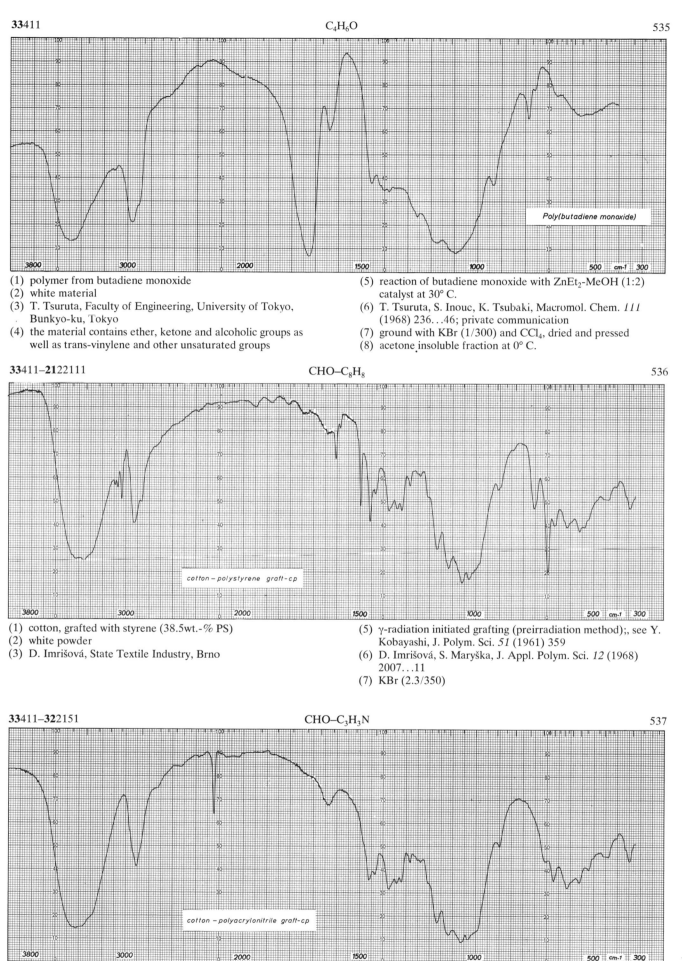

Poly(butadiene monoxide)

(1) polymer from butadiene monoxide
(2) white material
(3) T. Tsuruta, Faculty of Engineering, University of Tokyo, Bunkyo-ku, Tokyo
(4) the material contains ether, ketone and alcoholic groups as well as trans-vinylene and other unsaturated groups
(5) reaction of butadiene monoxide with ZnEt$_2$-MeOH (1:2) catalyst at 30° C.
(6) T. Tsuruta, S. Inoue, K. Tsubaki, Macromol. Chem. *111* (1968) 236...46; private communication
(7) ground with KBr (1/300) and CCl$_4$, dried and pressed
(8) acetone insoluble fraction at 0° C.

cotton – polystyrene graft-cp

(1) cotton, grafted with styrene (38.5wt.-% PS)
(2) white powder
(3) D. Imrišová, State Textile Industry, Brno
(5) γ-radiation initiated grafting (preirradiation method);, see Y. Kobayashi, J. Polym. Sci. *51* (1961) 359
(6) D. Imrišová, S. Maryška, J. Appl. Polym. Sci. *12* (1968) 2007...11
(7) KBr (2.3/350)

cotton – polyacrylonitrile graft-cp

(1) cotton, grafted with acrylonitrile (42.9 wt.-% PAN)
(2) white powder
(3) D. Imrišová, State Textile Research Institute, Center for the Application of Radio Active Isotopes in the Textile Industry, Brno
(5) γ-radiation initiated grafting (preirradiation method); see Y. Kobayashi, J. Polym. Sci. *51* (1961) 359
(6) D. Imrišová, S. Maryška, J. Appl. Sci. *11* (1967) 901...7
(7) KBr (2.5/350)

334122 $C_{18}H_{20}O_3$ 538

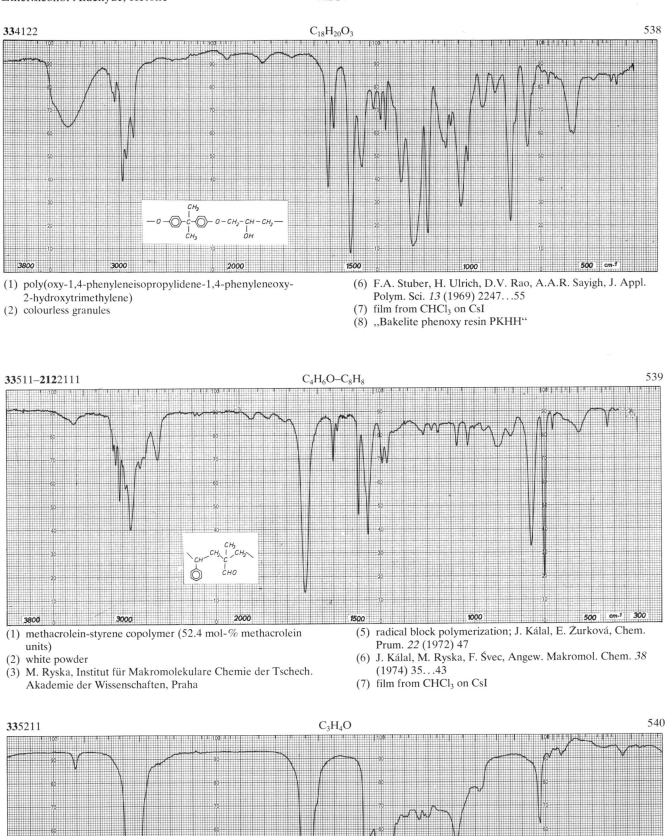

(1) poly(oxy-1,4-phenyleneisopropylidene-1,4-phenyleneoxy-2-hydroxytrimethylene)
(2) colourless granules

(6) F.A. Stuber, H. Ulrich, D.V. Rao, A.A.R. Sayigh, J. Appl. Polym. Sci. *13* (1969) 2247...55
(7) film from CHCl$_3$ on CsI
(8) „Bakelite phenoxy resin PKHH"

33511–**2122**111 $C_4H_6O–C_8H_8$ 539

(1) methacrolein-styrene copolymer (52.4 mol-% methacrolein units)
(2) white powder
(3) M. Ryska, Institut für Makromolekulare Chemie der Tschech. Akademie der Wissenschaften, Praha

(5) radical block polymerization; J. Kálal, E. Žurková, Chem. Prum. *22* (1972) 47
(6) J. Kálal, M. Ryska, F. Švec, Angew. Makromol. Chem. *38* (1974) 35...43
(7) film from CHCl$_3$ on CsI

335211 C_3H_4O 540

(1) ethylene-carbonmonoxide copolymer (21.8% CO)
(2) colourless material
(3) T.K. Wu, Plastic Products and Resins Department, E.I. Du Pont de Nemours & Comp., Experimental Station, Wilmington, Dela.

(5) high-pressure radical polymerization of ethylene and carbonmonoxide; M.M. Brubaker, D.D. Coffman, H.H. Hoehn, J. Am. Chem. Soc. *74* (1952) 1509; T.K. Wu, J. Phys. Chem. *73* (1969) 1801
(6) T.K. Wu, D.W. Ovenall, ACS Polym. Preprints *17/2* (1976) 693

335211   C₃H₄O   541

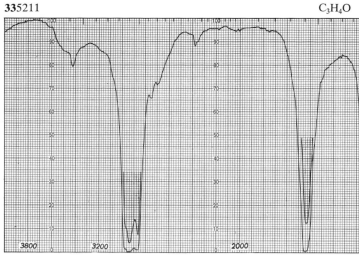
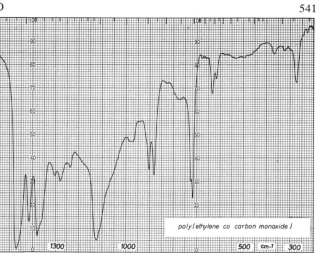

poly(ethylene co carbon monoxide)

(1) ethylene-carbonmonoxide copolymer (15.7 mol-% CO units)
(2) white, soft material
(3) H. Hoyer, Bayer AG, Leverkusen

(5) copolymerization of a mixture of 90% ethylene and 10% CO
    (0.8…1·10⁷ Pa in toluene with Co-carbonyl as an initiator
(6) H. Hoyer, H.G. Fitzky, Makromol. Chem. *161* (1972)
    49…56
(7) film on CsI

335211   C₃H₄O   542

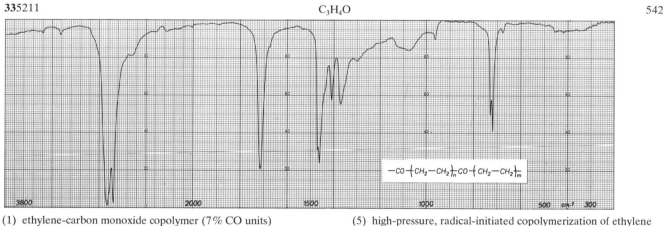

$-CO-(CH_2-CH_2)_n-CO-(CH_2-CH_2)_m-$

(1) ethylene-carbon monoxide copolymer (7% CO units)
(2) colourless granules
(3) T.K. Wu, du Pont de Nemours & Comp., Wilmington, Dela.

(5) high-pressure, radical-initiated copolymerization of ethylene
    with carbonmonoxide; see M.M. Brubaker, D.D. Coffman,
    H.H. Hoehn, J. Am. Chem. Soc. *74* (1952) 1509; T.K. Wu, J.
    Phys. Chem. *73* (1969) 1801
(6) T.K. Wu, D.W. Ovenall, Polym. Preprints *17*/2 (1976) 693
(7) melting film on CsI

335212   C₂₅H₁₈O₂   543

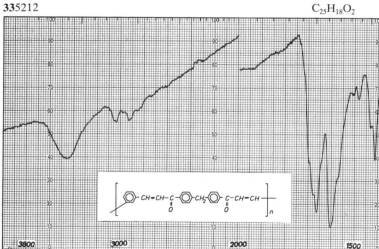

(1) polychalcone, poly(1,3-phenylene-vinylene-carbonyl-1,4-
    phenylene-methylene-1,4-phenylene-carbonyl-vinylene)
(2) light-yellow powder
(3) H. Oleinek, Institut für Makromolekulare Chemie, Jassy

(5) polycondensation of isophthalic aldehyde with 4,4'-diacetyl-
    diphenylmethane in ethanol in the presence of NaOH
(6) H. Oleinek, I. Zugrávescu, Makromol. Chem. *131* (1970)
    265…72
(7) KBr (1.5/350)

335212 $C_{25}H_{18}O_2$ 544

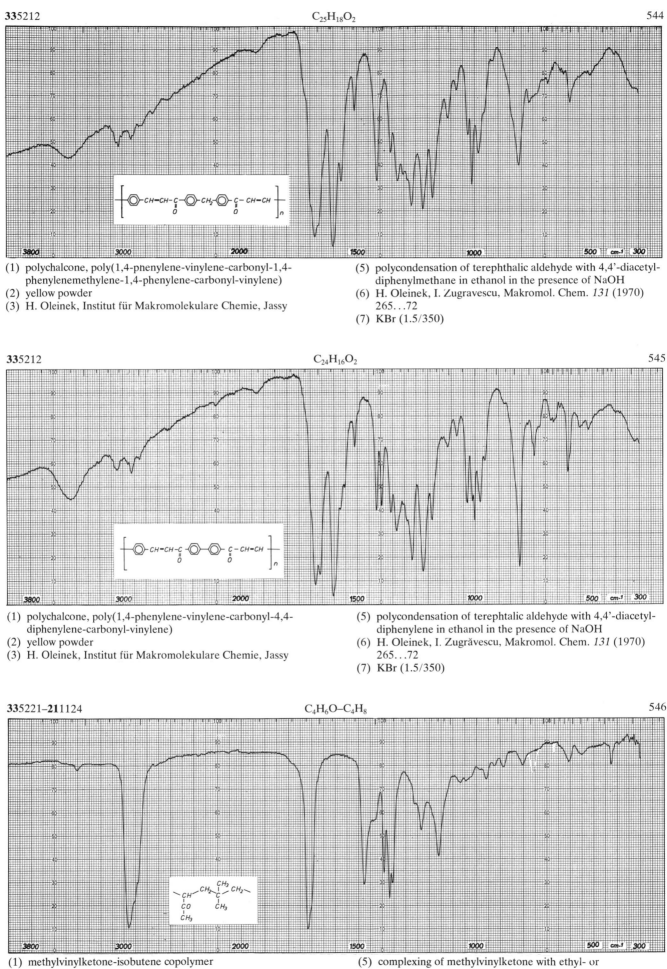

(1) polychalcone, poly(1,4-pnenylene-vinylene-carbonyl-1,4-phenylenemethylene-1,4-phenylene-carbonyl-vinylene)
(2) yellow powder
(3) H. Oleinek, Institut für Makromolekulare Chemie, Jassy
(5) polycondensation of terephthalic aldehyde with 4,4'-diacetyl-diphenylmethane in ethanol in the presence of NaOH
(6) H. Oleinek, I. Zugravescu, Makromol. Chem. *131* (1970) 265...72
(7) KBr (1.5/350)

335212 $C_{24}H_{16}O_2$ 545

(1) polychalcone, poly(1,4-phenylene-vinylene-carbonyl-4,4-diphenylene-carbonyl-vinylene)
(2) yellow powder
(3) H. Oleinek, Institut für Makromolekulare Chemie, Jassy
(5) polycondensation of terephtalic aldehyde with 4,4'-diacetyl-diphenylene in ethanol in the presence of NaOH
(6) H. Oleinek, I. Zugrăvescu, Makromol. Chem. *131* (1970) 265...72
(7) KBr (1.5/350)

335221–**21**1124 $C_4H_6O–C_4H_8$ 546

(1) methylvinylketone-isobutene copolymer
(2) colourless, tacky elastomer
(3) S. Pasynkiewicz, Department of Organic Technology I., Institute of Technology, Warszawa
(4) equimolar, alternating structure
(5) complexing of methylvinylketone with ethyl- or methylaluminumdichloride, copolymerization with isobutene in toluene at 195 K
(6) S. Pasynkiewicz, T. Diem, Anna Korol, Makromol. Chem. *137* (1970) 61....6
(7) film on CsI

33533/5 $C_{16}H_{14}O_3$ 547

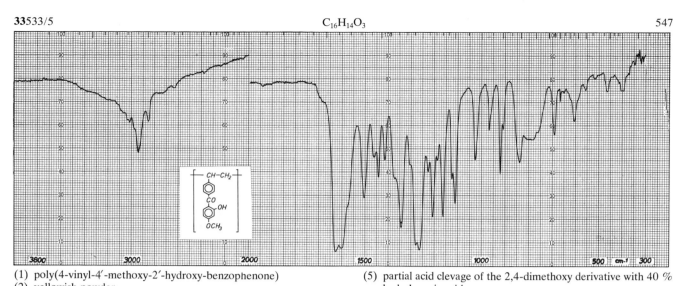

(1) poly(4-vinyl-4′-methoxy-2′-hydroxy-benzophenone)
(2) yellowish powder
(3) C. P. Pinazzi, Laboratoire de Chimie Organique
     Macromoléculaire, Le Mans

(5) partial acid clevage of the 2,4-dimethoxy derivative with 40 %
     hydrobromic acid
(6) C. P. Pinazzi, A. Fernandez, Makromol. Chem. *168* (1973)
     19...26
(7) film from CHCl₃ on CsI

33535 $C_{16}H_{13}O_2$ 548

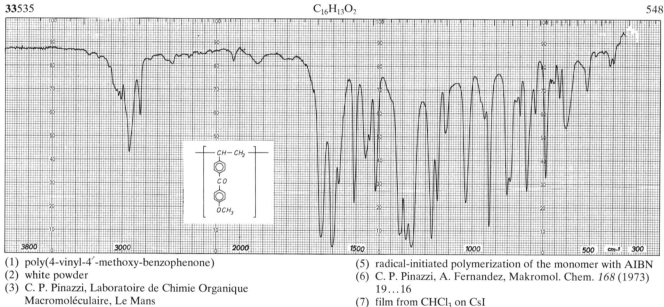

(1) poly(4-vinyl-4′-methoxy-benzophenone)
(2) white powder
(3) C. P. Pinazzi, Laboratoire de Chimie Organique
     Macromoléculaire, Le Mans

(5) radical-initiated polymerization of the monomer with AIBN
(6) C. P. Pinazzi, A. Fernandez, Makromol. Chem. *168* (1973)
     19...16
(7) film from CHCl₃ on CsI

33535 $C_{16}H_{13}O_2$ 549

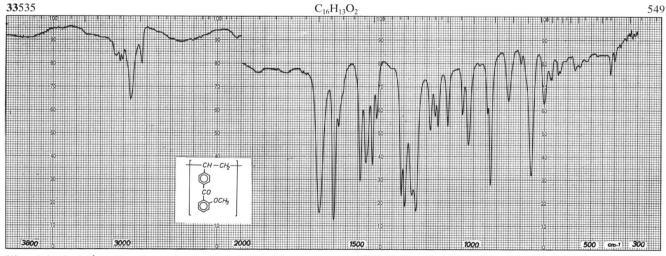

(1) poly(4-vinyl-2′-methoxy-benzophenone)
(2) white powder
(3) C. P. Pinazzi, Laboratoire de Chimie Organique
     Macromoléculaire, Le Mans
(5) radical-initiated polymerization of the monomer with AIBN

(6) C. P. Pinazzi, A. Fernandez, Makromol. Chem. *168* (1973)
     19...26
(7) film from CHCl₃ on CsI

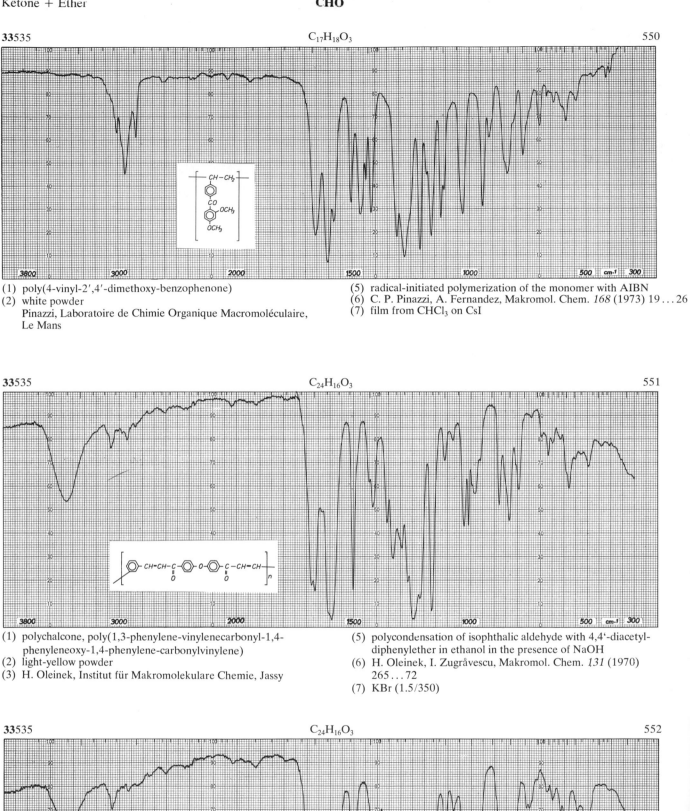

33535 $C_{17}H_{18}O_3$ 550

(1) poly(4-vinyl-2',4'-dimethoxy-benzophenone)
(2) white powder
    Pinazzi, Laboratoire de Chimie Organique Macromoléculaire,
    Le Mans

(5) radical-initiated polymerization of the monomer with AIBN
(6) C. P. Pinazzi, A. Fernandez, Makromol. Chem. *168* (1973) 19…26
(7) film from $CHCl_3$ on CsI

33535 $C_{24}H_{16}O_3$ 551

(1) polychalcone, poly(1,3-phenylene-vinylenecarbonyl-1,4-
    phenyleneoxy-1,4-phenylene-carbonylvinylene)
(2) light-yellow powder
(3) H. Oleinek, Institut für Makromolekulare Chemie, Jassy

(5) polycondensation of isophthalic aldehyde with 4,4'-diacetyl-
    diphenylether in ethanol in the presence of NaOH
(6) H. Oleinek, I. Zugrăvescu, Makromol. Chem. *131* (1970)
    265…72
(7) KBr (1.5/350)

33535 $C_{24}H_{16}O_3$ 552

(1) polychalcone, poly(1,4-phenylene-vinylene-carbonyl-1,4-
    phenyleneoxy-1,4-phenylene-carbonylvinylene)
(2) yellow powder
(3) H. Oleinek, Institut für Makromolekulare Chemie, Jassy

(5) polycondensation of terephthalic aldehyde with 4,4'-diacetyl-
    diphenylether in ethanol in the presence of NaOH
(6) H. Oleinek, I. Zugrăvescu, Makromol. Chem. *131* (1970)
    265…72
(7) KBr (1/350)

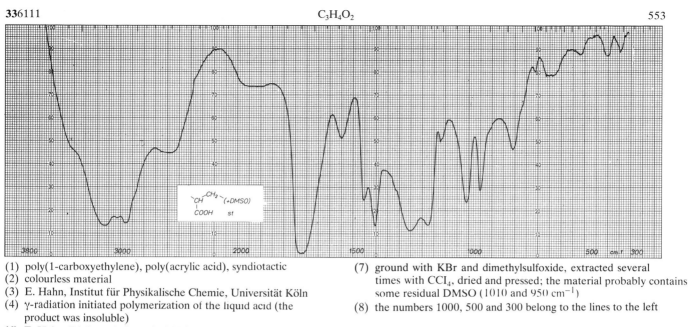

(1) poly(1-carboxyethylene), poly(acrylic acid), syndiotactic
(2) colourless material
(3) E. Hahn, Institut für Physikalische Chemie, Universität Köln
(4) γ-radiation initiated polymerization of the liquid acid (the product was insoluble)
(6) E. Hahn, Diplomarbeit, Köln 1975

(7) ground with KBr and dimethylsulfoxide, extracted several times with CCl$_4$, dried and pressed; the material probably contains some residual DMSO (1010 and 950 cm^{-1})
(8) the numbers 1000, 500 and 300 belong to the lines to the left

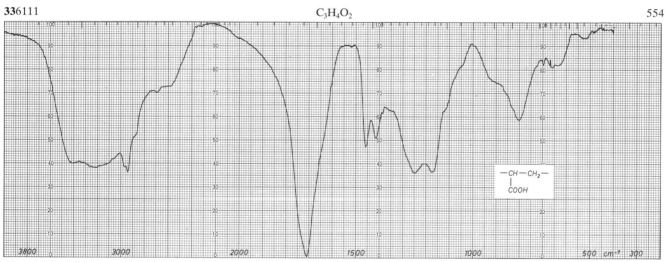

(1) poly(1-carboxyethylene), poly(acrylic acid), syndiotactic
(2) colourless material
(3) E. Hahn, Institut für Physikalische Chemie, Universität Köln

(4) γ-radiation initiated polymerization of the liquid acid (the product was insoluble)
(6) E. Hahn, Diplomarbeit, Köln 1975
(7) KBr (2/350)

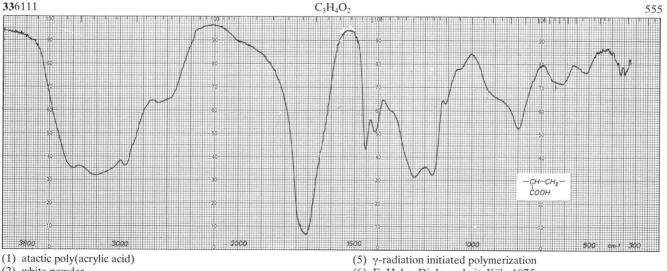

(1) atactic poly(acrylic acid)
(2) white powder
(3) E. Hahn, Institut für Physikalische Chemie, Universität Köln

(5) γ-radiation initiated polymerization
(6) E. Hahn, Diplomarbeit, Köln 1975
(7) KBr (1.2/350)

336111–4212127 $C_3H_4O_2$–C_6H_9NO 556

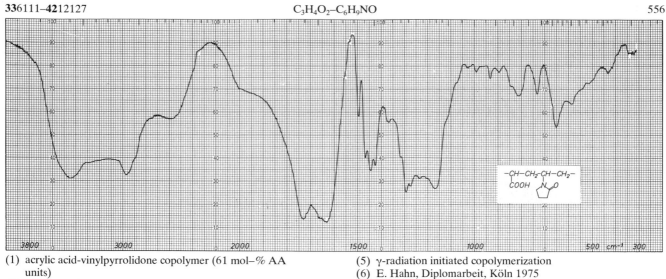

(1) acrylic acid-vinylpyrrolidone copolymer (61 mol–% AA units)
(2) white powder
(3) E. Hahn, Institut für Physikalische Chemie, Universität Köln
(5) γ-radiation initiated copolymerization
(6) E. Hahn, Diplomarbeit, Köln 1975
(7) KBr (3/350)

336112 $C_4H_6O_2$ 557

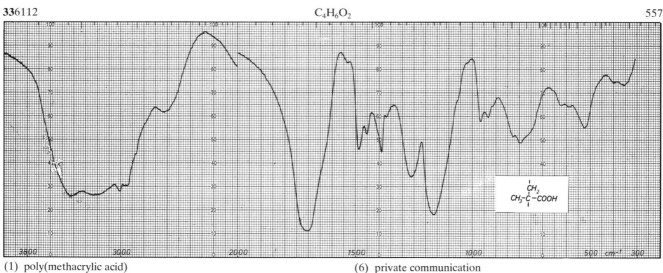

(1) poly(methacrylic acid)
(2) white granules
(3) Röhm GmbH, Darmstadt
(6) private communication
(7) ground with KBr (2/300) and H_2O, dried and pressed

336112 $C_5H_5O_4$ 558

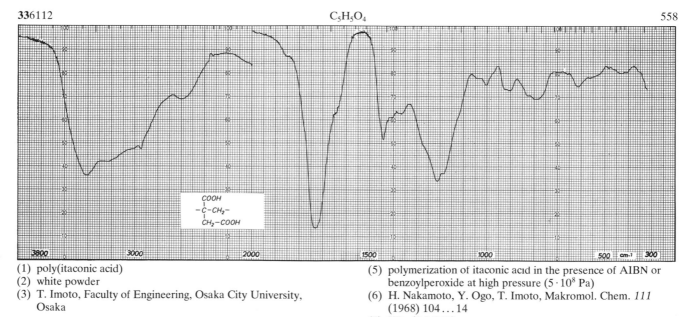

(1) poly(itaconic acid)
(2) white powder
(3) T. Imoto, Faculty of Engineering, Osaka City University, Osaka
(5) polymerization of itaconic acid in the presence of AIBN or benzoylperoxide at high pressure ($5 \cdot 10^8$ Pa)
(6) H. Nakamoto, Y. Ogo, T. Imoto, Makromol. Chem. *111* (1968) 104...14
(7) KBr (0.8/350)

336112 $C_5H_5O_4$ 559

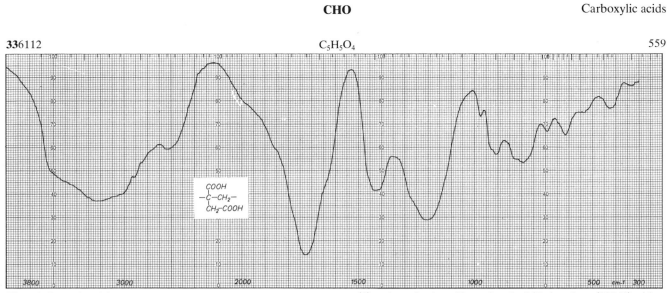

(1) poly(itaconic acid)
(2) colourless material
(3) K. Yokota, Materials Res. Lab., Nagoya Inst. of Technology, Nagoya

(5) polymerization of itaconic anhydride in xylene (333 K) with AIBN, hydrolysis of the polymer with water
(6) K. Yokota, T. Hirabayashi, T. Takashima, Makromol. Chem. *176* (1975) 1197...1205
(7) KBr (3/350)

336113 $C_{18}H_{24}O_{18}$ 560

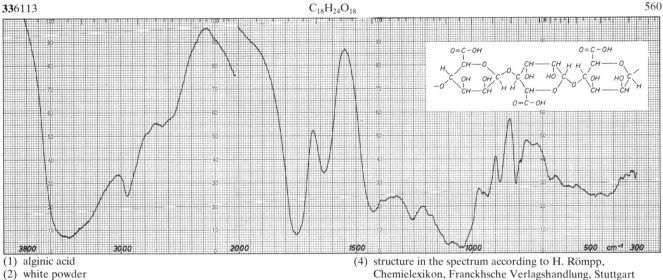

(1) alginic acid
(2) white powder
(3) P. Ander, Department of Chemistry, Seton Hall University, South Orange, N. J.

(4) structure in the spectrum according to H. Römpp, Chemielexikon, Franckhsche Verlagshandlung, Stuttgart
(5) from algae
(6) T. J. Podlas, P. Ander, Macromolecules *3* (1970) 154
(7) KBr (4.5/300)

336113–3331211–33831 $C_4H_2O_3$–C_3H_6O 561

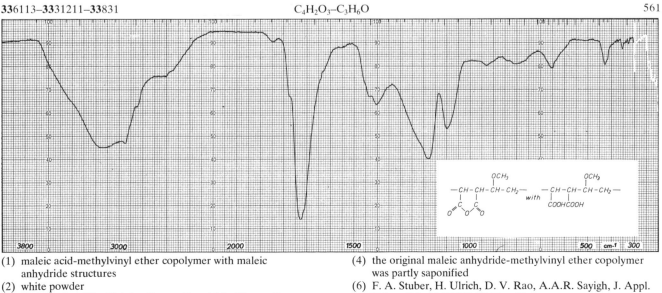

(1) maleic acid-methylvinyl ether copolymer with maleic anhydride structures
(2) white powder
(3) F. A. Stuber, The Upjohn Comp., Donald S. Gilmore Res. Labs., North Haven, Connecticut

(4) the original maleic anhydride-methylvinyl ether copolymer was partly saponified
(6) F. A. Stuber, H. Ulrich, D. V. Rao, A.A.R. Sayigh, J. Appl. Polym. Sci. *13* (1969) 2247...55
(7) film from CH_3OH/acetone on CsI

336113–3331211 $C_{10}H_{16}O_5$ 562

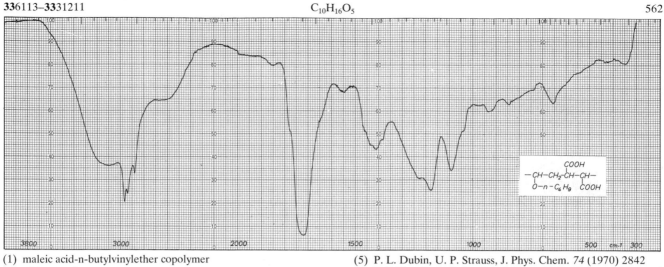

(1) maleic acid-n-butylvinylether copolymer
(2) white powder
(3) F. E. Treloar, School of Chemistry, University of Melbourne, Parkville, Victoria

(5) P. L. Dubin, U. P. Strauss, J. Phys. Chem. *74* (1970) 2842
(6) P. J. Kay, D. P. Kelly, G. I. Milgate, F. E. Treloar, Makromol. Chem. *177* (1976) 885 ... 93
(7) film from $CHCl_3$ on CsI

336213 $C_{18}H_{21}O_{18}K_3$ 563

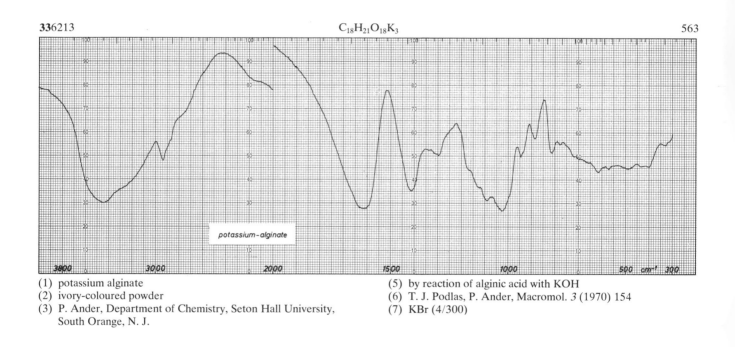

potassium-alginate

(1) potassium alginate
(2) ivory-coloured powder
(3) P. Ander, Department of Chemistry, Seton Hall University, South Orange, N. J.

(5) by reaction of alginic acid with KOH
(6) T. J. Podlas, P. Ander, Macromol. *3* (1970) 154
(7) KBr (4/300)

336213 $C_{18}H_{21}O_{18}K_3$ 564

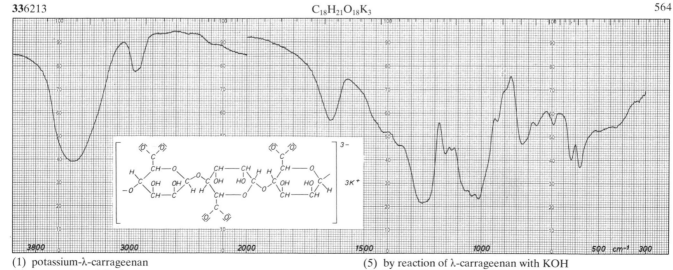

188

(1) potassium-λ-carrageenan
(2) ivory-coloured flocks
(3) P. Ander, Department of Chemistry, Seton Hall University, South Orange, N. J.

(5) by reaction of λ-carrageenan with KOH
(6) T. J. Podlas, P. Ander, Macromol. *3* (1970) 154
(7) KBr (2/300)

336213 $C_{18}H_{21}O_{18}K_3$ 565

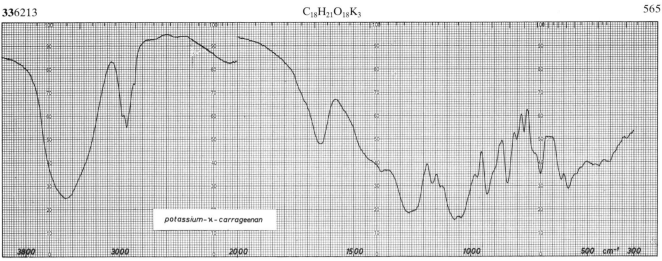

potassium-x-carrageenan

(1) potassium-x-carrageenan
(2) ivory-coloured powder
(3) P. Ander, Department of Chemistry, Seton Hall University, South Orange, N. J.

(5) by reaction of x-carrageenan with KOH
(6) T. J. Podlas, P. Ander, Macromol. 3 (1970) 154
(7) KBr (4.5/300)

336212 $C_4H_5O_2K$ 566

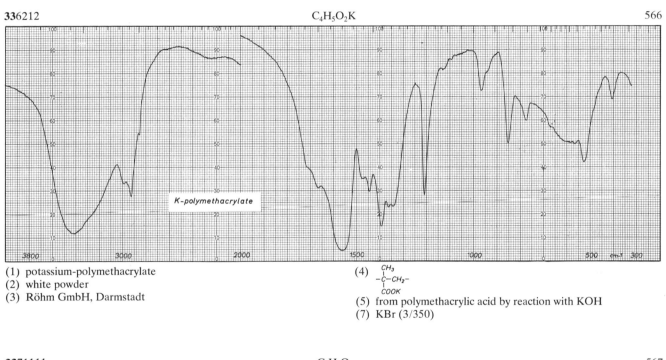

K-polymethacrylate

(1) potassium-polymethacrylate
(2) white powder
(3) Röhm GmbH, Darmstadt

(4)
$$-\overset{\overset{\displaystyle CH_3}{|}}{\underset{\underset{\displaystyle COOK}{|}}{C}}-CH_2-$$

(5) from polymethacrylic acid by reaction with KOH
(7) KBr (3/350)

3371111 $C_3H_4O_2$ 567

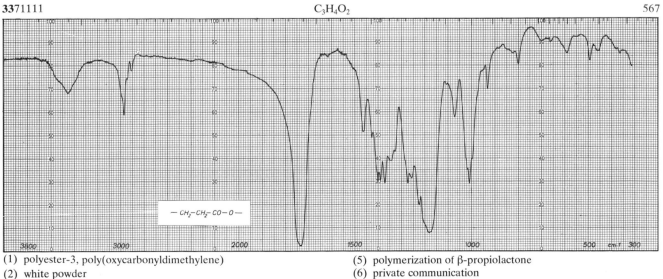

— CH₂—CH₂— CO—O —

(1) polyester-3, poly(oxycarbonyldimethylene)
(2) white powder
(3) H. Cherdron, Hoechst AG, Ffm.-Höchst

(5) polymerization of β-propiolactone
(6) private communication
(7) KBr (1/350)

189

3371111 $C_3H_4O_2$ 568

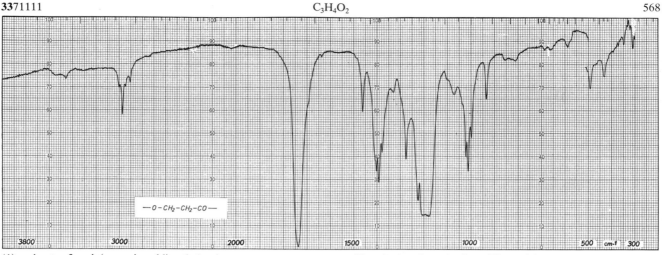

(1) polyester-3, poly(oxycarbonyldimethylene)
(2) white powder
(3) M. Okada, Department of Synthetic Chemistry, Faculty of Engineering, Nagoya University, Nagoya

(5) anionic polymerization of β-propiolactone
(6) private communication: see also Y. Yamashita, T. Tsuda, H. Ishida, A. Uchikawa, Y. Kuriyama, Chem. *113* (1968) 139...46

3371111 $C_5H_8O_2$ 569

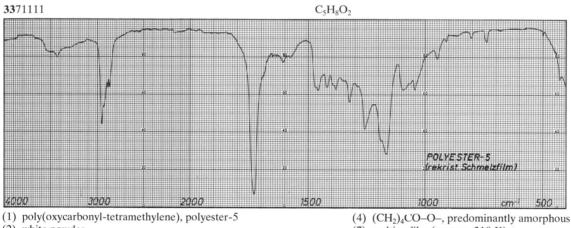

POLYESTER-5
(rekrist Schmelzfilm)

(1) poly(oxycarbonyl-tetramethylene), polyester-5
(2) white powder
(3) G. Sielaff, Institut für Physikalische Chemie, Universität Köln/Hoechst AG, Ffm.-Höchst

(4) (CH$_2$)$_4$CO–O–, predominantly amorphous
(7) melting film (approx. 310 K)

3371111 $C_5H_8O_2$ 570

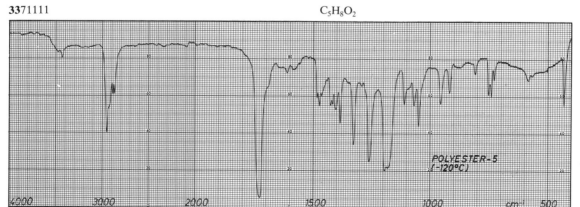

POLYESTER-5
(-120°C)

(1) (1)...(3), see above
(7) recrystallized melting film (approx. 153 K)

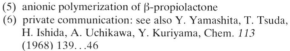
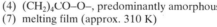
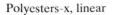

3371111 $C_6H_{10}O_2$ 571

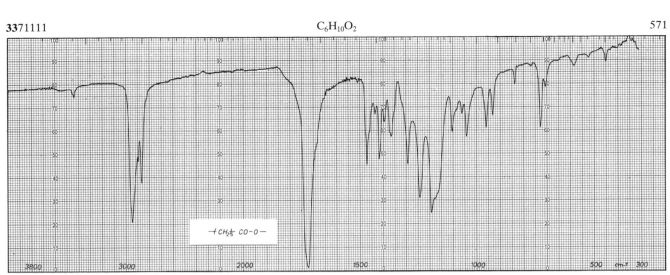

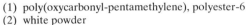

(1) poly(oxycarbonyl-pentamethylene), polyester-6
(2) white powder
(3) H. Cherdron, Hoechst AG, Ffm.-Höchst

(5) polymerization of ε-caprolactone
(7) film from $CHCl_3$ on CsI

3371111 $C_6H_{10}O_2$ 572

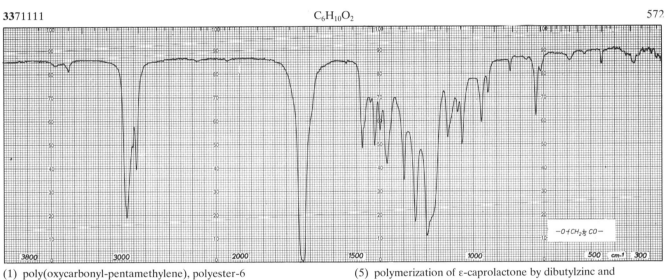

(1) poly(oxycarbonyl-pentamethylene), polyester-6
(2) white powder
(3) J. V. Koleske, Union Carbide Corp., Chemicals and Plastics, Technical Centre, South Charleston, W. Va.

(5) polymerization of ε-caprolactone by dibutylzinc and triisobutylaluminum
(6) R. D. Lundberg, J. V. Koleske, K. B. Wischmann, J. Polym. Sci. A-1 7 (1969) 2915...30
(7) film from $CH–Cl_3$ on CsI

3371111 $C_6H_{10}O_2$ 573

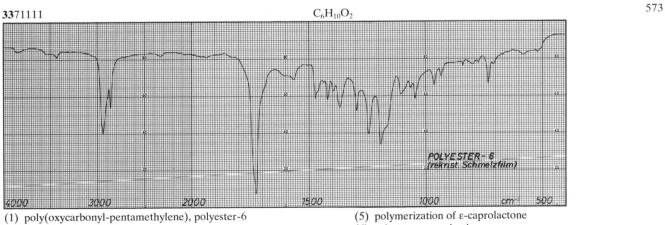

(1) poly(oxycarbonyl-pentamethylene), polyester-6
(2) white powder
(3) G. Sielaff, Institut für Physikalische Chemie, Universität Köln/Hoechst AG, Ffm-Höchst
(4) predominantly amorphous

(5) polymerization of ε-caprolactone
(6) private communication
(7) melting film (approx. 310 K)

3371111 $C_6H_{10}O_2$ 574

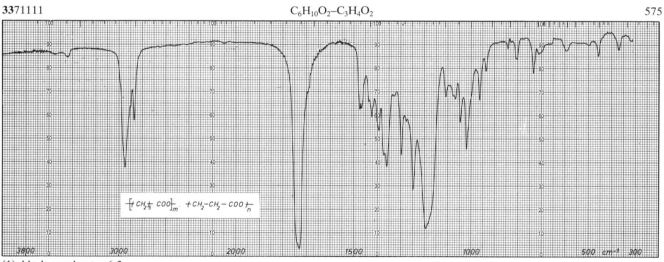

POLYESTER-6
(-120°C)

(1) ....(3) see above
(4) crystalline
(7) film from the melt (approx. 153 K)

3371111 $C_6H_{10}O_2-C_3H_4O_2$ 575

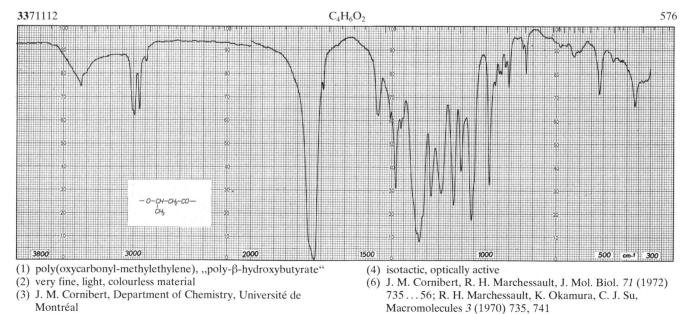

$-[CH_2\frac{}{5} COO]_m +CH_2-CH_2-COO+_n$

(1) block-copolyester-6,3
(2) white powder
(7) partly recrystallized film from $CHCl_3$ on CsI

3371112 $C_4H_6O_2$ 576

$-O-CH-CH_2-CO-$
$\quad\quad|$
$\quad\quad CH_3$

(1) poly(oxycarbonyl-methylethylene), „poly-ß-hydroxybutyrate"
(2) very fine, light, colourless material
(3) J. M. Cornibert, Department of Chemistry, Université de
Montréal
(4) isotactic, optically active
(6) J. M. Cornibert, R. H. Marchessault, J. Mol. Biol. 71 (1972)
735...56; R. H. Marchessault, K. Okamura, C. J. Su,
Macromolecules 3 (1970) 735, 741
(7) KBr (0,7/300)

3371112   C$_4$H$_6$O$_2$ 577

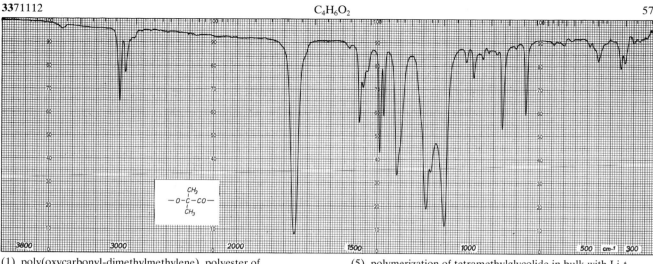

(1) poly(oxycarbonyl-dimethylmethylene), polyester of α-hydroxy-isobutyric acid
(2) colourless material
(3) H. Deibig, Battelle Institut, Frankfurt/M.
(4) crystalline
(5) polymerization of tetramethylglycolide in bulk with Li-t-butylate at 393...413 K
(6) H. Deibig, J. Geiger, M. Sander, Makromol. Chem. 145 (1971) 23...31
(7) film from ChCl$_3$ on CsI

3371112   C$_5$H$_8$O$_2$ 578

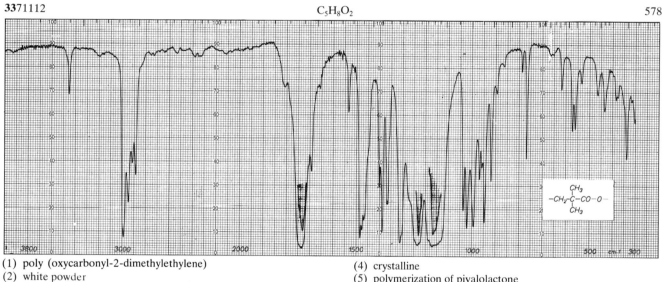

(1) poly (oxycarbonyl-2-dimethylethylene)
(2) white powder
(3) T. E. Mackey, E. I. Du Pont de Nemours & Comp., Wilmington, Dela.
(4) crystalline
(5) polymerization of pivalolactone
(6) R. G. Beaman, Polymer Preprints 11 (1970) 21
(7) recrystallized film from the melt

3371112   C$_5$H$_8$O$_2$ 579

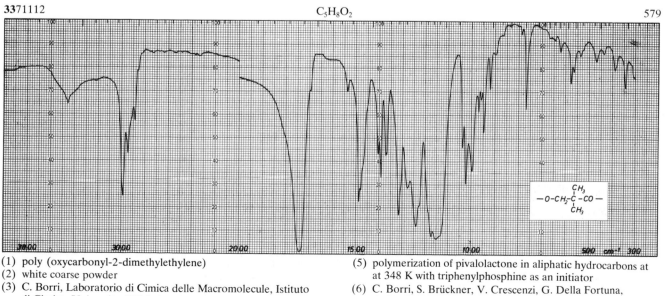

(1) poly (oxycarbonyl-2-dimethylethylene)
(2) white coarse powder
(3) C. Borri, Laboratorio di Cimica delle Macromolecule, Istituto di Cimica, Universita di Trieste
(4) crystalline
(5) polymerization of pivalolactone in aliphatic hydrocarbons at at 348 K with triphenylphosphine as an initiator
(6) C. Borri, S. Brückner, V. Crescenzi, G. Della Fortuna, A. Mariano, P. Scarazzato, Europ. Polym. J. 7 (1971) 1515...26
(7) ground with KBr (1/300) and CHCl$_3$, dried and pressed

3371112 $C_4H_8O_2$ 580

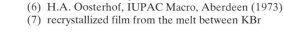

(1) poly(oxycarbonyl-2-dimethylethylene)
(2) white powder
(3) H.A. Oosterhof, Koninklijke Shell-Laboratorium, Amsterdam
(4) crystalline
(5) polymerization of pivalolactone; N.R. Mayne, Chem. Tech., December 1972, p. 728
(6) H.A. Oosterhof, IUPAC Macro, Aberdeen (1973)
(7) recrystallized film from the melt between KBr

3371112–**32**2153 $C_4H_6O_2$–C_4H_5N 581

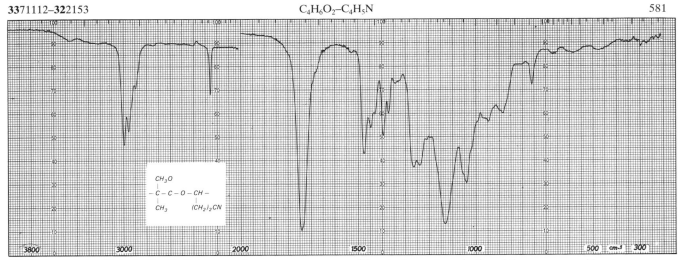

(1) β-cyanopropionaldehyde-dimethylketene copolymer [39 mol-% OCH–(CH$_2$)$_2$CN units]; copoly(oxycarbonyldimethylmethylene-2-cyanoethylene-me-thylene)
(2) white powder
(3) K. Hashimoto, Faculty of Agriculture, Nagoya University
(5) anionic copolymerization of the monomers with benzophenone-dilithium complex as initiator
(6) K. Hashimoto, H. Sumitomo, Polym J. *1* (1970) 190...7
(7) film from CHCl$_3$ on CsI

3371113 $C_{21}H_{34}O_2$ 582

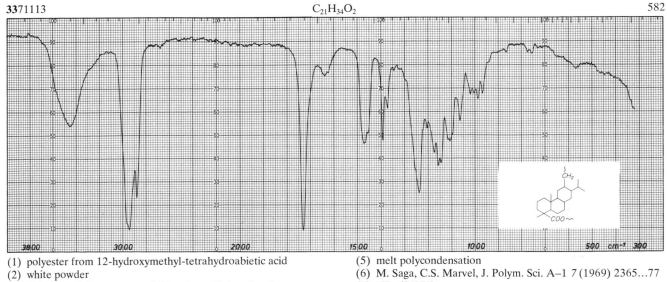

(1) polyester from 12-hydroxymethyl-tetrahydroabietic acid
(2) white powder
(3) C.S. Marvel, Department of Chemistry, University of Arizona, Tucson, Ariz.
(5) melt polycondensation
(6) M. Saga, C.S. Marvel, J. Polym. Sci. A–1 7 (1969) 2365...77
(7) KBr (2/350)

3371113 $C_{21}H_{32}O_2$ 583

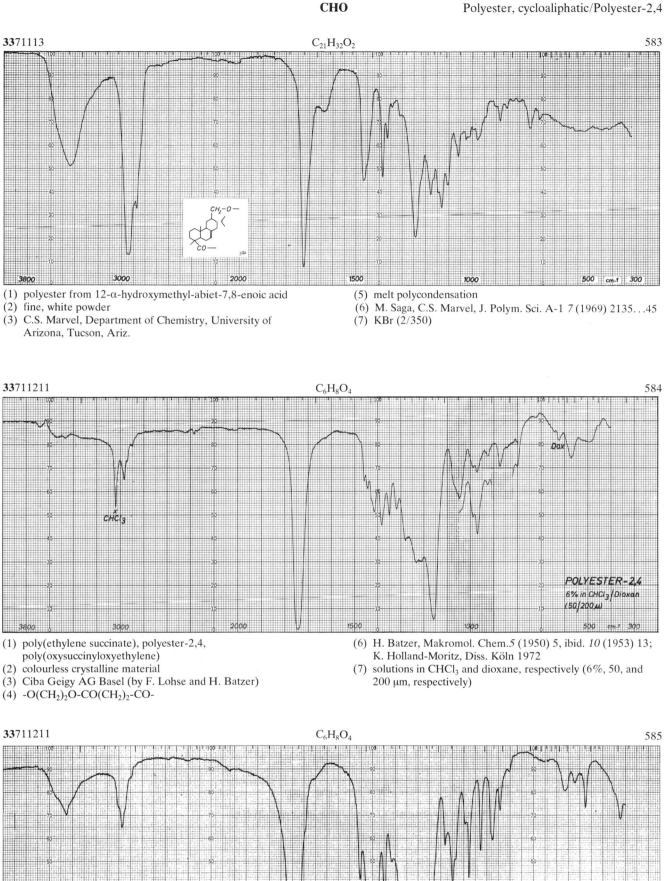

(1) polyester from 12-α-hydroxymethyl-abiet-7,8-enoic acid
(2) fine, white powder
(3) C.S. Marvel, Department of Chemistry, University of Arizona, Tucson, Ariz.
(5) melt polycondensation
(6) M. Saga, C.S. Marvel, J. Polym. Sci. A-1 7 (1969) 2135...45
(7) KBr (2/350)

3371211 $C_6H_8O_4$ 584

POLYESTER-2,4
6% in CHCl₃ / Dioxan
(50/200 μ)

CHCl₃

(1) poly(ethylene succinate), polyester-2,4, poly(oxysuccinyloxyethylene)
(2) colourless crystalline material
(3) Ciba Geigy AG Basel (by F. Lohse and H. Batzer)
(4) -O(CH₂)₂O-CO(CH₂)₂-CO-
(6) H. Batzer, Makromol. Chem.5 (1950) 5, ibid. 10 (1953) 13; K. Holland-Moritz, Diss. Köln 1972
(7) solutions in CHCl₃ and dioxane, respectively (6%, 50, and 200 μm, respectively)

3371211 $C_6H_8O_4$ 585

-O-(CH₂)₂O-CO-(CH₂)₂CO-

(1) poly(ethylene succinate), polyester-2,4, poly(oxysuccinyloxyethylene)
(2) colourless material
(3) H. Tadokoro, Department of Polymer Science, Osaka University, Toyonaka
(5) obtained by polycondensation
(6) private communication
(7) KBr (1/350)

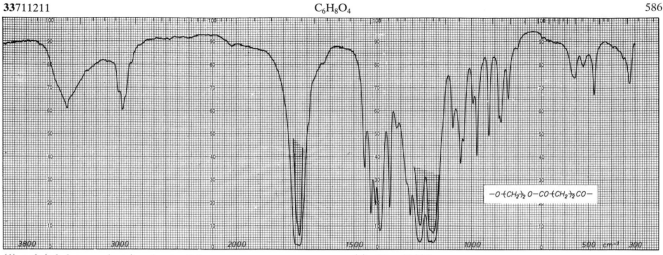

(1) poly(ethylene succinate), polyester-2,4,
   poly(oxysuccinyloxyethylene)
(2) colourless material
(3) K. Ueberreiter, Fritz-Haber-Institut der Max-Planck-
   Gesellschaft, Berlin

(4) M ≈ 10000
(6) K. Ueberreiter, K.-J. Lucas, Makromol. Chem. *140* (1970)
   65...81
(7) KBr (1/350)

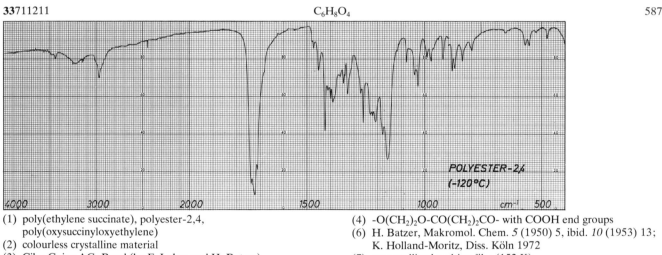

(1) poly(ethylene succinate), polyester-2,4,
   poly(oxysuccinyloxyethylene)
(2) colourless crystalline material
(3) Ciba-Geigy AG, Basel (by F. Lohse and H. Batzer)

(4) -O(CH$_2$)$_2$O-CO(CH$_2$)$_2$CO- with COOH end groups
(6) H. Batzer, Makromol. Chem. *5* (1950) 5, ibid. *10* (1953) 13;
   K. Holland-Moritz, Diss. Köln 1972
(7) recrystallized melting film (152 K)

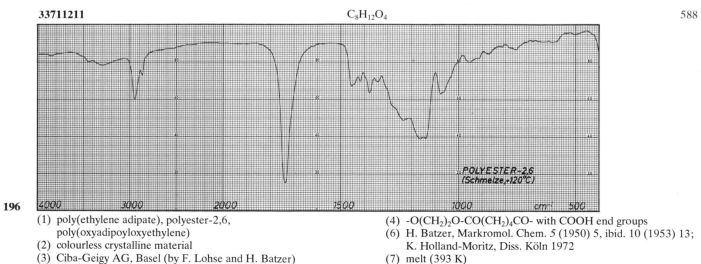

(1) poly(ethylene adipate), polyester-2,6,
   poly(oxyadipoyloxyethylene)
(2) colourless crystalline material
(3) Ciba-Geigy AG, Basel (by F. Lohse and H. Batzer)

(4) -O(CH$_2$)$_2$O-CO(CH$_2$)$_4$CO- with COOH end groups
(6) H. Batzer, Markromol. Chem. *5* (1950) 5, ibid. 10 (1953) 13;
   K. Holland-Moritz, Diss. Köln 1972
(7) melt (393 K)

33711211 $C_8H_{12}O_4$ 589

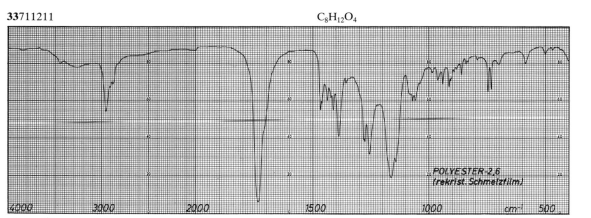

POLYESTER-2,6
(rekrist. Schmelzfilm)

(1) ... (6) see above
(7) recrystallized melting film (300 K)

33711211 $C_8H_{12}O_4$ 590

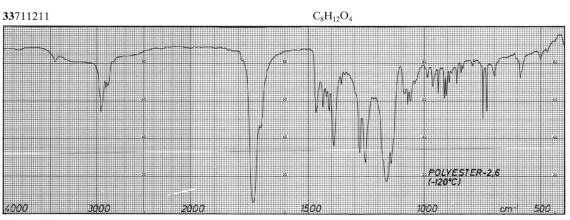

POLYESTER-2,6
(-120°C)

(1) ... (6) see above
(7) recrystallized melting film (153 K)

33711211 $C_{10}H_{16}O_4$ 591

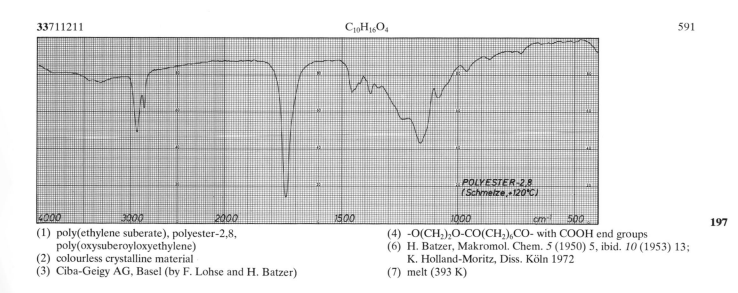

POLYESTER-2,8
(Schmelze,+120°C)

(1) poly(ethylene suberate), polyester-2,8,   (4) -O(CH$_2$)$_2$O-CO(CH$_2$)$_6$CO- with COOH end groups
    poly(oxysuberoyloxyethylene)   (6) H. Batzer, Makromol. Chem. 5 (1950) 5, ibid. 10 (1953) 13;
(2) colourless crystalline material   K. Holland-Moritz, Diss. Köln 1972
(3) Ciba-Geigy AG, Basel (by F. Lohse and H. Batzer) (7) melt (393 K)

33711211 $C_{10}H_{16}O_4$ 592

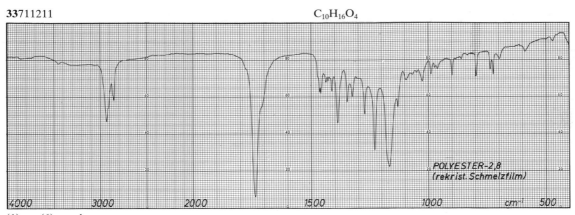

POLYESTER-2,8
(rekrist. Schmelzfilm)

(1) ...(6) see above
(7) recrystallized melting film (300 K)

33711211 $C_{10}H_{16}O_4$ 593

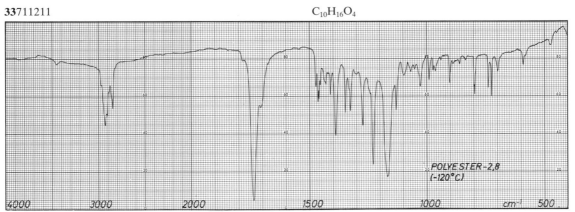

POLYESTER-2,8
(-120°C)

(1) ...(6) see above
(7) recrystallized melting film (153 K)

33711211 $C_{12}H_{20}O_4$ 594

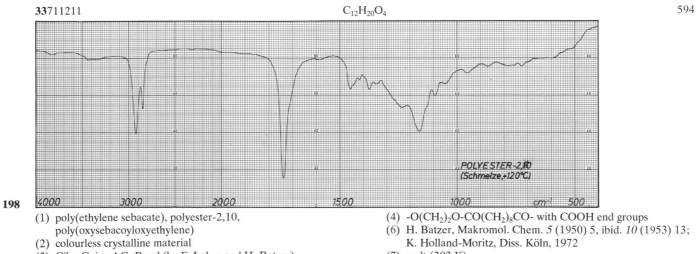

POLYESTER-2,10
(Schmelze,+120°C)

(1) poly(ethylene sebacate), polyester-2,10,
    poly(oxysebacoyloxyethylene)
(2) colourless crystalline material
(3) Ciba-Geigy AG, Basel (by F. Lohse and H. Batzer)

(4) $-O(CH_2)_2O-CO(CH_2)_8CO-$ with COOH end groups
(6) H. Batzer, Makromol. Chem. *5* (1950) 5, ibid. *10* (1953) 13;
    K. Holland-Moritz, Diss. Köln, 1972
(7) melt (393 K)

33711211 $C_{12}H_{20}O_4$ 595

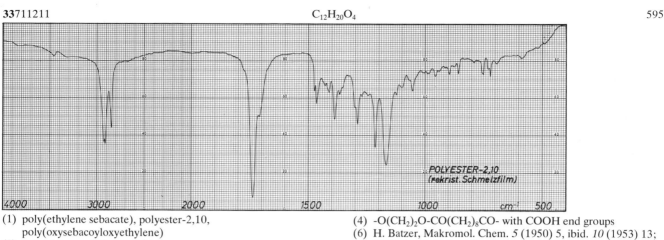

POLYESTER-2,10
(rekrist. Schmelzfilm)

(1) poly(ethylene sebacate), polyester-2,10,
     poly(oxysebacoyloxyethylene)
(2) colourless crystalline material
(3) Ciba-Geigy AG, Basel (by F. Lohse and H. Batzer)

(4) -O(CH$_2$)$_2$O-CO(CH$_2$)$_8$CO- with COOH end groups
(6) H. Batzer, Makromol. Chem. *5* (1950) 5, ibid. *10* (1953) 13;
     K. Holland-Moritz, Diss. Köln, 1972
(7) recrystallized melting film

33711211 $C_{12}H_{20}O_4$ 596

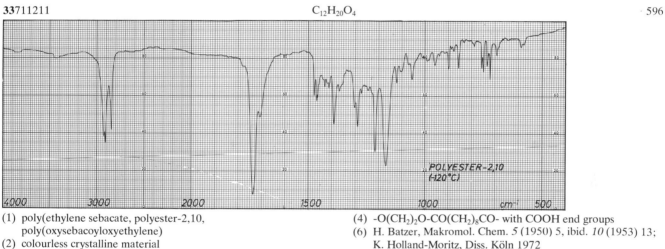

POLYESTER-2,10
(-120°C)

(1) poly(ethylene sebacate, polyester-2,10,
     poly(oxysebacoyloxyethylene)
(2) colourless crystalline material
(3) Ciba-Geigy AG, Basel (by F. Lohse and H. Batzer)

(4) -O(CH$_2$)$_2$O-CO(CH$_2$)$_8$CO- with COOH end groups
(6) H. Batzer, Makromol. Chem. *5* (1950) 5, ibid. *10* (1953) 13;
     K. Holland-Moritz, Diss. Köln 1972
(7) recrystallized melting film (153 K)

33711211 $C_8H_{12}O_4$ 597

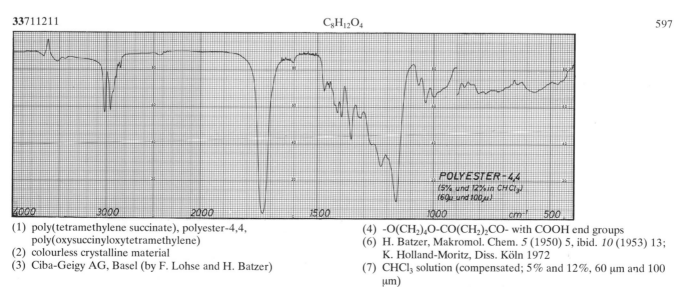

POLYESTER-4,4
(5% und 12% in CHCl$_3$)
(60μ und 100μ)

(1) poly(tetramethylene succinate), polyester-4,4,
     poly(oxysuccinyloxytetramethylene)
(2) colourless crystalline material
(3) Ciba-Geigy AG, Basel (by F. Lohse and H. Batzer)

(4) -O(CH$_2$)$_4$O-CO(CH$_2$)$_2$CO- with COOH end groups
(6) H. Batzer, Makromol. Chem. *5* (1950) 5, ibid. *10* (1953) 13;
     K. Holland-Moritz, Diss. Köln 1972
(7) CHCl$_3$ solution (compensated; 5% and 12%, 60 μm and 100 μm)

33711211 $C_8H_{12}O_4$ 598

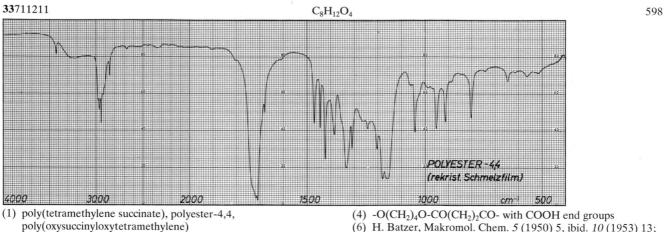

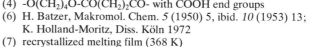

(1) poly(tetramethylene succinate), polyester-4,4, poly(oxysuccinyloxytetramethylene)
(2) colourless material
(3) Ciba-Geigy AG, Basel (by F. Lohse and H. Batzer)

(4) $-O(CH_2)_4O-CO(CH_2)_2CO-$ with COOH end groups
(6) H. Batzer, Makromol. Chem. *5* (1950) 5, ibid. *10* (1953) 13; K. Holland-Moritz, Diss. Köln 1972
(7) recrystallized melting film (368 K)

33711211 $C_8H_{12}O_4$ 599

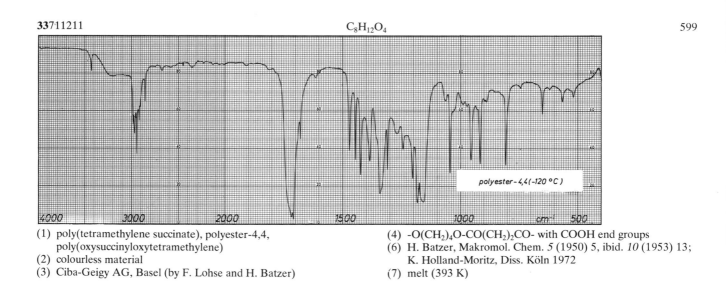

(1) poly(tetramethylene succinate), polyester-4,4, poly(oxysuccinyloxytetramethylene)
(2) colourless material
(3) Ciba-Geigy AG, Basel (by F. Lohse and H. Batzer)

(4) $-O(CH_2)_4O-CO(CH_2)_2CO-$ with COOH end groups
(6) H. Batzer, Makromol. Chem. *5* (1950) 5, ibid. *10* (1953) 13; K. Holland-Moritz, Diss. Köln 1972
(7) melt (393 K)

33711211 $C_8H_{12}O_4$ 600

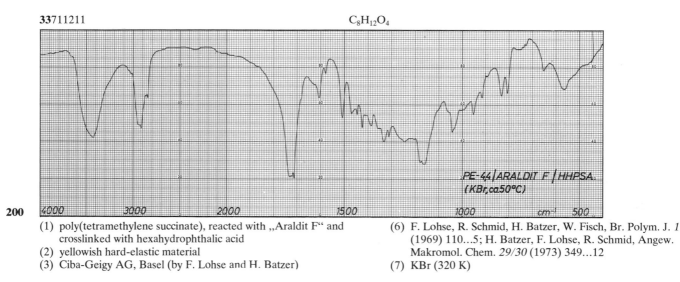

(1) poly(tetramethylene succinate), reacted with „Araldit F" and crosslinked with hexahydrophthalic acid
(2) yellowish hard-elastic material
(3) Ciba-Geigy AG, Basel (by F. Lohse and H. Batzer)

(6) F. Lohse, R. Schmid, H. Batzer, W. Fisch, Br. Polym. J. *1* (1969) 110...5; H. Batzer, F. Lohse, R. Schmid, Angew. Makromol. Chem. *29/30* (1973) 349...12
(7) KBr (320 K)

33711211 $C_8H_{12}O_4$ 601

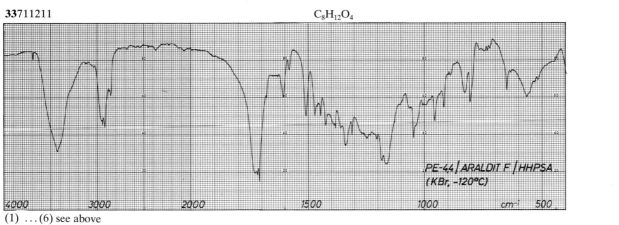

PE-44 / ARALDIT F / HHPSA
(KBr, -120°C)

(1) ...(6) see above
(7) KBr (153 K)

33711211 $C_{10}H_{16}O_4$ 602

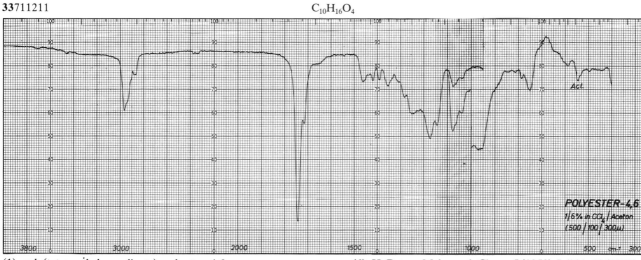

POLYESTER-4,6
1/6% in CCl₄ / Aceton
(500 / 100 / 300μ)

(1) poly(tetramethylene adipate), polyester-4,6,
poly(oxyadipoyloxytetramethylene)
(3) Ciba-Geigy AG, Basel (by F. Lohse and H. Batzer)
(4) -O(CH₂)₄O-CO(CH₂)₄CO- with carboxyl end groups

(6) H. Batzer, Makromol. Chem. *5* (1950) 5, ibid. *10* (1953) 13;
K. Holland-Moritz, Diss. Köln 1972
(7) solutions (1% and 6%) in CCl₄ and acetone, respectively (0,5
mm, 0,1 mm, and 0,3 mm, respectively)

33711211 $C_{10}H_{16}O_4$ 603

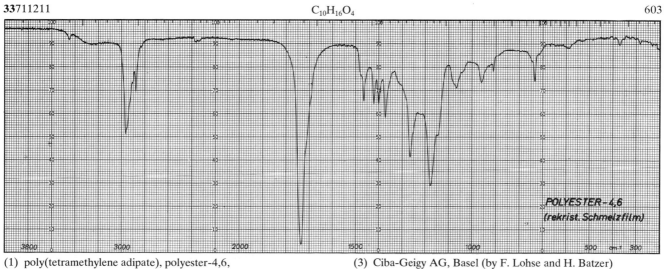

POLYESTER-4,6
(rekrist. Schmelzfilm)

(1) poly(tetramethylene adipate), polyester-4,6,
poly(oxyadipoyloxytetramethylene)
(2) colourless crystalline material

(3) Ciba-Geigy AG, Basel (by F. Lohse and H. Batzer)
(4) -O(CH₂)₄O-CO(CH₂)₄CO- with carboxyl end groups
(7) recrystallized melting film (323 K)

33711211 $C_{10}H_{16}O_4$ 604

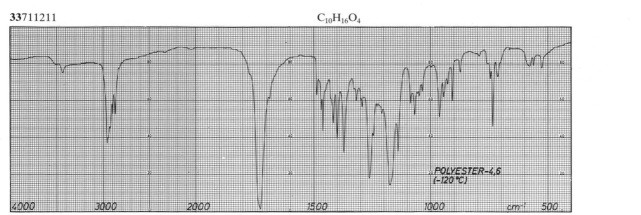

(1) poly(tetramethylene adipate), polyester-4,6, poly(oxyadipoyloxytetramethylene)
(3) Ciba-Geigy AG, Basel (by F. Lohse and H. Batzer)

(4) -O(CH$_2$)$_4$O-CO(CH$_2$)$_4$CO- with carboxyl end groups
(7) recrystallized melting film (153 K)

33711211 $C_{12}H_{20}O_4$ 605

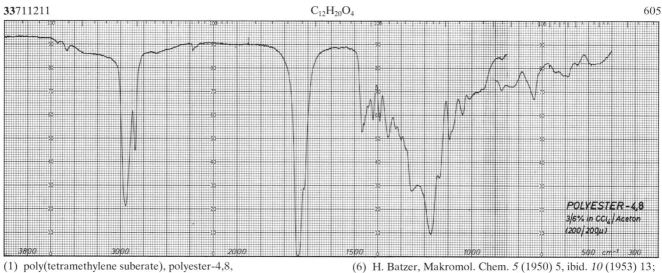

(1) poly(tetramethylene suberate), polyester-4,8, poly(oxysuberoyloxytetramethylene)
(3) Ciba-Geigy AG, Basel (by F. Lohse and H. Batzer)
(4) -O(CH$_2$)$_4$O-CO(CH$_2$)$_6$CO- with carboxyl end groups

(6) H. Batzer, Makromol. Chem. *5* (1950) 5, ibid. *10* (1953) 13; K. Holland-Moritz, Diss. Köln 1972
(7) solutions (3% and 6%) in CCl$_4$ and acetone, respectively (0,2 mm)

33711211 $C_{12}H_{20}O_4$ 606

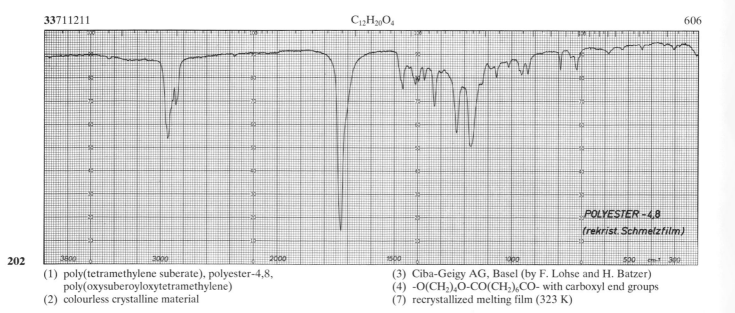

(1) poly(tetramethylene suberate), polyester-4,8, poly(oxysuberoyloxytetramethylene)
(2) colourless crystalline material

(3) Ciba-Geigy AG, Basel (by F. Lohse and H. Batzer)
(4) -O(CH$_2$)$_4$O-CO(CH$_2$)$_6$CO- with carboxyl end groups
(7) recrystallized melting film (323 K)

33711211   C$_{12}$H$_{20}$O$_4$ 607

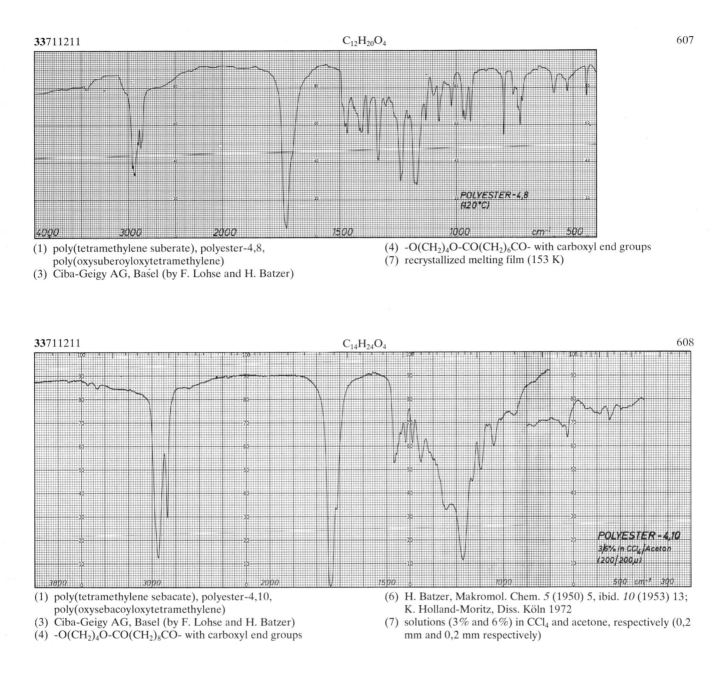

(1) poly(tetramethylene suberate), polyester-4,8, poly(oxysuberoyloxytetramethylene)

(3) Ciba-Geigy AG, Basel (by F. Lohse and H. Batzer)

(4) -O(CH$_2$)$_4$O-CO(CH$_2$)$_6$CO- with carboxyl end groups

(7) recrystallized melting film (153 K)

33711211   C$_{14}$H$_{24}$O$_4$ 608

(1) poly(tetramethylene sebacate), polyester-4,10, poly(oxysebacoyloxytetramethylene)

(3) Ciba-Geigy AG, Basel (by F. Lohse and H. Batzer)

(4) -O(CH$_2$)$_4$O-CO(CH$_2$)$_8$CO- with carboxyl end groups

(6) H. Batzer, Makromol. Chem. *5* (1950) 5, ibid. *10* (1953) 13; K. Holland-Moritz, Diss. Köln 1972

(7) solutions (3% and 6%) in CCl$_4$ and acetone, respectively (0,2 mm and 0,2 mm respectively)

33711211   C$_{14}$H$_{24}$O$_4$ 609

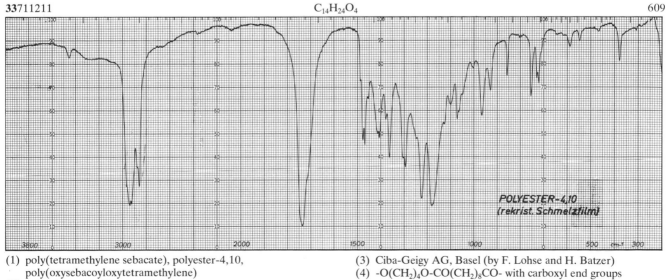

(1) poly(tetramethylene sebacate), polyester-4,10, poly(oxysebacoyloxytetramethylene)

(2) colourless crystalline material

(3) Ciba-Geigy AG, Basel (by F. Lohse and H. Batzer)

(4) -O(CH$_2$)$_4$O-CO(CH$_2$)$_8$CO- with carboxyl end groups

(7) recrystallized melting film (323 K)

33711211 $C_{14}H_{24}O_4$ 610

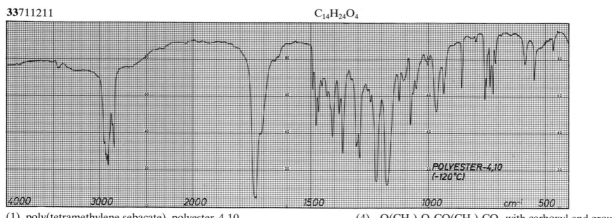

POLYESTER-4,10
(-120°C)

(1) poly(tetramethylene sebacate), polyester-4,10,
poly(oxysebacoyloxytetramethylene)
(3) Ciba-Geigy AG, Basel (by F. Lohse and H. Batzer)

(4) -O(CH₂)₄O-CO(CH₂)₈CO- with carboxyl end groups
(7) recrystallized melting film (153 K)

33711211 $C_{10}H_{16}O_4$ 611

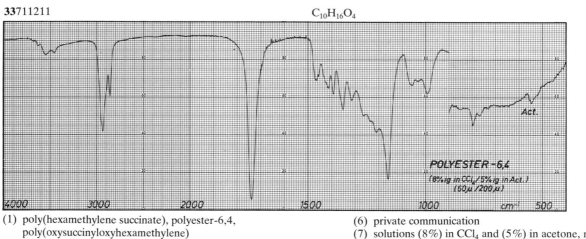

POLYESTER-6,4
(8%ig in CCl₄/5%ig in Act.)
(60μ/200μ)
Act.

(1) poly(hexamethylene succinate), polyester-6,4,
poly(oxysuccinyloxyhexamethylene)
(3) E. Knappe, Glasurit-Werke, Hiltrup
(4) -O(CH₂)₆O-CO(CH₂)₂CO- with alcoholic end groups

(6) private communication
(7) solutions (8%) in CCl₄ and (5%) in acetone, respectively
(0,06 mm and 0,2 mm, respectively)

33711211 $C_{10}H_{16}O_4$ 612

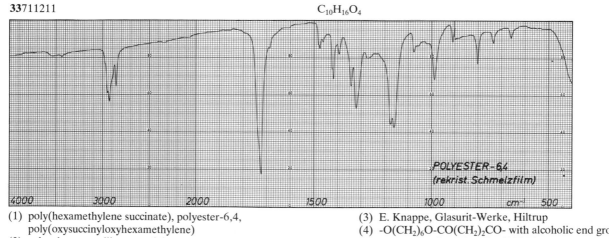

POLYESTER-6,4
(rekrist. Schmelzfilm)

(1) poly(hexamethylene succinate), polyester-6,4,
poly(oxysuccinyloxyhexamethylene)
(2) colourless crystalline material

(3) E. Knappe, Glasurit-Werke, Hiltrup
(4) -O(CH₂)₆O-CO(CH₂)₂CO- with alcoholic end groups
(7) recrystallized melting film (323 K)

33711211   C$_{10}$H$_{16}$O$_4$ 613

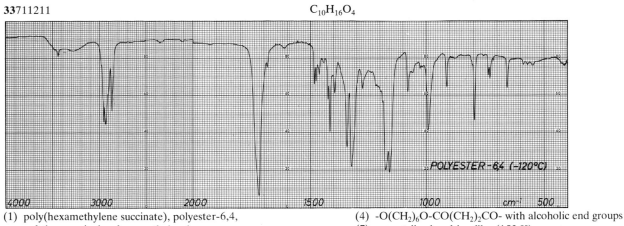

(1) poly(hexamethylene succinate), polyester-6,4,
    poly(oxysuccinyloxyhexamethylene)
(3) E. Knappe, Glasurit-Werke, Hiltrup

(4) -O(CH$_2$)$_6$O-CO(CH$_2$)$_2$CO- with alcoholic end groups
(7) recrystallzed melting film (153 K)

3311211   C$_{12}$H$_{20}$O$_4$ 614

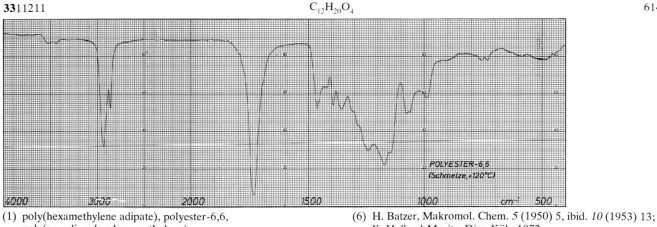

(1) poly(hexamethylene adipate), polyester-6,6,
    poly(oxyadipoyloxyhexamethylene)
(3) Ciba-Geigy AG, Basel (by F. Lohse and H. Batzer)
(4) -O(CH$_2$)$_6$O-C(CH$_2$)$_4$CO- with carboxyl end groups

(6) H. Batzer, Makromol. Chem. *5* (1950) 5, ibid. *10* (1953) 13;
    K. Holland-Moritz, Diss. Köln 1972
(7) melt (393 K)

33711211   C$_{12}$H$_{20}$O$_4$ 615

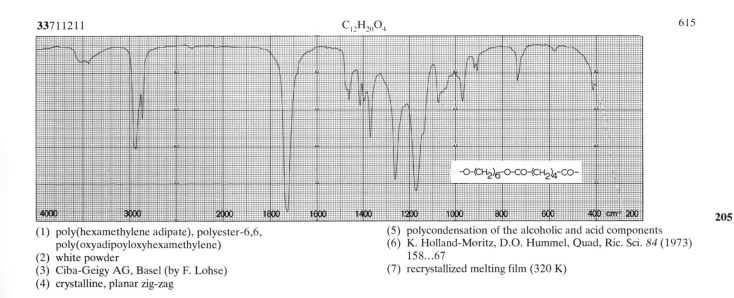

(1) poly(hexamethylene adipate), polyester-6,6,
    poly(oxyadipoyloxyhexamethylene)
(2) white powder
(3) Ciba-Geigy AG, Basel (by F. Lohse)
(4) crystalline, planar zig-zag

(5) polycondensation of the alcoholic and acid components
(6) K. Holland-Moritz, D.O. Hummel, Quad, Ric. Sci. *84* (1973)
    158...67
(7) recrystallized melting film (320 K)

33711211 $C_{12}H_{20}O_4$ 616

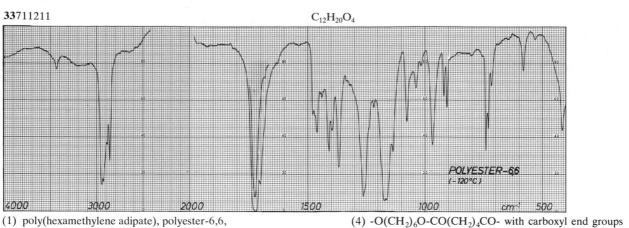

POLYESTER-66
(–120°C)

(1) poly(hexamethylene adipate), polyester-6,6,
     poly(oxyadipoyloxyhexamethylene)
(3) Ciba-Geigy AG, Basel (by F. Lohse and H. Batzer)

(4) -O(CH$_2$)$_6$O-CO(CH$_2$)$_4$CO- with carboxyl end groups
(7) recrystallized melting film (153 K)

33711211 $C_{12}H_{20}O_4$ 617

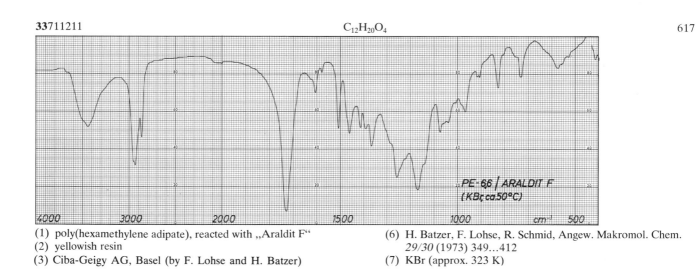

PE-66 / ARALDIT F
(KBr, ca. 50°C)

(1) poly(hexamethylene adipate), reacted with ,,Araldit F"
(2) yellowish resin
(3) Ciba-Geigy AG, Basel (by F. Lohse and H. Batzer)

(6) H. Batzer, F. Lohse, R. Schmid, Angew. Makromol. Chem.
     29/30 (1973) 349...412
(7) KBr (approx. 323 K)

33711211 $C_{12}H_{20}O_4$ 618

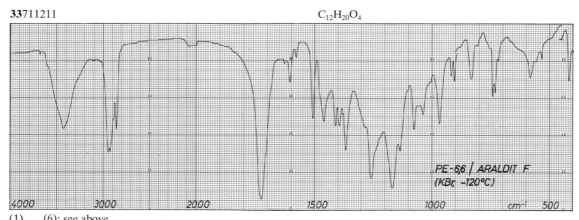

PE-66 / ARALDIT F
(KBr, –120°C)

(1) ...(6): see above
(7) KBr (153 K)

33711211 $C_{12}H_{20}O_4$ 619

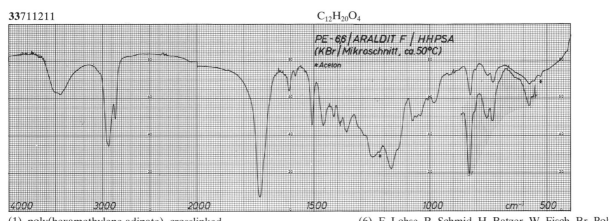

(1) poly(hexamethylene adipate), crosslinked
(2) yellowish elastomer
(3) Ciba-Geigy AG, Basel (by F. Lohse and H. Batzer)
(4) PE-6,6 with acid end groups, prolonged with Araldite F and
    crosslinked with hexahydrophthalic anhydride

(6) F. Lohse, R. Schmid, H. Batzer, W. Fisch, Br. Polym. J. *1*
    (1969) 110...5; H. Batzer, F. Lohse, R. Schmid, Angew.
    Makromol. Chem. *29/30* (1973) 349...412
(7) microslice, KBr (323 K)

33711211 $C_{12}H_{20}O_4$ 620

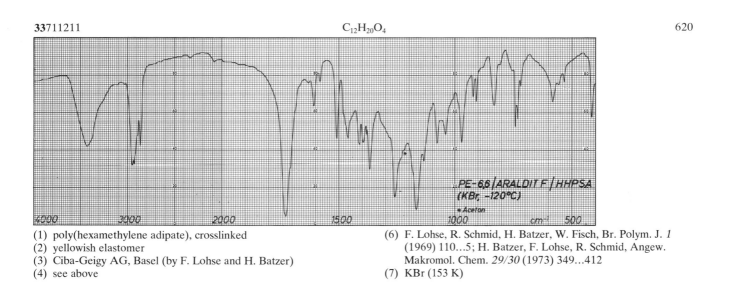

(1) poly(hexamethylene adipate), crosslinked
(2) yellowish elastomer
(3) Ciba-Geigy AG, Basel (by F. Lohse and H. Batzer)
(4) see above

(6) F. Lohse, R. Schmid, H. Batzer, W. Fisch, Br. Polym. J. *1*
    (1969) 110...5; H. Batzer, F. Lohse, R. Schmid, Angew.
    Makromol. Chem. *29/30* (1973) 349...412
(7) KBr (153 K)

33711211 $C_{12}H_{20}O_4 – C_{20}H_{36}O_4$ 621

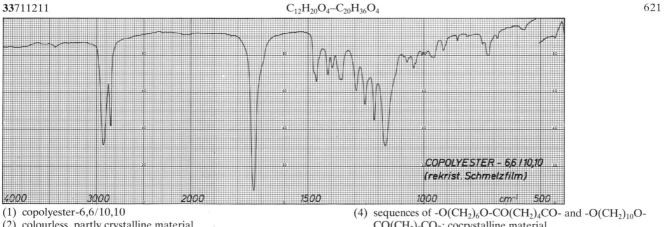

(1) copolyester-6,6/10,10
(2) colourless, partly crystalline material
(3) G.J. Howard, Dept. of Polymer and Fibre Science, Institute of
    Science and Technology, University of Manchester

(4) sequences of -O(CH$_2$)$_6$O-CO(CH$_2$)$_4$CO- and -O(CH$_2$)$_{10}$O-
    CO(CH$_2$)$_8$CO-; cocrystalline material
(5) ester interchange between polyester-6,6 and polyester-10,10
(6) G.J. Howard, S. Knutton, Polymer. *9* (1968) 527...34
(7) recrystallized film (323 K)

33711211   C$_{12}$H$_{20}$O$_4$–C$_{20}$H$_{36}$O$_4$ 622

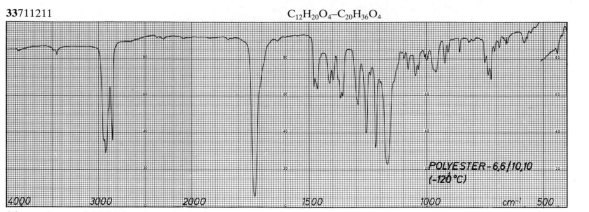

POLYESTER-6,6/10,10
(-120°C)

(1) copolyester-6,6/10,10
(3) G.J. Howard, Dept. of Polymer and Fibre Science, Institute of Science and Technology, University of Manchester
(4) cocrystalline material
(5) ester interchange between polyester-6,6 and polyester-10,10
(6) G.J. Howard, S. Knutton, Polymer *9* (1968) 527...34
(7) recrystallized film (153 K)

33711211   C$_{14}$H$_{24}$O$_4$ 623

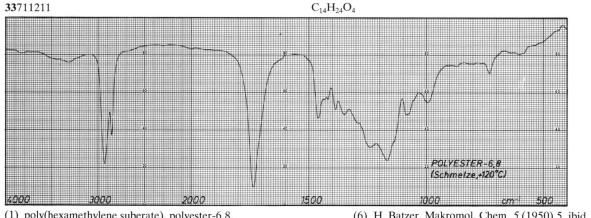

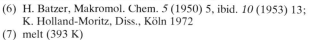
POLYESTER-6,8
(Schmelze,+120°C)

(1) poly(hexamethylene suberate), polyester-6,8, poly(oxysuberoyloxyhexamethylene)
(3) Ciba Geigy AG, Basel (by F. Lohse and H. Batzer)
(4) -O(CH$_2$)$_6$O-CO(CH$_2$)$_6$CO- with carboxyl end groups
(6) H. Batzer, Makromol. Chem. *5* (1950) 5, ibid. *10* (1953) 13; K. Holland-Moritz, Diss., Köln 1972
(7) melt (393 K)

33711211   C$_{14}$H$_{24}$O$_4$ 624

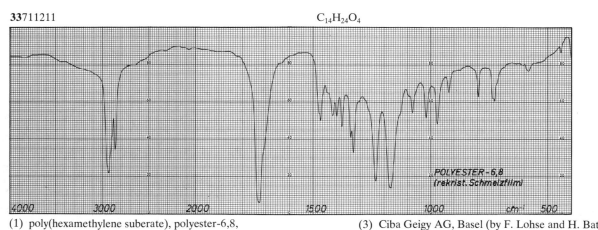

POLYESTER-6,8
(rekrist. Schmelzfilm)

(1) poly(hexamethylene suberate), polyester-6,8, poly(oxysuberoyloxyhexamethylene)
(2) colourless crystalline material
(3) Ciba Geigy AG, Basel (by F. Lohse and H. Batzer)
(4) -O(CH$_2$)$_6$O-CO(CH$_2$)$_6$CO- with carboxyl end groups
(7) recrystallized melting film (323 K)

33711211 $C_{14}H_{24}O_4$ 625

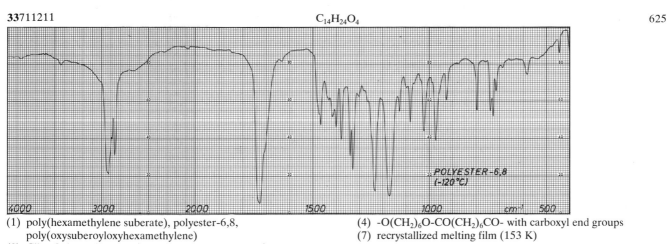
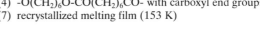

(1) poly(hexamethylene suberate), polyester-6,8,
    poly(oxysuberoyloxyhexamethylene)
(3) Ciba-Geigy AG, Basel (by F. Lohse and H. Batzer)

(4) -O(CH₂)₆O-CO(CH₂)₆CO- with carboxyl end groups
(7) recrystallized melting film (153 K)

33711211 $C_{16}H_{28}O_4$ 626

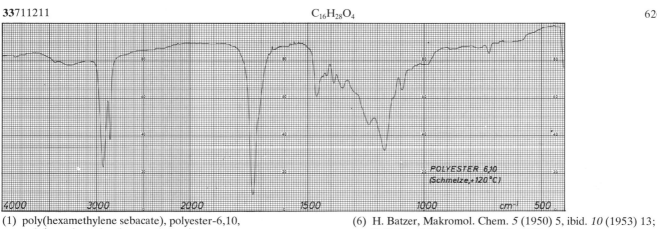
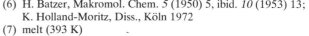

(1) poly(hexamethylene sebacate), polyester-6,10,
    poly(oxysebacoyloxyhexamethylene)
(3) Ciba-Geigy AG, Basel (by F. Lohse and H. Batzer)
(4) -O(CH₂)₆O-CO(CH₂)₈CO- with carboxyl end groups

(6) H. Batzer, Makromol. Chem. *5* (1950) 5, ibid. *10* (1953) 13;
    K. Holland-Moritz, Diss., Köln 1972
(7) melt (393 K)

33711211 $C_{16}H_{28}O_4$ 627

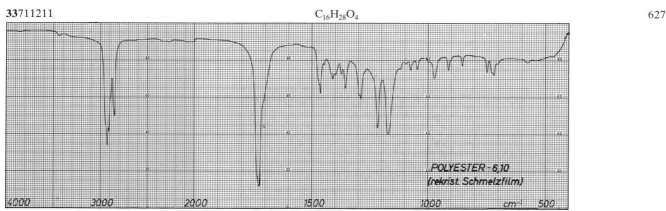

(1) ... (6): see above
(7) recrystallized melting film (323 K)

33711211 $C_{16}H_{28}O_4$ 628

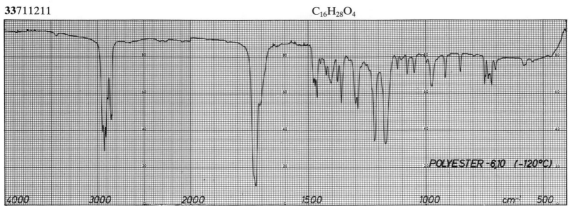

POLYESTER-6,10 (-120°C)

(1) ...(6): see above
(7) recrystallized melting film (153 K)

33711211 $C_{16}H_{28}O_4$ 629

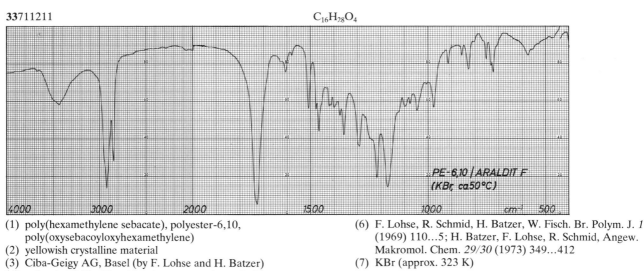

PE-6,10 / ARALDIT F
(KBr, ca 50°C)

(1) poly(hexamethylene sebacate), polyester-6,10, poly(oxysebacoyloxyhexamethylene)
(2) yellowish crystalline material
(3) Ciba-Geigy AG, Basel (by F. Lohse and H. Batzer)
(4) polyester-6,10 with acid end groups, prolonged with „Araldit F"

(6) F. Lohse, R. Schmid, H. Batzer, W. Fisch. Br. Polym. J. *1* (1969) 110...5; H. Batzer, F. Lohse, R. Schmid, Angew. Makromol. Chem. *29/30* (1973) 349...412
(7) KBr (approx. 323 K)

33711211 $C_{16}H_{28}O_4$ 630

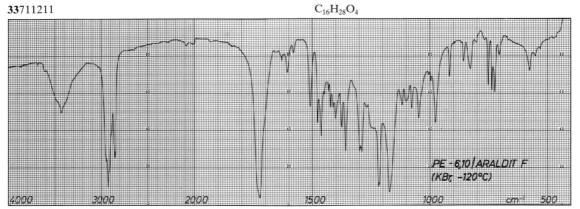

PE-6,10 / ARALDIT F
(KBr, -120°C)

(1) ...(6): see above
(7) KBr (approx. 153 K)

33711211 $C_{16}H_{28}O_4$ 631

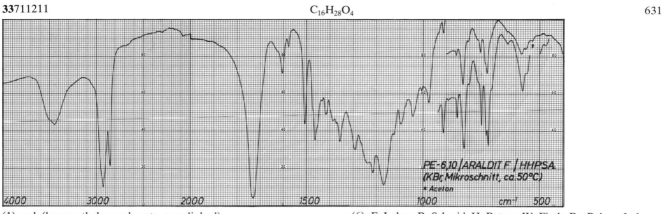

PE-6,10 / ARALDIT F / HHPSA.
(KBr, Mikroschnitt, ca. 50°C)
* Aceton

(1) poly(hexamethylene sebacate, crosslinked)
(2) yellowish elastomer
(3) Ciba-Geigy AG, Basel (by F. Lohse and H. Batzer)
(4) polyester-6,10 with acid end groups, prolonged with „Araldit F" and crosslinked with hexahydrophthalic anhydride

(6) F. Lohse, R. Schmid, H. Batzer, W. Fisch, Br. Polym. J. *1* (1969) 110...5; H. Batzer, F. Lohse, R. Schmid, Angew. Makromol. Chem. *29/30* (1973) 349...412
(7) KBr, microslice (323 K)

33711211 $C_{16}H_{28}O_4$ 632

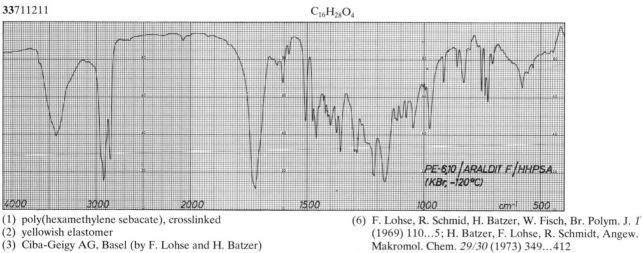

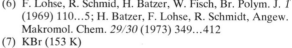

PE-6,10 / ARALDIT F / HHPSA.
(KBr, -120°C)

(1) poly(hexamethylene sebacate), crosslinked
(2) yellowish elastomer
(3) Ciba-Geigy AG, Basel (by F. Lohse and H. Batzer)
(4) see above

(6) F. Lohse, R. Schmid, H. Batzer, W. Fisch, Br. Polym. J. *1* (1969) 110...5; H. Batzer, F. Lohse, R. Schmidt, Angew. Makromol. Chem. *29/30* (1973) 349...412
(7) KBr (153 K)

33711211 $C_{12}H_{20}O_4$ 633

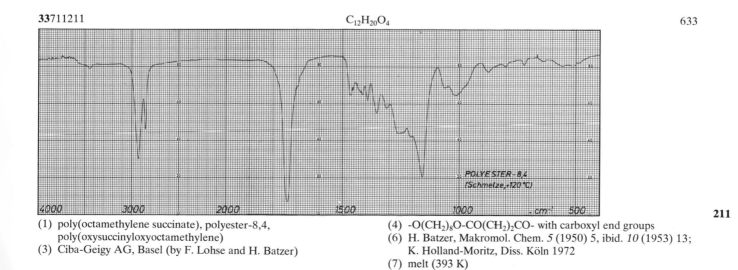

POLYESTER-8,4
(Schmelze, -120°C)

(1) poly(octamethylene succinate), polyester-8,4, poly(oxysuccinyloxyoctamethylene)
(3) Ciba-Geigy AG, Basel (by F. Lohse and H. Batzer)

(4) -O(CH$_2$)$_8$O-CO(CH$_2$)$_2$CO- with carboxyl end groups
(6) H. Batzer, Makromol. Chem. *5* (1950) 5, ibid. *10* (1953) 13; K. Holland-Moritz, Diss. Köln 1972
(7) melt (393 K)

33711211 $C_{12}H_{20}O_4$ 634

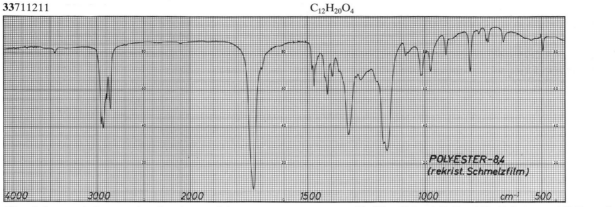

POLYESTER-8,4
(rekrist. Schmelzfilm)

(1) poly(octamethylene succinate), polyester-8,4,
  poly(oxysuccinyloxyoctamethylene)
(2) colourless crystalline material

(3) Ciba-Geigy AG, Basel (by F. Lohse and H. Batzer)
(4) -O(CH$_2$)$_8$O-CO(CH$_2$)$_2$CO- with carboxyl end groups
(7) recrystallized melting film (323 K)

33711211 $C_{12}H_{20}O_4$ 635

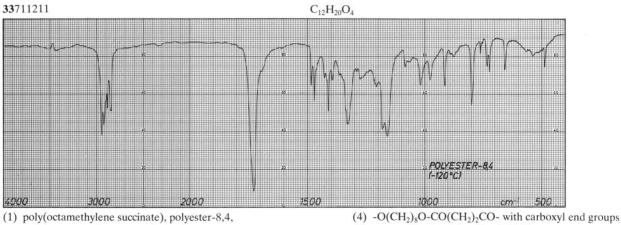

POLYESTER-8,4
(-120°C)

(1) poly(octamethylene succinate), polyester-8,4,
  poly(oxysuccinyloxyoctamethylene)
(3) Ciba-Geigy AG, Basel (by F. Lohse and H. Batzer)

(4) -O(CH$_2$)$_8$O-CO(CH$_2$)$_2$CO- with carboxyl end groups
(7) recrystallized melting film (153 K)

33711211 $C_{14}H_{24}O_4$ 636

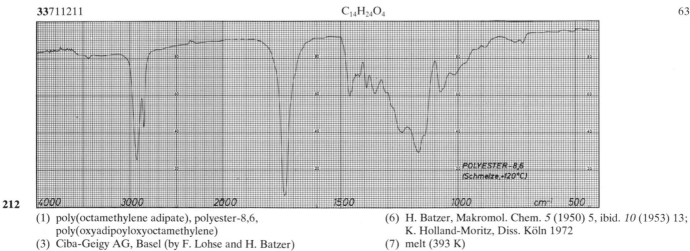

POLYESTER-8,6
(Schmelze,-120°C)

(1) poly(octamethylene adipate), polyester-8,6,
  poly(oxyadipoyloxyoctamethylene)
(3) Ciba-Geigy AG, Basel (by F. Lohse and H. Batzer)
(4) -O(CH$_2$)$_8$O-CO(CH$_2$)$_4$CO- with carboxyl end groups

(6) H. Batzer, Makromol. Chem. *5* (1950) 5, ibid. *10* (1953) 13;
  K. Holland-Moritz, Diss. Köln 1972
(7) melt (393 K)

33711211　　　　　　　　　　　$C_{14}H_{24}O_4$　　　　　　　　　　637

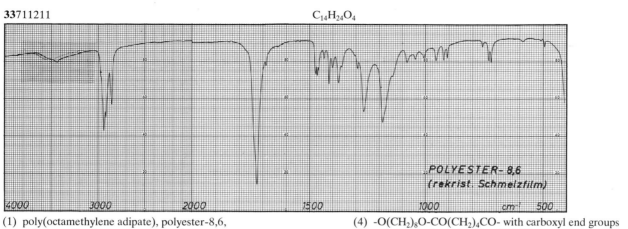

(1) poly(octamethylene adipate), polyester-8,6,
　　poly(oxyadipoyloxyoctamethylene)
(2) colourless crystalline material
(3) Ciba-Geigy AG, Basel (by F. Lohse and H. Batzer)

(4) -O(CH_2)_8O-CO(CH_2)_4CO- with carboxyl end groups
(7) recrystallized melting film (323 K)

33711211　　　　　　　　　　　$C_{14}H_{24}O_4$　　　　　　　　　　638

(1) poly(octamethylene adipate), polyester-8,6,
　　poly(oxyadipoyloxyoctamethylene)
(3) Ciba-Geigy AG, Basel (by F. Lohse and H. Batzer)

(4) -O(CH_2)_8O-CO(CH_2)_4CO- with carboxyl end groups
(7) recrystallized melting film (153 K)

33711211　　　　　　　　　　　$C_{16}H_{28}O_4$　　　　　　　　　　639

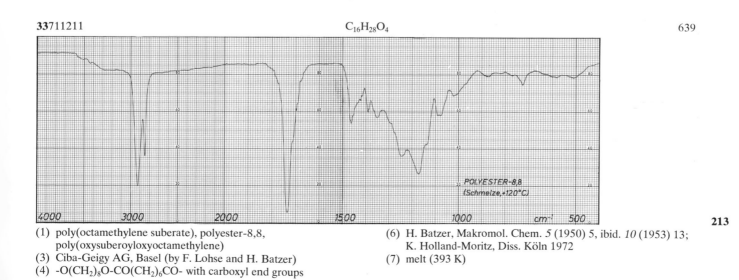

(1) poly(octamethylene suberate), polyester-8,8,
　　poly(oxysuberoyloxyoctamethylene)
(3) Ciba-Geigy AG, Basel (by F. Lohse and H. Batzer)
(4) -O(CH_2)_8O-CO(CH_2)_6CO- with carboxyl end groups

(6) H. Batzer, Makromol. Chem. *5* (1950) 5, ibid. *10* (1953) 13;
　　K. Holland-Moritz, Diss. Köln 1972
(7) melt (393 K)

33711211 $C_{16}H_{28}O_4$ 640

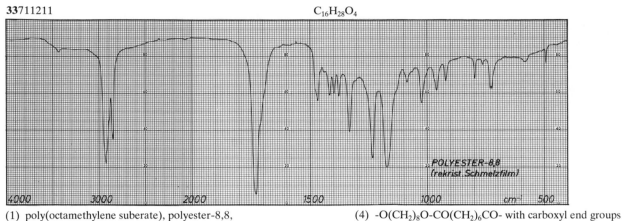

POLYESTER-8,8
(rekrist Schmelzfilm)

(1) poly(octamethylene suberate), polyester-8,8,
    poly(oxysuberoyloxyoctamethylene)
(2) colourless crystalline material
(3) Ciba-Geigy AG, Basel (by F. Lohse and H. Batzer)

(4) $-O(CH_2)_8O-CO(CH_2)_6CO-$ with carboxyl end groups
(7) recrystallized melting film (323 K)

33711211 $C_{16}H_{28}O_4$ 641

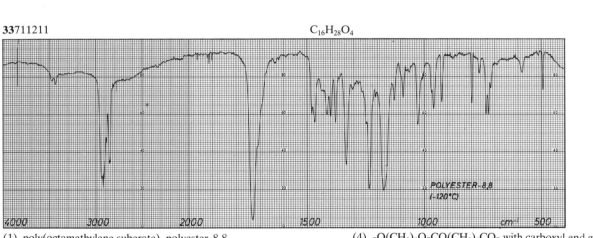

POLYESTER-8,8
(-120°C)

(1) poly(octamethylene suberate), polyester-8,8,
    poly(oxysuberoyloxyoctamethylene)
(3) Ciba-Geigy AG, Basel (by F. Lohse and H. Batzer)

(4) $-O(CH_2)_8O-CO(CH_2)_6CO-$ with carboxyl end groups
(7) recrystallized melting film (153 K)

33711211 $C_{18}H_{32}O_4$ 642

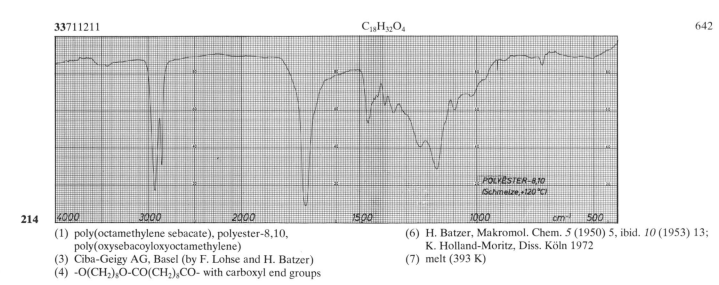

POLYESTER-8,10
(Schmelze,+120°C)

(1) poly(octamethylene sebacate), polyester-8,10,
    poly(oxysebacoyloxyoctamethylene)
(3) Ciba-Geigy AG, Basel (by F. Lohse and H. Batzer)
(4) $-O(CH_2)_8O-CO(CH_2)_8CO-$ with carboxyl end groups

(6) H. Batzer, Makromol. Chem. *5* (1950) 5, ibid. *10* (1953) 13;
    K. Holland-Moritz, Diss. Köln 1972
(7) melt (393 K)

33711211   C₁₈H₃₂O₄   643

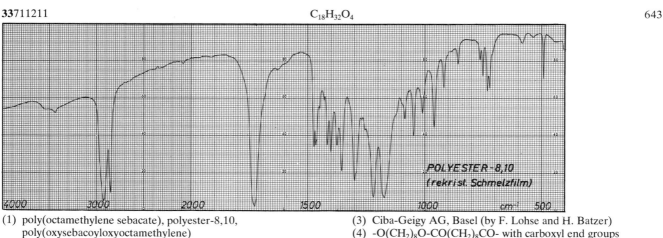

(1) poly(octamethylene sebacate), polyester-8,10,
    poly(oxysebacoyloxyoctamethylene)
(2) colourless crystalline material

(3) Ciba-Geigy AG, Basel (by F. Lohse and H. Batzer)
(4) -O(CH₂)₈O-CO(CH₂)₈CO- with carboxyl end groups
(7) recrystallized melting film (323 K)

33711211   C₁₈H₃₂O₄   644

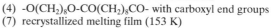

(1) poly(octamethylene sebacate), polyester-8,10,
    poly(oxysebacoyloxyoctamethylene)
(3) Ciba-Geigy AG, Basel (by F. Lohse and H. Batzer)

(4) -O(CH₂)₈O-CO(CH₂)₈CO- with carboxyl end groups
(7) recrystallized melting film (153 K)

33711211   C₁₄H₂₄O₄   645

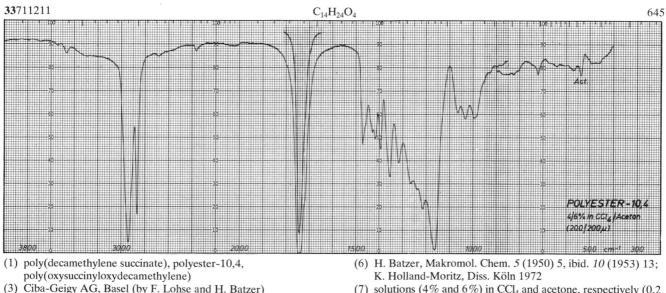

(1) poly(decamethylene succinate), polyester-10,4,
    poly(oxysuccinyloxydecamethylene)
(3) Ciba-Geigy AG, Basel (by F. Lohse and H. Batzer)
(4) -O(CH₂)₁₀O-CO(CH₂)₂CO- with carboxyl end groups

(6) H. Batzer, Makromol. Chem. 5 (1950) 5, ibid. 10 (1953) 13;
    K. Holland-Moritz, Diss. Köln 1972
(7) solutions (4% and 6%) in CCl₄ and acetone, respectively (0,2
    mm and 0,2 mm, respectively)

33711211 $C_{14}H_{24}O_4$ 646

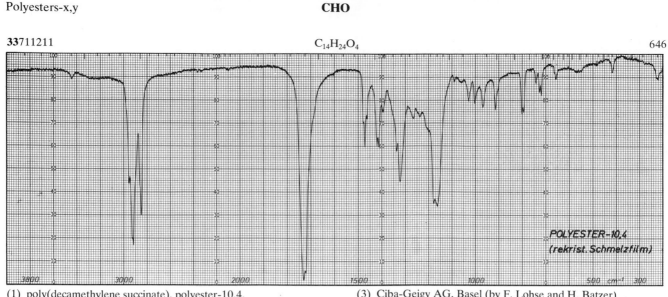

POLYESTER-10,4
(rekrist. Schmelzfilm)

(1) poly(decamethylene succinate), polyester-10,4,
    poly(oxysuccinyloxydecamethylene)
(2) colourless crystalline material
(3) Ciba-Geigy AG, Basel (by F. Lohse and H. Batzer)
(4) $-O(CH_2)_{10}O-CO(CH_2)_2CO-$ with carboxyl end groups
(7) recrystallized melting film (300 K)

33711211 $C_{14}H_{24}O_4$ 647

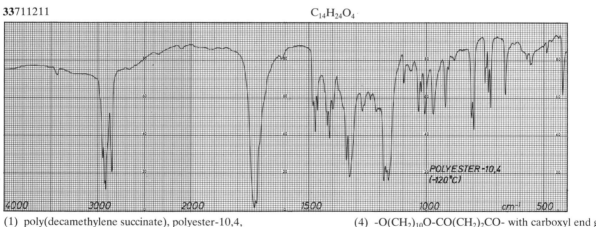

POLYESTER-10,4
(-120°C)

(1) poly(decamethylene succinate), polyester-10,4,
    poly(oxysuccinyloxydecamethylene)
(3) Ciba-Geigy AG, Basel (by F. Lohse and H. Batzer
(4) $-O(CH_2)_{10}O-CO(CH_2)_2CO-$ with carboxyl end groups
(7) recrystallized melting film (153 K)

33711211 $C_{16}H_{28}O_4$ 648

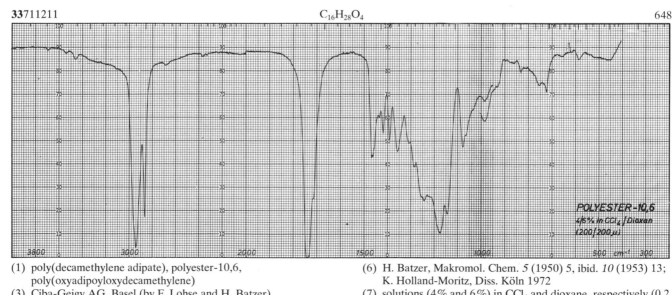

POLYESTER-10,6
4/6% in CCl₄/Dioxan
(200/200 μ)

(1) poly(decamethylene adipate), polyester-10,6,
    poly(oxyadipoyloxydecamethylene)
(3) Ciba-Geigy AG, Basel (by F. Lohse and H. Batzer)
    $-O(CH_2)_{10}O-CO(CH_2)_4CO-$ with carboxyl end groups
(6) H. Batzer, Makromol. Chem. *5* (1950) 5, ibid. *10* (1953) 13;
    K. Holland-Moritz, Diss. Köln 1972
(7) solutions (4% and 6%) in CCl₄ and dioxane, respectively (0,2
    mm and 0,2 mm respectively)

33711211 $C_{16}H_{28}O_4$ 649

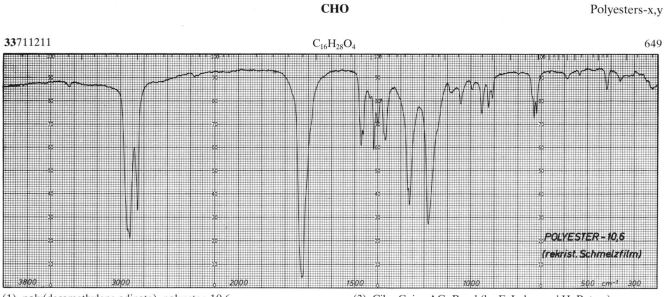

POLYESTER-10,6
(rekrist. Schmelzfilm)

(1) poly(decamethylene adipate), polyester-10,6,
     poly(oxyadipoyloxydecamethylene)
(2) colourless crystalline material

(3) Ciba-Geigy AG, Basel (by F. Lohse and H. Batzer)
(4) -O(CH$_2$)$_{10}$O-CO(CH$_2$)$_4$CO- with carboxyl end groups
(7) recrystallized melting film (300 K)

33711211 $C_{16}H_{28}O_4$ 650

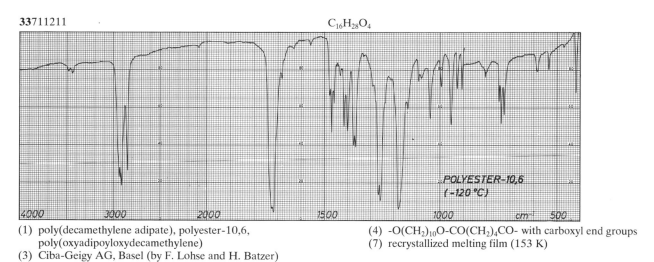

POLYESTER-10,6
(-120°C)

(1) poly(decamethylene adipate), polyester-10,6,
     poly(oxyadipoyloxydecamethylene)
(3) Ciba-Geigy AG, Basel (by F. Lohse and H. Batzer)

(4) -O(CH$_2$)$_{10}$O-CO(CH$_2$)$_4$CO- with carboxyl end groups
(7) recrystallized melting film (153 K)

33711211 $C_{18}H_{32}O_4$ 651

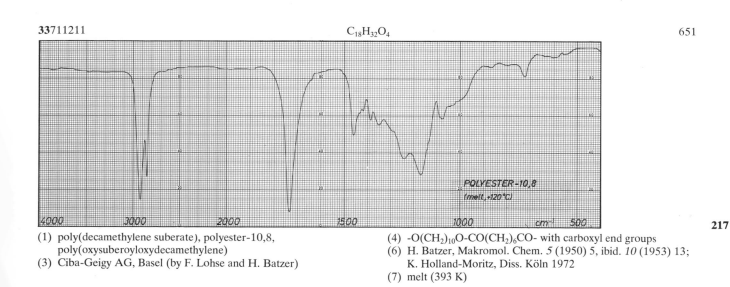

POLYESTER-10,8
(melt, +120°C)

(1) poly(decamethylene suberate), polyester-10,8,
     poly(oxysuberoyloxydecamethylene)
(3) Ciba-Geigy AG, Basel (by F. Lohse and H. Batzer)

(4) -O(CH$_2$)$_{10}$O-CO(CH$_2$)$_6$CO- with carboxyl end groups
(6) H. Batzer, Makromol. Chem. *5* (1950) 5, ibid. *10* (1953) 13;
     K. Holland-Moritz, Diss. Köln 1972
(7) melt (393 K)

33711211 $C_{18}H_{32}O_4$ 652

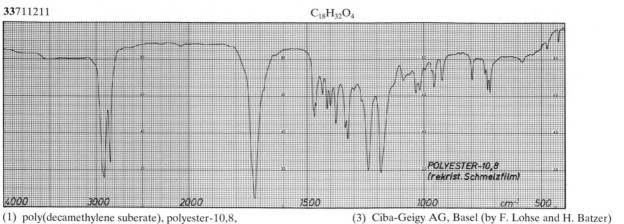

(1) poly(decamethylene suberate), polyester-10,8, poly(oxysuberoyloxydecamethylene)
(2) colourless crystalline material
(3) Ciba-Geigy AG, Basel (by F. Lohse and H. Batzer)
(4) $-O(CH_2)_{10}O-CO(CH_2)_6CO-$ with carboxyl end groups
(7) recrystallized melting film (323 K)

33711211 $C_{18}H_{32}O_4$ 653

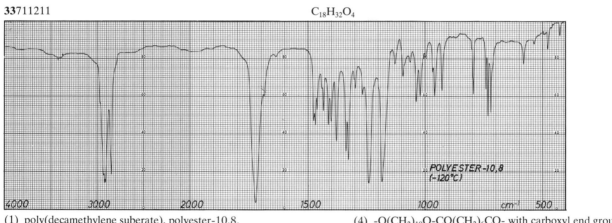

(1) poly(decamethylene suberate), polyester-10,8, poly(oxysuberoyloxydecamethylene)
(3) Ciba-Geigy AG, Basel (by F. Lohse and H. Batzer)
(4) $-O(CH_2)_{10}O-CO(CH_2)_6CO-$ with carboxyl end groups
(7) recrystallized melting film (153 K)

33711211 $C_{20}H_{36}O_4$ 654

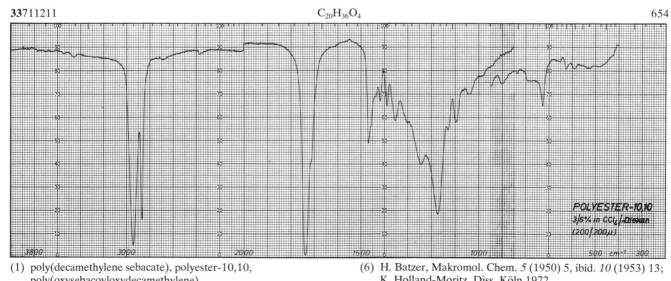

(1) poly(decamethylene sebacate), polyester-10,10, poly(oxysebacoyloxydecamethylene)
(3) Ciba-Geigy AG, Basel (by F. Lohse and H. Batzer)
(4) $-O(CH_2)_{10}O-CO(CH_2)_8CO-$ with carboxyl end groups
(6) H. Batzer, Makromol. Chem. *5* (1950) 5, ibid. *10* (1953) 13; K. Holland-Moritz, Diss. Köln 1972
(7) solutions (3% and 6%) in CCl_4 and dioxane, respectively (0,2 mm and 0,2 mm respectively)

33711211   C$_{20}$H$_{36}$O$_4$ 655

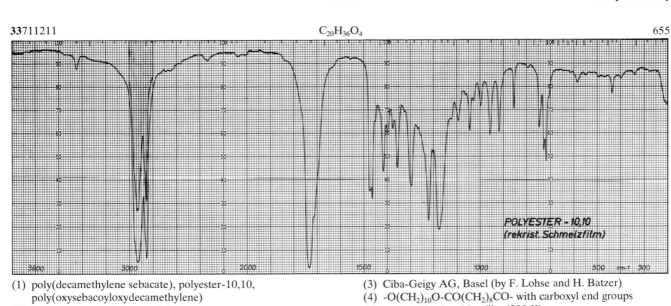

(1) poly(decamethylene sebacate), polyester-10,10, poly(oxysebacoyloxydecamethylene)
(2) colourless crystalline material

(3) Ciba-Geigy AG, Basel (by F. Lohse and H. Batzer)
(4) -O(CH$_2$)$_{10}$O-CO(CH$_2$)$_8$CO- with carboxyl end groups
(7) recrystallized melting film (300 K)

33711211   C$_{20}$H$_{36}$O$_4$ 656

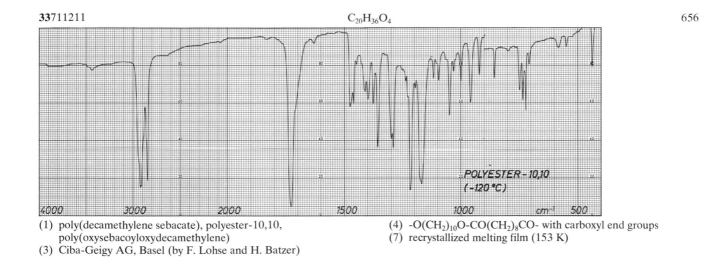

(1) poly(decamethylene sebacate), polyester-10,10, poly(oxysebacoyloxydecamethylene)
(3) Ciba-Geigy AG, Basel (by F. Lohse and H. Batzer)

(4) -O(CH$_2$)$_{10}$O-CO(CH$_2$)$_8$CO- with carboxyl end groups
(7) recrystallized melting film (153 K)

33711211   C$_{24}$H$_{44}$O$_4$ 657

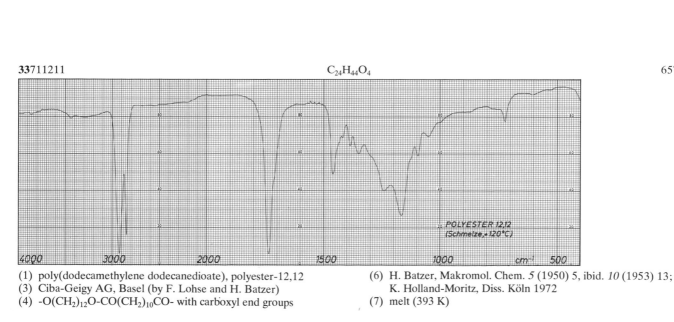

(1) poly(dodecamethylene dodecanedioate), polyester-12,12
(3) Ciba-Geigy AG, Basel (by F. Lohse and H. Batzer)
(4) -O(CH$_2$)$_{12}$O-CO(CH$_2$)$_{10}$CO- with carboxyl end groups

(6) H. Batzer, Makromol. Chem. *5* (1950) 5, ibid. *10* (1953) 13; K. Holland-Moritz, Diss. Köln 1972
(7) melt (393 K)

33711211   C$_{24}$H$_{44}$O$_4$ 658

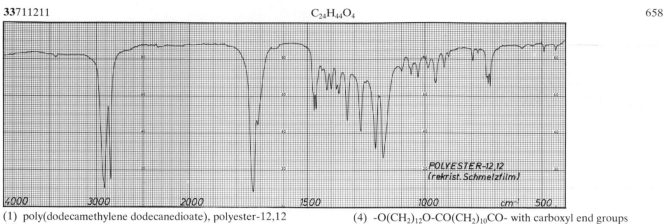

POLYESTER-12,12
(rekrist. Schmelzfilm)

(1) poly(dodecamethylene dodecanedioate), polyester-12,12
(2) colourless crystalline material
(3) Ciba-Geigy AG, Basel (by F. Lohse and H. Batzer)
(4) -O(CH$_2$)$_{12}$O-CO(CH$_2$)$_{10}$CO- with carboxyl end groups
(7) recrystallized melting film (323 K)

33711211   C$_{24}$H$_{44}$O$_4$ 659

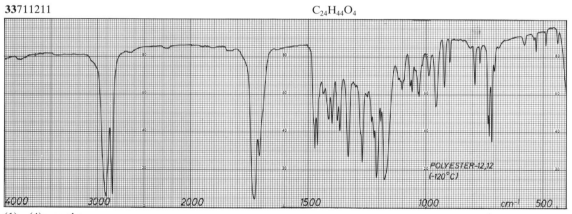

POLYESTER-12,12
(-120°C)

(1)...(4): see above
(7) recrystallized melting film (153 K)

33711212   C$_7$H$_{10}$O$_4$ 660

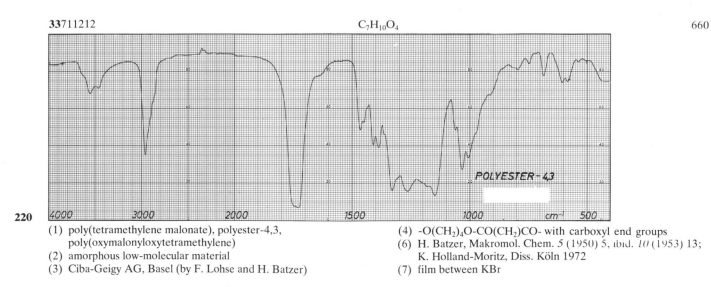

POLYESTER-4,3

(1) poly(tetramethylene malonate), polyester-4,3,
    poly(oxymalonyloxytetramethylene)
(2) amorphous low-molecular material
(3) Ciba-Geigy AG, Basel (by F. Lohse and H. Batzer)
(4) -O(CH$_2$)$_4$O-CO(CH$_2$)CO- with carboxyl end groups
(6) H. Batzer, Makromol. Chem. 5 (1950) 5, ibid. 10 (1953) 13;
    K. Holland-Moritz, Diss. Köln 1972
(7) film between KBr

33711212 $C_7H_{10}O_4$ 661

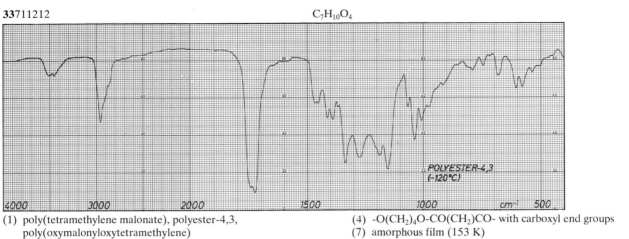

(1) poly(tetramethylene malonate), polyester-4,3,
poly(oxymalonyloxytetramethylene)
(3) Ciba-Geigy AG, Basel (by F. Lohse and H. Batzer)

(4) -O(CH$_2$)$_4$O-CO(CH$_2$)CO- with carboxyl end groups
(7) amorphous film (153 K)

33711212 $C_9H_{14}O_4$ 662

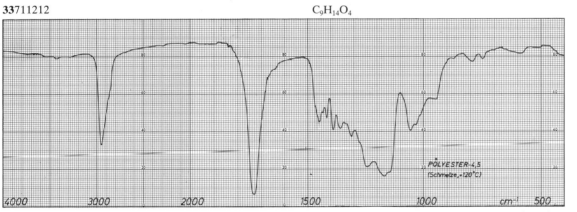

(1) poly(tetramethylene glutarate), polyester-4,5,
poly(oxyglutaroyloxytetramethylene)
(3) Ciba-Geigy AG, Basel (by F. Lohse and H. Batzer)
(4) -O(CH$_2$)$_4$O-CO(CH$_2$)$_3$CO- with carboxyl end groups

(6) H. Batzer, Makromol. Chem. *5* (1950) 5, ibid. *10* (1953) 13;
K. Holland-Moritz, Diss. Köln 1972
(7) melt (393 K)

33711212 $C_9H_{14}O_4$ 663

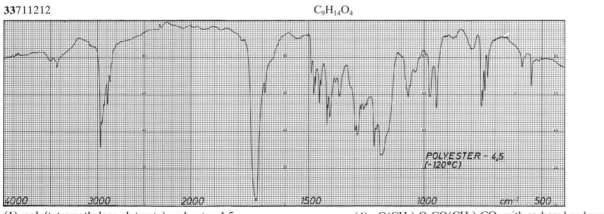

(1) poly(tetramethylene glutarate), polyester-4,5,
poly(oxyglutaroyloxytetramethylene)
(3) Ciba-Geigy AG, Basel (by F. Lohse and H. Batzer)

(4) -O(CH$_2$)$_4$O-CO(CH$_2$)$_3$CO- with carboxyl end groups
(7) recrystallized melting film (153 K)

33711212 $C_{11}H_{18}O_4$ 664

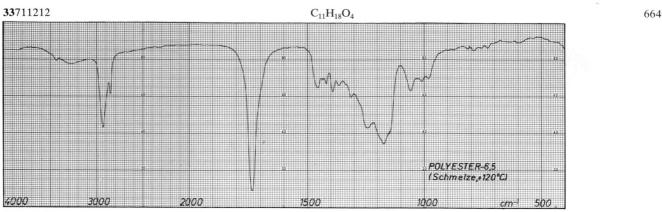

POLYESTER-6,5
(Schmelze,+120°C)

(1) poly(hexamethylene glutarate), polyester-6,5,
    poly(oxyglutaroyloxyhexamethylene)
(3) Ciba-Geigy AG, Basel (by F. Lohse and H. Batzer)
(4) -O(CH₂)₆O-CO(CH₂)₃CO- with carboxyl end groups

(6) H. Batzer, Makromol. Chem. *5* (1950), 5, ibid. *10* (1953) 13;
    K. Holland-Moritz, Diss. Köln 1972
(7) melt (393 K)

33711212 $C_{11}H_{18}O_4$ 665

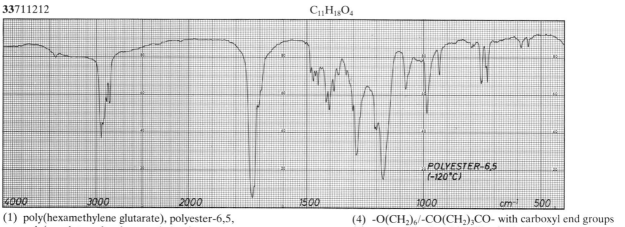

POLYESTER-6,5
(-120°C)

(1) poly(hexamethylene glutarate), polyester-6,5,
    poly(oxyglutaroyloxyhexamethylene)
(3) Ciba-Geigy AG, Basel (by F. Lohse and H. Batzer)

(4) -O(CH₂)₆/-CO(CH₂)₃CO- with carboxyl end groups
(7) recrystallized melting film (153 K)

33711212 $C_{13}H_{22}O_4$ 666

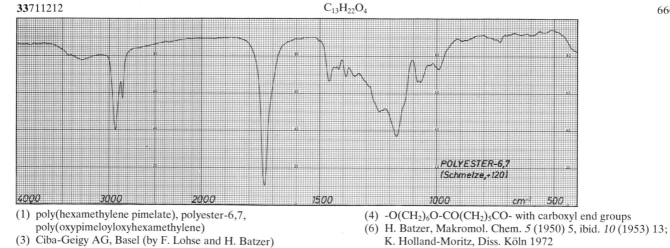

POLYESTER-6,7
(Schmelze,+120)

222

(1) poly(hexamethylene pimelate), polyester-6,7,
    poly(oxypimeloyloxyhexamethylene)
(3) Ciba-Geigy AG, Basel (by F. Lohse and H. Batzer)

(4) -O(CH₂)₆O-CO(CH₂)₅CO- with carboxyl end groups
(6) H. Batzer, Makromol. Chem. *5* (1950) 5, ibid. *10* (1953) 13;
    K. Holland-Moritz, Diss. Köln 1972
(7) melt (393 K)

33711212 C₁₃H₂₂O₄ 667

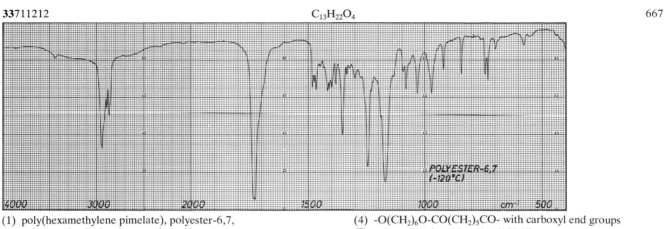
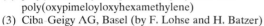

(1) poly(hexamethylene pimelate), polyester-6,7,
poly(oxypimeloyloxyhexamethylene)
(3) Ciba-Geigy AG, Basel (by F. Lohse and H. Batzer)

(4) -O(CH₂)₆O-CO(CH₂)₅CO- with carboxyl end groups
(7) recrystallized melting film (153 K)

33711212 C₁₅H₂₆O₄ 668

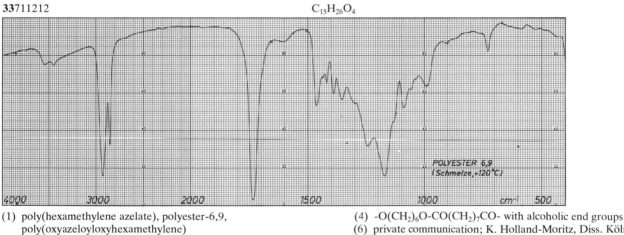
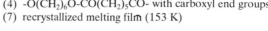

(1) poly(hexamethylene azelate), polyester-6,9,
poly(oxyazeloyloxyhexamethylene)
(3) E. Knappe, Glasurit-Werke, Hiltrup

(4) -O(CH₂)₆O-CO(CH₂)₇CO- with alcoholic end groups
(6) private communication; K. Holland-Moritz, Diss. Köln 1972
(7) melt (393 K)

33711212 C₁₅H₂₆O₄ 669

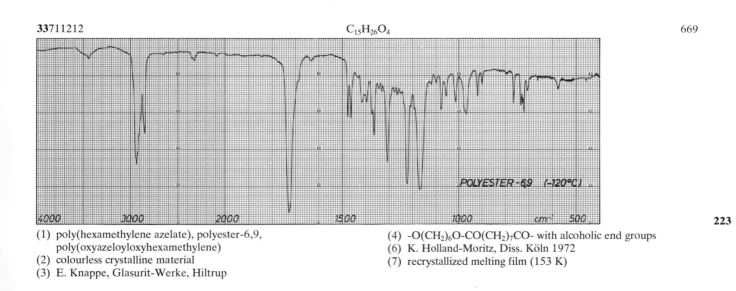

(1) poly(hexamethylene azelate), polyester-6,9,
poly(oxyazeloyloxyhexamethylene)
(2) colourless crystalline material
(3) E. Knappe, Glasurit-Werke, Hiltrup

(4) -O(CH₂)₆O-CO(CH₂)₇CO- with alcoholic end groups
(6) K. Holland-Moritz, Diss. Köln 1972
(7) recrystallized melting film (153 K)

33711213 · $C_7H_{10}O_4$ · 670

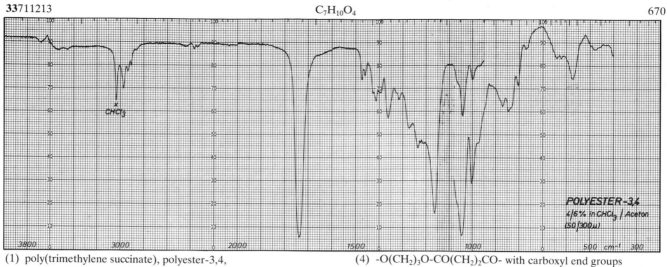

POLYESTER-3,4
4/6% in CHCl₃ / Aceton
(50/300μ)

CHCl₃

(1) poly(trimethylene succinate), polyester-3,4,
poly(oxysuccinyloxy-trimethylene)
(2) colourless viscous liquid
(3) Ciba-Geigy AG, Basel (by F. Lohse and H. Batzer)

(4) -O(CH₂)₃O-CO(CH₂)₂CO- with carboxyl end groups
(6) private communication
(7) solutions in CHCl₃ (4 %, 50 μm) and acetone (6 %, 300 μm),
respectively; compensated

33711213 · $C_7H_{10}O_4$ · 671

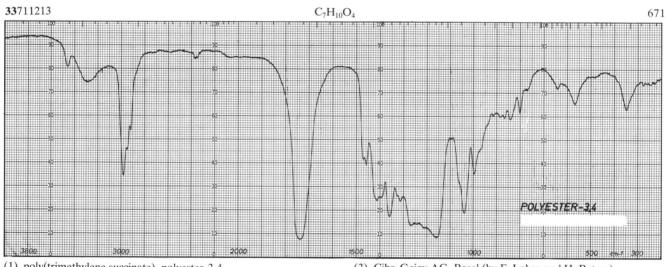

POLYESTER-3,4

(1) poly(trimethylene succinate), polyester-3,4,
poly(oxysuccinyloxy-trimethylene)
(2) colourless viscous liquid

(3) Ciba-Geigy AG, Basel (by F. Lohse and H. Batzer)
(7) liquid film (300 K)

33711213 · $C_7H_{10}O_4$ · 672

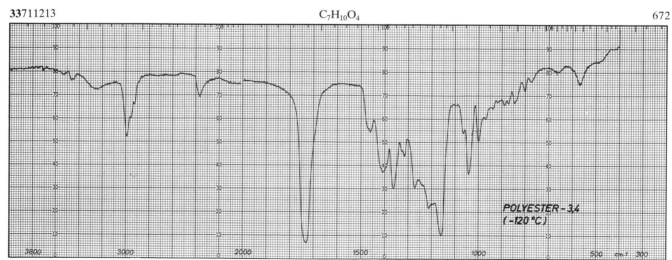

POLYESTER-3,4
(-120 °C)

(1) ...(4): see above
(7) amorphous film between KBr (153 K)

33711213 $C_7H_{10}O_4$ 673

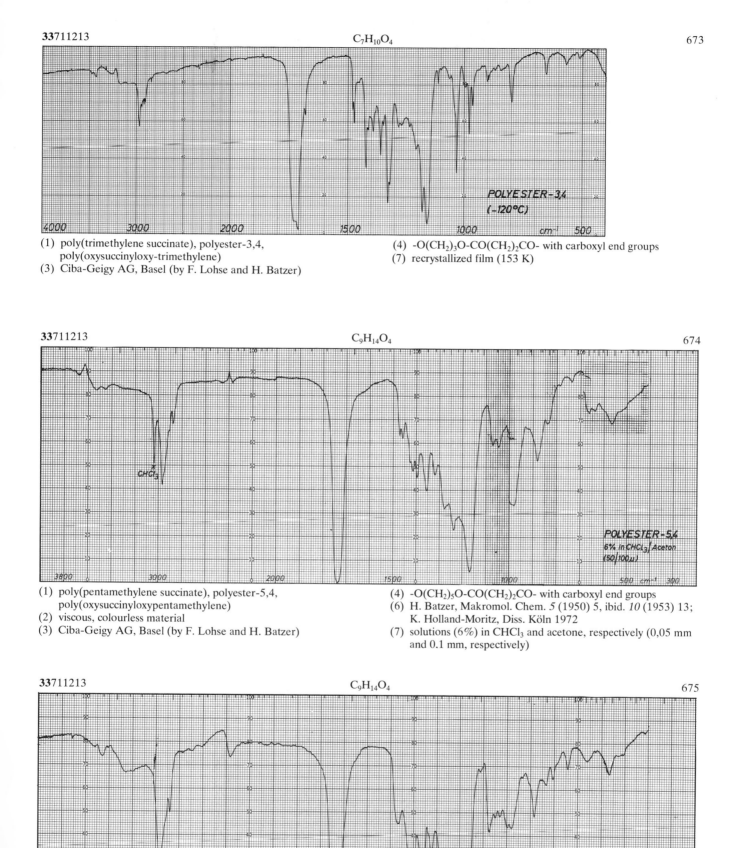

POLYESTER-3,4
(-120°C)

(1) poly(trimethylene succinate), polyester-3,4,
    poly(oxysuccinyloxy-trimethylene)
(3) Ciba-Geigy AG, Basel (by F. Lohse and H. Batzer)

(4) -O(CH₂)₃O-CO(CH₂)₂CO- with carboxyl end groups
(7) recrystallized film (153 K)

33711213 $C_9H_{14}O_4$ 674

CHCl₃

POLYESTER-5,4
6% in CHCl₃/Aceton
(50/100μ)

(1) poly(pentamethylene succinate), polyester-5,4,
    poly(oxysuccinyloxypentamethylene)
(2) viscous, colourless material
(3) Ciba-Geigy AG, Basel (by F. Lohse and H. Batzer)

(4) -O(CH₂)₅O-CO(CH₂)₂CO- with carboxyl end groups
(6) H. Batzer, Makromol. Chem. *5* (1950) 5, ibid. *10* (1953) 13;
    K. Holland-Moritz, Diss. Köln 1972
(7) solutions (6%) in CHCl₃ and acetone, respectively (0,05 mm
    and 0.1 mm, respectively)

33711213 $C_9H_{14}O_4$ 675

POLYESTER-5,4
(-120°C)

(1) ...(6): see above
(7) amorphous film between KBr (153 K)

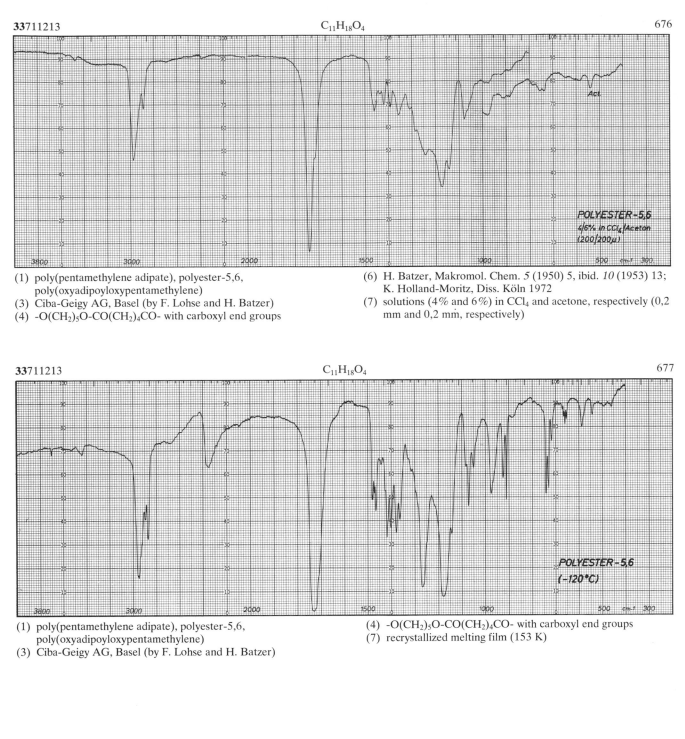

POLYESTER-5,6
4/6% in CCl₄ /Aceton
(200/200μ)

(1) poly(pentamethylene adipate), polyester-5,6, poly(oxyadipoyloxypentamethylene)
(3) Ciba-Geigy AG, Basel (by F. Lohse and H. Batzer)
(4) -O(CH₂)₅O-CO(CH₂)₄CO- with carboxyl end groups

(6) H. Batzer, Makromol. Chem. *5* (1950) 5, ibid. *10* (1953) 13; K. Holland-Moritz, Diss. Köln 1972
(7) solutions (4% and 6%) in CCl₄ and acetone, respectively (0,2 mm and 0,2 mm, respectively)

POLYESTER-5,6
(-120°C)

(1) poly(pentamethylene adipate), polyester-5,6, poly(oxyadipoyloxypentamethylene)
(3) Ciba-Geigy AG, Basel (by F. Lohse and H. Batzer)

(4) -O(CH₂)₅O-CO(CH₂)₄CO- with carboxyl end groups
(7) recrystallized melting film (153 K)

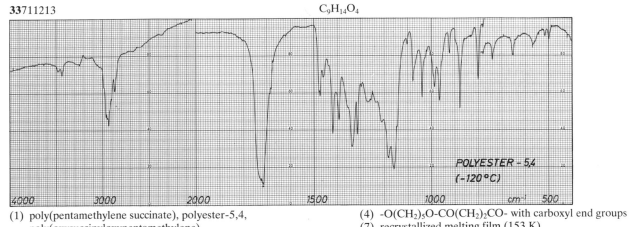

POLYESTER - 5,4
(-120°C)

(1) poly(pentamethylene succinate), polyester-5,4, poly(oxysuccinyloxypentamethylene)
(3) Ciba-Geigy AG, Basel (by F. Lohse and H. Batzer)

(4) -O(CH₂)₅O-CO(CH₂)₂CO- with carboxyl end groups
(7) recrystallized melting film (153 K)

33711213   C₁₁H₁₈O₄   679

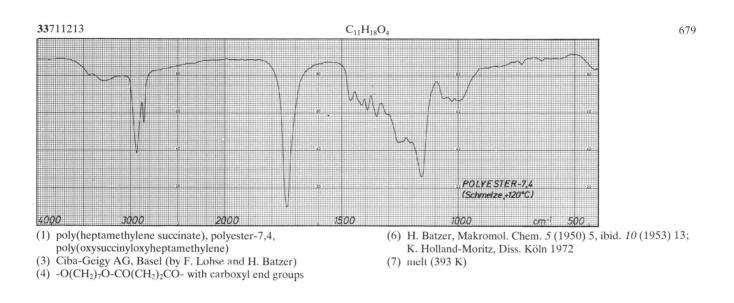

POLYESTER-7,4
(Schmelze,+120°C)

(1) poly(heptamethylene succinate), polyester-7,4,
    poly(oxysuccinyloxyheptamethylene)
(3) Ciba-Geigy AG, Basel (by F. Lohse and H. Batzer)
(4) -O(CH₂)₇O-CO(CH₂)₂CO- with carboxyl end groups

(6) H. Batzer, Makromol. Chem. *5* (1950) 5, ibid. *10* (1953) 13;
    K. Holland-Moritz, Diss. Köln 1972
(7) melt (393 K)

33711213   C₁₁H₁₈O₄   680

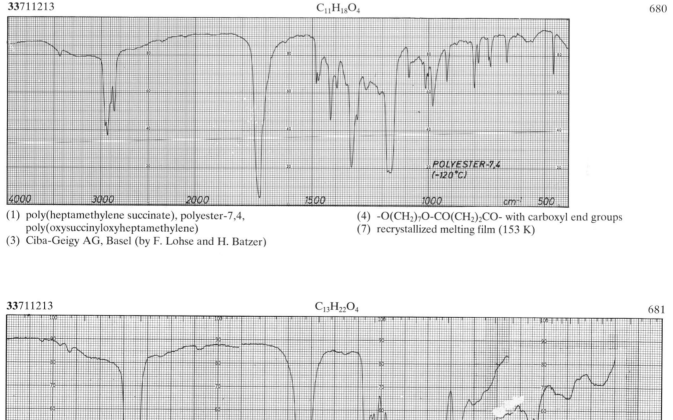

POLYESTER-7,4
(-120°C)

(1) poly(heptamethylene succinate), polyester-7,4,
    poly(oxysuccinyloxyheptamethylene)
(3) Ciba-Geigy AG, Basel (by F. Lohse and H. Batzer)

(4) -O(CH₂)₇O-CO(CH₂)₂CO- with carboxyl end groups
(7) recrystallized melting film (153 K)

33711213   C₁₃H₂₂O₄   681

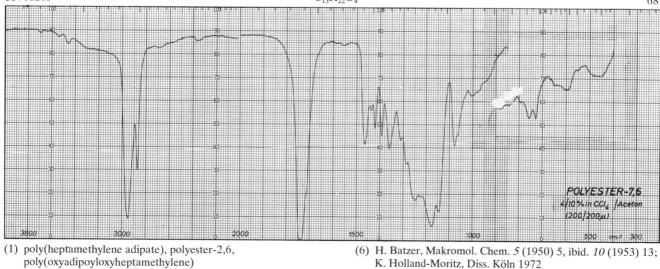

POLYESTER-7,6
4/10% in CCl₄ /Aceton
(200/200μ)

(1) poly(heptamethylene adipate), polyester-2,6,
    poly(oxyadipoyloxyheptamethylene)
(3) Ciba-Geigy AG, Basel (by F. Lohse and H. Batzer)
(4) -O(CH₂)₇O-CO(CH₂)₄CO- with carboxyl end groups

(6) H. Batzer, Makromol. Chem. *5* (1950) 5, ibid. *10* (1953) 13;
    K. Holland-Moritz, Diss. Köln 1972
(7) solutions (4% and 10%) in CCl₄ and acetone, respectively
    (0,2 mm and 0,2 mm, respectively)

33711213   C_{13}H_{22}O_4   682

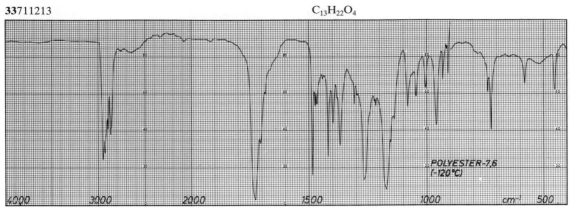

POLYESTER-7,6
(-120°C)

(1) ...(6): see above
(7) crystallized film (153 K)

33711213   C_{13}H_{22}O_4   683

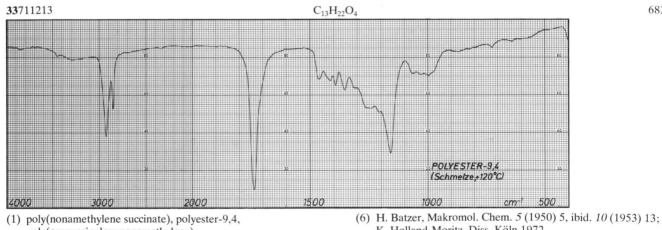

POLYESTER-9,4
(Schmelze,+120°C)

(1) poly(nonamethylene succinate), polyester-9,4,
 poly(oxysuccinyloxynonamethylene)
(3) Ciba-Geigy AG, Basel (by F. Lohse and H. Batzer)
(4) -O(CH₂)₉O-CO(CH₂)₂CO- with carboxyl end groups

(6) H. Batzer, Makromol. Chem. *5* (1950) 5, ibid. *10* (1953) 13;
 K. Holland-Moritz, Diss. Köln 1972
(7) melt (393 K)

33711213   C_{13}H_{22}O_4   684

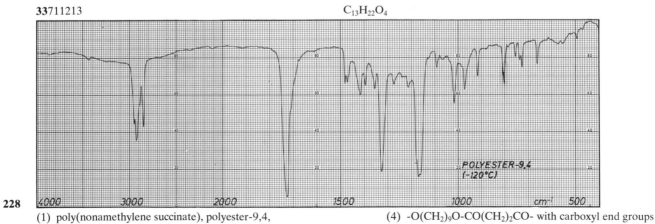

POLYESTER-9,4
(-120°C)

228

(1) poly(nonamethylene succinate), polyester-9,4,
 poly(oxysuccinyloxynonamethylene)
(3) Ciba-Geigy AG, Basel (by F. Lohse and H. Batzer)

(4) -O(CH₂)₉O-CO(CH₂)₂CO- with carboxyl end groups
(7) recrystallized melting film (153 K)

33711214 $C_{12}H_{20}O_4$ 685

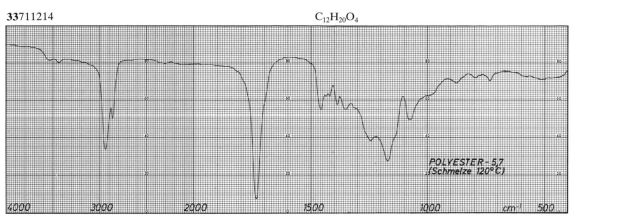

POLYESTER - 5,7
(Schmelze 120°C)

(1) poly(pentamethylene pimelate), polyester-5,7,
poly(oxypimeloyloxypentamethylene)
(3) Ciba-Geigy AG, Basel (by F. Lohse and H. Batzer)
(4) -O(CH₂)₅O-CO(CH₂)5CO- with carboxyl end groups

(6) H. Batzer, Makromol. Chem. *5* (1950) 5, ibid. *10* (1953) 13;
K. Holland-Moritz, Diss. Köln 1972
(7) melt (393 K)

33711214 $C_{12}H_{20}O_4$ 686

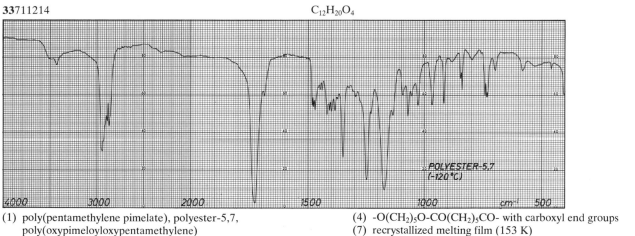
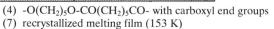
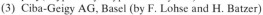

POLYESTER-5,7
(-120°C)

(1) poly(pentamethylene pimelate), polyester-5,7,
poly(oxypimeloyloxypentamethylene)
(3) Ciba-Geigy AG, Basel (by F. Lohse and H. Batzer)

(4) -O(CH₂)₅O-CO(CH₂)₅CO- with carboxyl end groups
(7) recrystallized melting film (153 K)

3371124   687

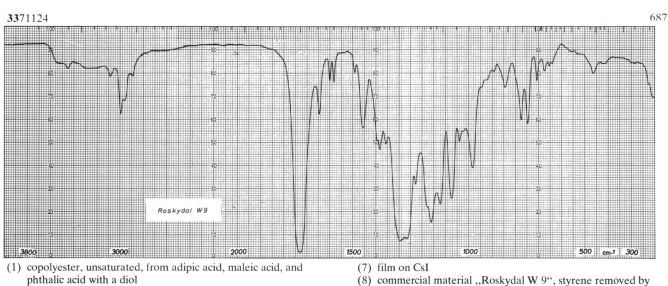

Roskydal W 9

(1) copolyester, unsaturated, from adipic acid, maleic acid, and
phthalic acid with a diol
(2) colourless, clear, viscous material
(3) Bayer AG, Leverkusen

(7) film on CsI
(8) commercial material „Roskydal W 9", styrene removed by
drying

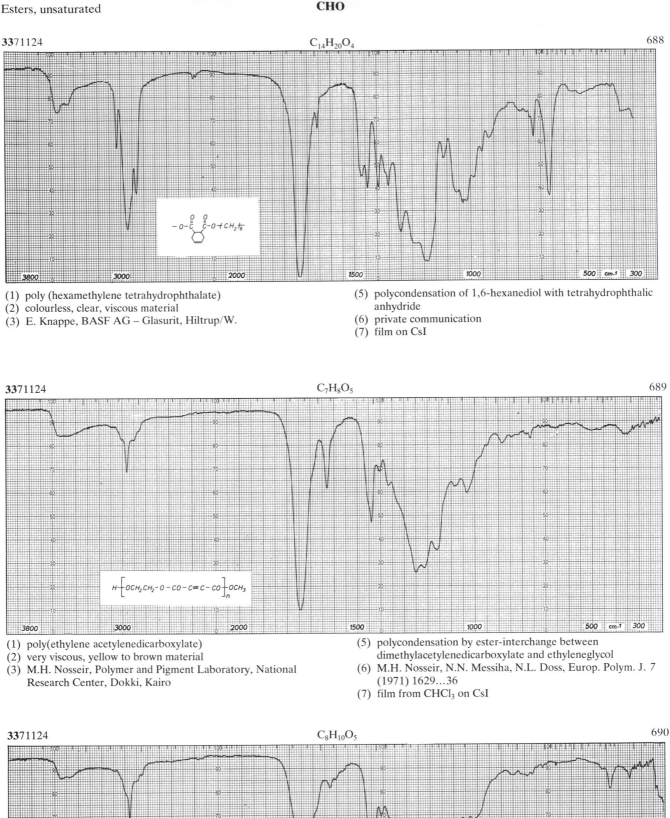

3371124 $C_{14}H_{20}O_4$ 688

(1) poly (hexamethylene tetrahydrophthalate)
(2) colourless, clear, viscous material
(3) E. Knappe, BASF AG – Glasurit, Hiltrup/W.

(5) polycondensation of 1,6-hexanediol with tetrahydrophthalic anhydride
(6) private communication
(7) film on CsI

3371124 $C_7H_8O_5$ 689

(1) poly(ethylene acetylenedicarboxylate)
(2) very viscous, yellow to brown material
(3) M.H. Nosseir, Polymer and Pigment Laboratory, National Research Center, Dokki, Kairo

(5) polycondensation by ester-interchange between dimethylacetylenedicarboxylate and ethyleneglycol
(6) M.H. Nosseir, N.N. Messiha, N.L. Doss, Europ. Polym. J. 7 (1971) 1629...36
(7) film from CHCl₃ on CsI

3371124 $C_8H_{10}O_5$ 690

(1) poly(1,2-propylene acetylenedicarboxylate)
(2) brown resinous material
(3) M.H. Nosseir, Polymer and Pigment Laboratory, National Research Center, Dokki, Kairo

(5) polycondensation by ester-interchange between dimethylacetylenedicarboxylate and propylene glycol
(6) M.H. Nosseir, N.N. Messiha, N.L. Doss, Europ. Polym. J. 7 (1971) 1629...36

3371124 $C_7H_8O_5$ 691

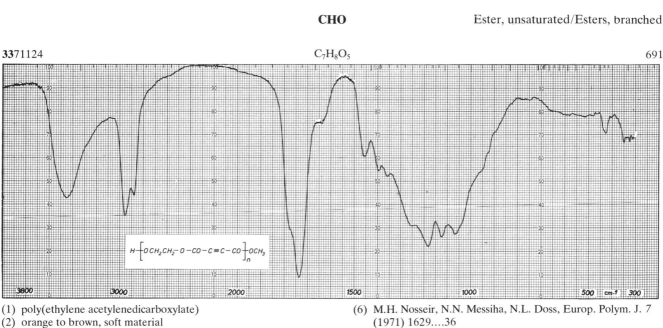

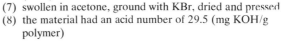

(1) poly(ethylene acetylenedicarboxylate)
(2) orange to brown, soft material
(3) M.H. Nosseir, Polymer and Pigment Laboratory, National Research Center, Dokki, Kairo   ·
(5) reaction of acetylenedicarboxylic acid with ethyleneoxide in tetrahydrofuran at room temperature

(6) M.H. Nosseir, N.N. Messiha, N.L. Doss, Europ. Polym. J. 7 (1971) 1629....36
(7) swollen in acetone, ground with KBr, dried and pressed
(8) the material had an acid number of 29.5 (mg KOH/g polymer)

3371132 $C_4H_6O_3$ 692

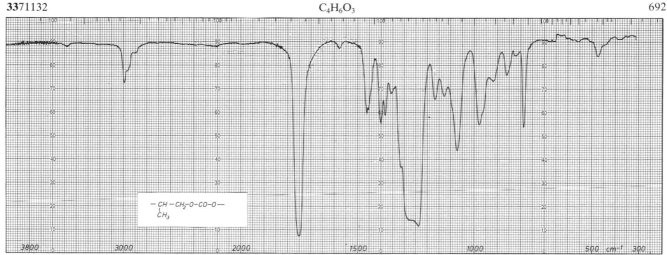

(1) poly(oxycarbonyloxy-1,2-propylene), poly(propylene carbonate)
(2) eggshell-coloured material
(3) W. Kuran, Institut of Organic Chemistry and Technology, Technical University, Warzawa

(5) copolymerization of carbondioxide and propylene oxide with, e.g., diethylzinc/resorcinol (equimolar) as a catalyst (in 1,3-dioxane)
(6) W. Kuran, S. Pasynkiewicz, Jadwiga Skupińska, A. Rokicki, Makromol. Chem. *177* (1976) 11...20
(7) film from $CHCl_3$ on CsI

3371132 $C_4H_6O_3$ 693

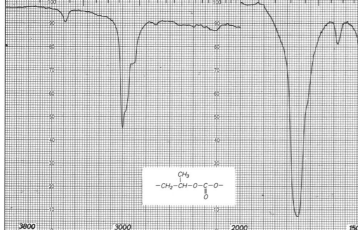

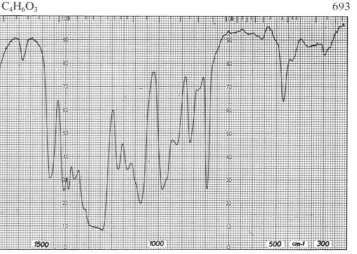

(1) poly(1,2-propylene carbonate), propyleneoxide-CO_2 copolymer (1:1)
(2) colourless material
(3) S. Inoue, University of Tokyo, Faculty of Engineering, Tokyo

(5) copolymerization with $Zn(C_2H_5)_2/H_2O$
(6) S. Inoue, H. Koinuma, T. Tsuruta, Makromol. Chem. *130* (1969) 210...20

3371221 $C_{10}H_8O_4$ 694

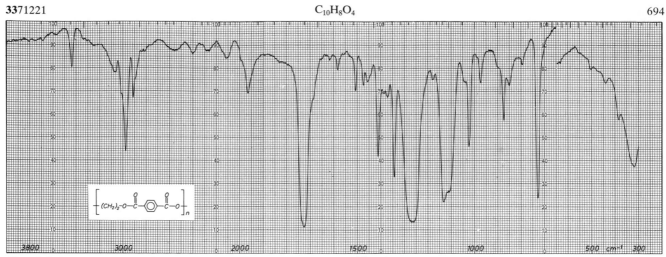

(1) poly(ethylene terephthalate)
(2) white, coarse powder
(3) H.G. Weyland, AKZO Research and Engineering N.V., Arnhem

(6) private communication
(7) melting film between KBr (300 K)

3371221 $C_{11}H_{10}O_4$ 695

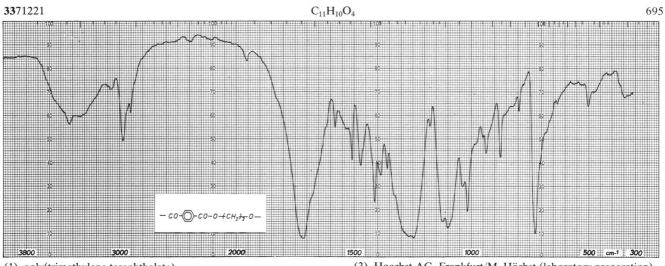

(1) poly(trimethylene terephthalate)
(2) white granules

(3) Hoechst AG, Frankfurt/M. Höchst (laboratory preparation)
(7) KBr (2/350), ordinate expanded

3371221 $C_{11}H_{10}O_4$ 696

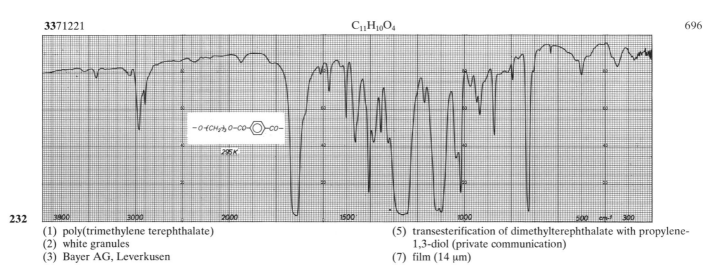

(1) poly(trimethylene terephthalate)
(2) white granules
(3) Bayer AG, Leverkusen

(5) transesterification of dimethylterephthalate with propylene-1,3-diol (private communication)
(7) film (14 μm)

3371221 $C_{12}H_{12}O_4$ 697

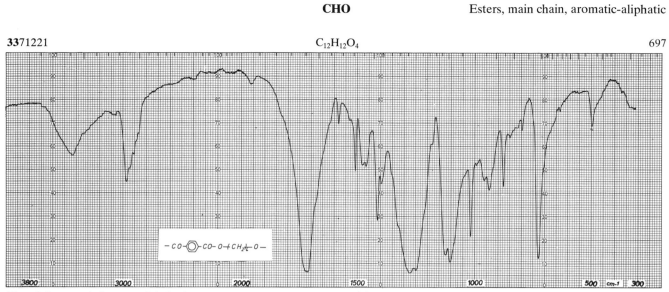

(1) poly(tetramethylene terephthalate)
(2) white granules

(3) Hoechst AG, Frankfurt/M. Höchst (laboratory preparation)
(7) KBr (2/350), ordinate expanded

3371221 $C_{12}H_{12}O_4$ 698

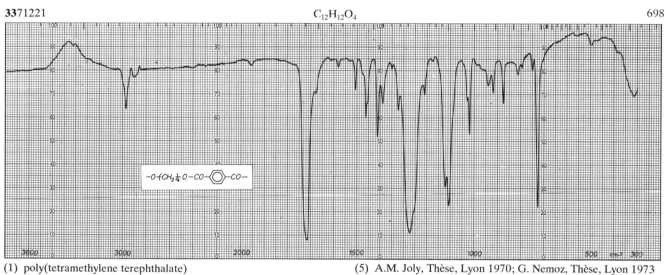

(1) poly(tetramethylene terephthalate)
(2) white granules
(3) G. Nemoz, Centre de Recherche de la Soierie et des Industries Textiles, Lyon

(5) A.M. Joly, Thèse, Lyon 1970; G. Nemoz, Thèse, Lyon 1973
(6) A.M. Joly, G. Nemoz, A. Douillard, G. Vallet, Makromol. Chem. *176* (1975) 479...94
(7) melting film on KBr

3371221 $C_{12}H_{12}O_4$ 699

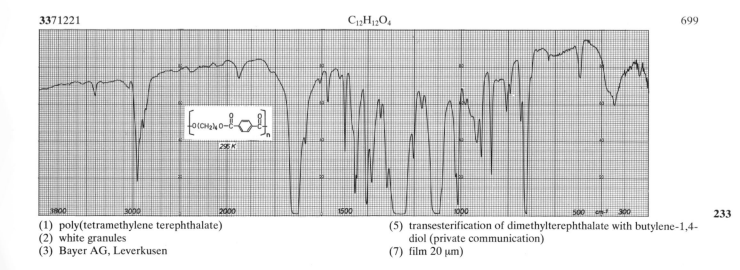

(1) poly(tetramethylene terephthalate)
(2) white granules
(3) Bayer AG, Leverkusen

(5) transesterification of dimethylterephthalate with butylene-1,4-diol (private communication)
(7) film 20 μm)

3371221   C$_{13}$H$_{14}$O$_4$ 700

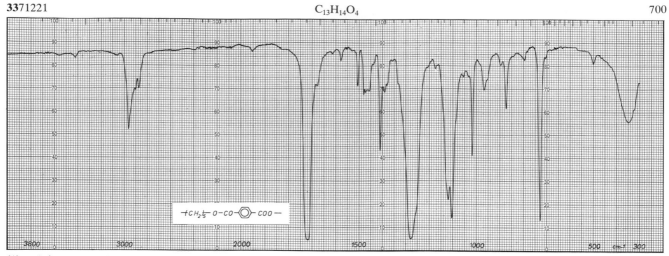

(1) poly(pentamethylene terephthalate)
(2) white granules
(3) G. Nemoz, Centre de Recherche de la Soierie et des
   Industries Textiles, Lyon

(5) A.M. Joly, Thèse, Lyon 1970; G. Nemoz, Thèse, Lyon 1973
(6) A.M. Joly, G. Nemoz, A. Douillard, G. Vallet, Makromol.
   Chem. *176* (1975) 479...94
(7) melting film on CsI

3371221   C$_{14}$H$_{16}$O$_4$ 701

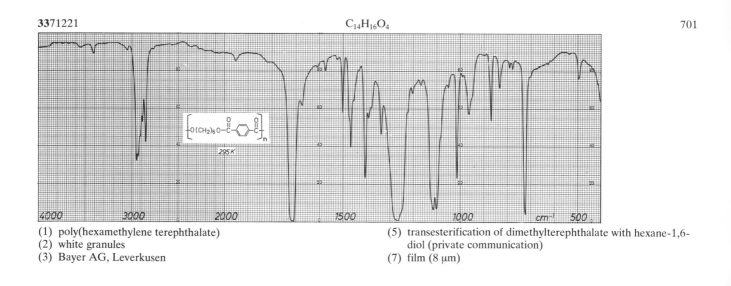

(1) poly(hexamethylene terephthalate)
(2) white granules
(3) Bayer AG, Leverkusen

(5) transesterification of dimethylterephthalate with hexane-1,6-
   diol (private communication)
(7) film (8 μm)

3371221   C$_{14}$H$_{16}$O$_4$ 702

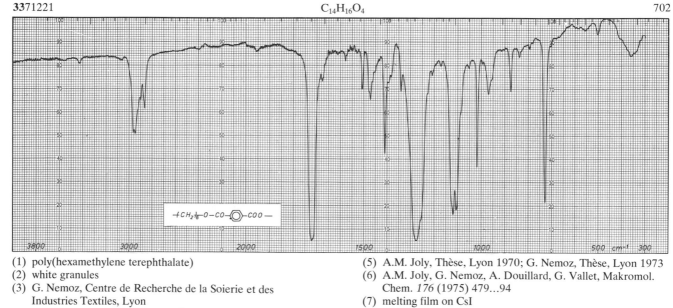

(1) poly(hexamethylene terephthalate)
(2) white granules
(3) G. Nemoz, Centre de Recherche de la Soierie et des
   Industries Textiles, Lyon

(5) A.M. Joly, Thèse, Lyon 1970; G. Nemoz, Thèse, Lyon 1973
(6) A.M. Joly, G. Nemoz, A. Douillard, G. Vallet, Makromol.
   Chem. *176* (1975) 479...94
(7) melting film on CsI

3371221   C$_{20}$H$_{24}$O$_4$ 703

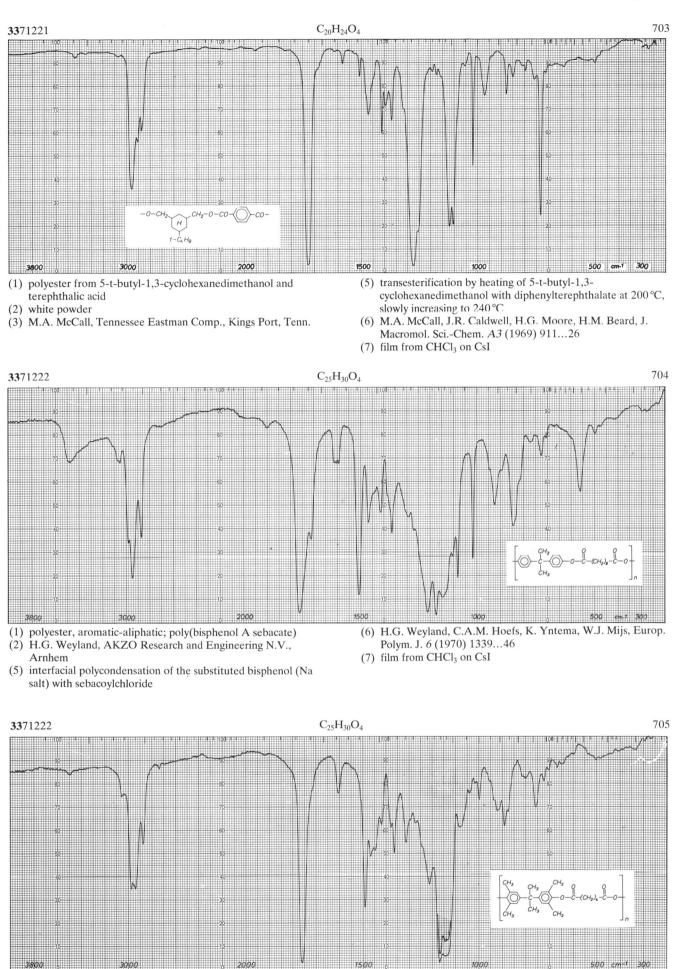

(1) polyester from 5-t-butyl-1,3-cyclohexanedimethanol and terephthalic acid
(2) white powder
(3) M.A. McCall, Tennessee Eastman Comp., Kings Port, Tenn.

(5) transesterification by heating of 5-t-butyl-1,3-cyclohexanedimethanol with diphenylterephthalate at 200 °C, slowly increasing to 240 °C
(6) M.A. McCall, J.R. Caldwell, H.G. Moore, H.M. Beard, J. Macromol. Sci.-Chem. *A3* (1969) 911...26
(7) film from CHCl$_3$ on CsI

3371222   C$_{25}$H$_{30}$O$_4$ 704

(1) polyester, aromatic-aliphatic; poly(bisphenol A sebacate)
(2) H.G. Weyland, AKZO Research and Engineering N.V., Arnhem
(5) interfacial polycondensation of the substituted bisphenol (Na salt) with sebacoylchloride

(6) H.G. Weyland, C.A.M. Hoefs, K. Yntema, W.J. Mijs, Europ. Polym. J. *6* (1970) 1339...46
(7) film from CHCl$_3$ on CsI

3371222   C$_{25}$H$_{30}$O$_4$ 705

(1) polyester, aromatic-aliphatic, poly(tetramethyl-bisphenol A adipate)
(2) H.G. Weyland, AKZO Research and Engineering N.V., Arnhem

(5) interfacial polycondensation of the substituted bisphenol (Na salt) with adipoylchloride
(6) H.G. Weyland, C.A.M. Hoefs, K. Yntema, W.J. Mijs, Europ. Polym. J. *6* (1970) 1339...46
(7) film from CHCl$_3$ on CsI

3371222 $C_{26}H_{32}O_4$ 706

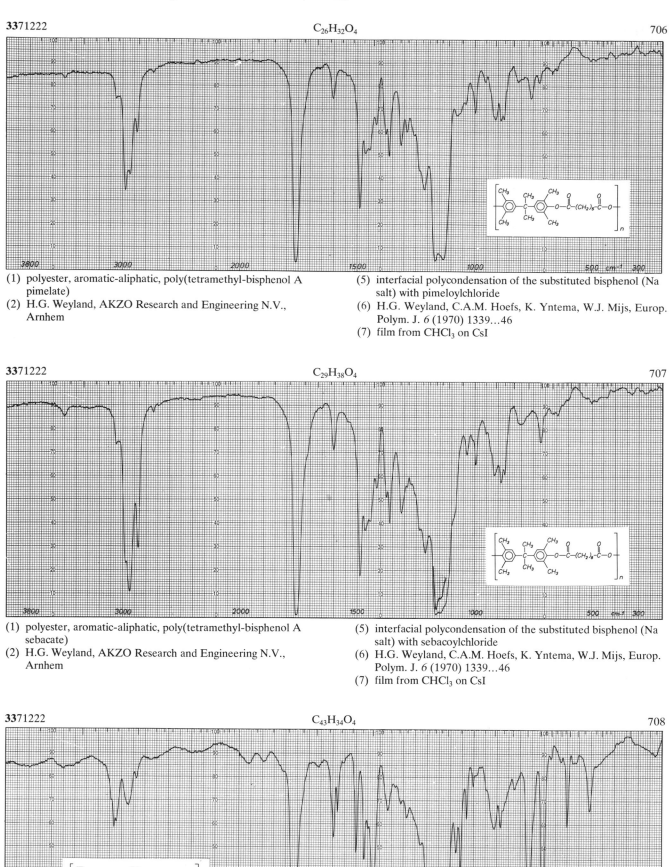

(1) polyester, aromatic-aliphatic, poly(tetramethyl-bisphenol A pimelate)
(2) H.G. Weyland, AKZO Research and Engineering N.V., Arnhem

(5) interfacial polycondensation of the substituted bisphenol (Na salt) with pimeloylchloride
(6) H.G. Weyland, C.A.M. Hoefs, K. Yntema, W.J. Mijs, Europ. Polym. J. *6* (1970) 1339...46
(7) film from $CHCl_3$ on CsI

3371222 $C_{29}H_{38}O_4$ 707

(1) polyester, aromatic-aliphatic, poly(tetramethyl-bisphenol A sebacate)
(2) H.G. Weyland, AKZO Research and Engineering N.V., Arnhem

(5) interfacial polycondensation of the substituted bisphenol (Na salt) with sebacoylchloride
(6) H.G. Weyland, C.A.M. Hoefs, K. Yntema, W.J. Mijs, Europ. Polym. J. *6* (1970) 1339...46
(7) film from $CHCl_3$ on CsI

3371222 $C_{43}H_{34}O_4$ 708

(1) polyester, aromatic-aliphatic, poly[bis(diphenylphenylene) methane adipate]
(2) H.G. Weyland, AKZO Research and Engineering N.V., Arnhem

(5) interfacial polycondensation of the substituted bisphenol (Na salt) with adipoylchloride
(6) H.G. Weyland, C.A.M. Hoefs, K. Yntema, W.J. Mijs, Europ. Polym. J. *6* (1970) 1339...46
(7) film from $CHCl_3$ on CsI

3371222 C_44H_36O_4 709

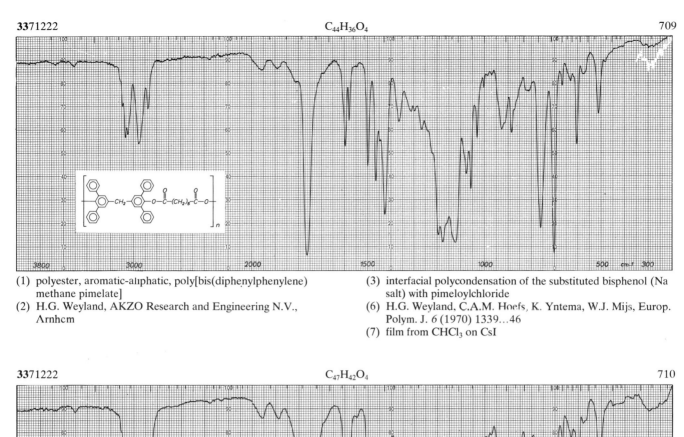

(1) polyester, aromatic-aliphatic, poly[bis(diphenylphenylene) methane pimelate]
(2) H.G. Weyland, AKZO Research and Engineering N.V., Arnhem
(3) interfacial polycondensation of the substituted bisphenol (Na salt) with pimeloylchloride
(6) H.G. Weyland, C.A.M. Hoefs, K. Yntema, W.J. Mijs, Europ. Polym. J. *6* (1970) 1339...46
(7) film from CHCl_3 on CsI

3371222 C_47H_42O_4 710

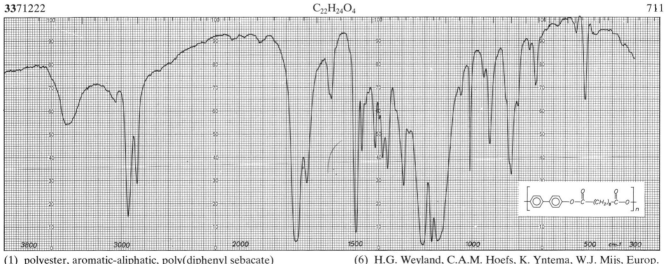

(1) polyester, aromatic-aliphatic, poly[bis(diphenylphenylene)methane sebacate]
(2) H.G. Weyland, AKZO Research and Engineering N.V., Arnhem
(5) interfacial polycondensation of the substituted bisphenol (Na salt) with sebacoylchloride
(6) H.G. Weyland, C.A.M. Hoefs, K. Yntema, W.J. Mijs, Europ. Polym. J. *6* (1970) 1339...46
(7) film from CHCl_3 on CsI

3371222 C_22H_24O_4 711

(1) polyester, aromatic-aliphatic, poly(diphenyl sebacate)
(2) H.G. Weyland, AKZO Research and Engineering N.V., Arnhem
(5) interfacial polycondensation of the bisphenol (Na salt) with sebacoylchloride
(6) H.G. Weyland, C.A.M. Hoefs, K. Yntema, W.J. Mijs, Europ. Polym. J. *6* (1970) 1339...46
(7) film from CHCl_3 on CsI

3371222 $C_{22}H_{24}O_4$ 712

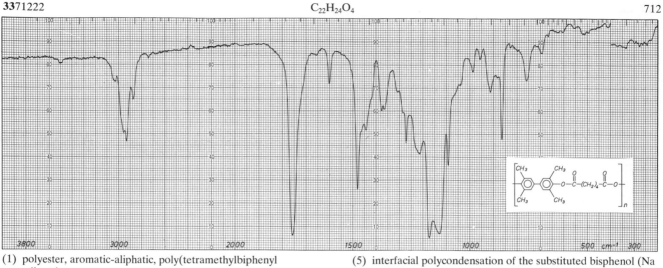

(1) polyester, aromatic-aliphatic, poly(tetramethylbiphenyl adipate)
(2) H.G. Weyland, AKZO Research and Engineering N.V., Arnhem
(5) interfacial polycondensation of the substituted bisphenol (Na salt) with adipoylchloride
(6) H.G. Weyland, C.A.M. Hoefs, K. Yntema, W.J. Mijs, Europ. Polym. J. *6* (1970) 1339...46
(7) film from $CHCl_3$ on CsI

3371222 $C_{23}H_{26}O_4$ 713

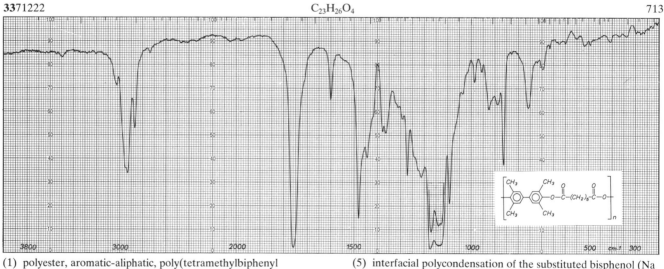

(1) polyester, aromatic-aliphatic, poly(tetramethylbiphenyl pimelate)
(2) H.G. Weyland, AKZO Research and Engineering N.V., Arnhem
(5) interfacial polycondensation of the substituted bisphenol (Na salt) with pimeloylchloride
(6) H.G. Weyland, C.A.M. Hoefs, K. Yntema, W.J. Mijs, Europ. Polym. J. *6* (1970) 1339...46
(7) film from $CHCl_3$ on CsI

3371222 $C_{26}H_{32}O_4$ 714

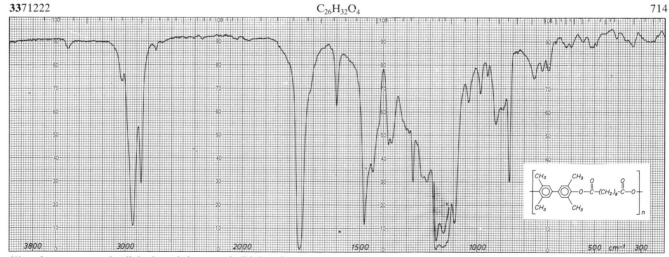

(1) polyester, aromatic-aliphatic, poly(tetramethylbiphenyl sebacate)
(2) H.G. Weyland, AKZO Research and Engineering N.V., Arnhem
(5) interfacial polycondensation of the substituted bisphenol (Na salt) with sebacoylchloride
(6) H.G. Weyland, C.A.M. Hoefs, K. Yntema, W.J. Mijs, Europ. Polym. J. *6* (1970) 1339...46
(7) film from $CHCl_3$ on CsI

3371222 $C_{46}H_{40}O_4$ 715

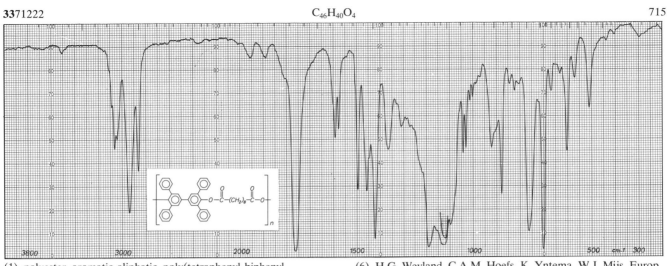

(1) polyester, aromatic-aliphatic, poly(tetraphenyl-biphenyl sebacate)
(2) H.G. Weyland, AKZO Research and Engineering N.V., Arnhem
(5) interfacial polycondensation of the substituted bisphenol (Na salt) with sebacoylchloride

(6) H.G. Weyland, C.A.M. Hoefs, K. Yntema, W.J. Mijs, Europ. Polym J. *6* (1970) 1339...46
(7) film from $CHCl_3$ on CsI

3371224 $C_{21}H_{14}O_4$ 716

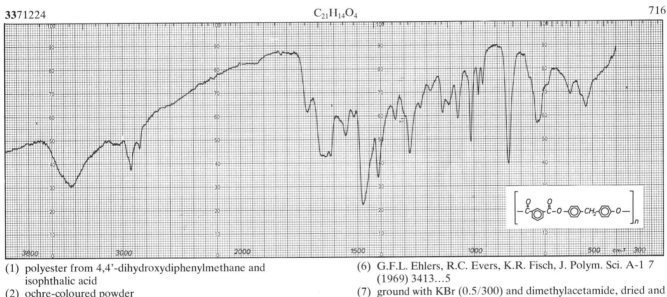

(1) polyester from 4,4'-dihydroxydiphenylmethane and isophthalic acid
(2) ochre-coloured powder
(3) G.F.L. Ehlers (Wright Patterson AFB, Ohio)
(5) interfacial polycondensation of isophthaloylchloride with the phenolate of 4,4'-dihydroxyphenylmethane

(6) G.F.L. Ehlers, R.C. Evers, K.R. Fisch, J. Polym. Sci. A-1 7 (1969) 3413...5
(7) ground with KBr (0.5/300) and dimethylacetamide, dried and pressed

3371224 $C_{23}H_{18}O_4$ 717

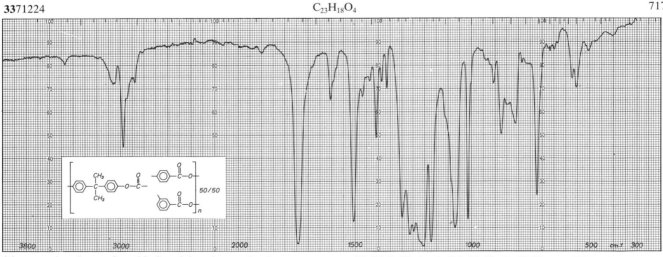

(1) aromatic polyester from bisphenol A and an equimolar amount of isophthalic and terephthalic acids
(2) white powder
(3) H.G. Weyland, AKZO Research and Engineering N.V., Arnhem
(5) interfacial polycondensation of the sodium phenolate and the acid chlorides

(6) H.G. Weyland, C.A.M. Hoefs, K. Yntema, W.J. Mijs, Europ. Polym. J. *6* (1970) 1339...46
(7) film from $CHCl_3$ on CsI

3371224   C_{23}H_{18}O_4   718

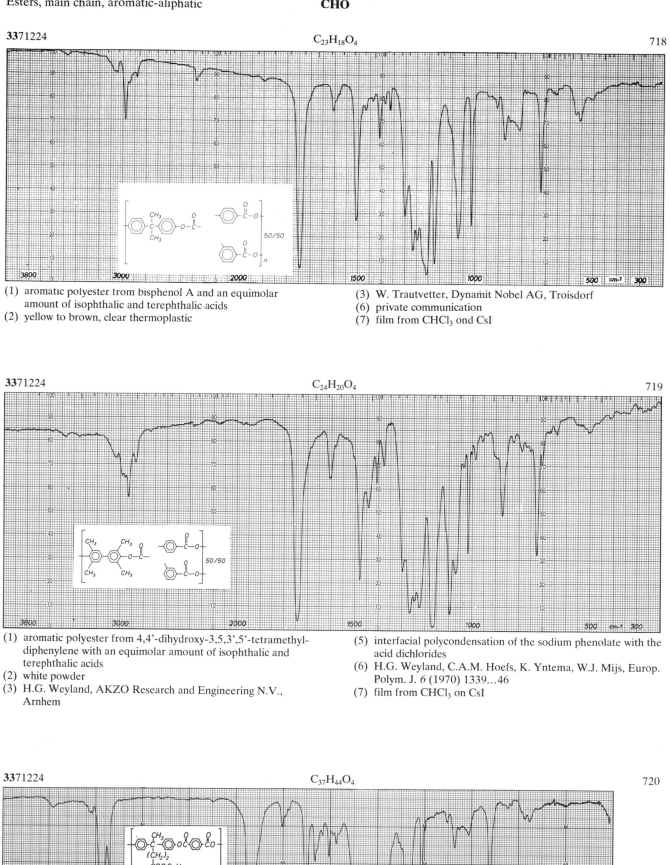

(1) aromatic polyester from bisphenol A and an equimolar amount of isophthalic and terephthalic acids
(2) yellow to brown, clear thermoplastic
(3) W. Trautvetter, Dynamit Nobel AG, Troisdorf
(6) private communication
(7) film from CHCl$_3$ ond CsI

3371224   C_{24}H_{20}O_4   719

(1) aromatic polyester from 4,4'-dihydroxy-3,5,3',5'-tetramethyl-diphenylene with an equimolar amount of isophthalic and terephthalic acids
(2) white powder
(3) H.G. Weyland, AKZO Research and Engineering N.V., Arnhem
(5) interfacial polycondensation of the sodium phenolate with the acid dichlorides
(6) H.G. Weyland, C.A.M. Hoefs, K. Yntema, W.J. Mijs, Europ. Polym. J. *6* (1970) 1339...46
(7) film from CHCl$_3$ on CsI

3371224   C_{37}H_{44}O_4   720

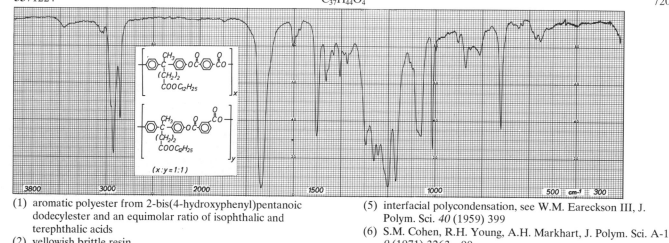

(1) aromatic polyester from 2-bis(4-hydroxyphenyl)pentanoic dodecylester and an equimolar ratio of isophthalic and terephthalic acids
(2) yellowish brittle resin
(3) S.M. Cohen, Monsanto Comp., Research Department, Plastic Product & Resin Div., Springfield, Mass.
(5) interfacial polycondensation, see W.M. Eareckson III, J. Polym. Sci. *40* (1959) 399
(6) S.M. Cohen, R.H. Young, A.H. Markhart, J. Polym. Sci. A-1 *9* (1971) 3263...99
(7) film from CHCl$_3$ on CsI

3371224 $C_{35}H_{32}O_5$ 721

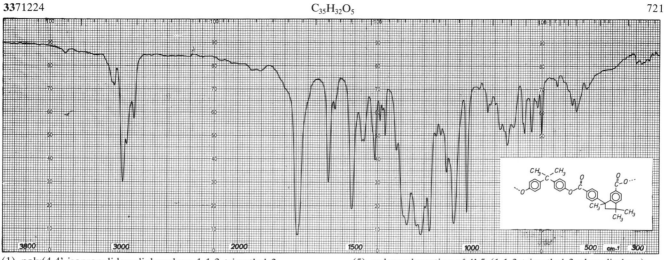

(1) poly(4,4'-isopropylidenediphenylene-1,1,3-trimethyl-3-phenylindane-4',5-dicarboxylate)
(2) white material
(3) Julia S. Tan, Research Laboratories, Eastman Kodak Comp., Rochester, N.Y.

(5) polycondensation of 4',5-(1,1,3-trimethyl-3-phenylindane) dicarboxylic acid (probably in the form of the acid chloride) and 2,2-bis(4'-hydroxyphenyl)propane
(6) Julia S. Tan, J. Polym. Sci. A-2 *12* (1974) 175...86
(7) film from $CHCl_3$ on CsI

3371224–3371234 $C_{23}H_{18}O_4$–$C_{16}H_{14}O_3$ 722

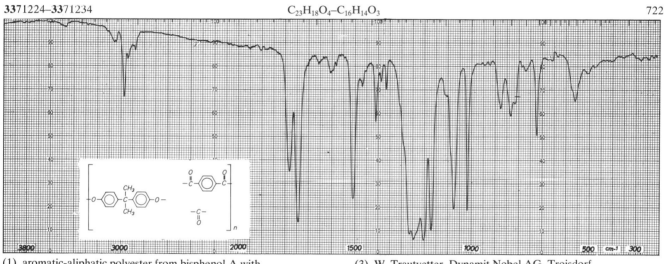

(1) aromatic-aliphatic polyester from bisphenol A with terephthalic acid and carbonic acid in equimolar ratio
(2) light-brown, clear thermoplastic

(3) W. Trautvetter, Dynamit Nobel AG. Troisdorf
(6) private communication
(7) film from $CHCl_3$ on CsI

3371234 $C_{16}H_{14}O_3$ 723

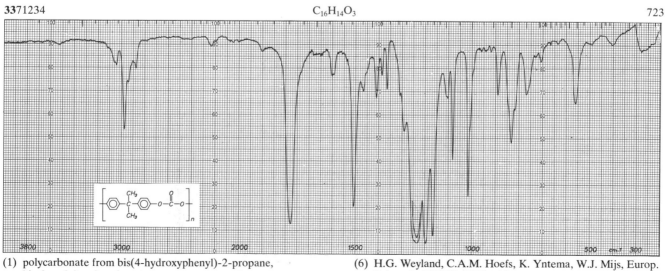

(1) polycarbonate from bis(4-hydroxyphenyl)-2-propane, bisphenol A polycarbonate
(2) colourless material
(3) H.G. Weyland, AKZO Research and Engineering N.V., Arnhem

(6) H.G. Weyland, C.A.M. Hoefs, K. Yntema, W.J. Mijs, Europ. Polym. J. *6* (1970) 1339...46
(7) film from $CHCl_3$ on CsI
(8) commercial "Makrolon"

241

3371234 $C_{25}H_{24}O_3$ 724

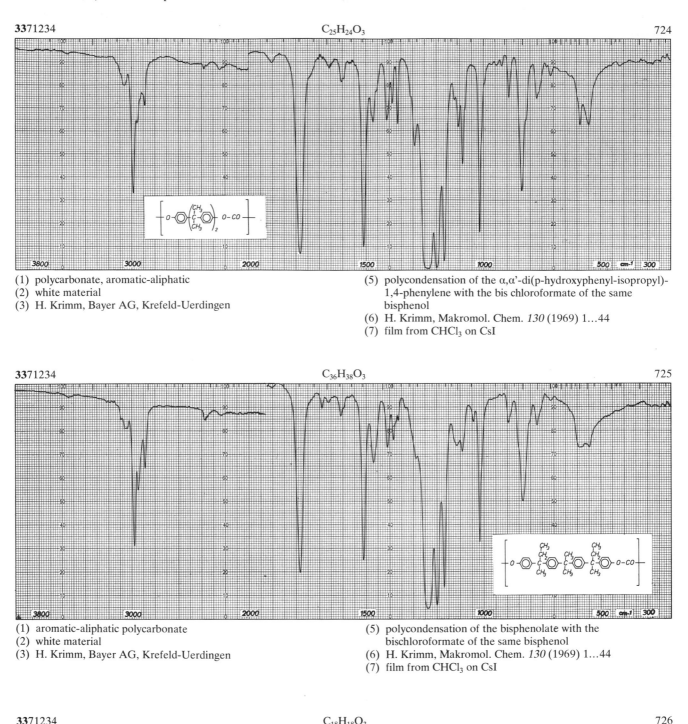

(1) polycarbonate, aromatic-aliphatic
(2) white material
(3) H. Krimm, Bayer AG, Krefeld-Uerdingen

(5) polycondensation of the α,α'-di(p-hydroxyphenyl-isopropyl)-1,4-phenylene with the bis chloroformate of the same bisphenol
(6) H. Krimm, Makromol. Chem. *130* (1969) 1...44
(7) film from CHCl₃ on CsI

3371234 $C_{36}H_{38}O_3$ 725

(1) aromatic-aliphatic polycarbonate
(2) white material
(3) H. Krimm, Bayer AG, Krefeld-Uerdingen

(5) polycondensation of the bisphenolate with the bischloroformate of the same bisphenol
(6) H. Krimm, Makromol. Chem. *130* (1969) 1...44
(7) film from CHCl₃ on CsI

3371234 $C_{18}H_{18}O_3$ 726

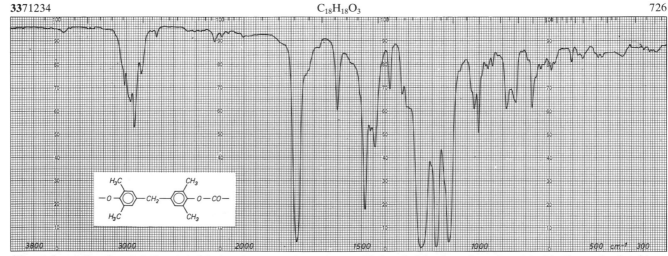

(1) poly(oxycarbonyloxy-2,6-dimethyl-1,4-phenylene-methylene-3,5-dimethyl-1,4-phenylene); polycarbonate from methylene-bis(3,5-dimethyl-4-hydroxyphenyl)
(2) milky-white granules
(3) V. Serini, Zentralbereich Zentrale Forschung, Wissenschaftliches Hauptlaboratorium, Bayer AG, Krefeld-Uerdingen

(5) interfacial polycondensation of the bischlorocarbonic acid ester of the bisphenol
(6) V. Serini, D. Freitag, H. Vernaleken, Angew. Makromol. Chem. *55* (1976) 175....89
(7) film from CH₂Cl₂ on CsI

CHOC
Carbonic, ester, aromatic-aliphatic
Esters, main chain, aromatic

3371234 C$_{20}$H$_{22}$O$_3$ 727

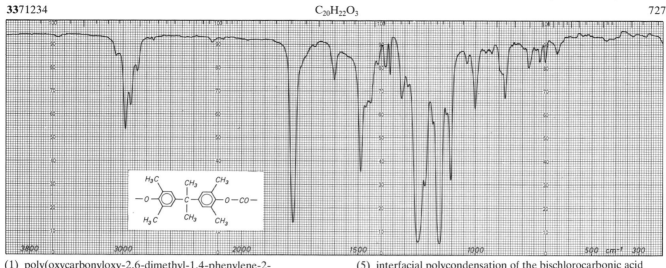

(1) poly(oxycarbonyloxy-2,6-dimethyl-1,4-phenylene-2-isopropylidene-3,5-dimethyl-1,4-phenylene); polycarbonate from tetramethylbisphenol A
(2) glassy clear granules
(3) V. Serini, Zentralbereich Zentrale Forschung, Wissenschaftliches Hauptlaboratorium, Bayer AG, Krefeld-Uerdingen

(5) interfacial polycondensation of the bischlorocarbonic acid ester of tetramethylbisphenol A
(6) V. Serini, D. Freitag, H. Vernaleken, Angew. Makromol. Chem. *55* (1976) 175...89
(7) film from CH$_2$Cl$_2$ on CsI

337132 C$_{20}$H$_{12}$O$_4$ 728

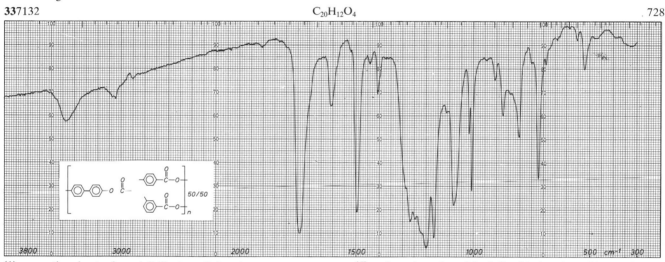

(1) aromatic polyester from 4,4'dihydroxydiphenylene, isophthalic and terephthalic acids
(2) white powder
(3) H.G. Weyland, AKZO Research and Engineering N.V., Arnhem

(5) polycondensation of the kaliumbisphenolate with the acid chloride
(6) H.G. Weyland, C.A.M. Hoefs, K. Yntema, W.J. Mijs, Europ. Polym. J. *6* (1970) 1339...46
(7) KBr (1/350)

337132 C$_{44}$H$_{28}$O$_4$ 729

(1) aromatic polyester from 4,4'-dihydroxy-3,5,3',5'-tetraphenyl-diphenylene, isophthalic and terephthalic acids
(2) white powder
(3) H.G. Weyland, AKZO Research and Engineering N.V., Arnhem

(5) polycondensation of the K-bisphenolate with the acid chloride
(6) H.G. Weyland, C.A.M. Hoefs, K. Yntema, W.J. Mijs, Europ. Polym. J. *6* (1970) 1339...46
(7) KBr (2/350)

337132–3371224 $C_{28}H_{16}O_8$–$C_{57}H_{56}O_{12}$ 730

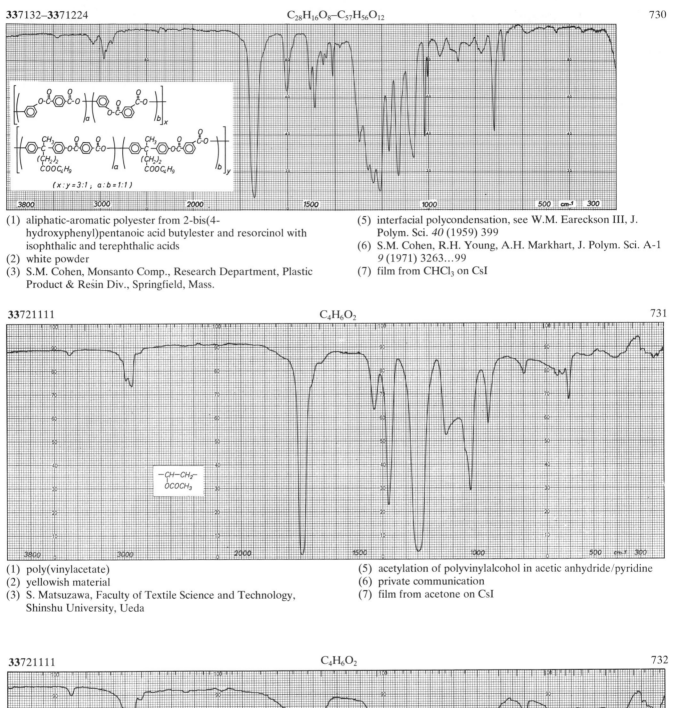

(1) aliphatic-aromatic polyester from 2-bis(4-hydroxyphenyl)pentanoic acid butylester and resorcinol with isophthalic and terephthalic acids
(2) white powder
(3) S.M. Cohen, Monsanto Comp., Research Department, Plastic Product & Resin Div., Springfield, Mass.
(5) interfacial polycondensation, see W.M. Eareckson III, J. Polym. Sci. *40* (1959) 399
(6) S.M. Cohen, R.H. Young, A.H. Markhart, J. Polym. Sci. A-1 *9* (1971) 3263…99
(7) film from CHCl$_3$ on CsI

33721111 $C_4H_6O_2$ 731

(1) poly(vinylacetate)
(2) yellowish material
(3) S. Matsuzawa, Faculty of Textile Science and Technology, Shinshu University, Ueda
(5) acetylation of polyvinylalcohol in acetic anhydride/pyridine
(6) private communication
(7) film from acetone on CsI

33721111 $C_4H_6O_2$ 732

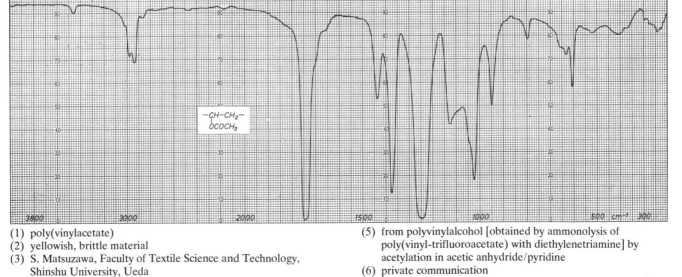

(1) poly(vinylacetate)
(2) yellowish, brittle material
(3) S. Matsuzawa, Faculty of Textile Science and Technology, Shinshu University, Ueda
(4) 51 mol-% syndiotactic dyads
(5) from polyvinylalcohol [obtained by ammonolysis of poly(vinyl-trifluoroacetate) with diethylenetriamine] by acetylation in acetic anhydride/pyridine
(6) private communication
(7) film from acetone on CsI

33721111   C₄H₆O₂   733

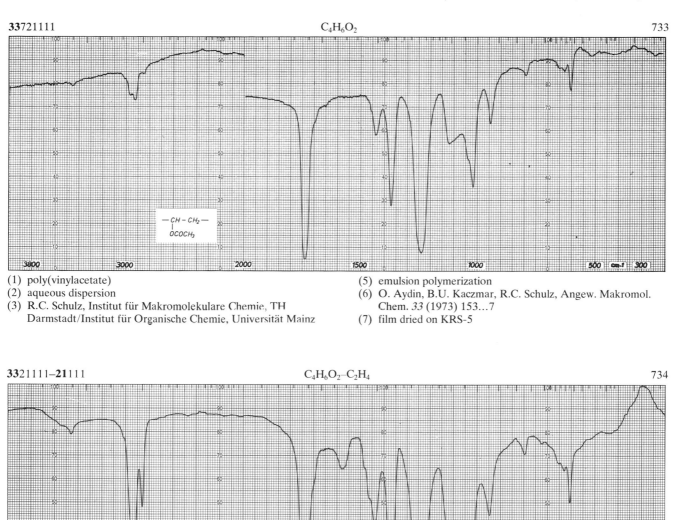

(1) poly(vinylacetate)
(2) aqueous dispersion
(3) R.C. Schulz, Institut für Makromolekulare Chemie, TH Darmstadt/Institut für Organische Chemie, Universität Mainz

(5) emulsion polymerization
(6) O. Aydin, B.U. Kaczmar, R.C. Schulz, Angew. Makromol. Chem. *33* (1973) 153...7
(7) film dried on KRS-5

3321111–21111   C₄H₆O₂–C₂H₄   734

(1) vinylacetate-ethylene copolymer
(2) yellowish, transparent, soft material
(3) T. Yatsu, Mitsui Petrochemical Ind., Research Center, Waki-Cho, Kuga-Gun
(4) alternating structure

(5) complexed copolymerization of the monomers in hexane solution with a tricomponent catalytic system (e.g., AlEt₃t-butylperoxyisobutyrate and diacetylperoxide)
(6) E. Yatsu, S. Moriuchi, H. Fujii, Polym. Preprints *16*/(1975) 373...8
(7) melting film between CsI

33721111   C₄H₆O₂–C₅H₈O₂   735

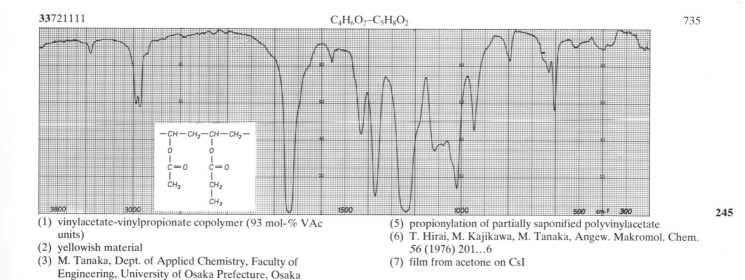

(1) vinylacetate-vinylpropionate copolymer (93 mol-% VAc units)
(2) yellowish material
(3) M. Tanaka, Dept. of Applied Chemistry, Faculty of Engineering, University of Osaka Prefecture, Osaka

(5) propionylation of partially saponified polyvinylacetate
(6) T. Hirai, M. Kajikawa, M. Tanaka, Angew. Makromol. Chem. *56* (1976) 201...6
(7) film from acetone on CsI

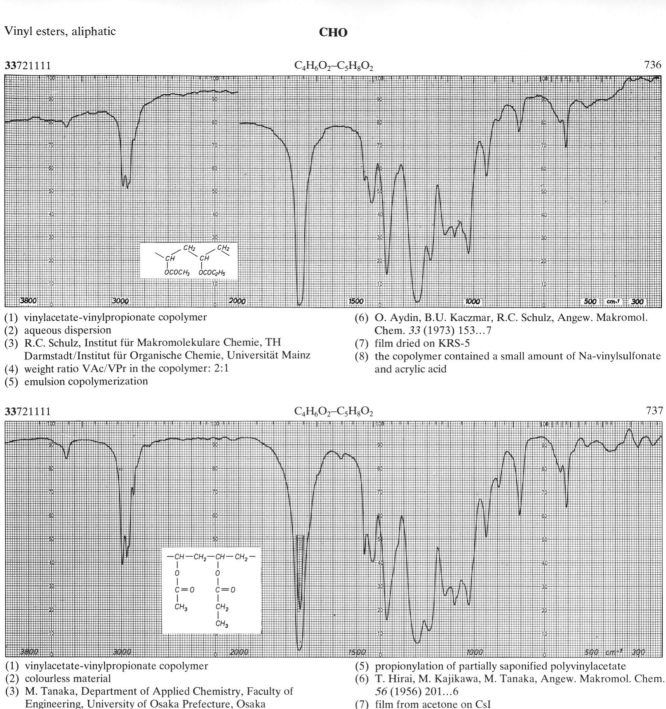

(1) vinylacetate-vinylpropionate copolymer
(2) aqueous dispersion
(3) R.C. Schulz, Institut für Makromolekulare Chemie, TH Darmstadt/Institut für Organische Chemie, Universität Mainz
(4) weight ratio VAc/VPr in the copolymer: 2:1
(5) emulsion copolymerization
(6) O. Aydin, B.U. Kaczmar, R.C. Schulz, Angew. Makromol. Chem. *33* (1973) 153...7
(7) film dried on KRS-5
(8) the copolymer contained a small amount of Na-vinylsulfonate and acrylic acid

(1) vinylacetate-vinylpropionate copolymer
(2) colourless material
(3) M. Tanaka, Department of Applied Chemistry, Faculty of Engineering, University of Osaka Prefecture, Osaka
(4) 53 mol-% vinylacetate units in the copolymer
(5) propionylation of partially saponified polyvinylacetate
(6) T. Hirai, M. Kajikawa, M. Tanaka, Angew. Makromol. Chem. *56* (1956) 201...6
(7) film from acetone on CsI

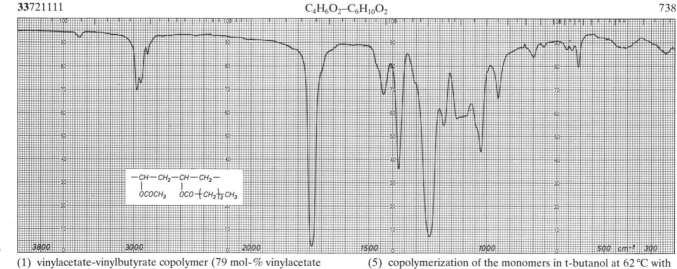

(1) vinylacetate-vinylbutyrate copolymer (79 mol-% vinylacetate units)
(2) colourless elastic material
(3) R. van der Meer, Laboratory of Polymer Technology, Eindhoven University of Technology, Eindhoven
(5) copolymerization of the monomers in t-butanol at 62 °C with AIBN
(6) R.v.d. Meer, A.L. German, Angew. Makromol. Chem. *56* (1976) 27...36
(7) film from CHCl₃ on CsI

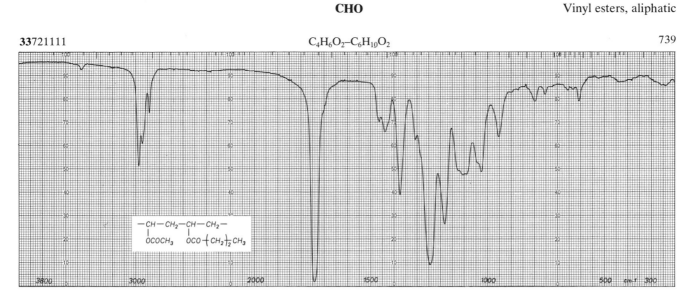

(1) vinylacetate-vinylbutyrate copolymer (50 mol-% vinylacetate units)
(2) colourless, transparent elastomer
(3) R. van der Meer, Laboratory of Polymer Technology, Eindhoven University of Technology, Eindhoven
(5) copolymerization of monomers in t-butanol at 62 °C with AIBN
(6) R.v.d. Meer, A.I.. German, Angew. Makromol. Chem. *56* (1976) 27...36
(7) film from CHCl₃ on CsI

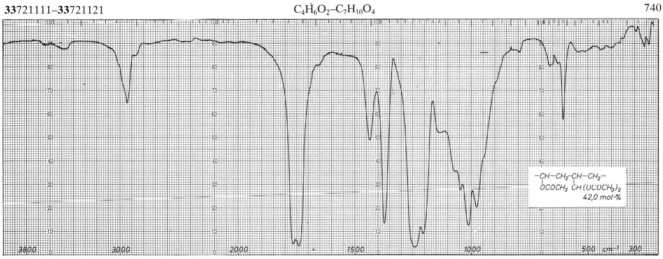

(1) vinylacetate-allylidenediacetate copolymer
(2) colourless material
(3) K. Noro, Central Research Laboratory, The Nippon Synthetic Chemical Industry Co., Hyogo
(4) the copolymer contains 42.0 mol-% allylidenediacetate units
(5) bulk-copolymerization with AIBN
(6) M. Sadamichi, K. Noro, J. Macromol. Sci.-Chem. *A3* (1969) 845...52
(7) film from acetone on CsI

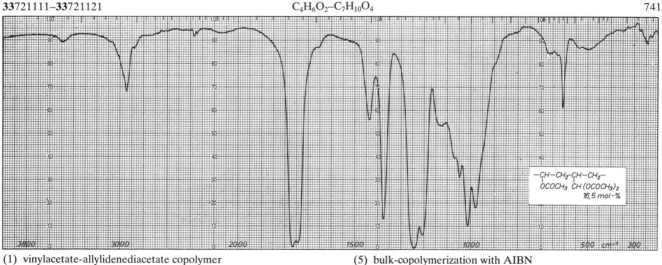

(1) vinylacetate-allylidenediacetate copolymer
(2) colourless material
(3) K. Noro, Central Research Laboratory, The Nippon Synthetic Chemical Industry., Hyogo
(4) the copolymer contains 16.5 mol-% allylidenediacetate units
(5) bulk-copolymerization with AIBN
(6) M. Sadamichi, K. Noro, J. Macromol. Sci.-Chem. *A3* (1969) 845...52
(7) film from acetone on CsI

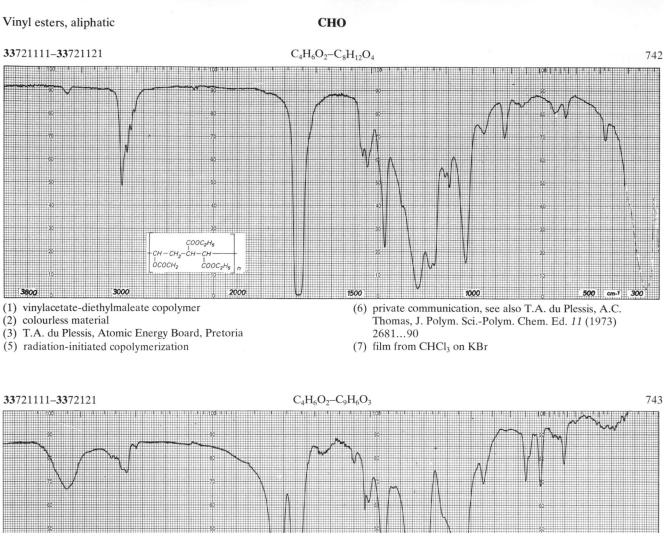

(1) vinylacetate-diethylmaleate copolymer
(2) colourless material
(3) T.A. du Plessis, Atomic Energy Board, Pretoria
(5) radiation-initiated copolymerization

(6) private communication, see also T.A. du Plessis, A.C. Thomas, J. Polym. Sci.-Polym. Chem. Ed. *11* (1973) 2681…90
(7) film from $CHCl_3$ on KBr

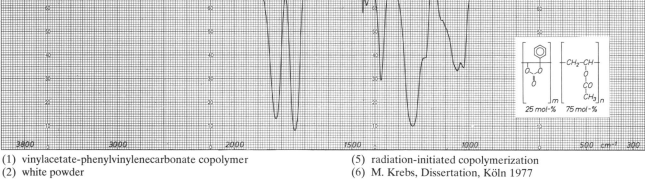

(1) vinylacetate-phenylvinylenecarbonate copolymer
(2) white powder
(3) M. Krebs, Institut für Physikalische Chemie, Universität Köln
(4) the copolymer contains 25% phenylvinylenecarbonate units

(5) radiation-initiated copolymerization
(6) M. Krebs, Dissertation, Köln 1977
(7) KBr (1/300)

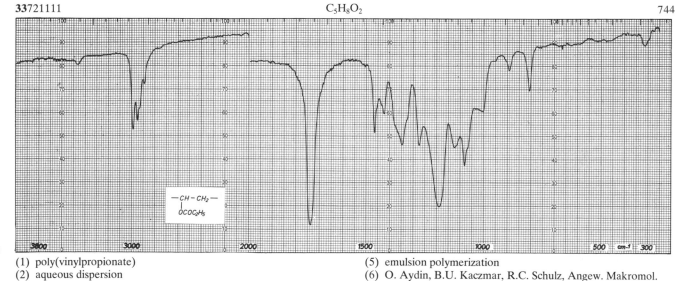

(1) poly(vinylpropionate)
(2) aqueous dispersion
(3) R.C. Schulz, Institut für Makromolekulare Chemie, TH Darmstadt/Institut für Organische Chemie, Universität Mainz

(5) emulsion polymerization
(6) O. Aydin, B.U. Kaczmar, R.C. Schulz, Angew. Makromol. Chem. *33* (1973) 153…7
(7) film dried on KRS-5

33721111   C$_5$H$_8$O$_2$ 745

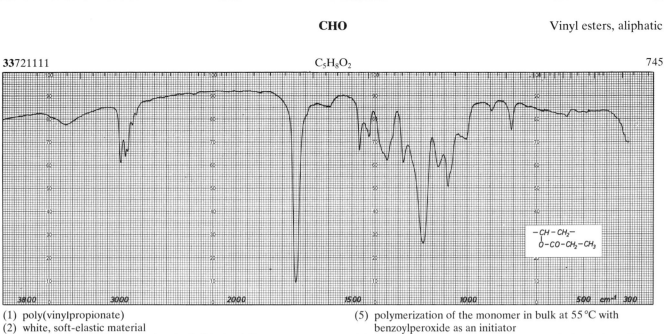

(1) poly(vinylpropionate)
(2) white, soft-elastic material
(3) P.L. Magagnini, Centro Nazionale di Chimica delle Macromolecole, Istituto di Chimica Industriale ed Applicata del Università di Pisa, Pisa

(5) polymerization of the monomer in bulk at 55 °C with benzoylperoxide as an initiator
(6) P.L. Magagnini, F. Sardelli, Giovanna Pizzirani, Ann. Chim. 57 (1967) 805...16
(7) film from benzene on KBr

33721111   C$_5$H$_8$O$_2$–C$_4$H$_6$O$_2$ 746

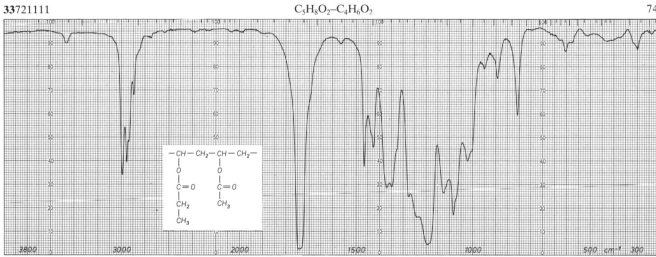

(1) vinylpropionate-vinylacetate copolymer (12% vinylacetate units)
(2) yellow material
(3) M. Tanaka, Department of Applied Chemistry, Faculty of Engineering, University of Osaka Prefecture, Osaka

(5) partial saponification of polyvinylacetate and subsequent propionylation; T. Hirai, M. Kajikawa, M. Tanaka, Angew. Makromol. Chem. in print
(6) T. Hirai, M. Kajikawa, M. Tanaka, Angew. Makromol. Chem. 56 (1976) 201...6
(7) film from CHCl$_3$ on CsI

33721111   C$_5$H$_8$O$_2$–C$_4$H$_6$O$_2$ 747

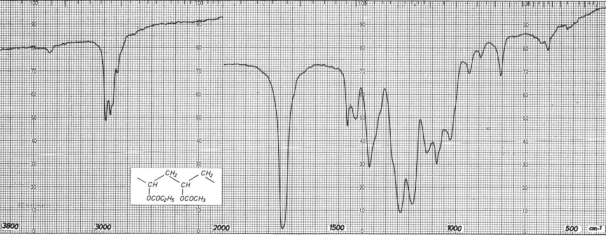

(1) vinylpropionate-vinylacetate copolymer
(2) aqueous dispersion
(3) R.C. Schulz, Institut für Makromolekulare Chemie, TH Darmstadt/Institut für Organische Chemie, Universität Mainz
(4) weight ratio of the monomer units in the copolymer approx. 2:1, VPr:VAc

(5) emulsion copolymerization
(6) O. Aydin, B.U. Kaczmar, R.C. Schulz, Angew. Makromol. Chem. 33 (1973) 153...7
(7) film on KRS-5
(8) the copolymer contained a small amount of Na-vinylsulfonate and acrylic acid units

33721111 $C_6H_{10}O_2$ 748

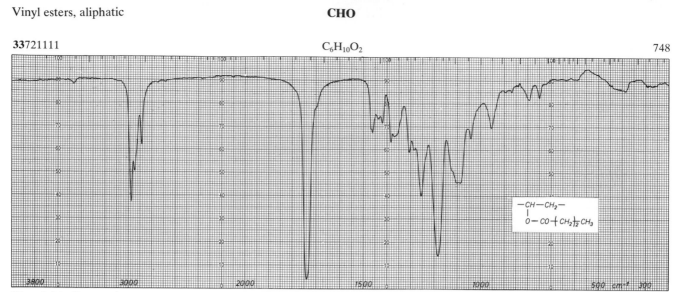

(1) poly(vinylbutyrate)
(2) colourless elastomer
(3) R. van der Meer, Laboratory of Polymer Technology, Eindhoven University of Technology, Eindhoven
(5) polymerization of commercial vinyl butyrate with AIBN
(6) R.v.d. Meer, A.L. German, Angew. Makromol. Chem. *56* (1976) 27...36
(7) film from CHCl₃ on CsI

33721111 $C_6H_{10}O_2 - C_4H_6O_2$ 749

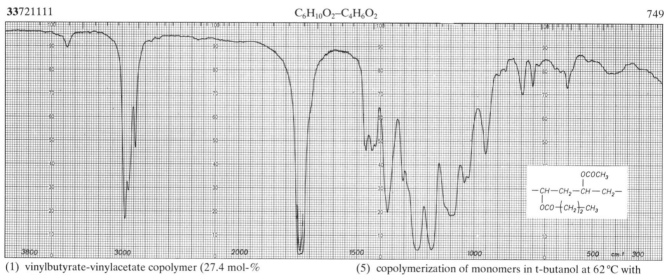

(1) vinylbutyrate-vinylacetate copolymer (27.4 mol-% vinylacetate units)
(2) yellowish, transparent elastomer
(3) R. van der Meer, Laboratory of Polymer Technology, Eindhoven University of Technology, Eindhoven
(5) copolymerization of monomers in t-butanol at 62 °C with AIBN
(6) R.v.d. Meer, A.L. German, Angew. Makromol. Chem. *56* (1976) 27...36
(7) film from CHCl₃ on CsI

33721111 $C_7H_{12}O_2$ 750

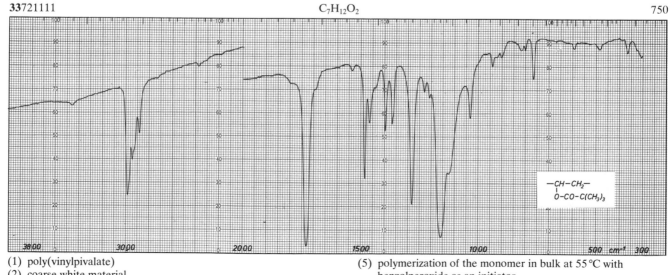

(1) poly(vinylpivalate)
(2) coarse white material
(3) P.L. Magagnini, Centro Nazionale di Chimica delle Macromolecole, Istituto di Chimica Industriale ed Applicata del Università di Pisa, Pisa
(5) polymerization of the monomer in bulk at 55 °C with benzolperoxide as an initiator
(6) P.L. Magagnini, F. Sardelli, Giovanna Pizzirani, Ann. Chim. *57* (1967) 805...16
(7) film from CHCl₃ on KBr

33721111 C₇H₁₀O₂ 751

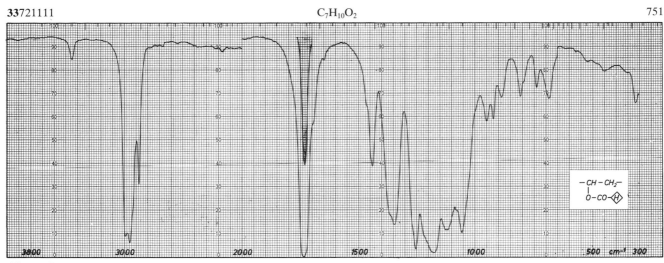

(1) poly(vinyl-cyclobutylcarboxylate)
(2) colourless material
(3) P.L. Magagnini, Centro Nazionale di Chimica delle
Macromolecole, Istituto di Chimica Industriale ed Applicata
del Università di Pisa, Pisa

(5) radical polymerization
(6) P.L. Magagnini, Gazz. Chim. Ital. 97 (1967) 1891; private
communication
(7) film from CHCl₃ on CsI

33721111 C₉H₁₄O₂ 752

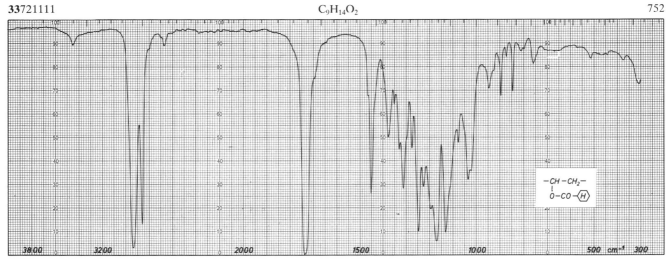

(1) poly(vinyl cyclohexylcarboxylate)
(2) white powder
(3) P.L. Magagnini, Centro Nazionale di Chimica delle
Macromolecole, Istituto di Chimica Industriale ed Applicata
del Università di Pisa, Pisa

(5) radical polymerization
(6) V. Frosini, P.L. Magagnini, E. Butta, M. Baccaredda, Kolloid-
Z.Z. Polym. 213 (1966) 115
(7) film from CHCl₃ on KBr

33721111–4131721111 C₄H₆O₂–C₅H₅F₃O₂ 753

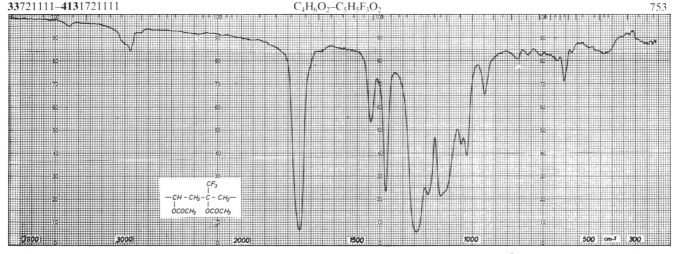

(1) vinylacetate-α-trifluoromethylvinylacetate copolymer
(2) coarse material
(3) H.C. Haas, Chemical Research Laboratories, Polaroid Corp.,
Cambridge, Mass.
(4) equimolar composition

(5) bulk copolymerization at 70⁰C with AIBN; see also H.C.
Haas, N.W. Schuler, J. Polym. Sci. A2 (1964) 1941
(6) H.C. Haas, R.L. MacDonald, C.K. Chiklis, J. Polym. Sci. A-1
7 (1969) 633...41
(7) film from CHCl₃ on CsI

33721112 $C_{13}H_{14}O_3$ 754

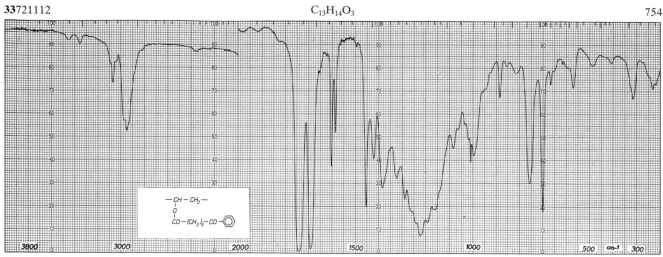

(1) poly(vinyl-4-benzoylbutyrate)
(2) colourless, tough material
(3) H. Hopff, Institut für Organische Technologie, ETH Zürich

(5) AIBN-initiated polymerization in bulk
(6) H. Hopff, M.A. Osman, Angew. Makromol. Chem. *6* (1969) 39...45

33721112 $C_{14}H_{16}O_3$ 755

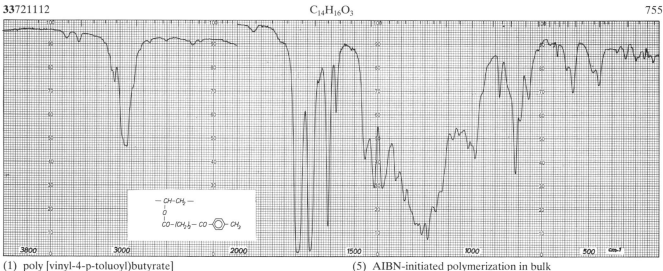

(1) poly [vinyl-4-p-toluoyl)butyrate]
(2) colourless plastic material
(3) H. Hopff, Institut für Organische Technologie, ETH Zürich

(5) AIBN-initiated polymerization in bulk
(6) H. Hopff, M.A. Osman, Angew. Makromol. Chem. *6* (1969) 39...45

33721113 $C_9H_8O_2$ 756

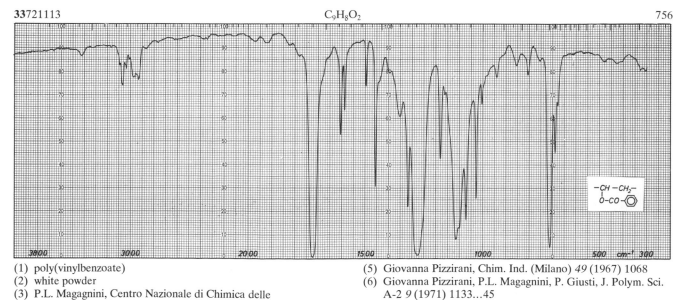

(1) poly(vinylbenzoate)
(2) white powder
(3) P.L. Magagnini, Centro Nazionale di Chimica delle Macromolecole, Istituto di Chimica Industriale ed Applicata del Università di Pisa, Pisa

(5) Giovanna Pizzirani, Chim. Ind. (Milano) *49* (1967) 1068
(6) Giovanna Pizzirani, P.L. Magagnini, P. Giusti, J. Polym. Sci. A-2 *9* (1971) 1133...45
(7) film from C_6H_6 on KBr

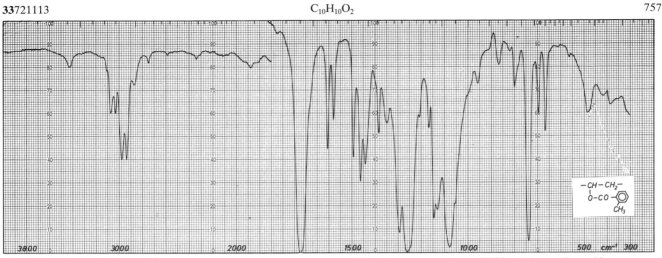

(1) poly(vinyl o-methylbenzoate)
(2) colourless màterial
(3) P.L. Magagnini, Centro Nazionale di Chimica delle
Macromolecole, Istituto di Chimica Industriale ed Applicata
del Università di Pisa, Pisa

(5) bulk polymerization at 65 °C with benzoylperoxide as an
initiator
(6) Giovanna Pizzirani, P.L. Magagnini, P. Giusti, J. Polym. Sci.
A-2 *9* (1971) 1133...45
(7) film from CHCl₃ on KBr

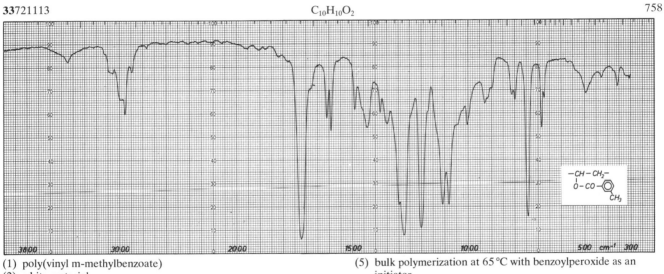

(1) poly(vinyl m-methylbenzoate)
(2) white material
(3) P.L. Magagnini, Centro Nazionale di Chimica delle
Macromolecole, Istituto di Chimica Industriale ed Applicata
del Università di Pisa, Pisa

(5) bulk polymerization at 65 °C with benzoylperoxide as an
initiator
(6) Giovanna Pizzirani, P.L. Magagnini, P. Giusti, J. Polym. Sci.
A-2 *9* (1971) 1133...45
(7) film from CHCl₃ on CsI

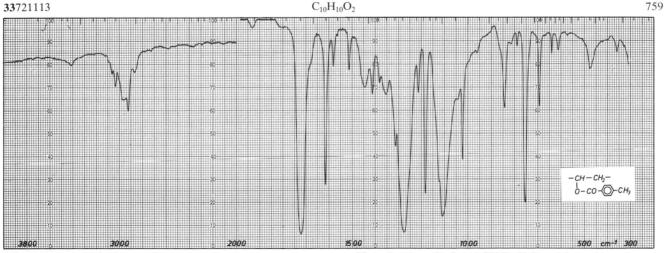

(1) poly(vinyl p-methylbenzoate)
(2) white powder
(3) P.L. Magagnini, Centro Nazionale di Chimica delle
Macromolecole, Istituto di Chimica Industriale ed Applicata
del Università di Pisa, Pisa

(5) bulk polymerization at 65 °C with benzoylperoxide as an
initiator
(6) Giovanna Pizzirani, P.L. Magagnini, P. Giusti, J. Polym. Sci.
A-2 *9* (1971) 1133...45
(7) film from CHCl₃ on KBr

33721113 $C_{13}H_{16}O_2$ 760

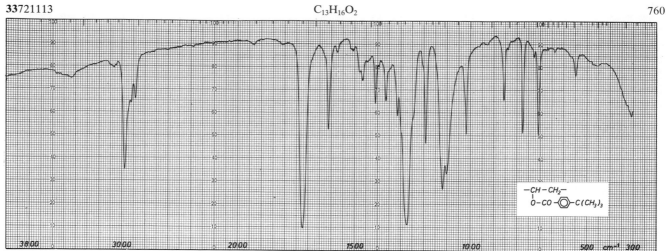

(1) poly(vinyl p-t-butylbenzoate)
(2) white coarse material
(3) P.L. Magagnini, Centro Nazionale di Chimica delle
    Macromolecole, Istituto di Chimica Industriale ed Applicata
    del Università di Pisa, Pisa

(5) bulk polymerization at 65 °C with benzoylperoxide as an
    initiator
(6) Giovanna Pizzirani, P.L. Magagnini, P. Giusti, J. Polym. Sci.
    A-2 *9* (1971) 1133...45
(7) film from benzene on KBr

33721113 $C_{13}H_{16}O_2$ 761

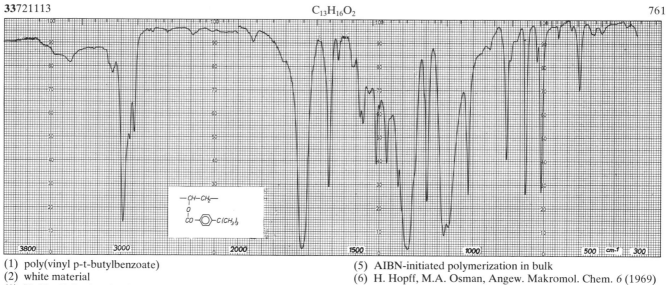

(1) poly(vinyl p-t-butylbenzoate)
(2) white material
(3) H. Hopff, Institut für Organische Technologie, ETH Zürich

(5) AIBN-initiated polymerization in bulk
(6) H. Hopff, M.A. Osman, Angew. Makromol. Chem. *6* (1969)
    39...45
(7) KBr (1/350)

33721121–**33**721111 $C_7H_{10}O_4–C_4H_6O_2$ 762

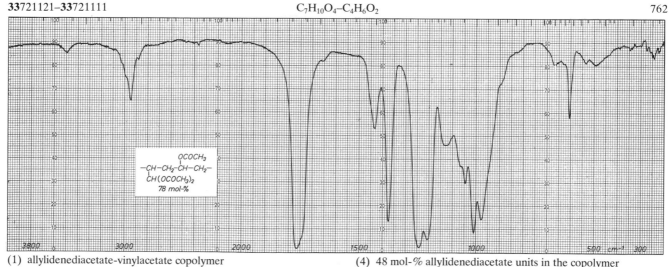

(1) allylidenediacetate-vinylacetate copolymer
(2) colourless material
(3) K. Noro, Central Research Laboratory, The Nippon Synthetic
    Chemical Industry, Co., Hyogo

(4) 48 mol-% allylidenediacetate units in the copolymer
(6) M. Sadamichi, K. Noro, J. Macromol. Sci.-Chem. *A3* (1969)
    845...52
(7) film from acetone on CsI

33721121

C$_3$H$_2$O$_2$

763

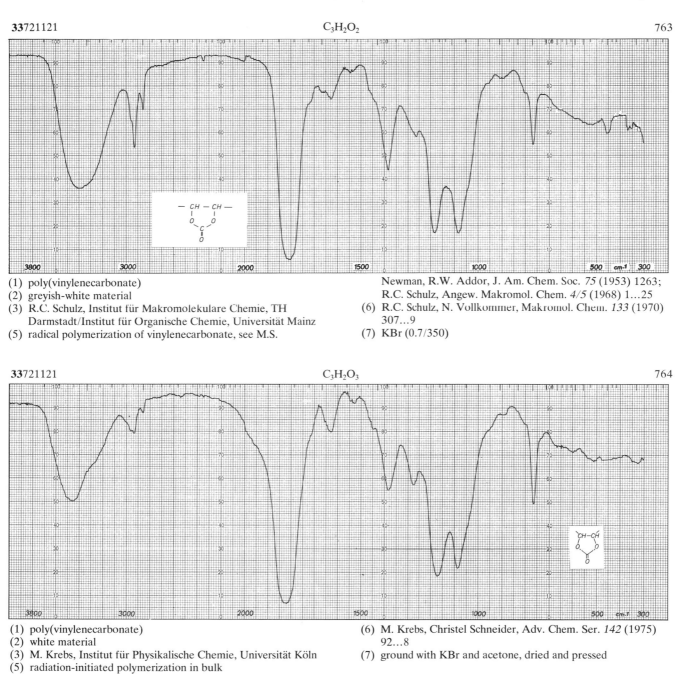

(1) poly(vinylenecarbonate)
(2) greyish-white material
(3) R.C. Schulz, Institut für Makromolekulare Chemie, TH Darmstadt/Institut für Organische Chemie, Universität Mainz
(5) radical polymerization of vinylenecarbonate, see M.S.

Newman, R.W. Addor, J. Am. Chem. Soc. *75* (1953) 1263; R.C. Schulz, Angew. Makromol. Chem. *4/5* (1968) 1...25
(6) R.C. Schulz, N. Vollkommer, Makromol. Chem. *133* (1970) 307...9
(7) KBr (0.7/350)

33721121

C$_3$H$_2$O$_3$

764

(1) poly(vinylenecarbonate)
(2) white material
(3) M. Krebs, Institut für Physikalische Chemie, Universität Köln
(5) radiation-initiated polymerization in bulk

(6) M. Krebs, Christel Schneider, Adv. Chem. Ser. *142* (1975) 92...8
(7) ground with KBr and acetone, dried and pressed

33721121–35111

C$_3$H$_2$O$_3$–C$_2$F$_3$Cl

765

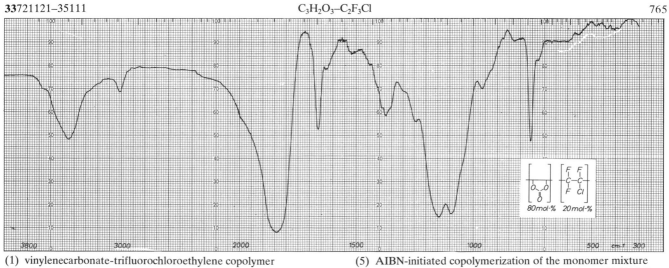

(1) vinylenecarbonate-trifluorochloroethylene copolymer
(2) white powder
(3) M. Krebs, Institut für Physikalische Chemie, Universität Köln
(4) 80 mol-% vinylenecarbonate units in the copolymer

(5) AIBN-initiated copolymerization of the monomer mixture
(6) M. Krebs, Christel Schneider, Adv. Chem. Ser. *142* (1975) 92...8
(7) KBr (1/350)

33721121 $C_4H_4O_3$ 766

33372121 $C_9H_6O_3$ 767

3372121–33721111 $C_9H_6O_3$–$C_4H_6O_2$ 768

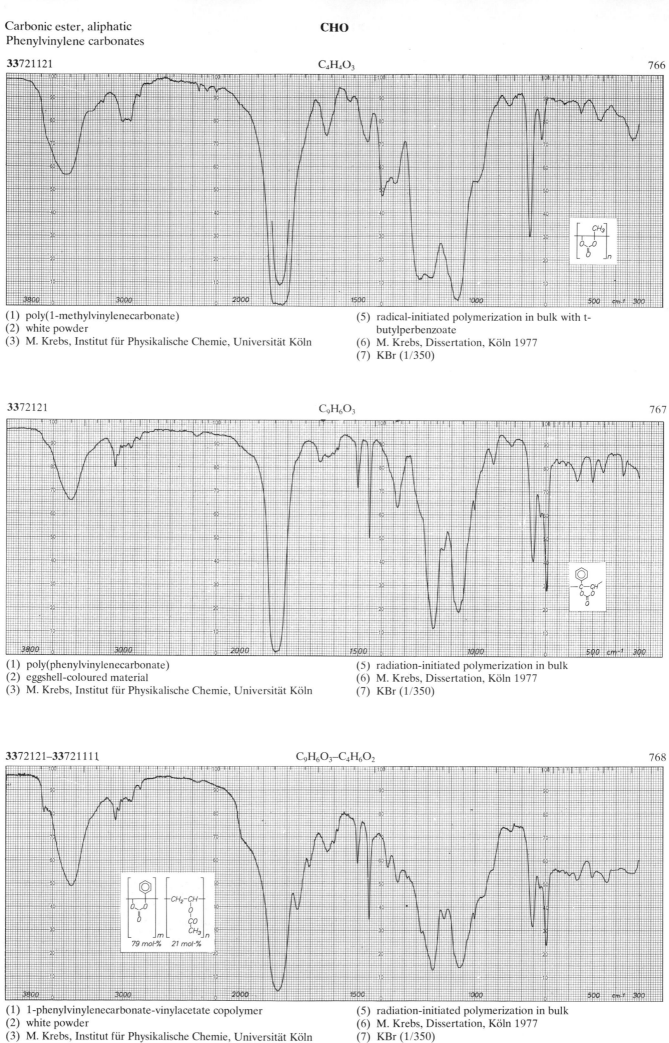

(1) poly(1-methylvinylenecarbonate)
(2) white powder
(3) M. Krebs, Institut für Physikalische Chemie, Universität Köln
(5) radical-initiated polymerization in bulk with t-butylperbenzoate
(6) M. Krebs, Dissertation, Köln 1977
(7) KBr (1/350)

(1) poly(phenylvinylenecarbonate)
(2) eggshell-coloured material
(3) M. Krebs, Institut für Physikalische Chemie, Universität Köln
(5) radiation-initiated polymerization in bulk
(6) M. Krebs, Dissertation, Köln 1977
(7) KBr (1/350)

(1) 1-phenylvinylenecarbonate-vinylacetate copolymer
(2) white powder
(3) M. Krebs, Institut für Physikalische Chemie, Universität Köln
(4) 79 mol-% 1-phenylvinylenecarbonate units in the copolymer
(5) radiation-initiated polymerization in bulk
(6) M. Krebs, Dissertation, Köln 1977
(7) KBr (1/350)

3372121–3372111 $C_9H_6O_3–C_4H_6O_2$ 769

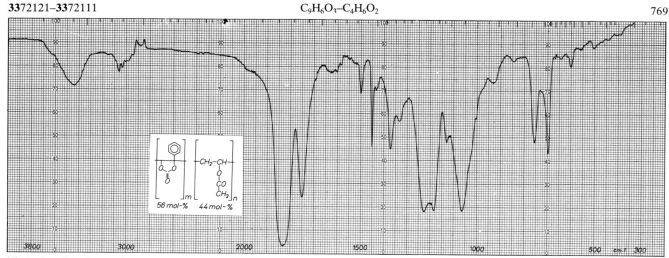

(1) 1-phenylvinylenecarbonate-vinylacetate copolymer
(2) white powder
(3) M. Krebs, Institut für Physikalische Chemie, Universität Köln
(4) 56 mol-% 1-phenylvinylenecarbonate units in the copolymer

(5) radiation-initiated polymerization in bulk
(6) M. Krebs, Dissertation, Köln 1977
(7) KBr (1/350)

3372121–35111 $C_3H_2O_3–C_2F_3Cl$ 770

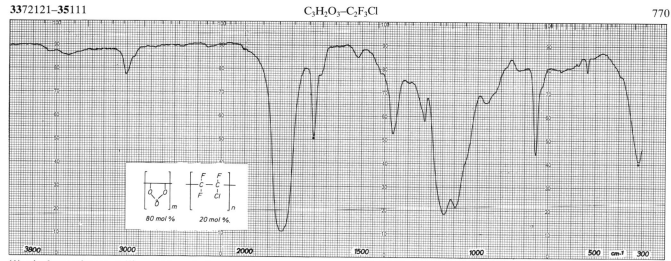

(1) vinylenecarbonate-trifluorochloroethylene copolymer
(2) white powder
(3) M. Krebs, Institut für Physikalische Chemie, Universität Köln
(4) 80 mol-% vinylenecarbonate units

(6) M. Krebs, Christel Schneider, Adv. Chem. Ser. *142* (1975)
     92...8
(7) clear film from acetone on KBr

3372121–42124212 $C_9H_6O_3–C_4H_3NO_2$ 771

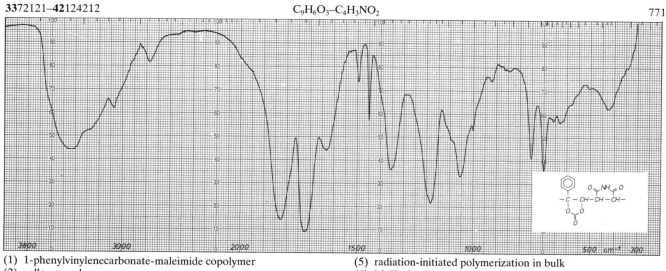

(1) 1-phenylvinylenecarbonate-maleimide copolymer
(2) yellow powder
(3) M. Krebs, Institut für Physikalische Chemie, Universität Köln
(4) 54 mol-% 1-phenylvinylenecarbonate units in the copolymer

(5) radiation-initiated polymerization in bulk
(6) M. Krebs, Dissertation, Köln 1977
(7) KBr (1/350)

3372132 $C_{17}H_{14}O_2$ 772

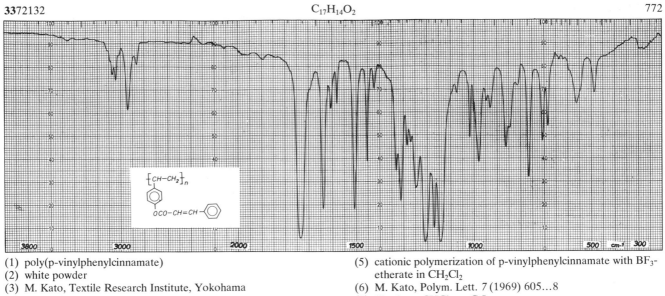

(1) poly(p-vinylphenylcinnamate)
(2) white powder
(3) M. Kato, Textile Research Institute, Yokohama

(5) cationic polymerization of p-vinylphenylcinnamate with BF$_3$-etherate in CH$_2$Cl$_2$
(6) M. Kato, Polym. Lett. 7 (1969) 605...8
(7) film from CHCl$_3$ on CsI

337221111 $C_4H_6O_2$ 773

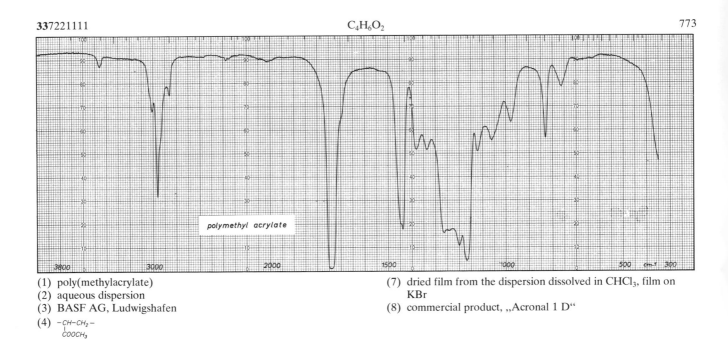

polymethyl acrylate

(1) poly(methylacrylate)
(2) aqueous dispersion
(3) BASF AG, Ludwigshafen
(4) $-CH-CH_2-$
          $COOCH_3$

(7) dried film from the dispersion dissolved in CHCl$_3$, film on KBr
(8) commercial product, „Acronal 1 D"

337221111 $C_4H_6O_2$ 774

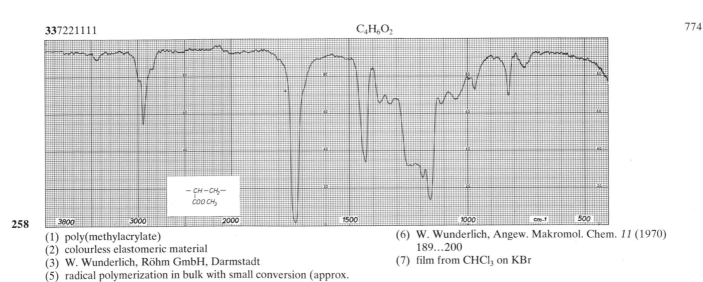

$-CH-CH_2-$
$COO\,CH_3$

(1) poly(methylacrylate)
(2) colourless elastomeric material
(3) W. Wunderlich, Röhm GmbH, Darmstadt
(5) radical polymerization in bulk with small conversion (approx. 5%)

(6) W. Wunderlich, Angew. Makromol. Chem. 11 (1970) 189...200
(7) film from CHCl$_3$ on KBr

337221111–21111   C₄H₆O₂–C₂H₄   775

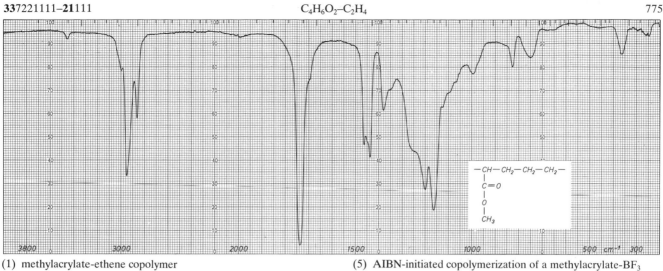

(1) methylacrylate-ethene copolymer
(2) colourless elastomer
(3) A.L. Logothetis, Elastomer Chemistry Department, E.I. Du
Pont de Nemours & Comp., Wilmington, Dela.
(4) equimolar, alternating structure
(5) AIBN-initiated copolymerization of a methylacrylate-BF₃
complex with ethylene.
(6) A.L. Logothetis, J.M. McKenna, Polymer Lett. *12* (1974)
131...7, ACS Polymer Preprints *17/2* (1976) 642
(7) film from CHCl₃ on CsI

337221111–2111211   C₄H₆O₂–C₃H₆   776

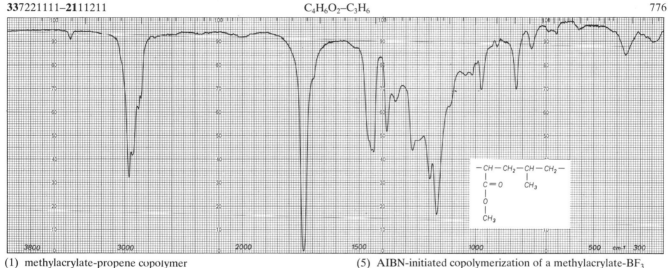

(1) methylacrylate-propene copolymer
(2) colourless elastomer
(3) A.L. Logothetis, Elastomer Chemistry Department, E.I. Du
Pont de Nemours & Comp., Wilmington, Dela
(4) equimolar, alternating structure
(5) AIBN-initiated copolymerization of a methylacrylate-BF₃
complex with propene
(6) A.L. Logothetis, J.M. McKenna, Polymer Lett. *12* (1974)
131...7, ACS Polym. Prepr. *17/2* (1976) 642
(7) film from CHCl₃ on CsI

337221111–337221121   C₄H₆O₂–C₅H₈O₂   777

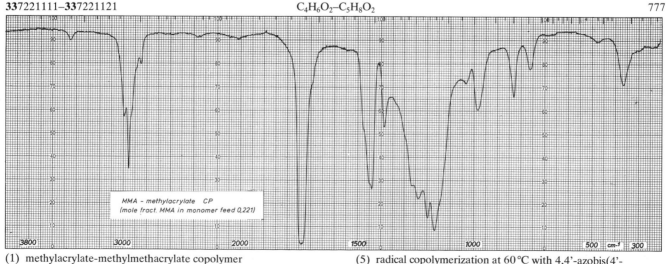

MMA - methylacrylate   CP
(mole fract. MMA in monomer feed 0.221)

(1) methylacrylate-methylmethacrylate copolymer
(2) milky-glassy material
(3) A.K. Chaudhuri, Department of Physical Chemistry, Indian
Association for Cultivation of Science, Jadavpur, Calcutta
(4) mol fraction of MMA in the monomer mixture: 0.221
(5) radical copolymerization at 60 °C with 4,4'-azobis(4'-
cyanopentanoic acid); low conversion (up to 5 %)
(6) A.K. Chaudhuri, S.R. Palit, J. Polym. Sci. A-1 *6* (1968)
2187...96
(7) film from CHCl₃ on CsI

337221111–421512 $C_5H_8O_2–C_4H_5NO_2$ 778

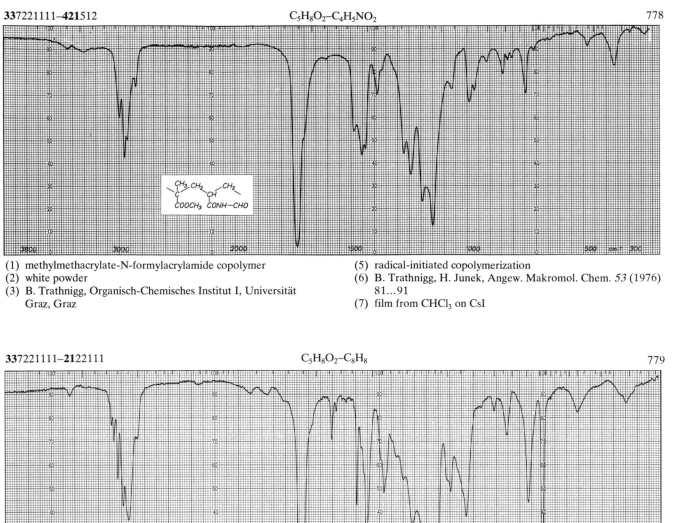

(1) methylmethacrylate-N-formylacrylamide copolymer
(2) white powder
(3) B. Trathnigg, Organisch-Chemisches Institut I, Universität Graz, Graz

(5) radical-initiated copolymerization
(6) B. Trathnigg, H. Junek, Angew. Makromol. Chem. *53* (1976) 81...91
(7) film from $CHCl_3$ on CsI

337221111–2122111 $C_5H_8O_2–C_8H_8$ 779

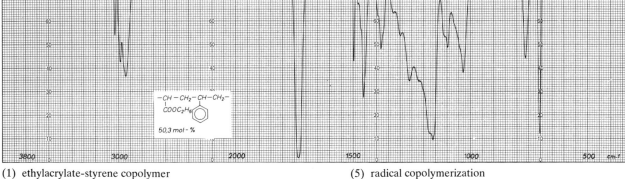

(1) ethylacrylate-styrene copolymer
(2) glassy granules
(3) P. Wittmer, BASF AG, Ludwigshafen
(4) almost equimolar composition

(5) radical copolymerization
(6) P. Wittmer, Makromolekulares Kolloquium, Freiburg 1972; private communication
(7) film from $CHCl_3$ on CsI

337221111–2122111 $C_5H_8O_2–C_8H_8$ 780

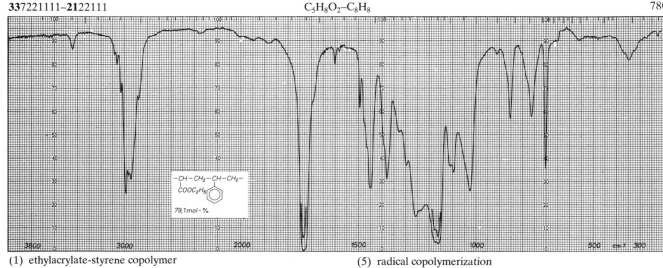

(1) ethylacrylate-styrene copolymer
(2) colourless elastomer
(3) P. Wittmer, BASF AG, Ludwigshafen
(4) 79.1 mol-% ethylacrylate

(5) radical copolymerization
(6) P. Wittmer, Makromolekulares Kolloquium, Freiburg 1972; private communication
(7) film from $CHCl_3$ on CsI

337221111–337221121   C$_7$H$_{12}$O$_2$–C$_5$H$_8$O$_2$ 781

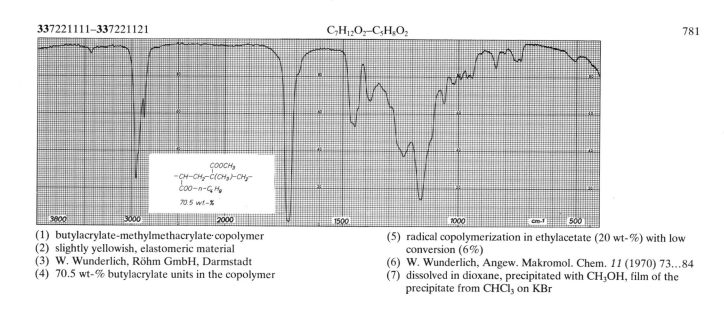

COOCH$_3$
|
–CH–CH$_2$–C(CH$_3$)–CH$_2$–
|
COO–n–C$_4$H$_9$

70.5 wt.-%

(1) butylacrylate-methylmethacrylate copolymer
(2) slightly yellowish, elastomeric material
(3) W. Wunderlich, Röhm GmbH, Darmstadt
(4) 70.5 wt-% butylacrylate units in the copolymer

(5) radical copolymerization in ethylacetate (20 wt-%) with low conversion (6%)
(6) W. Wunderlich, Angew. Makromol. Chem. *11* (1970) 73...84
(7) dissolved in dioxane, precipitated with CH$_3$OH, film of the precipitate from CHCl$_3$ on KBr

337221111   C$_{19}$H$_{40}$O$_2$ 782

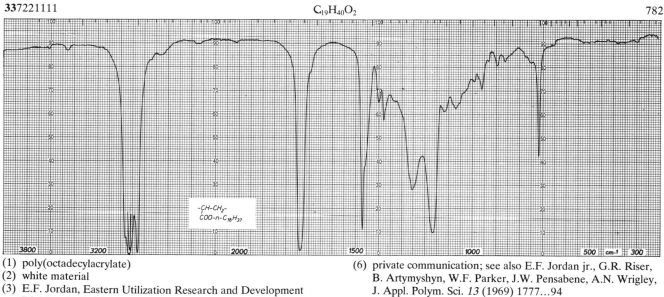

–CH–CH$_2$–
|
COO–n–C$_{18}$H$_{37}$

(1) poly(octadecylacrylate)
(2) white material
(3) E.F. Jordan, Eastern Utilization Research and Development Division, Philadelphia, Pa.

(6) private communication; see also E.F. Jordan jr., G.R. Riser, B. Artymyshyn, W.F. Parker, J.W. Pensabene, A.N. Wrigley, J. Appl. Polym. Sci. *13* (1969) 1777...94
(7) film from CHCl$_3$ on CsI

337221111–3121112   C$_{21}$H$_{40}$O$_2$–C$_2$H$_2$Cl$_2$ 783

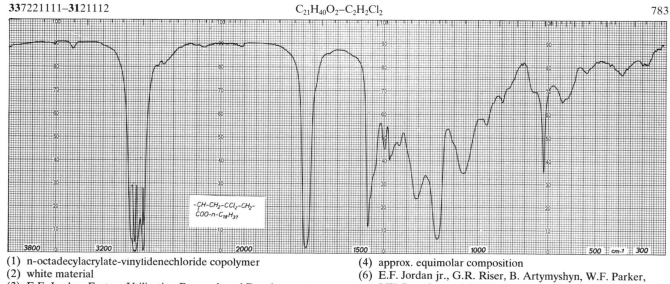

–CH–CH$_2$–CCl$_2$–CH$_2$–
|
COO–n–C$_{18}$H$_{37}$

(1) n-octadecylacrylate-vinylidenechloride copolymer
(2) white material
(3) E.F. Jordan, Eastern Utilization Research and Development Division, Philadelphia, Pa.

(4) approx. equimolar composition
(6) E.F. Jordan jr., G.R. Riser, B. Artymyshyn, W.F. Parker, J.W. Pensabene, A.N. Wrigley, J. Appl. Polym. Sci. *13* (1969) 1777...94
(7) film from CHCl$_3$ on CsI

337221111–33612 $C_{11}H_{20}O_2$–$C_4H_6O_2$ 784

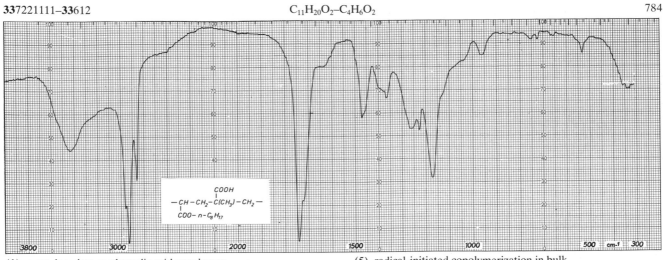

(1) n-octylacrylate-methacrylic acid copolymer
(2) yellowish material
(3) A.V. Tobolsky, Department of Chemistry, Princeton University, N.J.
(4) approx. equimolar composition, slightly crosslinked

(5) radical-initiated copolymerization in bulk
(6) A.V. Tobolsky, I.L. Hopkins, J. Polym. Sci. A-1 7 (1969) 2431...2
(7) KBr (2/350), ordinate expanded

337221111 $C_{14}H_{26}O_2$ 785

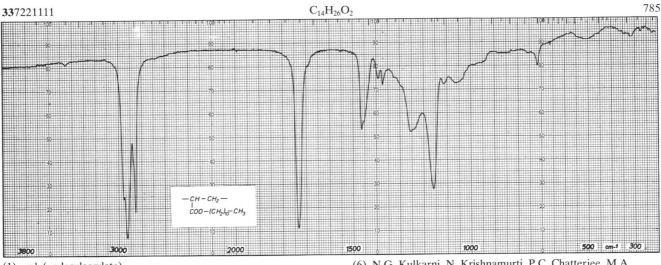

(1) poly(undecylacrylate)
(2) colourless material
(3) N.G. Kulkarni, Regional Research Laboratory, Hyderabad
(5) radical-initiated polymerization in benzene solution with benzoylperoxide as an initiator

(6) N.G. Kulkarni, N. Krishnamurti, P.C. Chatterjee, M.A. Sivasamban, Makromol. Chem. *147* (1971) 149...53
(7) film from $CHCl_3$ on CsI

337221111 $C_9H_{14}O_2$ 786

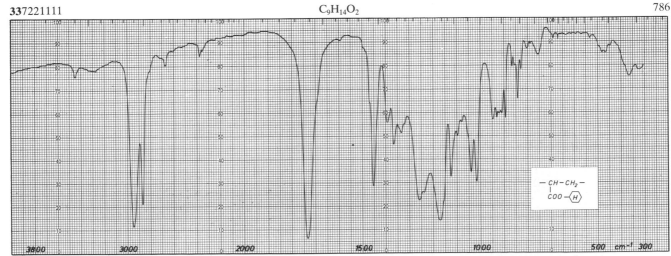

(1) poly(cyclohexylacrylate)
(2) colourless material
(3) P.L. Magagnini, Centro Nazionale di Chimica delle Macromolecole, Istituto di Chimica Industriale ed Applicata del Università di Pisa, Pisa

(5) bulk polymerization of cyclohexylacrylate at 70 °C with benzoylperoxide as an initiator
(6) V. Frosini, P.L. Magagnini, E. Butta, M. Baccaredda, Kolloid-Z.Z. Polym. *213* (1966) 115...20
(7) film from $CHCl_3$ on KBr

337221111   C₂₄H₃₁O₄   787

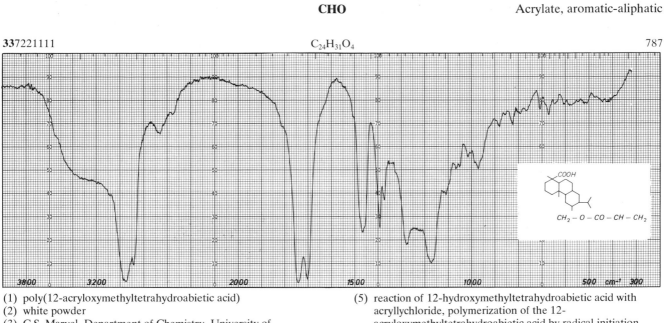

(1) poly(12-acryloxymethyltetrahydroabietic acid)
(2) white powder
(3) C.S. Marvel, Department of Chemistry, University of Arizona, Tucson, Az.

(5) reaction of 12-hydroxymethyltetrahydroabietic acid with acryllychloride, polymerization of the 12-acryloxymethyltetrahydroabietic acid by radical initiation
(6) M. Saga, C.S. Marvel, J. Polym. Sci. A-1 *7* (1969) 2365...77
(7) KBr (6/1000)

337221111   C₈H₁₄O₂   788

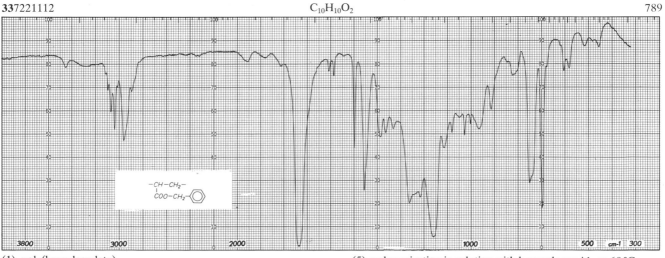

(1) poly[(+)2-methylbutylacrylate]
(2) glassy-clear, very tough material
(3) K. Ohara, Shinshu University, Tokiiri, Ueda

(5) radical polymerization
(6) K. Ohara, Makromol. Chem. *142* (1971) 75
(7) film from CHCl₃ on CsI

337221112   C₁₀H₁₀O₂   789

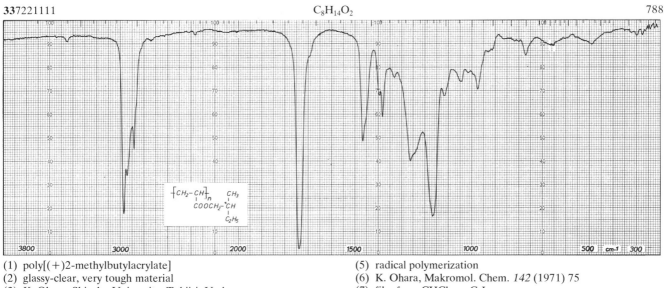

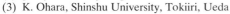

(1) poly(benzylacrylate)
(2) colourless material
(3) G.G. Cameron, Department of Chemistry, University of Aberdeen, Old Aberdeen

(5) polymerization in solution with benzoylperoxide at 60 °C
(6) G.G. Cameron, D.R. Kane, Polymer *9* (1968) 461...70
(7) film from acetone on KBr

337221113   C₉H₈O₂   790

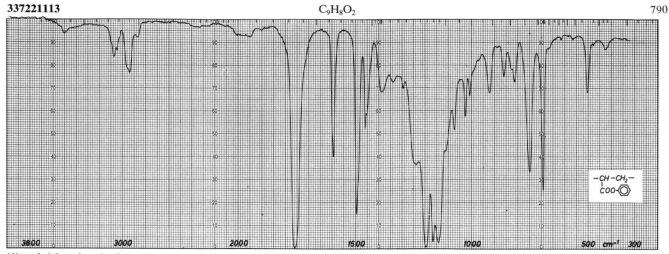

(1) poly(phenylacrylate)
(2) white powder
(3) P.L. Magagnini, Centro Nazionale di Chimica delle Macromolecole, Istituto di Chimica Industriale ed Applicata del Università di Pisa, Pisa

(5) polymerization in benzene solution at 60 °C with benzoylperoxide as an initiator
(6) Giovanna Pizzirani, P.L. Magagnini, P. Giusti, J. Polym. Sci. A-2 *9* (1971) 1133...45
(7) film from CHCl₃ on KBr

337221113   C₉H₈O₂   791

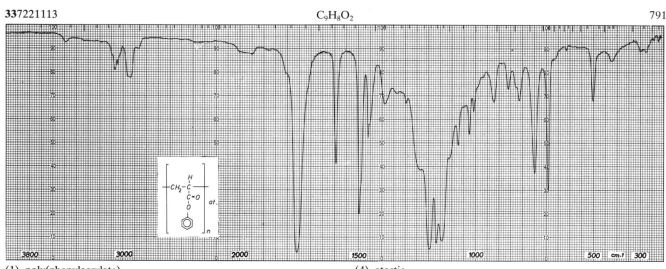

(1) poly(phenylacrylate)
(2) white powder
(3) H. Guéniffey, Laboratoire de Chimie Macromoléculaire, Le Mans (Université de Caën)

(4) atactic
(6) private communication; see also H. Guéniffey, H. Kämmerer, C.P. Pinazzi, Makromol. Chem. *136* (1970) 173...8
(7) film from CHCl₃ on CsI

337221113   C₁₀H₁₀O₂   792

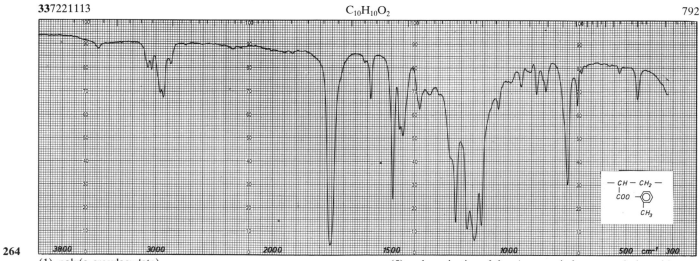

(1) poly(o-cresylacrylate)
(2) colourless material
(3) P.L. Magagnini, Centro Nazionale di Chimica delle Macromolecole, Istituto di Chimica Industriale ed Applicata del Università di Pisa, Pisa

(5) polymerization of the monomer in benzene solution with benzoylperoxide as an initiator at 60 °C
(6) Giovanna Pizzirani, P.L. Magagnini, P. Giusti, J. Polym. Sci. A-2 *9* (1971) 1133...45
(7) film from CHCl₃ on KBr

337221113 $C_{10}H_{10}O_2$ 793

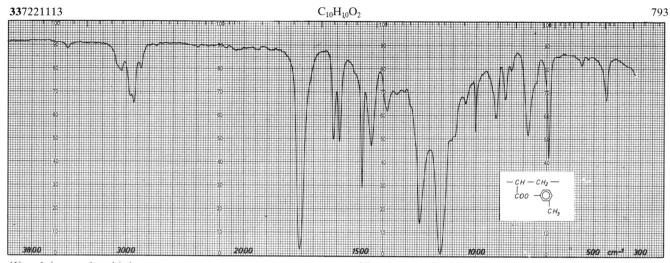

(1) poly(m-cresylacrylate)
(2) colourless material
(3) P.L. Magagnini, Centro Nazionale di Chimica delle Macromolecole, Istituto di Chimica Industriale ed Applicata del Università di Pisa, Pisa

(5) polymerization of the monomer in benzene solution with benzoylperoxide as an initiator at 60 °C
(6) Giovanna Pizzirani, P.L. Magagnini, P. Giusti, J. Polym. Sci. A-2 *9* (1971) 1133...45
(7) film from CHCl₃ on KBr

337221113 $C_{10}H_{10}O_2$ 794

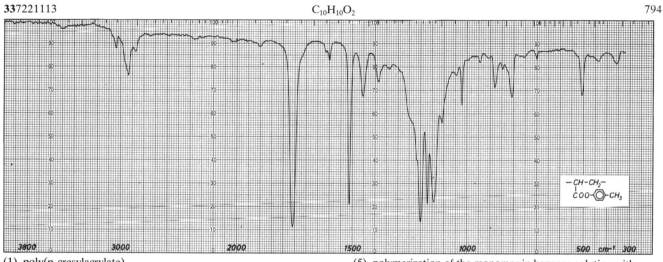

(1) poly(p-cresylacrylate)
(2) slightly yellowish material
(3) P.L. Magagnini, Centro Nazionale di Chimica delle Macromolecole, Istituto di Chimica Industriale ed Applicatá del Università di Pisa, Pisa

(5) polymerization of the monomer in benzene solution with benzoylperoxide as an initiator at 60 °C
(6) Giovanna Pizzirani, P.L. Magagnini, P. Giusti, J. Polym. Sci. A-2 *9* (1971) 1133...45
(7) film from CHCl₃ on KBr

337221113 $C_{10}H_{10}O_2$ 795

(1) poly(p-cresylacrylate)
(2) white powder
(3) H. Guéniffey, Laboratoire de Chimie Macromoléculaire, Le Mans (Université de Caën)

(4) atactic
(6) private communication; see also H. Guéniffey, H. Kämmerer, C.P. Pinazzi, Makromol. Chem. *136* (1970) 173...8
(7) film from CHCl₃ on CsI

337221113   C$_{13}$H$_{16}$O$_2$ 796

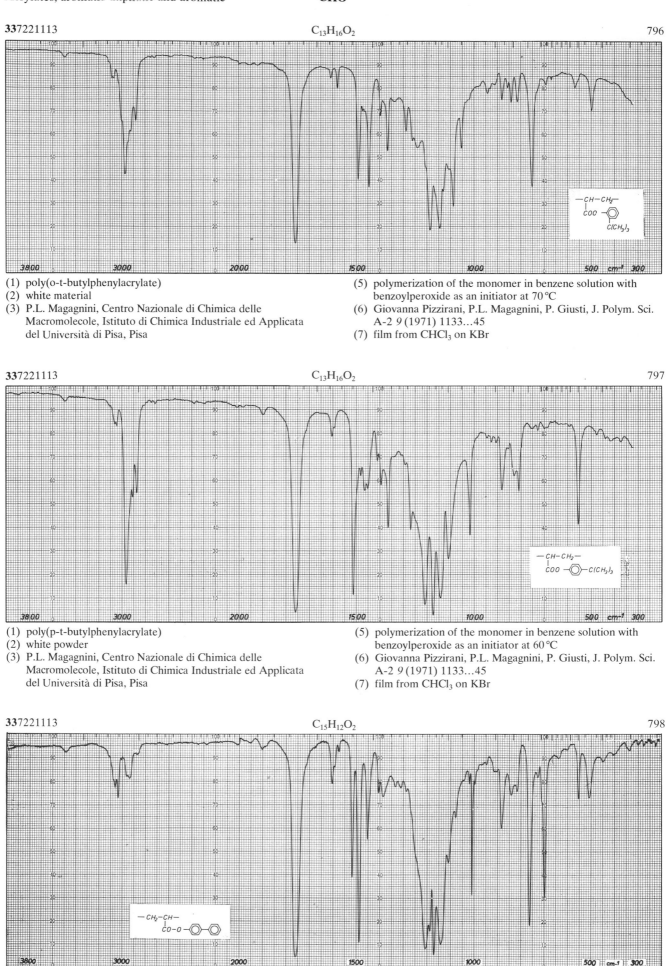

(1) poly(o-t-butylphenylacrylate)
(2) white material
(3) P.L. Magagnini, Centro Nazionale di Chimica delle
    Macromolecole, Istituto di Chimica Industriale ed Applicata
    del Università di Pisa, Pisa

(5) polymerization of the monomer in benzene solution with
    benzoylperoxide as an initiator at 70 °C
(6) Giovanna Pizzirani, P.L. Magagnini, P. Giusti, J. Polym. Sci.
    A-2 *9* (1971) 1133...45
(7) film from CHCl$_3$ on KBr

337221113   C$_{13}$H$_{16}$O$_2$ 797

(1) poly(p-t-butylphenylacrylate)
(2) white powder
(3) P.L. Magagnini, Centro Nazionale di Chimica delle
    Macromolecole, Istituto di Chimica Industriale ed Applicata
    del Università di Pisa, Pisa

(5) polymerization of the monomer in benzene solution with
    benzoylperoxide as an initiator at 60 °C
(6) Giovanna Pizzirani, P.L. Magagnini, P. Giusti, J. Polym. Sci.
    A-2 *9* (1971) 1133...45
(7) film from CHCl$_3$ on KBr

337221113   C$_{15}$H$_{12}$O$_2$ 798

(1) poly(p-biphenylacrylate)
(2) white powder
(3) P.L. Magagnini, Centro Nazionale di Chimica delle
    Macromolecole, Istituto di Chimica Industriale ed Applicata
    del Università di Pisa, Pisa

(6) P.L. Magagnini, V. Frosini, IUPAC Macro, Madrid 1974
    (preprints p. 587...9)
(7) film from CHCl$_3$ on CsI

337221121   C₅H₈O₂   799

(1) poly(methylmethacrylate), isotactic
(2) white material
(3) G. Smets, Laboratory of Macromolecular Chemistry, University of Louvain
(5) polymerization of methylmethacrylate in toluene at room

temperature with (C₆H₅MgBr)-CoCl₂ at room temperature, fractionation with benzene-methanol
(6) H. Berghmans, G. Smets, Makromol. Chem. *115* (1968) 187...97
(7) film from cyclohexanone on CsI

337221121   C₅H₈O₂   800

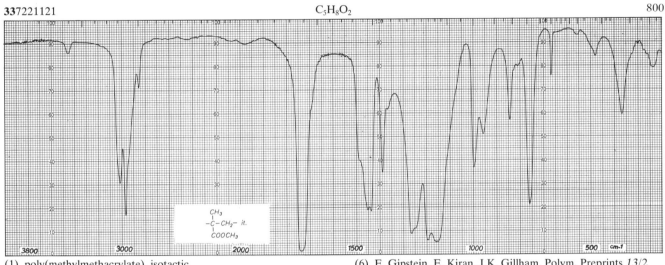

(1) poly(methylmethacrylate), isotactic
(2) white powder
(3) E. Gipstein, IBM, San Jose, Calif.
(5) W. Sorenson, T. Campbell, Preparative Methods of Polymer Chemistry, 2nd ed., Interscience, New York 1968; W. Goode et al., J. Polym. Sci. *46* (1960) 317

(6) E. Gipstein, E. Kiran, J.K. Gillham, Polym. Preprints *13/2* (1972) 1212...7
(7) film from CHCl₃ on CsI
(8) band at 760 cm⁻¹ partly from residual CHCl₃; 667 cm⁻¹: CHCl₃

337221121   C₅H₈O₂   801

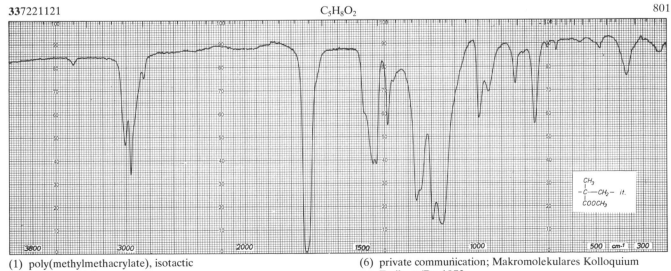

(1) poly(methylmethacrylate), isotactic
(2) white material
(3) W. Borchard, Institut für Physikalische Chemie, TU Clausthal
(4) 93% isotactic, 2% syndiotactic and 5% heterotactic triads (by NMR)

(6) private communication; Makromolekulares Kolloquium Freiburg/Br. 1972
(7) film from CHCl₃ on CsI
(8) band at 760 cm⁻¹ partly from CHCl₃; 667 cm⁻¹: CHCl₃

337221121 $C_5H_8O_2$ 802

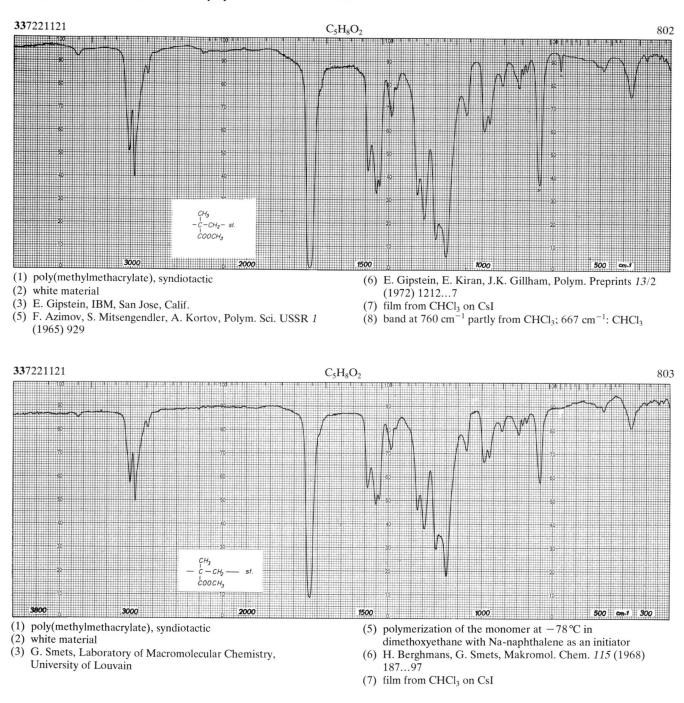

(1) poly(methylmethacrylate), syndiotactic
(2) white material
(3) E. Gipstein, IBM, San Jose, Calif.
(5) F. Azimov, S. Mitsengendler, A. Kortov, Polym. Sci. USSR *1* (1965) 929

(6) E. Gipstein, E. Kiran, J.K. Gillham, Polym. Preprints *13/2* (1972) 1212...7
(7) film from $CHCl_3$ on CsI
(8) band at 760 cm^{-1} partly from $CHCl_3$; 667 cm^{-1}: $CHCl_3$

337221121 $C_5H_8O_2$ 803

(1) poly(methylmethacrylate), syndiotactic
(2) white material
(3) G. Smets, Laboratory of Macromolecular Chemistry, University of Louvain

(5) polymerization of the monomer at $-78\,°C$ in dimethoxyethane with Na-naphthalene as an initiator
(6) H. Berghmans, G. Smets, Makromol. Chem. *115* (1968) 187...97
(7) film from $CHCl_3$ on CsI

337221121 $C_5H_8O_2$ 804

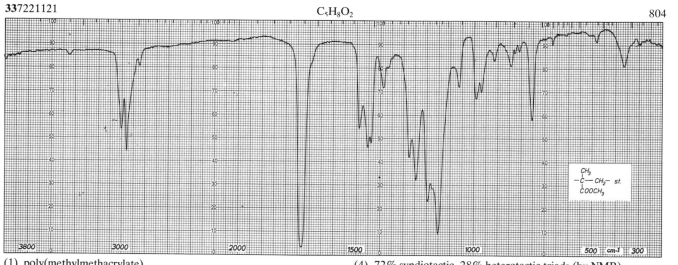

(1) poly(methylmethacrylate)
(2) white material
(3) W. Borchard, Institut für Physikalische Chemie, TU Clausthal

(4) 72% syndiotactic, 28% heterotactic triads (by NMR)
(6) private communication; Makromolekulares Colloquium, Freiburg/Br. 1972
(7) film from $CHCl_3$ on CsI

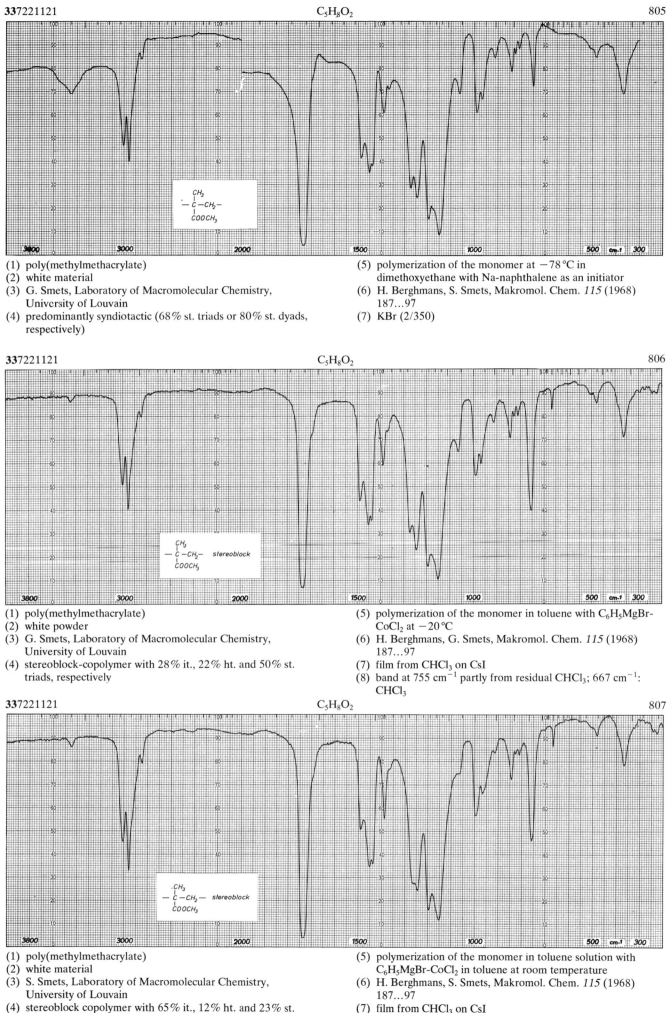

337221121 $C_5H_8O_2$ 805

(1) poly(methylmethacrylate)
(2) white material
(3) G. Smets, Laboratory of Macromolecular Chemistry, University of Louvain
(4) predominantly syndiotactic (68% st. triads or 80% st. dyads, respectively)

(5) polymerization of the monomer at −78 °C in dimethoxyethane with Na-naphthalene as an initiator
(6) H. Berghmans, S. Smets, Makromol. Chem. *115* (1968) 187...97
(7) KBr (2/350)

337221121 $C_5H_8O_2$ 806

(1) poly(methylmethacrylate)
(2) white powder
(3) G. Smets, Laboratory of Macromolecular Chemistry, University of Louvain
(4) stereoblock-copolymer with 28% it., 22% ht. and 50% st. triads, respectively

(5) polymerization of the monomer in toluene with C_6H_5MgBr-$CoCl_2$ at −20 °C
(6) H. Berghmans, G. Smets, Makromol. Chem. *115* (1968) 187...97
(7) film from $CHCl_3$ on CsI
(8) band at 755 cm^{-1} partly from residual $CHCl_3$; 667 cm^{-1}: $CHCl_3$

337221121 $C_5H_8O_2$ 807

(1) poly(methylmethacrylate)
(2) white material
(3) S. Smets, Laboratory of Macromolecular Chemistry, University of Louvain
(4) stereoblock copolymer with 65% it., 12% ht. and 23% st. triads, respectively

(5) polymerization of the monomer in toluene solution with C_6H_5MgBr-$CoCl_2$ in toluene at room temperature
(6) H. Berghmans, S. Smets, Makromol. Chem. *115* (1968) 187...97
(7) film from $CHCl_3$ on CsI
(8) band at 758 cm^{-1} partly due to residual $CHCl_3$; 667 cm^{-1}: $CHCl_3$

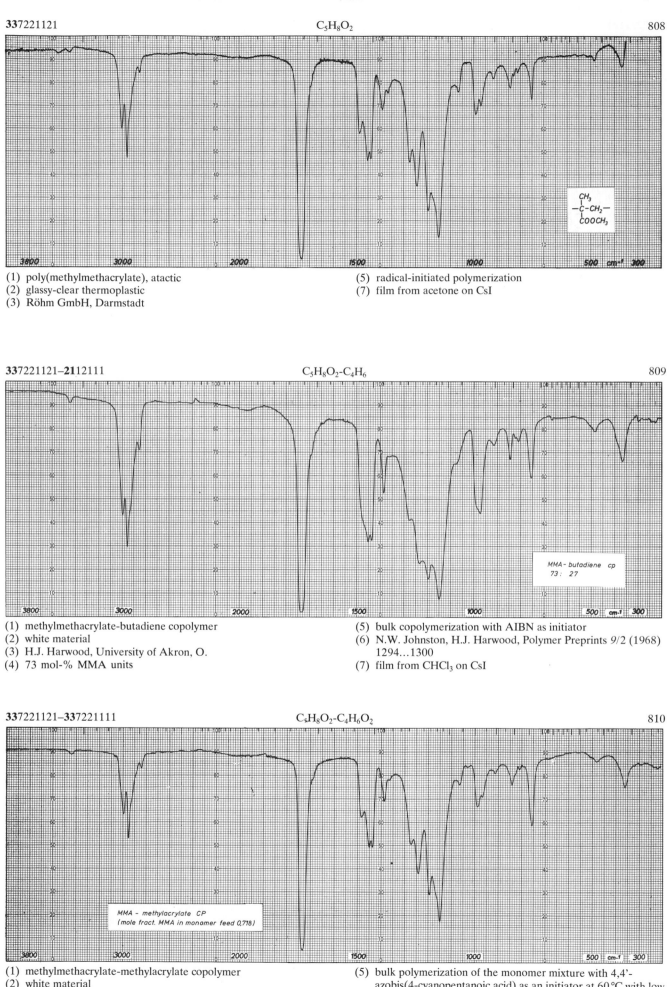

337221121 $C_5H_8O_2$ 808

$$\begin{array}{c} CH_3 \\ | \\ -C-CH_2- \\ | \\ COOCH_3 \end{array}$$

(1) poly(methylmethacrylate), atactic
(2) glassy-clear thermoplastic
(3) Röhm GmbH, Darmstadt
(5) radical-initiated polymerization
(7) film from acetone on CsI

337221121–2112111 $C_5H_8O_2$-C_4H_6 809

MMA-butadiene cp
73 : 27

(1) methylmethacrylate-butadiene copolymer
(2) white material
(3) H.J. Harwood, University of Akron, O.
(4) 73 mol-% MMA units
(5) bulk copolymerization with AIBN as initiator
(6) N.W. Johnston, H.J. Harwood, Polymer Preprints *9/2* (1968) 1294...1300
(7) film from $CHCl_3$ on CsI

337221121–337221111 $C_5H_8O_2$-$C_4H_6O_2$ 810

MMA - methylacrylate CP
(mole fract. MMA in monomer feed 0,718)

(1) methylmethacrylate-methylacrylate copolymer
(2) white material
(3) A.K. Chaudhuri, Indian Association for the Cultivation of Science, Calcutta
(4) mol fraction of MMA in monomer feed: 0.718
(5) bulk polymerization of the monomer mixture with 4,4'-azobis(4-cyanopentanoic acid) as an initiator at 60 °C with low conversion (up to 5 %)
(6) A.K. Chaudhuri, S.R. Palit, J. Polym. Sci. A-1 *6* (1968) 2187...96
(7) film from $CHCl_3$ on CsI

337221121–337221111 C$_5$H$_8$O$_2$-C$_4$H$_6$O$_2$ 811

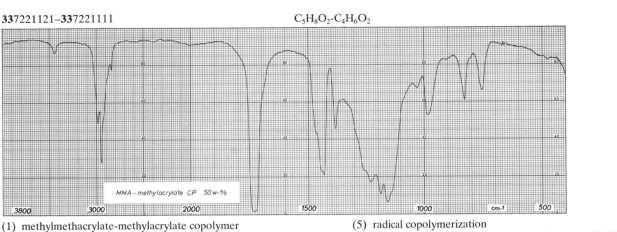

MMA – methylacrylate CP 50 w-%

(1) methylmethacrylate-methylacrylate copolymer
(2) colourless material
(3) W. Wunderlich, Röhm GmbH, Darmstadt
(4) approx. 50 wt-% of both monomer units in the copolymer

(5) radical copolymerization
(6) W. Wunderlich, Angew. Makromol. Chem. *11* (1970) 189...200
(7) film from CHCl$_3$ on KBr

337221121–337221111 C$_5$H$_8$O$_2$-C$_5$H$_8$O$_2$ 812

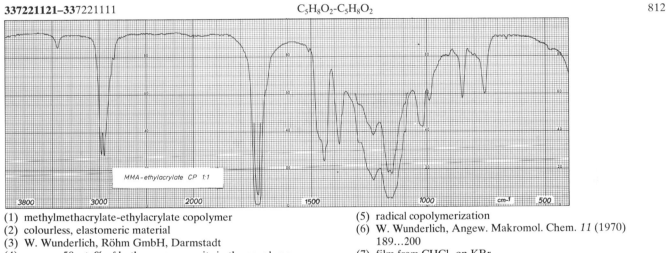

MMA – ethylacrylate CP 1:1

(1) methylmethacrylate-ethylacrylate copolymer
(2) colourless, elastomeric material
(3) W. Wunderlich, Röhm GmbH, Darmstadt
(4) approx. 50 wt-% of both monomer units in the copolymer

(5) radical copolymerization
(6) W. Wunderlich, Angew. Makromol. Chem. *11* (1970) 189...200
(7) film from CHCl$_3$ on KBr

337221121–337221111 C$_5$H$_8$O$_2$-C$_7$H$_{12}$O$_2$ 813

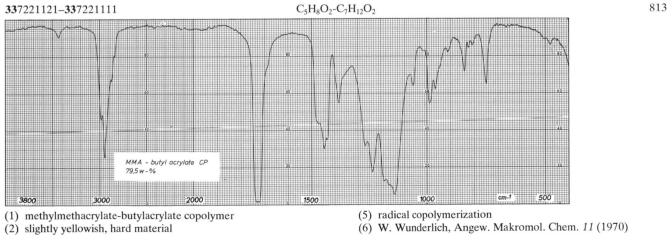

MMA – butyl acrylate CP 79,5 w-%

(1) methylmethacrylate-butylacrylate copolymer
(2) slightly yellowish, hard material
(3) W. Wunderlich, Röhm GmbH, Darmstadt
(4) 79.5 wt-% MMA units

(5) radical copolymerization
(6) W. Wunderlich, Angew. Makromol. Chem. *11* (1970) 189...200
(7) reprecipitated with CH$_3$OH from dioxane solution; film from CHCl$_3$ on KBr

337221121–337221111 C$_5$H$_8$O$_2$-C$_7$H$_{12}$O$_2$ 814

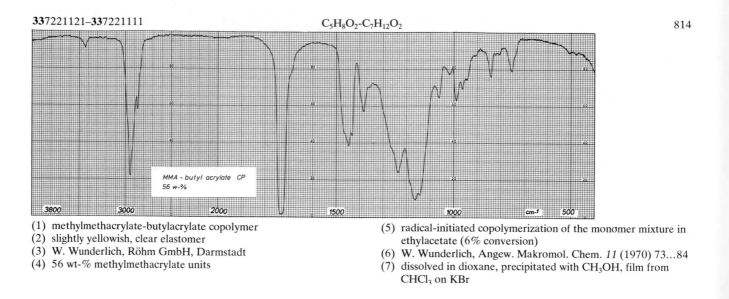

MMA - butyl acrylate CP
56 w-%

(1) methylmethacrylate-butylacrylate copolymer
(2) slightly yellowish, clear elastomer
(3) W. Wunderlich, Röhm GmbH, Darmstadt
(4) 56 wt-% methylmethacrylate units

(5) radical-initiated copolymerization of the monomer mixture in ethylacetate (6% conversion)
(6) W. Wunderlich, Angew. Makromol. Chem. *11* (1970) 73...84
(7) dissolved in dioxane, precipitated with CH$_3$OH, film from CHCl$_3$ on KBr

337221121 C$_5$H$_8$O$_2$-C$_8$H$_{14}$O$_2$ 815

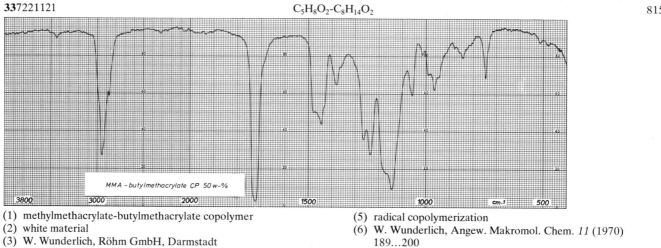

MMA - butylmethacrylate CP 50 w-%

(1) methylmethacrylate-butylmethacrylate copolymer
(2) white material
(3) W. Wunderlich, Röhm GmbH, Darmstadt
(4) approx. 50 wt-% of both monomer units

(5) radical copolymerization
(6) W. Wunderlich, Angew. Makromol. Chem. *11* (1970) 189...200
(7) film from CHCl$_3$ on KBr

337221121–2122111 C$_5$H$_8$O$_2$-C$_8$H$_8$ 816

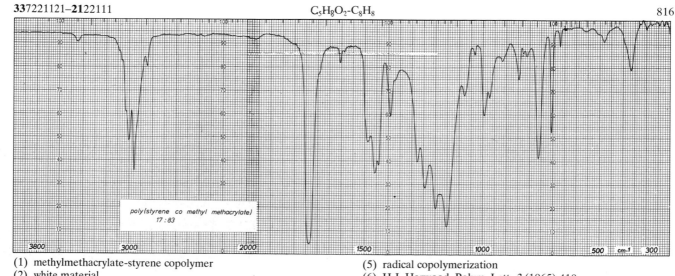

poly(styrene co methyl methacrylate)
17 : 83

(1) methylmethacrylate-styrene copolymer
(2) white material
(3) H.J. Harwood, University of Akron, O.
(4) 83 mol-% methylmethacrylate units

(5) radical copolymerization
(6) H.J. Harwood, Polym. Lett. *3* (1965) 419
(7) film from CHCl$_3$ in CsI
(8) band at 670 cm^{-1} due to residual CHCl$_3$

337221121–2122111   C$_5$H$_8$O$_2$-C$_8$H$_8$-C$_5$H$_8$O$_2$ 817

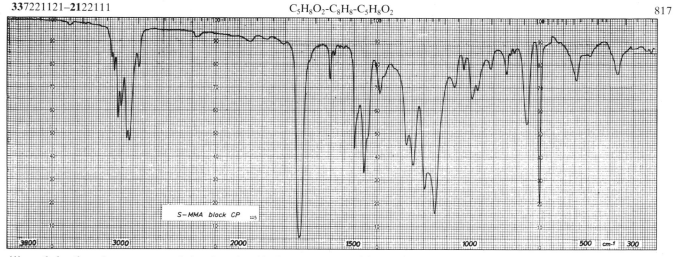

S–MMA block CP

(1) methylmethacrylate-styrene-methylmethacrylate block
    copolymer; (mole fraction styrene: 0.47)
(2) white material
(3) T. Kotaka, Institute for Chemical Research, Kyoto University

(5) anionic copolymerization (see above)
(6) T. Kotaka, T. Tanaka, H. Ohnuma, Y. Murakami, H. Inagaki,
    Polymer J. *1* (1970) 245...59
(7) film from ethylacetate on CsI

337221121–2122111   C$_5$H$_8$O$_2$-C$_8$H$_8$ 818

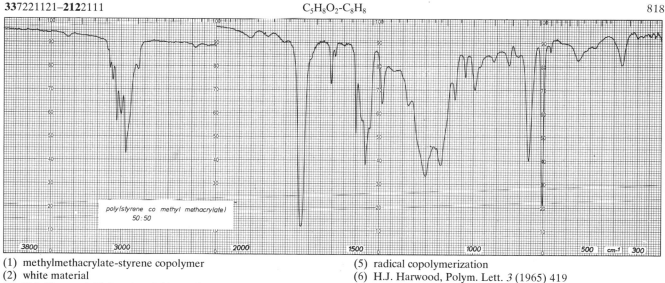

poly(styrene co methyl methacrylate)
50:50

(1) methylmethacrylate-styrene copolymer
(2) white material
(3) H.J. Harwood, University of Akron, O.
(4) equimolar composition, statistical distribution

(5) radical copolymerization
(6) H.J. Harwood, Polym. Lett. *3* (1965) 419
(7) film from CHCl$_3$ on CsI

337221121–2122111–3121111   C$_5$H$_8$O$_2$-C$_8$H$_8$-C$_2$H$_3$Cl   819

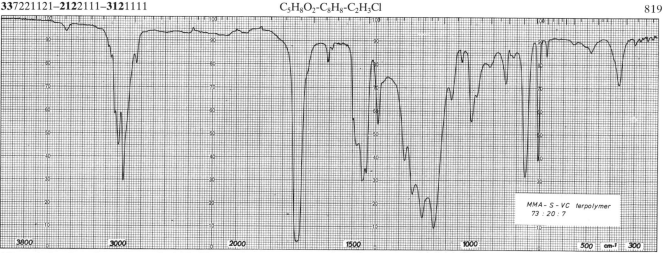

MMA – S – VC terpolymer
73 : 20 : 7

(1) methylmethacrylate-styrene-vinylchloride terpolymer
(2) white powder
(3) H.J. Harwood, University of Akron, O.
(4) molar ratio MMA-S-VC 73:20:7

(5) radical copolymerization
(6) H.J. Harwood, private communication
(7) film from CHCl$_3$ on CsI

337221121–2122111–312111 $C_5H_8O_2\text{-}C_8H_8\text{-}C_2H_3Cl$ 820

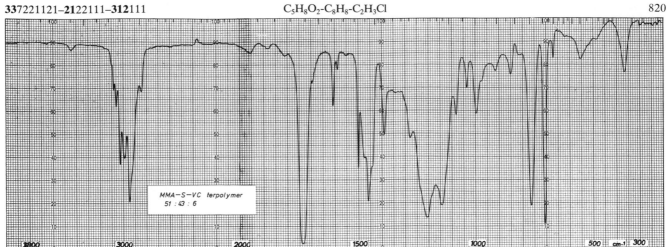

MMA–S–VC terpolymer 51 : 43 : 6

(1) methylmethacrylate-styrene-vinylchloride terpolymer
(2) white powder
(3) H.J. Harwood, University of Akron, O.
(4) molar ratio MMA-S-VC 51:43:6
(5) radical copolymerization
(6) H.J. Harwood, private communication
(7) film from $CHCl_3$ on CsI

337221121–3121112 $C_5H_8O_2\text{-}C_2H_2Cl$ 821

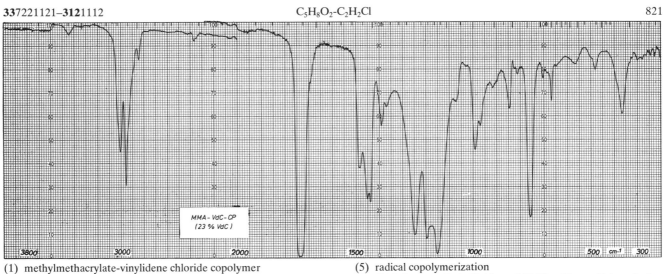

MMA - VdC - CP (23 % VdC)

(1) methylmethacrylate-vinylidene chloride copolymer
(2) white powder
(3) J.N. Hay, Chemistry Department, University of Birmingham
(4) 23 mol-% vinylidene chloride·units
(5) radical copolymerization
(6) G.M. Burnett, R.A. Haldron, J.N. Hay, Europ. Polym. J. *4* (1968) 82...92
(7) film from $CHCl_3$ on CsI

337221121–322151 $C_5H_8O_2\text{-}C_3H_3N$ 822

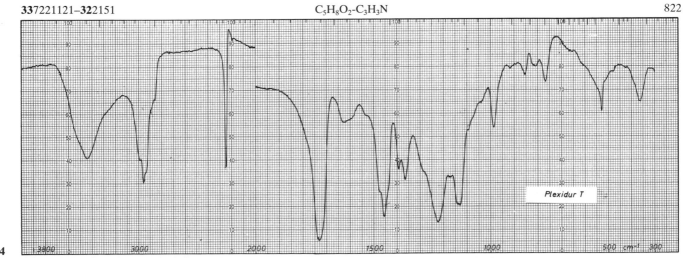

Plexidur T

(1) methylmethacrylate-acrylonitrile copolymer
(2) clear, colourless material
(3) Röhm GmbH, Darmstadt
(4) statistical
(5) radical copolymerization
(7) KBr (4/300)
(8) commercial „Plexidur T"

337221121–337221122 C₅H₈O₂-C₁₁H₁₂O₂ 823

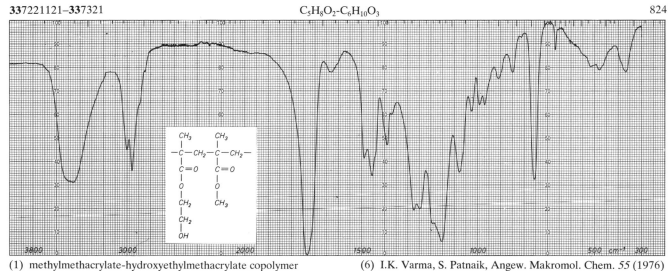

(1) methylmethacrylate-benzylmethacrylate copolymer
(2) white powder
(3) K. Ito, Department of Synthetic Chemistry, Faculty of Engineering, Nagoya University, Nagoya
(4) approx. equimolar composition

(5) anionic copolymerization of the monomer mixture in tetrahydrofuran solution with LiAlH₄ as an initiator
(6) K. Ito, T. Sugie, Y. Yamashita, Makromol. Chem. *125* (1969) 291...3
(7) film from CHCl₃ on CsI

337221121–337321 C₅H₈O₂-C₆H₁₀O₃ 824

(1) methylmethacrylate-hydroxyethylmethacrylate copolymer
(2) colourless, hard material
(3) I.K. Varma, Indian Institute of Technology, Delhi
(5) bulk copolymerization with benzoylperoxide

(6) I.K. Varma, S. Patnaik, Angew. Makromol. Chem. *55* (1976) 109...16; private communication
(7) KBr (2/350)
(8) 30 wt-% HEMA in the monomer feed

337221121–337321 C₅H₈O₂-C₆H₁₀O₃ 825

(1) methylmethacrylate-hydroxyethylmethacrylate copolymer
(2) colourless, hard material
(3) I.K. Varma, Indian Institute of Technology, Delhi
(5) bulk copolymerization with benzoylperoxide

(6) I.K. Varma, S. Patnaik, Angew. Makromol. Chem. *55* (1976) 109...16; private communication
(7) KBr (2/350)
(8) 40 wt-% HEMA in the monomer feed

337221121–337321 $C_5H_8O_2$-$C_6H_{10}O_3$

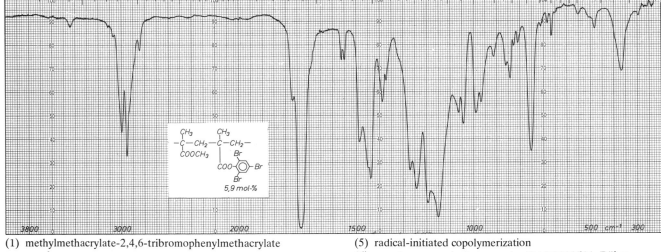

(1) methylmethacrylate-hydroxyethylmethacrylate copolymer
(2) colourless, hard material
(3) I.K. Varma, Indian Institute of Technology, Delhi
(5) bulk copolymerization with benzoylperoxide

(6) I.K. Varma, S. Patnaik, Angew. Makromol. Chem. *55* (1976) 109...16; private communication
(7) KBr (2/350)
(8) 50 wt-% HEMA in the monomer feed

337221121–41337221123 $C_5H_8O_2$-$C_{10}H_7Br_3O_2$ 827

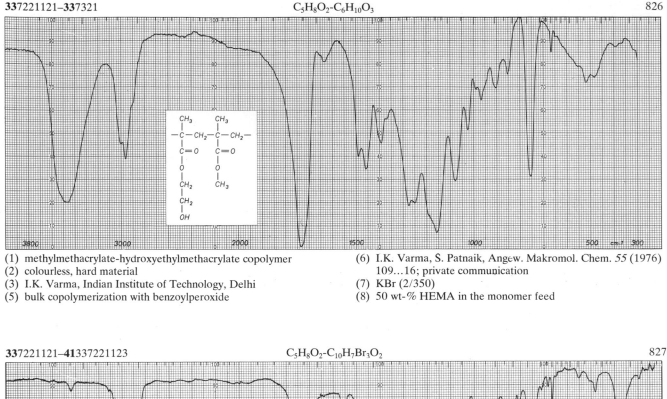

(1) methylmethacrylate-2,4,6-tribromophenylmethacrylate copolymer
(2) glassy-clear, colourless material
(3) Röhm GmbH, Darmstadt (by F. Kollinsky)
(4) 20 wt-% 2,4,6-tribromophenylmethacrylate units

(5) radical-initiated copolymerization
(6) private communication, see also DAS 2202791, Röhm GmbH, Darmstadt; Angew. Chem. *86* (1974) 456
(7) film from $CHCl_3$ on CsI

337221121–4215212 $C_5H_8O_2$-$C_6H_7NO_2$ 828

(1) methylmethacrylate-N-vinylsuccinimide copolymer
(2) colourless, clear plate
(3) W. Gänzler, Röhm GmbH, Darmstadt
(4) 70 wt-% MMA units

(5) copolymerization in bulk at 50 °C with benzoylperoxide as an initiator
(6) W. Gänzler, G. Schreyer, G. Schröder, Angew. Makromol. Chem. *11* (1970) 135...44
(7) film from $CHCl_3$ on KBr

337221121–322151 $C_6H_{10}O_2$–C_3H_3N 829

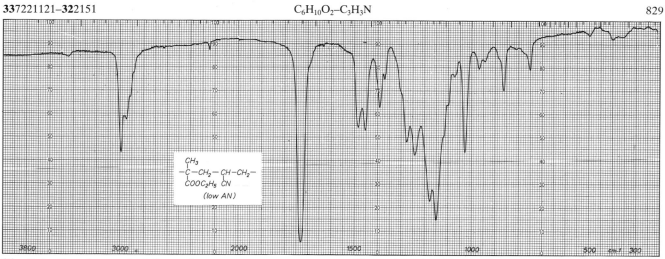

(1) ethylmethacrylate-acrylonitrile copolymer
(2) white coarse material
(3) M.Z. El-Sabee, Department of Chemistry, Faculty of Science, University of Kairo, Giza
(4) low acrylonitrile content

(5) copolymerization of the monomer mixture in bulk at 70°C
(6) M.Z. El-Sabee, A.H. Ahmed, Europ. Polym. J. *10* (1974) 1149...52
(7) film from $CHCl_3$ on CsI

337221121 $C_8H_{14}O_2$ 830

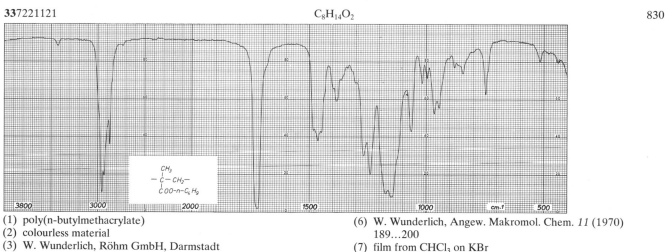

(1) poly(n-butylmethacrylate)
(2) colourless material
(3) W. Wunderlich, Röhm GmbH, Darmstadt
(5) radical-initiated polymerization of the monomer in bulk, low conversion (approx. 5%)

(6) W. Wunderlich, Angew. Makromol. Chem. *11* (1970) 189...200
(7) film from $CHCl_3$ on KBr

3372211211 $C_{15}H_{28}O_2$ 831

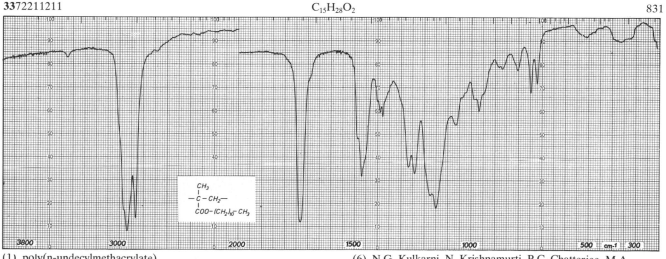

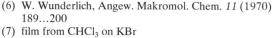

(1) poly(n-undecylmethacrylate)
(2) white material
(3) N.G. Kulkarni, Regional Research Laboratory, Hyderabad
(5) polymerization in benzene solution with benzoylperoxide as an initiator

(6) N.G. Kulkarni, N. Krishnamurti, P.C. Chatterjee. M.A. Sivasamban, Makromol. Chem. *147* (1971) 149...53
(7) film from $CHCl_3$ on CsI

337221121 C$_{16}$H$_{33}$O$_2$ 832

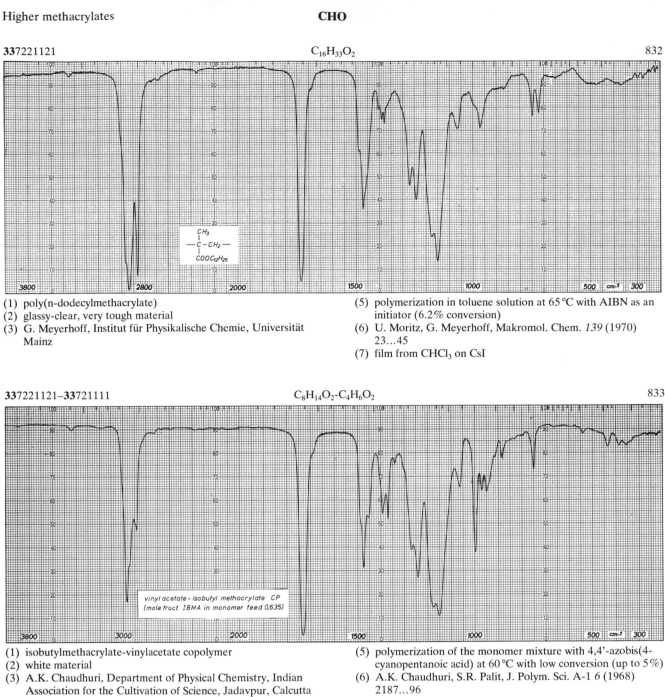

(1) poly(n-dodecylmethacrylate)
(2) glassy-clear, very tough material
(3) G. Meyerhoff, Institut für Physikalische Chemie, Universität Mainz

(5) polymerization in toluene solution at 65 °C with AIBN as an initiator (6.2% conversion)
(6) U. Moritz, G. Meyerhoff, Makromol. Chem. *139* (1970) 23...45
(7) film from CHCl$_3$ on CsI

337221121–33721111 C$_8$H$_{14}$O$_2$-C$_4$H$_6$O$_2$ 833

vinyl acetate - isobutyl methacrylate CP
(mole fract. IBMA in monomer feed 0,635)

(1) isobutylmethacrylate-vinylacetate copolymer
(2) white material
(3) A.K. Chaudhuri, Department of Physical Chemistry, Indian Association for the Cultivation of Science, Jadavpur, Calcutta
(4) mol fraction of IBMA in the monomer feed: 0.635

(5) polymerization of the monomer mixture with 4,4'-azobis(4-cyanopentanoic acid) at 60 °C with low conversion (up to 5%)
(6) A.K. Chaudhuri, S.R. Palit, J. Polym. Sci. A-1 *6* (1968) 2187...96
(7) film from CHCl$_3$ on CsI

337221121 C$_8$H$_{14}$O$_2$ 834

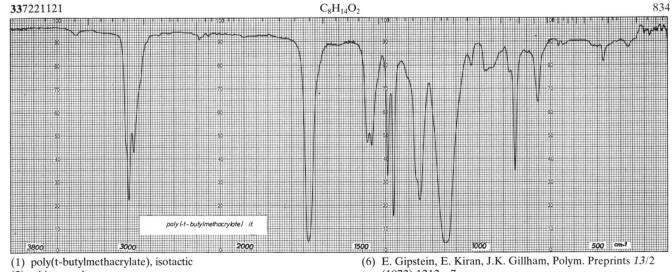

poly (-t- butylmethacrylate) it.

(1) poly(t-butylmethacrylate), isotactic
(2) white powder
(3) E. Gipstein, IBM, San Jose, Calif.
(5) F. Azimov, S. Mitsengendler, A. Korotov, Polym. Sci. USSR *1* (1965) 929

(6) E. Gipstein, E. Kiran, J.K. Gillham, Polym. Preprints *13/2* (1972) 1212...7
(7) film from CHCl$_3$ on CsI

33722112 $C_8H_{15}O_2$ 835

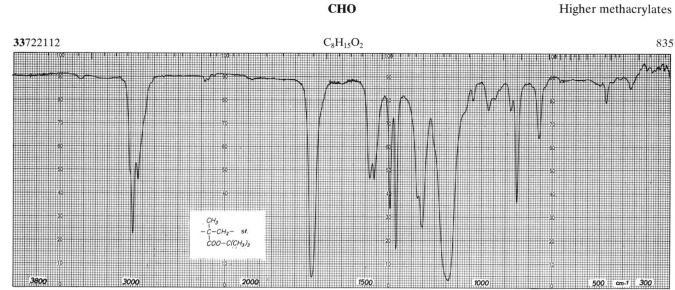

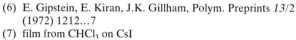

(1) poly(t-butylmethacrylate), syndiotactic
(2) white powder
(3) E. Gipstein, IBM, San Jose, Calif.
(5) F. Azimov, S. Mitsengendler, A. Korotov, Polym. Sci. USSR *1* (1965 929

(6) E. Gipstein, E. Kiran, J.K. Gillham, Polym. Preprints *13/2* (1972) 1212...7
(7) film from CHCl₃ on CsI

337221121 $C_8H_{14}O_2$ 836

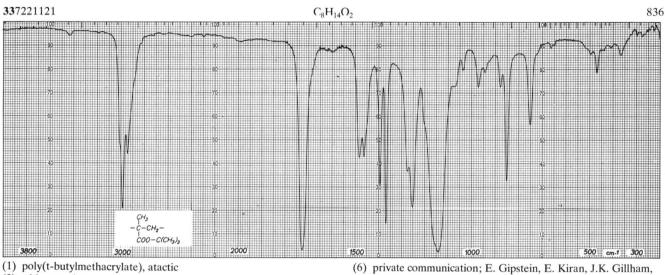

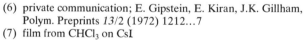

(1) poly(t-butylmethacrylate), atactic
(2) white powder
(3) E. Gipstein, IBM, San Jose, Calif.
(5) radical polymerization

(6) private communication; E. Gipstein, E. Kiran, J.K. Gillham, Polym. Preprints *13/2* (1972) 1212...7
(7) film from CHCl₃ on CsI

337221121 $C_8H_{14}O_2$ 837

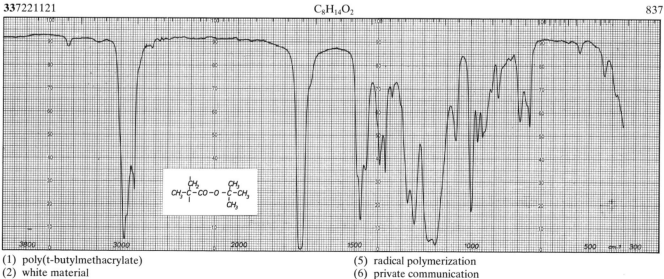

(1) poly(t-butylmethacrylate)
(2) white material
(3) W. Wunderlich, Röhm GmbH, Darmstadt

(5) radical polymerization
(6) private communication
(7) film from CCl₄ on KBr

337221121 $C_9H_{16}O_2$ 838

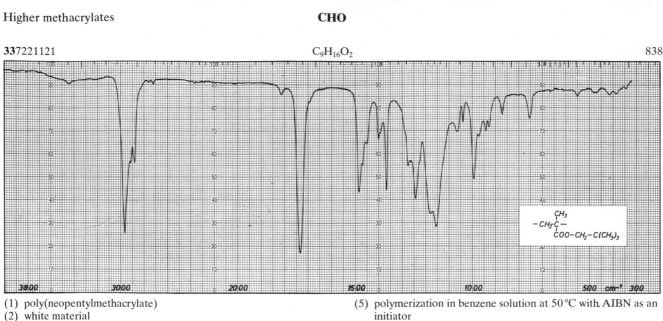

(1) poly(neopentylmethacrylate)
(2) white material
(3) J. Niezette, Department of Physical Chemistry, University of Liège, Sart Tilman
(4) 57% syndiotactic, 32% heterotactic and 11% isotactic triads (by NMR)
(5) polymerization in benzene solution at 50 °C with AIBN as an initiator
(6) J. Niezette, V. Desreux, Makromol. Chem. *149* (1971) 177…83
(7) film from CHCl$_3$ on KBr

337221121 $C_9H_{16}O_2$ 839

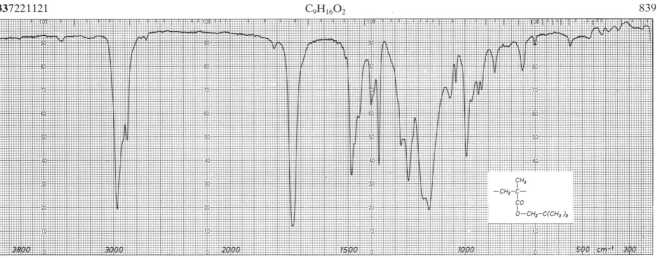

(1) poly(neopentylmethacrylate)
(2) white powder
(3) Ligia Gargallo, Instituto de Ciencias Quimicas, Universidad Católica de Chile, Santiago
(5) polymerization of the monomer in benzene solution at 50 °C with AIBN as an initiator
(6) Ligia Gargallo, M. Russo, Makromol. Chem. *176* (1975) 2735…44
(7) film from CHCl$_3$ on CsI

337221121 $C_{11}H_{20}O_2$ 840

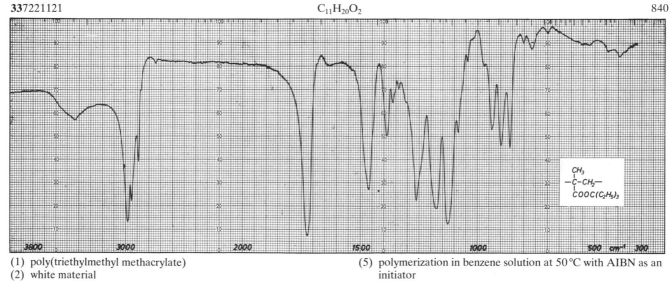

(1) poly(triethylmethyl methacrylate)
(2) white material
(3) J. Niezette, Department of Physical Chemistry, University of Liège, Sart Tilman
(4) 53% heterotactic, 33% syndiotactic and 14% isotactic triads (by NMR)
(5) polymerization in benzene solution at 50 °C with AIBN as an initiator
(6) J. Niezette, V. Desreux, Makromol. Chem. *149* (1971) 177…83
(7) KBr (1.2/350)

337221121 $C_{14}H_{24}O_2$ 841

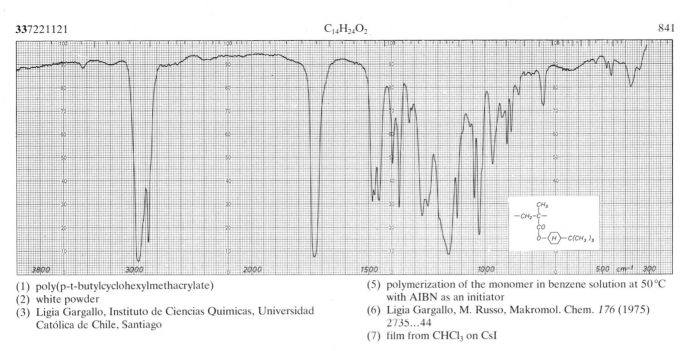

(1) poly(p-t-butylcyclohexylmethacrylate)
(2) white powder
(3) Ligia Gargallo, Instituto de Ciencias Quimicas, Universidad Católica de Chile, Santiago

(5) polymerization of the monomer in benzene solution at 50 °C with AIBN as an initiator
(6) Ligia Gargallo, M. Russo, Makromol. Chem. *176* (1975) 2735...44
(7) film from CHCl$_3$ on CsI

337221121 $C_6H_8O_2$ 842

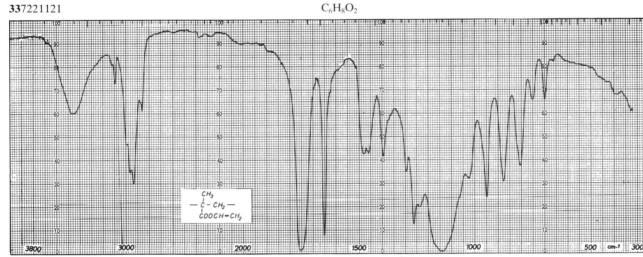

(1) poly(vinylmethacrylate)
(2) colourless material
(3) J.P.J. Higgins, Department of Chemical Engineering and Chemical Technology, Imperial College of Science and Technology, London

(5) polymerization in bulk or in solution at 60 °C with benzoylperoxide as an initiator
(6) private communication; see also J.P.J. Higgins, K.E. Weale, J. Polym. Sci. A-1 *6* (1968) 3007...13
(7) toluene solution ground with KBr, dried and pressed

337221121 $C_7H_{10}O_2$ 843

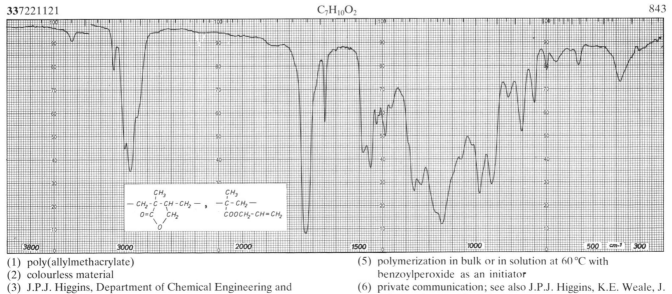

(1) poly(allylmethacrylate)
(2) colourless material
(3) J.P.J. Higgins, Department of Chemical Engineering and Chemical Technology, Imperial College of Science and Technology, London
(4) the polymer contained some lactone groups

(5) polymerization in bulk or in solution at 60 °C with benzoylperoxide as an initiator
(6) private communication; see also J.P.J. Higgins, K.E. Weale, J. Polym. Sci. A-1 *6* (1968) 3007...13
(7) film from toluene on CsI

337221121 $C_{31}H_{50}O_2$ 844

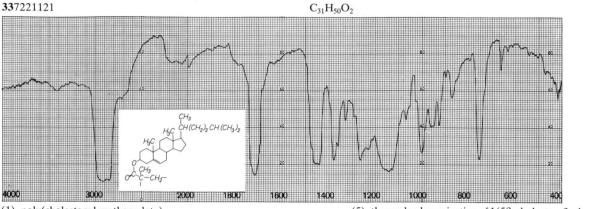

(1) poly(cholestanyl methacrylate)
(3) A.C. de Visser, University of Utah, Salt Lake City/
Department of Material Science, School of Medicine and
Dentistry, Free University, Amsterdam
(4) amorphous, probably with pre dominant syndiotactic
structures

(5) thermal polymerization of 1(5β-cholestan-3-yloxycarbonyl)-
ethylene in bulk in the mesophase (83.5 °C at the start)
(6) Anthonie C. de Visser, J.W.A. van den Berg, A. Bantjes,
Makromol. Chem. *176* (1975) 495...9
(7) film from $CHCl_3$ on KBr (spectrum by R. Visser)
(8) change of absorption at 2000 cm^{-1} is due to the change of
grating

337221121 $C_{31}H_{50}O_2$ 845

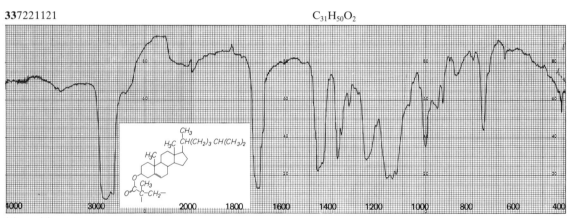

(1) ...(4) see above
(5) anionic polymerization of 1(5β-cholestan-3-yloxycarbonyl)-
ethylene in dry toluene with butyllithium as initiator (273 K,
then 243 K)
(6) ...(8) see above

337221121 $C_{16}H_{30}O_2$ 846

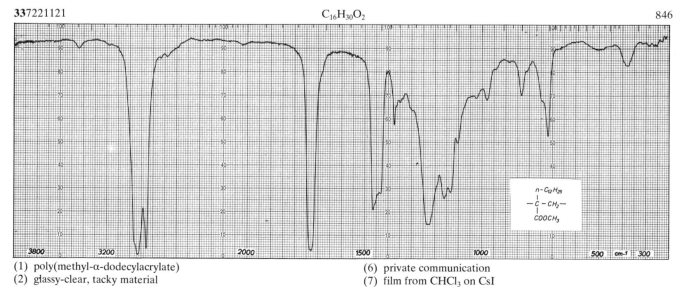

(1) poly(methyl-α-dodecylacrylate)
(2) glassy-clear, tacky material
(3) J.L. Sites, Department of the Army, Washington, D.C.

(6) private communication
(7) film from $CHCl_3$ on CsI

337221121 $C_{20}H_{38}O_2$ 847

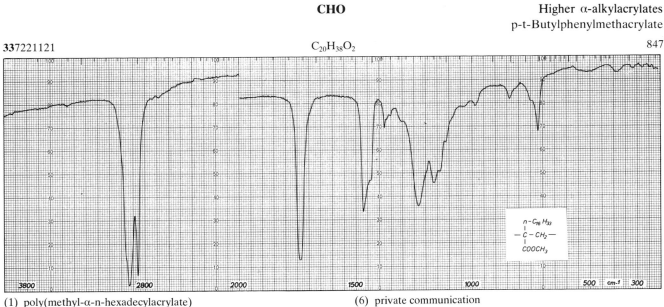

(1) poly(methyl-α-n-hexadecylacrylate)
(2) white material
(3) J.L. Sites, Department of the Army, Washington, D.C.

(6) private communication
(7) film from CHCl₃ on CsI

337221121 $C_{22}H_{42}O_2$ 848

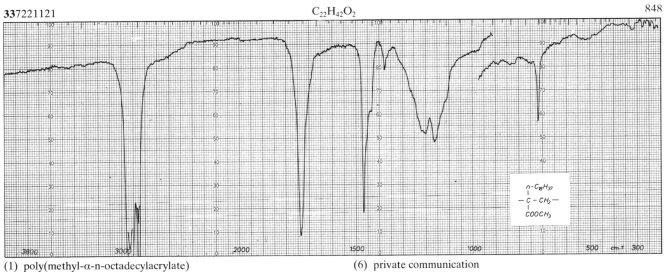

(1) poly(methyl-α-n-octadecylacrylate)
(2) white material
(3) J.L. Sites, Department of the Army, Washington, D.C.

(6) private communication
(7) film from CHCl₃ on CsI, ordinate expanded

337221122 $C_{14}H_{18}O_2$ 849

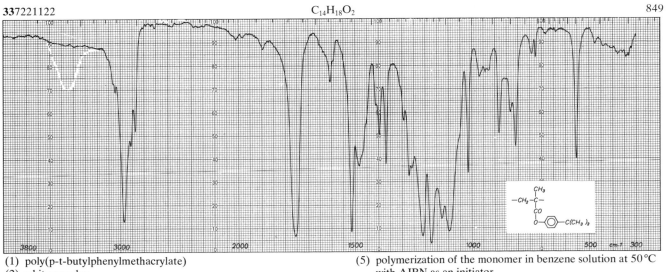

(1) poly(p-t-butylphenylmethacrylate)
(2) white powder
(3) Ligia Gargallo, Instituto de Ciencias Quimicas, Universidad Católica de Chile, Santiago

(5) polymerization of the monomer in benzene solution at 50 °C with AIBN as an initiator
(6) Ligia Gargallo, M. Russo, Makromol. Chem. *176* (1975) 2735...44
(7) KBr (2/350)

337221122   C₁₁H₁₂O₂   850

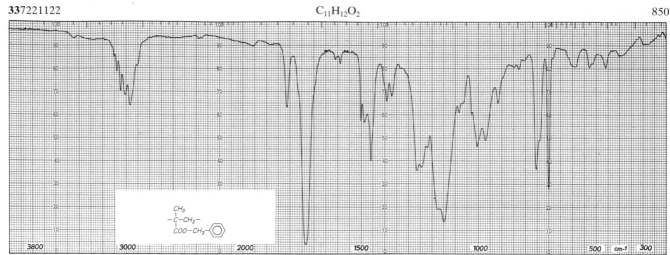

(1) poly(benzylmethacrylate)
(2) white powder
(3) H.J. Harwood, Institute of Polymer Science, University of Akron, Akron, O.
(5) radical-initiated polymerization at 60 °C
(6) private communication
(7) film from CHCl₃ on CsI

337221122   C₁₂H₁₄O₂   851

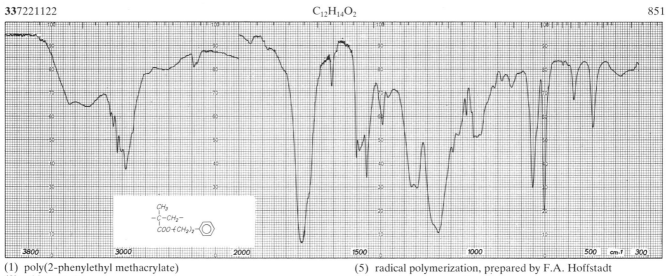

(1) poly(2-phenylethyl methacrylate)
(2) white powder
(3) H.J. Harwood, Institute of Polymer Science, University of Akron, Akron, O.
(5) radical polymerization, prepared by F.A. Hoffstadt
(6) private communication
(7) KBr (2/300)

337221123   C₁₀H₁₀O₂   852

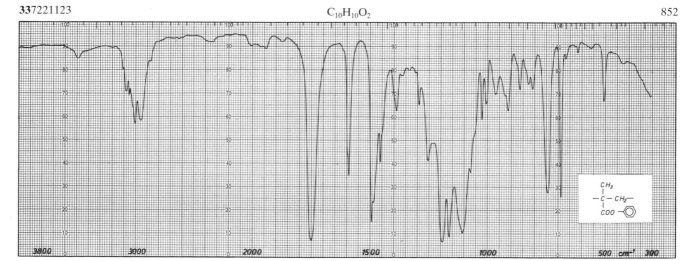

(1) poly(phenylmethacrylate)
(2) white powder
(3) P.L. Magagnini, Istitute di Chimica Industriale ed Applicata. Facoltà di Ingegneria, Università di Pisa, Pisa
(5) S. Krause, J.J. Gormley, N. Roman, J.A. Shetter, W.H. Watanabe, J. Polym. Sci. A3 (1965) 3573
(6) private communication, see also Giovanna Pizzirani, P.L. Magagnini, P. Giusti, J. Polym. Sci. A-2 9 (1971) 1133...45
(7) film from CHCl₃ on KBr

337221123   C₁₀H₁₀O₂   853

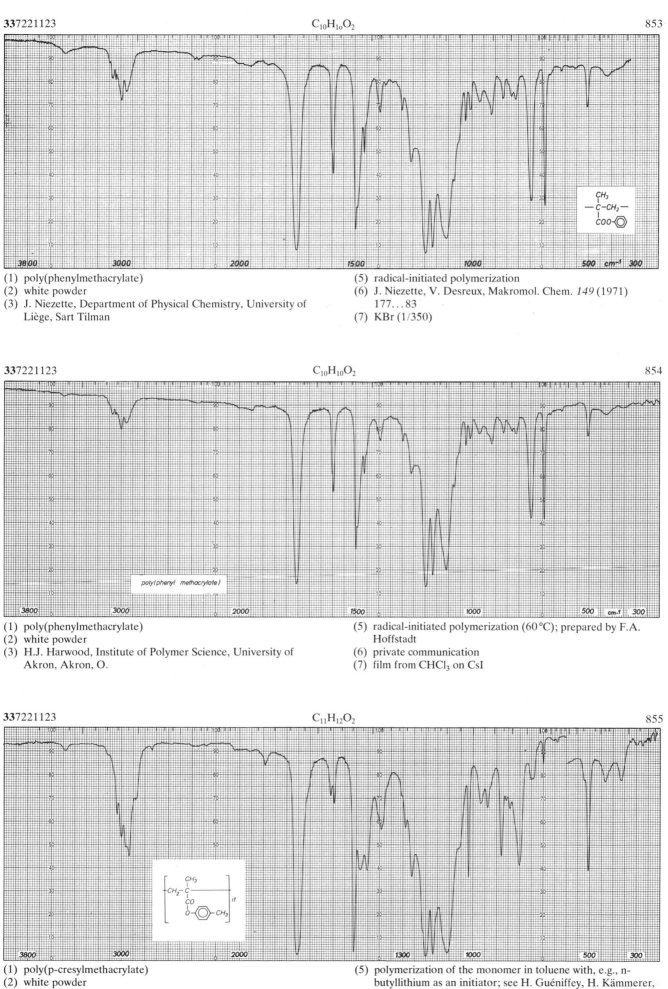

(1) poly(phenylmethacrylate)
(2) white powder
(3) J. Niezette, Department of Physical Chemistry, University of
   Liège, Sart Tilman

(5) radical-initiated polymerization
(6) J. Niezette, V. Desreux, Makromol. Chem. *149* (1971)
   177...83
(7) KBr (1/350)

337221123   C₁₀H₁₀O₂   854

poly(phenyl methacrylate)

(1) poly(phenylmethacrylate)
(2) white powder
(3) H.J. Harwood, Institute of Polymer Science, University of
   Akron, Akron, O.

(5) radical-initiated polymerization (60 °C); prepared by F.A.
   Hoffstadt
(6) private communication
(7) film from CHCl₃ on CsI

337221123   C₁₁H₁₂O₂   855

(1) poly(p-cresylmethacrylate)
(2) white powder
(3) K. Guéniffey, Laboratoire de Chimie Organique
   Macromoléculaire, Le Mans
(4) predominantly isotactic

(5) polymerization of the monomer in toluene with, e.g., n-
   butyllithium as an initiator; see H. Guéniffey, H. Kämmerer,
   C. Pinazzi, Makromol. Chem. *136* (1970) 173
(6) H. Guéniffey, E. Klesper, H. Kämmerer, Makromol. Chem.
   162 (1972) 199...204
(7) film from CHCl₃ on CsI

337221123 $C_{11}H_{12}O_2$ 856

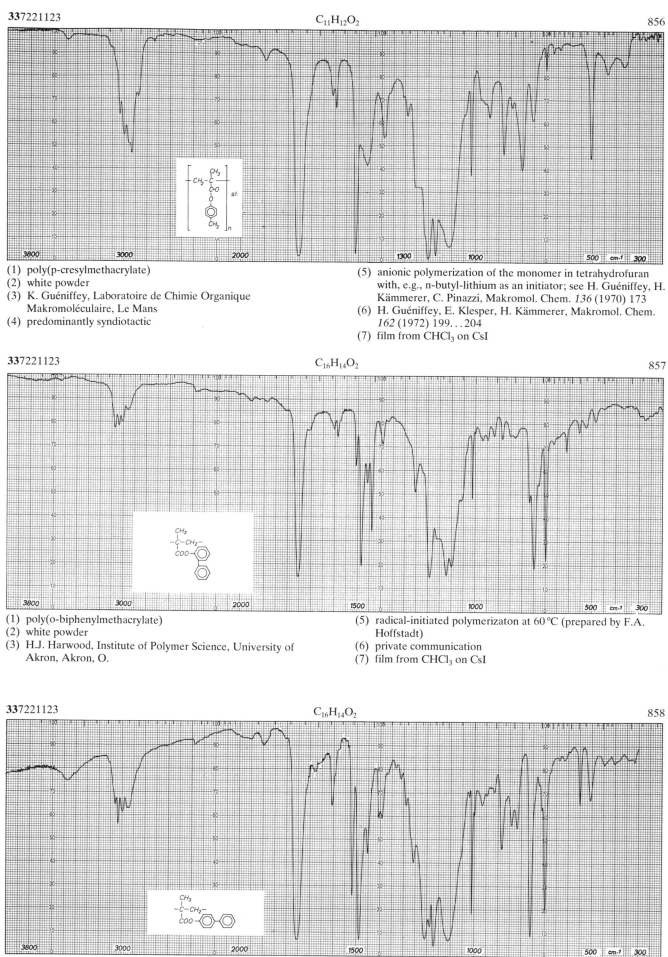

(1) poly(p-cresylmethacrylate)
(2) white powder
(3) K. Guéniffey, Laboratoire de Chimie Organique Macromoléculaire, Le Mans
(4) predominantly syndiotactic
(5) anionic polymerization of the monomer in tetrahydrofuran with, e.g., n-butyl-lithium as an initiator; see H. Guéniffey, H. Kämmerer, C. Pinazzi, Makromol. Chem. *136* (1970) 173
(6) H. Guéniffey, E. Klesper, H. Kämmerer, Makromol. Chem. *162* (1972) 199...204
(7) film from $CHCl_3$ on CsI

337221123 $C_{16}H_{14}O_2$ 857

(1) poly(o-biphenylmethacrylate)
(2) white powder
(3) H.J. Harwood, Institute of Polymer Science, University of Akron, Akron, O.
(5) radical-initiated polymerizaton at 60 °C (prepared by F.A. Hoffstadt)
(6) private communication
(7) film from $CHCl_3$ on CsI

337221123 $C_{16}H_{14}O_2$ 858

(1) poly(p-biphenylmethacrylate)
(2) white powder
(3) H.J. Harwood, Institute of Polymer Science, University of Akron, Akron, O.
(5) radical-initiated polymerization at 60 °C (prepared by F.A. Hoffstadt)
(6) private communication
(7) KBr (2/300)

337221123 $C_{14}H_{12}O_2$ 859

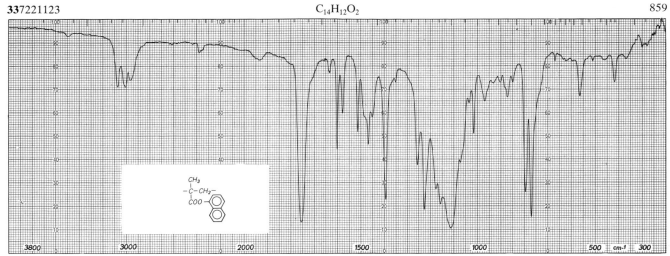

(1) poly(1-naphthylmethacrylate)
(2) white powder
(3) H.J. Harwood, Institute of Polymer Science, University of Akron, Akron, O.
(5) radical-initiated polymerization at 60 °C (prepared by F.A. Hoffstadt)
(6) private communication
(7) film from $CHCl_3$ on CsI

337221123 $C_{14}H_{12}O_2$ 860

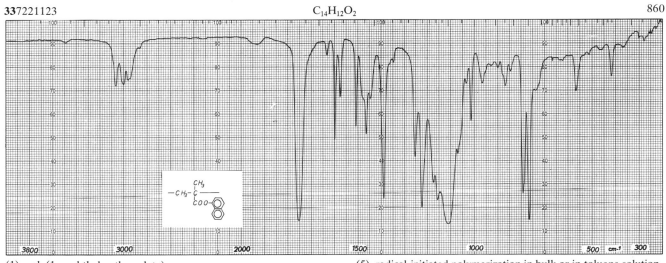

(1) poly(1-naphthylmethacrylate)
(2) white powder
(3) J.E. Guillet, Department of Chemistry, University of Toronto, Toronto
(5) radical-initiated polymerization in bulk or in toluene solution at 60 °C with benzoylperoxide as an initiator
(6) A.C. Somersall, J.E. Guillet, Macromolecules 6 (1973) 218...23
(7) film from $CHCl_3$ on CsI

337221123 $C_{14}H_{12}O_2$ 861

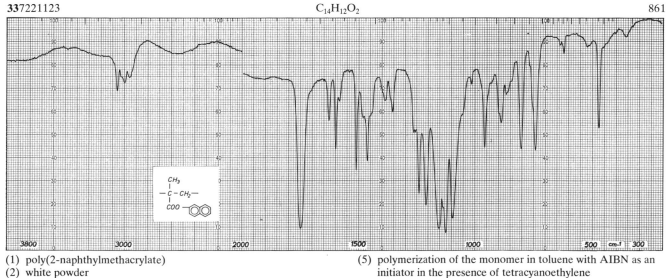

(1) poly(2-naphthylmethacrylate)
(2) white powder
(3) H. Boudevska, Institute of Organic Chemistry, Bulgarian Academy of Sciences, Sofia
(5) polymerization of the monomer in toluene with AIBN as an initiator in the presence of tetracyanoethylene
(6) H. Boudevska, M. Mintcheva, Europ. Polym. J. 10 (1974) 875...7
(7) film from $CHCl_3$ on CsI

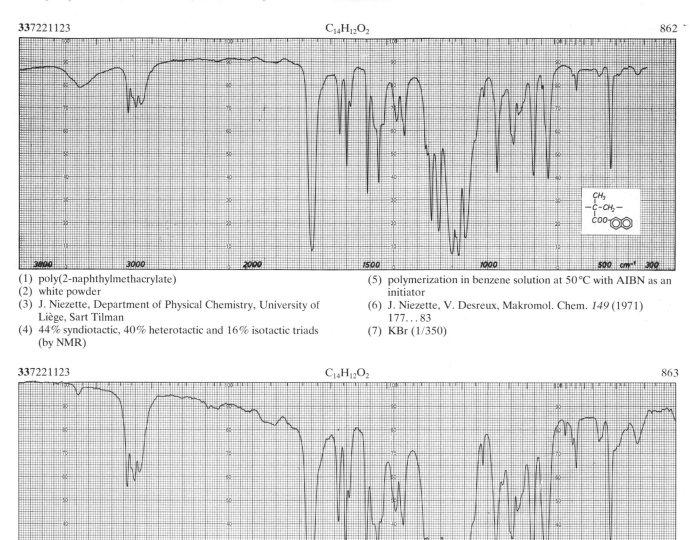

337221123 $C_{14}H_{12}O_2$ 862

(1) poly(2-naphthylmethacrylate)
(2) white powder
(3) J. Niezette, Department of Physical Chemistry, University of Liège, Sart Tilman
(4) 44% syndiotactic, 40% heterotactic and 16% isotactic triads (by NMR)
(5) polymerization in benzene solution at 50 °C with AIBN as an initiator
(6) J. Niezette, V. Desreux, Makromol. Chem. *149* (1971) 177...83
(7) KBr (1/350)

337221123 $C_{14}H_{12}O_2$ 863

(1) poly(2-naphthylmethacrylate)
(2) white powder
(3) H.J. Harwood, Institute of Polymer Science, University of Akron, Akron, O.
(5) radical-initiated polymerization at 60 °C (prepared by F.A. Hoffstadt)
(6) private communication
(7) film from $CHCl_3$ on CsI

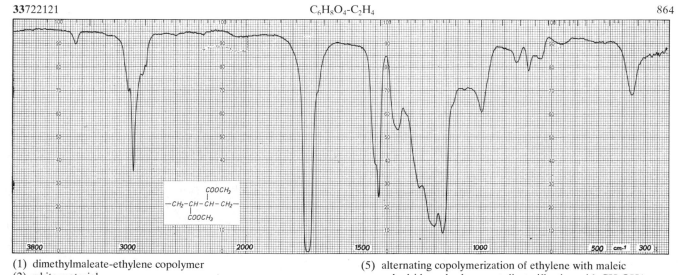

33722121 $C_6H_8O_4$-C_2H_4 864

(1) dimethylmaleate-ethylene copolymer
(2) white material
(3) T. Otsu, Department of Applied Chemistry, Faculty of Engineering, Osaka City University, Osaka
(4) head-to-head-tail-to-tail poly(methylacrylate)
(5) alternating copolymerization of ethylene with maleic anhydride and subsequent diesterification with CH_3OH/H_2SO_4
(6) T. Otsu, S. Aoki, R. Nakatani, Makromol. Chem. *134* (1970) 331...3
(7) film from $CHCl_3$ on CsI

288

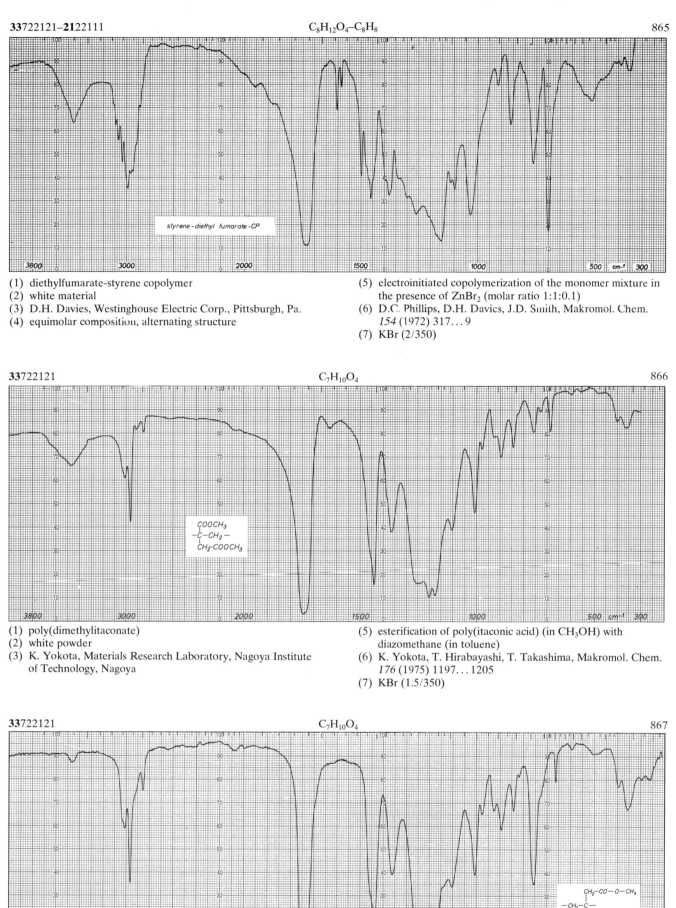

styrene - diethyl fumarate -CP

(1) diethylfumarate-styrene copolymer
(2) white material
(3) D.H. Davies, Westinghouse Electric Corp., Pittsburgh, Pa.
(4) equimolar composition, alternating structure
(5) electroinitiated copolymerization of the monomer mixture in the presence of ZnBr$_2$ (molar ratio 1:1:0.1)
(6) D.C. Phillips, D.H. Davies, J.D. Smith, Makromol. Chem. *154* (1972) 317…9
(7) KBr (2/350)

$$\begin{array}{c} COOCH_3 \\ | \\ -C-CH_2- \\ | \\ CH_2-COOCH_3 \end{array}$$

(1) poly(dimethylitaconate)
(2) white powder
(3) K. Yokota, Materials Research Laboratory, Nagoya Institute of Technology, Nagoya
(5) esterification of poly(itaconic acid) (in CH$_3$OH) with diazomethane (in toluene)
(6) K. Yokota, T. Hirabayashi, T. Takashima, Makromol. Chem. *176* (1975) 1197…1205
(7) KBr (1.5/350)

$$\begin{array}{c} CH_2-CO-O-CH_3 \\ | \\ -CH_2-C- \\ | \\ CO-O-CH_3 \end{array}$$

(1) poly(dimethylitaconate)
(2) colourless material
(3) J. Veličković, Tehnolosko-metalurški fakultet, Beograd
(5) radical polymerization with AIBN
(6) J. Veličković, Jovanka Vukajlović-Filipović, Angew. Makromol. Chem. *13* (1970) 79…88; J. Veličković, Viera Juraničova, Jovanka Filipović, IUPAC Macro Leiden, 1970; J. Veličković, Slavica Vasović, ibid.
(7) film from CHCl$_3$ on CsI

33722121 $C_{17}H_{30}O_4$ 868

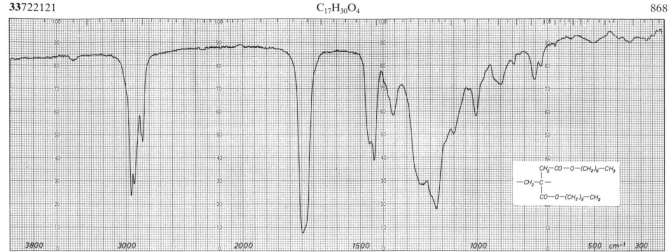

(1) poly(di-n-hexylitaconate)
(2) colourless material
(3) J. Veličković, Tehnolosko-metalurški fakultet, Beograd
(5) radical polymerization with AIBN

(6) J. Veličković, Jovanka Vukajlović-Filipović, Angew. Makromol. Chem. *13* (1970) 79...88; J. Veličković, Viera Juranicóva, Jovanka Filipović, IUPAC Macro Leiden, 1970; J. Veličković, Slavica Vasović, ibid.
(7) film from CHCl₃ on CsI

33722121 $C_{27}H_{50}O_4$ 869

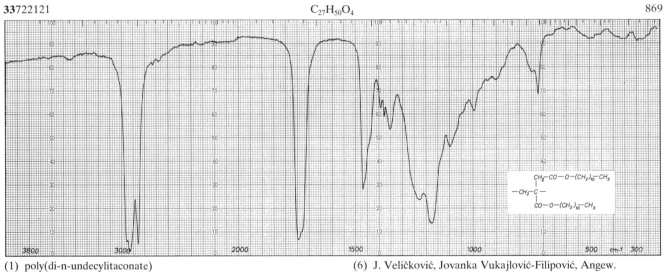

(1) poly(di-n-undecylitaconate)
(2) white material
(3) J. Veličković, Tehnolosko-metalurški fakultet, Beograd
(5) radical polymerization with AIBN

(6) J. Veličković, Jovanka Vukajlović-Filipović, Angew. Makromol. Chem. *13* (1970) 79...88; J. Veličković, Viera Juranicóva, Jovanka Filipović, IUPAC Macro Leiden, 1970; J. Veličković, Slavica Vasović, ibid.
(7) film from CHCl₃ on CsI

33722121 $C_{21}H_{38}O_4$ 870

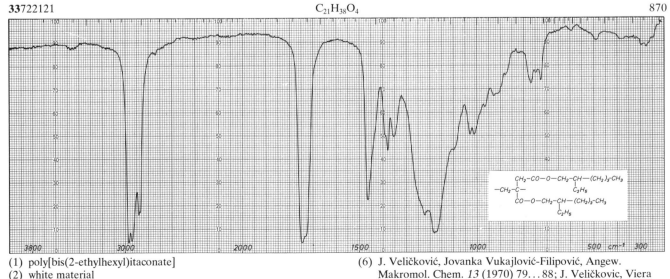

(1) poly[bis(2-ethylhexyl)itaconate]
(2) white material
(3) J. Veličković, Tehnolosko-metalurški fakultet, Beograd
(5) radical polymerization with AIBN

(6) J. Veličković, Jovanka Vukajlović-Filipović, Angew. Makromol. Chem. *13* (1970) 79...88; J. Veličkovic, Viera Juraničova, Jovanka Filipović, IUPAC Macro Leiden, 1970; J. Veličković, Slavica Vasović, ibid.
(7) film from CHCl₃ on CsI

33722121 $C_{17}H_{26}O_4$ 871

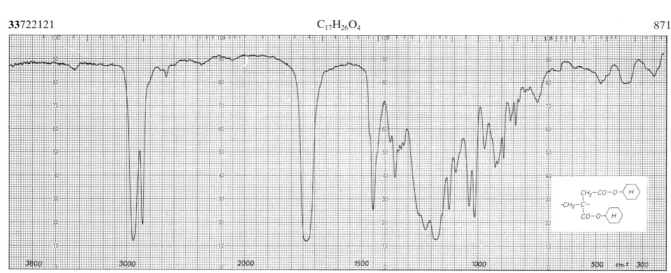

(1) poly(dicyclohexylitaconate)
(2) white material
(3) J. Veličković, Tehnolosko-metalurški fakultet, Beograd
(5) radical polymerization with AIBN

(6) J. Veličković, S. Čoševa, R. Fort, Europ. Polym. J. *11* (1975) 377
(7) film from $CHCl_3$ on CsI

33722121 $C_{19}H_{30}O_4$ 872

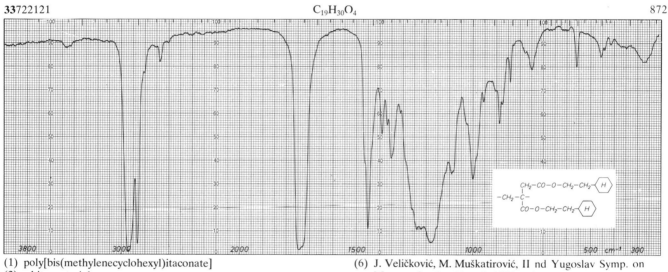

(1) poly[bis(methylenecyclohexyl)itaconate]
(2) white material
(3) J. Veličković, Tehnolosko-metalurški fakultet, Beograd
(5) radical polymerization with AIBN

(6) J. Veličković, M. Muškatirović, II nd Yugoslav Symp. on Macromolecules, Zagreb 1971; private communication
(7) film from $CHCl_3$ on CsI

33722121 $C_{21}H_{34}O_4$ 873

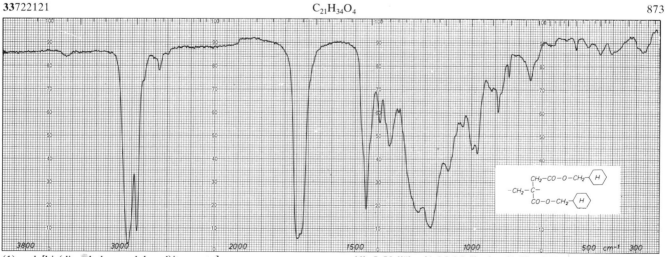

(1) poly[bis(dimethylenecyclohexyl)itaconate]
(2) white powder
(3) J. Veličković, Tehnolosko-metalurški fakultet, Beograd
(5) radical polymerization with AIBN

(6) J. Veličković, M. Muškatirović, II nd Yugoslav Symp. on Macromolecules, Zagreb 1971; private communication
(7) film from $CHCl_3$ on CsI

33722122 $C_{21}H_{22}O_4$ 874

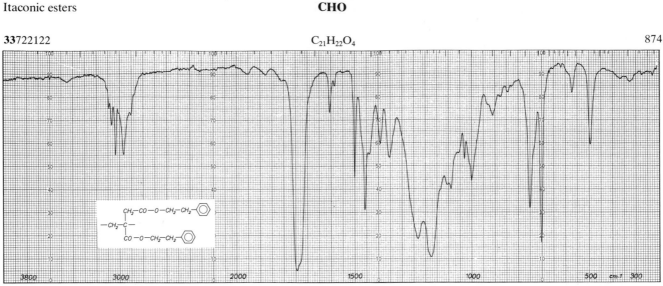

(1) poly[bis(dimethylenephenyl)itaconate]
(2) glassy material
(3) J. Veličković, Tehnolosko-metalurški fakultet, Beograd

(5) radical polymerization with AIBN
(6) J. Veličković, M. Muškatirović, II nd Yugoslav Symp. on Macromolecules, Zagreb 1971, private communication
(7) film from $CHCl_3$ on CsI

33722122 $C_{19}H_{18}O_4$ 875

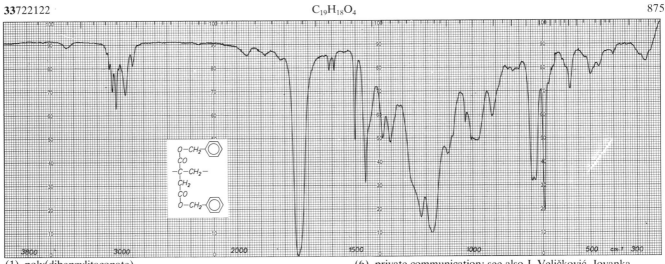
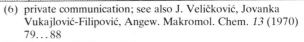

(1) poly(dibenzylitaconate)
(2) white powder
(3) J. Veličković, Faculty of Technology and Metallurgy, Beograd
(5) bulk polymerization of the monomer with AIBN

(6) private communication; see also J. Veličković, Jovanka Vukajlović-Filipović, Angew. Makromol. Chem. *13* (1970) 79...88
(7) film from $CHCl_3$ on CsI

33722123 $C_{19}H_{18}O_4$ 876

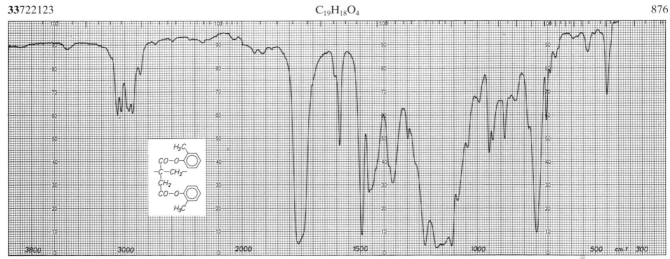

(1) poly(di-o-tolylitaconate)
(2) white powder
(3) J. Veličković, Faculty of Technology and Metallurgy, Beograd
(5) bulk polymerization of the monomer with AIBN

(6) private communication; see also J. Veličković, Jovanka Vukajlović-Filipović, Angew. Makromol. Chem. *13* (1970) 79...88
(7) film from $CHCl_3$ on CsI

3372222   C$_{19}$H$_{18}$O$_4$ 877

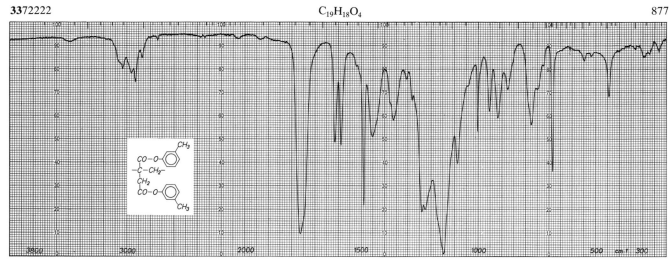

(1) poly(di-m-tolylitaconate)
(2) white powder
(3) J. Veličković, Faculty of Technology and Metallurgy, Beograd
(5) bulk polymerization of the monomer with AIBN

(6) private communication; see also J. Veličković, Jovanka Vukajlović-Filipović, Angew. Makromol. Chem. *13* (1970) 79...88
(7) film from CHCl$_3$ on CsI

33722123   C$_{19}$H$_{18}$O$_4$ 878

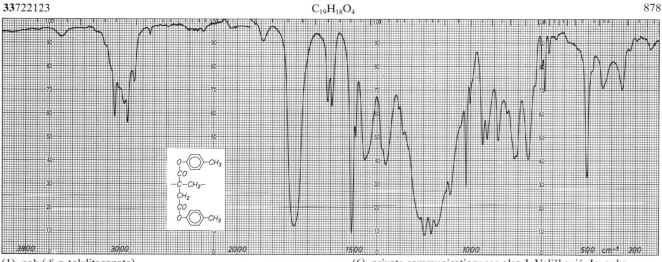

(1) poly(di-p-tolylitaconate)
(2) white powder
(3) J. Veličković, Faculty of Technology and Metallurgy, Beograd
(5) bulk polymerization of the monomer with AIBN

(6) private communication; see also J. Veličković, Jovanka Vukajlović-Filipović, Angew. Makromol. Chem. *13* (1970) 79...88
(7) film from CHCl$_3$ on CsI

33722123   C$_{17}$H$_{14}$O$_4$ 879

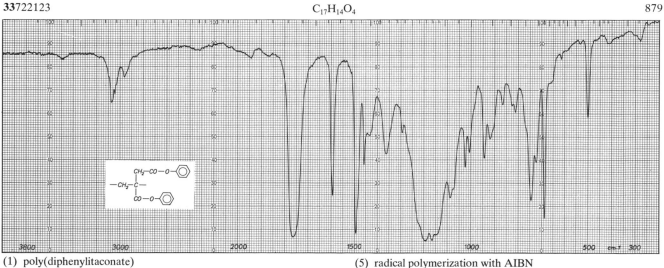

(1) poly(diphenylitaconate)
(2) white powder
(3) J. Veličković, Tehnolosko-metalurški fakultet, Beograd

(5) radical polymerization with AIBN
(6) J. Veličković, M. Plavšić, Europ. Polym. J. *12* (1976) 151
(7) film from CHCl$_3$ on CsI

3372221 $C_{10}H_{10}O_2$ 880

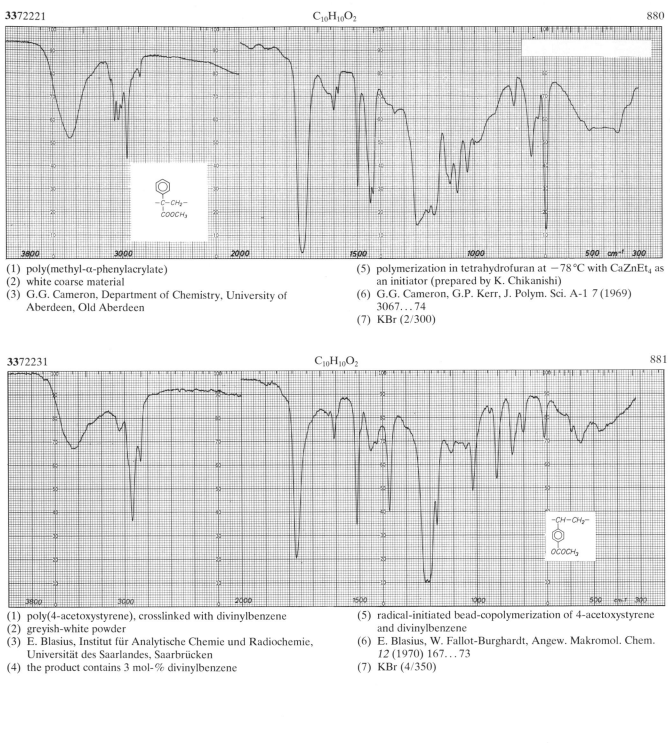

(1) poly(methyl-α-phenylacrylate)
(2) white coarse material
(3) G.G. Cameron, Department of Chemistry, University of Aberdeen, Old Aberdeen

(5) polymerization in tetrahydrofuran at −78 °C with CaZnEt₄ as an initiator (prepared by K. Chikanishi)
(6) G.G. Cameron, G.P. Kerr, J. Polym. Sci. A-1 7 (1969) 3067...74
(7) KBr (2/300)

3372231 $C_{10}H_{10}O_2$ 881

(1) poly(4-acetoxystyrene), crosslinked with divinylbenzene
(2) greyish-white powder
(3) E. Blasius, Institut für Analytische Chemie und Radiochemie, Universität des Saarlandes, Saarbrücken
(4) the product contains 3 mol-% divinylbenzene

(5) radical-initiated bead-copolymerization of 4-acetoxystyrene and divinylbenzene
(6) E. Blasius, W. Fallot-Burghardt, Angew. Makromol. Chem. *12* (1970) 167...73
(7) KBr (4/350)

337321 $C_6H_{10}O_3$ 882

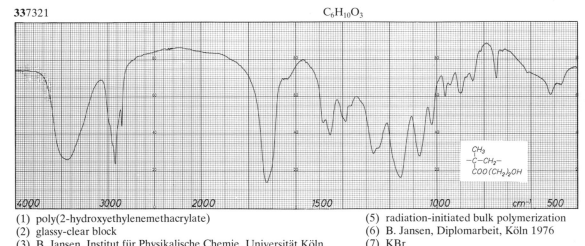

(1) poly(2-hydroxyethylenemethacrylate)
(2) glassy-clear block
(3) B. Jansen, Institut für Physikalische Chemie, Universität Köln

(5) radiation-initiated bulk polymerization
(6) B. Jansen, Diplomarbeit, Köln 1976
(7) KBr

337321   C_{26}H_{36}O_5   883

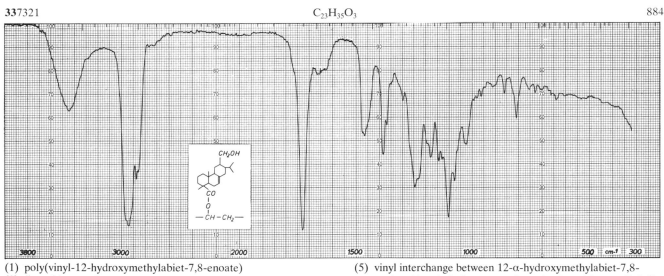

(1) poly(vinylcholate), poly(vinyl-3α, 7α, 12α,-trihydroxy-5-β-cholan-24-oate)
(2) white powder
(3) K. Takemoto, Faculty of Engineering, Osaka University, Suita
(5) radical-initiated polymerization with AIBN
(6) M. Miyata, M. Sato, T. Ishikawa, K. Takemoto, Makromol. Chem. *176* (1975) 2139...42
(7) KBr (2/350)

337321   C_{23}H_{35}O_3   884

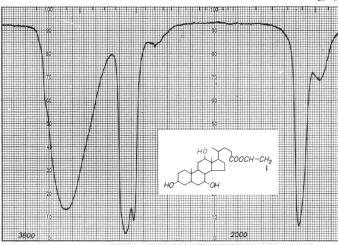

(1) poly(vinyl-12-hydroxymethylabiet-7,8-enoate)
(2) fine white powder
(3) C.S. Marvel, Department of Chemistry, University of Arizona, Tucson, Ariz.
(5) vinyl interchange between 12-α-hydroxymethylabiet-7,8-enoic acid and vinylacetate, polymerization with, e.g., K_2S_2O_8 in an emulsion system
(6) M. Saga, C.S. Marvel, J. Polym. Sci. A-1 *7* (1969) 2135...45
(7) ground with KBr (1.5/350) and CHCl_3, dried and pressed

337322   C_7H_{12}O_4   885

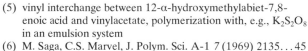

(1) poly(2,3-dihydroxypropylmethacrylate)
(2) coarse, greyish-white material
(3) G. Beinert, Centre de Recherches sur les Macromolécules, Strasbourg
(5) anionic polymerization of (2,2-dimethyl-1,3-dioxolan-4-yl)methylmethacrylate, acid hydrolysis
(6) G. Beinert, G. Hild, P. Rempp, Makromol. Chem. *175* (1974) 2069...77
(7) ground with KBr (1.3/350) and CH_3OH, dried and pressed

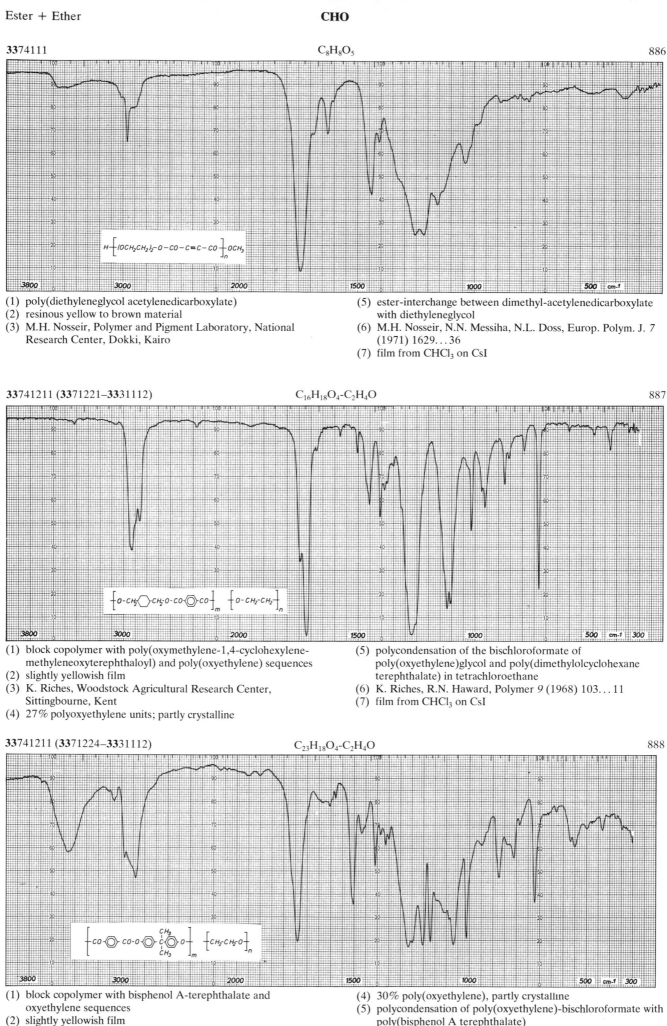

3374111   C$_8$H$_8$O$_5$ 886

H$-$[(OCH$_2$CH$_2$)$_2$$-O-CO-C\equiv$C$-CO-$]$_nOCH_3$

(1) poly(diethyleneglycol acetylenedicarboxylate)
(2) resinous yellow to brown material
(3) M.H. Nosseir, Polymer and Pigment Laboratory, National Research Center, Dokki, Kairo

(5) ester-interchange between dimethyl-acetylenedicarboxylate with diethyleneglycol
(6) M.H. Nosseir, N.N. Messiha, N.L. Doss, Europ. Polym. J. 7 (1971) 1629...36
(7) film from CHCl$_3$ on CsI

33741211 (3371221–3331112)   C$_{16}$H$_{18}$O$_4$-C$_2$H$_4$O   887

[O$-$CH$_2$-⬡-CH$_2$-O$-$CO-◯-CO]$_m$ [O$-$CH$_2$-CH$_2$]$_n$

(1) block copolymer with poly(oxymethylene-1,4-cyclohexylene-methyleneoxyterephthaloyl) and poly(oxyethylene) sequences
(2) slightly yellowish film
(3) K. Riches, Woodstock Agricultural Research Center, Sittingbourne, Kent
(4) 27% polyoxyethylene units; partly crystalline

(5) polycondensation of the bischloroformate of poly(oxyethylene)glycol and poly(dimethylolcyclohexane terephthalate) in tetrachloroethane
(6) K. Riches, R.N. Haward, Polymer 9 (1968) 103...11
(7) film from CHCl$_3$ on CsI

33741211 (3371224–3331112)   C$_{23}$H$_{18}$O$_4$-C$_2$H$_4$O   888

[CO-◯-CO-O-◯-C(CH$_3$)(CH$_3$)-◯-O]$_m$ [CH$_2$-CH$_2$-O]$_n$

(1) block copolymer with bisphenol A-terephthalate and oxyethylene sequences
(2) slightly yellowish film
(3) K. Riches, Woodstock Agricultural Research Center, Sittingbourne, Kent

(4) 30% poly(oxyethylene), partly crystalline
(5) polycondensation of poly(oxyethylene)-bischloroformate with poly(bisphenol A terephthalate)
(6) K. Riches, R.N. Haward, Polym. 9 (1968) 103...11
(7) KBr

33741212   C$_9$H$_8$O$_3$ 889

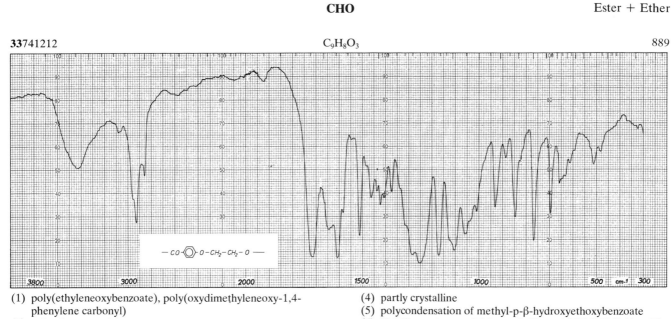

(1) poly(ethyleneoxybenzoate), poly(oxydimethyleneoxy-1,4-phenylene carbonyl)
(2) colourless material
(3) K. Mihara, Mitsubishi Chemical Industries, Yokkaichi Plant, Mie

(4) partly crystalline
(5) polycondensation of methyl-p-β-hydroxyethoxybenzoate
(6) K. Mihara, Angew. Makromol. Chem. 40/41 (1974) 41...55
(7) ground with KBr (2/350) and dimethylacetamide, dried and pressed

33741212   C$_{18}$H$_{16}$O$_6$ 890

(1) poly(ethylene-1,2-diphenoxyethane-p,p'-dicarboxylate)
(2) colourless granules
(3) M. Morita, Noguchi Institute, Tokyo
(4) partly crystalline

(5) polycondensation of ethyleneglycol with the dimethyl ester of bis-p-carboxyphenoxyethane
(6) M. Morita, T. Yamada, T. Kubo, S. Mihara, S. Okajima, J. Polym. Sci. Pt. C 23 (1968) 683...93
(7) KBr (2/350)

33741212   891

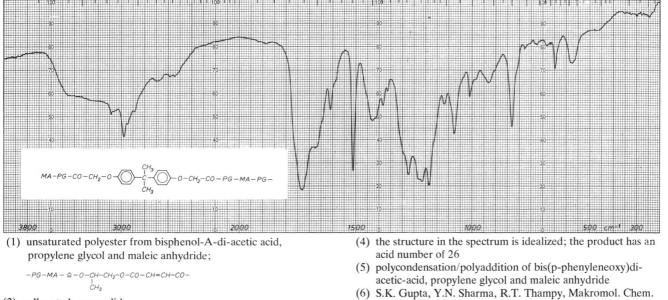

(1) unsaturated polyester from bisphenol-A-di-acetic acid, propylene glycol and maleic anhydride;

$-PG-MA- \hateq -O-CH_2-CH_2-O-CO-CH=CH-CO-$
$\qquad\qquad\qquad CH_3$

(2) yellow to brown solid
(3) R.T. Thampy, Shri Ram Institute for Industrial Research, Delhi

(4) the structure in the spectrum is idealized; the product has an acid number of 26
(5) polycondensation/polyaddition of bis(p-phenyleneoxy)di-acetic-acid, propylene glycol and maleic anhydride
(6) S.K. Gupta, Y.N. Sharma, R.T. Thampy, Makromol. Chem. 120 (1968) 137...47
(7) film from acetone on CsI

33741222 $C_{26}H_{24}O_5$ 892

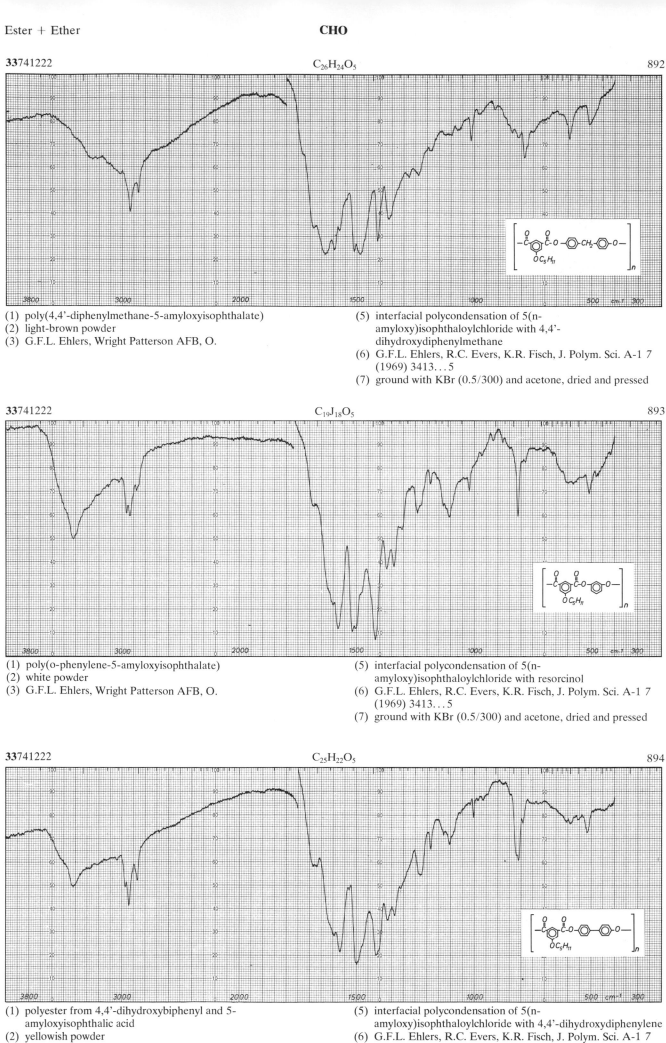

(1) poly(4,4'-diphenylmethane-5-amyloxyisophthalate)
(2) light-brown powder
(3) G.F.L. Ehlers, Wright Patterson AFB, O.

(5) interfacial polycondensation of 5(n-amyloxy)isophthaloylchloride with 4,4'-dihydroxydiphenylmethane
(6) G.F.L. Ehlers, R.C. Evers, K.R. Fisch, J. Polym. Sci. A-1 7 (1969) 3413...5
(7) ground with KBr (0.5/300) and acetone, dried and pressed

33741222 $C_{19}J_{18}O_5$ 893

(1) poly(o-phenylene-5-amyloxyisophthalate)
(2) white powder
(3) G.F.L. Ehlers, Wright Patterson AFB, O.

(5) interfacial polycondensation of 5(n-amyloxy)isophthaloylchloride with resorcinol
(6) G.F.L. Ehlers, R.C. Evers, K.R. Fisch, J. Polym. Sci. A-1 7 (1969) 3413...5
(7) ground with KBr (0.5/300) and acetone, dried and pressed

33741222 $C_{25}H_{22}O_5$ 894

(1) polyester from 4,4'-dihydroxybiphenyl and 5-amyloxyisophthalic acid
(2) yellowish powder
(3) G.F.L. Ehlers, Wright Patterson AFB, O.

(5) interfacial polycondensation of 5(n-amyloxy)isophthaloylchloride with 4,4'-dihydroxydiphenylene
(6) G.F.L. Ehlers, R.C. Evers, K.R. Fisch, J. Polym. Sci. A-1 7 (1969) 3413...5
(7) ground with KBr (0.3/300) and acetone, dried and pressed

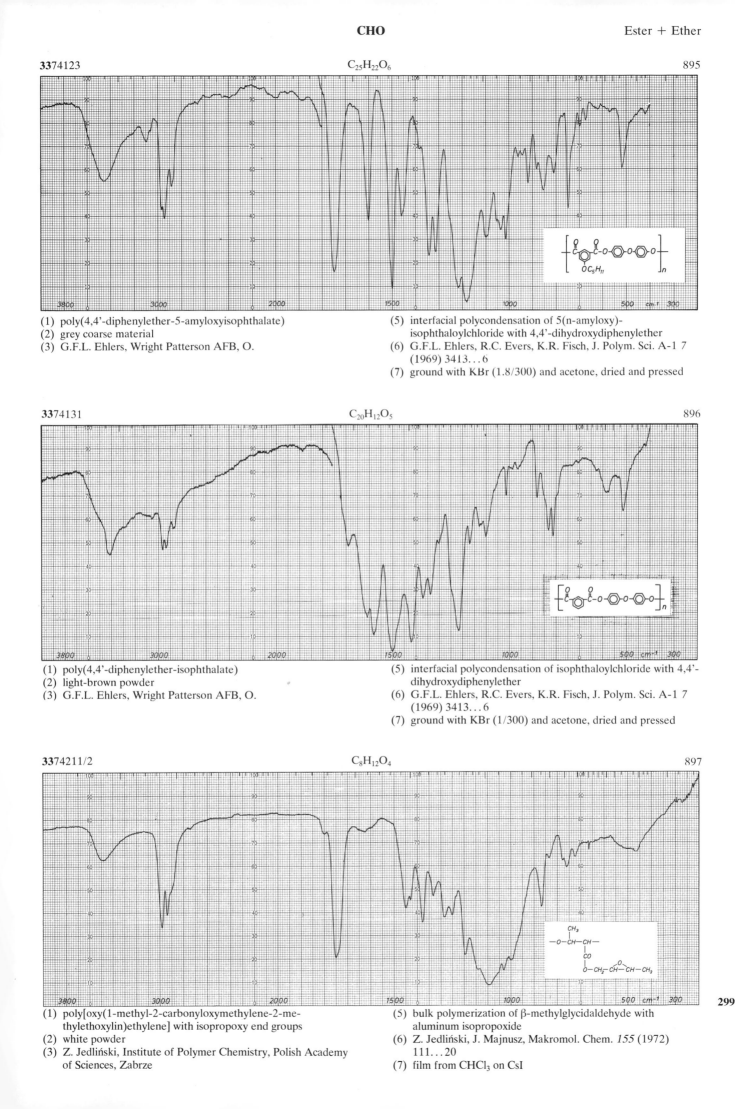

3374123 $C_{25}H_{22}O_6$ 895

(1) poly(4,4'-diphenylether-5-amyloxyisophthalate)
(2) grey coarse material
(3) G.F.L. Ehlers, Wright Patterson AFB, O.

(5) interfacial polycondensation of 5(n-amyloxy)-isophthaloylchloride with 4,4'-dihydroxydiphenylether
(6) G.F.L. Ehlers, R.C. Evers, K.R. Fisch, J. Polym. Sci. A-1 7 (1969) 3413...6
(7) ground with KBr (1.8/300) and acetone, dried and pressed

3374131 $C_{20}H_{12}O_5$ 896

(1) poly(4,4'-diphenylether-isophthalate)
(2) light-brown powder
(3) G.F.L. Ehlers, Wright Patterson AFB, O.

(5) interfacial polycondensation of isophthaloylchloride with 4,4'-dihydroxydiphenylether
(6) G.F.L. Ehlers, R.C. Evers, K.R. Fisch, J. Polym. Sci. A-1 7 (1969) 3413...6
(7) ground with KBr (1/300) and acetone, dried and pressed

3374211/2 $C_8H_{12}O_4$ 897

(1) poly[oxy(1-methyl-2-carbonyloxymethylene-2-methylethoxylin)ethylene] with isopropoxy end groups
(2) white powder
(3) Z. Jedliński, Institute of Polymer Chemistry, Polish Academy of Sciences, Zabrze

(5) bulk polymerization of β-methylglycidaldehyde with aluminum isopropoxide
(6) Z. Jedliński, J. Majnusz, Makromol. Chem. 155 (1972) 111...20
(7) film from $CHCl_3$ on CsI

3374212 $C_{10}H_{16}O_4$ 898

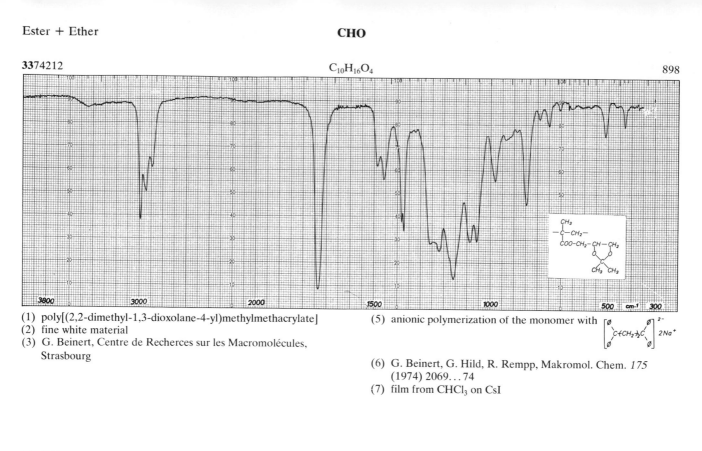

(1) poly[(2,2-dimethyl-1,3-dioxolane-4-yl)methylmethacrylate]
(2) fine white material
(3) G. Beinert, Centre de Recherces sur les Macromolécules, Strasbourg

(5) anionic polymerization of the monomer with
(6) G. Beinert, G. Hild, R. Rempp, Makromol. Chem. *175* (1974) 2069...74
(7) film from CHCl₃ on CsI

3374213 $C_{12}H_{16}O_8$ 899

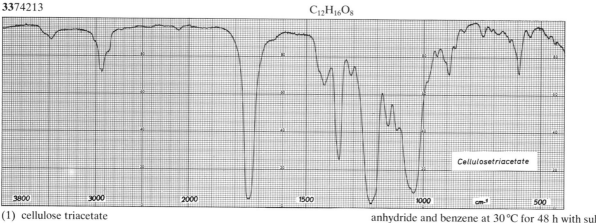

Cellulosetriacetate

(1) cellulose triacetate
(2) M. Takai, Department of Applied Chemistry, Faculty of Engineering, Hokkaido University, Sapporo
(5) acetylation of cellulose fibers in glacial acetic acid at 30 °C for 24 h, followed by acetylation in a 25:75 mixture of acetic

anhydride and benzene at 30 °C for 48 h with sulfuric acid as catalyst
(6) S. Watanabe, M. Takai, J. Hayashi, J. Polym. Sci. C *23* (1968) 825...33; S. Watanabe, J. Hayashi, K. Imai, ibid. 809...23
(7) film from CHCl₃ on KBr

3374213 $C_{12}H_{18}O_6$ 900

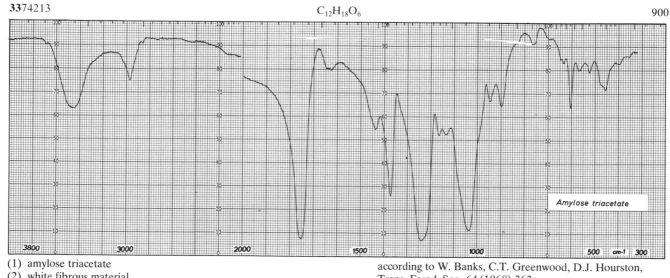

Amylose triacetate

(1) amylose triacetate
(2) white fibrous material
(3) C.T. Greenwood, Department of Chemistry, University of Edinburgh
(5) linear amylose from potatoe starch, fractionated from dimethylsulfoxide by addition of butanol, acetylation

according to W. Banks, C.T. Greenwood, D.J. Hourston, Trans. Farad. Soc. *64* (1968) 363
(6) W. Banks, C.T. Greenwood, Europ. Polym. J. *4* (1968) 457...64
(7) KBr (4/1000)

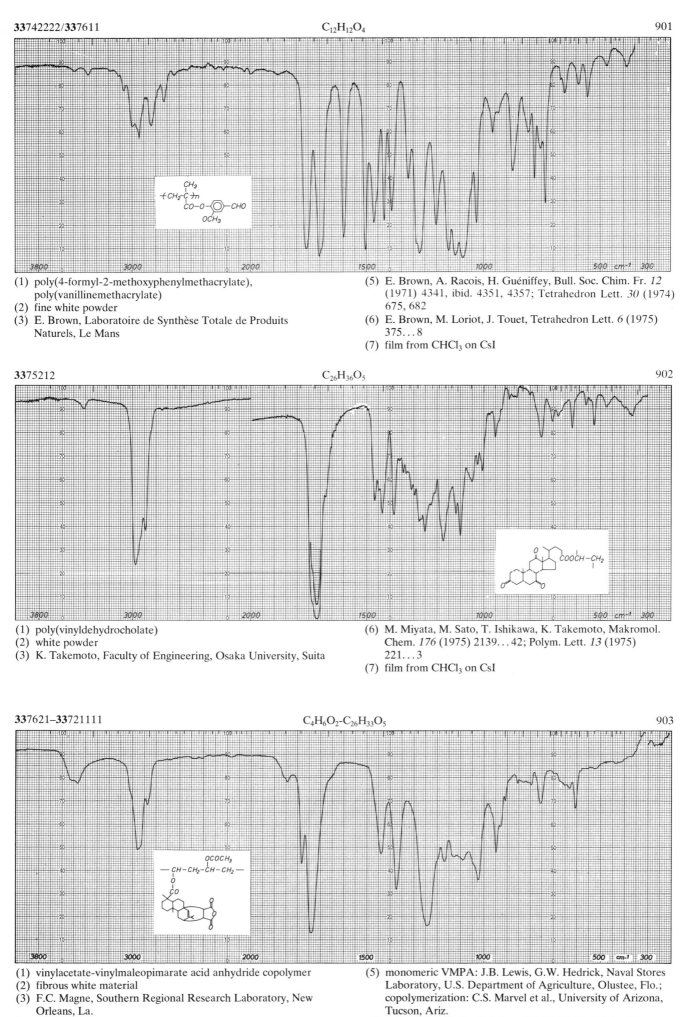

(1) poly(4-formyl-2-methoxyphenylmethacrylate),
poly(vanillinemethacrylate)
(2) fine white powder
(3) E. Brown, Laboratoire de Synthèse Totale de Produits
Naturels, Le Mans

(5) E. Brown, A. Racois, H. Guéniffey, Bull. Soc. Chim. Fr. *12*
(1971) 4341, ibid. 4351, 4357; Tetrahedron Lett. *30* (1974)
675, 682
(6) E. Brown, M. Loriot, J. Touet, Tetrahedron Lett. *6* (1975)
375...8
(7) film from CHCl_{3} on CsI

(1) poly(vinyldehydrocholate)
(2) white powder
(3) K. Takemoto, Faculty of Engineering, Osaka University, Suita

(6) M. Miyata, M. Sato, T. Ishikawa, K. Takemoto, Makromol.
Chem. *176* (1975) 2139...42; Polym. Lett. *13* (1975)
221...3
(7) film from CHCl_{3} on CsI

(1) vinylacetate-vinylmaleopimarate acid anhydride copolymer
(2) fibrous white material
(3) F.C. Magne, Southern Regional Research Laboratory, New
Orleans, La.
(4) 20% VMPA units in the copolymer

(5) monomeric VMPA: J.B. Lewis, G.W. Hedrick, Naval Stores
Laboratory, U.S. Department of Agriculture, Olustee, Flo.;
copolymerization: C.S. Marvel et al., University of Arizona,
Tucson, Ariz.
(6) F.C. Magne, J. Appl. Polym. Sci. *12* (1968) 2079...82
(7) film from CHCl_{3} on CsI

33773 $C_4H_2O_3$-C_3H_6O ($C_7H_8O_4$)   904

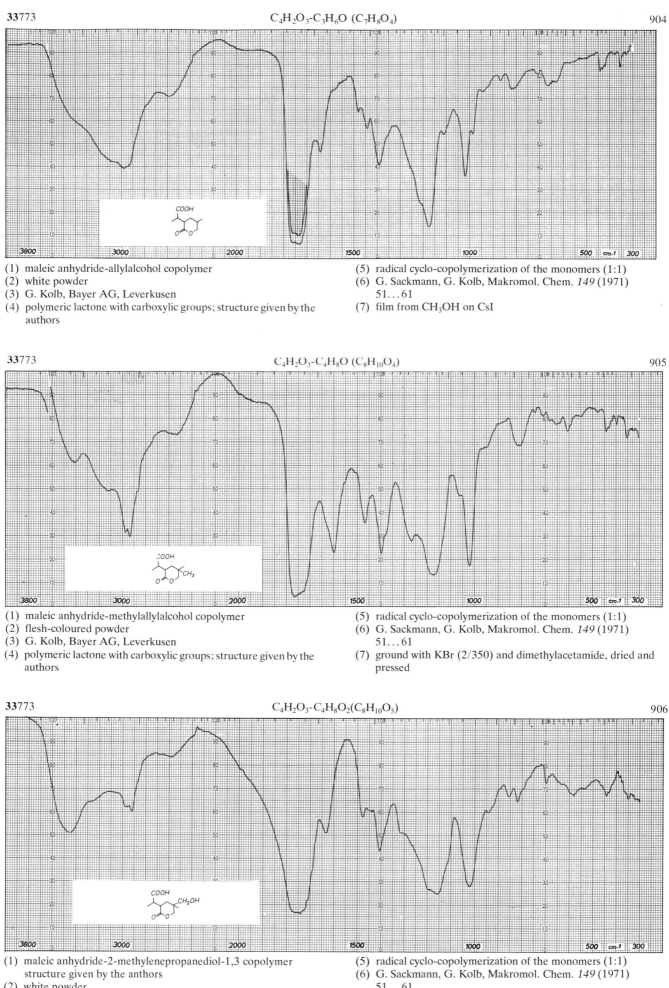

(1) maleic anhydride-allylalcohol copolymer
(2) white powder
(3) G. Kolb, Bayer AG, Leverkusen
(4) polymeric lactone with carboxylic groups; structure given by the authors

(5) radical cyclo-copolymerization of the monomers (1:1)
(6) G. Sackmann, G. Kolb, Makromol. Chem. *149* (1971) 51...61
(7) film from CH_3OH on CsI

33773 $C_4H_2O_3$-C_4H_8O ($C_8H_{10}O_4$)   905

(1) maleic anhydride-methylallylalcohol copolymer
(2) flesh-coloured powder
(3) G. Kolb, Bayer AG, Leverkusen
(4) polymeric lactone with carboxylic groups; structure given by the authors

(5) radical cyclo-copolymerization of the monomers (1:1)
(6) G. Sackmann, G. Kolb, Makromol. Chem. *149* (1971) 51...61
(7) ground with KBr (2/350) and dimethylacetamide, dried and pressed

33773 $C_4H_2O_3$-$C_4H_8O_2$($C_8H_{10}O_5$)   906

(1) maleic anhydride-2-methylenepropanediol-1,3 copolymer structure given by the anthors
(2) white powder
(3) G. Kolb, Bayer AG, Leverkusen
(4) polymeric lactone with carboxylic and alcoholic groups; structure given by the authors

(5) radical cyclo-copolymerization of the monomers (1:1)
(6) G. Sackmann, G. Kolb, Makromol. Chem. *149* (1971) 51...61
(7) KBr (2/350)

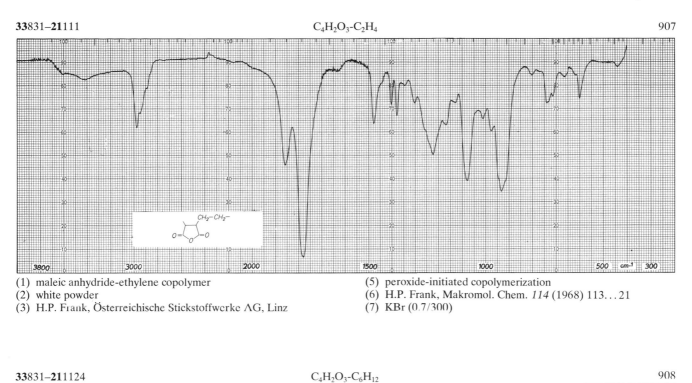

(1) maleic anhydride-ethylene copolymer
(2) white powder
(3) H.P. Frank, Österreichische Stickstoffwerke AG, Linz

(5) peroxide-initiated copolymerization
(6) H.P. Frank, Makromol. Chem. *114* (1968) 113...21
(7) KBr (0.7/300)

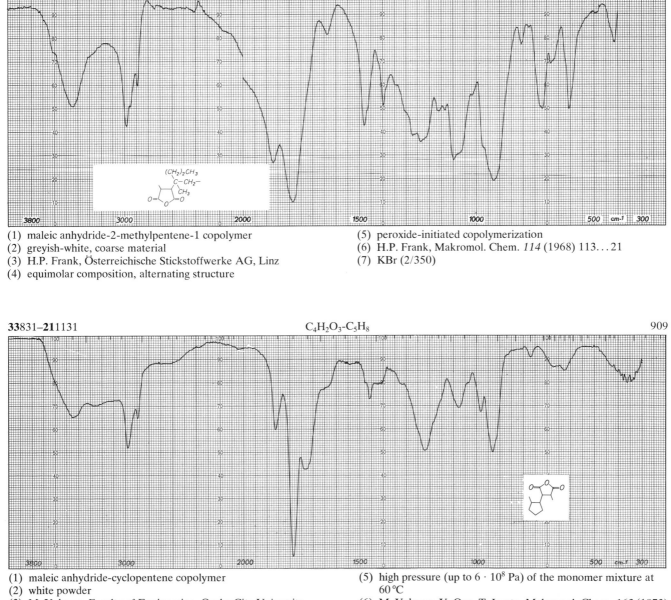

(1) maleic anhydride-2-methylpentene-1 copolymer
(2) greyish-white, coarse material
(3) H.P. Frank, Österreichische Stickstoffwerke AG, Linz
(4) equimolar composition, alternating structure

(5) peroxide-initiated copolymerization
(6) H.P. Frank, Makromol. Chem. *114* (1968) 113...21
(7) KBr (2/350)

(1) maleic anhydride-cyclopentene copolymer
(2) white powder
(3) M. Yokawa, Faculty of Engineering, Osaka City University, Osaka
(4) almost equimolar composition

(5) high pressure (up to 6 · 10⁸ Pa) of the monomer mixture at 60 °C
(6) M. Yokawa, Y. Ogo, T. Imoto, Makromol. Chem. *163* (1973) 135...42
(7) KBr (1/350)

33831–2122111 $C_4H_2O_3$–C_8H_8 910

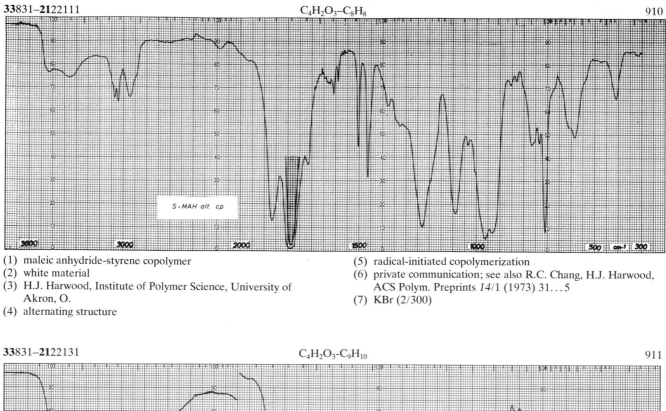

S - MAH alt. cp

(1) maleic anhydride-styrene copolymer
(2) white material
(3) H.J. Harwood, Institute of Polymer Science, University of Akron, O.
(4) alternating structure

(5) radical-initiated copolymerization
(6) private communication; see also R.C. Chang, H.J. Harwood, ACS Polym. Preprints *14*/1 (1973) 31...5
(7) KBr (2/300)

33831–2122131 $C_4H_2O_3$-C_9H_{10} 911

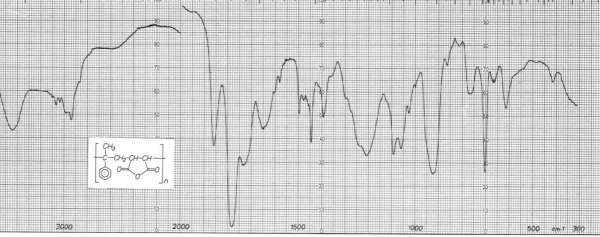

(1) maleic anhydride-α-methylstyrene copolymer
(2) white coarse material
(3) R.B. Seymor, Department of Chemistry, University of Houston, Houston, Tex.
(4) equimolar composition, alternating structure

(5) copolymerization of the monomer mixture in decalin with AIBN; see also K. Oshima, Kogyo Kagaku Zasshi, *67* (1964) 2159
(6) R.B. Seymor, D.P. Garner, Polymer *17* (1976) 21...4
(7) ground with KBr (1/350) and acetone, dried and pressed

33831–3331211 $C_4H_2O_3$-$C_6H_{12}O$ 912

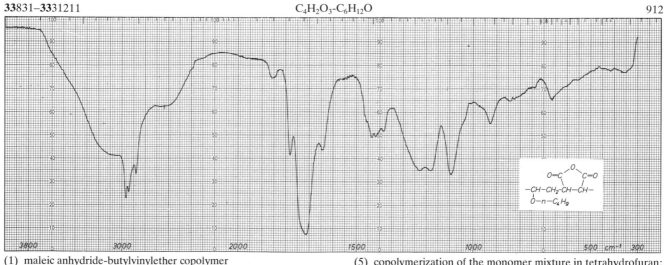

(1) maleic anhydride-butylvinylether copolymer
(2) white powder
(3) P.L. Dubin, Rutgers University, New Brunswick, N.J.; F.E. Treloar, Chemistry School, University of Melbourne, Parkville, Victoria

(5) copolymerization of the monomer mixture in tetrahydrofuran; see P.L. Dubin, U.P. Strauss, J. Phys. Chem. *74* (1970) 2842
(6) P.J. Kay, D.P. Kelly, G.I. Milgate, F.E. Treloar, Macromol. Chem. *177* (1976) 885...93
(7) film from tetrahydrofuran on CsI

342111   CH₂S   913

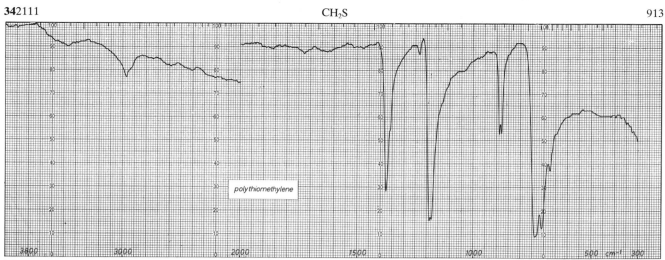

polythiomethylene

(1) poly(thiomethylene)
(2) white powder
(3) J.-I. Takeda, Department of Polymer Chemistry, Faculty of Engineering, Kyoto University, Kyoto
(4) -S-CH₂-

(5) catalytic solid-state polymerization of trithiane at 180 °C; catalysts: e.g., halogen, HCl, metal halides
(6) J.-I. Takeda, K. Hayashi, S. Okamura, J. Appl. Polym. Sci. *13* (1969) 1435...46
(7) ground with CsBr (3/500) and toluene, dried and pressed
(8) polymerized by bromine

342111   CH₂S   914

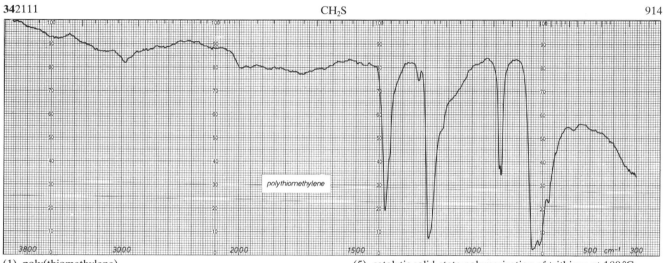

polythiomethylene

(1) poly(thiomethylene)
(2) white powder
(3) J.-I. Takeda, Department of Polymer Chemistry, Faculty of Engineering, Kyoto University, Kyoto
(4) -S-CH₂-

(5) catalytic solid-state polymerization of trithiane at 180 °C; catalysts: e.g., halogen, HCl, metal halides
(6) J.-I. Takeda, K. Hayashi, S. Okamura, J. Appl. Polym. Sci. *13* (1969) 1435...46
(7) ground with CsBr (3/500) and toluene, dried and pressed
(8) polymerized by benzylchloride

342111   C₂H₄S   915

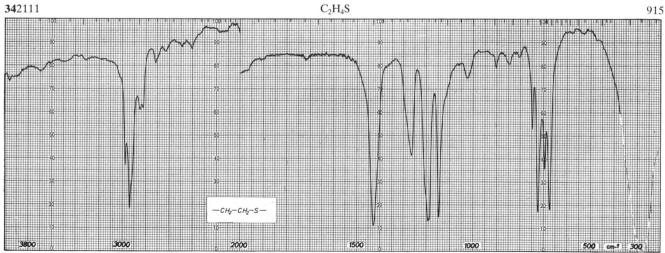

—CH₂—CH₂—S—

(1) poly(thioethylene)
(2) white, coarse powder
(3) A. Nicco, Société Ethylène Plastique, Centre de Recherches, F-62 Mazingarbe

(5) S. Boileau, J. Coste, J.N. Raynal, P. Sigwalt, C.R. hebd. Séanc. Acad. Sci. *254* (1962) 2774...6
(6) A. Nicco, J.P. Machon, H. Fremaux, J.Ph. Pied, B. Zindy, M. Thiery, Europ. Polym. J. *6* (1970) 1427...35
(7) film between KBr (pressed at 240 °C)

342111 C_2H_4S 916

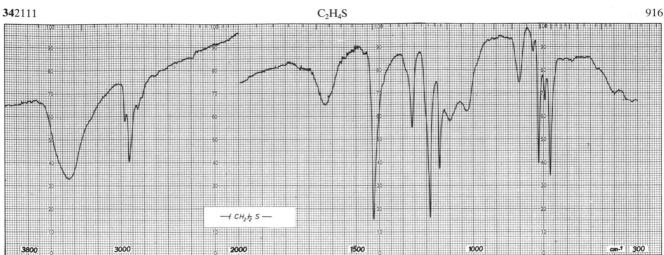

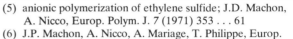

(1) poly(thioethylene)
(2) white powder
(3) J.P. Machon, Centre de Recherches, Société Ethylène
     Plastique, F-62 Mazingarbe

(5) anionic polymerization of ethylene sulfide; J.D. Machon,
     A. Nicco, Europ. Polym. J. 7 (1971) 353 . . . 61
(6) J.P. Machon, A. Nicco, A. Mariage, T. Philippe, Europ.
     Polym. J. *8* (1972) 547...59
(7) KBr (2.5/350)

342111 C_2H_4S 917

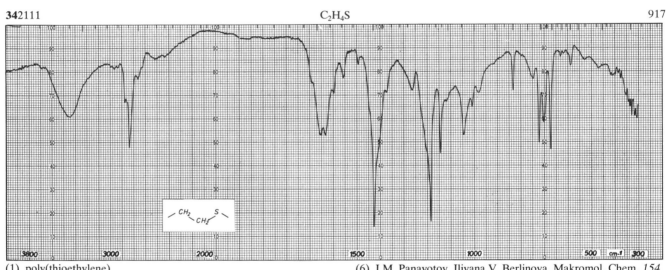

(1) poly(thioethylene)
(2) white powder
(3) I.M. Panayotov, Institute of Organic Chemistry, Bulgarian
     Academy of Sciences, Sofia
(5) polymerization of ethylene sulfide with an alkali metal
     complex of an aromatic nitrile or ketone, e.g., the anion
     radical from benzophenone and kalium

(6) I.M. Panayotov, Iliyana V. Berlinova, Makromol. Chem. *154*
     (1972) 139...49
(7) KBr (2/350)
(8) contains probably residual catalyst (carbonyl absorptions near
     1650 cm^{-1}, aromatic absorpitions, especially the one at
     833 cm^{-1})

342111 C_2H_4S 918

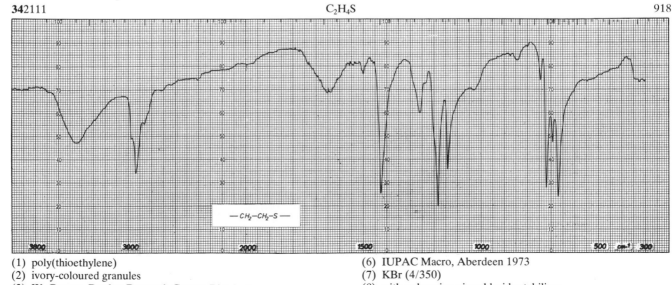

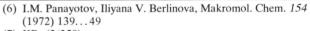

(1) poly(thioethylene)
(2) ivory-coloured granules
(3) W. Cooper, Dunlop Research Center, Birmingham

(6) IUPAC Macro, Aberdeen 1973
(7) KBr (4/350)
(8) with polyamine-zinc chloride stabilizer

342111   C₃H₆S   919

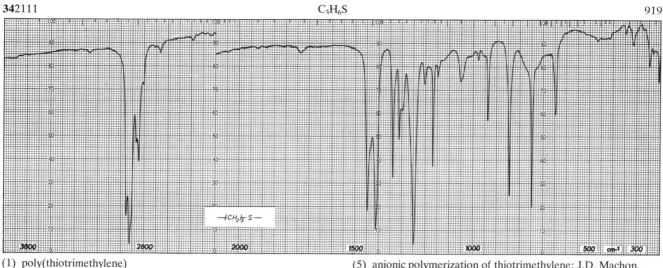

(1) poly(thiotrimethylene)
(2) white fibrous material
(3) J.P. Machon, Centre de Recherches, Société Ethylène Plastique, F-62 Mazingarbe

(5) anionic polymerization of thiotrimethylene; J.D. Machon, A. Nicco, Europ. Polym. J. 7 (1971) 353...61
(6) J.P. Machon, A. Nicco, A. Mariage, T. Philippe, Europ. Polym. J. 8 (1972) 547...59
(7) film from CHCl₃ on CsI

342112   C₃H₆S   920

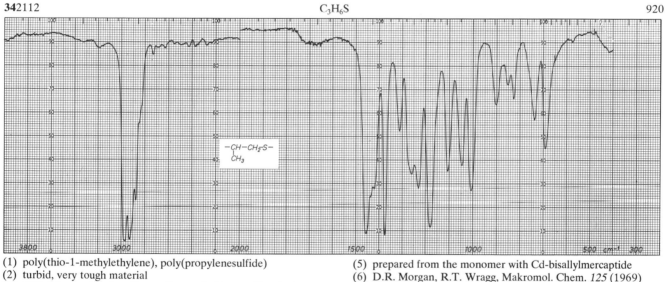

(1) poly(thio-1-methylethylene), poly(propylenesulfide)
(2) turbid, very tough material
(3) D.R. Morgan, Dunlop Comp., Research Centre, Chemical Research Dept., Erdingthon, Birmingham

(5) prepared from the monomer with Cd-bisallylmercaptide
(6) D.R. Morgan, R.T. Wragg, Makromol. Chem. 125 (1969) 220...30
(7) film from benzene on KBr

342112   C₃H₆S   921

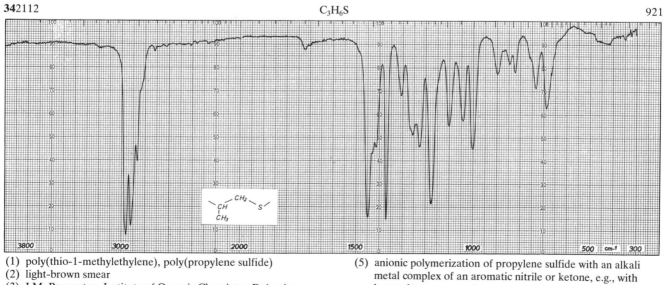

(1) poly(thio-1-methylethylene), poly(propylene sulfide)
(2) light-brown smear
(3) I.M. Panayotov, Institute of Organic Chemistry, Bulgarian Academy of Sciences, Sofia

(5) anionic polymerization of propylene sulfide with an alkali metal complex of an aromatic nitrile or ketone, e.g., with benzophenone-potassium complex
(6) I.M. Panayotov, Iliyana V. Berlinova, Makromol. Chem. 154 (1972) 139...49
(7) film from CHCl₃ on CsI

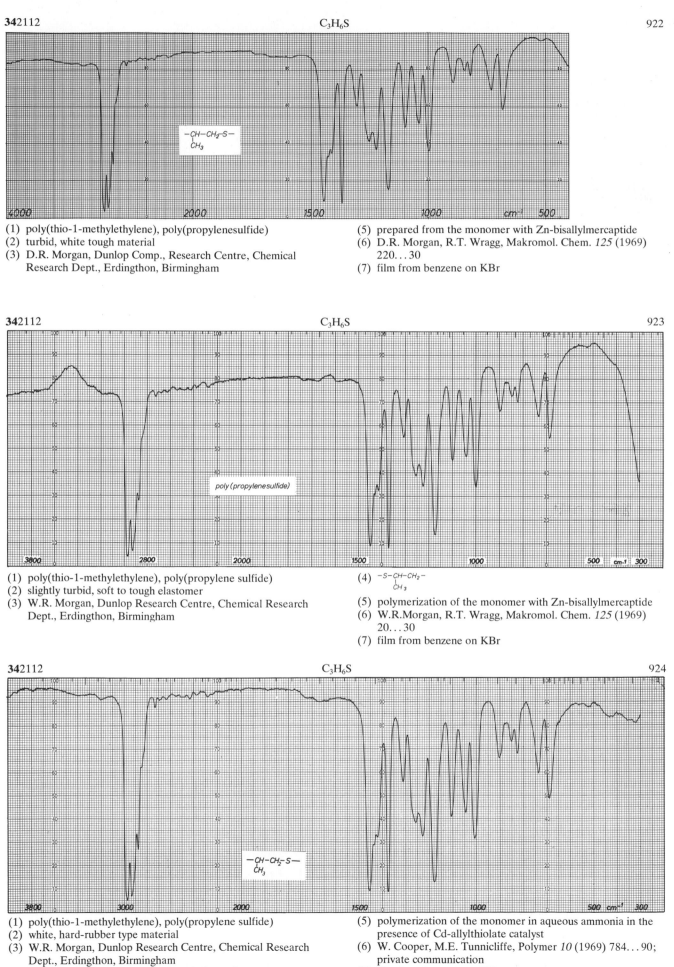

342112   C₃H₆S   922

−CH−CH₂−S−
  |
  CH₃

(1) poly(thio-1-methylethylene), poly(propylenesulfide)
(2) turbid, white tough material
(3) D.R. Morgan, Dunlop Comp., Research Centre, Chemical
    Research Dept., Erdingthon, Birmingham
(5) prepared from the monomer with Zn-bisallylmercaptide
(6) D.R. Morgan, R.T. Wragg, Makromol. Chem. *125* (1969)
    220...30
(7) film from benzene on KBr

342112   C₃H₆S   923

poly (propylenesulfide)

(1) poly(thio-1-methylethylene), poly(propylene sulfide)
(2) slightly turbid, soft to tough elastomer
(3) W.R. Morgan, Dunlop Research Centre, Chemical Research
    Dept., Erdingthon, Birmingham
(4) −S−CH−CH₂−
        |
        CH₃
(5) polymerization of the monomer with Zn-bisallylmercaptide
(6) W.R.Morgan, R.T. Wragg, Makromol. Chem. *125* (1969)
    20...30
(7) film from benzene on KBr

342112   C₃H₆S   924

−CH−CH₂−S−
  |
  CH₃

(1) poly(thio-1-methylethylene), poly(propylene sulfide)
(2) white, hard-rubber type material
(3) W.R. Morgan, Dunlop Research Centre, Chemical Research
    Dept., Erdingthon, Birmingham
(4) partly crystalline, with predominantly isotactic structure
(5) polymerization of the monomer in aqueous ammonia in the
    presence of Cd-allylthiolate catalyst
(6) W. Cooper, M.E. Tunnicliffe, Polymer *10* (1969) 784...90;
    private communication
(7) film from benzene on KBr

342112   C$_3$H$_6$S   925

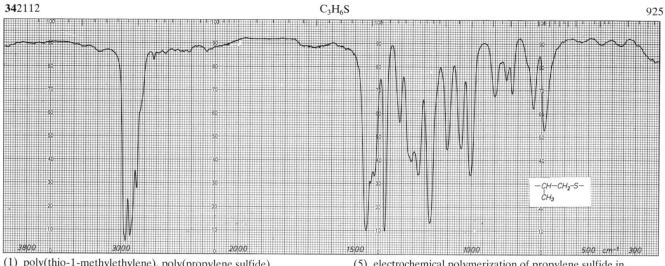

(1) poly(thio-1-methylethylene), poly(propylene sulfide)
(2) slightly coloured, clear elastomer
(3) G. Mengoli, Laboratorio di Polarografia ed Elettrochimica Preparativa del C.N.R., Padova

(5) electrochemical polymerization of propylene sulfide in dimethylformamide in the presence of tetrabutylamonium and natrium counterions
(6) G. Mengoli, S. Daolio, Polym. Lett. *13* (1975) 743...51
(7) film from CS$_2$ on CsI

342112   C$_3$H$_6$S   926

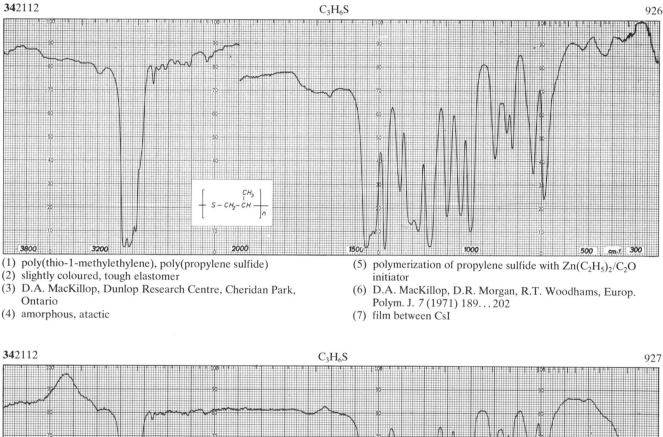

(1) poly(thio-1-methylethylene), poly(propylene sulfide)
(2) slightly coloured, tough elastomer
(3) D.A. MacKillop, Dunlop Research Centre, Cheridan Park, Ontario
(4) amorphous, atactic

(5) polymerization of propylene sulfide with Zn(C$_2$H$_5$)$_2$/C$_2$O initiator
(6) D.A. MacKillop, D.R. Morgan, R.T. Woodhams, Europ. Polym. J. *7* (1971) 189...202
(7) film between CsI

342112   C$_3$H$_6$S   927

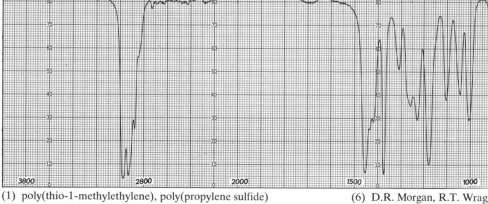

(1) poly(thio-1-methylethylene), poly(propylene sulfide)
(2) milky-turbid, very tough material
(3) D.R. Morgan, Dunlop Research Centre, Birmingham
(5) polymerization of propylene sulfide with Cd-bisallylmercaptide

(6) D.R. Morgan, R.T. Wragg, Makromol. Chem. *125* (1969) 220...30
(7) film from benzene on KBr
(8) absorption increase beyond 400 cm^{-1} due to KBr

342112   C_3H_6S   928

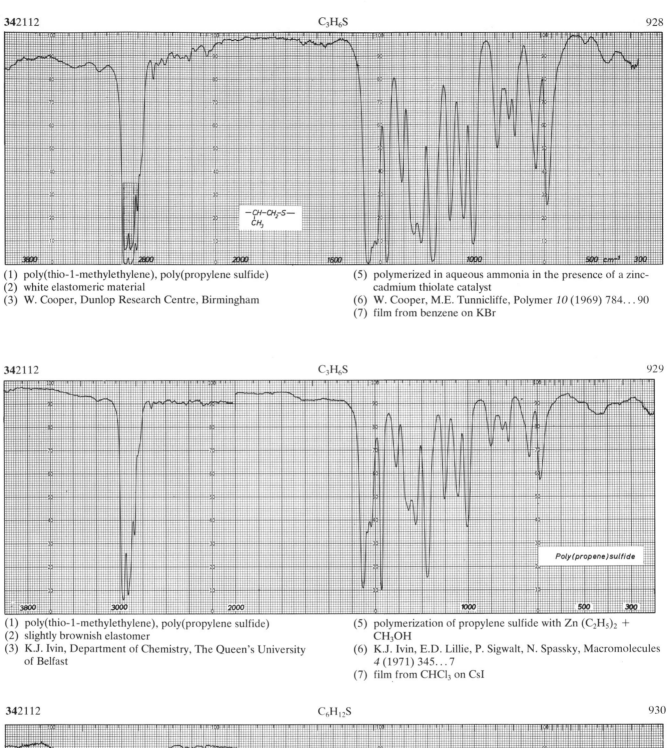

−CH−CH_2−S−
CH_3

(1) poly(thio-1-methylethylene), poly(propylene sulfide)
(2) white elastomeric material
(3) W. Cooper, Dunlop Research Centre, Birmingham

(5) polymerized in aqueous ammonia in the presence of a zinc-cadmium thiolate catalyst
(6) W. Cooper, M.E. Tunnicliffe, Polymer *10* (1969) 784...90
(7) film from benzene on KBr

342112   C_3H_6S   929

Poly(propene)sulfide

(1) poly(thio-1-methylethylene), poly(propylene sulfide)
(2) slightly brownish elastomer
(3) K.J. Ivin, Department of Chemistry, The Queen's University of Belfast

(5) polymerization of propylene sulfide with Zn (C_2H_5)_2 + CH_3OH
(6) K.J. Ivin, E.D. Lillie, P. Sigwalt, N. Spassky, Macromolecules *4* (1971) 345...7
(7) film from CHCl_3 on CsI

342112   C_6H_12S   930

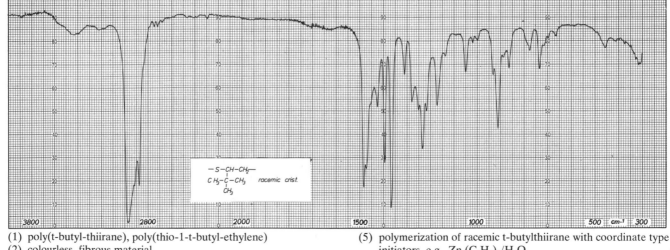

−S−CH−CH_2−
CH_3−C−CH_3   *racemic crist.*
CH_3

310

(1) poly(t-butyl-thiirane), poly(thio-1-t-butyl-ethylene)
(2) colourless, fibrous material
(3) Ph. Dumas, Laboratoire de Chimie Macromoléculaire, Université de Paris, Paris 5^e
(4) racemic, crystalline

(5) polymerization of racemic t-butylthiirane with coordinate type initiators, e.g., Zn (C_2H_5)_2/H_2O
(6) P. Dumas, N. Spassky, P. Sigwalt, Makromol. Chem. *156* (1972) 55...64
(7) KBr (2/350)

342112   C₆H₁₁S   931

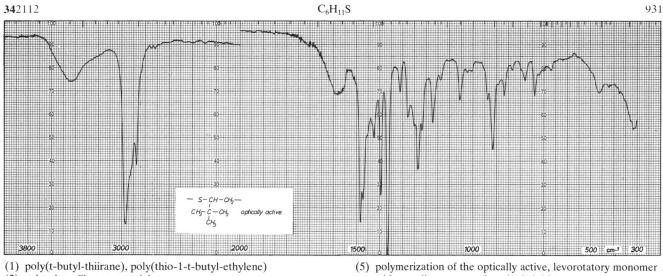

(1) poly(t-butyl-thiirane), poly(thio-1-t-butyl-ethylene)
(2) colourless, fibrous material
(3) Ph. Dumas, Laboratoire de Chimie Macromoléculaire,
    Université de Paris, Paris 5ᵉ
(4) levorotatory, crystalline polymer

(5) polymerization of the optically active, levorotatory monomer
    with coordinate or purely anionic initiators
(6) P. Dumas, N. Spassky, P. Sigwalt, Makromol. Chem. *156*
    (1972) 55...64
(7) KBr (2/350)

342112   C₆H₁₁S   932

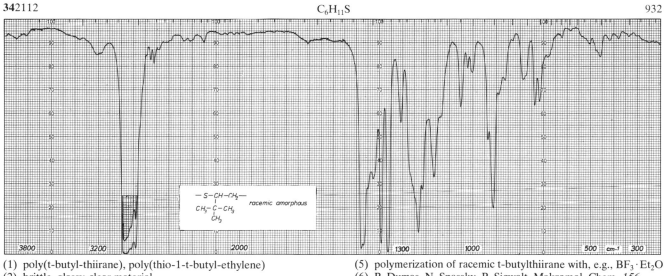

(1) poly(t-butyl-thiirane), poly(thio-1-t-butyl-ethylene)
(2) brittle, glassy-clear material
(3) Ph. Dumas, Laboratoire de Chimie Macromoléculaire,
    Université de Paris, Paris 5ᵉ
(4) racemic, amorphous

(5) polymerization of racemic t-butylthiirane with, e.g., BF₃·Et₂O
(6) P. Dumas, N. Spassky, P. Sigwalt, Makromol. Chem. *156*
    (1972) 55...64
(7) film from CHCl₃ on CsI

342112   C₄H₈S   933

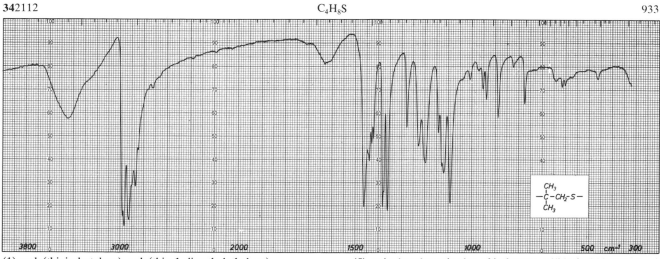

(1) poly(thioisobutylene), poly(thio-1-dimethylethylene)
(2) eggshell-coloured powder
(3) S. Boileau, Laboratoire de Chimie Macromoléculaire, Faculté
    des Sciences de Paris, Paris
(4) crystalline

(5) anionic polymerization of isobutene sulfide (epithioisobutane)
(6) S. Boileau, P. Sigwalt, Makromol. Chem. *131* (1970) 7...13
(7) KBr (2.2/350)

342112 $C_5H_{10}S$ 934

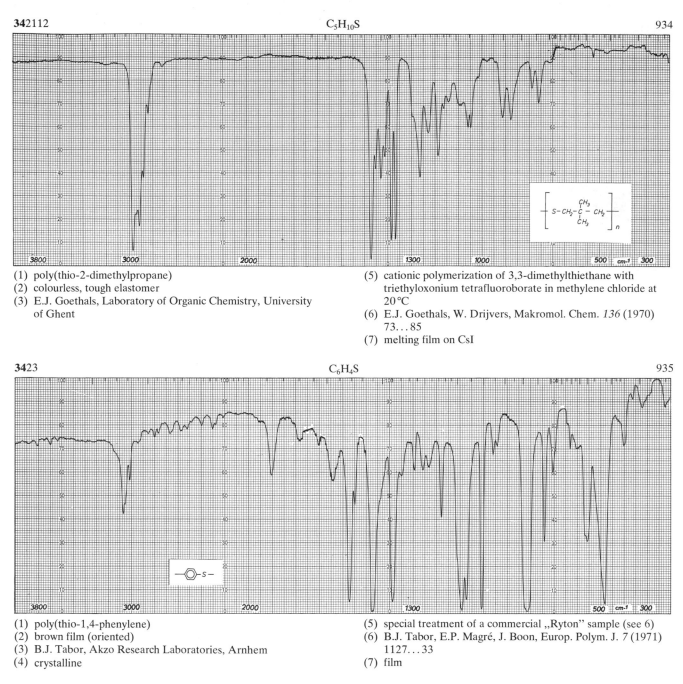

(1) poly(thio-2-dimethylpropane)
(2) colourless, tough elastomer
(3) E.J. Goethals, Laboratory of Organic Chemistry, University of Ghent

(5) cationic polymerization of 3,3-dimethylthiethane with triethyloxonium tetrafluoroborate in methylene chloride at 20 °C
(6) E.J. Goethals, W. Drijvers, Makromol. Chem. *136* (1970) 73...85
(7) melting film on CsI

3423 C_6H_4S 935

(1) poly(thio-1,4-phenylene)
(2) brown film (oriented)
(3) B.J. Tabor, Akzo Research Laboratories, Arnhem
(4) crystalline

(5) special treatment of a commercial „Ryton" sample (see 6)
(6) B.J. Tabor, E.P. Magré, J. Boon, Europ. Polym. J. 7 (1971) 1127...33
(7) film

3423 C_6H_4S 936

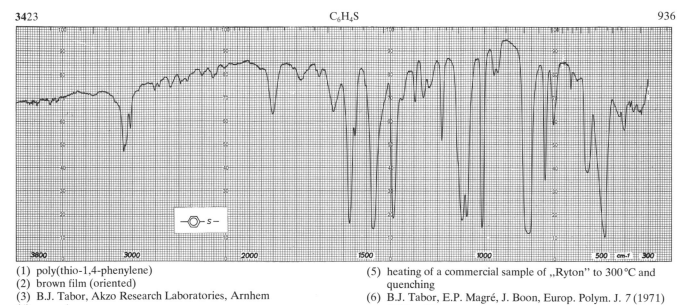

(1) poly(thio-1,4-phenylene)
(2) brown film (oriented)
(3) B.J. Tabor, Akzo Research Laboratories, Arnhem
(4) amorphous

(5) heating of a commercial sample of „Ryton" to 300 °C and quenching
(6) B.J. Tabor, E.P. Magré, J. Boon, Europ. Polym. J. 7 (1971) 1127...33
(7) film (scratched)'

3423   C$_6$H$_4$S   937

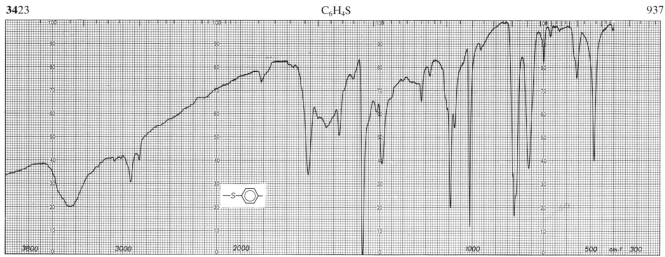

(1) poly(thio-1,4-phenylene)
(2) light-yellow powder
(3) J.M. Barrales-Rienda, Instituto de Plásticos y Caucho, Madrid

(6) J.M. Barrales-Rienda, IUPAC Macro, Aberdeen 1973
(7) ground with KBr (1/350) and CHCl$_3$, dried and pressed

3423   C$_6$H$_4$S   938

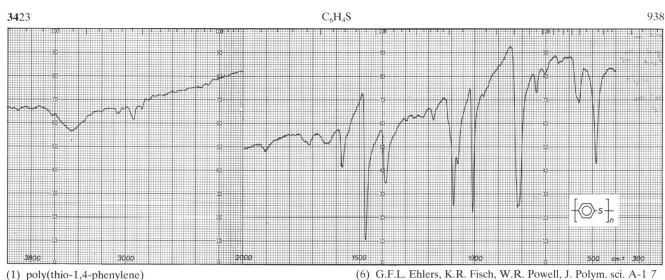

(1) poly(thio-1,4-phenylene)
(2) grey powder
(3) G.F.L. Ehlers, Wright Patterson AFB, Ohio
(5) heating of cuprous p-bromothiophenoxide in sealed ampoules under argon at 200 °C for two days (synthesis by H.A. Smith and C.E. Handlovits)

(6) G.F.L. Ehlers, K.R. Fisch, W.R. Powell, J. Polym. sci. A-1 7 (1969) 2955...67
(7) ground with KBr (2.2/300) and acetone, dried and pressed

3423-32235 (**42**223235)   C$_{12}$H$_8$S$_2$-C$_7$H$_3$N   939

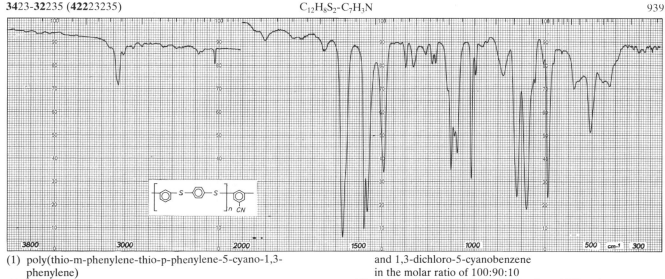

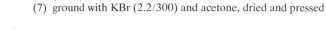

(1) poly(thio-m-phenylene-thio-p-phenylene-5-cyano-1,3-phenylene)
(2) greyish-white powder
(3) C.S. Marvel, Department of Chemistry, University of Arizona, Tucson, Ariz.
(5) polycondensation of m-dimercaptobenzene, p-dibromobenzene

and 1,3-dichloro-5-cyanobenzene in the molar ratio of 100:90:10
(6) C.S. Marvel, IUPAC Macro, Aberdeen 1973; private communication
(7) film from CHCl$_3$ on CsI

344111 $C_2H_4S_2$ 940

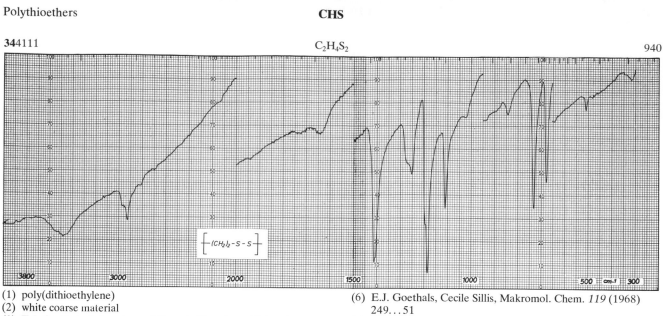

(1) poly(dithioethylene)
(2) white coarse material
(3) E.J. Goethals, Laboratory of Organic Chemistry, University of Ghent
(5) oxidative polycondensation of ethane-1,2-dithiol with dimethylsulfoxide

(6) E.J. Goethals, Cecile Sillis, Makromol. Chem. *119* (1968) 249...51
(7) KBr (3.5/300)

344111 $C_6H_{12}S_2$ 941

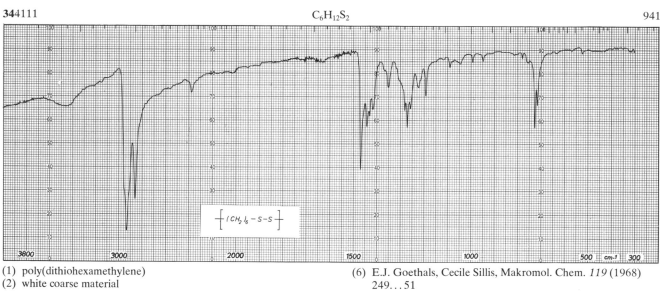
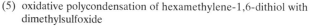

(1) poly(dithiohexamethylene)
(2) white coarse material
(3) E.J. Goethals, Laboratory of Organic Chemistry, University of Ghent
(5) oxidative polycondensation of hexamethylene-1,6-dithiol with dimethylsulfoxide

(6) E.J. Goethals, Cecile Sillis, Makromol. Chem. *119* (1968) 249...51
(7) KBr (2.5/350)

344111 $C_{10}H_{20}S_2$ 942

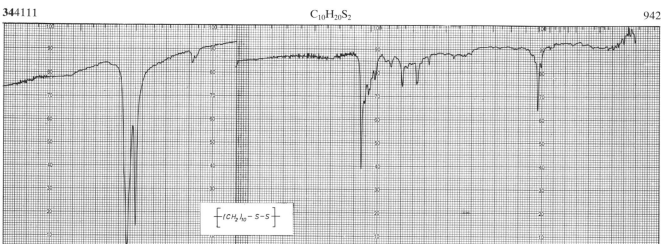

(1) poly(dithiodecamethylene)
(2) white coarse material
(3) E.J. Goethals, Laboratory of Organic Chemistry, University of Ghent
(5) oxidative polycondensation of decamethylene-1,10-dithiol

(6) E.J. Goethals, Cecile Sillis, Makromol. Chem. *119* (1968) 249...51
(7) KBr (1/300)

344212 $C_{18}H_{20}S_4$ 943

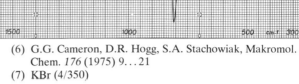

(1) poly(hexamethylene-dithio-1,4-diphenylene-dithioether
(2) yellowish powder
(3) G.G. Cameron, Department of Chemistry, University of Aberdeen, Old Aberdeen
(5) polycondensation of 4,4'-diphenyldisulfenylchloride with hexamethylene-1,6-dithiol

(6) G.G. Cameron, D.R. Hogg, S.A. Stachowiak, Makromol. Chem. *176* (1975) 9...21
(7) KBr (4/350)

344213 $C_{19}H_{14}S_4$ 944

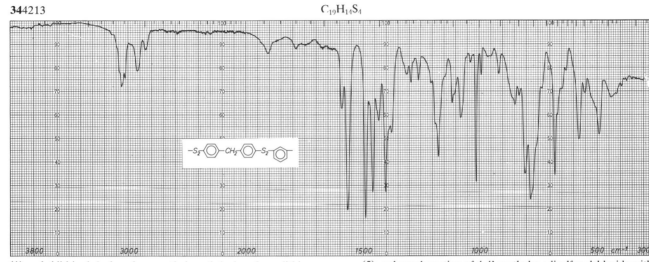

(1) poly(dithio-1,4-phenylene-methylene-1,4-phenylene-dithio-1,3-phenylene)
(2) yellowish powder
(3) G.G. Cameron, Department of Chemistry, University of Aberdeen, Old Aberdeen

(5) polycondensation of 4,4'-methylenedisulfenylchloride with 1,3-dimercaptobenzene
(6) G.G. Cameron, D.R. Hogg, S.A. Stachowiak, Makromol. Chem. *176* (1975) 9...21
(7) film from CHCl$_3$ on CsI

344213–**4142** $C_{13}H_{10}S_2$-$C_6H_3ClS_2$ 945

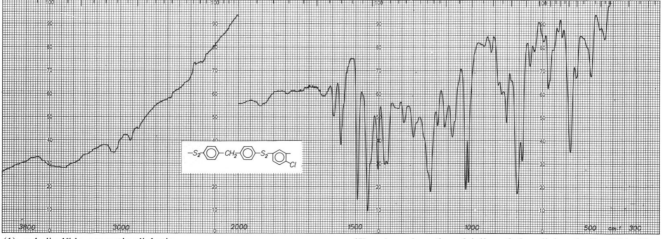

(1) polydisulfide, aromatic-aliphatic
(2) white powder
(3) G.G. Cameron, Department of Chemistry, University of Aberdeen, Old Aberdeen
(4) alternating structure

(5) polycondensation of 4,4'-methylenediphenylsulfenylchloride with 2-chlorobenzene-1,5-dithiol
(6) private communication; see also G.G. Cameron, S.A. Stachowiak, Makromol. Chem. *176* (1975) 1523...8
(7) KBr (3/350)

3443 C$_{12}$H$_8$S$_2$ 946

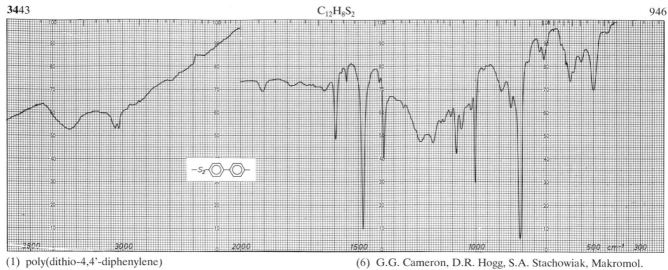

(1) poly(dithio-4,4'-diphenylene)
(2) yellowish powder
(3) G.G. Cameron, Department of Chemistry, University of Aberdeen, Old Aberdeen
(5) reductive polycondensation of biphenyldisulfenylchloride with lithium metal

(6) G.G. Cameron, D.R. Hogg, S.A. Stachowiak, Makromol. Chem. *176* (1975) 9...21
(7) KBr (2/350)

348112 C$_{14}$H$_{10}$S 947

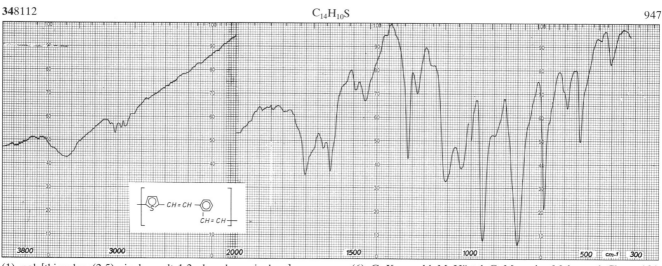

(1) poly[thienylene(2,5)-vinylene-alt-1,2-phenylene-vinylene]
(2) light-brown powder
(3) G. Koßmehl, Organisch-Chemisches Institut, FU Berlin
(5) polycondensation of 2,5-bis(triphenylphosphoniomethyl)thiophenedichloride with phthalic aldehyde

(6) G. Kossmehl, M. Härtel, G. Manecke, Makromol. Chem. 131 (1970) 37...54
(7) KBr (0.8/350, 4/350)

348112 C$_{14}$H$_{10}$S 948

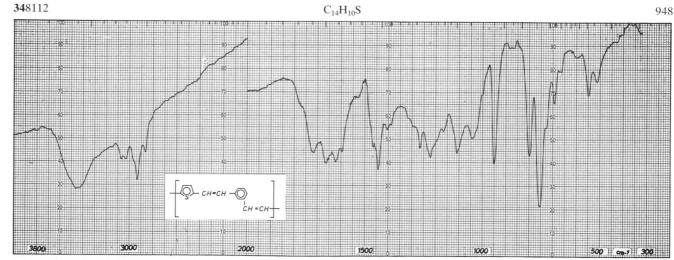

(1) poly[thienylene(2,5)-vinylene-alt-1,3-phenylene-vinylene]
(2) red-brown powder
(3) G. Koßmehl, Organisch-Chemisches Institut, FU Berlin
(5) polycondensation of 2,5-bis(triphenylphosphoniomethyl)thiophenedichloride with isophthalic aldehyde

(6) G. Kossmehl, M. Härtel, G. Manecke, Makromol. Chem. 131 (1970) 37...54
(7) KBr (4/350)

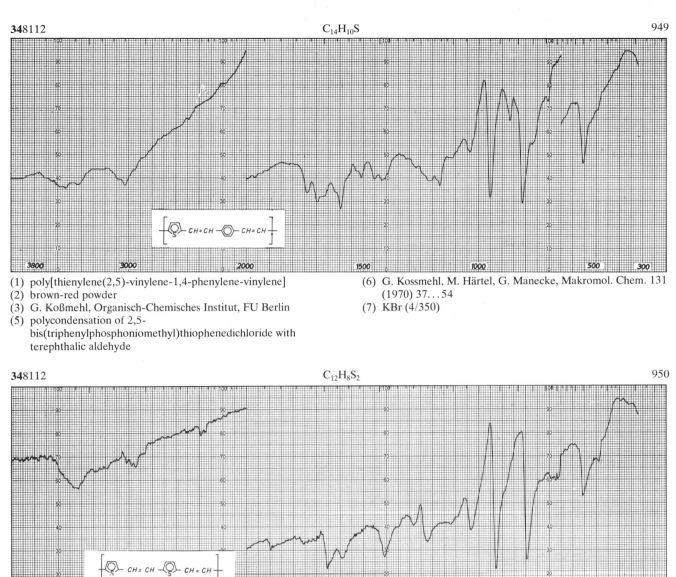

(1) poly[thienylene(2,5)-vinylene-1,4-phenylene-vinylene]
(2) brown-red powder
(3) G. Koßmehl, Organisch-Chemisches Institut, FU Berlin
(5) polycondensation of 2,5-bis(triphenylphosphoniomethyl)thiophenedichloride with terephthalic aldehyde

(6) G. Kossmehl, M. Härtel, G. Manecke, Makromol. Chem. 131 (1970) 37...54
(7) KBr (4/350)

(1) poly[thienylene(2,5)-vinylene]
(2) black powder
(3) G. Koßmehl, Organisch-Chemisches Institut, FU Berlin
(5) polycondensation of 2,5-bis-(triphenylphosphoniomethyl)thiophene dichloride with thiophene-2,5-dialdehyde (Wittig reaction)

(6) G. Kossmehl, M. Härtel, G. Manecke, Makromol. Chem. 131 (1970) 15...36
(7) KBr (2/350), ordinate expanded

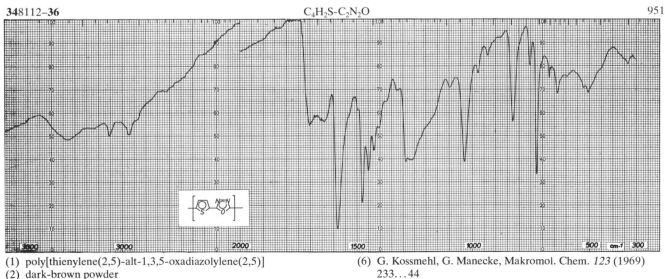

(1) poly[thienylene(2,5)-alt-1,3,5-oxadiazolylene(2,5)]
(2) dark-brown powder
(3) G. Koßmehl, Organisch-Chemisches Institut, FU Berlin
(5) cyclodihydration of polymeric thiophene-2,5-dicarboxylic acid hydrazide; the latter was obtained by polycondensation of the dihydrazide and the dichloride of thiophene-2,5-dicarboxylic acid

(6) G. Kossmehl, G. Manecke, Makromol. Chem. 123 (1969) 233...44
(7) ground with KBr (2/300) and dimethylacetamide, dried and pressed

35111 C_2F_3Cl 952

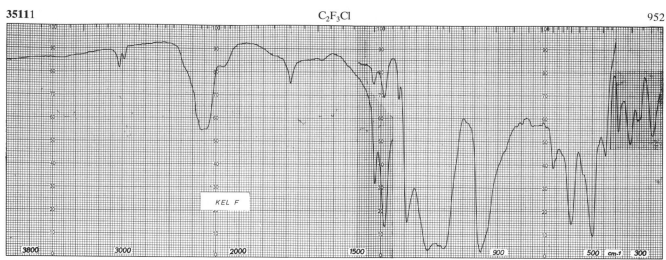

KEL F

(1) poly(trifluorochloroethylene)
(2) colourless film
(3) 3M Comp. (commercial product)

(7) original film (150 μm; 4000...1350 cm^{-1}); thin film (swollen in 3-chloro-1-trifluoromethyl-benzene, pressed and measured between KBr)

35111 C_2F_3Cl 953

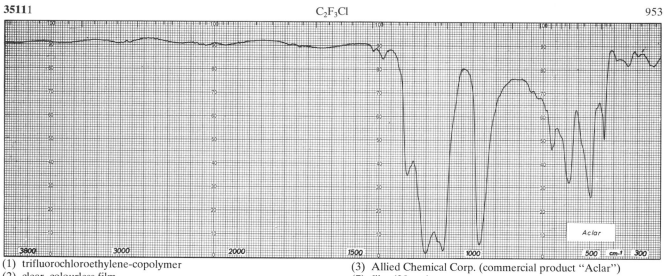

Aclar

(1) trifluorochloroethylene-copolymer
(2) clear, colourless film

(3) Allied Chemical Corp. (commercial product "Aclar")
(7) film (20 μm)

35111–21111 C_2F_3Cl-C_2H_4 954

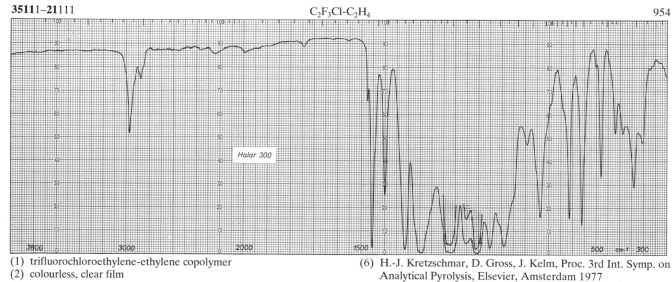

Halar 300

(1) trifluorochloroethylene-ethylene copolymer
(2) colourless, clear film
(3) Allied Chemicals Plastics Division, Morristown, N.J.
(4) close to alternating structure / almost equimolar composition

(6) H.-J. Kretzschmar, D. Gross, J. Kelm, Proc. 3rd Int. Symp. on Analytical Pyrolysis, Elsevier, Amsterdam 1977
(7) melting film
(8) commercial product "Halar 300"

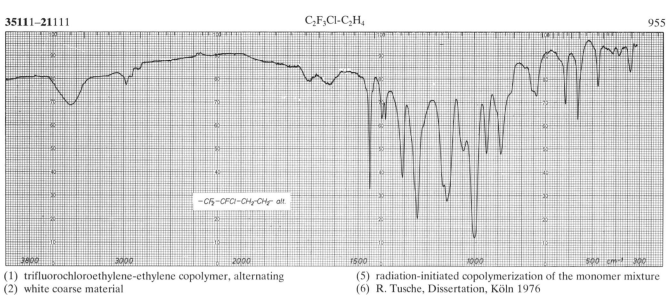

$-CF_2-CFCl-CH_2-CH_2-$ alt.

(1) trifluorochloroethylene-ethylene copolymer, alternating
(2) white coarse material
(3) R. Tusche, Institut für Physikalische Chemie, Universität Köln

(5) radiation-initiated copolymerization of the monomer mixture
(6) R. Tusche, Dissertation, Köln 1976
(7) ground with KBr (3/350) and $CHCl_3$, dried and pressed

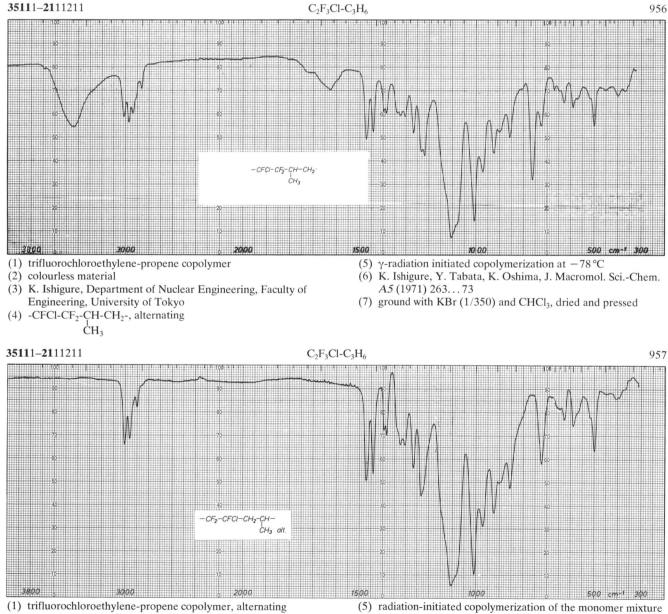

$-CFCl-CF_2-CH-CH_2-$
$\quad\quad\quad\quad\quad\; CH_3$

(1) trifluorochloroethylene-propene copolymer
(2) colourless material
(3) K. Ishigure, Department of Nuclear Engineering, Faculty of Engineering, University of Tokyo
(4) -$CFCl$-CF_2-CH-CH_2-, alternating
$\quad\quad\quad\quad\quad\;\; CH_3$

(5) γ-radiation initiated copolymerization at −78 °C
(6) K. Ishigure, Y. Tabata, K. Oshima, J. Macromol. Sci.-Chem. A5 (1971) 263...73
(7) ground with KBr (1/350) and $CHCl_3$, dried and pressed

$-CF_2-CFCl-CH_2-CH-$
$\quad\quad\quad\quad\quad\quad\;\; CH_3$ alt.

(1) trifluorochloroethylene-propene copolymer, alternating
(2) white material
(3) R. Tusche, Institut für Physikalische Chemie, Universität Köln

(5) radiation-initiated copolymerization of the monomer mixture
(6) R. Tusche, Dissertation, Köln 1976
(7) film from $CHCl_3$ on CsI

35111–2111212   C$_2$F$_3$Cl–C$_4$H$_8$ 958

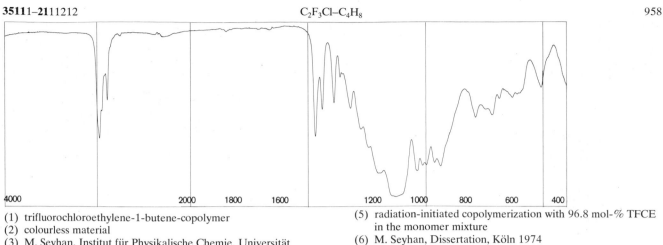

(1) trifluorochloroethylene-1-butene-copolymer
(2) colourless material
(3) M. Seyhan, Institut für Physikalische Chemie, Universität Köln
(4) almost alternating equimolar structure
(5) radiation-initiated copolymerization with 96.8 mol-% TFCE in the monomer mixture
(6) M. Seyhan, Dissertation, Köln 1974
(7) film

35111–2111212   C$_2$F$_3$Cl-C$_4$H$_8$ 959

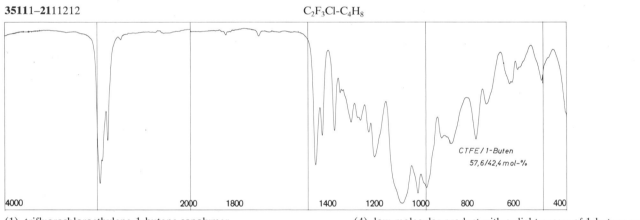

CTFE / 1-Buten
57,6/42,4 mol-%

(1) trifluorochloroethylene-1-butene copolymer
(2) colourless material
(3) M. Seyhan, Institut für Physikalische Chemie, Universität Köln
(4) low-molecular product with a slight excess of 1-butene units (probably hydrocarbon end-groups)
(6) M. Seyhan, Dissertation, Köln 1974
(7) film

35111–211122   C$_2$F$_3$Cl-C$_5$H$_{10}$ 960

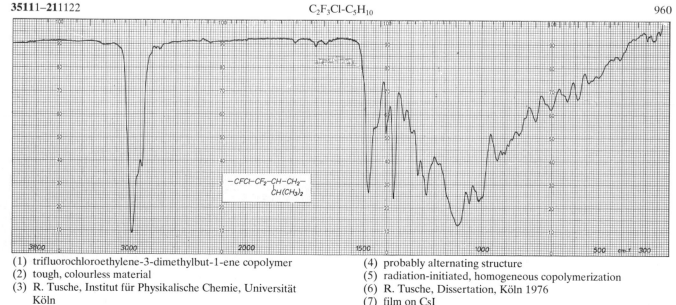

–CFCl–CF$_2$–CH–CH$_2$–
CH(CH$_3$)$_2$

(1) trifluorochloroethylene-3-dimethylbut-1-ene copolymer
(2) tough, colourless material
(3) R. Tusche, Institut für Physikalische Chemie, Universität Köln
(4) probably alternating structure
(5) radiation-initiated, homogeneous copolymerization
(6) R. Tusche, Dissertation, Köln 1976
(7) film on CsI

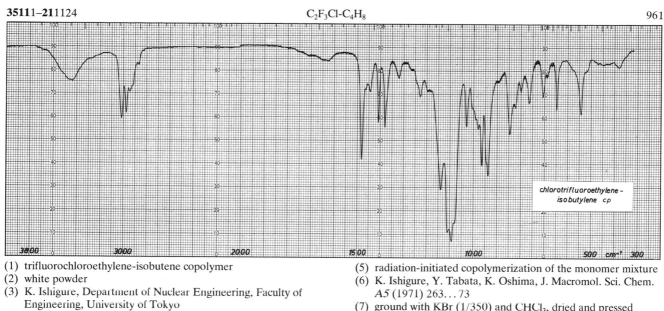

chlorotrifluoroethylene - isobutylene cp

(1) trifluorochloroethylene-isobutene copolymer
(2) white powder
(3) K. Ishigure, Department of Nuclear Engineering, Faculty of Engineering, University of Tokyo
(4) alternating structure

(5) radiation-initiated copolymerization of the monomer mixture
(6) K. Ishigure, Y. Tabata, K. Oshima, J. Macromol. Sci. Chem. *A5* (1971) 263...73
(7) ground with KBr (1/350) and $CHCl_3$, dried and pressed

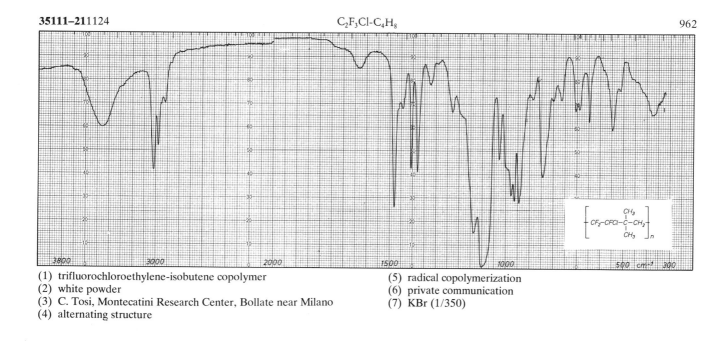

(1) trifluorochloroethylene-isobutene copolymer
(2) white powder
(3) C. Tosi, Montecatini Research Center, Bollate near Milano
(4) alternating structure

(5) radical copolymerization
(6) private communication
(7) KBr (1/350)

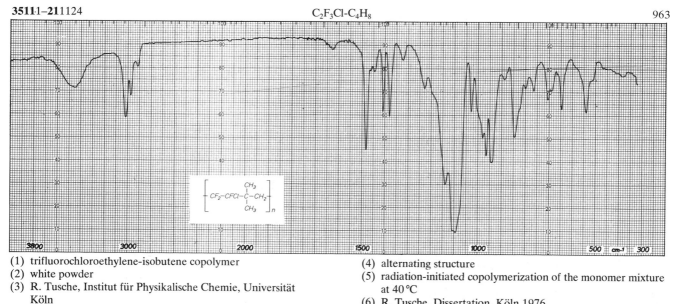

(1) trifluorochloroethylene-isobutene copolymer
(2) white powder
(3) R. Tusche, Institut für Physikalische Chemie, Universität Köln
(4) alternating structure
(5) radiation-initiated copolymerization of the monomer mixture at 40 °C
(6) R. Tusche, Dissertation, Köln 1976
(7) KBr (1.5/350)

35111–211121 C_2F_3Cl-C_6H_{12} 964

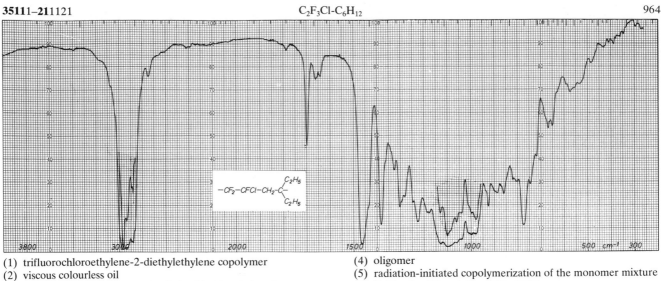

(1) trifluorochloroethylene-2-diethylethylene copolymer
(2) viscous colourless oil
(3) R. Tusche, Institut für Physikalische Chemie, Universität Köln
(4) oligomer
(5) radiation-initiated copolymerization of the monomer mixture
(6) R. Tusche, Dissertation, Köln 1976
(7) film between CsI

35111–3121121 C_2F_3Cl-C_3H_5Cl 965

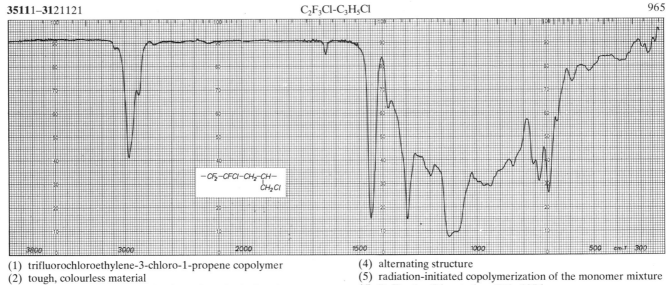

(1) trifluorochloroethylene-3-chloro-1-propene copolymer
(2) tough, colourless material
(3) R. Tusche, Institut für Physikalische Chemie, Universität Köln
(4) alternating structure
(5) radiation-initiated copolymerization of the monomer mixture
(6) R. Tusche, Dissertation, Köln 1976
(7) film between CsI

35111–33721121 C_2F_3Cl-$C_3H_2O_4$ 966

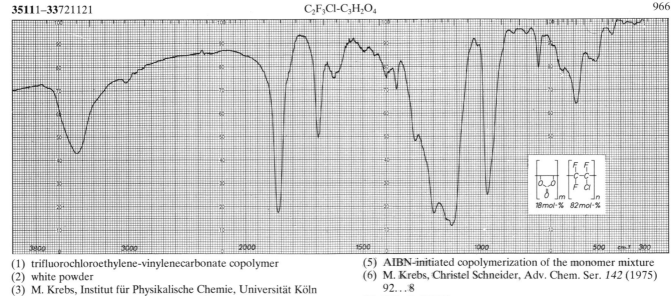

(1) trifluorochloroethylene-vinylenecarbonate copolymer
(2) white powder
(3) M. Krebs, Institut für Physikalische Chemie, Universität Köln
(4) 82 mol-% trifluoroethylene units in the copolymer
(5) AIBN-initiated copolymerization of the monomer mixture
(6) M. Krebs, Christel Schneider, Adv. Chem. Ser. *142* (1975) 92…8
(7) KBr (1.5/350)

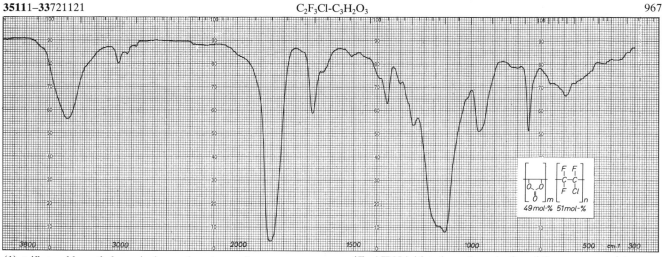

(1) trifluorochloroethylene-vinylenecarbonate copolymer
(2) white powder
(3) M. Krebs, Institut für Physikalische Chemie, Universität Köln
(4) 51 mol-% trifluorochloroethylene units in the copolymer

(5) AIBN-initiated copolymerization of the monomer mixture
(6) M. Krebs, Christel Schneider, Adv. Chem. Ser. *142* (1975) 92...8
(7) KBr (1/300)

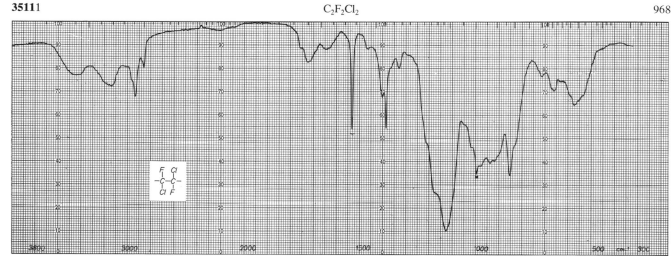

(1) poly(1,2-difluoro-1,2-dichloroethylene)
(2) white, coarse material
(3) D.W. Brown, National Bureau of Standards, Washington, D.C.
(5) high-pressure polymerization of the monomer; see D.W. Brown, L.A. Wall, Polym. Preprints *5* (1964) 907

(6) D.W. Brown, L.A. Wall, J. Polym. Sci. A-2 *7* (1969) 601...8
(7) swollen in C_6F_6, ground with KBr, dried and pressed
(8) * bands of hexafluorobenzene

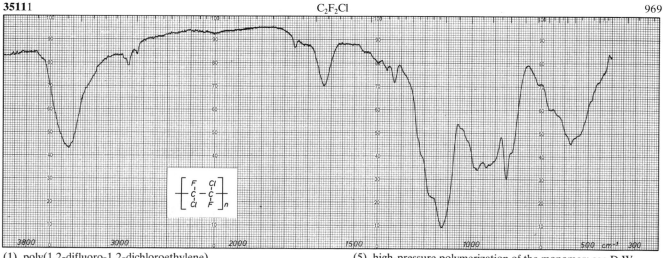

(1) poly(1,2-difluoro-1,2-dichloroethylene)
(2) white, coarse material
(3) D.W. Brown, National Bureau of Standards, Washington, D.C.

(5) high-pressure polymerization of the monomer; see D.W. Brown, L.A. Wall, Polym. Preprints *5* (1964) 907
(6) D.W. Brown, L.A. Wall, J. Polym. Sci. A-2 *7* (1969) 601...8
(7) KBr (4/400)

352　　　　　　　　　　　　　　$C_{12}F_{19}N_3$　　　　　　　　　　　　970

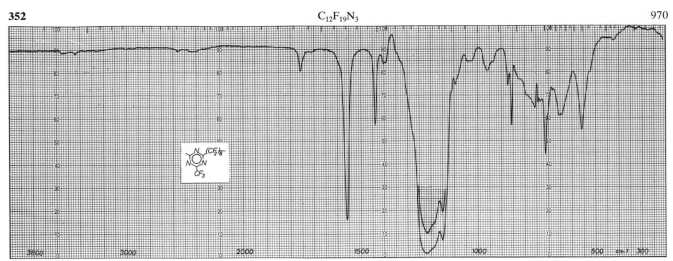

(1) poly(2,4-perfluorooctamethylene-6-perfluoromethyl-triazine)
(2) colourless elastomer
(3) E. Dorfman, Hooker Chemical Corp., Niagara Falls, N.Y.

(5) laboratory preparation
(6) private communication
(7) film from C_6F_6 on CsI

352　　　　　　　　　　　　　　$C_{12}F_{19}N_3$　　　　　　　　　　　　971

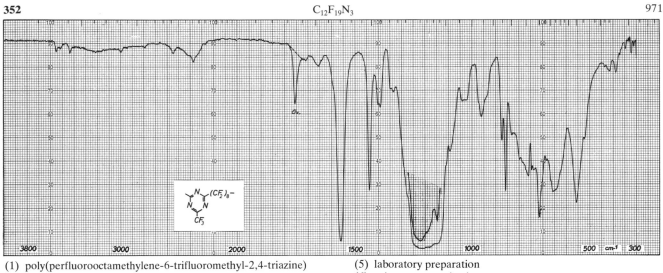

(1) poly(perfluorooctamethylene-6-trifluoromethyl-2,4-triazine)
(2) colourless elastomer
(3) B.M. Rushton, Hooker Chemical Corp., Niagara Falls, N.Y.

(5) laboratory preparation
(6) private communication
(7) melting film between CsI (120 °C)

35313112–**21**111　　　　　　　　$C_3F_6O-C_2H_4$　　　　　　　　972

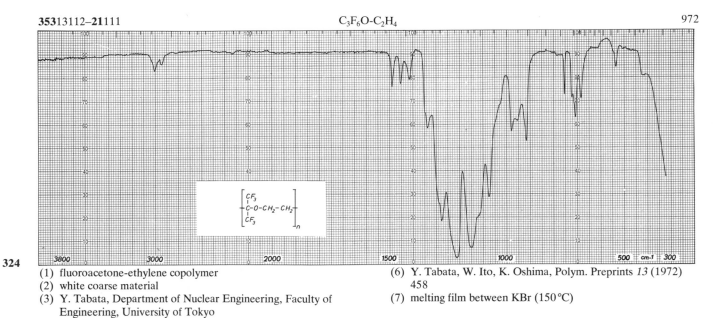

(1) fluoroacetone-ethylene copolymer
(2) white coarse material
(3) Y. Tabata, Department of Nuclear Engineering, Faculty of Engineering, University of Tokyo
(5) radiation-induced copolymerization (ionic at low temperature, radical at high temperature)

(6) Y. Tabata, W. Ito, K. Oshima, Polym. Preprints *13* (1972) 458
(7) melting film between KBr (150 °C)

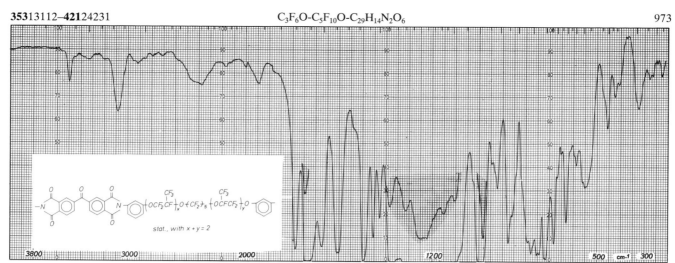

(1) poly(perfluoroalkylene-ether), linked with imide-bridges, on the basis of benzophenone-tetracarboxylic anhydride
(2) yellow film
(3) J.A. Webster, Monsanto Research Corp., Dayton, O.
(5) reaction of the aromatic diamine (with polyperfluoroalkylene-ether bridges) with benzophenonetetracarboxylic dianhydride

(6) J.A. Webster, J.M. Butler, T.J. Morrow, Polym. Preprints *13*/1 (1972) 612...6
(7) original film (approx. 30 μm), KBr

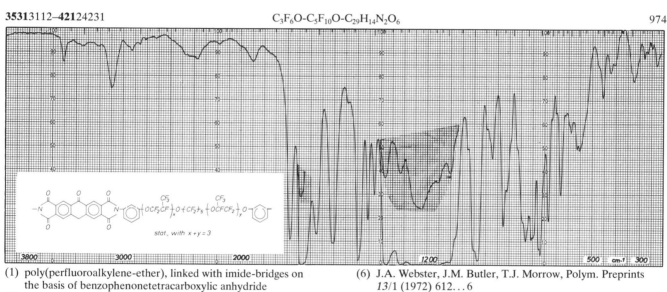
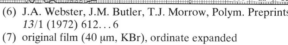

(1) poly(perfluoroalkylene-ether), linked with imide-bridges on the basis of benzophenonetetracarboxylic anhydride
(2) yellow film
(3) J.A. Webster, Monsanto Research Corp., Dayton, O.
(5) reaction of the aromatic diamine (with polyperfluoroalkylene-ether bridges) with benzophenonetetracarboxylic dianhydride

(6) J.A. Webster, J.M. Butler, T.J. Morrow, Polym. Preprints *13*/1 (1972) 612...6
(7) original film (40 μm, KBr), ordinate expanded

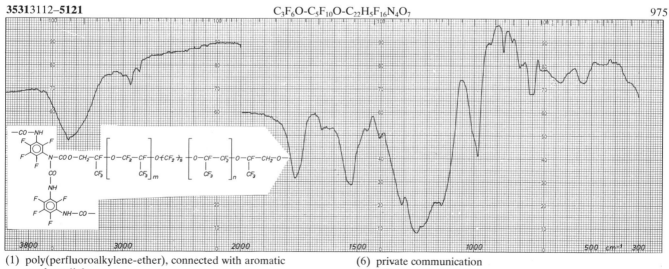

(1) poly(perfluoroalkylene-ether), connected with aromatic urethane links
(2) colourless film
(3) A.H. McLeod/F.D. Trischler, Whittaker Corp., Research & Development, San Diego, Calif.

(6) private communication
(7) KBr

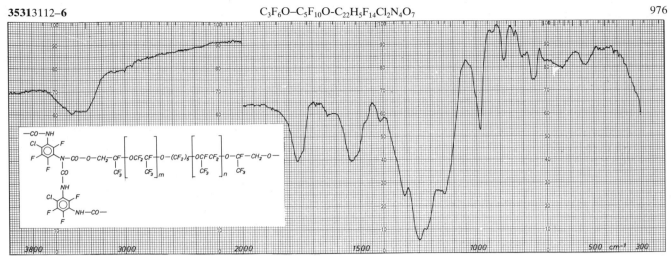

(1) poly(perfluoroalkylene-ether), connected with aromatic urethane links
(2) colourless film
(3) A.H. McLeod/F.D. Trischler, Whittaker Corp., Research & Development, San Diego, Calif.

(5) polyaddition of chlorotrifluoro-m-phenylenediisocyanate and the poly(perfluoroether)diol
(6) private communication
(7) KBr (ordinate expanded)

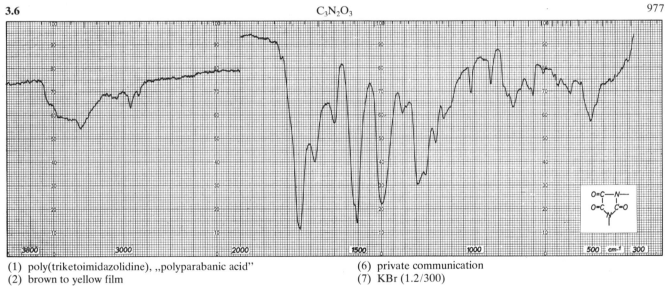

(1) poly(triketoimidazolidine), „polyparabanic acid"
(2) brown to yellow film
(3) Hoechst AG (by K. Weissermel)

(6) private communication
(7) KBr (1.2/300)

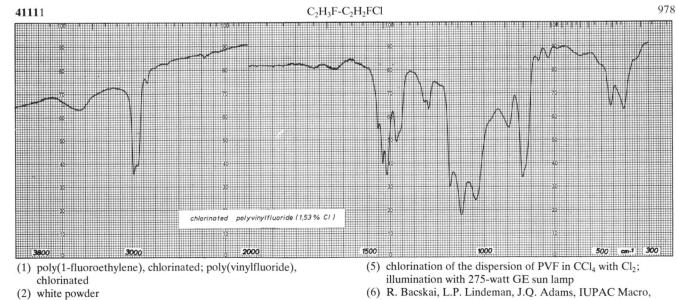

chlorinated polyvinylfluoride (1,53 % Cl)

(1) poly(1-fluoroethylene), chlorinated; poly(vinylfluoride), chlorinated
(2) white powder
(3) R. Bacskai, Chevron Research Comp., Richmond, Calif.
(4) 1.53 % Cl

(5) chlorination of the dispersion of PVF in CCl_4 with Cl_2; illumination with 275-watt GE sun lamp
(6) R. Bacskai, L.P. Lindeman, J.Q. Adams, IUPAC Macro, Toronto 1968; A 4.6
(7) KBr (4/1000)

41111 $C_2H_3F-C_2H_2FCl$ 979

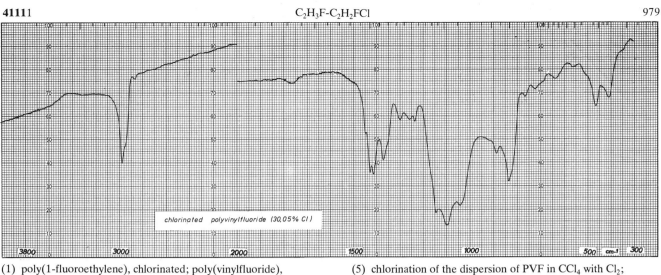

chlorinated   polyvinylfluoride (30,05% Cl)

(1) poly(1-fluoroethylene), chlorinated; poly(vinylfluoride),
    chlorinated
(2) white powder
(3) R. Bacskai, Chevron Research Comp., Richmond, Calif.
(4) 30 % Cl

(5) chlorination of the dispersion of PVF in CCl_4 with Cl_2;
    illumination with 275-watt GE sun lamp
(6) R. Bacskai, L.P. Lindeman, J.Q. Adams, IUPAC Macro,
    Toronto 1968; A 4.6
(7) KBr (7/1000)

41111 $C_2H_3F-C_2H_2FCl$ 980

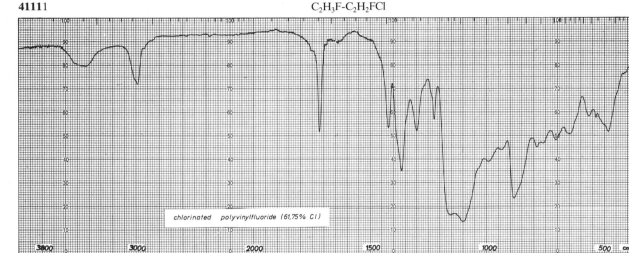

chlorinated   polyvinylfluoride (61,75% Cl)

(1) poly(1-fluoroethylene), chlorinated; poly(vinylfluoride),
    chlorinated
(2) white coarse material
(3) R. Bacskai, Chevron Research Comp., Richmond, Calif.
(4) 62 % Cl

(5) chlorination of the dispersion of PVF in CCl_4 with Cl_2;
    illumination with 275-watt GE sun lamp
(6) R. Bacskai, L.P. Lindeman, J.Q. Adams, IUPAC, Toronto
    1968; A 4.6
(7) KBr (11.4/1000)

41214 $C_{26}H_{14}F_4N_2$ 981

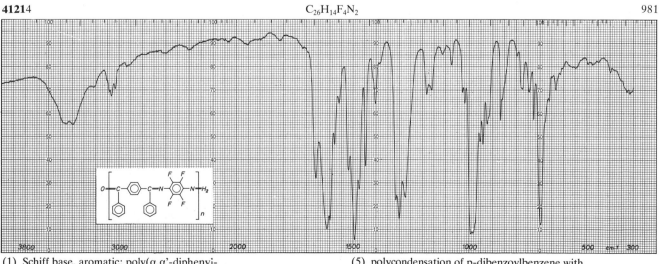

327

(1) Schiff base, aromatic; poly(α,α'-diphenyi-
    p-xylylidenetetrafluoro-p-phenylenediamine)
(2) greenish powder
(3) A.A. Volpe, Department of Chemistry and Chemical
    Engineering, Stevens Institute of Technology, Hoboken, N.J.

(5) polycondensation of p-dibenzoylbenzene with
    terephthaloylchloride in decalin in the presence of p-toluene
    sulfonic acid
(6) L.G. Kaufman, P.T. Funke, A.A. Volpe, Macromolecules *3*
    (1970) 358...62
(7) KBr

41214   C_26H_14F_4N_2   982

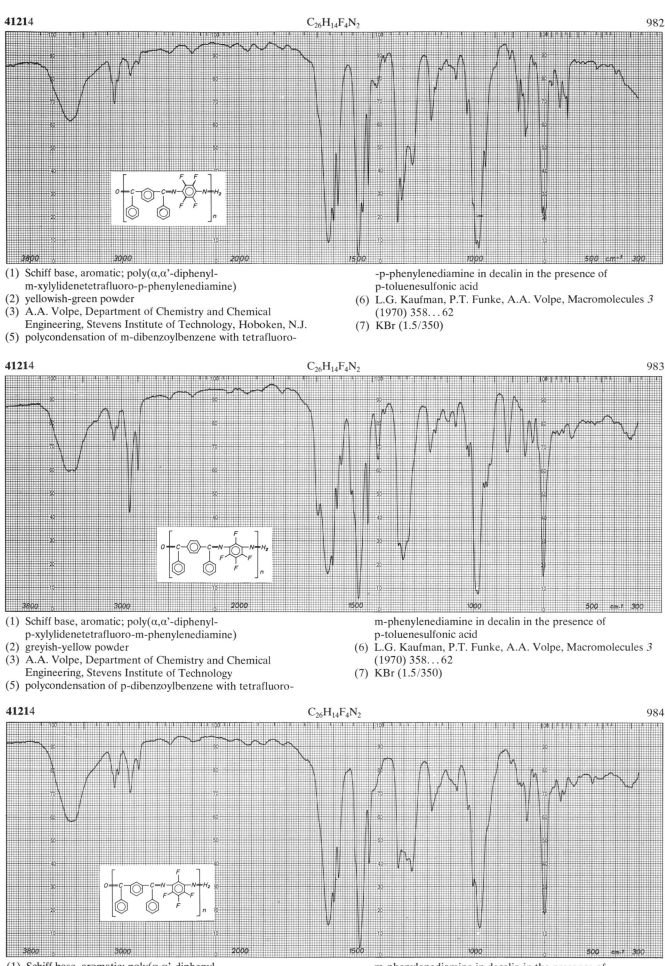

(1) Schiff base, aromatic; poly(α,α'-diphenyl-
    m-xylylidenetetrafluoro-p-phenylenediamine)
(2) yellowish-green powder
(3) A.A. Volpe, Department of Chemistry and Chemical
    Engineering, Stevens Institute of Technology, Hoboken, N.J.
(5) polycondensation of m-dibenzoylbenzene with tetrafluoro-

-p-phenylenediamine in decalin in the presence of
p-toluenesulfonic acid
(6) L.G. Kaufman, P.T. Funke, A.A. Volpe, Macromolecules *3*
    (1970) 358...62
(7) KBr (1.5/350)

41214   C_26H_14F_4N_2   983

(1) Schiff base, aromatic; poly(α,α'-diphenyl-
    p-xylylidenetetrafluoro-m-phenylenediamine)
(2) greyish-yellow powder
(3) A.A. Volpe, Department of Chemistry and Chemical
    Engineering, Stevens Institute of Technology
(5) polycondensation of p-dibenzoylbenzene with tetrafluoro-

m-phenylenediamine in decalin in the presence of
p-toluenesulfonic acid
(6) L.G. Kaufman, P.T. Funke, A.A. Volpe, Macromolecules *3*
    (1970) 358...62
(7) KBr (1.5/350)

41214   C_26H_14F_4N_2   984

(1) Schiff base, aromatic; poly(α,α'-diphenyl-
    m-xylylidenetetrafluoro-m-phenylenediamine)
(2) greyish-green powder
(3) A.A. Volpe, Department of Chemistry and Chemical
    Engineering, Stevens Institute of Technology
(5) polycondensation of m-dibenzoylbenzene with tetrafluoro-

m-phenylenediamine in decalin in the presence of
p-toluenesulfonic acid
(6) L.G. Kaufman, P.T. Funke, A.A. Volpe, Macromolecules *3*
    (1970) 358...62
(7) KBr (1.7/350)

41211   C₃H₂ClN   985

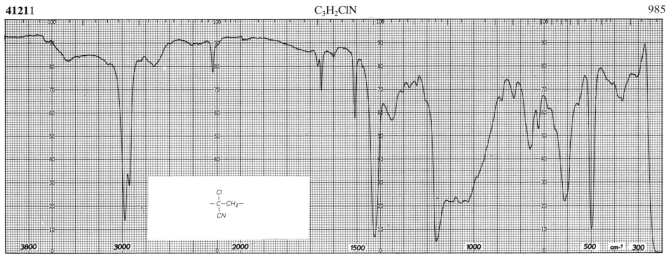

(1) poly(2-chloroacrylonitrile); poly(1-chloro-1-cyanaoethylene)
(2) yellowish material
(3) F. Winther, Institut für Physikalische Chemie, Universität
    Köln/Institut für Physikalische Chemie, Universität Kiel

(5) spontaneous polymerization
(6) private communication
(7) ground with KBr (20/1000) and CH₃OH, dried and pressed
(8) absorption beyond 270 cm⁻¹ due to KBr

41222   C₉H₆ClN   986

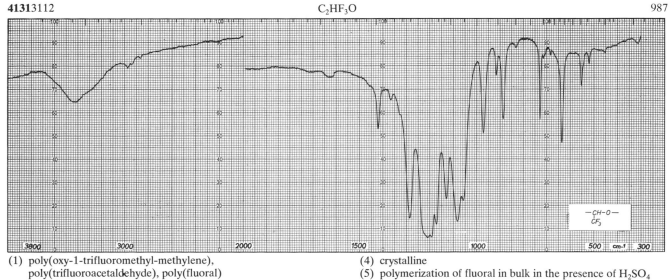

(1) poly[α(4-chlorophenyl)acrylonitrile]; poly[1(4-chlorophenyl)-
    1-cyanoethylene]
(2) white powder
(3) W. Funke, Forschungsinstitut für Pigmente und Lacke,
    Universität Stuttgart

(5) anionic polymerization of the monomer in dimethylformamide
    solution with n-butyllithium
(6) M. Sonntag, W. Funke, Makromol. Chem. 137 (1970) 23...8
(7) KBr (2/350)

41313112   C₂HF₃O   987

(1) poly(oxy-1-trifluoromethyl-methylene),
    poly(trifluoroacetaldehyde), poly(fluoral)
(2) yellowish-white, coarse material
(3) W.K. Busfield, Department of Chemistry, University of
    Dundee

(4) crystalline
(5) polymerization of fluoral in bulk in the presence of H₂SO₄
(6) W.K. Busfield, Polymer 9 (1968) 479...88
(7) KBr (1/300)

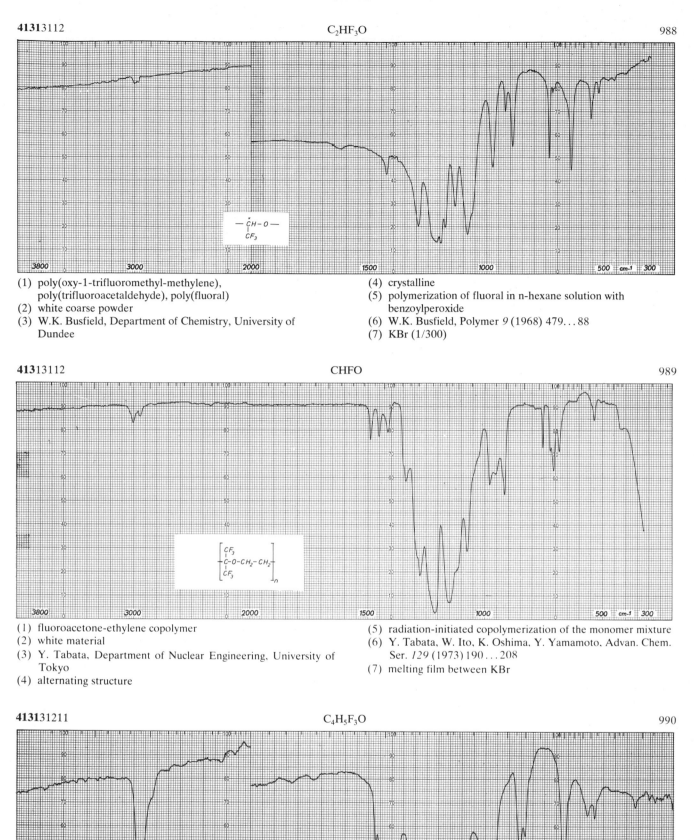

41313112 C_2HF_3O 988

- CH – O –
  |
  CF_3

(1) poly(oxy-1-trifluoromethyl-methylene),
    poly(trifluoroacetaldehyde), poly(fluoral)
(2) white coarse powder
(3) W.K. Busfield, Department of Chemistry, University of
    Dundee

(4) crystalline
(5) polymerization of fluoral in n-hexane solution with
    benzoylperoxide
(6) W.K. Busfield, Polymer 9 (1968) 479...88
(7) KBr (1/300)

41313112   CHFO   989

⎡ CF_3
│ |
─C–O–CH_2–CH_2─
│ |
⎣ CF_3 ⎦_n

(1) fluoroacetone-ethylene copolymer
(2) white material
(3) Y. Tabata, Department of Nuclear Engineering, University of
    Tokyo
(4) alternating structure

(5) radiation-initiated copolymerization of the monomer mixture
(6) Y. Tabata, W. Ito, K. Oshima, Y. Yamamoto, Advan. Chem.
    Ser. 129 (1973) 190...208
(7) melting film between KBr

413131211 $C_4H_5F_3O$ 990

–CH – CH_2–
|
O — CH_2 – CF_3

(1) poly(2,2,2-trifluoroethyl vinylether)
(2) colourless, glassy-clear elastomer
(3) C.K. Chiklis, Chemical Research Laboratories, Polaroid
    Corp., Cambridge, Mass.
(4) amorphous

(5) cationic polymerization of the monomer in $CHCl_3$/n-pentane
    solution with BF_3 at $-78\,°C$
(6) C.K. Chiklis, H.C. Haas, J. Polym. Sci. A-1 6 (1968)
    2573...84
(7) film from acetone on CsI

413171221 $C_{13}H_8F_6O_5$ 991

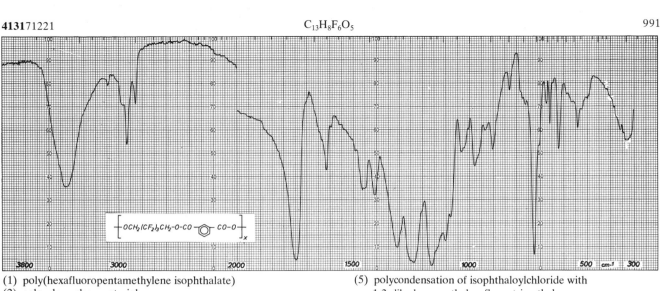

(1) poly(hexafluoropentamethylene isophthalate)
(2) colourless, clear material
(3) F.D. Trischler, Narmco Research & Development Division, Whittaker Corp., San Diego, Calif.

(5) polycondensation of isophthaloylchloride with 1,3-dihydroxymethylperfluorotrimethylene
(6) F.D. Trischler, J. Hollander, J. Polym. Sci. A-1 7 (1969) 971...5
(7) KBr, ordinate expanded

41317412 $C_{18}H_{18}F_6O_5$ 992

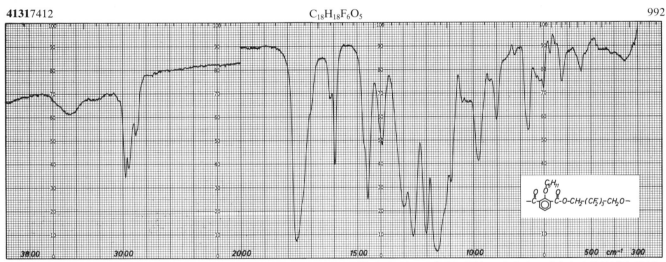
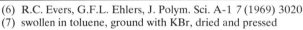

(1) poly(hexafluoropentamethylene 2-n-amyloxyisophthalate)
(2) brown, very tough, somewhat tacky material
(3) G.F.L. Ehlers, Wright-Patterson AFB, O.
(5) interfacial polycondensation of 1,3-dihydroxymethyl-perfluorotrimethylene with 2(n-amyloxy)isophthaloylchloride

(6) R.C. Evers, G.F.L. Ehlers, J. Polym. Sci. A-1 7 (1969) 3020
(7) swollen in toluene, ground with KBr, dried and pressed

41317412 $C_{18}H_{18}F_6O_5$ 993

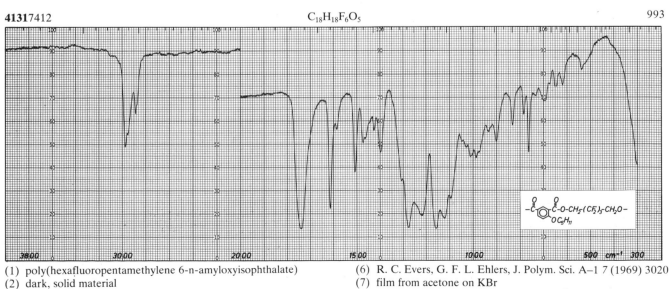

(1) poly(hexafluoropentamethylene 6-n-amyloxyisophthalate)
(2) dark, solid material
(3) G. F. L. Ehlers, Wright-Patterson AFB, O.
(5) interfacial polycondensation of 1,3-dihydroxymethyl-perfluoro-trimethylene with 6(n-amyloxy)isophthaloylchloride

(6) R. C. Evers, G. F. L. Ehlers, J. Polym. Sci. A–1 7 (1969) 3020
(7) film from acetone on KBr
(8) the absorption increase beyond 400 cm^{-1} is due to KBr

41317412 $C_{18}H_{18}F_6O_5$ 994

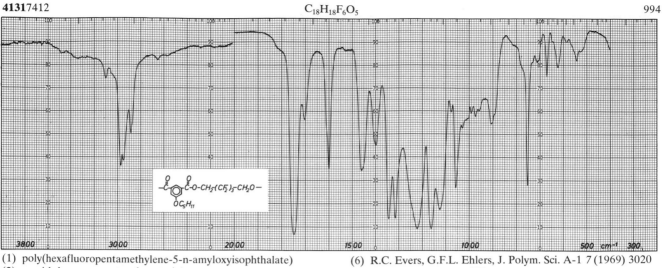

(1) poly(hexafluoropentamethylene-5-n-amyloxyisophthalate)
(2) greyish-brown, very tough material
(3) G.F.L. Ehlers, Wright-Patterson AFB, O.
(5) interfacial polycondensation of 1,3-dihydroxymethyl-
     perfluorotrimethylene with 5(n-amyloxy)isophthaloylchloride

(6) R.C. Evers, G.F.L. Ehlers, J. Polym. Sci. A-1 7 (1969) 3020
(7) film from acetone on KBr

41321121 C_3H_5ClO 995

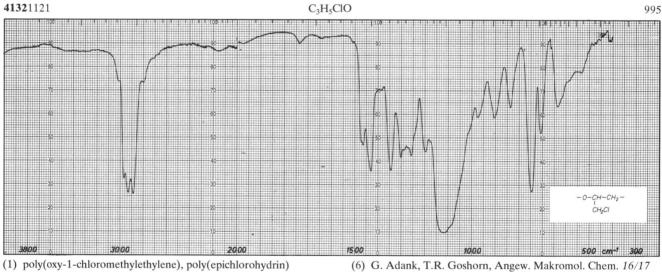

(1) poly(oxy-1-chloromethylethylene), poly(epichlorohydrin)
(2) porous, white elastomer
(3) G. Adank, B.F. Goodrich Chem. Comp., Akron, O.
(5) cationic polymerization

(6) G. Adank, T.R. Goshorn, Angew. Makromol. Chem. *16/17*
     (1971) 103...15
(7) film from CHCl_3/Cl_4 on KBr
(8) "Hydrin 100"

413231121–**3331**111 C_3H_5ClO-C_2H_4O 996

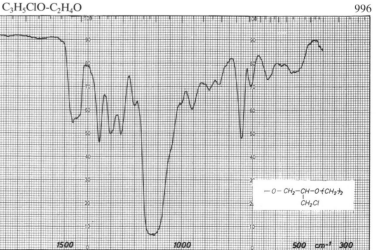

(1) epichlorohydrin-ethyleneoxide copolymer
(2) porous, yellowish elastomer
(3) G. Adank, B.F. Goodrich Chem. Comp., Akron, O.
(5) cationic copolymerization

(6) G. Adank, T.R. Goshorn, Angew. Makromol. Chem. *16/17*
     (1971) 103...15
(7) film from CHCl_3/Cl_4 on KBr
(8) "Hydrin 200"

413231121 $C_4H_5Cl_3O$ 997

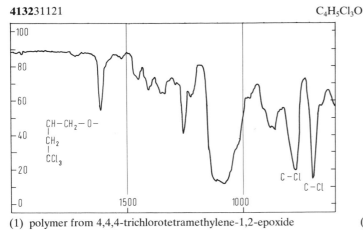

(1) polymer from 4,4,4-trichlorotetramethylene-1,2-epoxide
(2) colourless material
(3) P.E. Wei, Esso Research and Engng. Comp., Linden, N.J.
(5) catalyst system: triisobutyl aluminium: acetyl acetone: H_2O =
     1:1:0,5

(6) P.E. Wei, P.E. Butler, J. Polym. Sci. A-1 *6* (1968) 2461...75
(7) film (spectrum by the autors)

413231121–333111 $C_5H_8Cl_2O\text{-}C_4H_6O$ 998

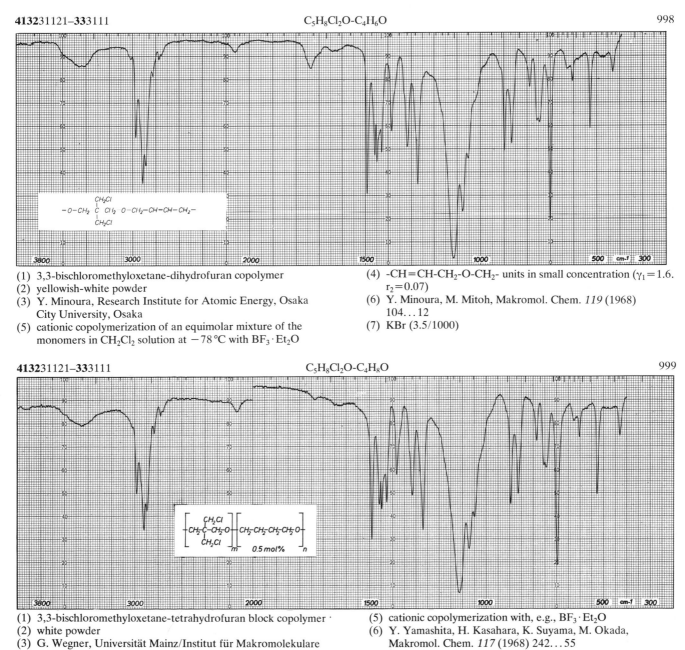

(1) 3,3-bischloromethyloxetane-dihydrofuran copolymer
(2) yellowish-white powder
(3) Y. Minoura, Research Institute for Atomic Energy, Osaka
     City University, Osaka
(5) cationic copolymerization of an equimolar mixture of the
     monomers in CH_2Cl_2 solution at $-78\,°C$ with $BF_3 \cdot Et_2O$

(4) $-CH=CH\text{-}CH_2\text{-}O\text{-}CH_2\text{-}$ units in small concentration ($\gamma_1=1.6$.
     $r_2=0.07$)
(6) Y. Minoura, M. Mitoh, Makromol. Chem. *119* (1968)
     104...12
(7) KBr (3.5/1000)

413231121–333111 $C_5H_8Cl_2O\text{-}C_4H_8O$ 999

(1) 3,3-bischloromethyloxetane-tetrahydrofuran block copolymer
(2) white powder
(3) G. Wegner, Universität Mainz/Institut für Makromolekulare
     Chemie, Universität Freiburg/Br.
(4) 0,5 mol-% oxytetramethylene units

(5) cationic copolymerization with, e.g., $BF_3 \cdot Et_2O$
(6) Y. Yamashita, H. Kasahara, K. Suyama, M. Okada,
     Makromol. Chem. *117* (1968) 242...55
(7) KBr (2/400)

413231121–333111 $C_5H_8Cl_2O–C_4H_8O$ 1000

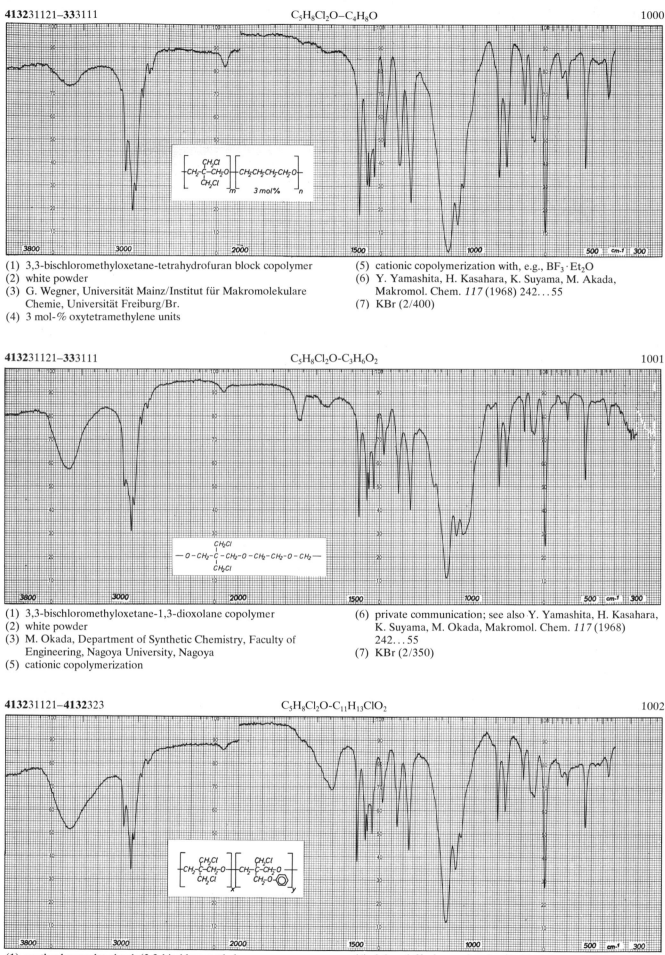

(1) 3,3-bischloromethyloxetane-tetrahydrofuran block copolymer
(2) white powder
(3) G. Wegner, Universität Mainz/Institut für Makromolekulare Chemie, Universität Freiburg/Br.
(4) 3 mol-% oxytetramethylene units
(5) cationic copolymerization with, e.g., $BF_3 \cdot Et_2O$
(6) Y. Yamashita, H. Kasahara, K. Suyama, M. Akada, Makromol. Chem. *117* (1968) 242...55
(7) KBr (2/400)

413231121–333111 $C_5H_8Cl_2O–C_3H_6O_2$ 1001

(1) 3,3-bischloromethyloxetane-1,3-dioxolane copolymer
(2) white powder
(3) M. Okada, Department of Synthetic Chemistry, Faculty of Engineering, Nagoya University, Nagoya
(5) cationic copolymerization
(6) private communication; see also Y. Yamashita, H. Kasahara, K. Suyama, M. Okada, Makromol. Chem. *117* (1968) 242...55
(7) KBr (2/350)

413231121–4132323 $C_5H_8Cl_2O–C_{11}H_{13}ClO_2$ 1002

(1) partly phenoxylated poly(3,3-bischloromethyl-oxatetramethylene)
(2) white material
(3) G. Wegner, Universität Mainz/Institut für Makromolekulare Chemie, Universität Freiburg/Br.
(4) 0.8 mol-% phenoxylated units, block-type copolymer
(5) phenoxylation of crystalline "Penton" at 80 °C in dimethylformamide
(6) Y. Minoura et al., J. Polym. Sci. *A-5* (1968) 2843
(7) KBr (2/400)

413231121–4132323 $C_5H_8Cl_2O$-$C_{11}H_{13}ClO_2$ 1003

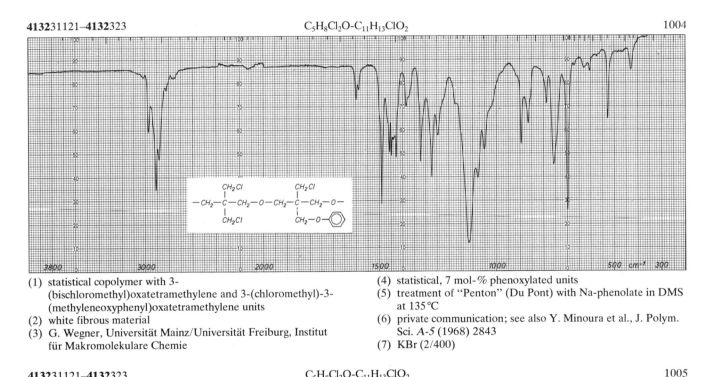

(1) partly phenoxylated poly(3,3-bischloromethyl-
     oxatetramethylene)
(2) white material
(3) G. Wegner, Universität Mainz/Institut für Makromolekulare
     Chemie, Universität Freiburg/Br.

(4) 1.4 mol-% phenoxylated units, block-type copolymer
(5) phenoxylation of crystalline "Penton" at 80 °C. in
     dimethylformamide
(6) Y. Minoura et al., J. Polym. Sci. *A-5* (1968) 2843
(7) KBr (2/400)

413231121–4132323 $C_5H_8Cl_2O$-$C_{11}H_{13}ClO_2$ 1004

(1) statistical copolymer with 3-
     (bischloromethyl)oxatetramethylene and 3-(chloromethyl)-3-
     (methyleneoxyphenyl)oxatetramethylene units
(2) white fibrous material
(3) G. Wegner, Universität Mainz/Universität Freiburg, Institut
     für Makromolekulare Chemie

(4) statistical, 7 mol-% phenoxylated units
(5) treatment of "Penton" (Du Pont) with Na-phenolate in DMS
     at 135 °C
(6) private communication; see also Y. Minoura et al., J. Polym.
     Sci. *A-5* (1968) 2843
(7) KBr (2/400)

413231121–4132323 $C_5H_8Cl_2O$-$C_{11}H_{13}ClO_2$ 1005

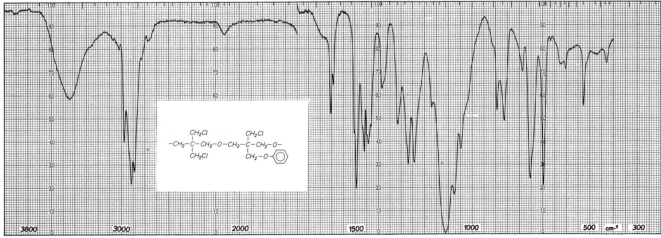

(1) poly(bischloromethyloxatetramethylene) with 10.7 mol-%
     statistically distributed phenoxylated units
(2) white material
(3) G. Wegner, Universität Mainz/Institut für Makromolekulare
     Chemie, Universität Freiburg/Br.

(5) phenoxylation of "Penton" with Na-phenolate in
     dimethylformamide at 135 °C.
(6) private communication; see also Y. Minoura et al., J. Polym.
     Sci. *A-5* (1968) 2843
(7) KBr (2/400)

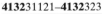

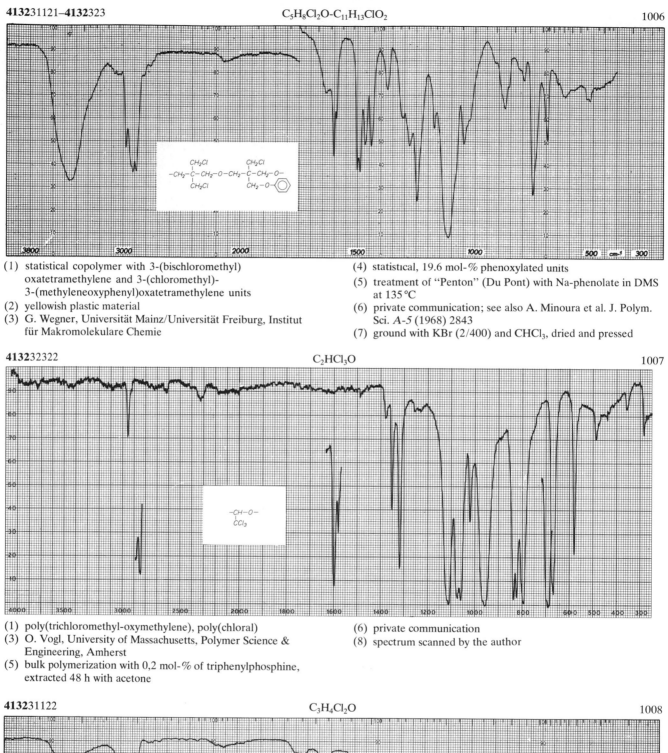

413231121–4132323 $C_5H_8Cl_2O$-$C_{11}H_{13}ClO_2$ 1006

(1) statistical copolymer with 3-(bischloromethyl)
oxatetramethylene and 3-(chloromethyl)-
3-(methyleneoxyphenyl)oxatetramethylene units

(2) yellowish plastic material

(3) G. Wegner, Universität Mainz/Universität Freiburg, Institut
für Makromolekulare Chemie

(4) statistical, 19.6 mol-% phenoxylated units

(5) treatment of "Penton" (Du Pont) with Na-phenolate in DMS
at 135 °C

(6) private communication; see also A. Minoura et al. J. Polym.
Sci. *A-5* (1968) 2843

(7) ground with KBr (2/400) and CHCl₃, dried and pressed

413232322 C_2HCl_3O 1007

(1) poly(trichloromethyl-oxymethylene), poly(chloral)

(3) O. Vogl, University of Massachusetts, Polymer Science &
Engineering, Amherst

(5) bulk polymerization with 0,2 mol-% of triphenylphosphine,
extracted 48 h with acetone

(6) private communication

(8) spectrum scanned by the author

413231122 $C_3H_4Cl_2O$ 1008

(1) poly[(1,2-dichloroethyl)oxymethylene]

(2) white powder

(3) H. Sumitomo, Department of Chemical Technology, Faculty
of Engineering, Osaka University, Osaka

(5) cationic polymerization

(6) H. Sumitomo, T. Nakagawa, J. Polym. Sci. *B 7* (1969)
739...42

(7) KBr (2/350)

413231211–311112 C₂HCl₃-C₄H₇ClO 1009

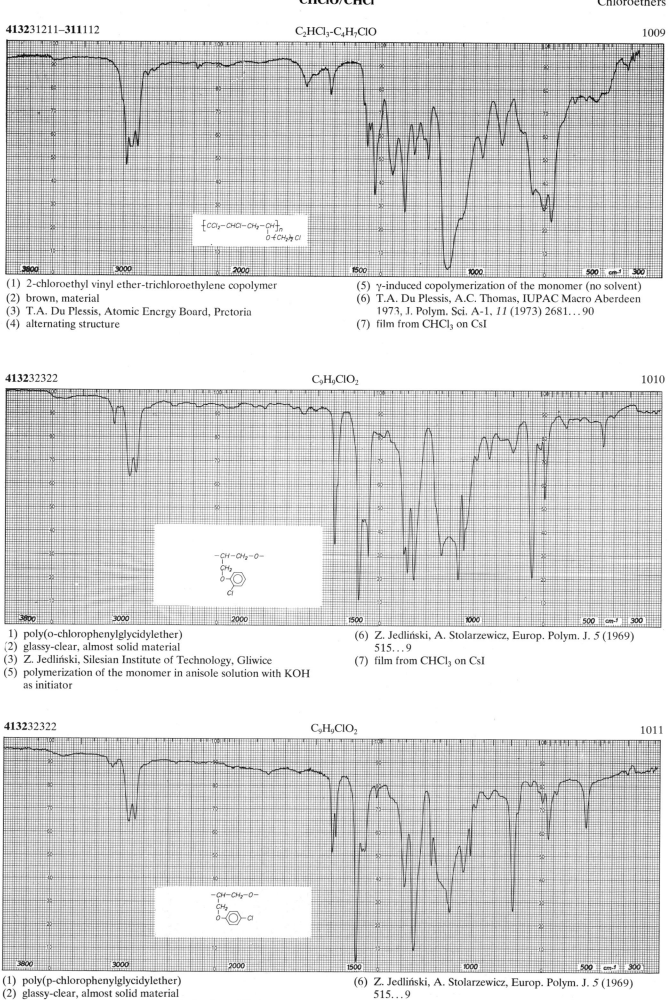

(1) 2-chloroethyl vinyl ether-trichloroethylene copolymer
(2) brown, material
(3) T.A. Du Plessis, Atomic Encrgy Board, Prctoria
(4) alternating structure

(5) γ-induced copolymerization of the monomer (no solvent)
(6) T.A. Du Plessis, A.C. Thomas, IUPAC Macro Aberdeen 1973, J. Polym. Sci. A-1, *11* (1973) 2681...90
(7) film from CHCl₃ on CsI

413232322 C₉H₉ClO₂ 1010

1) poly(o-chlorophenylglycidylether)
(2) glassy-clear, almost solid material
(3) Z. Jedliński, Silesian Institute of Technology, Gliwice
(5) polymerization of the monomer in anisole solution with KOH as initiator

(6) Z. Jedliński, A. Stolarzewicz, Europ. Polym. J. *5* (1969) 515...9
(7) film from CHCl₃ on CsI

413232322 C₉H₉ClO₂ 1011

(1) poly(p-chlorophenylglycidylether)
(2) glassy-clear, almost solid material
(3) Z. Jedliński, Silesian Institute of Technology, Gliwice
(5) polymerization of the monomer in anisole solution with KOH as initiator

(6) Z. Jedliński, A. Stolarzewicz, Europ. Polym. J. *5* (1969) 515...9
(7) film from CHCl₃ on CsI

413232322 $C_9H_8Cl_2O_2$ 1012

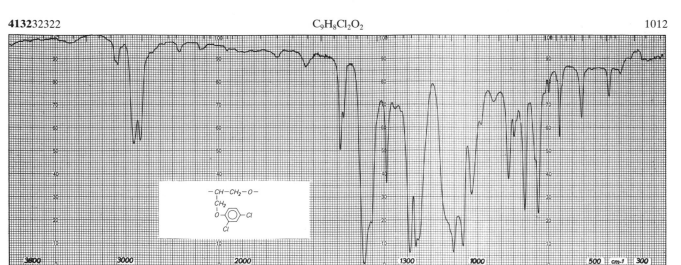

(1) poly(2,4-dichlorophenylglycidylether)
(2) glassy-clear, almost solid material
(3) Z. Jedliński, Silesian Institute of Technology, Gliwice
(5) polymerization of the monomer in anisole solution with KOH as initiator
(6) Z. Jedliński, A. Stolarzewicz, Europ. Polym. J. *5* (1969) 515...9
(7) film from $CHCl_3$ on CsI

4132331 $C_6H_2Cl_2O$ 1013

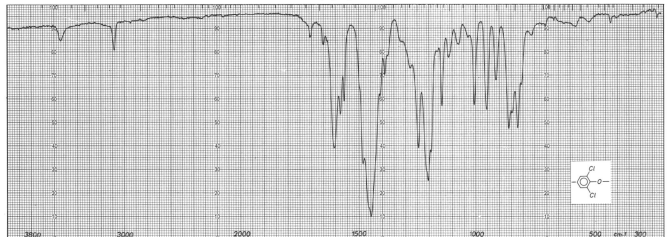

(1) poly(oxy-2,6-dichlorophenylene)
(2) light-yellow powder
(3) S. Tsuruya, Department of Hydrocarbon Chemistry, Faculty of Engineering, Kyoto University, Kyoto
(5) oxidative polycondensation of 2,6-dichlorophenol with $CuCl_2$/ CH_3ONa in CH_3OH
(6) S. Tsuruya, T. Kawamura, S. Tsutsiya, T. Yonezawa , Polymer Letters *7* (1969) 709...11
(7) film from $CHCl_3$ on CsI

4132511–**2122**111 C_3H_3ClO-C_8H_8 1014

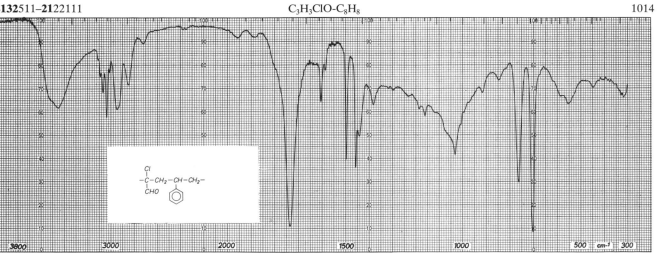

(1) α-chloroacrolein-styrene copolymer
(2) eggshell-coloured powder
(3) H.-G. Elias, TU Zürich/Midland Macromolecular Institute, Midland, Mich.
(4) the copolymer contains a small amount of -CH(CCl=CH₂)O- units.
(5) radical-initiated copolymerization of the monomer mixture in bulk with AIBN at 60 °C
(6) H.-G. Elias, W. Lengweiler, Makromol. Chem. *113* (1968) 155...70
(7) KBr (2/350)

41325211   C$_2$H$_3$Cl-CO   1015

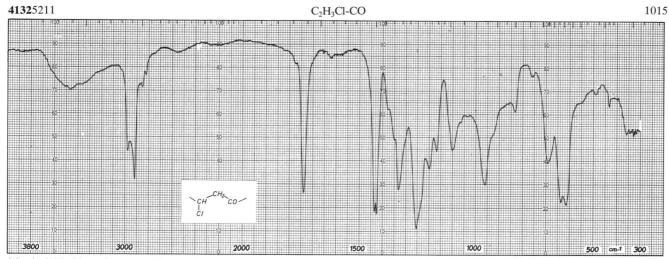

(1) vinylchloride-carbonmonoxide copolymer
(2) colourless film
(3) W. Kawai, Government Industrial Research Institute, Osaka
(4) alternating structure, α-keto group
(5) aqueous emulsion copolymerization with ammonium persulfate as initiator; alternatively: copolymerization in bulk

with AlEt$_2$OEt-CuCl-CCl$_4$ as initiator (see W. Kawai, T. Ichihashi, J. Polym. Sci. A-1 *10* (1972) 1709
(6) W. Kawai, Europ. Polym. J. *10* (1974) 805...8
(7) film

413271224   C$_{23}$H$_{14}$Cl$_4$O$_4$-C$_{23}$H$_{14}$Cl$_4$O$_4$ 1016

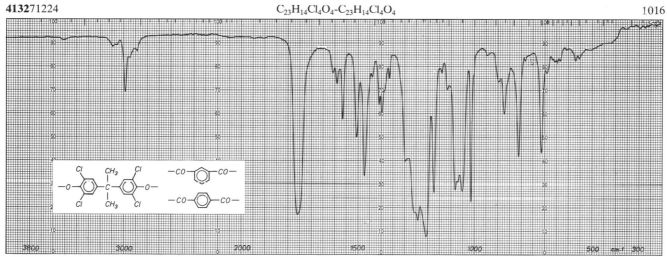
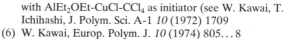

(1) copolyester, aromatic, chlorinated
(2) white, coarse powder
(3) R. Ismail, Zentrallabor der Dynamit Nobel AG, Troisdorf
(5) polycondensation of 2 equivalents 2,2-bis(3,5-dichloro-4-hydroxyphenyl)propane with 1 eq. isophthaloylchloride and 1

eq. terephthaloylchloride in o-dichlorobenzene in the presence of a catalyst, e. g., quinoline
(6) R.M. Ismail, Angew. Makromol. Chem. *8* (1969) 99...116
(7) film from CHCl$_3$ on CsI

413271224   C$_{23}$H$_{14}$Cl$_4$O$_4$-C$_{23}$H$_{14}$Cl$_4$O$_4$ 1017

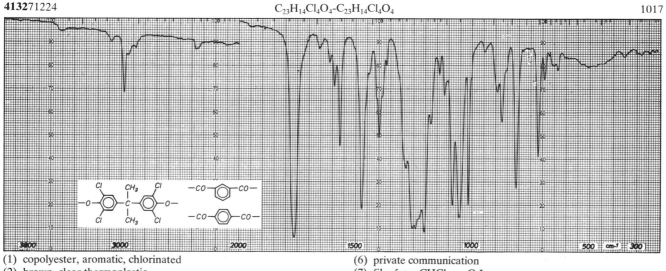

(1) copolyester, aromatic, chlorinated
(2) brown, clear thermoplastic
(3) Dynamit Nobel AG, Troisdorf (by W. Trautvetter)

(6) private communication
(7) film from CHCl$_3$ on CsI

41327221121   C$_4$H$_5$ClO$_2$ 1018

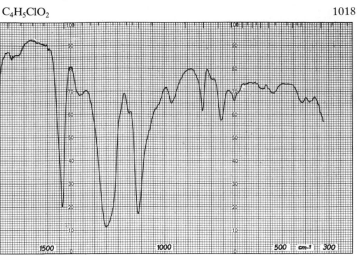

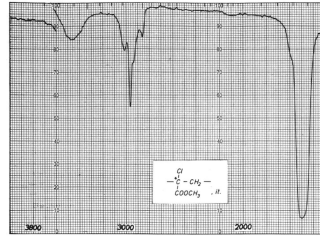

(1) poly(methyl-α-chloroacrylate), isotactic; poly(1-chloro-1-carbonyloxymethyl-ethylene)

(2) white, light powder

(3) K. Matsuzaki, Faculty of Engineering, University of Tokyo

(5) anionic polymerization with phenylmagnesiumbromide in toluene

(6) K. Matsuzaki, T. Uryu, K. Ito, Makromol. Chem. *126* (1969) 292...5

(7) ground with KBr (1.2/350) and CHCl$_3$, dried and pressed

41327221121   C$_4$H$_5$ClO$_2$ 1019

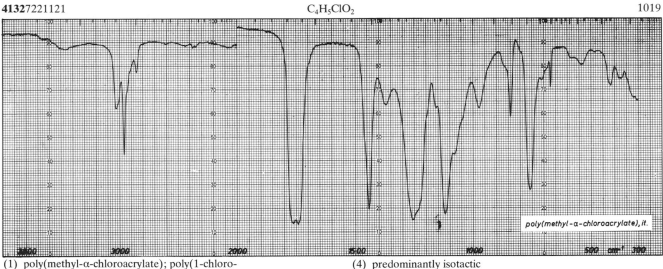

poly(methyl-α-chloroacrylate), it.

(1) poly(methyl-α-chloroacrylate); poly(1-chloro-1-carbonyloxymethyl-ethylene)

(2) white powder

(3) G.R. Dever, Polymer Science & Engineering Department, University of Massachusetts, Amherst, Mass.

(4) predominantly isotactic

(5) polymerization with, e.g., Li-fluorenyl in toluene at −78 °C

(6) R. Lenz, B. Wesslén, Macromolecules *4* (1971) 20...4

(7) film from CHCl$_3$ on CsI

(8) band at 667 cm^{-1} due to residual CHCl$_3$

41327221121   C$_4$H$_5$ClO$_2$ 1020

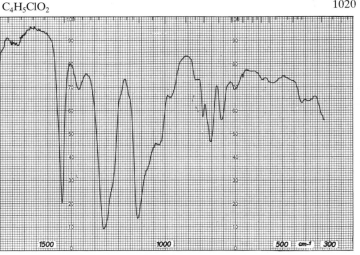

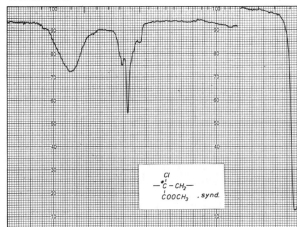

(1) poly(methyl-α-chloroacrylate), syndiotactic; poly(1-chloro-1-carbonyloxymethyl-ethylene)

(2) white light powder

(3) K. Matsuzaki, Faculty of Engineering, University of Tokyo

(4) 81% syndiotactic sequences

(5) polymerization of the monomer in toluene solution by UV light, photosensitized with benzoin

(6) K. Matsuzaki, T. Uryu, K. Ito, Makromol. Chem. *126* (1969) 292...95

(7) ground with KBr (1.2/350) and CHCl$_3$, dried and pressed

41327221121 $C_4H_5ClO_2$ 1021

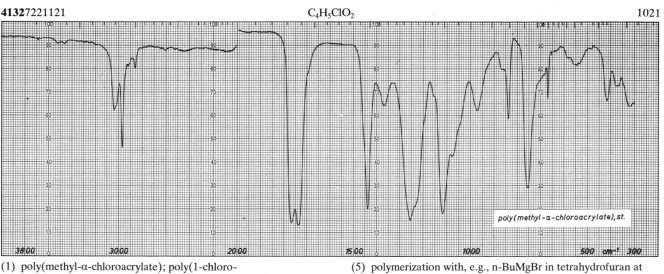

poly(methyl-α-chloroacrylate),st.

(1) poly(methyl-α-chloroacrylate); poly(1-chloro-
1-carbonyloxymethyl-ethylene)
(2) white powder
(3) G.R. Dever, Polymer Science & Engineering Dept.,
University of Massachusetts, Amherst, Mass.
(4) predominantly syndiotactic

(5) polymerization with, e.g., n-BuMgBr in tetrahydrofuran at
−78 °C
(6) B. Wesslén, R. Lenz, Makromolecules 4 (1971) 20...4
(7) film from $CHCl_3$ on CsI
(8) band at 667 cm^{-1} due to residual $CHCl_3$

41327221121 $C_4H_5ClO_2$ 1022

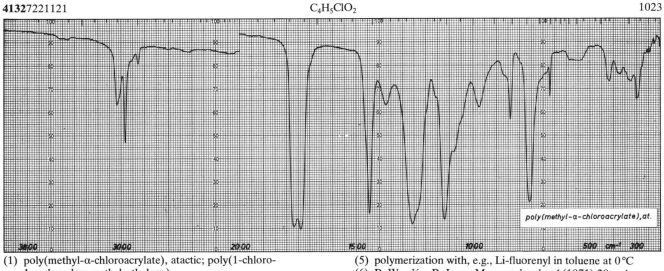

(1) poly(methyl-α-chloroacrylate), atactic; poly(1-chloro-
1-carbonyloxymethyl-ethylene)
(2) white powder
(3) K. Matsuzaki, Faculty of Engineering, University of Tokyo
(5) anionic polymerization of the monomer in toluene solution
with n-butyllithium at −40 °C

(6) K. Matsuzaki, T. Uryu, K. Ito, Makromol. Chem. 126 (1969)
292...95
(7) ground with KBr (1.2/350) and $CHCl_3$, dried and pressed

41327221121 $C_4H_5ClO_2$ 1023

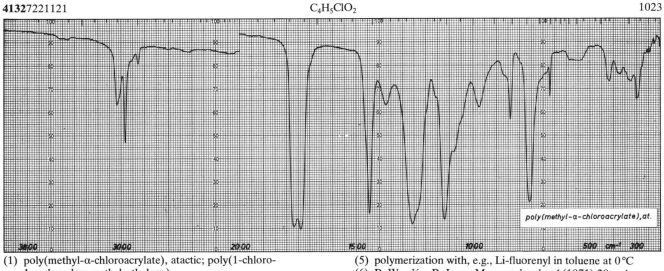

poly(methyl-α-chloroacrylate),at.

(1) poly(methyl-α-chloroacrylate), atactic; poly(1-chloro-
1-carbonyloxymethyl-ethylene)
(2) white powder
(3) G.R. Dever, Polymer Science & Engineering Dept.,
University of Massachusetts, Amherst, Mass.

(5) polymerization with, e.g., Li-fluorenyl in toluene at 0 °C
(6) B. Wesslén, R. Lenz, Macromolecules 4 (1971) 20...4
(7) film from $CHCl_3$ on CsI
(8) band at 667 cm^{-1} due to residual $CHCl_3$

41327221121 $C_5H_7ClO_2$ 1024

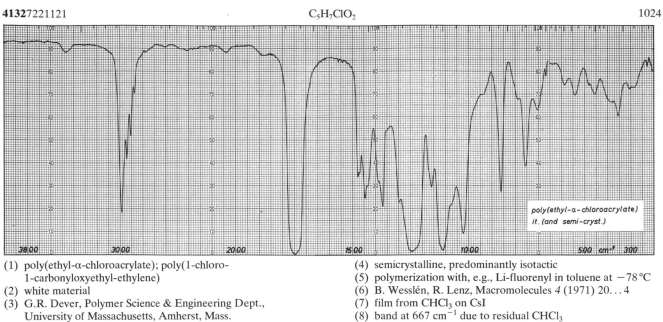

poly(ethyl-α-chloroacrylate)
it. (and semi-cryst.)

(1) poly(ethyl-α-chloroacrylate); poly(1-chloro-
    1-carbonyloxyethyl-ethylene)
(2) white material
(3) G.R. Dever, Polymer Science & Engineering Dept.,
    University of Massachusetts, Amherst, Mass.

(4) semicrystalline, predominantly isotactic
(5) polymerization with, e.g., Li-fluorenyl in toluene at $-78\,°C$
(6) B. Wesslén, R. Lenz, Macromolecules *4* (1971) 20…4
(7) film from $CHCl_3$ on CsI
(8) band at 667 cm^{-1} due to residual $CHCl_3$

41327221121 $C_5H_7ClO_2$ 1025

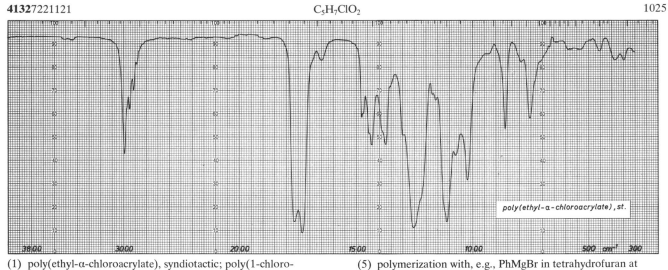

poly(ethyl-α-chloroacrylate), st.

(1) poly(ethyl-α-chloroacrylate), syndiotactic; poly(1-chloro-
    1-carbonyloxyethyl-ethylene)
(2) white material
(3) G.R. Dever, Polymer Science & Engineering Dept.,
    University of Massachusetts, Amherst, Mass.

(5) polymerization with, e.g., PhMgBr in tetrahydrofuran at
    $-78\,°C$
(6) B. Wesslén, R. Lenz, Macromolecules *4* (1971) 20…4
(7) film from $CHCl_3$ on CsI

41327221121 $C_5H_7ClO_2$ 1026

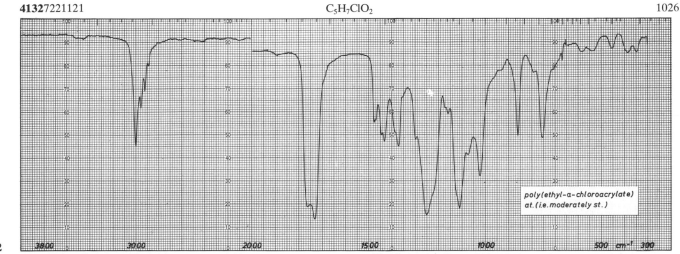

poly(ethyl-α-chloroacrylate)
at. (i.e. moderately st.)

(1) poly(ethyl-α-chloroacrylate), atactic; poly(1-chloro-
    1-carbonyloxyethyl-ethylene)
(2) white material
(3) G.R. Dever, Polymer Science & Engineering Dept.,
    University of Massachusetts, Amherst, Mass.

(5) photo-chemical polymerization in bulk at room temperature
(6) B. Wesslén, R. Lenz, Macromolecules *4* (1971) 20…4
(7) film from $CHCl_3$ on CsI
(8) band at 667 cm^{-1} due to residual $CHCl_3$

41327221121 $C_6H_9ClO_2$ 1027

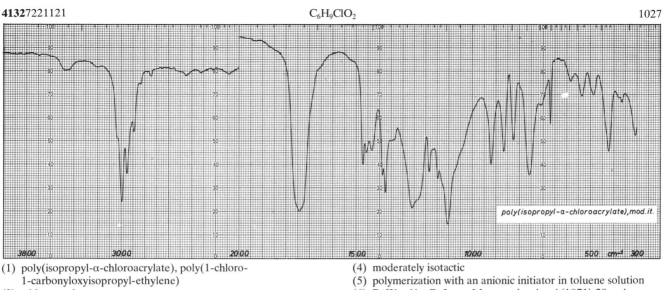

poly(isopropyl-α-chloroacrylate), mod. it.

(1) poly(isopropyl-α-chloroacrylate), poly(1-chloro-1-carbonyloxyisopropyl-ethylene)
(2) white powder
(3) G.R. Dever, Polymer Science & Engineering Dept., University of Massachusetts, Amherst, Mass.
(4) moderately isotactic
(5) polymerization with an anionic initiator in toluene solution
(6) B. Wesslén, R. Lenz, Macromolecules *4* (1971) 20...4
(7) film from $CHCl_3$ on KBr
(8) band at 667 cm^{-1} due to residual $CHCl_3$

41327221121 $C_6H_9ClO_2$ 1028

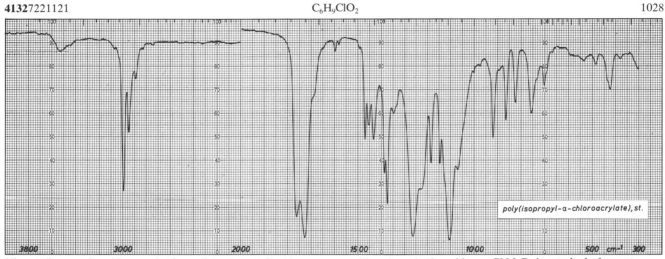

poly(isopropyl-α-chloroacrylate), st.

(1) poly(isopropyl-α-chloroacrylate), syndiotactic; poly(1-chloro-1-carbonyloxyisopropyl-ethylene)
(2) white powder
(3) G.R. Dever, Polymer Science & Engineering Dept., University of Massachusetts, Amherst, Mass.
(5) polymerization with, e.g. PhMgBr in tetrahydrofuran at −78 °C
(6) B. Wesslén, R. Lenz, Macromolecules *4* (1971) 20...4
(7) film from $CHCl_3$ on KBr

41327221121 $C_6H_9ClO_2$ 1029

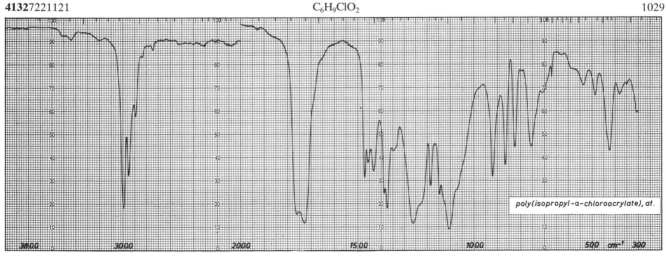

poly(isopropyl-α-chloroacrylate), at.

(1) poly(isopropyl-α-chloroacrylate), atactic; poly(1-chloro-1-carbonyloxyisopropyl-ethylene)
(2) white powder
(3) G.R. Dever, Polymer Science & Engineering Dept., University of Massachusetts, Amherst, Mass.
(5) polymerization in toluene solution at room temperature with an anionic initiator, e.g., Li-fluorenyl
(6) B. Wesslén, R. Lenz, Macromolecules *4* (1971) 20...4
(7) film from $CHCl_3$ on KBr
(8) band at 667 cm^{-1} due to residual $CHCl_3$

4132741212 $C_{36}H_{36}Cl_4O_{14}$ 1030

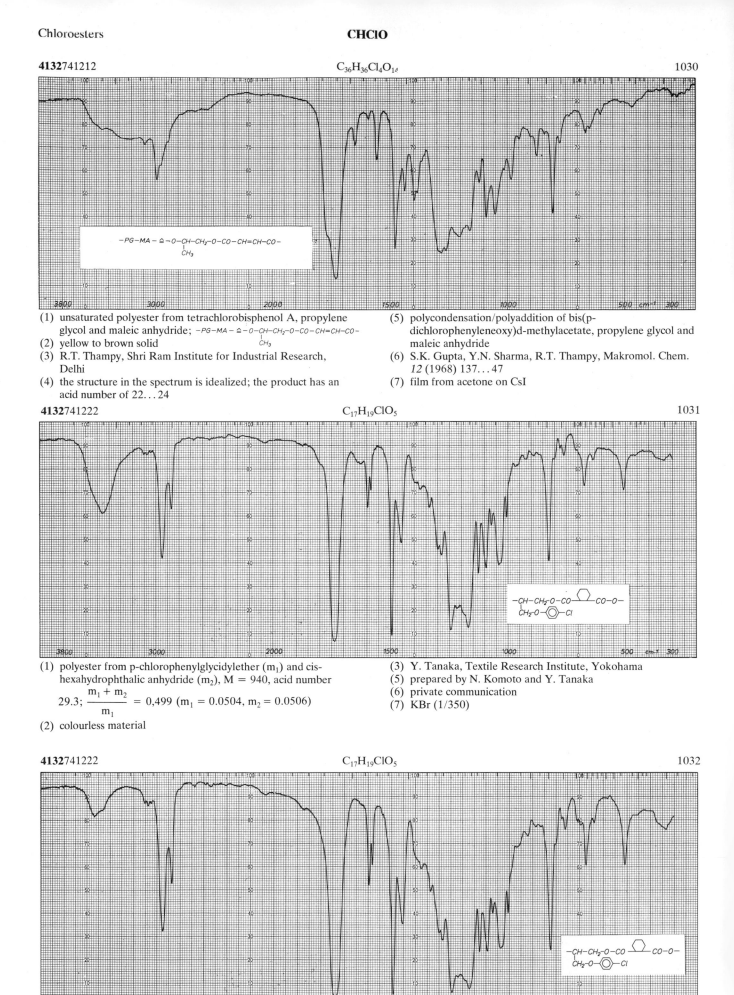

(1) unsaturated polyester from tetrachlorobisphenol A, propylene glycol and maleic anhydride; $-PG-MA- \hat{=} -O-CH-CH_2-O-CO-CH=CH-CO-$
$\quad\quad\quad\quad\quad\quad\quad\quad\quad\quad\quad\quad CH_3$
(2) yellow to brown solid
(3) R.T. Thampy, Shri Ram Institute for Industrial Research, Delhi
(4) the structure in the spectrum is idealized; the product has an acid number of 22...24

(5) polycondensation/polyaddition of bis(p-dichlorophenyleneoxy)d-methylacetate, propylene glycol and maleic anhydride
(6) S.K. Gupta, Y.N. Sharma, R.T. Thampy, Makromol. Chem. *12* (1968) 137...47
(7) film from acetone on CsI

4132741222 $C_{17}H_{19}ClO_5$ 1031

(1) polyester from p-chlorophenylglycidylether (m_1) and cis-hexahydrophthalic anhydride (m_2), M = 940, acid number 29.3; $\dfrac{m_1 + m_2}{m_1} = 0{,}499$ (m_1 = 0.0504, m_2 = 0.0506)
(2) colourless material

(3) Y. Tanaka, Textile Research Institute, Yokohama
(5) prepared by N. Komoto and Y. Tanaka
(6) private communication
(7) KBr (1/350)

4132741222 $C_{17}H_{19}ClO_5$ 1032

(1) polyester from p-chlorophenylglycidyl ether (m_1) and cis-hexahydrophthalic anhydride (m_2), M = 1340, acid number 28.1; $\dfrac{m_1 + m_2}{m_1} = 0.590$ (m_1 = 0.0607, m_2 = 0.0421)
(2) colourless material

(3) Y. Tanaka, Textile Research Institute, Yokohama
(5) prepared by N. Komoto and Y. Tanaka
(6) private communication
(7) KBr (2/350)

41327711–2121111 $C_6H_2Cl_2O_2–C_8H_8$ 1033

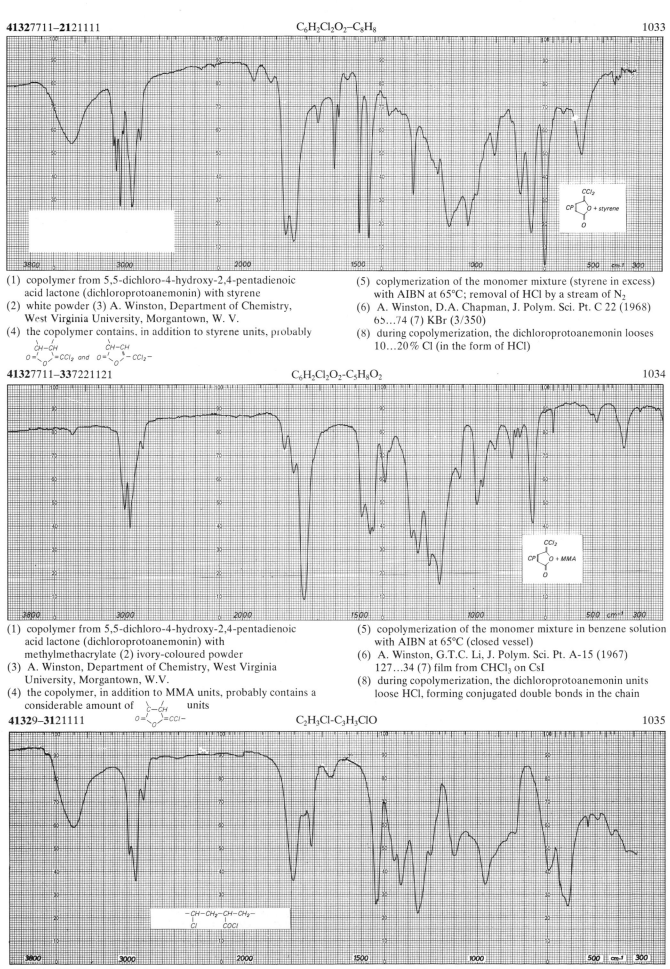

(1) copolymer from 5,5-dichloro-4-hydroxy-2,4-pentadienoic
acid lactone (dichloroprotoanemonin) with styrene
(2) white powder (3) A. Winston, Department of Chemistry,
West Virginia University, Morgantown, W. V.
(4) the copolymer contains, in addition to styrene units, probably

(5) copolymerization of the monomer mixture (styrene in excess)
with AIBN at 65°C; removal of HCl by a stream of N_2
(6) A. Winston, D.A. Chapman, J. Polym. Sci. Pt. C 22 (1968)
65...74 (7) KBr (3/350)
(8) during copolymerization, the dichloroprotoanemonin looses
10...20% Cl (in the form of HCl)

41327711–337221121 $C_6H_2Cl_2O_2-C_5H_8O_2$ 1034

(1) copolymer from 5,5-dichloro-4-hydroxy-2,4-pentadienoic
acid lactone (dichloroprotoanemonin) with
methylmethacrylate (2) ivory-coloured powder
(3) A. Winston, Department of Chemistry, West Virginia
University, Morgantown, W.V.
(4) the copolymer, in addition to MMA units, probably contains a
considerable amount of units

(5) copolymerization of the monomer mixture in benzene solution
with AIBN at 65°C (closed vessel)
(6) A. Winston, G.T.C. Li, J. Polym. Sci. Pt. A-15 (1967)
127...34 (7) film from $CHCl_3$ on CsI
(8) during copolymerization, the dichloroprotoanemonin units
loose HCl, forming conjugated double bonds in the chain

41329–3121111 $C_2H_3Cl-C_3H_3ClO$ 1035

(1) vinylchloride-carbonmonoxide copolymer
(2) white, hygroscopic material
(3) L. Ratti, Montecatini Edison, Centro Ricerche, Bollate, Milano
(4) in addition to 1-chloroethylene units, the copolymer contains
1-chlorocarbonyl-ethylene (acrylchloride) units
(5) copolymerization in bulk at 50°C with bis(4-t-

butylcyclohexyl)-peroxydicarbonate as initiator
(6) R. Ratti, F. Visani, M. Ragazzini, Europ. Polym. J. 9 (1973)
429...33
(7) ground with KBr (2/350) and $CHCl_3$, dried and pressed
(8) during preparation, some of the acid chloride units were
hydrolyzed

4133331 $C_6H_2Br_2O$ 1036

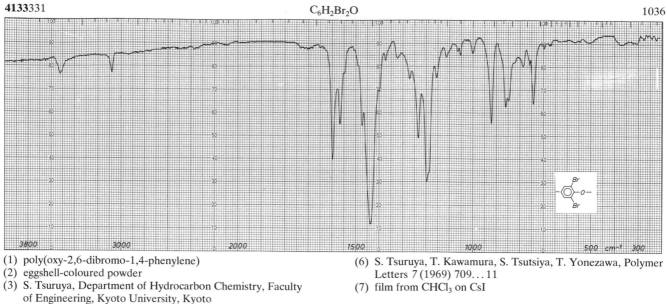

(1) poly(oxy-2,6-dibromo-1,4-phenylene)
(2) eggshell-coloured powder
(3) S. Tsuruya, Department of Hydrocarbon Chemistry, Faculty of Engineering, Kyoto University, Kyoto
(5) oxidative polycondensation of 2,6-dichlorophenol with $CuCl_2$/ CH_3ONa in CH_3OH

(6) S. Tsuruya, T. Kawamura, S. Tsutsiya, T. Yonezawa, Polymer Letters *7* (1969) 709...11
(7) film from $CHCl_3$ on CsI

41337221111 $C_{14}H_{25}BrO_2$ 1037

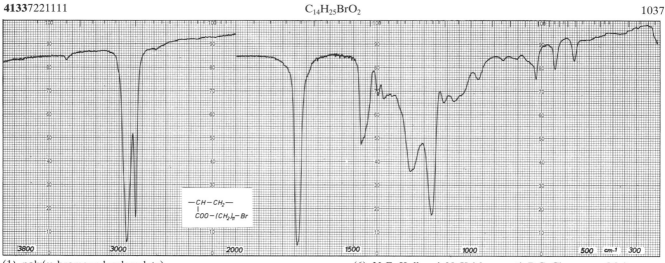
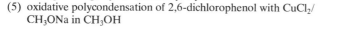

(1) poly(ω-bromoundecylacrylate)
(3) N.G. Kulkarni, Regional Research Lab., Hyderabad
(5) radical-initiated polymerization in benzene solution with bezoylperoxide as initiator

(6) N.G. Kulkarni, N. Krishnamurti, P.C. Chatterjee, M.A. Sivasamban, Makromol. Chem. *147* (1971) 149...53
(7) film from $CHCl_3$ on CsI

41337221121 $C_{15}H_{27}BrO_2$ 1038

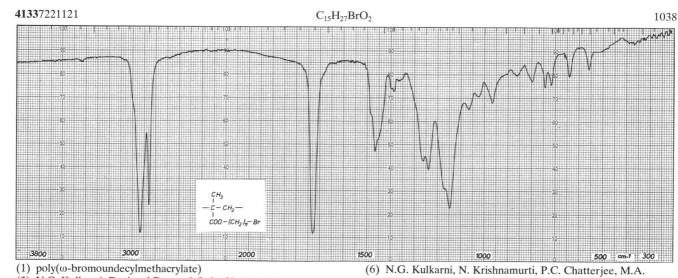
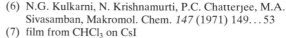

(1) poly(ω-bromoundecylmethacrylate)
(3) N.G. Kulkarni, Regional Research Lab., Hyderabad
(5) radical-initiated polymerization in benzene solution with benzoylperoxide as initiator

(6) N.G. Kulkarni, N. Krishnamurti, P.C. Chatterjee, M.A. Sivasamban, Makromol. Chem. *147* (1971) 149...53
(7) film from $CHCl_3$ on CsI

4133741212   C₃₆H₃₆Br₄O₁₄   1039

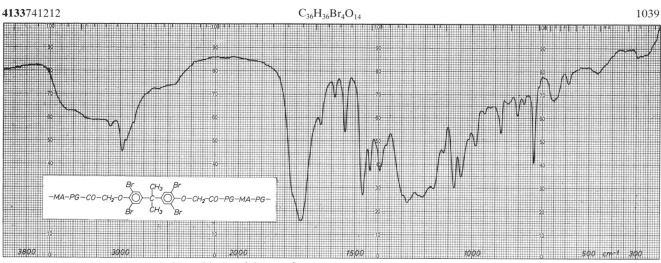

(1) unsaturated polyester from tetrabromobisphenol A, propylene
    glycol and maleic anhydride
(2) yellow to brown solid
(3) R.T. Thampy, Shri Ram Institute for Industrial Research,
    Delhi
(4) the structure in the spectrum is idealized; the product has an
    acid number of 22

(5) polycondensation/polyaddition of isopropylydene-2-bis(p-
    dibromophenyleneoxy)di-methylacetate, propylene glycol and
    maleic anhydride
(6) S.K. Gupta, Y.N. Sharma, R.T. Thampy, Makromol. Chem.
    120 (1968) 137...47
(7) film from acetone on CsI

41342   C₁₆H₂₁JO₄   1040

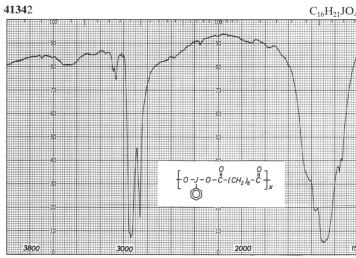
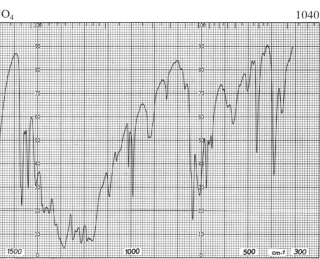

(1) polyester from iodosobenzene and sebacic acid
(2) white waxy material
(3) H.K. Livingston . ±, Wayne State University, Detroit, Mich.
(5) reaction of iodobenzenedichloride with silversebacate in
    acetone solution

(6) H.K. Livingston, J.W. Sullivan, J. Polym. Sci. C *22* (1968)
    195...202
(7) ground with KBr (7/1000) and acetone, dried and pressed

421114   C₇H₇NO   1041

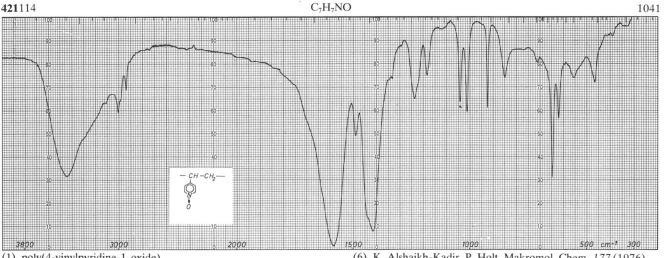

(1) poly(4-vinylpyridine-1-oxide)
(2) light-yellow powder
(3) K. Alshaikh-Kadir, Department of Chemistry, University of
    Reading, Berks.
(5) oxidation of poly(4-vinylpyridine) with H₂O₂ in CH₃COH;
    P.F. Holt, E.T. Nasrallah, J. Chem. Soc. B *1968*, 400

(6) K. Alshaikh-Kadir, P. Holt, Makromol. Chem. *177* (1976)
    311...7
(7) KBr (1.5/350)
(8) the material is strongly hygroscopic

421114   C₇H₇NO   1042

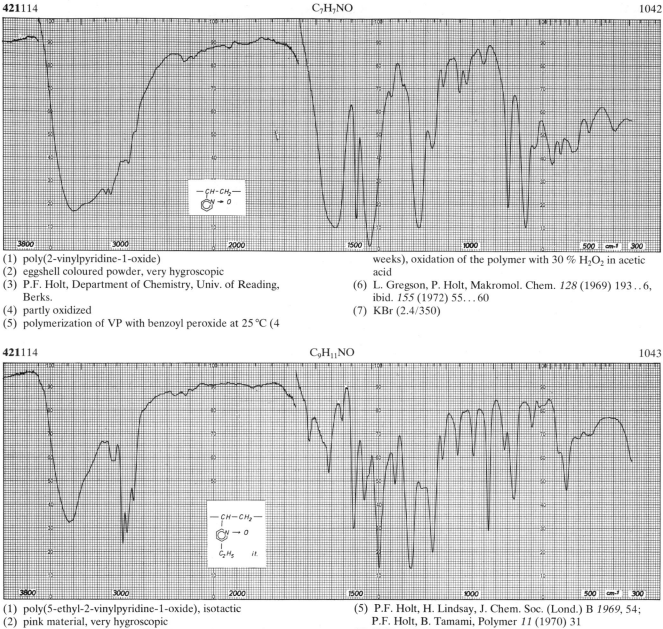

(1) poly(2-vinylpyridine-1-oxide)
(2) eggshell coloured powder, very hygroscopic
(3) P.F. Holt, Department of Chemistry, Univ. of Reading, Berks.
(4) partly oxidized
(5) polymerization of VP with benzoyl peroxide at 25 °C (4

weeks), oxidation of the polymer with 30 % H₂O₂ in acetic acid
(6) L. Gregson, P. Holt, Makromol. Chem. *128* (1969) 193..6, ibid. *155* (1972) 55...60
(7) KBr (2.4/350)

421114   C₉H₁₁NO   1043

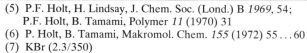

(1) poly(5-ethyl-2-vinylpyridine-1-oxide), isotactic
(2) pink material, very hygroscopic
(3) P.F. Holt, Department of Chemistry, Univ. of Reading, Berks.
(5) P.F. Holt, H. Lindsay, J. Chem. Soc. (Lond.) B *1969*, 54; P.F. Holt, B. Tamami, Polymer *11* (1970) 31
(6) P. Holt, B. Tamami, Makromol. Chem. *155* (1972) 55...60
(7) KBr (2.3/350)

421114   C₉H₁₁NO   1044

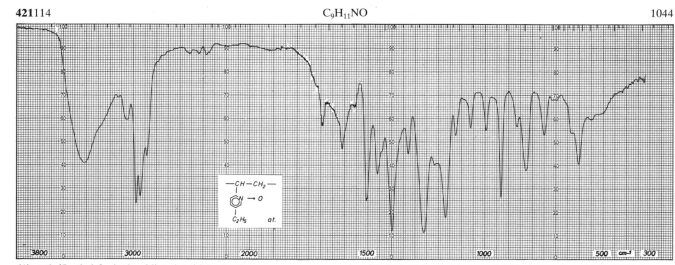

(1) poly(5-ethyl-2-vinylpyridine-1-oxide), atactic
(2) pink material, very hygroscopic
(3) P.F. Holt, Department of Chemistry, Univ. of Reading, Berks.
(5) P.F. Holt, H. Lindsay, J. Chem. Soc. (Lond.) B *1969*, 54; P.F. Holt, B. Tamami, Polymer *11* (1970) 31
(6) P. Holt, B. Tamami, Makromol. Chem. *155* (1952) 55...60
(7) KBr (2.3/350)

421121 $C_8H_{14}N_2O_3$ 1045

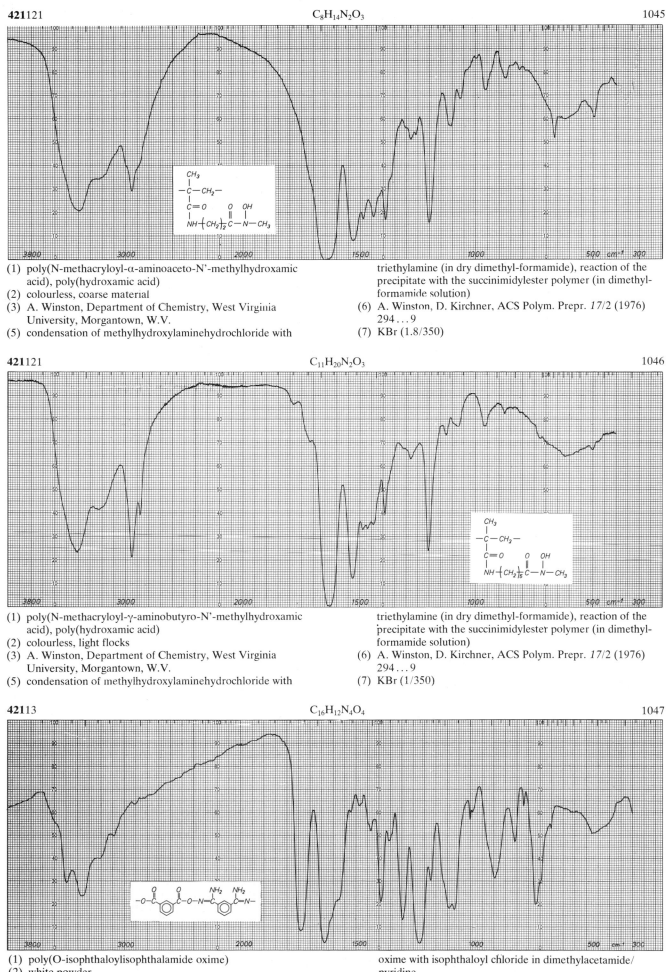

(1) poly(N-methacryloyl-α-aminoaceto-N'-methylhydroxamic
    acid), poly(hydroxamic acid)
(2) colourless, coarse material
(3) A. Winston, Department of Chemistry, West Virginia
    University, Morgantown, W.V.
(5) condensation of methylhydroxylaminehydrochloride with

triethylamine (in dry dimethyl-formamide), reaction of the
precipitate with the succinimidylester polymer (in dimethylformamide solution)
(6) A. Winston, D. Kirchner, ACS Polym. Prepr. *17/2* (1976)
    294...9
(7) KBr (1.8/350)

421121 $C_{11}H_{20}N_2O_3$ 1046

(1) poly(N-methacryloyl-γ-aminobutyro-N'-methylhydroxamic
    acid), poly(hydroxamic acid)
(2) colourless, light flocks
(3) A. Winston, Department of Chemistry, West Virginia
    University, Morgantown, W.V.
(5) condensation of methylhydroxylaminehydrochloride with

triethylamine (in dry dimethyl-formamide), reaction of the
precipitate with the succinimidylester polymer (in dimethylformamide solution)
(6) A. Winston, D. Kirchner, ACS Polym. Prepr. *17/2* (1976)
    294...9
(7) KBr (1/350)

42113 $C_{16}H_{12}N_4O_4$ 1047

(1) poly(O-isophthaloylisophthalamide oxime)
(2) white powder
(3) J.J. Lindberg, Department of Wood and Polymer Chemistry,
    University of Helsinki, Helsinki
(5) low-temperature solution polycondensation of isophthalamide

oxime with isophthaloyl chloride in dimethylacetamide/
pyridine
(6) A. Lehtinen, S. Purokoski, J.J. Lindberg, Makromol. Chem.
    176 (1975) 1553...66
(7) KBr (2/350)

4211522   C$_{32}$H$_{26}$N$_2$O$_{10}$ 1048

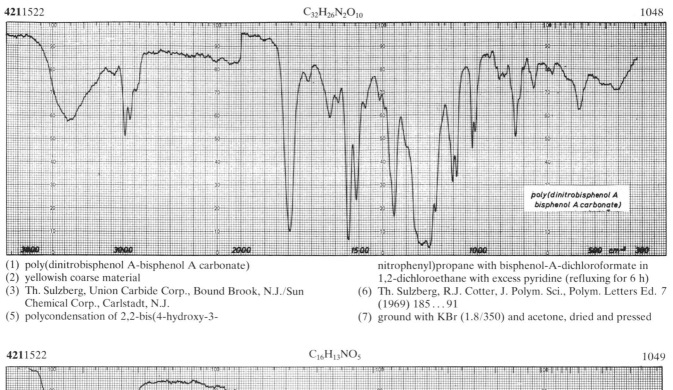

poly(dinitrobisphenol A bisphenol A carbonate)

(1) poly(dinitrobisphenol A-bisphenol A carbonate)
(2) yellowish coarse material
(3) Th. Sulzberg, Union Carbide Corp., Bound Brook, N.J./Sun Chemical Corp., Carlstadt, N.J.
(5) polycondensation of 2,2-bis(4-hydroxy-3-

nitrophenyl)propane with bisphenol-A-dichloroformate in 1,2-dichloroethane with excess pyridine (refluxing for 6 h)
(6) Th. Sulzberg, R.J. Cotter, J. Polym. Sci., Polym. Letters Ed. 7 (1969) 185...91
(7) ground with KBr (1.8/350) and acetone, dried and pressed

4211522   C$_{16}$H$_{13}$NO$_5$ 1049

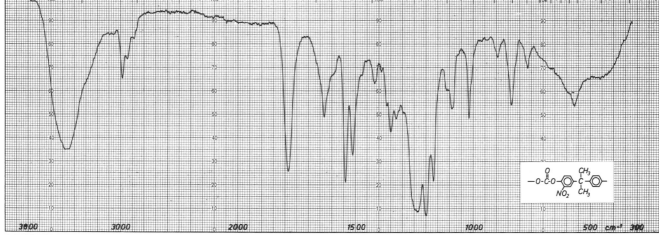

(1) bisphenol A, polycarbonate of nitro derivative, polycarbonate of 3-nitrobisphenol A
(2) bright-yellow powder
(3) Th. Sulzberg, Sun Chemical Corporation, Carlstadt, N.Y.

(5) polycondensation of bisphenol A dichloroformate and AgNo$_3$ in acetonitrile
(6) T. Sulzberg, R.J. Cotter, Polymer Letters 7 (1969) 185...91
(7) KBr (1/350)

4211522   C$_{16}$H$_{12}$N$_2$O$_7$ 1050

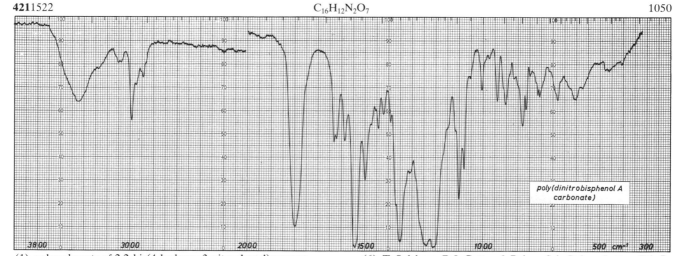

poly(dinitrobisphenol A carbonate)

(1) polycarbonate of 2,2-bis(4-hydroxy-3-nitrophenyl)propane
(2) light yellow powder
(3) Th. Sulzberg, Sun Chemical Corporation, Carlstadt, N.Y.
(5) polycondensation of dinitrobisphenol A with phosgene in pyridine at 50 °C

(6) T. Sulzberg, R.J. Cotter, J. Polym. Sci., Polym. Letters Ed. 7 (1969) 185...81
(7) KBr (2/350)

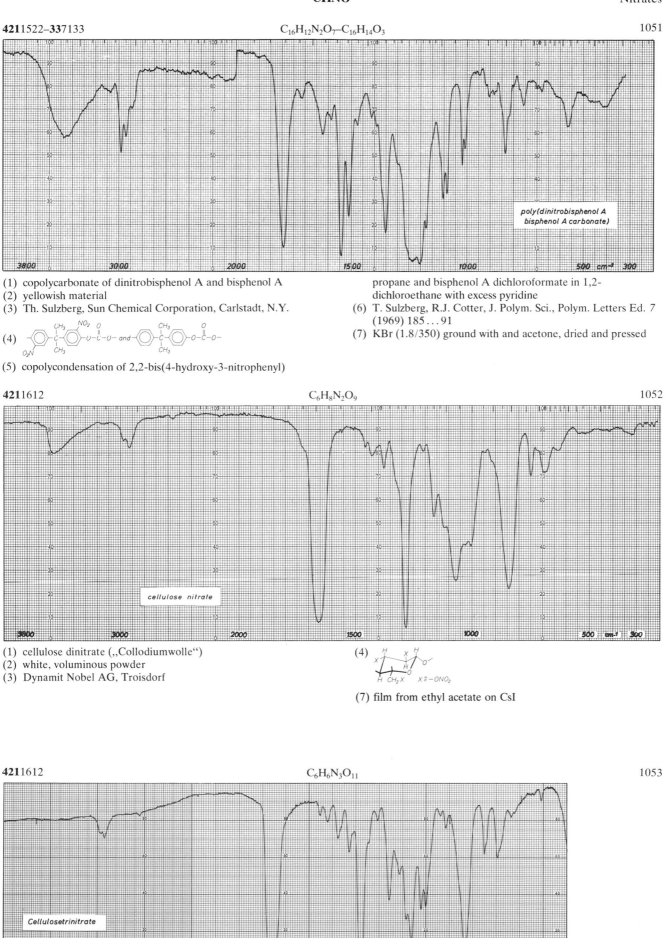

poly(dinitrobisphenol A bisphenol A carbonate)

(1) copolycarbonate of dinitrobisphenol A and bisphenol A
(2) yellowish material
(3) Th. Sulzberg, Sun Chemical Corporation, Carlstadt, N.Y.

(4)

(5) copolycondensation of 2,2-bis(4-hydroxy-3-nitrophenyl)

propane and bisphenol A dichloroformate in 1,2-dichloroethane with excess pyridine
(6) T. Sulzberg, R.J. Cotter, J. Polym. Sci., Polym. Letters Ed. 7 (1969) 185...91
(7) KBr (1.8/350) ground with and acetone, dried and pressed

cellulose nitrate

(1) cellulose dinitrate („Collodiumwolle")
(2) white, voluminous powder
(3) Dynamit Nobel AG, Troisdorf

(4) $X \hat{=} -ONO_2$

(7) film from ethyl acetate on CsI

Cellulosetrinitrate

(1) cellulosetrinitrate
(2) turbid film
(3) M. Takai, Faculty of Engineering, Hokkaido University, Sapporo

(4) $X = -ONO_2$

(5) nitration of purified ramie
(6) S. Watanabe, J. Hayashi, K. Imai, J. Polym. Sci. C 23 (1968) 809...23
(7) film

42121111   C$_2$H$_3$NO   1054

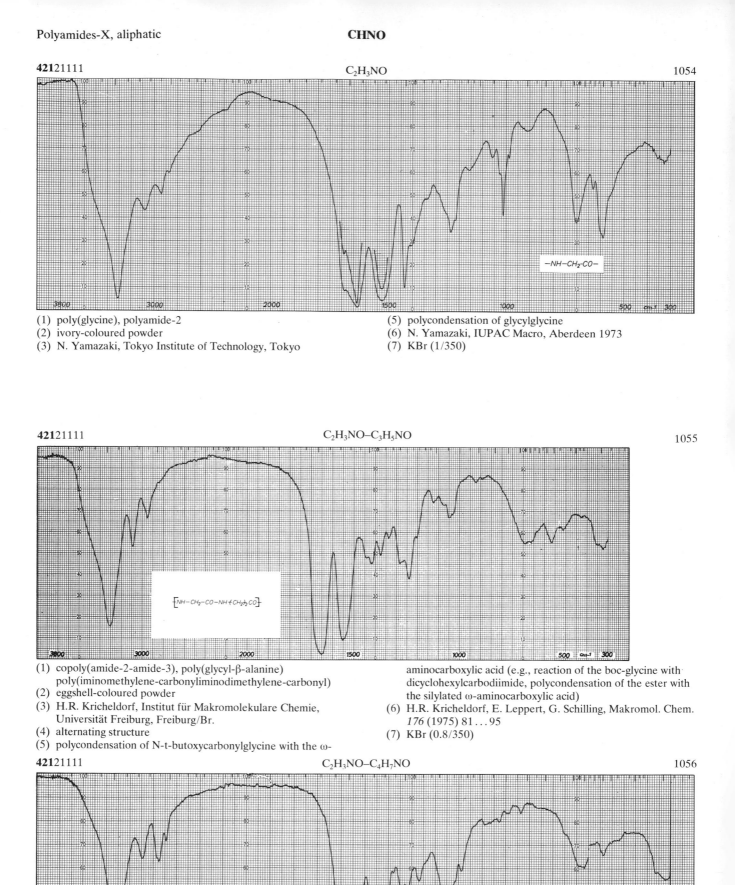

−NH−CH$_2$−CO−

(1) poly(glycine), polyamide-2
(2) ivory-coloured powder
(3) N. Yamazaki, Tokyo Institute of Technology, Tokyo
(5) polycondensation of glycylglycine
(6) N. Yamazaki, IUPAC Macro, Aberdeen 1973
(7) KBr (1/350)

42121111   C$_2$H$_3$NO–C$_3$H$_5$NO   1055

⁅NH−CH$_2$−CO−NH−(CH$_2$)$_2$−CO⁆

(1) copoly(amide-2-amide-3), poly(glycyl-β-alanine)
poly(iminomethylene-carbonyliminodimethylene-carbonyl)
(2) eggshell-coloured powder
(3) H.R. Kricheldorf, Institut für Makromolekulare Chemie,
Universität Freiburg, Freiburg/Br.
(4) alternating structure
(5) polycondensation of N-t-butoxycarbonylglycine with the ω-
aminocarboxylic acid (e.g., reaction of the boc-glycine with
dicyclohexylcarbodiimide, polycondensation of the ester with
the silylated ω-aminocarboxylic acid)
(6) H.R. Kricheldorf, E. Leppert, G. Schilling, Makromol. Chem.
176 (1975) 81 … 95
(7) KBr (0.8/350)

42121111   C$_2$H$_3$NO–C$_4$H$_7$NO   1056

⁅NH−CH$_2$−CO−NH−(CH$_2$)$_3$−CO⁆

(1) poly(glycyl-γ-butyramide), copolyamide from glycine and γ-
aminobutyric acid; copoly(amide-2-amide-4),
poly(iminomethylene-carbonyliminotrimethylenecarbonyl)
(2) greyish-brown powder
(3) H.R. Kricheldorf, Institut für Makromolekulare Chemie,
Universität Freiburg, Freiburg/Br.
(4) alternating structure
(5) polycondensation of N-t-butoxycarbonylglycine with the ω-
aminocarboxylic acid (e.g.; reaction of the boc-glycine with
dicyclohexylcarbodiimide, polycondensation of the ester with
the silylated ω-aminocarboxylic acid)
(6) H.R. Kricheldorf, E. Leppert, G. Schilling, Makromol. Chem.
176 (1975) 81 … 95
(7) KBr (0.8/350)

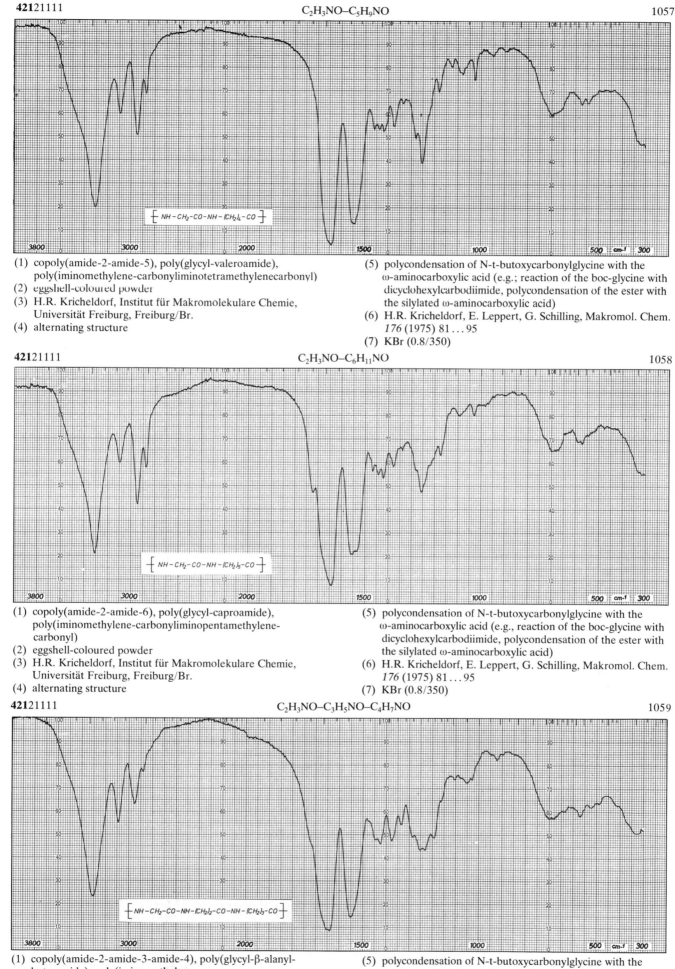

(1) copoly(amide-2-amide-5), poly(glycyl-valeroamide), poly(iminomethylene-carbonyliminotetramethylenecarbonyl)
(2) eggshell-coloured powder
(3) H.R. Kricheldorf, Institut für Makromolekulare Chemie, Universität Freiburg, Freiburg/Br.
(4) alternating structure
(5) polycondensation of N-t-butoxycarbonylglycine with the ω-aminocarboxylic acid (e.g.; reaction of the boc-glycine with dicyclohexylcarbodiimide, polycondensation of the ester with the silylated ω-aminocarboxylic acid)
(6) H.R. Kricheldorf, E. Leppert, G. Schilling, Makromol. Chem. *176* (1975) 81...95
(7) KBr (0.8/350)

(1) copoly(amide-2-amide-6), poly(glycyl-caproamide), poly(iminomethylene-carbonyliminopentamethylene-carbonyl)
(2) eggshell-coloured powder
(3) H.R. Kricheldorf, Institut für Makromolekulare Chemie, Universität Freiburg, Freiburg/Br.
(4) alternating structure
(5) polycondensation of N-t-butoxycarbonylglycine with the ω-aminocarboxylic acid (e.g., reaction of the boc-glycine with dicyclohexylcarbodiimide, polycondensation of the ester with the silylated ω-aminocarboxylic acid)
(6) H.R. Kricheldorf, E. Leppert, G. Schilling, Makromol. Chem. *176* (1975) 81...95
(7) KBr (0.8/350)

(1) copoly(amide-2-amide-3-amide-4), poly(glycyl-β-alanyl-butyramide), poly(iminomethylene-carbonyliminodimethylene-carbonyliminotrimethylenecarbonyl)
(2) greyish-brown powder
(3) H.R. Kricheldorf, Institut für Makromolekulare Chemie, Universität Freiburg, Freiburg/Br.
(4) alternating structure
(5) polycondensation of N-t-butoxycarbonylglycine with the ω-aminocarboxylic acid (e.g., reaction of the boc-glycine with dicyclohexylcarbodiimide, polycondensation of the ester with the silylated ω-aminocarboxylic acid)
(6) H.R. Kricheldorf, E. Leppert, G. Schilling, Makromol. Chem. *176* (1975) 81...95
(7) KBr (0.8/350)

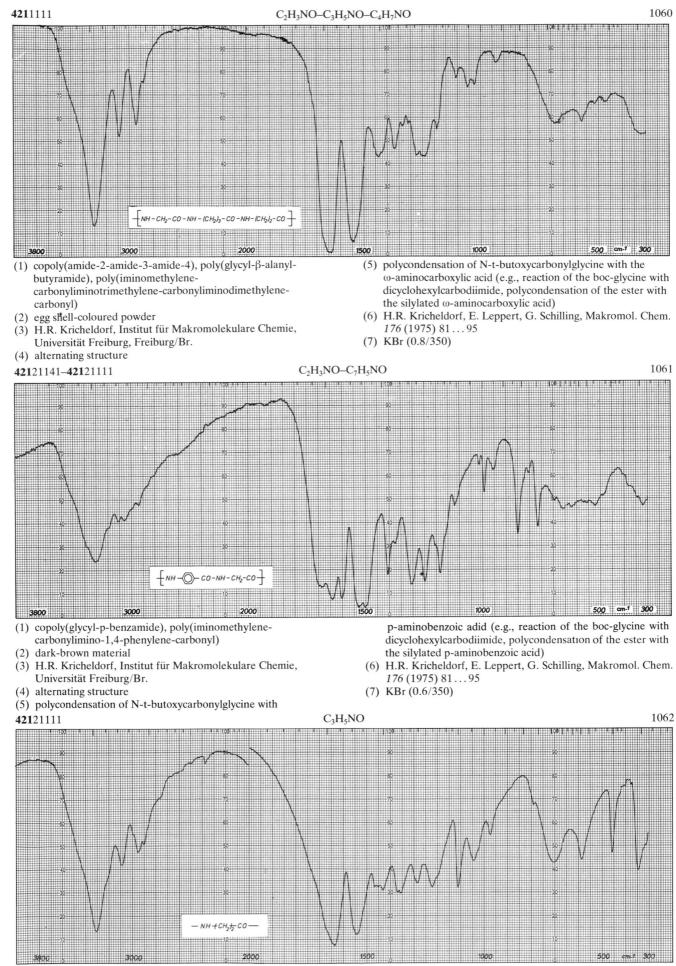

4211111 $C_2H_3NO–C_3H_5NO–C_4H_7NO$ 1060

[NH–CH₂–CO–NH–(CH₂)₃–CO–NH–(CH₂)₂–CO]

(1) copoly(amide-2-amide-3-amide-4), poly(glycyl-β-alanyl-butyramide), poly(iminomethylene-carbonyliminotrimethylene-carbonyliminodimethylene-carbonyl)
(2) egg shell-coloured powder
(3) H.R. Kricheldorf, Institut für Makromolekulare Chemie, Universität Freiburg, Freiburg/Br.
(4) alternating structure

(5) polycondensation of N-t-butoxycarbonylglycine with the ω-aminocarboxylic acid (e.g., reaction of the boc-glycine with dicyclohexylcarbodiimide, polycondensation of the ester with the silylated ω-aminocarboxylic acid)
(6) H.R. Kricheldorf, E. Leppert, G. Schilling, Makromol. Chem. *176* (1975) 81...95
(7) KBr (0.8/350)

42121141–**42121**111 $C_2H_3NO–C_7H_5NO$ 1061

[NH–⬡–CO–NH–CH₂–CO]

(1) copoly(glycyl-p-benzamide), poly(iminomethylene-carbonylimino-1,4-phenylene-carbonyl)
(2) dark-brown material
(3) H.R. Kricheldorf, Institut für Makromolekulare Chemie, Universität Freiburg/Br.
(4) alternating structure
(5) polycondensation of N-t-butoxycarbonylglycine with

p-aminobenzoic adid (e.g., reaction of the boc-glycine with dicyclohexylcarbodiimide, polycondensation of the ester with the silylated p-aminobenzoic acid)
(6) H.R. Kricheldorf, E. Leppert, G. Schilling, Makromol. Chem. *176* (1975) 81...95
(7) KBr (0.6/350)

42121111 C_3H_5NO 1062

— NH–(CH₂)₂–CO —

(1) polyamide-3, poly(β-alanine), poly(iminodimethylenecarbonyl)
(2) yellow material
(3) Y. Iwakura, K. Haga, Department of Synthetic Chemistry, Faculty of Engineering, University of Tokyo, Tokyo

(5) polymerization of perhydro-1,5-diazocine-2,6-dione
(6) Y. Iwakura, K. Uno, M. Akiyama, K. Haga, J. Polym. Sci. A 7 (1969) 657...66
(7) KBr (2.6/300)

42121111 C₃H₅NO 1063

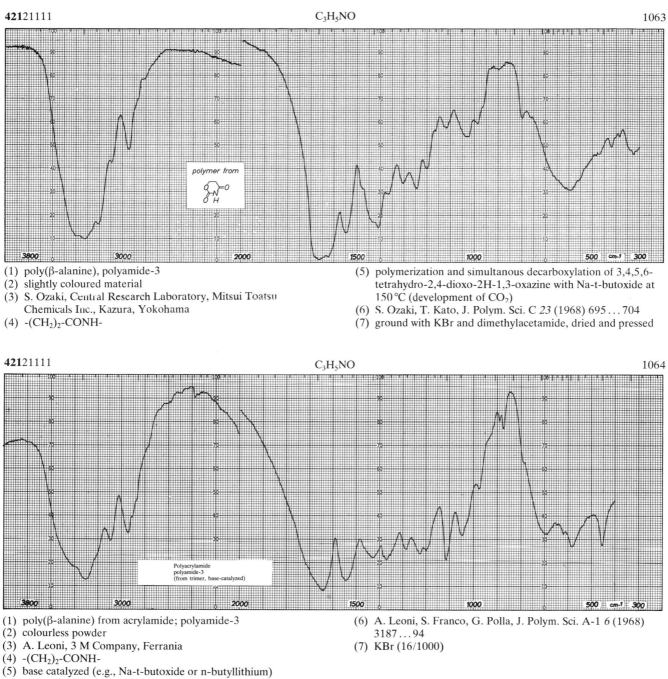

(1) poly(β-alanine), polyamide-3
(2) slightly coloured material
(3) S. Ozaki, Central Research Laboratory, Mitsui Toatsu Chemicals Inc., Kazura, Yokohama
(4) -(CH₂)₂-CONH-

(5) polymerization and simultanous decarboxylation of 3,4,5,6-tetrahydro-2,4-dioxo-2H-1,3-oxazine with Na-t-butoxide at 150 °C (development of CO₂)
(6) S. Ozaki, T. Kato, J. Polym. Sci. C 23 (1968) 695...704
(7) ground with KBr and dimethylacetamide, dried and pressed

42121111 C₃H₅NO 1064

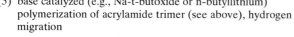

Polyacrylamide
polyamide-3
(from trimer, base-catalyzed)

(1) poly(β-alanine) from acrylamide; polyamide-3
(2) colourless powder
(3) A. Leoni, 3 M Company, Ferrania
(4) -(CH₂)₂-CONH-
(5) base catalyzed (e.g., Na-t-butoxide or n-butyllithium) polymerization of acrylamide trimer (see above), hydrogen migration

(6) A. Leoni, S. Franco, G. Polla, J. Polym. Sci. A-1 6 (1968) 3187...94
(7) KBr (16/1000)

42121111 C₃H₅NO 1065

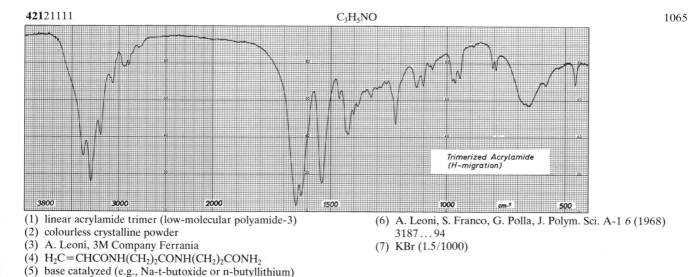

Trimerized Acrylamide
(H-migration)

(1) linear acrylamide trimer (low-molecular polyamide-3)
(2) colourless crystalline powder
(3) A. Leoni, 3M Company Ferrania
(4) H₂C=CHCONH(CH₂)₂CONH(CH₂)₂CONH₂
(5) base catalyzed (e.g., Na-t-butoxide or n-butyllithium) polymerization of acrylamide in dioxane, and dioxane extraction of the polymer

(6) A. Leoni, S. Franco, G. Polla, J. Polym. Sci. A-1 6 (1968) 3187...94
(7) KBr (1.5/1000)

42121111   C₃H₅NO–C₄H₇NO   1066

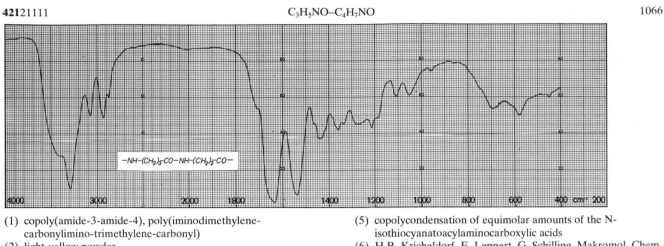

(1) copoly(amide-3-amide-4), poly(iminodimethylene-carbonylimino-trimethylene-carbonyl)
(2) light-yellow powder
(3) H.R. Kricheldorf, Institut für Makromolekulare Chemie, Universität Freiburg, Freiburg/Br.
(4) alternating structure
(5) copolycondensation of equimolar amounts of the N-isothiocyanatoacylaminocarboxylic acids
(6) H.R. Kricheldorf, E. Leppert, G. Schilling, Makromol. Chem. *175* (1974) 1705...29
(7) KBr (0.9/350), ordinate expanded

42121111   C₃H₅NO–C₅H₉NO   1067

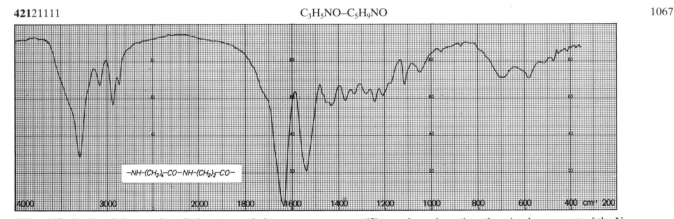

(1) poly(iminodimethylene-carbonyliminotetramethylene-carbonyl) copoly(amide-3-amide-5)
(2) light-yellow powder
(3) H.R. Kricheldorf, Institut für Makromolekulare Chemie, Universität Freiburg, Freiburg/Br.
(4) alternating structure
(5) copolycondensation of equimolar amounts of the N-isothiocyanatoacylaminocarboxylic acids
(6) H.R. Kricheldorf, E. Leppert, G. Schilling, Makromol. Chem. *175* (1974) 1705...29
(7) KBr (0.5/350), ordinate expanded

42121111   C₃H₅NO–C₆H₁₁NO   1068

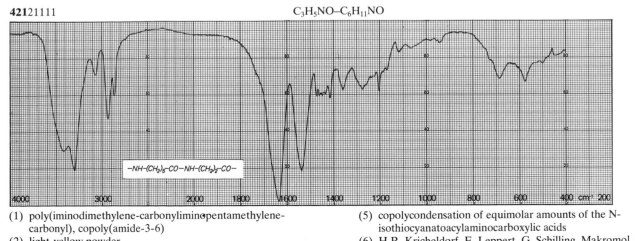

(1) poly(iminodimethylene-carbonyliminopentamethylene-carbonyl), copoly(amide-3-6)
(2) light-yellow powder
(3) H.R. Kricheldorf, Institut für Makromolekulare Chemie, Universität Freiburg, Freiburg/Br.
(4) alternating structure
(5) copolycondensation of equimolar amounts of the N-isothiocyanatoacylaminocarboxylic acids
(6) H.R. Kricheldorf, E. Leppert, G. Schilling, Makromol. Chem. *175* (1974) 1705...29
(7) KBr (0.7/350), ordinate expanded

42121111–42121141   C$_3$H$_5$NO–C$_7$H$_5$NO   1069

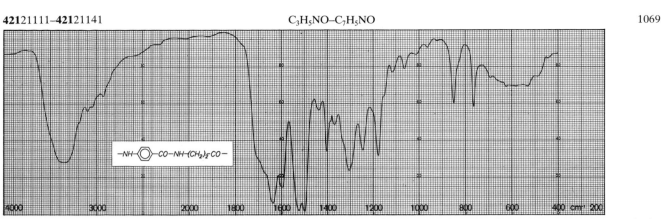

(1) copoly(amide-3-benzamide), poly(imino-dimethylene-
    carbonylimino-1,4-phenylene-carbonyl)
(2) pink powder
(3) H.R. Kricheldorf, Institut für Makromolekulare Chemie,
    Universität Freiburg, Freiburg/Br.
(5) copolyconcensation of equimolar amounts of

4-isothiocyanatabenzoic acid with 3-isothio-cyanatopropionic
acid
(6) H.R. Kricheldorf, E. Leppert, G. Schilling, Makromol. Chem.
    175 (1974) 1705...29
(7) KBr (0.7/300), ordinate expanded

42121111   C$_4$H$_7$NO   1070

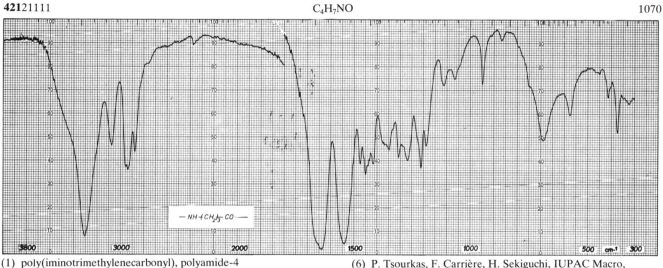

(1) poly(iminotrimethylenecarbonyl), polyamide-4
(2) white material
(3) F.J. Carrière, Laboratoire de Chimie Macromoléculaire,
    CNRS, Ecole Superieure de Physique et Chimie Industrielles,
    Paris

(6) P. Tsourkas, F. Carrière, H. Sekiguchi, IUPAC Macro,
    Madrid, 1974 (II, 2–4)
(7) dissolved in HCOOH and ground with KBr, dried and pressed

42121111   C$_4$H$_7$NO–C$_5$H$_9$NO   1071

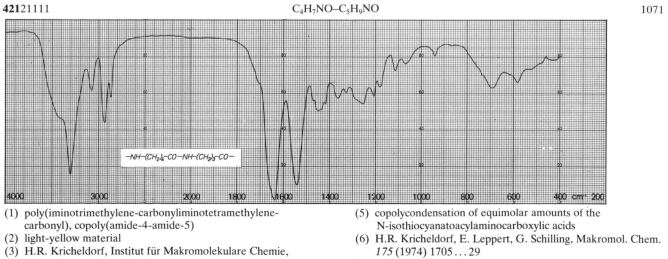

(1) poly(iminotrimethylene-carbonyliminotetramethylene-
    carbonyl), copoly(amide-4-amide-5)
(2) light-yellow material
(3) H.R. Kricheldorf, Institut für Makromolekulare Chemie,
    Universität Freiburg, Freiburg/Br.
(4) alternating structure

(5) copolycondensation of equimolar amounts of the
    N-isothiocyanatoacylaminocarboxylic acids
(6) H.R. Kricheldorf, E. Leppert, G. Schilling, Makromol. Chem.
    175 (1974) 1705...29
(7) KBr (0.3/350), ordinate expanded

42121111   C$_4$H$_7$NO–C$_6$H$_{11}$NO   1072

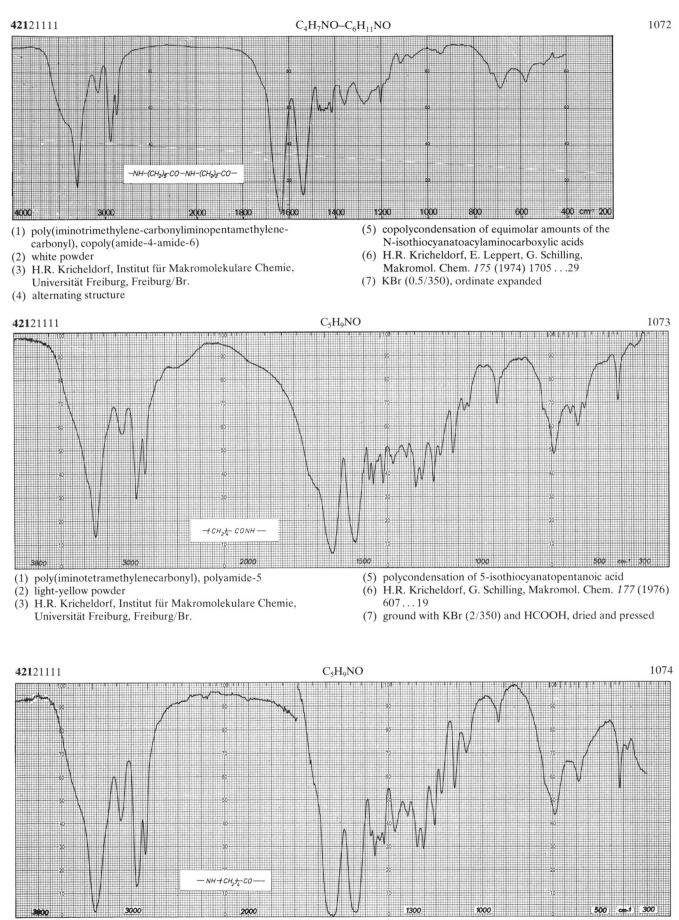

—NH—(CH$_2$)$_5$—CO—NH—(CH$_2$)$_5$—CO—

(1) poly(iminotrimethylene-carbonyliminopentamethylene-carbonyl), copoly(amide-4-amide-6)
(2) white powder
(3) H.R. Kricheldorf, Institut für Makromolekulare Chemie, Universität Freiburg, Freiburg/Br.
(4) alternating structure

(5) copolycondensation of equimolar amounts of the N-isothiocyanatoacylaminocarboxylic acids
(6) H.R. Kricheldorf, E. Leppert, G. Schilling, Makromol. Chem. *175* (1974) 1705...29
(7) KBr (0.5/350), ordinate expanded

42121111   C$_5$H$_9$NO   1073

—(CH$_2$)$_4$—CONH—

(1) poly(iminotetramethylenecarbonyl), polyamide-5
(2) light-yellow powder
(3) H.R. Kricheldorf, Institut für Makromolekulare Chemie, Universität Freiburg, Freiburg/Br.

(5) polycondensation of 5-isothiocyanatopentanoic acid
(6) H.R. Kricheldorf, G. Schilling, Makromol. Chem. *177* (1976) 607...19
(7) ground with KBr (2/350) and HCOOH, dried and pressed

42121111   C$_5$H$_9$NO   1074

—NH—(CH$_2$)$_4$—CO—

(1) poly(iminotetramethylenecarbonyl), polyamide-5
(2) white, fibrous material
(3) F.J. Carrière, Laboratoire de Chimie Macromoléculaire, CNRS, Ecole Superieure de Physique et Chimie Industrielles, Paris

(6) P. Tsourkas, F. Carrière, H. Sekiguchi, IUPAC, Macro, Madrid, 1974 (II, 2–4)
(7) dissolved in HCOOH, ground with KBr, dried and pressed

42121111 $C_5H_9NO–C_6H_{11}NO$ 1075

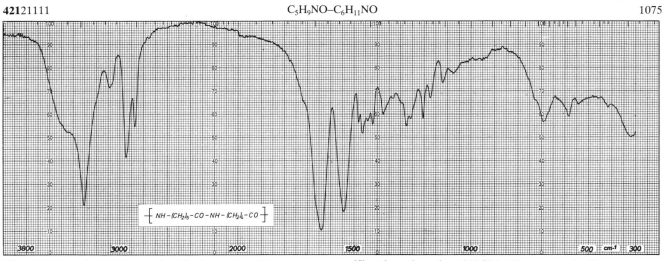

(1) poly(iminotetramethylene-carbonyliminopentamethylene-
     carbonyl), copoly(amide-5-amide-6)
(2) egg shell-coloured material
(3) H.R. Kricheldorf, Institut für Makromolekulare Chemie,
     Universität Freiburg, Freiburg/Br.
(4) alternating structure

(5) polycondensation of N-(5-isothiocyanatovaleryl)-
     4-aminobutyric acid
(6) H.R. Kricheldorf, G. Schilling, Makromol. Chem. *177* (1976)
     607…19
(7) KBr (0.8/350)

42121111–42121141 $C_5H_9NO–C_7H_5NO$ 1076

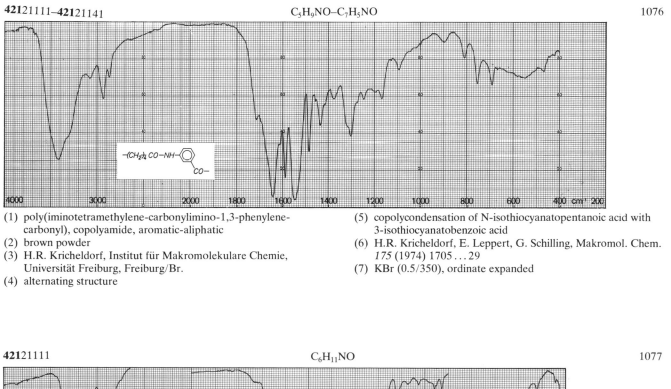

(1) poly(iminotetramethylene-carbonylimino-1,3-phenylene-
     carbonyl), copolyamide, aromatic-aliphatic
(2) brown powder
(3) H.R. Kricheldorf, Institut für Makromolekulare Chemie,
     Universität Freiburg, Freiburg/Br.
(4) alternating structure

(5) copolycondensation of N-isothiocyanatopentanoic acid with
     3-isothiocyanatobenzoic acid
(6) H.R. Kricheldorf, E. Leppert, G. Schilling, Makromol. Chem.
     175 (1974) 1705…29
(7) KBr (0.5/350), ordinate expanded

42121111 $C_6H_{11}NO$ 1077

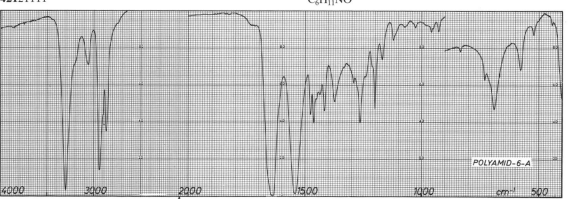

(1) poly(iminopentamethylenecarbonyl), polyamide-6
(2) colourless thermoplastic
(3) BASF AG, Ludwigshafen
(4) crystalline, modification A (α-form)

(6) R. Schürmann, Thesis, Universität Köln, 1973
(7) film from HCOOH solution (300 K)
(8) prepared from commercial „Ultramid BK"

42121111   C₆H₁₁NO   1078

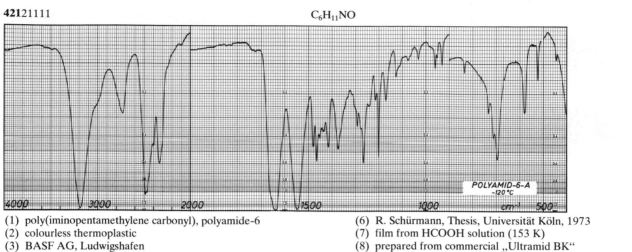

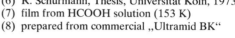

(1) poly(iminopentamethylene carbonyl), polyamide-6
(2) colourless thermoplastic
(3) BASF AG, Ludwigshafen
(4) crystalline, modification A (α-form)

(6) R. Schürmann, Thesis, Universität Köln, 1973
(7) film from HCOOH solution (153 K)
(8) prepared from commercial „Ultramid BK"

42121111   C₆H₁₁NO   1079

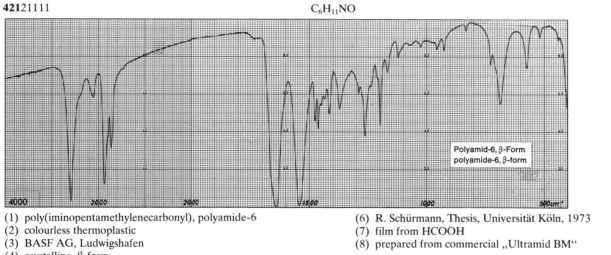

(1) poly(iminopentamethylenecarbonyl), polyamide-6
(2) colourless thermoplastic
(3) BASF AG, Ludwigshafen
(4) crystalline, β-form

(6) R. Schürmann, Thesis, Universität Köln, 1973
(7) film from HCOOH
(8) prepared from commercial „Ultramid BM"

42121111   C₆H₁₁NO   1080

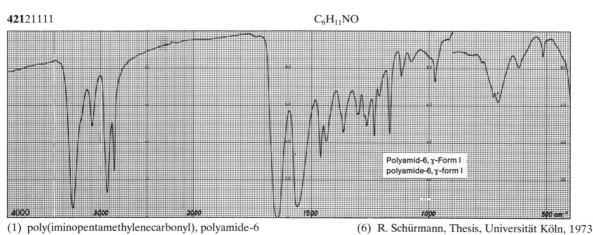

(1) poly(iminopentamethylenecarbonyl), polyamide-6
(2) colourless thermoplastic
(3) BASF AG, Ludwigshafen
(4) crystalline, γ-form I

(6) R. Schürmann, Thesis, Universität Köln, 1973
(7) film from HCOOH
(8) prepared from commercial „Ultramid BM"

42121111 $C_6H_{11}NO$ 1081

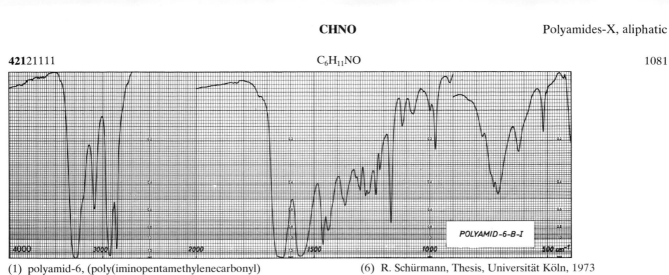

POLYAMID-6-B-I

(1) polyamid-6, (poly(iminopentamethylenecarbonyl)
(2) colourless thermoplastic
(3) BASF AG, Ludwigshafen
(4) crystalline, modification B–I (γ-form I)

(6) R. Schürmann, Thesis, Universität Köln, 1973
(7) film from HCOOH solution, treated with aqueous KI_3 and $Na_2S_2O_3$
(8) prepared from commercial „Ultramid BM"

42121111 $C_6H_{11}NO$ 1082

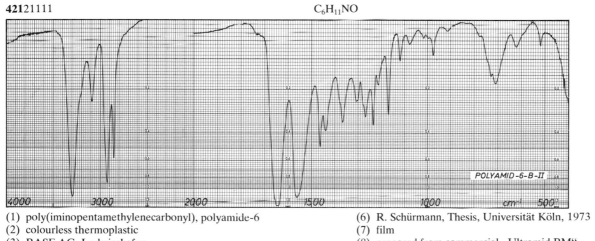

POLYAMID-6-B-II

(1) poly(iminopentamethylenecarbonyl), polyamide-6
(2) colourless thermoplastic
(3) BASF AG, Ludwigshafen
(4) crystalline, modification B–II (γ-form II)

(6) R. Schürmann, Thesis, Universität Köln, 1973
(7) film
(8) prepared from commercial „Ultramid BM"

42121111 + **2**1111 $C_6H_{11}NO + C_2H_4$ 1083

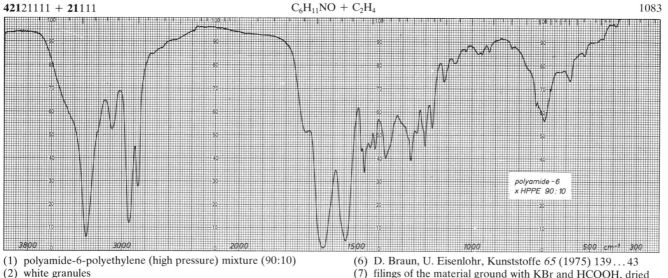

polyamide-6
x HPPE 90:10

(1) polyamide-6-polyethylene (high pressure) mixture (90:10)
(2) white granules
(3) D. Braun, Deutsches Kunststoff-Institut, Darmstadt

(6) D. Braun, U. Eisenlohr, Kunststoffe 65 (1975) 139...43
(7) filings of the material ground with KBr and HCOOH, dried and pressed

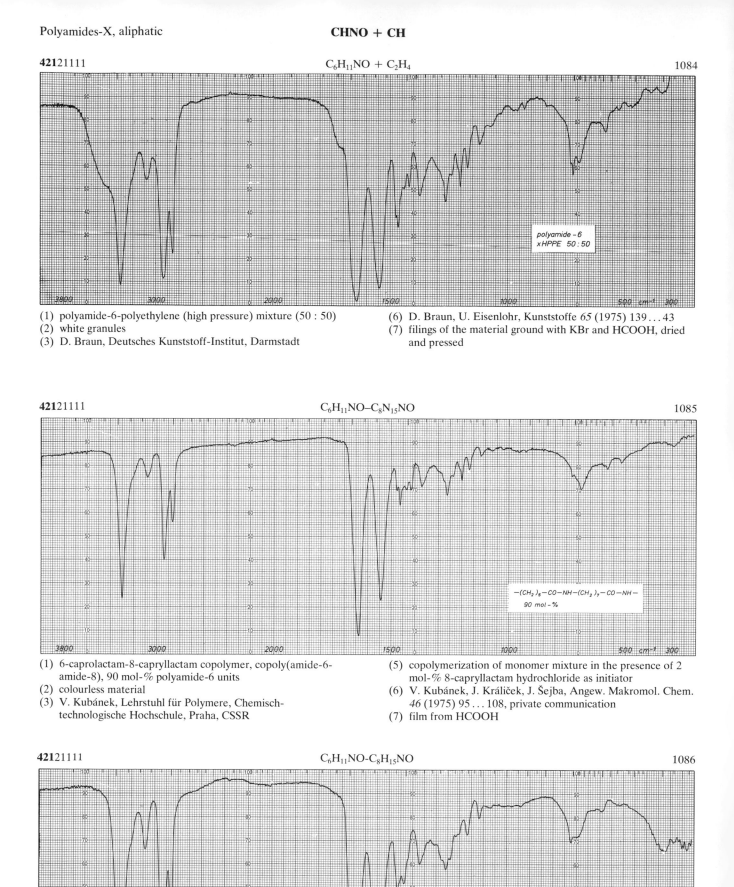

polyamide - 6
xHPPE 50 : 50

(1) polyamide-6-polyethylene (high pressure) mixture (50 : 50)
(2) white granules
(3) D. Braun, Deutsches Kunststoff-Institut, Darmstadt

(6) D. Braun, U. Eisenlohr, Kunststoffe *65* (1975) 139...43
(7) filings of the material ground with KBr and HCOOH, dried and pressed

$-(CH_2)_5-CO-NH-(CH_2)_7-CO-NH-$
90 mol - %

(1) 6-caprolactam-8-capryllactam copolymer, copoly(amide-6-amide-8), 90 mol-% polyamide-6 units
(2) colourless material
(3) V. Kubánek, Lehrstuhl für Polymere, Chemisch-technologische Hochschule, Praha, CSSR

(5) copolymerization of monomer mixture in the presence of 2 mol-% 8-capryllactam hydrochloride as initiator
(6) V. Kubánek, J. Králiček, J. Šejba, Angew. Makromol. Chem. *46* (1975) 95...108, private communication
(7) film from HCOOH

$-(CH_2)_5-CO-NH-(CH_2)_7-CO-NH-$
50 mol - %

(1) 6-caprolactam-8-capryllactam copolymer, copoly(amide-6-amide-8), 50 mol-% amide-6 units
(2) colourless, clear material
(3) V. Kubánek, Lehrstuhl für Polymere, Chemisch-technologische Hochschule, Praha, CSSR
(5) copolymerization of a nomomer mixture in the presence of

0.25 mol-% N-acetylcaprolactam and 0.25 mol-% Na salt of the lactam
(6) V. Kubánek, J. Králiček, J. Šejba, Angew. Makromol. Chem. *46* (1975) 95...108, private communication
(7) film from HCOOH

42121111 C₆H₁₁NO–C₁₂H₂₃NO 1087

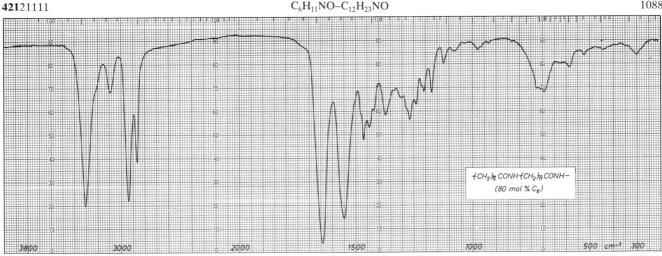

(1) 6-caprolactam-12-laurolactam copolymer, copoly(amide-6-amide-12), approximately 95 mol-% amide-6-units
(2) glassy-clear granules
(3) V. Kubánek, Lehrstuhl für Polymere, Chemisch-technologische Hochschule, Praha, CSSR
(5) copolymerization of a mixture of 94.7 mol-% 6-caprolactam, 5 mol-% 12-lauryllactam, 0,03 mol-% bis(2-

methoxyethoxy)sodiumdihydroaluminate („Synhydrid") (initiator) and 0,3 mol-% trimer phenylisocyanate (activator) at 240 °C; see V. Kubánek, J. Králiček, J. Mařík, J. Kondelíková, Chem. prum. 25 (1975) 628
(6) V. Kubánek, J. Králiček, K. Černý, Jaroslava Kondelíková, Angew. Makromol. Chem. 54 (1976) 127...39
(7) film from HCOOH

42121111 C₆H₁₁NO–C₁₂H₂₃NO 1088

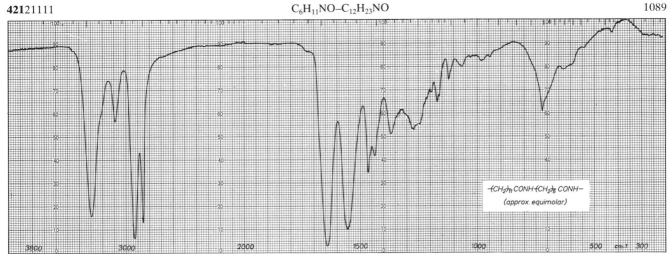

(1) 6-caprolactam-12-laurolactam copolymer, copoly(amide-6-amide-12), approximately 80 mol-% amide-6 units
(2) glassy-clear granules
(3) V. Kubánek, Lehrstuhl für Polymere, Chemisch-technologische Hochschule, Praha, CSSR
(5) copolymerization of a mixture of 97.7 mol-% 6-caprolactam, 20 mol-%-lauryllactam, 0,03 mol-% „Synhydrid" (initiator)

and 0,3 mol-% trimer phenylisocyanate (activator) at 240 °C; see V. Kubánek, J. Králiček, J. Mařík, J. Kondelíková, Chem. prum 25 (1975) 628
(6) V. Kubánek, J. Králiček, K. Černý, Jaroslava Kondelíková, Angew. Makromol. Chem. 54 (1976) 127...39
(7) film from HCOOH

42121111 C₆H₁₁NO–C₁₂H₂₃NO 1089

(1) 6-caprolactam-12-laurolactam copolymer, copoly(amide-6-amide-12), approx. equimolar composition
(2) greyish-white elastomer
(3) V. Kubánek, Lehrstuhl für Polymere, Chemisch-technologische Hochschule, Praha, CSSR
(5) copolymerization of the mixture of 50 mol-% 12-

lauryllactam, 48 mol-% 6-caprolactam, and 2 mol-% 6-aminocaproic acid as initiator
(6) V. Kubánek, J. Králiček, K. Černý, Jaroslava Kondelíková, Angew. Makromol. Chem. 54 (1976) 127...39
(7) film from HCOOH

42121111–**42**121112   C₆H₁₁NO–C₇H₁₃NO   1090

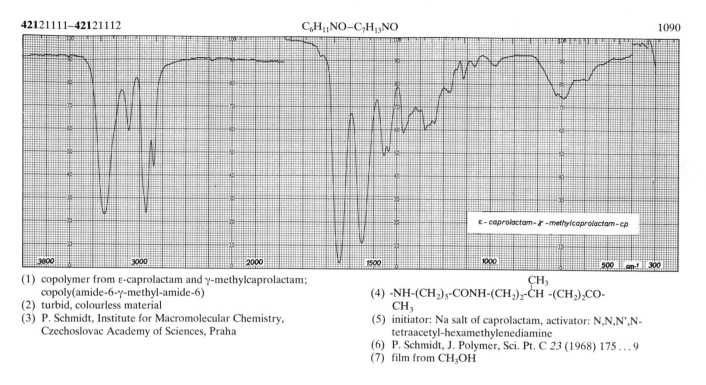

ε - caprolactam - γ -methylcaprolactam - cp

(1) copolymer from ε-caprolactam and γ-methylcaprolactam;
      copoly(amide-6-γ-methyl-amide-6)
(2) turbid, colourless material
(3) P. Schmidt, Institute for Macromolecular Chemistry,
      Czechoslovac Academy of Sciences, Praha

$$\text{CH}_3$$
(4) -NH-(CH₂)₅-CONH-(CH₂)₂-CH -(CH₂)₂CO-
      CH₃
(5) initiator: Na salt of caprolactam, activator: N,N,N',N-
      tetraacetyl-hexamethylenediamine
(6) P. Schmidt, J. Polymer, Sci. Pt. C *23* (1968) 175 … 9
(7) film from CH₃OH

42121111–**42**121141   C₆H₁₁NO-C₇H₅NO   1091

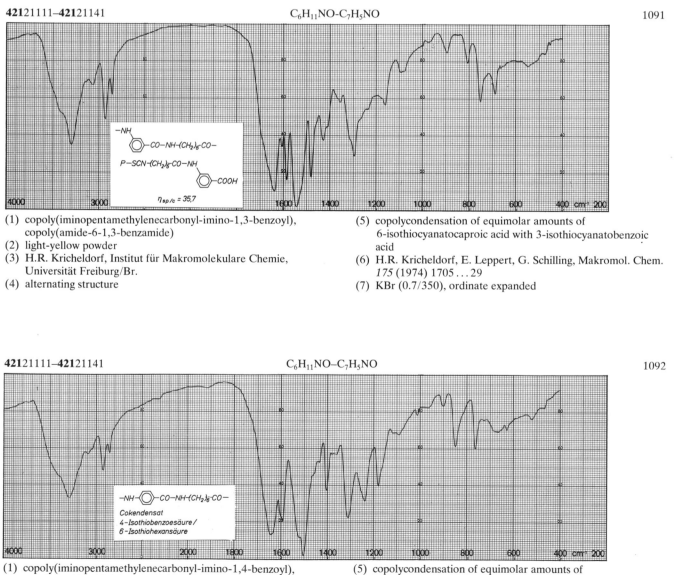

—NH—⬡—CO—NH-(CH₂)₅-CO—

P—SCN-(CH₂)₅-CO—NH

⬡—COOH

η_{sp/c} = 35,7

(1) copoly(iminopentamethylenecarbonyl-imino-1,3-benzoyl),
      copoly(amide-6-1,3-benzamide)
(2) light-yellow powder
(3) H.R. Kricheldorf, Institut für Makromolekulare Chemie,
      Universität Freiburg/Br.
(4) alternating structure
(5) copolycondensation of equimolar amounts of
      6-isothiocyanatocaproic acid with 3-isothiocyanatobenzoic
      acid
(6) H.R. Kricheldorf, E. Leppert, G. Schilling, Makromol. Chem.
      175 (1974) 1705 … 29
(7) KBr (0.7/350), ordinate expanded

42121111–**42**121141   C₆H₁₁NO–C₇H₅NO   1092

—NH—⬡—CO—NH-(CH₂)₅-CO—

Cokendensat
4-Isothiobenzoesäure/
6-Isothiohexansäure

(1) copoly(iminopentamethylenecarbonyl-imino-1,4-benzoyl),
      copoly(amide-6-1,4-benzamide)
(2) light-brown powder
(3) H.R. Kricheldorf, Institut für Makromolekulare Chemie,
      Universität Freiburg, Freiburg/Br.
(4) alternating structure
(5) copolycondensation of equimolar amounts of
      6-isothiocyanatocaproic and 4-isothiocyanatobenzoic acids
(6) H.R. Kricheldorf, E. Leppert, G. Schilling, Makromol. Chem.
      175 (1974) 1705 … 29
(7) KBr (0.5/350), ordinate expanded

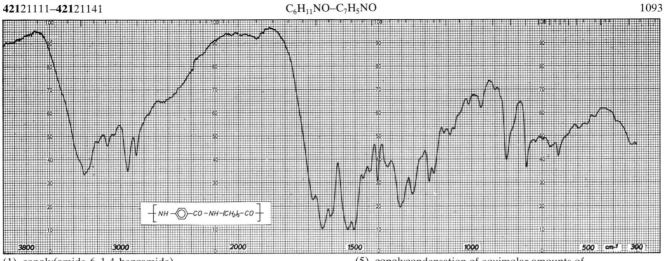

(1) copoly(amide-6-1,4-benzamide),
    poly(iminopentamethylenecarbonyl-imino-1,4-phenylene-
    carbonyl)
(2) dark-grey powder
(3) H.R. Kricheldorf, Institut für Makromolekulare Chemie,
    Universität Freiburg/Br.
(4) alternating structure

(5) copolycondensation of equimolar amounts of
    6-isothiocyanatocaproic acid with 4-isothiocyanatobenzoic
    acid
(6) H.R. Kricheldorf, E. Leppert, G. Schilling, Makromol. Chem.
    175 (1974) 1705...29
(7) KBr (2/350)

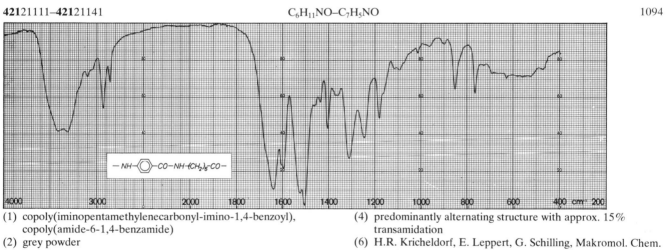

(1) copoly(iminopentamethylenecarbonyl-imino-1,4-benzoyl),
    copoly(amide-6-1,4-benzamide)
(2) grey powder
(3) H.R. Kricheldorf, Institut für Makromolekulare Chemie,
    Universität Freiburg, Freiburg/Br.

(4) predominantly alternating structure with approx. 15%
    transamidation
(6) H.R. Kricheldorf, E. Leppert, G. Schilling, Makromol. Chem.
    175 (1974) 1705...29
(7) KBr (0.5/350), ordinate expanded

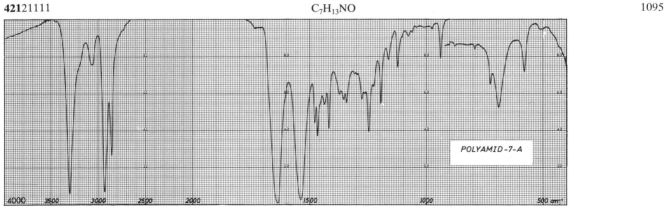

(1) polyamide-7
(2) colourless material
(3) British Nylon Spinners (laboratory preparation)

(4) -NH-(CH$_2$)$_6$-CO-, modification A, α-form
(6) R. Schürmann, Dissertation, Köln 1973
(7) film from HCOOH solution

42121111 $C_7H_{13}NO$ 1096

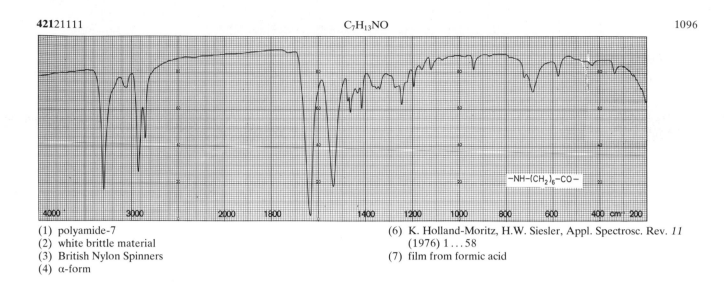

(1) polyamide-7
(2) white brittle material
(3) British Nylon Spinners
(4) α-form

(6) K. Holland-Moritz, H.W. Siesler, Appl. Spectrosc. Rev. *11*
    (1976) 1...58
(7) film from formic acid

42121111 $C_8H_{15}NO$ 1097

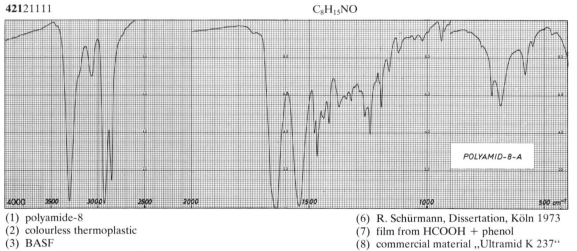

(1) polyamide-8
(2) colourless thermoplastic
(3) BASF
(4) -NH-$(CH_2)_7$-CO-, modification A (α form)

(6) R. Schürmann, Dissertation, Köln 1973
(7) film from HCOOH + phenol
(8) commercial material „Ultramid K 237"

42121111 $C_8H_{15}NO$ 1098

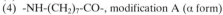

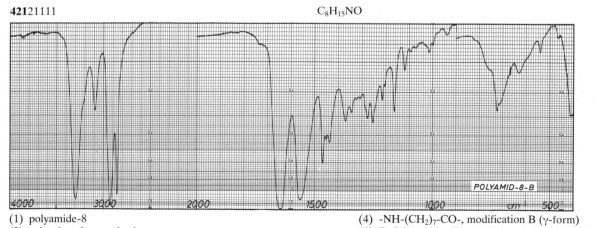

(1) polyamide-8
(2) colourless thermoplastic
(3) BASF

(4) -NH-$(CH_2)_7$-CO-, modification B (γ-form)
(6) R. Schürmann, Thesis, Universität Köln, 1973
(8) commercial material „Ultramid K 237"

42121111   C₈H₁₅NO–C₆H₁₁NO   1099

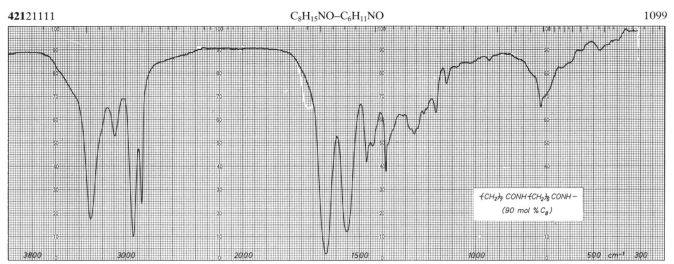

+CH₂+₇ CONH +CH₂+₅ CONH –

(90 mol % C₈)

(1) 8-capryllactam-6-caprolactam copolymer, copoly(amide-8-amide-6) (90 mol-% amide-8 units)
(2) white powder
(3) V. Kubánek, Lehrstuhl für Polymere, Chemisch-technologische Hochschule, Praha, CSSR
(5) copolymerization of a mixture of 90 mol-% 8-capryllactam 10

mol-% 6-caprolactam, 2 mol-% 8-capryllactam hydrochloride (initiator)
(6) V. Kubánek, J. Králiček, J. Šejba, Angew. Makromol. Chem. *46* (1975) 95 … 108
(7) ground with KBr (1.7/350) and HCOOH, dried and pressed

42121111   C₁₂H₂₃NO   1100

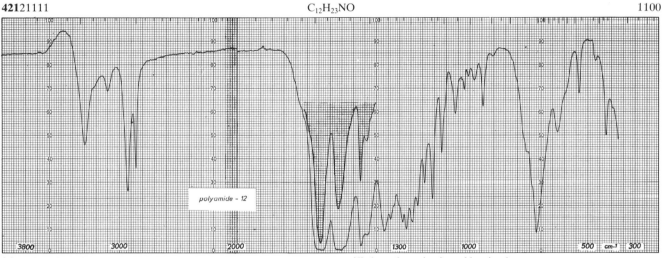

polyamide - 12

(1) polyamide-12
(2) colourless material
(3) H.-G. Elias, Technische Universität, Zürich
(4) -NH-(CH₂)₁₁-CO-, crystalline

(5) by polymerization of laurine lactam
(6) H.-G. Elias, A. Fritz, Makromol. Chem. *114* (1968) 31 … 50
(7) melting film (between KBr)

42121112   C₃H₅NO   1101

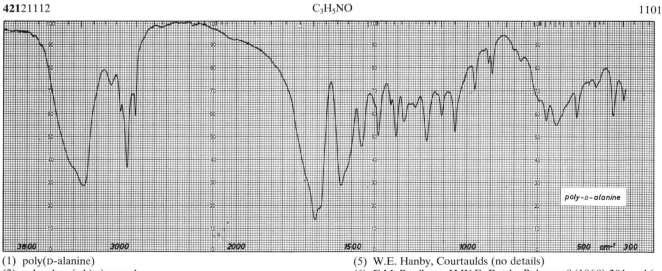

poly-D-alanine

(1) poly(D-alanine)
(2) colourless (white) granules
(3) E.M. Bradbury, Portsmouth College of Technology
(4) -NH-CH-CO-
       |
       CH₃

(5) W.E. Hanby, Courtaulds (no details)
(6) E.M. Bradbury, H.W.E. Rattle, Polymer *9* (1968) 201 … 16
(7) ground with KBr (1/350) and DMA, dried and pressed (twice)

42121112   C₃H₅NO   1102

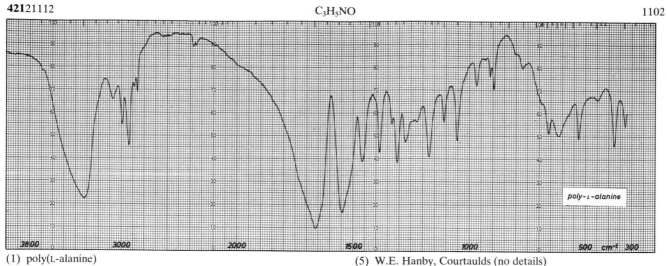

(1) poly(L-alanine)
(2) white material
(3) E.M. Bradbury, Portsmouth College of Technology
(4) —NH—CH—CO—
         |
         CH₃

(5) W.E. Hanby, Courtaulds (no details)
(6) E.M.Bradbury, H.W.E. Rattle, Polymer *9* (1968) 201 . . . 16
(7) ground with KBr (1/350) and DMA dried and pressed (three times)

42121112   C₃H₅NO   1103

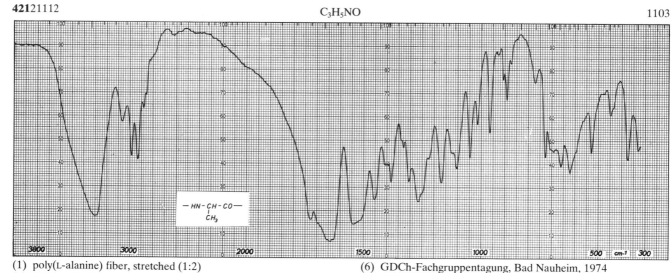

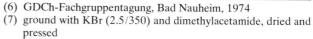

(1) poly(L-alanine) fiber, stretched (1:2)
(2) silky-white fiber
(3) G. Ebert, Philipps-Universität, Marburg

(6) GDCh-Fachgruppentagung, Bad Nauheim, 1974
(7) ground with KBr (2.5/350) and dimethylacetamide, dried and pressed

42121112   C₃H₅NO   1104

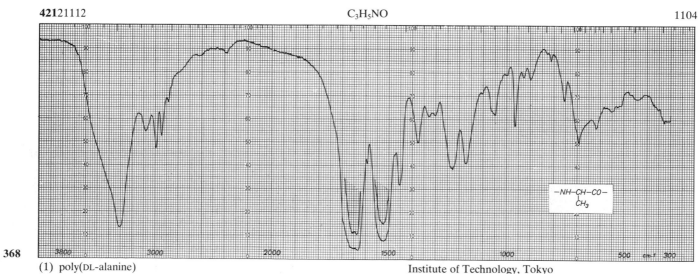

(1) poly(DL-alanine)
(2) ivory-coloured powder
(3) N. Yamazaki, Department of Polymer Science, Tokyo

Institute of Technology, Tokyo
(6) N. Yamazaki, IUPAC Macro, Aberdeen 1973
(7) KBr (1/350)

42121112-421211523   C₃H₅NO–C₁₄H₁₈N₂O₃   1105

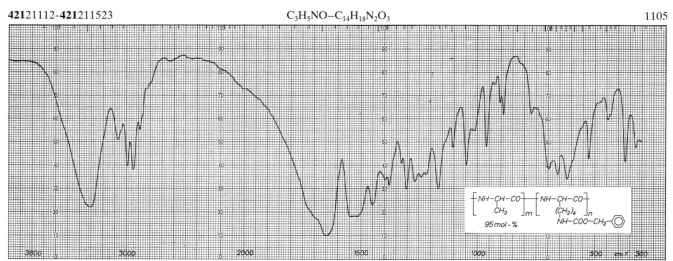

(1) copoly(L-alanine-N-ε-carbobenzoxy-L-lysine) fiber,
    95 mol-% L-alanine units
(2) silky-white fiber
(3) G. Ebert, Philipps-Universität, Marburg

(4) stretched (1:2)
(6) GDCh-Fachgruppentagung, Bad Nauheim, 1974
(7) ground with KBr (2/350) and dimethylacetamide, dried and
    pressed

42121112–421211523   C₃H₅NO–C₁₄H₁₈N₂O₃   1106

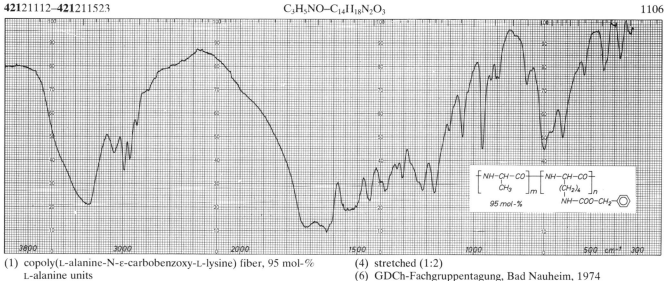

(1) copoly(L-alanine-N-ε-carbobenzoxy-L-lysine) fiber, 95 mol-%
    L-alanine units
(2) silky-white fiber
(3) G. Ebert, Philipps-Universität, Marburg

(4) stretched (1:2)
(6) GDCh-Fachgruppentagung, Bad Nauheim, 1974
(7) ground with KBr (2/350) and HCOOH, dried and pressed

42121112   C₄H₇NO   1107

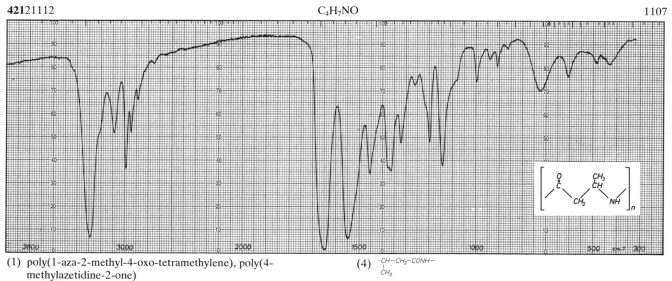

(1) poly(1-aza-2-methyl-4-oxo-tetramethylene), poly(4-
    methylazetidine-2-one)
(2) colourless flocks
(3) Hoechst AG (laboratory preparation)

(4) –CH–CH₂–CONH–
       |
       CH₃
(5) polymerization of 4-methylazetidine-2-one
(7) film from HCOOH solution

42121112   C₆H₁₁NO   1108

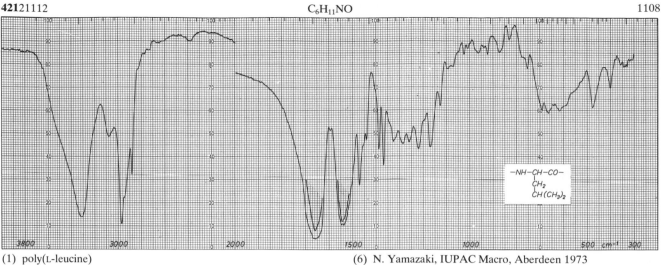

(1) poly(L-leucine)
(2) white powder
(3) N. Yamazaki, Department of Polymer Science, Tokyo
University of Technology, Tokyo

(6) N. Yamazaki, IUPAC Macro, Aberdeen 1973
(7) KBr (1/350)

42121112   C₇H₁₃NO   1109

(1) poly(ε-methyl-ε-caprolactam), poly(iminoethylidene-
tetramethylenecarbonyl)
(2) white, brittle material
(3) P. Schmidt, Institute for Macromolecular Chemistry,
Czechoslovac Academy of Sciences, Praha, ČSSR
(5) polymerization of ε-ethyl-ε-caprolactam in the presence of

Na-salt of caprolactam and N,N,N',N'-
tetraacetylhexamethylenediamine
(6) P. Čefelín, P. Schmidt, J. Šebenda, J. Polym. Sci. Pt. C *23*
(1968) 175 ... 9, private communication
(7) melting film between CsI

42121112   C₇H₁₃NO   1110

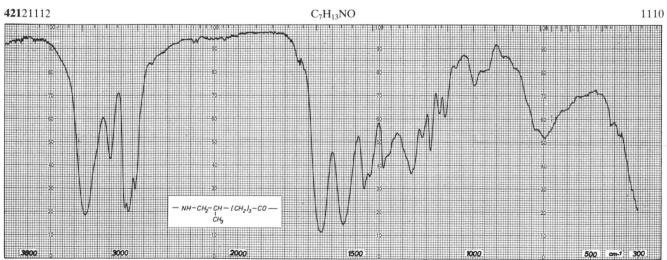

(1) poly(δ-methyl-ε-caprolactam), poly(iminomethylene-
ethylidene-trimethylene-carbonyl)
(2) white, brittle material
(3) P. Schmidt, Institute for Macromolecular Chemistry,
Czechoslovac Academy of Sciences, Praha, ČSSR
(5) polymerization of δ-methyl-ε-caprolactam in the presence of

Na-salt of caprolactam and N,N,N',N'-
tetraacetylhexamethylenediamine
(6) P. Čefelín, P. Schmidt, J. Šebenda, J. Polym. Sci. Pt. C *23*
(1968) 175 ... 9, private communication
(7) melting film between CsI

42121112   C$_7$H$_{13}$NO   1111

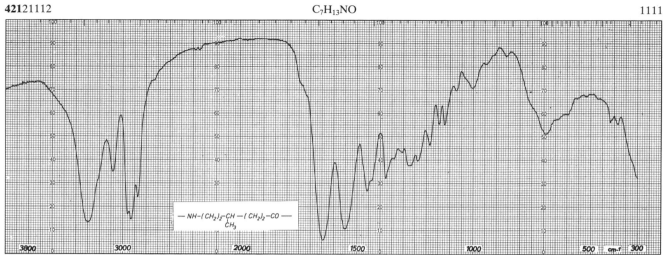

— NH—(CH$_2$)$_2$—CH—(CH$_2$)$_2$—CO —
            |
           CH$_3$

(1) poly(γ-methyl-ε-caprolactam), poly(iminodimethylene-
    ethylidene-dimethylenecarbonyl)
(2) clear, slightly coloured material
(3) P. Schmidt, Institute for Macromolecular Chemistry,
    Czechoslovac Academy of Sciences, Praha, ČSSR
(5) polymerization of γ-methyl-ε-caprolactam in the presence of

Na-salt of caprolactam and N,N,N',N'-
tetraacetylhexamethylenediamine
(6) P. Čefelín, P. Schmidt, J. Šebenda, J. Polym. Sci. Pt. C 23
    (1968) 175…9, private communication
(7) melting film between CsI

42121112   C$_7$H$_{13}$NO   1112

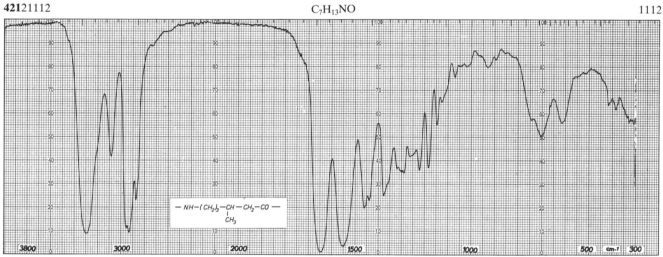

— NH—(CH$_2$)$_3$—CH—CH$_2$—CO —
              |
             CH$_3$

(1) poly(β-methyl-ε-caprolactam), poly(iminotrimethylene-
    ethylidene-methylenecarbonyl)
(2) white, brittle material
(3) P. Schmidt, Institute for Macromolecular Chemistry,
    Czechoslovac Academy of Sciences, Praha, ČSSR
(5) polymerization of β-methyl-ε-caprolactam in the presence of

Na-salt of caprolactam and N,N,N',N'-
tetraacetylhexamethylenediamine
(6) P. Čefelín, P. Schmidt, J. Šebenda, J. Polym. Sci. Pt. C 23
    (1968) 175…9, private communication
(7) melting film between CsI

42121112   C$_4$H$_7$NO   1113

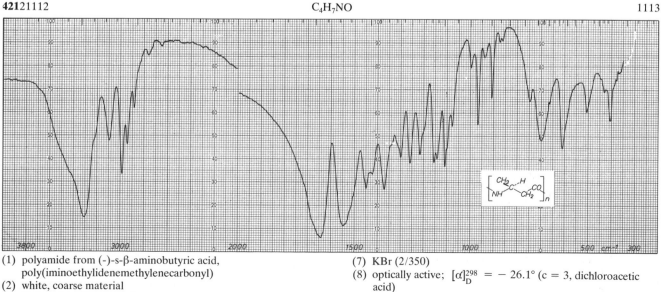

$$\left[\begin{array}{c} CH_3 \quad H \\ NH-C-C-CO \\ H \quad CH_2 \end{array}\right]_n$$

(1) polyamide from (-)-s-β-aminobutyric acid,
    poly(iminoethylidenemethylenecarbonyl)
(2) white, coarse material
(3) E. Schmidt, Hoechst AG, Frankfurt/M.
(6) E. Schmidt, Makromolekulares Kolloquium, Freiburg/Br.
    1970, private communication

(7) KBr (2/350)
(8) optically active; $[\alpha]_D^{298} = -26.1°$ (c = 3, dichloroacetic
    acid)

421121112   C$_5$H$_9$NO   1114

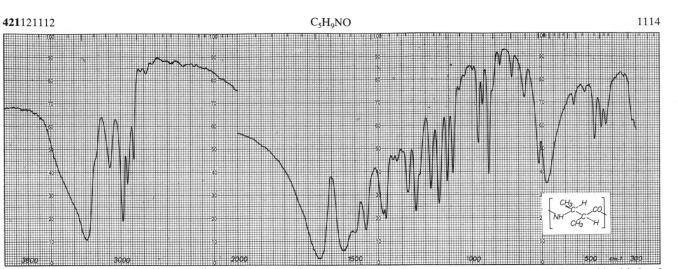

(1) poly[threo(-)-αs,βs-β-amino-α-methylbutyric acid],
    pola[imino(diethylidene)carbonyl], erythro-diisotactic

(2) white, hard, coarse material

(3) E. Schmidt, Hoechst AG, Frankfurt/M.

(6) E. Schmidt, Makromolekulares Kolloquium, Freiburg/Br.
    1970, private communication

(7) ground with KBr (0.7/350) and dimethylacetamide, dried and
    pressed

(8) optically active; $[\alpha]_D^{298} = -25.0°$ (c = 3, trifluoroacetic
    acid)

42121112   C$_5$H$_9$NO   1115

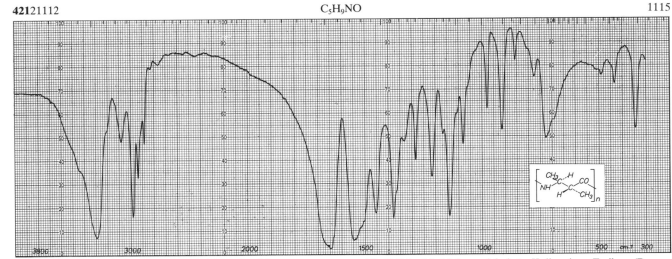
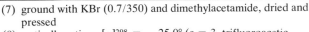

(1) poly(erythro-αr,βs-β-amino-α-methyl-butyric acid),
    poly[imino(diethylidene)carbonyl], erythro-diisotactic

(2) white powder

(3) E. Schmidt, Hoechst AG, Frankfurt/M.

(6) E. Schmidt, Makromolekulares Kolloquium, Freiburg/Br.
    1970, private communication

(7) KBr (2/350)

42121112   C$_5$H$_9$NO   1116

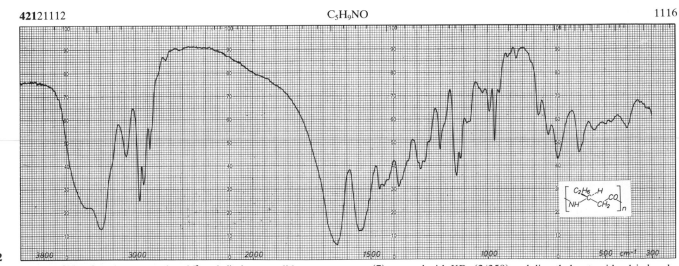

(1) poly[(-)-s-β-aminopentanoic acid], poly(iminopropylidene-
    methylenecarbonyl)

(2) grey material

(3) E. Schmidt, Hoechst AG, Frankfurt/M.

(6) E. Schmidt, Makromolekulares Kolloquium, Freiburg/Br.
    1970, private communication

(7) ground with KBr (2/350) and dimethylacetamide, dried and
    pressed

(8) optically active; $[\alpha]_D^{298} = -32.7°$ (c = 3, dichloroacetic
    acid)

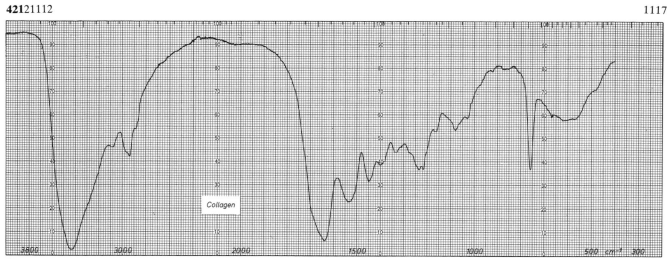

(1) Collagen
(2) colourless powder
(3) Carl Freudenberg KG, Weinheim/Bergstraße (by K. Bräumer)

(6) H. Zahn, F. Glowitz, G.C. von Heyl, Kolloid-Z.Z. Polym. *180* (1962) 26 . . . 35, and preceding papers; K. Bräumer, Angew. Makromol. Chem. *10/41* (1974) 485 . . . 92
(7) KBr (1/350)

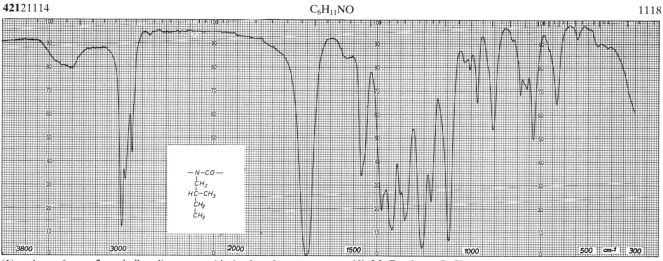

(1) polymer from s-2-methylbutylisocyanate (derivative of polyamide-1); poly[N-(2-methylbutyl)-carbonyl]
(2) colourless (white) powder
(3) M. Goodman, Polytechnic Institute of New York, Brooklyn, N.Y

(6) M. Goodman, S. Chen, Macromolecules *3* (1970) 398
(7) KBr (1/350)

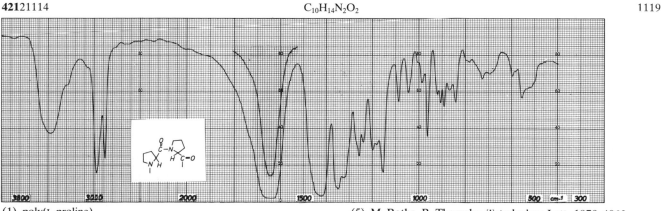

(1) poly(L-proline)
(2) white powder
(3) M. Rothe, Lehrstuhl für Organische Chemie II der Universität Ulm, Ulm
(4) cis-conformation of the peptide link

(5) M. Rothe, R. Theysohn, Tetrahedron Lett. *1970*, 4063; M. Rothe, J. Mazánek, ibid. *1972*, 3795
(6) M. Rothe, H. Rott, Angew. Chem. *88* (1976) 844 . . . 5
(7) KBr (2.8/350)

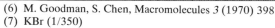

42121114 $C_{10}H_{14}N_2O_2$ 1120

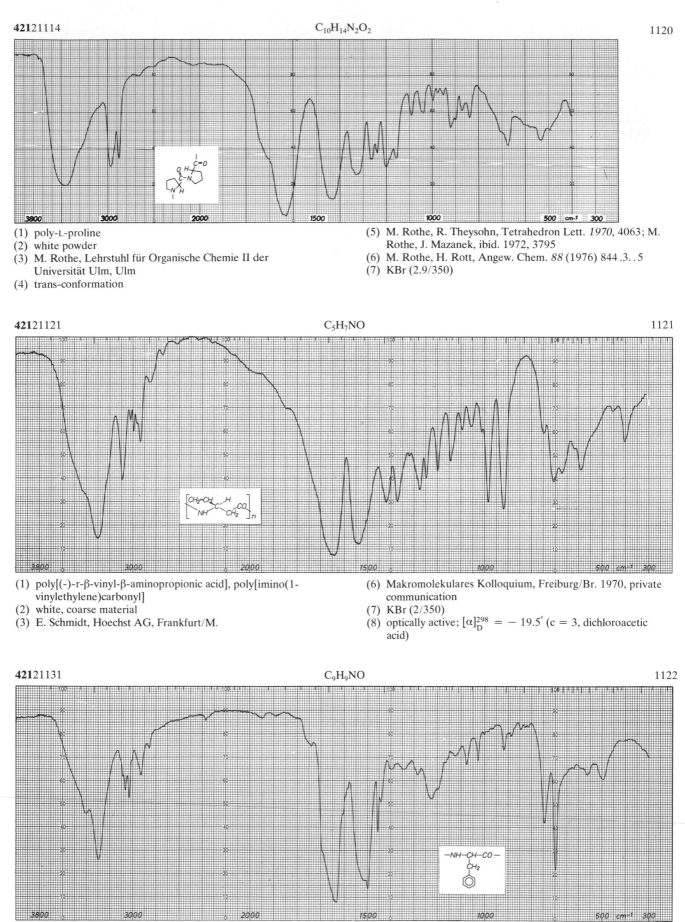

(1) poly-L-proline
(2) white powder
(3) M. Rothe, Lehrstuhl für Organische Chemie II der Universität Ulm, Ulm
(4) trans-conformation

(5) M. Rothe, R. Theysohn, Tetrahedron Lett. *1970*, 4063; M. Rothe, J. Mazanek, ibid. 1972, 3795
(6) M. Rothe, H. Rott, Angew. Chem. *88* (1976) 844 .3. . 5
(7) KBr (2.9/350)

42121121 C_5H_7NO 1121

(1) poly[(-)-r-β-vinyl-β-aminopropionic acid], poly[imino(1-vinylethylene)carbonyl]
(2) white, coarse material
(3) E. Schmidt, Hoechst AG, Frankfurt/M.

(6) Makromolekulares Kolloquium, Freiburg/Br. 1970, private communication
(7) KBr (2/350)
(8) optically active; $[\alpha]_D^{298} = -19.5°$ (c = 3, dichloroacetic acid)

42121131 C_9H_9NO 1122

(1) poly(L-phenylalanıne)
(2) ivory-coloured powder
(3) N. Yamazaki, Department of Polymer Science, Tokyo Institute of Technology, Tokyo

(6) N. Yamazaki, IUPAC Macro, Aberdeen 1973; private communication
(7) KBr (1/350)

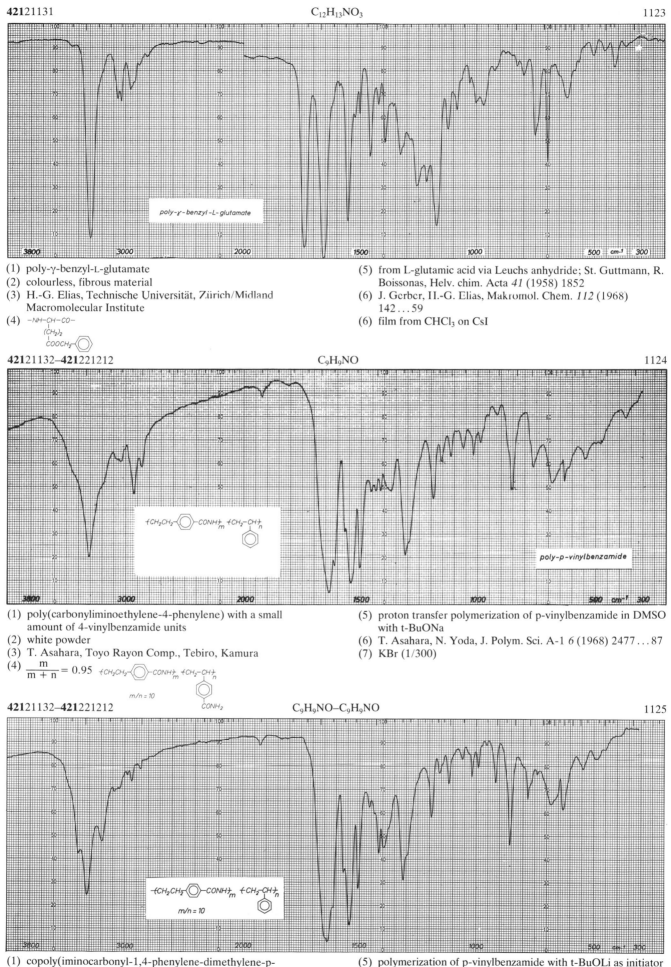

42121131 $C_{12}H_{13}NO_3$ 1123

poly-γ-benzyl-L-glutamate

(1) poly-γ-benzyl-L-glutamate
(2) colourless, fibrous material
(3) H.-G. Elias, Technische Universität, Zürich/Midland Macromolecular Institute
(4) $-NH-CH-CO-$
      $(CH_2)_2$
      $COOCH_2-$⟨○⟩

(5) from L-glutamic acid via Leuchs anhydride; St. Guttmann, R. Boissonas, Helv. chim. Acta *41* (1958) 1852
(6) J. Gerber, H.-G. Elias, Makromol. Chem. *112* (1968) 142...59
(6) film from $CHCl_3$ on CsI

42121132–421221212 C_9H_9NO 1124

$+CH_2CH_2-$⟨○⟩$-CONH\}_m$ $+CH_2-CH\}_n$
      ⟨○⟩

poly-p-vinylbenzamide

(1) poly(carbonyliminoethylene-4-phenylene) with a small amount of 4-vinylbenzamide units
(2) white powder
(3) T. Asahara, Toyo Rayon Comp., Tebiro, Kamura
(4) $\dfrac{m}{m+n} = 0.95$ $+CH_2CH_2-$⟨○⟩$-CONH\}_m$ $+CH_2-CH\}_n$

       $m/n = 10$ ⟨○⟩
                    $CONH_2$

(5) proton transfer polymerization of p-vinylbenzamide in DMSO with t-BuONa
(6) T. Asahara, N. Yoda, J. Polym. Sci. A-1 *6* (1968) 2477...87
(7) KBr (1/300)

42121132–421221212 $C_9H_9NO–C_9H_9NO$ 1125

$+CH_2CH_2-$⟨○⟩$-CONH\}_m$ $+CH_2-CH\}_n$
      $m/n = 10$ ⟨○⟩

(1) copoly(iminocarbonyl-1,4-phenylene-dimethylene-p-vinylbenzamide)
(2) white powder
(3) T. Asahara, Basic Research Laboratory, Toyo Rayon Comp. Ltd., Tebiro, Kamakura

(5) polymerization of p-vinylbenzamide with t-BuOLi as initiator (21 h, 130 °C)
(6) T. Asahara, N. Yoda, J. Polym. Sci. *A6* (1968) 2477...87
(7) KBr (1.2/350)

42121134 $C_{10}H_{11}NO$ 1126

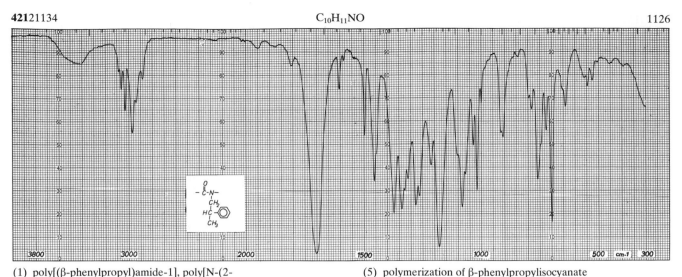

(1) poly[(β-phenylpropyl)amide-1], poly[N-(2-phenylpropyl)carbonyl]
(2) colourless (white) powder
(3) M. Goodman, Polymer Research Institute, Polytechnic Institute of Brooklyn, N.Y.

(5) polymerization of β-phenylpropylisocyanate
(6) M. Goodman, S. Chen, Macromolecules *3* (1970) 398...402

4212115121 $C_5H_9NO_2$ 1127

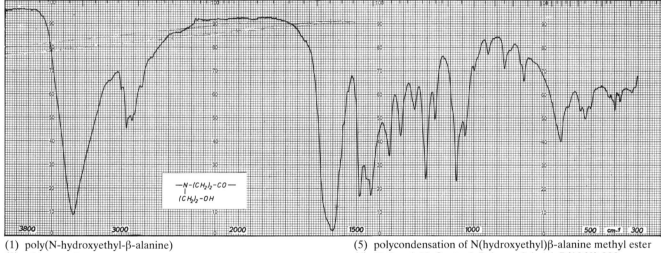

(1) poly(N-hydroxyethyl-β-alanine)
(2) white powder
(3) K. Sanui, Chemical Department, Sophia University, Chiyota-Ku, Tokyo

(5) polycondensation of N(hydroxyethyl)β-alanine methyl ester
(6) K. Sanui, N. Ogata, J. Polymer Sci. A1 7 (1969) 889
(7) KBr (1/350)

4212115124 $C_5H_7NO_3$ 1128

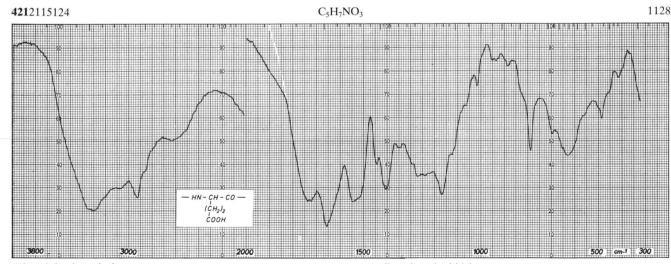

(1) poly(L-glutamine),
poly[imino(carboxyethylene)methylene-carbonyl]
(2) silky-white fiber
(3) G. Ebert, Fachbereich Physikalische Chemie/Polymere, Philipps-Universität, Marburg/Lahn
(5) thermal or anionic polymerization of the N-carboxyanhydride

(Leuchs anhydride)
(6) G. Ebert, Christa Ebert, V. Kroker, W. Werner, Angew. Makromol. Chem. 40/41 (1974) 493...506
(7) ground with KBr (2/350) and dimethylacetamide, dried and pressed

4212115125 $C_6H_9NO_3$ 1129

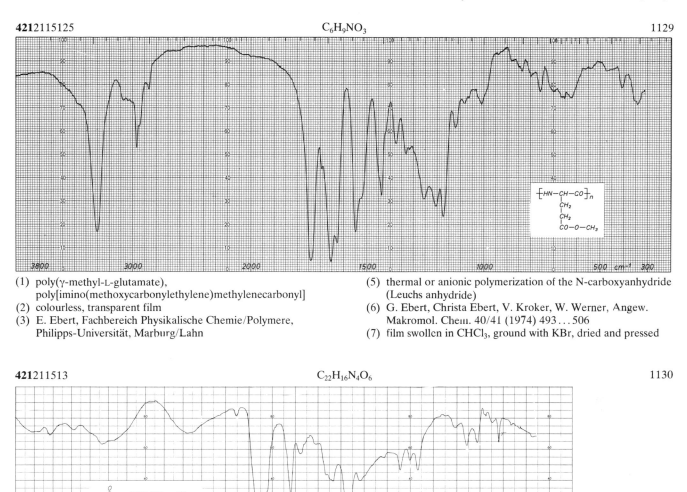

(1) poly(γ-methyl-L-glutamate),
poly[imino(methoxycarbonylethylene)methylenecarbonyl]
(2) colourless, transparent film
(3) E. Ebert, Fachbereich Physikalische Chemie/Polymere,
Philipps-Universität, Marburg/Lahn

(5) thermal or anionic polymerization of the N-carboxyanhydride
(Leuchs anhydride)
(6) G. Ebert, Christa Ebert, V. Kroker, W. Werner, Angew.
Makromol. Chem. 40/41 (1974) 493...506
(7) film swollen in CHCl₃, ground with KBr, dried and pressed

---

421211513 $C_{22}H_{16}N_4O_6$ 1130

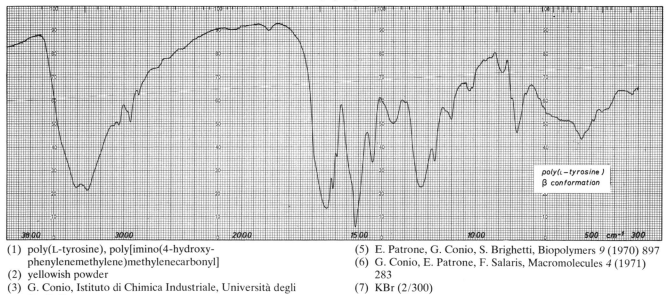

(1) poly(aminoamidocarboxylic acid), aromatic
(3) R.A. Jewell, Chemistry and Physics Branch, NASA Langley
Research Center, Langley Station, Hampton, Va.
(5) polyaddition of pyromellitic anhydride with
3,3'-diaminobenzidine

(6) R.A. Jewell, J. Makromol. Sci.-Chem. *A3* (1969) 1147...59
(7) thin film (spectrum by R.A. Jewell)

4212115221 $C_9H_8NO_2$ 1131

poly(L–tyrosine)
β conformation

(1) poly(L-tyrosine), poly[imino(4-hydroxy-
phenylenemethylene)methylenecarbonyl]
(2) yellowish powder
(3) G. Conio, Istituto di Chimica Industriale, Università degli
Studi, Genova
(4) -NH-CH-CO-
     |
     CH₂-⟨◯⟩-OH

(5) E. Patrone, G. Conio, S. Brighetti, Biopolymers *9* (1970) 897
(6) G. Conio, E. Patrone, F. Salaris, Macromolecules *4* (1971)
283
(7) KBr (2/300)

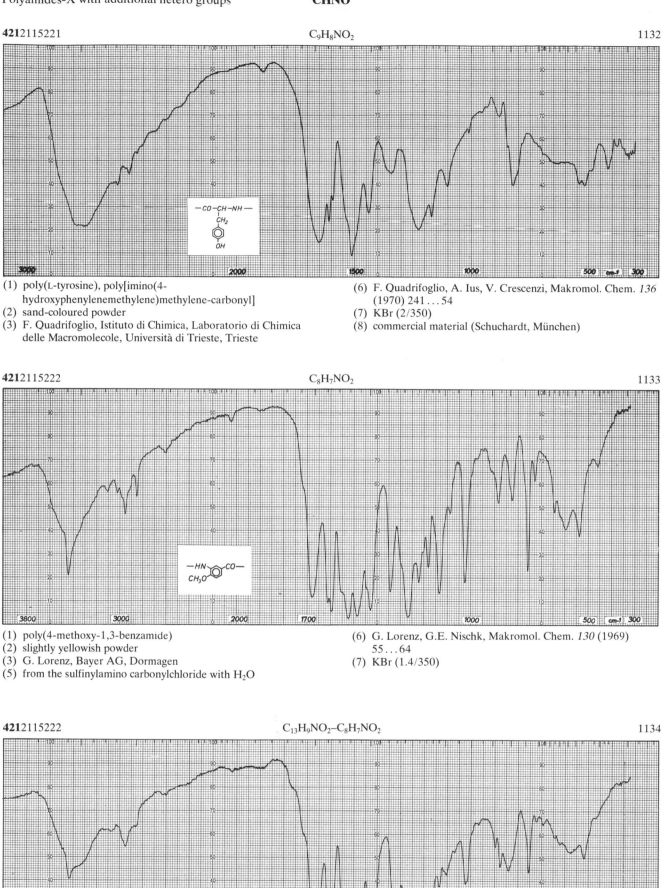

4212115221   C$_9$H$_8$NO$_2$ 1132

(1) poly(L-tyrosine), poly[imino(4-hydroxyphenylenemethylene)methylene-carbonyl]
(2) sand-coloured powder
(3) F. Quadrifoglio, Istituto di Chimica, Laboratorio di Chimica delle Macromolecole, Università di Trieste, Trieste

(6) F. Quadrifoglio, A. Ius, V. Crescenzi, Makromol. Chem. *136* (1970) 241...54
(7) KBr (2/350)
(8) commercial material (Schuchardt, München)

4212115222   C$_8$H$_7$NO$_2$ 1133

(1) poly(4-methoxy-1,3-benzamide)
(2) slightly yellowish powder
(3) G. Lorenz, Bayer AG, Dormagen
(5) from the sulfinylamino carbonylchloride with H$_2$O

(6) G. Lorenz, G.E. Nischk, Makromol. Chem. *130* (1969) 55...64
(7) KBr (1.4/350)

4212115222   C$_{13}$H$_9$NO$_2$–C$_8$H$_7$NO$_2$ 1134

(1) copolyamido ether aromatic
(2) white coarse material
(3) G. Lorenz, Organisch-Wissenschaftliches Laboratorium, Bayer AG, Dormagen
(5) polycondensation or interfacial polycondensation of sulfinylamino-1-4-phenyleneoxy-1,4-benzoylchloride and sulfinylamino-(2-methoxy)-1,3-benzoylchloride in a polar organic solvent with stoichiometrical quantity of water

(6) G. Lorenz, G.E. Nischk, Makromol. Chem. *130* (1969) 55...64
(7) ground with KBr (1.3/350) and tetrahydrofuran, dried and pressed

4212115322 $C_{13}H_9NO_2$ 1135

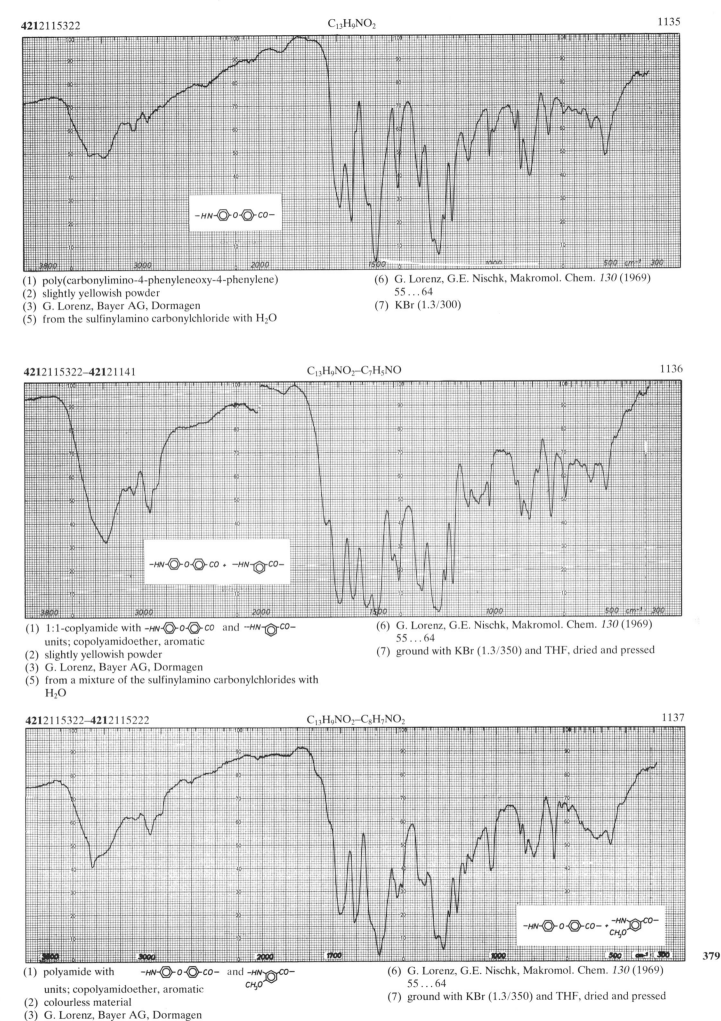

(1) poly(carbonylimino-4-phenyleneoxy-4-phenylene)
(2) slightly yellowish powder
(3) G. Lorenz, Bayer AG, Dormagen
(5) from the sulfinylamino carbonylchloride with H_2O

(6) G. Lorenz, G.E. Nischk, Makromol. Chem. *130* (1969)
    55...64
(7) KBr (1.3/300)

4212115322–**4212**1141 $C_{13}H_9NO_2$–C_7H_5NO 1136

(1) 1:1-coplyamide with $-HN\text{-}⟨O⟩\text{-}O\text{-}⟨O⟩\text{-}CO$ and $-HN\text{-}⟨O⟩\text{-}CO-$
    units; copolyamidoether, aromatic
(2) slightly yellowish powder
(3) G. Lorenz, Bayer AG, Dormagen
(5) from a mixture of the sulfinylamino carbonylchlorides with
    H_2O

(6) G. Lorenz, G.E. Nischk, Makromol. Chem. *130* (1969)
    55...64
(7) ground with KBr (1.3/350) and THF, dried and pressed

4212115322–**4212**115222 $C_{13}H_9NO_2$–$C_8H_7NO_2$ 1137

(1) polyamide with $-HN\text{-}⟨O⟩\text{-}O\text{-}⟨O⟩\text{-}CO-$ and $-HN\text{-}⟨O⟩\text{-}CO-$ with CH_3O
    units; copolyamidoether, aromatic
(2) colourless material
(3) G. Lorenz, Bayer AG, Dormagen
(5) from a mixture of the sulfinylamino carbonylchlorides with
    H_2O

(6) G. Lorenz, G.E. Nischk, Makromol. Chem. *130* (1969)
    55...64
(7) ground with KBr (1.3/350) and THF, dried and pressed

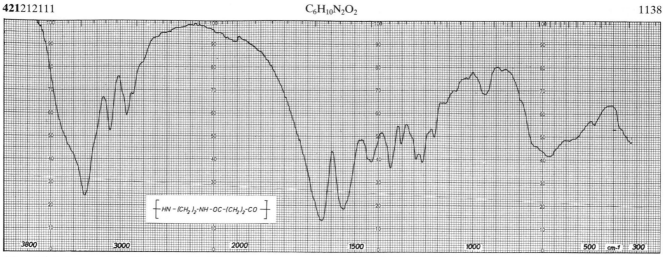

(1) poly(ethylene succinamide), polyamide-2,4
(2) greyish-white material
(3) J.P. Soulier, Académie de Lyon, Université Claude Bernard
(6) J.P. Soulier, IUPAC Macro, Aberdeen 1973
(7) KBr (2/350)

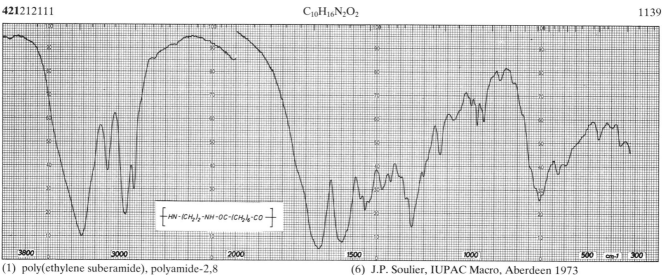

(1) poly(ethylene suberamide), polyamide-2,8
(2) greyish-white material
(3) J.P. Soulier, Académie de Lyon, Université Claude Bernard
(6) J.P. Soulier, IUPAC Macro, Aberdeen 1973
(7) dissolved in HCOOH, precipitated with CH_3OH, white powder pressed with KBr (2/350)

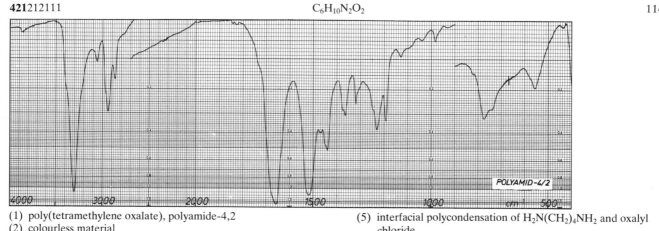

(1) poly(tetramethylene oxalate), polyamide-4,2
(2) colourless material
(3) R. Schürmann, Institut für Physikalische Chemie, Universität Köln
(4) semi-crystalline
(5) interfacial polycondensation of $H_2N(CH_2)_4NH_2$ and oxalyl chloride
(6) R. Schürmann, Thesis, Universität Köln, 1973
(7) film from HCOOH

421212111   C₈H₁₄N₂O₂   1141

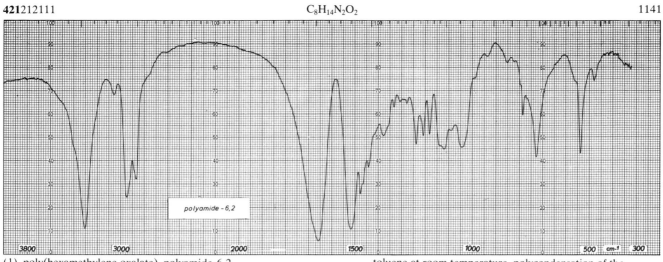

(1) poly(hexamethylene oxalate), polyamide-6,2
(2) colourless material
(3) S.W. Shalaby, Allied Chemical Corp., Morristown, N.J.
(4) -NH(CH₂)₆NH(CO)₂-
(5) reaction of hexamethylene diamine with diethyl oxalate in

toluene at room temperature, polycondensation of the
prepolymer at 65…75 °C (i.v.)
(6) S.W. Shalaby, Polymer Preprints *13*/2 (1972) 1054
(7) ground with KBr (1/350) with acetone, dried and pressed

421212111   C₈H₁₄N₂O₂   1142

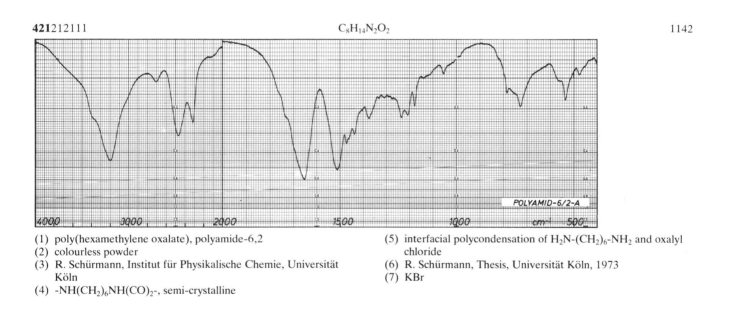

(1) poly(hexamethylene oxalate), polyamide-6,2
(2) colourless powder
(3) R. Schürmann, Institut für Physikalische Chemie, Universität Köln
(4) -NH(CH₂)₆NH(CO)₂-, semi-crystalline

(5) interfacial polycondensation of H₂N-(CH₂)₆-NH₂ and oxalyl chloride
(6) R. Schürmann, Thesis, Universität Köln, 1973
(7) KBr

421212111   C₈H₁₄N₂O₃   1143

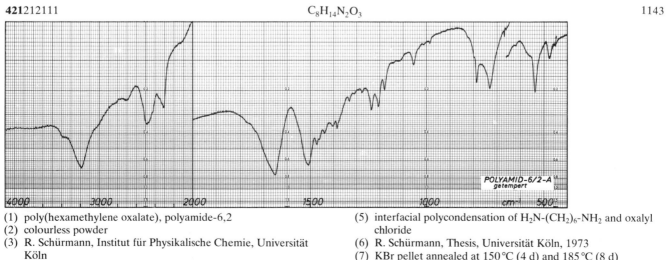

(1) poly(hexamethylene oxalate), polyamide-6,2
(2) colourless powder
(3) R. Schürmann, Institut für Physikalische Chemie, Universität Köln
(4) -NH(CH₂)₆-NH-(CO)₂, semi-crystalline, modification A (α-form)

(5) interfacial polycondensation of H₂N-(CH₂)₆-NH₂ and oxalyl chloride
(6) R. Schürmann, Thesis, Universität Köln, 1973
(7) KBr pellet annealed at 150 °C (4 d) and 185 °C (8 d)

42121211 $C_{12}H_{22}N_2O_2$ 1144

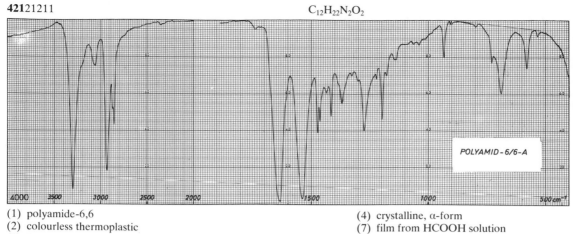

(1) polyamide-6,6
(2) colourless thermoplastic
(3) BASF AG, Ludwigshafen

(4) crystalline, α-form
(7) film from HCOOH solution
(8) commercial „Ultramid A"

421212111 $C_{12}H_{22}N_2O_2$ 1145

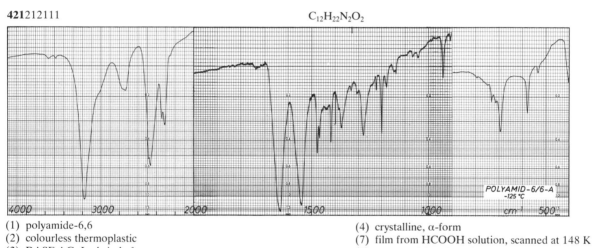

(1) polyamide-6,6
(2) colourless thermoplastic
(3) BASF AG, Ludwigshafen

(4) crystalline, α-form
(7) film from HCOOH solution, scanned at 148 K
(8) commercial „Ultramid A"

421212111 $C_{14}H_{26}N_2O_2$ 1146

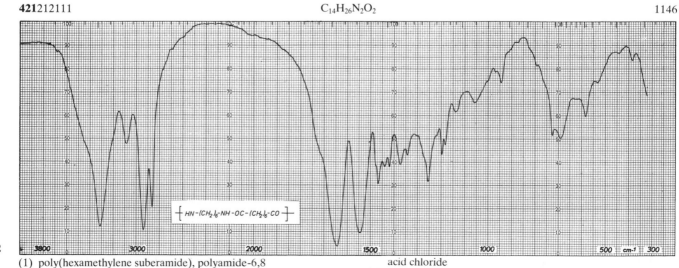

(1) poly(hexamethylene suberamide), polyamide-6,8
(2) colourless powder
(3) J.P. Soulier, Académie de Lyon, Université Claude Bernard
(5) interfacial polycondensation of H_2N-$(CH_2)_6$-NH_2 and suberic

acid chloride
(6) J.P. Soulier, IUPAC Macro, Aberdeen 1973
(7) ground with KBr (2.5/350) and DMSO, dried and pressed

421212111   C$_{16}$H$_{30}$N$_2$O$_2$ 1147

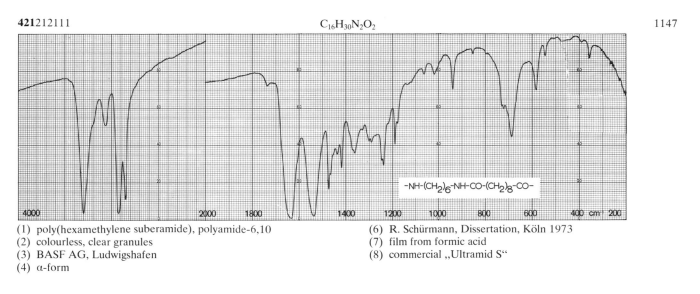

-NH-(CH$_2$)$_6$-NH-CO-(CH$_2$)$_8$-CO-

(1) poly(hexamethylene suberamide), polyamide-6,10
(2) colourless, clear granules
(3) BASF AG, Ludwigshafen
(4) α-form

(6) R. Schürmann, Dissertation, Köln 1973
(7) film from formic acid
(8) commercial „Ultramid S"

421212111–42121251   C$_{16}$H$_{30}$N$_2$O$_2$–C$_{17}$H$_{30}$N$_2$O$_3$ 1148

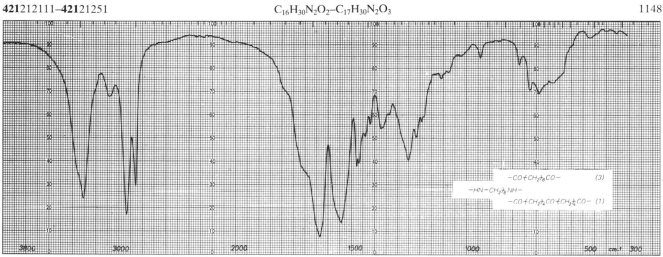

-CO+CH$_2$+$_8$CO-   (3)
-HN-CH$_2$+$_6$NH-
-CO+CH$_2$+$_4$CO+CH$_2$+$_4$CO- (1)

(1) copolyamide from sebacic acid and 6-keto-hendecane-dioic
    acid (3:1) with hexamethylenediisocyanate, (poly(ketoamide),
    copoly(amide-6, 10-ketoamide)
(2) white powder

(3) R. Obeso, Instituto de Plásticos y Caucho, Madrid
(6) R. Obeso. J. de Abajo, J. Fontán, private communication
(7) KBr (1.2/350)

421212111   C$_{10}$H$_{18}$N$_2$O$_2$ 1149

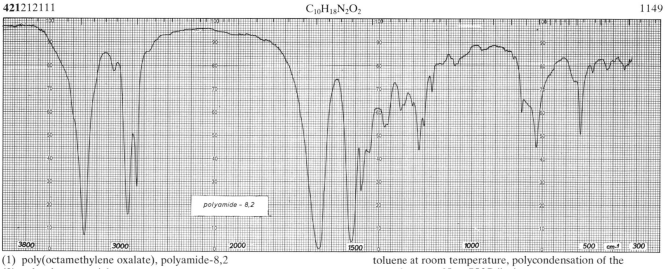

polyamide - 8,2

(1) poly(octamethylene oxalate), polyamide-8,2
(2) colourless material
(3) S.W. Shalaby, Allied Chemical Corp. Morristown, N.J.
(4) -NH(CH$_2$)$_8$NH(CO)$_2$-
(5) reaction of octamethylene diamine with di-n-butyloxalate in

toluene at room temperature, polycondensation of the
prepolymer at 65…75 °C (i.v.)

(6) S.W. Shalaby, Polymer Preprints *13*/2 (1972) 1054
(7) ground with KBr (1/350) and acetone, dried and pressed

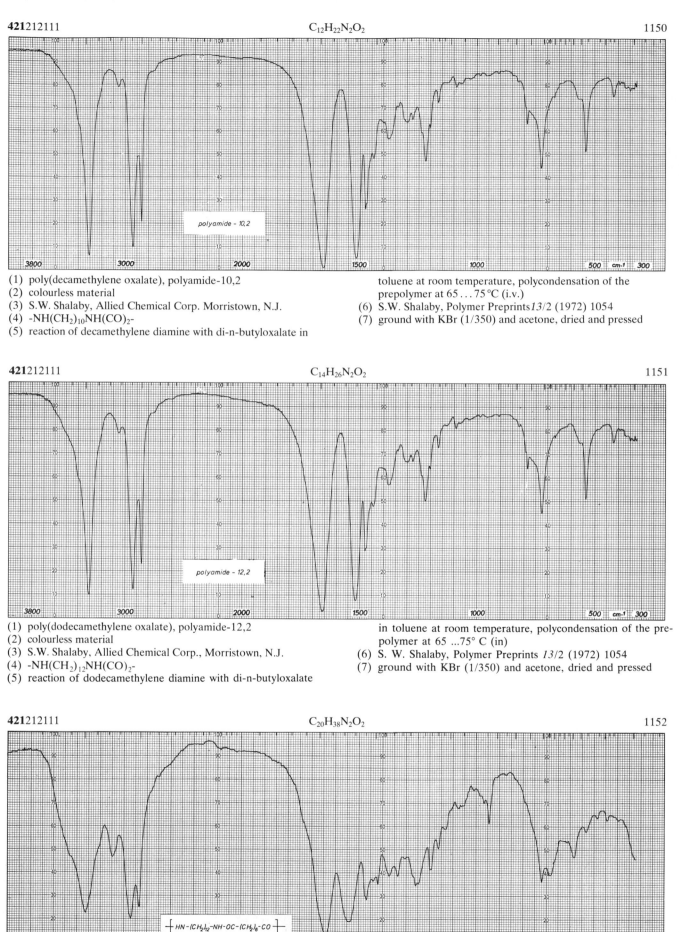

421212111 $C_{12}H_{22}N_2O_2$ 1150

polyamide - 10,2

(1) poly(decamethylene oxalate), polyamide-10,2
(2) colourless material
(3) S.W. Shalaby, Allied Chemical Corp. Morristown, N.J.
(4) -NH(CH$_2$)$_{10}$NH(CO)$_2$-
(5) reaction of decamethylene diamine with di-n-butyloxalate in

toluene at room temperature, polycondensation of the prepolymer at 65...75 °C (i.v.)
(6) S.W. Shalaby, Polymer Preprints *13*/2 (1972) 1054
(7) ground with KBr (1/350) and acetone, dried and pressed

421212111 $C_{14}H_{26}N_2O_2$ 1151

polyamide - 12,2

(1) poly(dodecamethylene oxalate), polyamide-12,2
(2) colourless material
(3) S.W. Shalaby, Allied Chemical Corp., Morristown, N.J.
(4) -NH(CH$_2$)$_{12}$NH(CO)$_2$-
(5) reaction of dodecamethylene diamine with di-n-butyloxalate

in toluene at room temperature, polycondensation of the prepolymer at 65 ...75° C (in)
(6) S. W. Shalaby, Polymer Preprints *13*/2 (1972) 1054
(7) ground with KBr (1/350) and acetone, dried and pressed

421212111 $C_{20}H_{38}N_2O_2$ 1152

$\{ HN-(CH_2)_{12}-NH-OC-(CH_2)_6-CO \}$

(1) poly(dodecamethylene suberamide), polyamide-12,8
(2) greyish material
(3) J.P. Soulier, Académie de Lyon, Université Claude Bernard
(5) interfacial polycondensation of H$_2$N(CH$_2$)$_{12}$NH$_2$ and suberic acid chloride
(6) J.P. Soulier, IUPAC Macro, Aberdeen 1973
(7) KBr (2/300)

421212114 $C_8H_{14}N_2O_2$ 1153

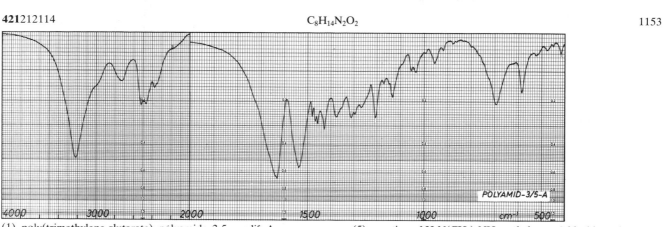

POLYAMID-3/5-A

(1) poly(trimethylene glutarate), polyamide-3,5, modif. A
(2) colourless material
(3) R. Schürmann, Institut für Physikalische Chemie, Universität Köln
(4) -NH(CH$_2$)$_3$NHCO(CH$_2$)$_3$CO-, α-form
(5) reaction of H$_2$N(CH$_2$)$_3$NH$_2$ and glutaroylchloride under cooling
(6) R. Schürmann, Thesis, Universität Köln, 1973
(7) KBr, tempered at 185 °C (4 d)

421212113 $C_7H_{12}N_2O_2$ 1154

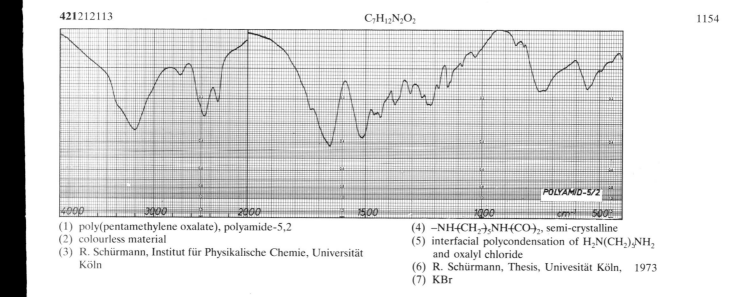

POLYAMID-5/2

(1) poly(pentamethylene oxalate), polyamide-5,2
(2) colourless material
(3) R. Schürmann, Institut für Physikalische Chemie, Universität Köln
(4) –NH(CH$_2$)$_5$NH(CO)$_2$, semi-crystalline
(5) interfacial polycondensation of H$_2$N(CH$_2$)$_5$NH$_2$ and oxalyl chloride
(6) R. Schürmann, Thesis, Univesität Köln, 1973
(7) KBr

421212113 $C_7H_{12}N_2O_2$ 1155

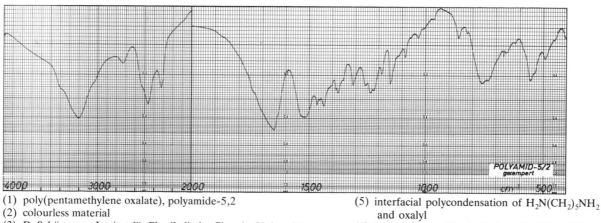

POLYAMID-5/2
gecempert

(1) poly(pentamethylene oxalate), polyamide-5,2
(2) colourless material
(3) R. Schürmann, Institut für Physikalische Chemie, Universität Köln
(4) -NH(CH$_2$)$_5$NH(CO)$_2$-, semi-crystalline
(5) interfacial polycondensation of H$_2$N(CH$_2$)$_5$NH$_2$ and oxalyl
(6) R. Schürmann, Thesis, Universität Köln, 1973
(7) KBr, tempered at 150 °C (4 d) and 185 °C (8 d)

421212114 $C_{12}H_{22}N_2O_2$ 1156

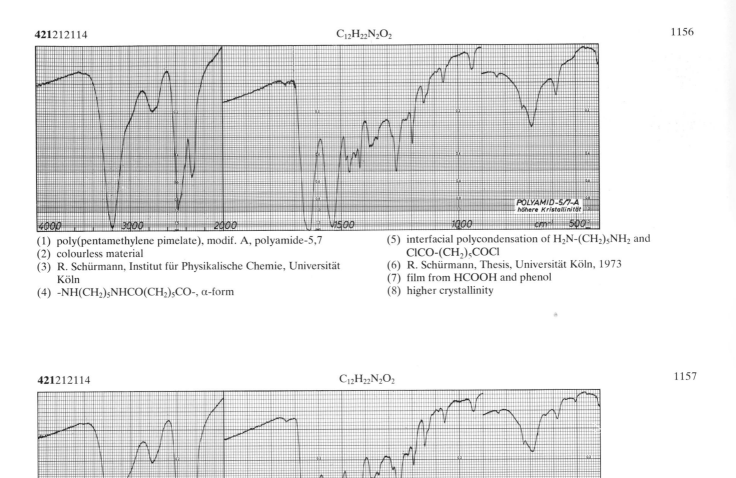

(1) poly(pentamethylene pimelate), modif. A, polyamide-5,7
(2) colourless material
(3) R. Schürmann, Institut für Physikalische Chemie, Universität Köln
(4) -NH(CH$_2$)$_5$NHCO(CH$_2$)$_5$CO-, α-form

(5) interfacial polycondensation of H$_2$N-(CH$_2$)$_5$NH$_2$ and ClCO-(CH$_2$)$_5$COCl
(6) R. Schürmann, Thesis, Universität Köln, 1973
(7) film from HCOOH and phenol
(8) higher crystallinity

421212114 $C_{12}H_{22}N_2O_2$ 1157

(1) poly(pentamethylene pimelate), modif. A, polyamide-5-7
(2) colourless material
(3) R. Schürmann, Institut für Physikalische Chemie, Universität Köln
(4) -NH(CH$_2$)$_5$NHCO(CH$_2$)$_5$CO-, α-form

(5) see above
(6) R. Schürmann, Thesis, Universität Köln, 1973
(7) film from HCOOH and phenol
(8) lower crystallinity

421212114 $C_{12}H_{22}N_2O_2$ 1158

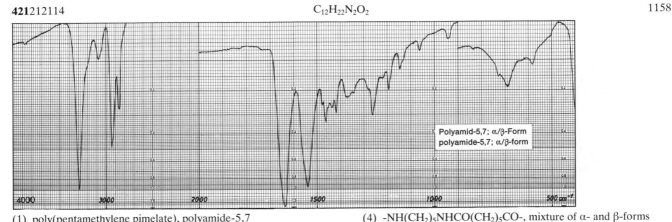

(1) poly(pentamethylene pimelate), polyamide-5,7
(2) colourless material
(3) R. Schürmann, Institut für Physikalische Chemie, Universität Köln

(4) -NH(CH$_2$)$_5$NHCO(CH$_2$)$_5$CO-, mixture of α- and β-forms
(5) see above
(6) R. Schürmann, Thesis, Universität Köln 1973
(7) film from HCOOH and phenol

421212114 $C_{12}H_{22}N_2O_2$ 1159

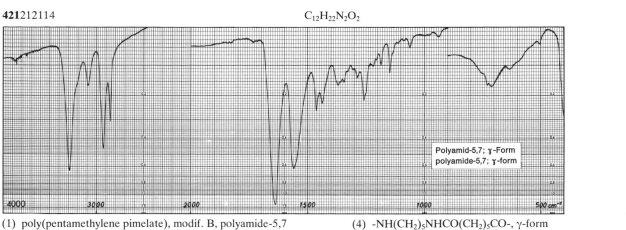

Polyamid-5,7; γ-Form
polyamide-5,7; γ-form

(1) poly(pentamethylene pimelate), modif. B, polyamide-5,7
(2) colourless material
(3) R. Schürmann, Inistut für Physikalische Chemie, Universität Köln
(4) -NH(CH$_2$)$_5$NHCO(CH$_2$)$_5$CO-, γ-form
(5) see above
(6) R. Schürmann, Thesis, Universität Köln, 1973
(7) film from HCOOH

421212114 $C_{12}H_{22}N_2O_2$ 1160

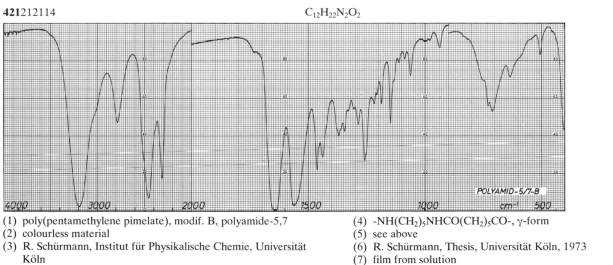

POLYAMID-5/7-B

(1) poly(pentamethylene pimelate), modif. B, polyamide-5,7
(2) colourless material
(3) R. Schürmann, Institut für Physikalische Chemie, Universität Köln
(4) -NH(CH$_2$)$_5$NHCO(CH$_2$)$_5$CO-, γ-form
(5) see above
(6) R. Schürmann, Thesis, Universität Köln, 1973
(7) film from solution

421212114 $C_{12}H_{22}N_2O_2$ 1161

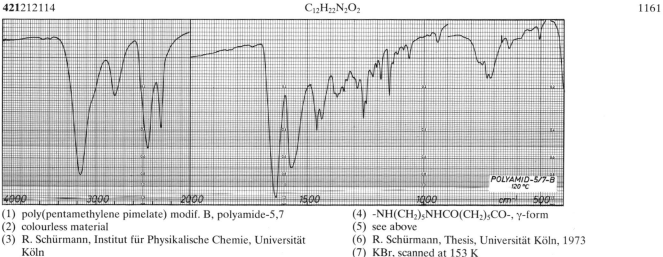

POLYAMID-5/7-B
120 °C

(1) poly(pentamethylene pimelate) modif. B, polyamide-5,7
(2) colourless material
(3) R. Schürmann, Institut für Physikalische Chemie, Universität Köln
(4) -NH(CH$_2$)$_5$NHCO(CH$_2$)$_5$CO-, γ-form
(5) see above
(6) R. Schürmann, Thesis, Universität Köln, 1973
(7) KBr, scanned at 153 K

42121212 $C_{19}H_{36}N_2O_2$ 1162

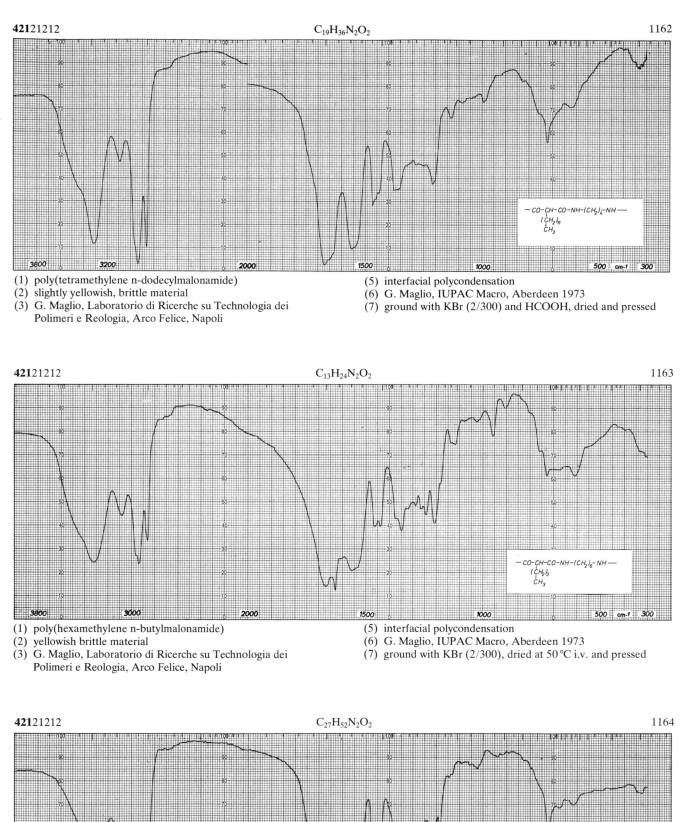

(1) poly(tetramethylene n-dodecylmalonamide)
(2) slightly yellowish, brittle material
(3) G. Maglio, Laboratorio di Ricerche su Technologia dei
      Polimeri e Reologia, Arco Felice, Napoli
(5) interfacial polycondensation
(6) G. Maglio, IUPAC Macro, Aberdeen 1973
(7) ground with KBr (2/300) and HCOOH, dried and pressed

42121212 $C_{13}H_{24}N_2O_2$ 1163

(1) poly(hexamethylene n-butylmalonamide)
(2) yellowish brittle material
(3) G. Maglio, Laboratorio di Ricerche su Technologia dei
      Polimeri e Reologia, Arco Felice, Napoli
(5) interfacial polycondensation
(6) G. Maglio, IUPAC Macro, Aberdeen 1973
(7) ground with KBr (2/300), dried at 50 °C i.v. and pressed

42121212 $C_{27}H_{52}N_2O_2$ 1164

(1) poly(hexamethylene n-octadecylmalonamide)
(2) colourless brittle material
(3) G. Maglio, Laboratorio di Ricerche su Technologia dei
      Polimeri e Reologia, Arco Felice, Napoli
(5) interfacial polycondensation
(6) G. Maglio, IUPAC Macro, Aberdeen 1973
(7) ground with KBr and HCOOH, dried and pressed

42121212 C$_{25}$H$_{48}$N$_2$O$_2$ 1165

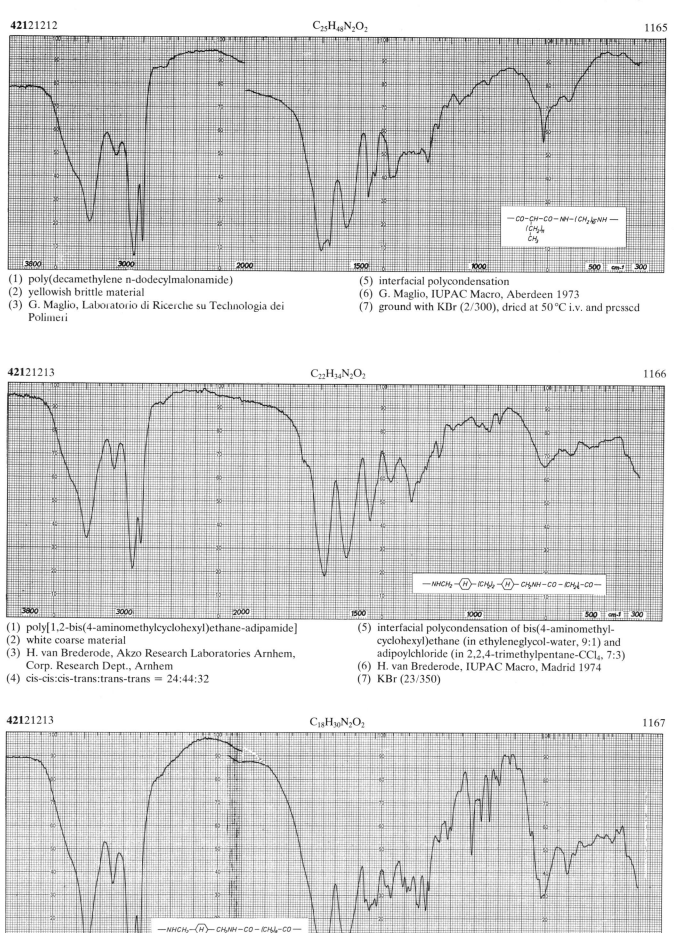

(1) poly(decamethylene n-dodecylmalonamide)
(2) yellowish brittle material
(3) G. Maglio, Laboratorio di Ricerche su Technologia dei Polimeri
(5) interfacial polycondensation
(6) G. Maglio, IUPAC Macro, Aberdeen 1973
(7) ground with KBr (2/300), dried at 50 °C i.v. and pressed

42121213 C$_{22}$H$_{34}$N$_2$O$_2$ 1166

(1) poly[1,2-bis(4-aminomethylcyclohexyl)ethane-adipamide]
(2) white coarse material
(3) H. van Brederode, Akzo Research Laboratories Arnhem, Corp. Research Dept., Arnhem
(4) cis-cis:cis-trans:trans-trans = 24:44:32
(5) interfacial polycondensation of bis(4-aminomethylcyclohexyl)ethane (in ethyleneglycol-water, 9:1) and adipoylchloride (in 2,2,4-trimethylpentane-CCl$_4$, 7:3)
(6) H. van Brederode, IUPAC Macro, Madrid 1974
(7) KBr (23/350)

42121213 C$_{18}$H$_{30}$N$_2$O$_2$ 1167

(1) poly(1,4-dimethylenecyclohexylene sebacamide)
(2) colourless material
(3) F.R. Prince, Allied Chemical Corp., Chemical Research Laboratory, Morristown, N.J.
(4) all-trans
(5) interfacial polycondensation of the diamine with sebacoylchloride
(6) F.R. Prince, R.J. Fredericks, Macromolecules 5 (1972) 168...70
(7) KBr (5/350)

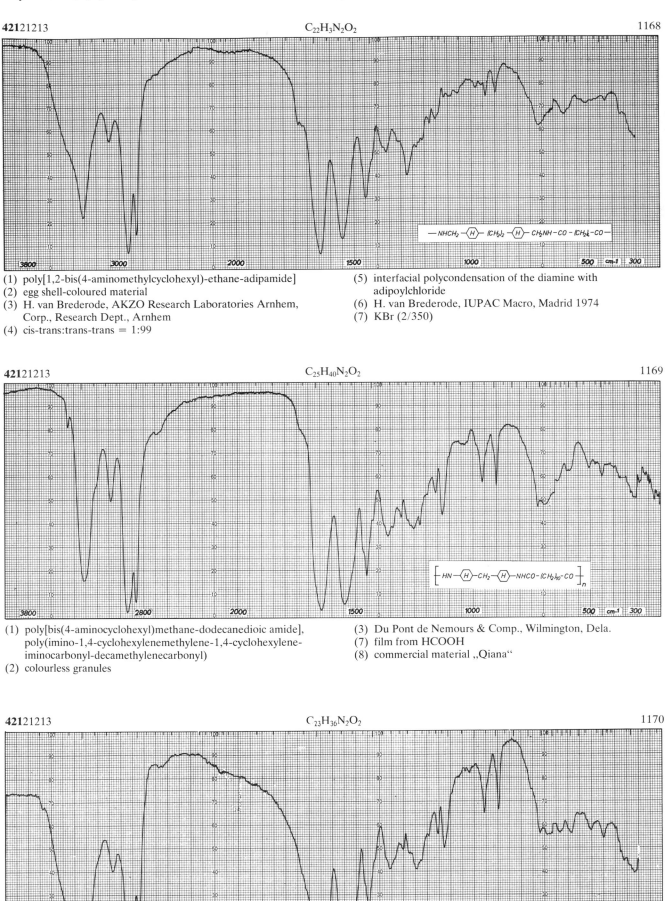

42121213 $C_{22}H_3N_2O_2$ 1168

(1) poly[1,2-bis(4-aminomethylcyclohexyl)-ethane-adipamide]
(2) egg shell-coloured material
(3) H. van Brederode, AKZO Research Laboratories Arnhem, Corp., Research Dept., Arnhem
(4) cis-trans:trans-trans = 1:99

(5) interfacial polycondensation of the diamine with adipoylchloride
(6) H. van Brederode, IUPAC Macro, Madrid 1974
(7) KBr (2/350)

42121213 $C_{25}H_{40}N_2O_2$ 1169

(1) poly[bis(4-aminocyclohexyl)methane-dodecanedioic amide], poly(imino-1,4-cyclohexylenemethylene-1,4-cyclohexylene-iminocarbonyl-decamethylenecarbonyl)
(2) colourless granules

(3) Du Pont de Nemours & Comp., Wilmington, Dela.
(7) film from HCOOH
(8) commercial material „Qiana"

42121213 $C_{23}H_{36}N_2O_2$ 1170

(1) poly[4,4'-bis(cyclohexylene)methylene sebacamide]
(2) colourless material
(3) F.R. Prince, Allied Chemical Corporation, Morristown, N.J.
(4) crystalline
(5) melt polycondensation of bis(4-aminocyclohexyl)methane and sebacic acid (250 °C)

(6) F.R. Prince, R.J. Fredericks, Macromolecules 5 (1972) 168...70
(7) KBr (3/350), ordinate expanded

42121213   C$_{19}$H$_{28}$N$_2$O$_6$ 1171

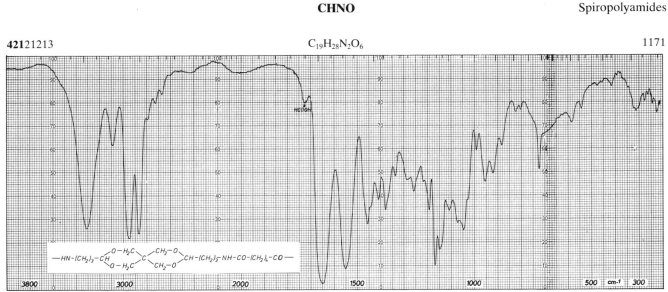

(1) spiropolyamide 3,9-bis(3-aminopropyl)-2,4,8,10-tetroxaspiro[5,5]undecane and adipoyl chloride
(2) colourless fibrous material
(3) L. Hoppe, Firma Wolff & Co., Walsrode
(5) interfacial polycondensation
(6) L. Hoppe, Makromol. Chem. *124* (1969) 274...7
(7) film from HCOOH solution

42121213   C$_{23}$H$_{36}$N$_2$O$_6$ 1172

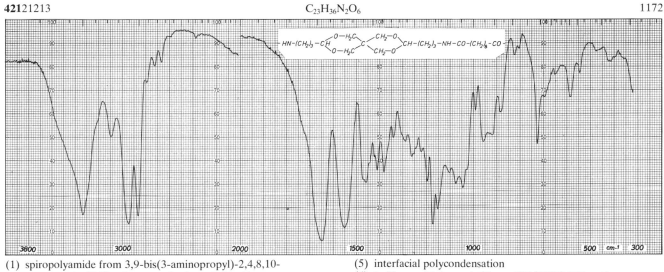

(1) spiropolyamide from 3,9-bis(3-aminopropyl)-2,4,8,10-tetraoxaspiro[5,5]undecane and sebazoyl chloride
(2) light, colourless material
(3) L. Hoppe, Firma Wolff & Co., Walsrode
(5) interfacial polycondensation
(6) L. Hoppe, Makromol. Chem. *124* (1969) 274...7
(7) KBr (3/350)

42121213   C$_{19}$H$_{28}$N$_2$O$_6$ 1173

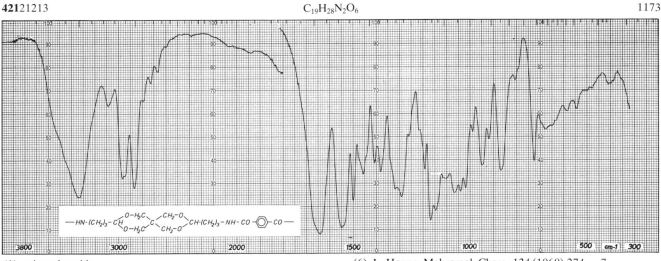

(1) spiropolyamide
(2) yellowish powder
(3) L. Hoppe, Firma Wolff & Co., Walsrode
(5) interfacial polycondensation of 3,9-bis(3-aminopropyl)-2,4,8,10-tetraoxaspiro[5,5]undecane and terephthaloyl chloride
(6) L. Hoppe, Makromol. Chem. *124* (1969) 274...7
(7) KBr (3/350)

42121221 $C_6H_8N_2O_2$ 1174

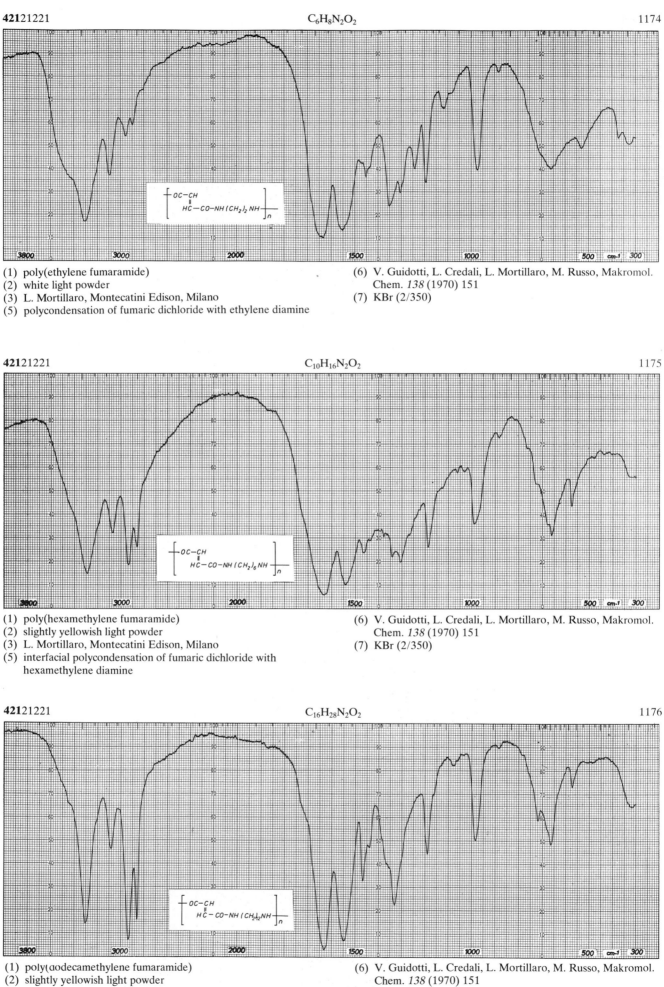

(1) poly(ethylene fumaramide)
(2) white light powder
(3) L. Mortillaro, Montecatini Edison, Milano
(5) polycondensation of fumaric dichloride with ethylene diamine

(6) V. Guidotti, L. Credali, L. Mortillaro, M. Russo, Makromol. Chem. *138* (1970) 151
(7) KBr (2/350)

42121221 $C_{10}H_{16}N_2O_2$ 1175

(1) poly(hexamethylene fumaramide)
(2) slightly yellowish light powder
(3) L. Mortillaro, Montecatini Edison, Milano
(5) interfacial polycondensation of fumaric dichloride with hexamethylene diamine

(6) V. Guidotti, L. Credali, L. Mortillaro, M. Russo, Makromol. Chem. *138* (1970) 151
(7) KBr (2/350)

42121221 $C_{16}H_{28}N_2O_2$ 1176

(1) poly(dodecamethylene fumaramide)
(2) slightly yellowish light powder
(3) L. Mortillaro, Montecatini Edison, Milano
(5) polycondensation of fumaric dichloride with dedecamethylene diamine

(6) V. Guidotti, L. Credali, L. Mortillaro, M. Russo, Makromol. Chem. *138* (1970) 151
(7) KBr (2/350)

42121221 $C_{11}H_{18}N_2O_2$ 1177

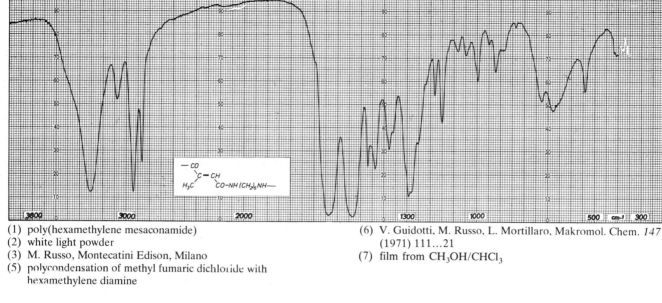

(1) poly(hexamethylene mesaconamide)
(2) white light powder
(3) M. Russo, Montecatini Edison, Milano
(5) polycondensation of methyl fumaric dichloride with
    hexamethylene diamine

(6) V. Guidotti, M. Russo, L. Mortillaro, Makromol. Chem. *147*
    (1971) 111...21
(7) film from $CH_3OH/CHCl_3$

42121221 $C_{16}H_{28}N_2O_2$ 1178

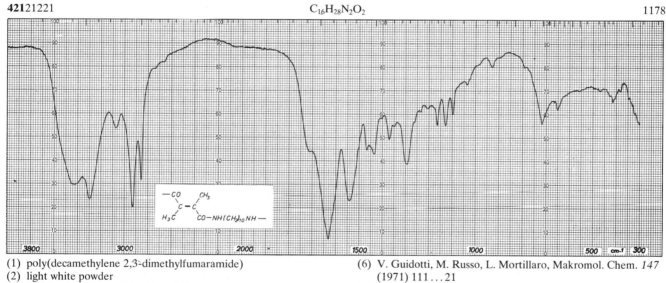

(1) poly(decamethylene 2,3-dimethylfumaramide)
(2) light white powder
(3) M. Russo, Montecatini Edison, Milano
(5) polycondensation of dimethyl fumaric dichloride with
    decamethylene diamine

(6) V. Guidotti, M. Russo, L. Mortillaro, Makromol. Chem. *147*
    (1971) 111...21
(7) ground with KBr (2/350) and HCOOH, dried and pressed

42121221 $C_{15}H_{26}N_2O_2$ 1179

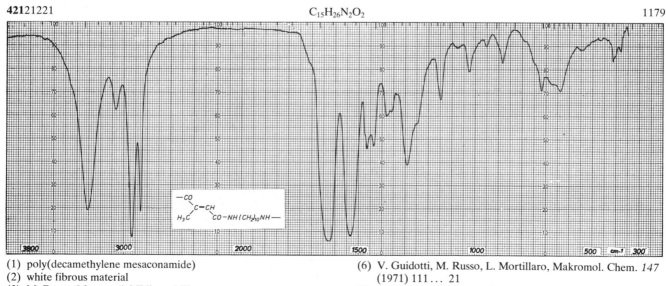

(1) poly(decamethylene mesaconamide)
(2) white fibrous material
(3) M. Russo, Montecatini Edison, Milano
(5) polycondensation of methyl fumaric dichloride with
    decamethylene diamine

(6) V. Guidotti, M. Russo, L. Mortillaro, Makromol. Chem. *147*
    (1971) 111...21
(7) dissolved in $CH_3OH + CHCl_3$, ground with KBr, dried and
    pressed

42121231 $C_{13}H_{14}N_2O_2$ 1180

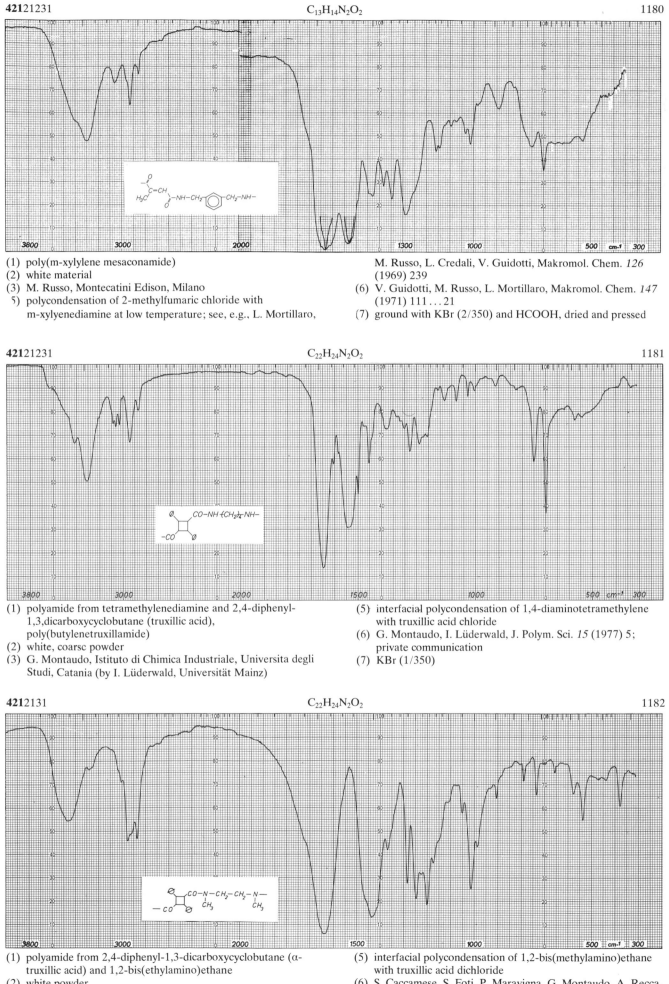

(1) poly(m-xylylene mesaconamide)
(2) white material
(3) M. Russo, Montecatini Edison, Milano
5) polycondensation of 2-methylfumaric chloride with
    m-xylyenediamine at low temperature; see, e.g., L. Mortillaro,

M. Russo, L. Credali, V. Guidotti, Makromol. Chem. *126*
(1969) 239
(6) V. Guidotti, M. Russo, L. Mortillaro, Makromol. Chem. *147*
    (1971) 111 ... 21
(7) ground with KBr (2/350) and HCOOH, dried and pressed

42121231 $C_{22}H_{24}N_2O_2$ 1181

(1) polyamide from tetramethylenediamine and 2,4-diphenyl-
    1,3,dicarboxycyclobutane (truxillic acid),
    poly(butylenetruxillamide)
(2) white, coarsc powder
(3) G. Montaudo, Istituto di Chimica Industriale, Universita degli
    Studi, Catania (by I. Lüderwald, Universität Mainz)

(5) interfacial polycondensation of 1,4-diaminotetramethylene
    with truxillic acid chloride
(6) G. Montaudo, I. Lüderwald, J. Polym. Sci. *15* (1977) 5;
    private communication
(7) KBr (1/350)

4212131 $C_{22}H_{24}N_2O_2$ 1182

(1) polyamide from 2,4-diphenyl-1,3-dicarboxycyclobutane (α-
    truxillic acid) and 1,2-bis(ethylamino)ethane
(2) white powder
(3) G. Montaudo, I. Lüderwald, Istituto di Chimica Industriale,
    Universita degli Studi, Catania/Institut für Organische
    Chemie, Universität Mainz, Mainz

(5) interfacial polycondensation of 1,2-bis(methylamino)ethane
    with truxillic acid dichloride
(6) S. Caccamese, S. Foti, P. Maravigna, G. Montaudo, A. Recca,
    I. Lüderwald, M. Przybylski, J. Polym. Sci. – Chem. Ed. *15*
    (1977) 5 ... 13
(7) KBr (2/350)

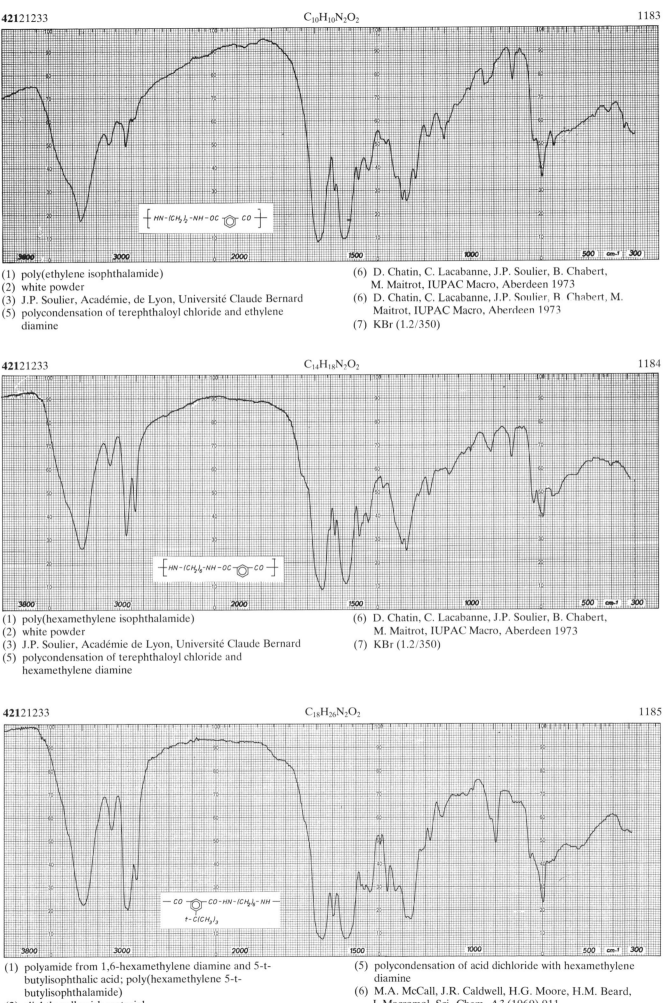

42121233 $C_{10}H_{10}N_2O_2$ 1183

$$\left[HN-(CH_2)_2-NH-OC-\bigcirc-CO \right]$$

(1) poly(ethylene isophthalamide)
(2) white powder
(3) J.P. Soulier, Académie, de Lyon, Université Claude Bernard
(5) polycondensation of terephthaloyl chloride and ethylene diamine

(6) D. Chatin, C. Lacabanne, J.P. Soulier, B. Chabert, M. Maitrot, IUPAC Macro, Aberdeen 1973
(6) D. Chatin, C. Lacabanne, J.P. Soulier, B. Chabert, M. Maitrot, IUPAC Macro, Aberdeen 1973
(7) KBr (1.2/350)

42121233 $C_{14}H_{18}N_2O_2$ 1184

$$\left[HN-(CH_2)_6-NH-OC-\bigcirc-CO \right]$$

(1) poly(hexamethylene isophthalamide)
(2) white powder
(3) J.P. Soulier, Académie de Lyon, Université Claude Bernard
(5) polycondensation of terephthaloyl chloride and hexamethylene diamine

(6) D. Chatin, C. Lacabanne, J.P. Soulier, B. Chabert, M. Maitrot, IUPAC Macro, Aberdeen 1973
(7) KBr (1.2/350)

42121233 $C_{18}H_{26}N_2O_2$ 1185

$$- CO-\bigcirc-CO-HN-(CH_2)_6-NH -$$
$$t-C(CH_3)_3$$

(1) polyamide from 1,6-hexamethylene diamine and 5-t-butylisophthalic acid; poly(hexamethylene 5-t-butylisophthalamide)
(2) slightly yellowish material
(3) M.A. McCall, Tennessee Eastman Company, Kingsport, Tenn.

(5) polycondensation of acid dichloride with hexamethylene diamine
(6) M.A. McCall, J.R. Caldwell, H.G. Moore, H.M. Beard, J. Macromol. Sci.-Chem. *A3* (1969) 911
(7) dissolved in HCOOH, ground with KBr, dried and pressed

42121233 $C_{20}H_{30}N_2O_2$ 1186

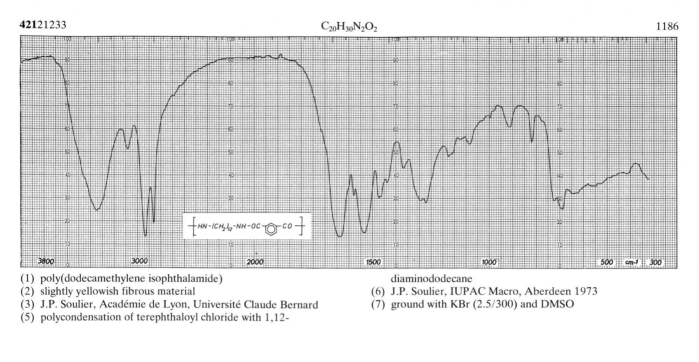

(1) poly(dodecamethylene isophthalamide)
(2) slightly yellowish fibrous material
(3) J.P. Soulier, Académie de Lyon, Université Claude Bernard
(5) polycondensation of terephthaloyl chloride with 1,12-
diaminododecane
(6) J.P. Soulier, IUPAC Macro, Aberdeen 1973
(7) ground with KBr (2.5/300) and DMSO

42121233 $C_{14}H_{18}N_2O_2$ 1187

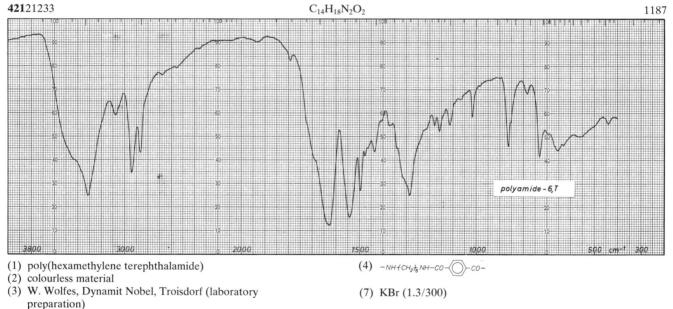

polyamide - 6,T

(1) poly(hexamethylene terephthalamide)
(2) colourless material
(3) W. Wolfes, Dynamit Nobel, Troisdorf (laboratory
preparation)

(4) $-NH{(CH_2)}_6NH-CO-\bigcirc-CO-$

(7) KBr (1.3/300)

42121233 $C_{17}H_{24}N_2O_2$ 1188

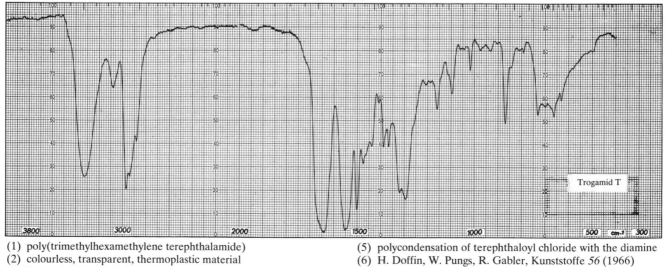

Trogamid T

(1) poly(trimethylhexamethylene terephthalamide)
(2) colourless, transparent, thermoplastic material
(3) Dynamit Nobel AG, Troisdorf
(4) polyamide from terephthalic acid and 2,2,4(2,4,4)-
trimethylhexamethylene-1,6-diamine (mixture of isomers)
(5) polycondensation of terephthaloyl chloride with the diamine
(6) H. Doffin, W. Pungs, R. Gabler, Kunststoffe 56 (1966)
542...6
(7) film from DMF solution (dried i.v. at 60°C)
(8) commercial material „Trogamid T"

42121233 $C_{20}H_{22}N_2O_2$ 1189

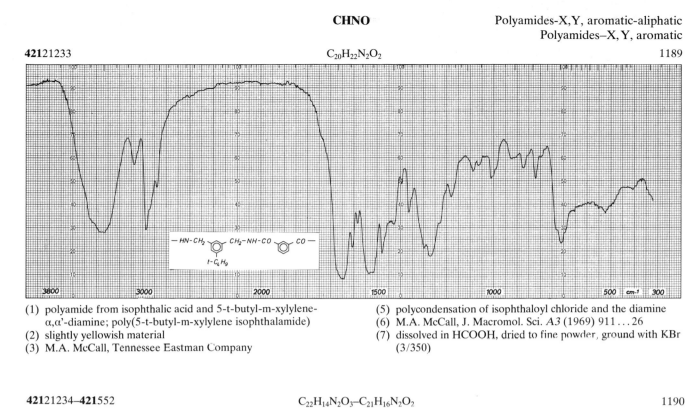

(1) polyamide from isophthalic acid and 5-t-butyl-m-xylylene-
α,α'-diamine; poly(5-t-butyl-m-xylylene isophthalamide)
(2) slightly yellowish material
(3) M.A. McCall, Tennessee Eastman Company
(5) polycondensation of isophthaloyl chloride and the diamine
(6) M.A. McCall, J. Macromol. Sci. *A3* (1969) 911...26
(7) dissolved in HCOOH, dried to fine powder, ground with KBr
(3/350)

42121234–**421**552 $C_{22}H_{14}N_2O_3–C_{21}H_{16}N_2O_2$ 1190

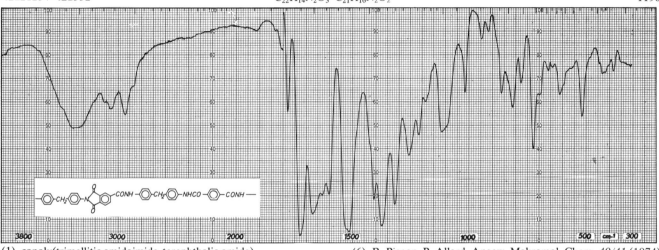

(1) copoly(trimellitic amidoimide-terephthalic amide)
(2) fine, yellow fiber
(3) R. Pigeon, Rhône-Poulenc-Textile, Lyon
(5) polycondensation of trimellitic acid anhydride, terephthalic
acid and 4,4'-diisocyanato-diphenylmethane in polar solvent
(6) R. Pigeon, P. Allard, Angew. Makromol. Chem. *40/41* (1974)
139...58
(7) ground with KBr (2.5/350) and dimethylacetamide, dried and
pressed

42121241 $C_{14}H_{10}N_2O_2$ 1191

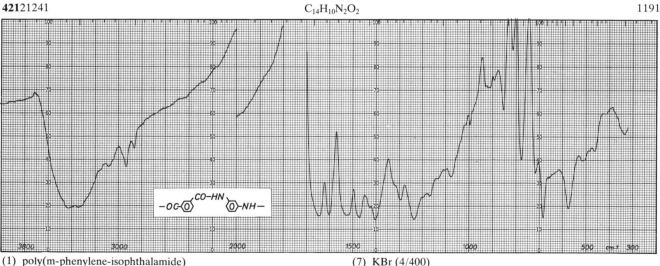

(1) poly(m-phenylene-isophthalamide)
(2) orange-coloured fiber
(3) Du Pont de Nemours & Comp., Wilmington, Dela.
(by J. Goldfarb, Wright-Patterson AFB, O.)
(7) KBr (4/400)
(8) commercial „Nomex"

42121241 $C_{14}H_{10}N_2O_2$ 1192

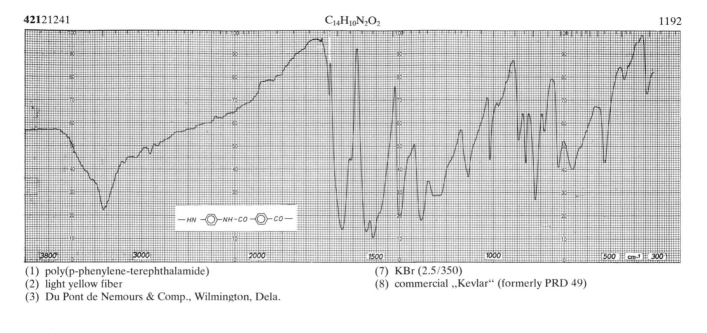

(1) poly(p-phenylene-terephthalamide)
(2) light yellow fiber
(3) Du Pont de Nemours & Comp., Wilmington, Dela.

(7) KBr (2.5/350)
(8) commercial „Kevlar" (formerly PRD 49)

42121241 $C_{14}H_{10}N_2O_2$ 1193

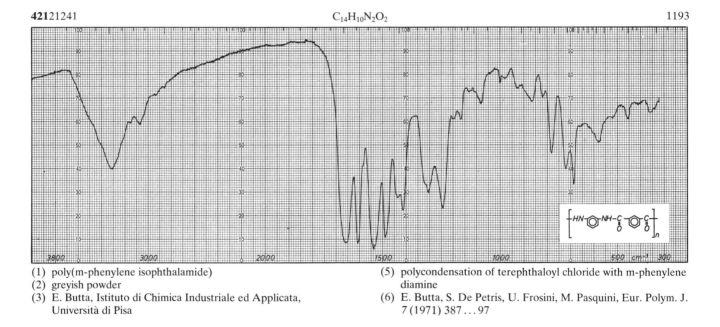

(1) poly(m-phenylene isophthalamide)
(2) greyish powder
(3) E. Butta, Istituto di Chimica Industriale ed Applicata,
Università di Pisa

(5) polycondensation of terephthaloyl chloride with m-phenylene
diamine
(6) E. Butta, S. De Petris, U. Frosini, M. Pasquini, Eur. Polym. J.
7 (1971) 387 . . . 97

42121241 $C_{14}H_{10}N_2O_2$ 1194

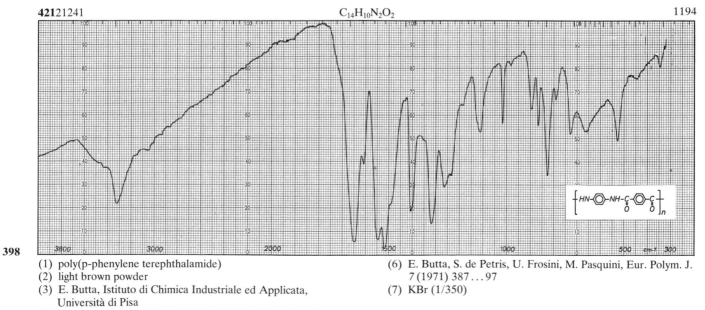

(1) poly(p-phenylene terephthalamide)
(2) light brown powder
(3) E. Butta, Istituto di Chimica Industriale ed Applicata,
Università di Pisa
(5) polycondensation of terephthalic chloride with p-phenylene
diamine

(6) E. Butta, S. de Petris, U. Frosini, M. Pasquini, Eur. Polym. J.
7 (1971) 387 . . . 97
(7) KBr (1/350)

42121242   C$_{20}$H$_{14}$N$_2$O$_2$ 1195

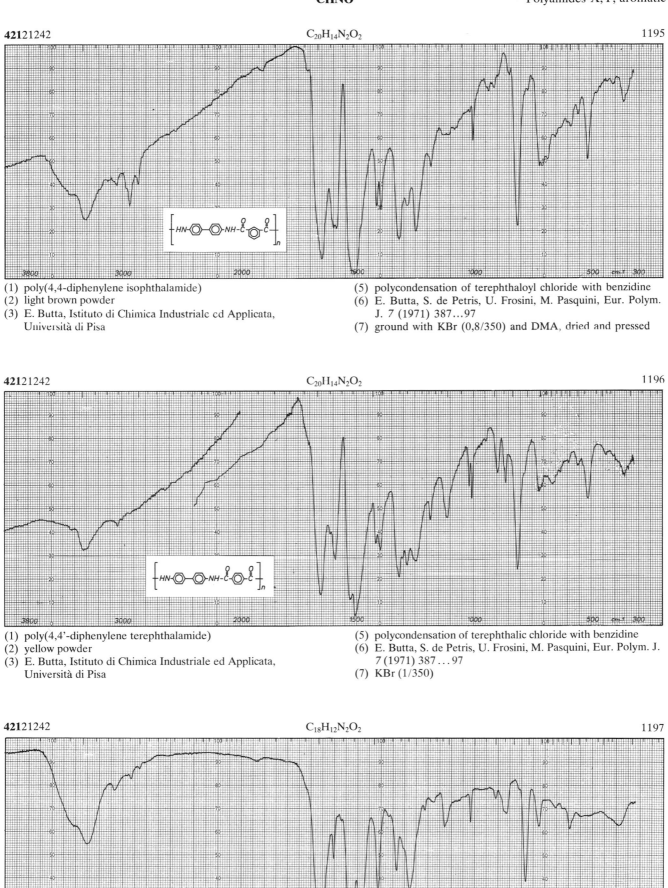

(1) poly(4,4-diphenylene isophthalamide)
(2) light brown powder
(3) E. Butta, Istituto di Chimica Industriale ed Applicata,
    Università di Pisa

(5) polycondensation of terephthaloyl chloride with benzidine
(6) E. Butta, S. de Petris, U. Frosini, M. Pasquini, Eur. Polym.
    J. 7 (1971) 387...97
(7) ground with KBr (0,8/350) and DMA, dried and pressed

42121242   C$_{20}$H$_{14}$N$_2$O$_2$ 1196

(1) poly(4,4'-diphenylene terephthalamide)
(2) yellow powder
(3) E. Butta, Istituto di Chimica Industriale ed Applicata,
    Università di Pisa

(5) polycondensation of terephthalic chloride with benzidine
(6) E. Butta, S. de Petris, U. Frosini, M. Pasquini, Eur. Polym. J.
    7 (1971) 387...97
(7) KBr (1/350)

42121242   C$_{18}$H$_{12}$N$_2$O$_2$ 1197

(1) poly(1,5-naphthalene terephthalamide)
(2) light brown powder
(3) E. Butta, Istituto di Chimica Industriale ed Applicata,
    Università di Pisa (5) polycondensation of terephthalic
    chloride with 1,5-diamino naphthalene

(6) E. Butta, S. de Petris, U. Frosini, M. Pasquini, Eur. Polym. J.
    7 (1971) 387...97
(7) KBr (1/350)

421212511   C$_{48}$H$_{28}$N$_6$O$_2$

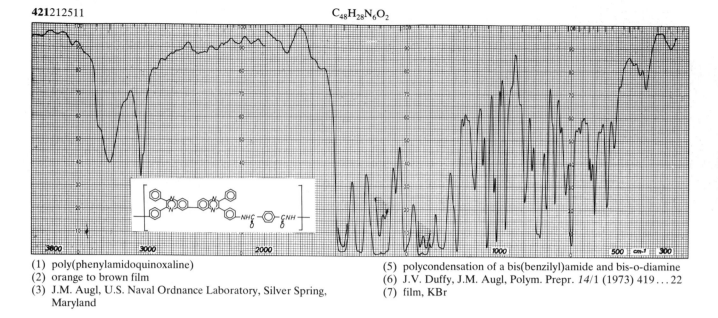

(1) poly(phenylamidoquinoxaline)
(2) orange to brown film
(3) J.M. Augl, U.S. Naval Ordnance Laboratory, Silver Spring, Maryland

(5) polycondensation of a bis(benzilyl)amide and bis-o-diamine
(6) J.V. Duffy, J.M. Augl, Polym. Prepr. *14*/1 (1973) 419...22
(7) film, KBr

4212125122–323131   C$_{40}$H$_{27}$N$_5$O$_4$ 1199

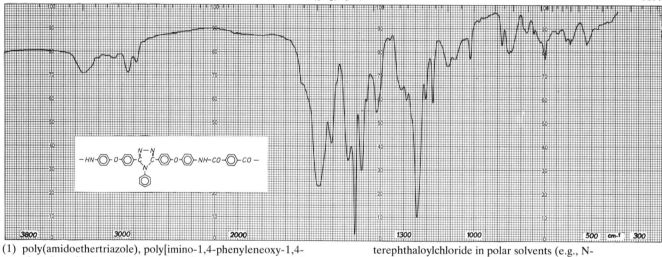

(1) poly(amidoethertriazole), poly[imino-1,4-phenyleneoxy-1,4-phenylene-(1-phenyl-2,5-triazolediyl)-1,4-phenyleneoxy-1,4-phenyleneimino-terephthaloyl]
(2) white to yellow, very fine fiber
(3) H.-E. Künzel, Organisch-Wissenschaftliches Laboratorium, Bayer AG, Werk Dormagen, Dormagen
(5) polycondensation of the heterocyclic diamine with

terephthaloylchloride in polar solvents (e.g., N-dimethylacetamide or N-methylpyrrolidone)
(6) H.-E. Künzel, G.D. Wolf, F. Bentz, G. Blankenstein, G.E. Nischk, Makromol. Chem. *130* (1969) 103...44
(7) fiber dissolved in dimethylformamide, film; ordinate expanded between 2000 cm^{-1} and 200 cm^{-1}

4212125123   C$_{13}$H$_{22}$N$_2$O$_3$ 1200

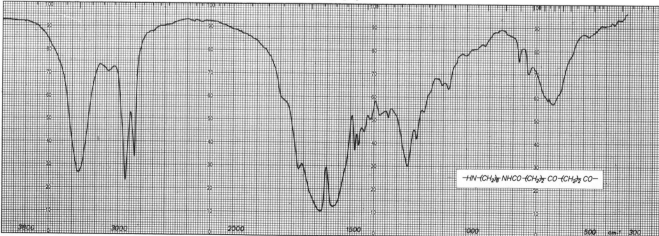

(1) poly(ketoamide), poly(9,12,15-trioxo-1,8-diaza-pentadecane)
(2) eggshell-coloured powder
(3) R. Obeso, Instituto de Plásticos y Caucho, Madrid

(6) R. Obeso, J. de Abajo, J. Fontán, private communication
(7) KBr (1.5/350)

4212125123   C$_{17}$H$_{30}$N$_2$O$_3$ 1201

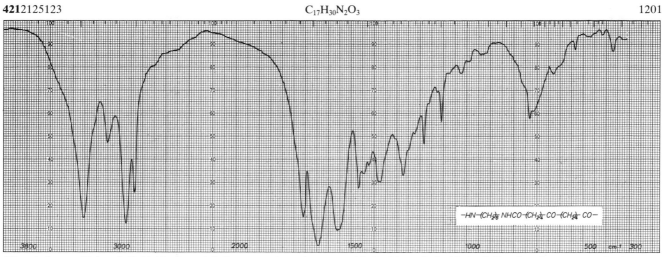

−HN−(CH$_2$)$_8$ NHCO−(CH$_2$)$_4$ CO−(CH$_2$)$_4$ CO−

(1) poly(ketoamide), poly(9,14,19-trioxo-1,8-diaza-nonadecane)
(2) yellowish coarse material
(3) R. Obeso, Instituto de Plásticos y Caucho, Madrid
(5) polycondensation of the salt of the diamine with keto-
    dicarboxylic acid
(6) R. Obeso, J. de Abajo, J. Fontán private communication
(7) KBr (2/350)

4212125123   C$_{17}$H$_{30}$N$_2$O$_3$ 1202

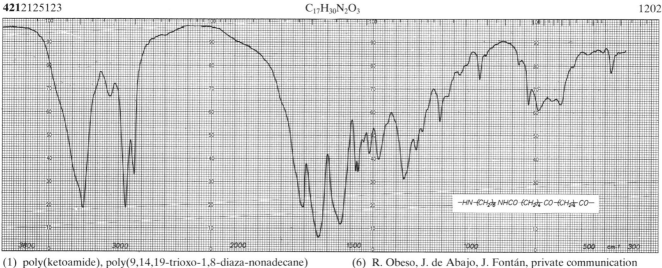

−HN−(CH$_2$)$_8$ NHCO (CH$_2$)$_4$ CO−(CH$_2$)$_4$ CO−

(1) poly(ketoamide), poly(9,14,19-trioxo-1,8-diaza-nonadecane)
(2) eggshell-coloured powder
(3) R. Obeso, Instituto de Plásticos y Caucho, Madrid
(6) R. Obeso, J. de Abajo, J. Fontán, private communication
(7) KBr (2/350)

4212125222   C$_{33}$H$_{23}$N$_2$O$_4$ 1203

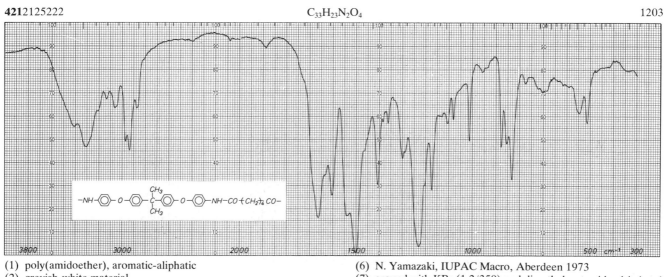

−NH−⟨O⟩−O−⟨O⟩−C(CH$_3$)(CH$_3$)−⟨O⟩−O−⟨O⟩−NH−CO−(CH$_2$)$_4$ CO−

(1) poly(amidoether), aromatic-aliphatic
(2) greyish-white material
(3) N. Yamazaki, Tokyo Institute of Technology, Tokyo
(6) N. Yamazaki, IUPAC Macro, Aberdeen 1973
(7) ground with KBr (1.2/350) and dimethylacetamide, dried and
    pressed

401

421212531 $C_{15}H_9N_3O_2$ 1204

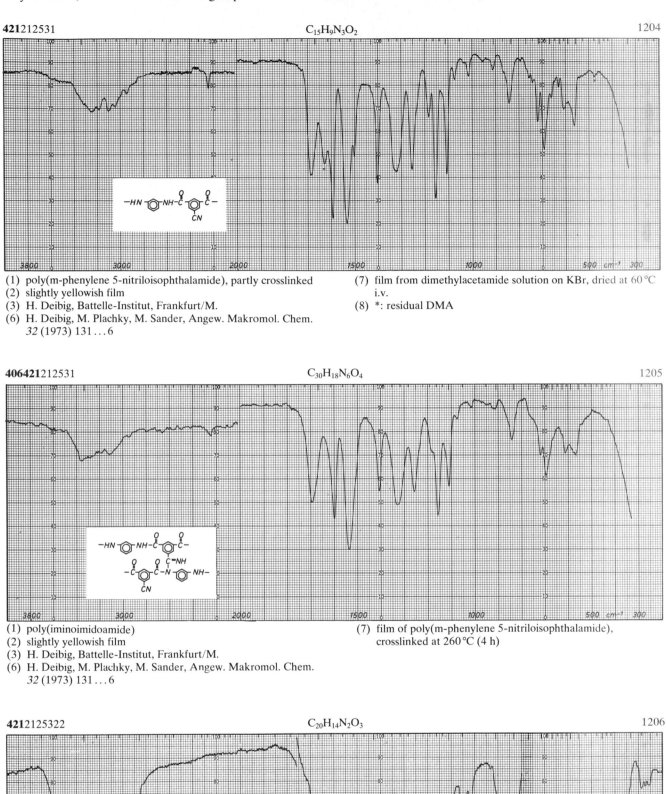

(1) poly(m-phenylene 5-nitriloisophthalamide), partly crosslinked
(2) slightly yellowish film
(3) H. Deibig, Battelle-Institut, Frankfurt/M.
(6) H. Deibig, M. Plachky, M. Sander, Angew. Makromol. Chem. *32* (1973) 131…6

(7) film from dimethylacetamide solution on KBr, dried at 60 °C
i.v.
(8) *: residual DMA

406421212531 $C_{30}H_{18}N_6O_4$ 1205

(1) poly(iminoimidoamide)
(2) slightly yellowish film
(3) H. Deibig, Battelle-Institut, Frankfurt/M.
(6) H. Deibig, M. Plachky, M. Sander, Angew. Makromol. Chem. *32* (1973) 131…6

(7) film of poly(m-phenylene 5-nitriloisophthalamide), crosslinked at 260 °C (4 h)

4212125322 $C_{20}H_{14}N_2O_3$ 1206

(1) poly(4,4'-oxydiphenylene isophthalamide)
(2) slightly yellowish film
(3) G. Lorenz, Bayer AG, Dormagen
(5) polycondensation of diamine and acid chloride

(6) G. Lorenz, G.E. Nischk, Makromol. Chem. *130* (1969) 55…64
(7) dissolved in DMA and THF, dispersed in KBr (1/400), dried and pressed

4212125322 $C_{20}H_{14}N_2O_3$ 1207

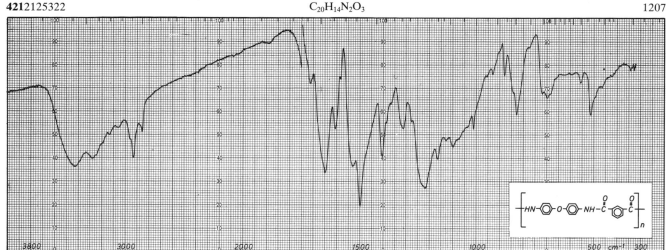

(1) poly(4,4'-oxydiphenylene isophthalamide)
(2) pinkish-grey powder
(3) E. Butta, Istituto di Chimica Industriale ed Applicata,
      Università di Pisa
(5) polycondensation of 4,4'-diaminodiphenylene ether with

isophthaloyl chloride
(6) E. Butta, S. De Petris, U. Frosini, M. Pasquini, Eur. Polym. J.
      7 (1971) 387...97
(7) ground with KBr (2/350) and acetone, dried and pressed

4212125322 $C_{20}H_{14}N_2O_3$ 1208

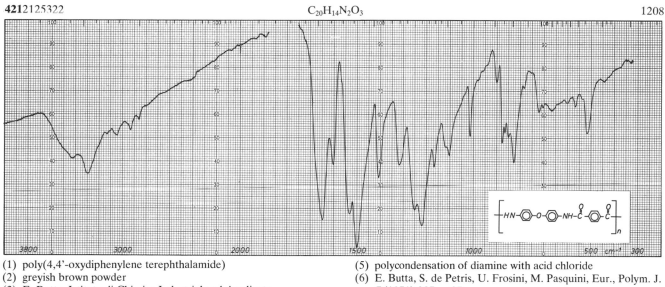

(1) poly(4,4'-oxydiphenylene terephthalamide)
(2) greyish brown powder
(3) E. Butta, Istituto di Chimica Industriale ed Applicata,
      Università di Pisa

(5) polycondensation of diamine with acid chloride
(6) E. Butta, S. de Petris, U. Frosini, M. Pasquini, Eur., Polym. J.
      7 (1971) 387...97
(7) KBr (1/350)

4212125322 $C_{13}H_9NO_2{-}C_{20}H_{14}N_2O_3$ 1209

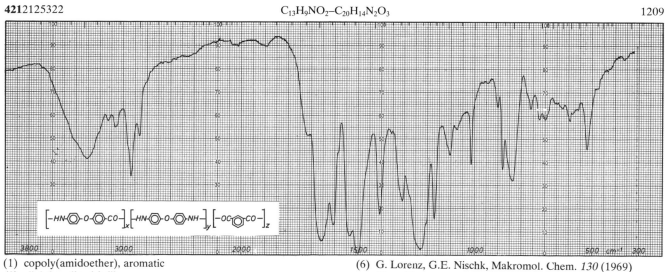

(1) copoly(amidoether), aromatic
(2) slightly yellowish film
(3) G. Lorenz, Bayer AG, Dormagen

(6) G. Lorenz, G.E. Nischk, Makromol. Chem. *130* (1969)
      55...64
(7) ground with KBr (1.3/300) and DMA, dried and pressed

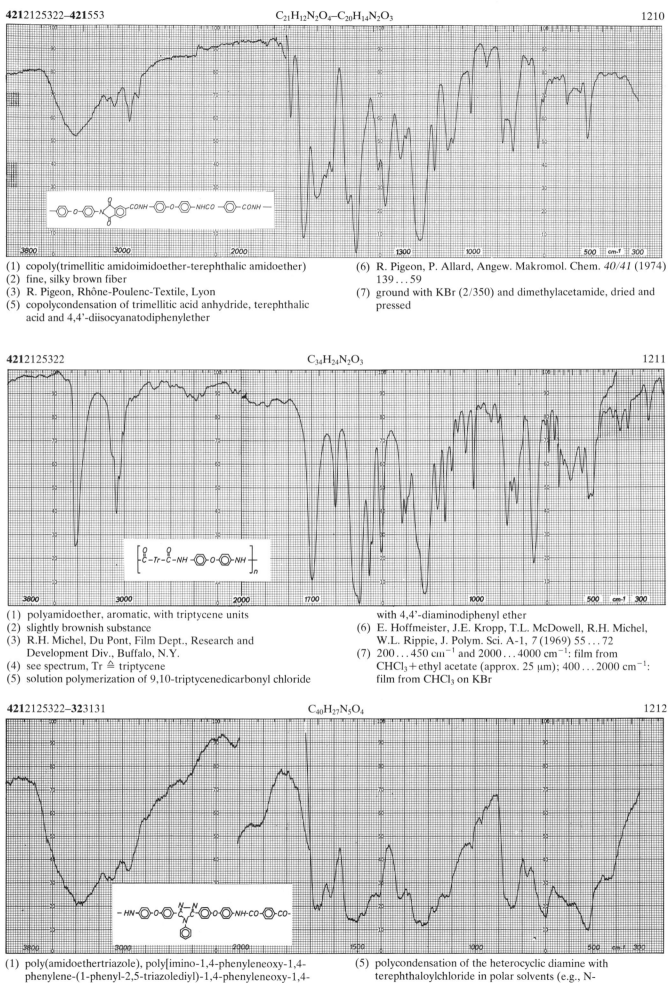

(1) copoly(trimellitic amidoimidoether-terephthalic amidoether)
(2) fine, silky brown fiber
(3) R. Pigeon, Rhône-Poulenc-Textile, Lyon
(5) copolycondensation of trimellitic acid anhydride, terephthalic acid and 4,4'-diisocyanatodiphenylether

(6) R. Pigeon, P. Allard, Angew. Makromol. Chem. *40/41* (1974) 139...59
(7) ground with KBr (2/350) and dimethylacetamide, dried and pressed

(1) polyamidoether, aromatic, with triptycene units
(2) slightly brownish substance
(3) R.H. Michel, Du Pont, Film Dept., Research and Development Div., Buffalo, N.Y.
(4) see spectrum, Tr ≙ triptycene
(5) solution polymerization of 9,10-triptycenedicarbonyl chloride

with 4,4'-diaminodiphenyl ether
(6) E. Hoffmeister, J.E. Kropp, T.L. McDowell, R.H. Michel, W.L. Rippie, J. Polym. Sci. A-1, 7 (1969) 55...72
(7) 200...450 cm⁻¹ and 2000...4000 cm⁻¹: film from CHCl₃ + ethyl acetate (approx. 25 μm); 400...2000 cm⁻¹: film from CHCl₃ on KBr

(1) poly(amidoethertriazole), poly[imino-1,4-phenyleneoxy-1,4-phenylene-(1-phenyl-2,5-triazolediyl)-1,4-phenyleneoxy-1,4-phenyleneimino-terephthaloyl]
(2) white to yellow, very fine fiber
(3) H.-E. Künzel, Organisch-Wissenschaftliches Laboratorium, Bayer AG, Werk Dormagen, Dormagen

(5) polycondensation of the heterocyclic diamine with terephthaloylchloride in polar solvents (e.g., N-dimethylacetamide or N-methylpyrrolidone)
(6) H.-E. Künzel, G.D. Wolf, F. Bentz, G. Blankenstein, G.E. Nischk, Makromol. Chem. *130* (1969) 103...44
(7) KBr

4212125322–42165122 | C$_{29}$H$_{20}$N$_4$O$_4$ | 1213

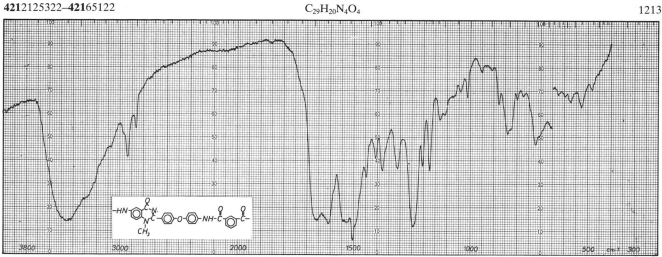

(1) poly(amidoetherquinazolone)
(2) yellow fiber
(3) H.-E. Künzel, Organisch-Wissenschaftliches Laboratorium, Bayer AG, Werk Dormagen, Dormagen
(5) polycondensation of the heterocyclic diamine with isophthaloylchloride in polar solvents (e.g., N-

dimethylacetamide or N-methylpyrrolidone)
(6) H.-E. Künzel, G.W. Wolf, F. Bentz, G. Blankenstein, G.E. Nischk, Makromol. Chem. *130* (1969) 103...44
(7) ground with KBr (1/350) and dimethylacetamide, dried and pressed

4212125325 | C$_{21}$H$_{14}$N$_2$O$_5$ | 1214

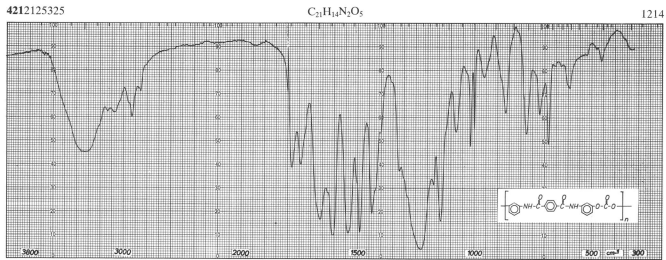

(1) poly[N,N'-bis(3-phenyl carbonate)terephthalamide]
(2) brownish-red fibrous material
(3) C. Giori, IIT Research Institute, Chicago, I11.
(5) polycondensation of m-aminophenol, terephthaloyl chloride and phosgene

(6) C. Giori, ACS Polym. Prepr. *11* (1970) 1023...6
(7) ground with KBr (1/350) and DMA, dried (14 d at 45 °C i.v.) and pressed

421212533–36–37 | C$_{34}$H$_{22}$N$_4$O$_5$–C$_{34}$H$_{22}$N$_4$O$_4$S | 1215

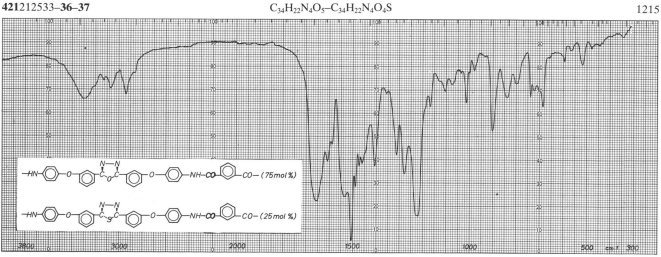

(1) copoly(amidoether) with heterocyclic rings
(2) eggshell-coloured fiber
(3) H.-E. Künzel, Organisch-Wissenschaftliches Laboratorium der Bayer AG, Werk Dormagen, Dormagen
(5) copolycondensation of a mixture of the heterocyclic-aromatic diamines with isophthaloyl chloride

(6) H.-E. Künzel, G.D. Wolf, F. Bentz, G. Blankenstein, G.E. Nischk, Makromol. Chem. *130* (1969) 103..44
(7) ground with KBr (1.5/350) and dimethylacetamide, dried and pressed

4212125324 $C_{25}H_{18}N_4O_8$ 1216

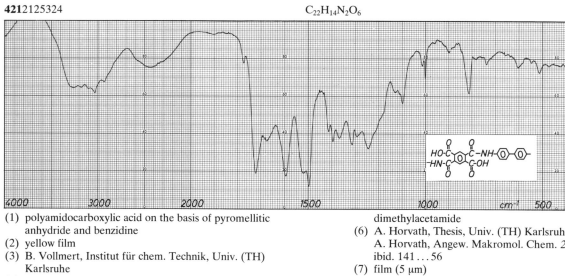

(1) poly(amidoacid-amide)
(3) Toyo Rayon Comp. Ltd., Sonoyama, Otsu (by M. Kurihara)
(5) polycondensation of methylene-bis(2-aminobenzamide) with pyromellitic dianhydride

(6) M. Kurihara, N. Yoda, Polym. Lett. *6* (1968) 875...82
(7) film (spectrum by M. Kurihara)

4212125324 $C_{22}H_{14}N_2O_6$ 1217

(1) polyamidocarboxylic acid on the basis of pyromellitic anhydride and benzidine
(2) yellow film
(3) B. Vollmert, Institut für chem. Technik, Univ. (TH) Karlsruhe
(5) polyaddition of dianhydride and diamine in dimethylacetamide

(6) A. Horvath, Thesis, Univ. (TH) Karlsruhe, 1970;B. Vollmert, A. Horvath, Angew. Makromol. Chem. *23* (1972) 117...39, ibid. 141...56
(7) film (5 µm)

4212132 $C_{16}H_{26}N_2O_2$ 1218

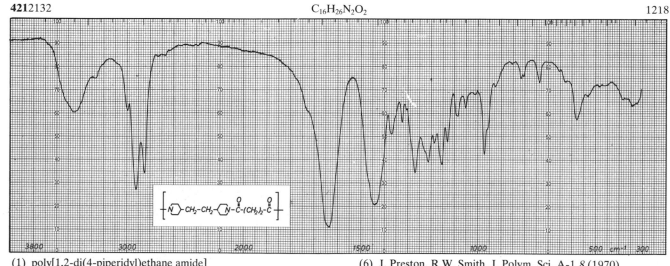

(1) poly[1,2-di(4-piperidyl)ethane amide]
(2) colourless material
(3) J. Preston, Chemstrand Research Center, Durham, N.C.
(5) interfacial polycondensation of 1,2-di(4-piperidyl)ethane with succinic acid chloride

(6) J. Preston, R.W. Smith, J. Polym. Sci. A-1 *8* (1970) 1841...50
(7) KBr (2–350)

4212132 $C_{18}H_{30}N_2O_2$ 1219

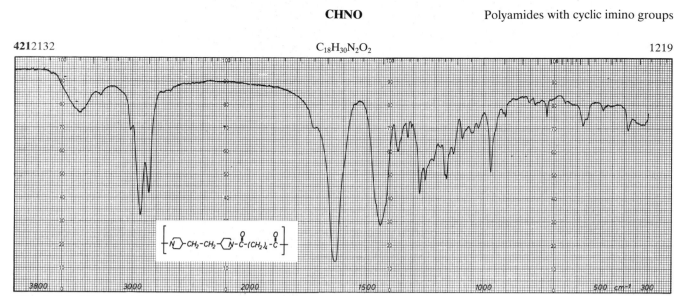

(1) poly[1,2-di(4-piperidyl)ethane] amide
(2) white powder
(3) J. Preston, Chemstrand Research Center, Durham, N.C.
(5) interfacial polycondensation of 1,2-di(4-piperidyl)ethane with adipoyl chloride

(6) J. Preston, R.W. Smith, J. Polym. Sci. A-1 *8* (1970) 1841...50
(7) KBr (1/350)

4212132 $C_{17}H_{28}N_2O_2$ 1220

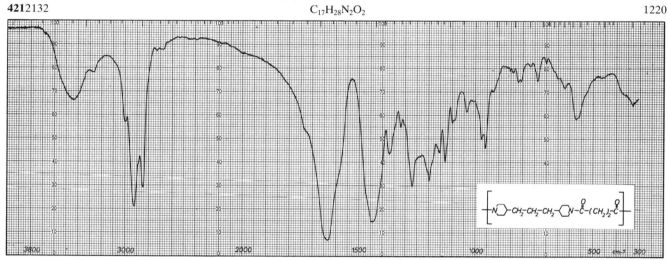

(1) poly[1,3-di(4-piperidyl)propane]amide
(2) white powder
(3) J. Preston, Chemstrand Research Center, Durham, N.C.
(5) interfacial polycondensation of 1,3-di(4-piperidyl)propane with adipoyl chloride

(6) J. Preston, R.W. Smith, J. Polym. Sci. A-1 *8* (1970) 1841...50
(7) KBr (2/350)

4212132 $C_{19}H_{32}N_2O_2$ 1221

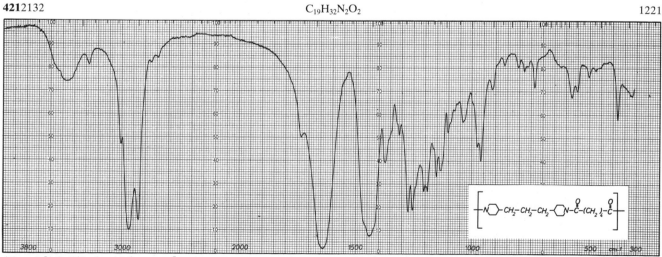

(1) poly[1,3-di(4-piperidyl)propane] amide
(2) white powder
(3) J. Preston, Chemstrand Research Center, Durham, N.C.
(5) interfacial polycondensation of 1,3-di(4-piperidyl)propane with adipoyl chloride

(6) J. Preston, R.W. Smith, J. Polym. Sci. A-1 *8* (1970) 1841...50

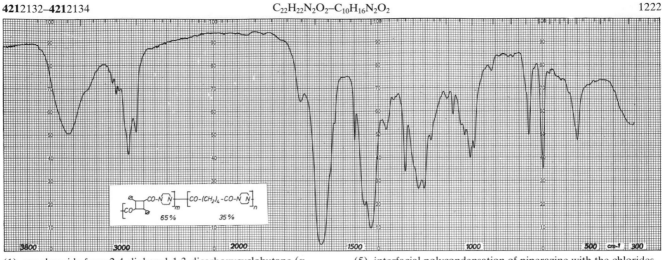

(1) copolyamide from 2,4-diphenyl-1,3-dicarboxycyclobutane (α-truxillic acid), adipic acid and piperazine (diethylene diamine)
(2) white material
(3) G. Montaudo, I. Lüderwald, Istituto di Chimica Industriale, Università degli Studi, Catania/Institut für Organische Chemie, Universität Mainz, Mainz
(5) interfacial polycondensation of piperazine with the chlorides of truxillic acid and adipic acid
(6) S. Caccamese, S. Foti, P. Maravigna, G. Montaudo, A. Recca, I. Lüderwald, M. Przybylski, J. Polym. Sci.-Chem. Ed. *15* (1977) 5 ... 13

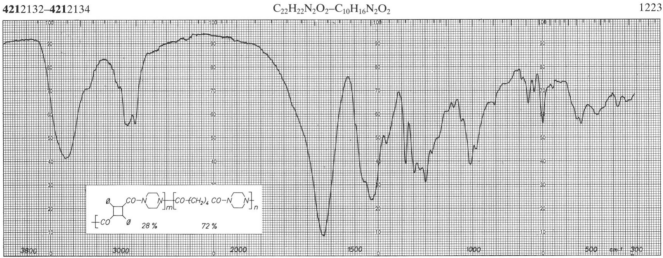

(1) copolyamide from 2,4-diphenyl-1,3-carboxycyclobutane, adipic acid and piperazine
(2) white, coarse powder
(3) G. Montaudo, Istituto di Chimica Industriale, Università degli Studie, Catania (by I. Lüderwald, Universität Mainz)
(4) molar ratio of adipic and truxillic acid: 72:28
(5) interfacial polycondensation of piperazine with the chlorides of truxillic acid and adipic acid
(6) G. Montaudo, I. Lüderwald, J. Polym. Sci. *15* (1977) 6
(7) KBr (2.5/350), ordinate expanded

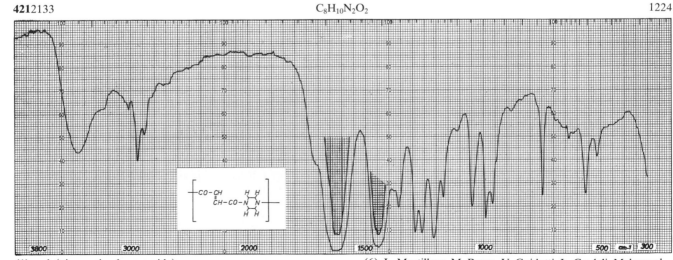

(1) poly(piperanzine fumaramide)
(2) ivory coloured substance
(3) L. Mortillaro, Montecatini Edison, Milano
(5) polycondensation of piperazine and fumaroyl chloride
(6) L. Mortillaro, M. Russo, V. Guidotti, L. Credali, Makromol. Chem. *138* (1970) 151 ... 61
(7) ground with KBr (1.5/350) and HCOOH, dried and pressed

4212133 C₉H₁₂N₂O₂ 1225

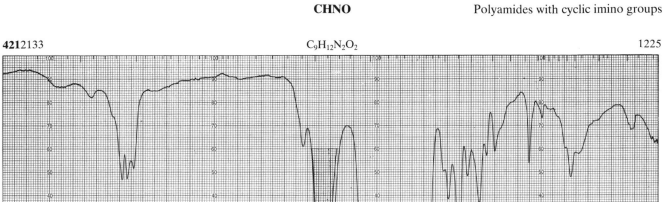

(1) poly(2-methylpiperazine fumaramide)
(2) light white substance
(3) L. Mortillaro, Montecatini Edison, Milano
(5) polycondensation of 2-methylpiperazine and fumaroyl chloride

(6) L. Mortillaro, M. Russo, V. Guidotti, L. Credali, Makromol. Chem. *138* (1970) 151...61
(7) film (10 μm) from HCOOH solution

4212133 C₁₀H₁₄N₂O₂ 1226

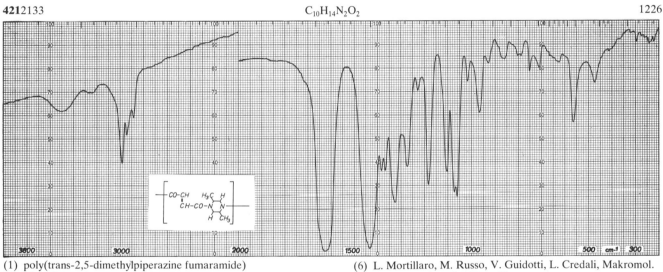

(1) poly(trans-2,5-dimethylpiperazine fumaramide)
(2) slight light substance
(3) L. Mortillaro, Montecatini Edison, Milano
(5) interfacial polycondensation of 2,5-dimethylpiperazine and fumaroyl chloride

(6) L. Mortillaro, M. Russo, V. Guidotti, L. Credali, Makromol. Chem. *138* (1970) 151...61
(7) film from CH₃OH/CHCl₃ on CsI

4212133 C₁₂H₁₈N₂O₂ 1227

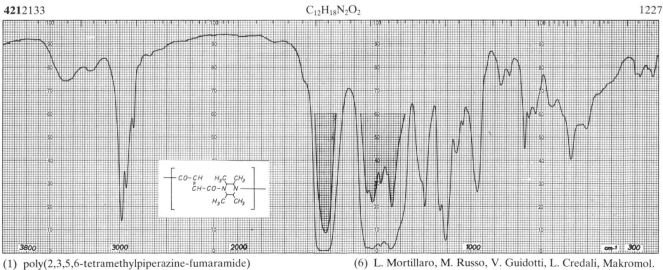

(1) poly(2,3,5,6-tetramethylpiperazine-fumaramide)
(2) lightly yellowish material
(3) L. Mortillaro, Montecatini Edison, Milano
(5) interfacial polycondensation of 2,3,5,6-tetramethylpiperazine and fumaroyl chloride

(6) L. Mortillaro, M. Russo, V. Guidotti, L. Credali, Makromol. Chem. *138* (1970) 151...61
(7) film from CH₃OH/CHCl₃ ond CsI

4212133 $C_9H_{12}N_2O_2$ 1228

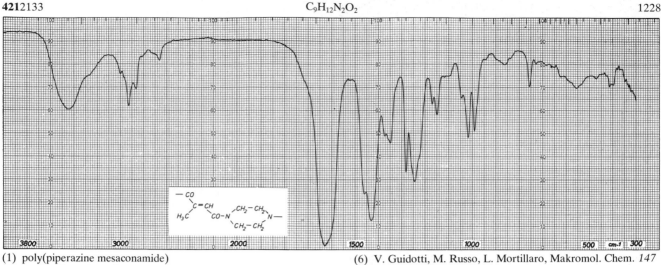

(1) poly(piperazine mesaconamide)
(2) ivory-coloured powder
(3) M. Russo, Montecatini Edison, Milano
(5) polycondensation of piperazine and methyl fumaroyl chloride

(6) V. Guidotti, M. Russo, L. Mortillaro, Makromol. Chem. *147* (1971) 111...21
(7) ground with KBr (0.5/350) and HCOOH, dried and pressed

4212134 $C_{22}H_{22}N_2O_2$ 1229

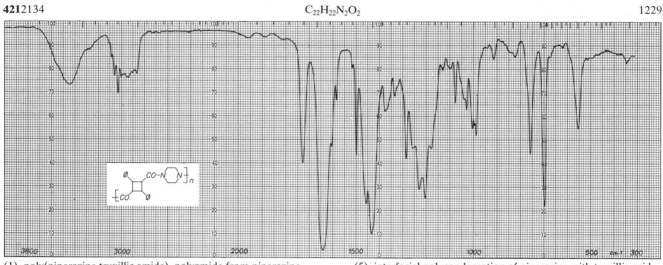

(1) poly(piperazine truxillic amide), polyamide from piperazine and 2,4-diphenyl-1,3-dicarboxy-cyclobutane
(2) white, coarse powder
(3) G. Montaudo, Istituto di Chimica Industriale, Università degli Studi, Catania

(5) interfacial polycondensation of piperazine with truxillic acid dichloride
(6) G. Montaudo, I. Lüderwald, J. Polym. Sci. *15* (1977) 5
(7) KBr (1.2/350)

4212134 $C_{21}H_{28}N_2O_2$ 1230

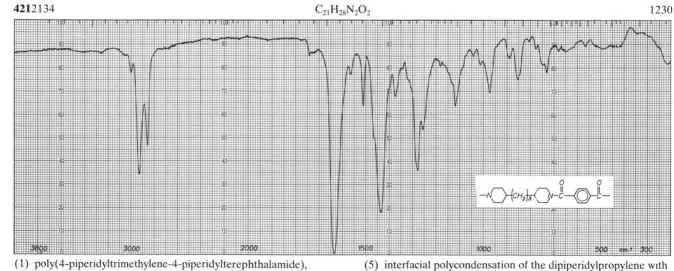

410

(1) poly(4-piperidyltrimethylene-4-piperidylterephthalamide), polyamide from 1,3-di-(4-piperidyl)-propylene and terephthalic acid
(2) white material
(3) J. Preston, Chemstrand Research Center, Durham, N.C.

(5) interfacial polycondensation of the dipiperidylpropylene with terephthaloylchloride
(6) J. Preston, R.W. Smith, J. Polym. Sci. A-1 *8* (1970) 1841...50; ACS Polym. Prepr. *11* (1970) 347...53
(7) film from CHCl₃ on CsI

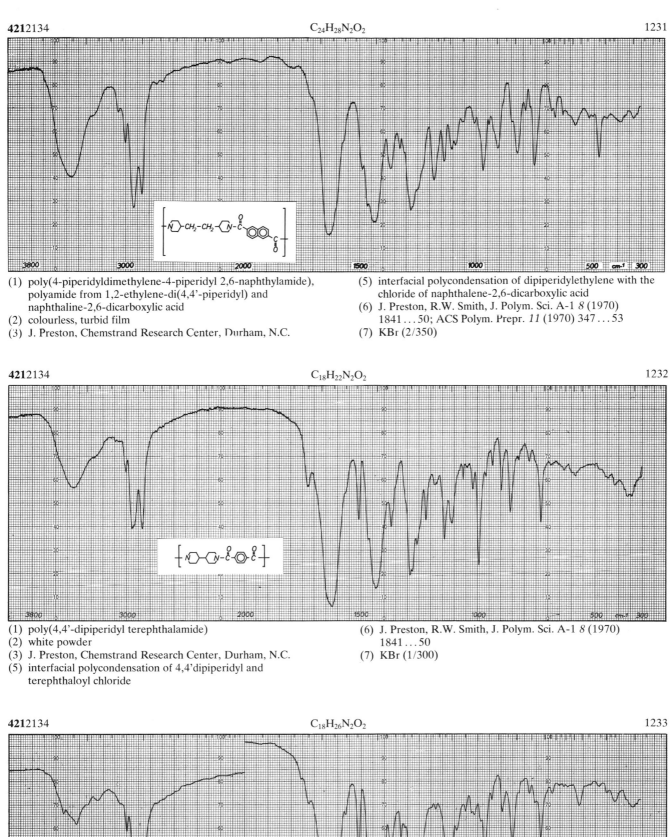

$C_{24}H_{28}N_2O_2$

(1) poly(4-piperidyldimethylene-4-piperidyl 2,6-naphthylamide),
    polyamide from 1,2-ethylene-di(4,4'-piperidyl) and
    naphthaline-2,6-dicarboxylic acid
(2) colourless, turbid film
(3) J. Preston, Chemstrand Research Center, Durham, N.C.

(5) interfacial polycondensation of dipiperidylethylene with the
    chloride of naphthalene-2,6-dicarboxylic acid
(6) J. Preston, R.W. Smith, J. Polym. Sci. A-1 *8* (1970)
    1841...50; ACS Polym. Prepr. *11* (1970) 347...53
(7) KBr (2/350)

$C_{18}H_{22}N_2O_2$

(1) poly(4,4'-dipiperidyl terephthalamide)
(2) white powder
(3) J. Preston, Chemstrand Research Center, Durham, N.C.
(5) interfacial polycondensation of 4,4'dipiperidyl and
    terephthaloyl chloride

(6) J. Preston, R.W. Smith, J. Polym. Sci. A-1 *8* (1970)
    1841...50
(7) KBr (1/300)

$C_{18}H_{26}N_2O_2$

(1) poly[1,2-di(4-piperidyl)ethane terephthalamide]
(2) colourless material
(3) J. Preston, Chemstrand Research Center, Durham, N.C.
(5) interfacial polycondensation of 1,2-di(4-piperidyl)ethane and
    terephthaloyl fluoride

(6) J. Preston, R.W. Smith, J. Polym. Sci. A-1, *8* (1970)
    1841...50
(7) KBr (1/350)

4212134 $C_{19}H_{28}N_2O_2$ 1234

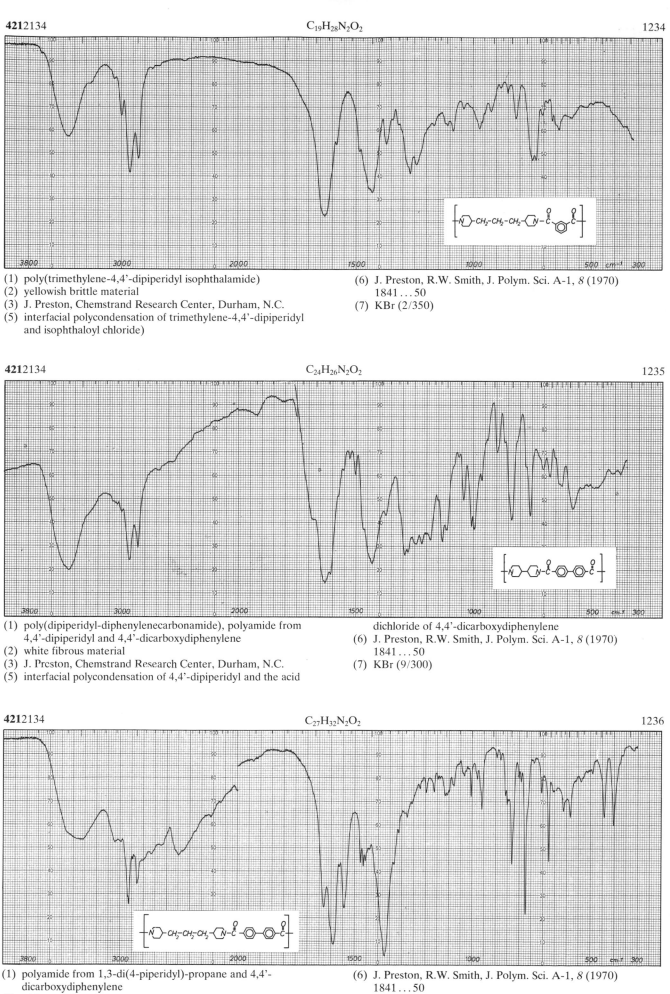

(1) poly(trimethylene-4,4'-dipiperidyl isophthalamide)
(2) yellowish brittle material
(3) J. Preston, Chemstrand Research Center, Durham, N.C.
(5) interfacial polycondensation of trimethylene-4,4'-dipiperidyl and isophthaloyl chloride)

(6) J. Preston, R.W. Smith, J. Polym. Sci. A-1, *8* (1970) 1841...50
(7) KBr (2/350)

4212134 $C_{24}H_{26}N_2O_2$ 1235

(1) poly(dipiperidyl-diphenylenecarbonamide), polyamide from 4,4'-dipiperidyl and 4,4'-dicarboxydiphenylene
(2) white fibrous material
(3) J. Preston, Chemstrand Research Center, Durham, N.C.
(5) interfacial polycondensation of 4,4'-dipiperidyl and the acid

dichloride of 4,4'-dicarboxydiphenylene
(6) J. Preston, R.W. Smith, J. Polym. Sci. A-1, *8* (1970) 1841...50
(7) KBr (9/300)

4212134 $C_{27}H_{32}N_2O_2$ 1236

412

(1) polyamide from 1,3-di(4-piperidyl)-propane and 4,4'-dicarboxydiphenylene
(2) white powder
(3) J. Preston, Chemstrand Research Center, Durham, N.C.
(5) interfacial polycondensation of 1,3-di(4-piperidyl) and the acid dichloride of 4,4'dicarboxydiphenylene

(6) J. Preston, R.W. Smith, J. Polym. Sci. A-1, *8* (1970) 1841...50
(7) KBr (1/350)

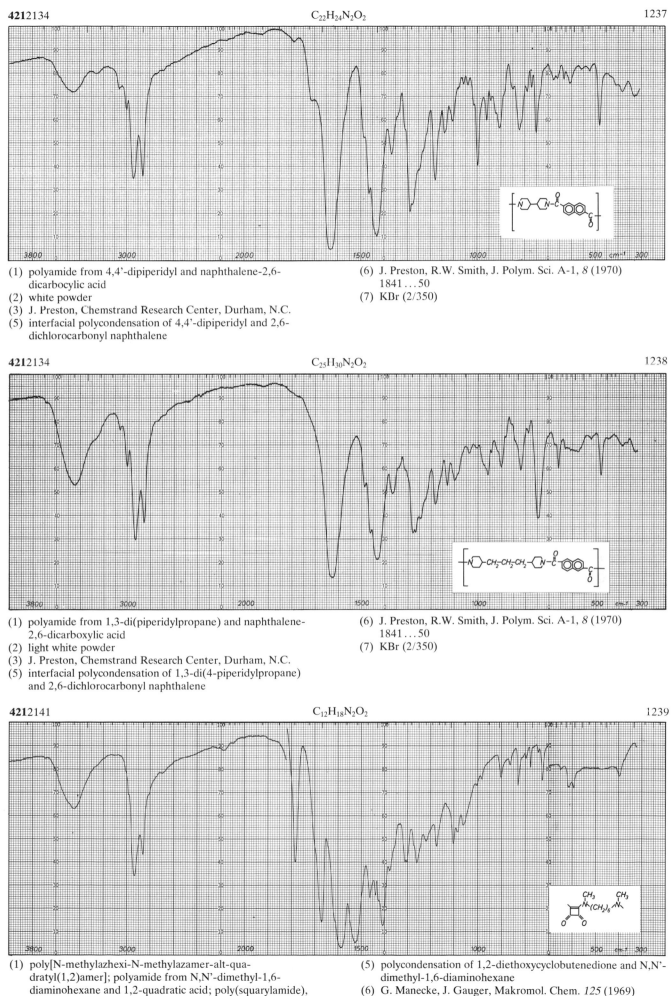

(1) polyamide from 4,4'-dipiperidyl and naphthalene-2,6-dicarbocylic acid
(2) white powder
(3) J. Preston, Chemstrand Research Center, Durham, N.C.
(5) interfacial polycondensation of 4,4'-dipiperidyl and 2,6-dichlorocarbonyl naphthalene

(6) J. Preston, R.W. Smith, J. Polym. Sci. A-1, *8* (1970) 1841...50
(7) KBr (2/350)

(1) polyamide from 1,3-di(piperidylpropane) and naphthalene-2,6-dicarboxylic acid
(2) light white powder
(3) J. Preston, Chemstrand Research Center, Durham, N.C.
(5) interfacial polycondensation of 1,3-di(4-piperidylpropane) and 2,6-dichlorocarbonyl naphthalene

(6) J. Preston, R.W. Smith, J. Polym. Sci. A-1, *8* (1970) 1841...50
(7) KBr (2/350)

(1) poly[N-methylazhexi-N-methylazamer-alt-quadratyl(1,2)amer]; polyamide from N,N'-dimethyl-1,6-diaminohexane and 1,2-quadratic acid; poly(squarylamide), aliphatic
(2) slightly orange powder
(3) G. Manecke, Fritz-Haber-Institut, Berlin (W)

(5) polycondensation of 1,2-diethoxycyclobutenedione and N,N'-dimethyl-1,6-diaminohexane
(6) G. Manecke, J. Gauger, Makromol. Chem. *125* (1969) 231...46
(7) KBr (1.5/1000)

4212141 $C_{14}H_{22}N_2O_2$ 1240

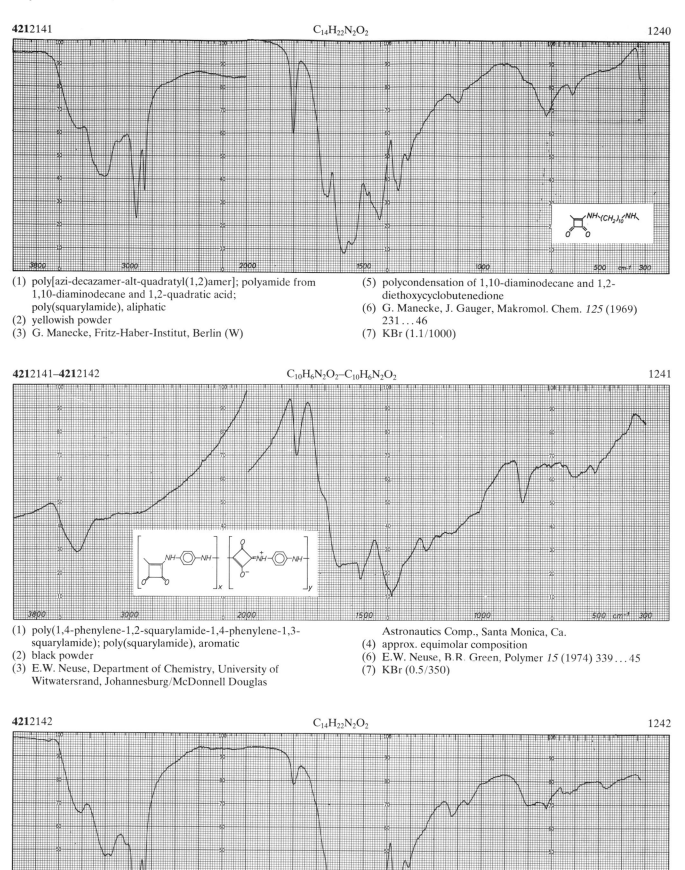

(1) poly[azi-decazamer-alt-quadratyl(1,2)amer]; polyamide from 1,10-diaminodecane and 1,2-quadratic acid; poly(squarylamide), aliphatic
(2) yellowish powder
(3) G. Manecke, Fritz-Haber-Institut, Berlin (W)
(5) polycondensation of 1,10-diaminodecane and 1,2-diethoxycyclobutenedione
(6) G. Manecke, J. Gauger, Makromol. Chem. *125* (1969) 231...46
(7) KBr (1.1/1000)

4212141–**421**2142 $C_{10}H_6N_2O_2$–$C_{10}H_6N_2O_2$ 1241

(1) poly(1,4-phenylene-1,2-squarylamide-1,4-phenylene-1,3-squarylamide); poly(squarylamide), aromatic
(2) black powder
(3) E.W. Neuse, Department of Chemistry, University of Witwatersrand, Johannesburg/McDonnell Douglas

Astronautics Comp., Santa Monica, Ca.
(4) approx. equimolar composition
(6) E.W. Neuse, B.R. Green, Polymer *15* (1974) 339...45
(7) KBr (0.5/350)

4212142 $C_{14}H_{22}N_2O_2$ 1242

(1) poly[azi-decazamer-alt-quadratyl(1,3)amer]; polyamide from 1,10-diaminodecane and 1,3-quadratic acid; poly(squarylamide), aliphatic
(2) slightly brownish powder
(3) G. Manecke, Fritz-Haber-Institut, Berlin (W)
(5) polycondensation of 1,10-diaminodecane-squarate-1,3
(6) G. Manecke, J. Gauger, Makromol. Chem. *125* (1969) 231...46
(7) KBr (1/1000)

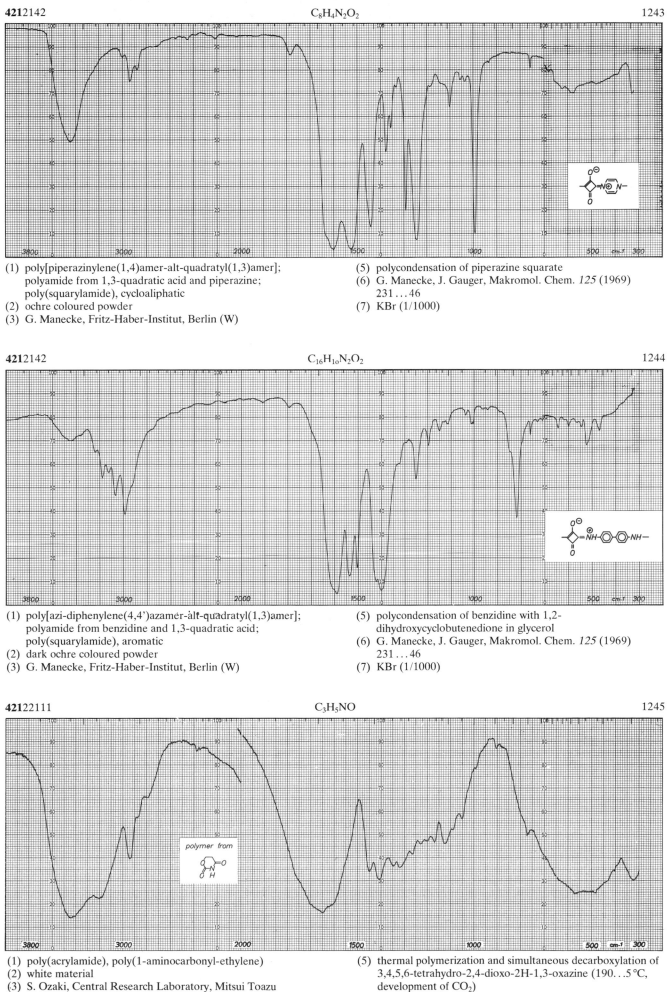

4212142   C₈H₄N₂O₂   1243

(1) poly[piperazinylene(1,4)amer-alt-quadratyl(1,3)amer];
    polyamide from 1,3-quadratic acid and piperazine;
    poly(squarylamide), cycloaliphatic
(2) ochre coloured powder
(3) G. Manecke, Fritz-Haber-Institut, Berlin (W)
(5) polycondensation of piperazine squarate
(6) G. Manecke, J. Gauger, Makromol. Chem. *125* (1969)
    231...46
(7) KBr (1/1000)

4212142   C₁₆H₁₀N₂O₂   1244

(1) poly[azi-diphenylene(4,4')azamer-alt-quadratyl(1,3)amer];
    polyamide from benzidine and 1,3-quadratic acid;
    poly(squarylamide), aromatic
(2) dark ochre coloured powder
(3) G. Manecke, Fritz-Haber-Institut, Berlin (W)
(5) polycondensation of benzidine with 1,2-
    dihydroxycyclobutenedione in glycerol
(6) G. Manecke, J. Gauger, Makromol. Chem. *125* (1969)
    231...46
(7) KBr (1/1000)

42122111   C₃H₅NO   1245

(1) poly(acrylamide), poly(1-aminocarbonyl-ethylene)
(2) white material
(3) S. Ozaki, Central Research Laboratory, Mitsui Toazu
    Chemicals Inc., Kazura, Yokohama
(5) thermal polymerization and simultaneous decarboxylation of
    3,4,5,6-tetrahydro-2,4-dioxo-2H-1,3-oxazine (190...5 °C,
    development of CO₂)
(6) S. Ozaki, T. Kato, J. Polym. Sci. C *23* (1968) 695...704
(7) KBr (3.5/350)

42122111–**322**251   C₃H₅NO–C₃H₃N   1246

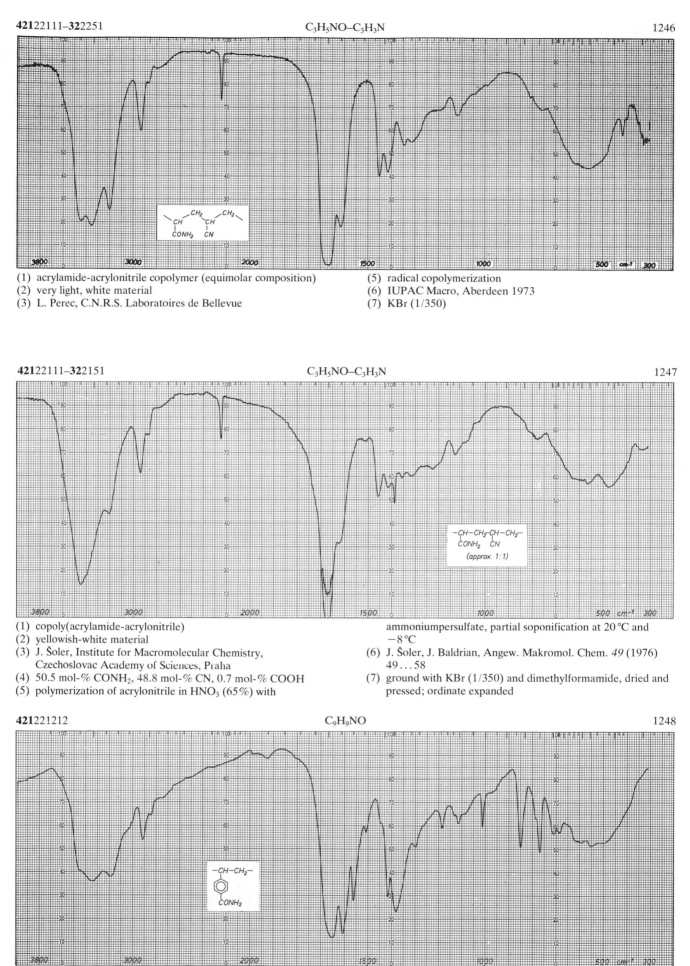

(1) acrylamide-acrylonitrile copolymer (equimolar composition)
(2) very light, white material
(3) L. Perec, C.N.R.S. Laboratoires de Bellevue

(5) radical copolymerization
(6) IUPAC Macro, Aberdeen 1973
(7) KBr (1/350)

42122111–**322**151   C₃H₅NO–C₃H₃N   1247

(1) copoly(acrylamide-acrylonitrile)
(2) yellowish-white material
(3) J. Šoler, Institute for Macromolecular Chemistry, Czechoslovac Academy of Sciences, Praha
(4) 50.5 mol-% CONH₂, 48.8 mol-% CN, 0.7 mol-% COOH
(5) polymerization of acrylonitrile in HNO₃ (65%) with

ammoniumpersulfate, partial soponification at 20 °C and −8 °C
(6) J. Šoler, J. Baldrian, Angew. Makromol. Chem. *49* (1976) 49...58
(7) ground with KBr (1/350) and dimethylformamide, dried and pressed; ordinate expanded

421221212   C₉H₉NO   1248

(1) poly(p-vinylbenzamide), poly[1-(4-aminocarbonyl-phenylene)ethylene]
(2) white powder
(3) T. Asahara, Basic Research Laboratory, Toyo Rayon Comp., Tebiro, Kamakura

(5) polymerization of p-vinylbenzamide with n-BuLi at 130 °C (47 h)
(6) T. Asahara, N. Yoda, J. Polym. Sci. A-1 *6* (1968) 2477...87
(7) KBr (1.5/350)

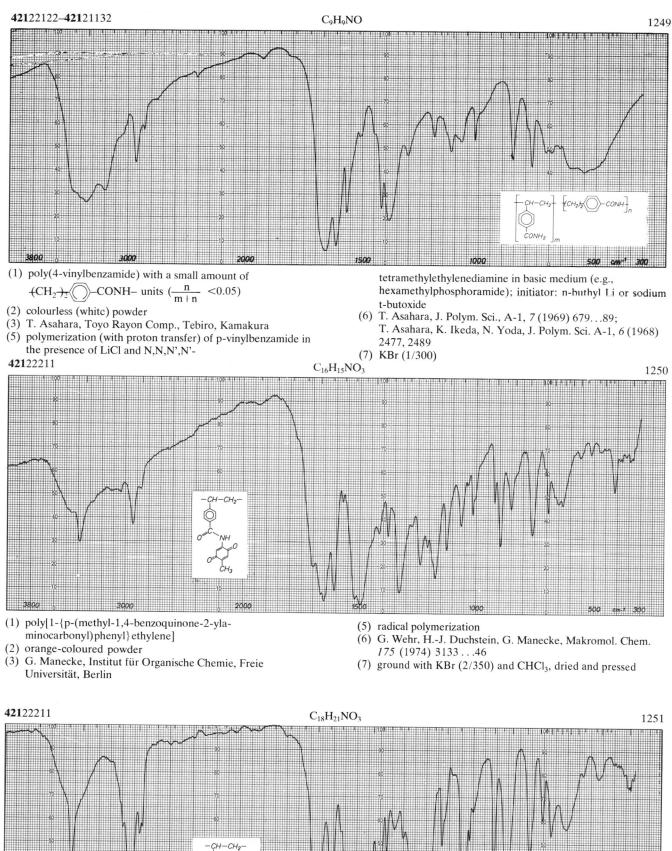

(1) poly(4-vinylbenzamide) with a small amount of

$+CH_2+_2$⟨◯⟩–CONH– units ($\frac{n}{m+n}$ <0.05)

(2) colourless (white) powder

(3) T. Asahara, Toyo Rayon Comp., Tebiro, Kamakura

(5) polymerization (with proton transfer) of p-vinylbenzamide in
the presence of LiCl and N,N,N',N'-

tetramethylethylenediamine in basic medium (e.g.,
hexamethylphosphoramide); initiator: n-buthyl Li or sodium
t-butoxide

(6) T. Asahara, J. Polym. Sci., A-1, 7 (1969) 679...89;
T. Asahara, K. Ikeda, N. Yoda, J. Polym. Sci. A-1, 6 (1968)
2477, 2489

(7) KBr (1/300)

(1) poly[1-{p-(methyl-1,4-benzoquinone-2-yla-
minocarbonyl)phenyl}ethylene]

(2) orange-coloured powder

(3) G. Manecke, Institut für Organische Chemie, Freie
Universität, Berlin

(5) radical polymerization

(6) G. Wehr, H.-J. Duchstein, G. Manecke, Makromol. Chem.
175 (1974) 3133...46

(7) ground with KBr (2/350) and CHCl₃, dried and pressed

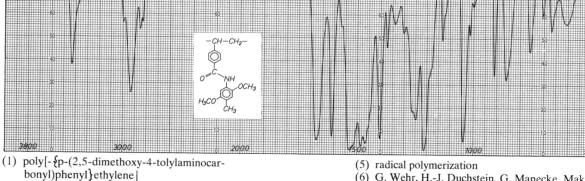

(1) poly[-{p-(2,5-dimethoxy-4-tolylaminocar-
bonyl)phenyl}ethylene]

(2) eggshell-coloured powder

(3) G. Manecke, Institut für Organische Chemie, Freie
Universität, Berlin

(5) radical polymerization

(6) G. Wehr, H.-J. Duchstein, G. Manecke, Makromol. Chem.
175 (1974) 3133...46

(7) ground with KBr (2/350) and CHCl₃, dried and pressed

42122211 C₅H₉NO 1252

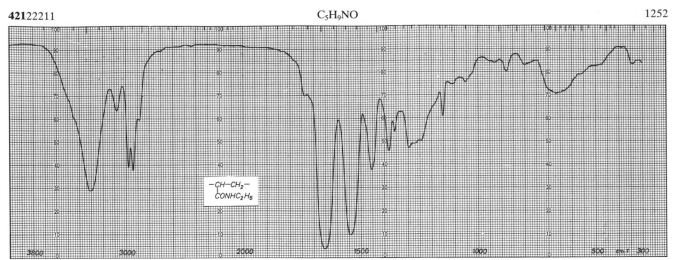

(1) poly(N-ethylacrylamide)
(2) white material
(3) J. Kopeček, Institute of Macromolecular Chemistry,
Czechoslovak Academy of Sciences, Praha
(5) radical-initiated polymerization with AIBN
(6) J. Strohalm, K. Ulbrich, J. Exner, J. Kopeček, Angew.
Makromol. Chem. *49* (1976) 83...92
(7) swollen in acetone, ground with KBr, dried and pressed

42122211 C₇H₁₃NO 1253

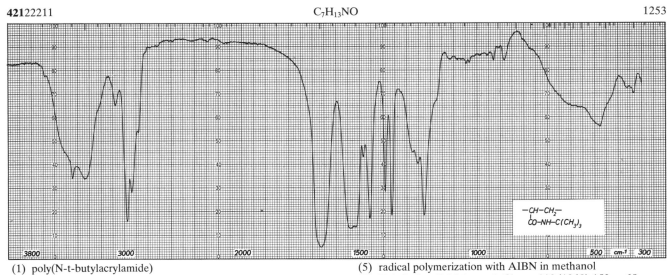

(1) poly(N-t-butylacrylamide)
(2) white powder
(3) E.A.S. Cavell, Department of Chemistry, University of
Southampton
(5) radical polymerization with AIBN in methanol
(6) E.A.S. Cavell, Makromol. Chem. *119* (1968) 153...60
(7) ground with KBr (0.5/300) and DMA, dried and pressed

42122211–**31**21112 C₇H₁₃NO–C₂H₂Cl₂ 1254

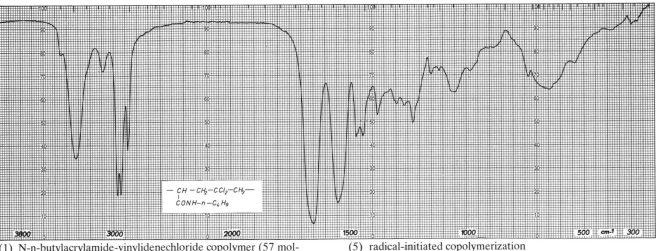

(1) N-n-butylacrylamide-vinylidenechloride copolymer (57 mol-
% BAA units)
(2) amber-coloured resin-like material
(3) E.F. Jordan, Eastern Utilization Research and Development
Division, Philadelphia, Pa.
(5) radical-initiated copolymerization
(6) E.F. Jordan, G.R. Riser, B. Artymyshyn, W.E. Parker, J.W.
Pensabene, A.N. Wrigley, J. Appl. Sci. *13* (1969) 1777...94
(7) reprecipitated with CHCl₃/pentane, film from CHCl₃ on CsI

42122211–3121112 C₁₁H₂₁NO–C₂H₂Cl₂ 1255

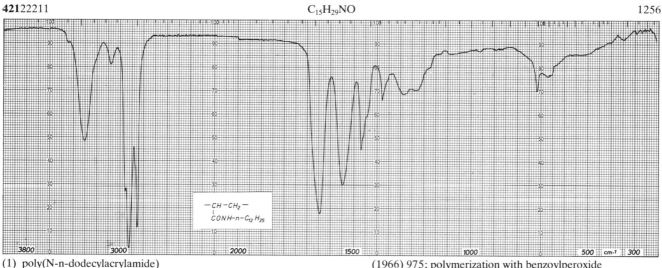

(1) poly(N-n-octylacrylamide-vinylidenechloride copolymer)
(2) orange coloured, resinous material
(3) E.F. Jordan, Eastern Utilization Research and Development Division, Philadelphia, Pa.
(4) 57 mol-% n-octylacrylamide units
(5) copolymerization in dispersion (with polyvinylalcohol and

MgCO₃) with benzoylperoxide
(6) private communication; see also E.F. Jordan, jr., G.R. Riser, B. Artymyshyn, W.F. Parker, J.W. Pensabene, A.N. Wrigley, J. Appl. Polym. Sci. *13* (1969) 1777...94
(7) film from CHCl₃ on CsI

42122211 C₁₅H₂₉NO 1256

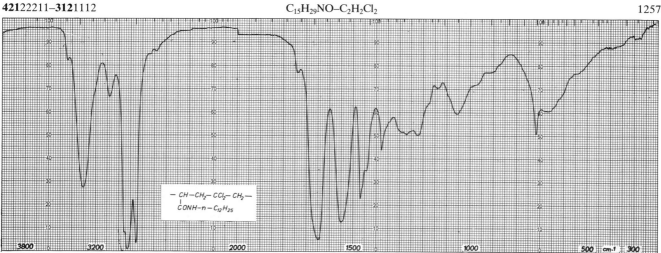

(1) poly(N-n-dodecylacrylamide)
(2) colourless, resinous material
(3) E.F. Jordan, Eastern Utilization Research and Development Division, Philadelphia, Pa.
(5) preparation of the monomer according to E.F. Jordan, G.R. Riser, W.E. Parker, A.N. Wrigley, J. Polym. Sci. A-2 *4*

(1966) 975; polymerization with benzoylperoxide
(6) private communication; see also E.F. Jordan jr., G.R. Riser, B. Artymyshyn, W.F. Parker, J.W. Pensabene, A.N. Wrigley, J. Appl. Polym. Sci. *13* (1969) 1777...94
(7) film from CHCl₃ on CsI

42122211–3121112 C₁₅H₂₉NO–C₂H₂Cl₂ 1257

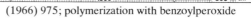

(1) N-n-dodecylacrylamide-vinylidenechloride copolymer
(2) orange-coloured, resinous material
(3) E.F. Jordan, Eastern Utilization Research and Development Division, Philadelphia, Pa.
(4) approx. equimolar composition
(5) copolymerization in dispersion (with polyvinylalcohol and

MgCO₃) with benzoylperoxide
(6) private communication; see also E.F. Jordan, jr., G.R. Riser, B. Artymyshyn, W.F. Parker, J.W. Pensabene, A.N. Wrigley, J. Appl. Polym. Sci. *13* (1969) 1777...94
(7) film from CHCl₃ on CsI

42122211 $C_{21}H_{41}NO$ 1258

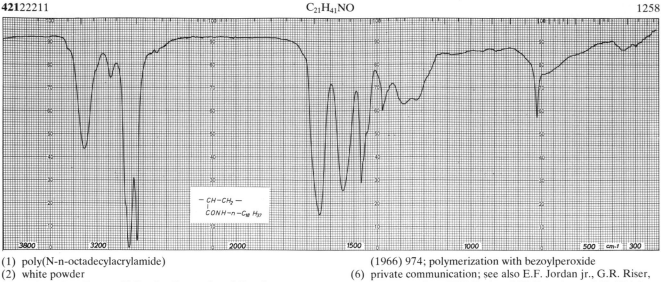

(1) poly(N-n-octadecylacrylamide)
(2) white powder
(3) E.F. Jordan, Eastern Utilization Research and Development Division, Philadelphia, Pa.
(5) preparation of the monomer according to E.F. Jordan, G.R. Riser, W.E. Parker, A.N. Wrigley, J. Polym. Sci. A-2 *4*

(1966) 974; polymerization with bezoylperoxide
(6) private communication; see also E.F. Jordan jr., G.R. Riser, B. Artymyshyn, W.F. Parker, J.W. Pensabene, A.N. Wrigley, J. Appl. Polym. Sci. *13* (1969) 1777...94
(7) film from $CHCl_3$ on CsI

42122211 $C_9H_{15}N_3O_3$ 1259

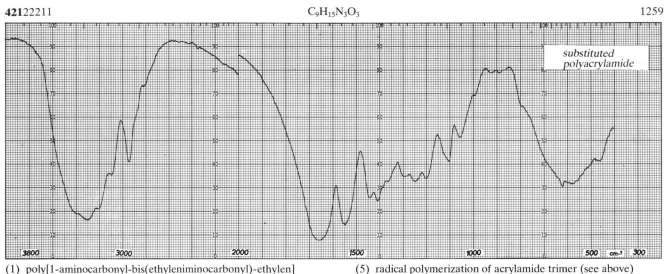

substituted polyacrylamide

(1) poly[1-aminocarbonyl-bis(ethyleniminocarbonyl)-ethylen]
(2) colourless powder
(3) A. Leoni, 3M Company, Ferrania
(4) $-CH-CH_2-$
   $CONH(CH_2)_2 CONH(CH_2)_2 CONH_2$

(5) radical polymerization of acrylamide trimer (see above)
(6) A. Leoni, S. Franco, G. Polla, J. Polym. Sci. A-1 *6* (1968)
(7) KBr (6.5/1000)

42122212 $C_7H_{13}NO_2$ 1260

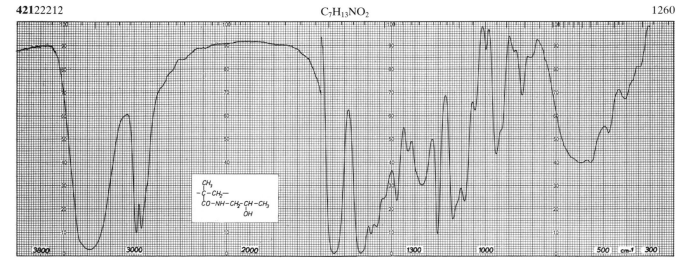

(1) poly[N-(2-hydroxypropyl)methacrylamide]
(2) colourless powder
(3) J. Kopeček, Institute for Macromolecular Chemistry, Czechoslovak Academy of Sciences, Praha

(5) radical polymerization with 2,2'-azo-bis(methylisobutyrate)
(6) J. Kopeček, H. Baźilová, Eur. Polym. J. *9* (1973) 7...14
(7) film from CH_3OH solution on CsI

42122212   C₈H₁₅NO₄   1261

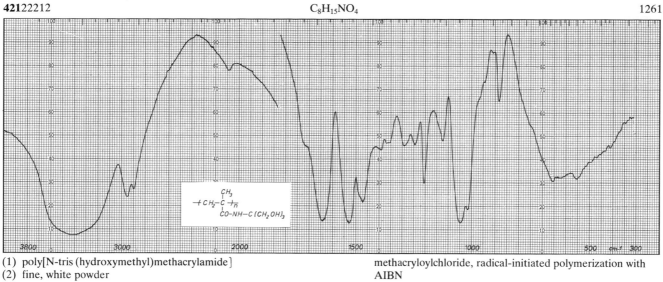

(1) poly[N-tris (hydroxymethyl)methacrylamide]
(2) fine, white powder
(3) E. Brown, Laboratoire de Synthèse Totale de Produits Naturels, Faculté des Sciences, Le Mans
(5) condensation of tris(hydroxymethyl)aminomethane with

methacryloylchloride, radical-initiated polymerization with AIBN
(6) E. Brown, M. Loriot, J. Touet, Tetrahedron Lett. 6 (1975) 357...8
(7) KBr (5/350)

42122212   C₆H₁₁NO   1262

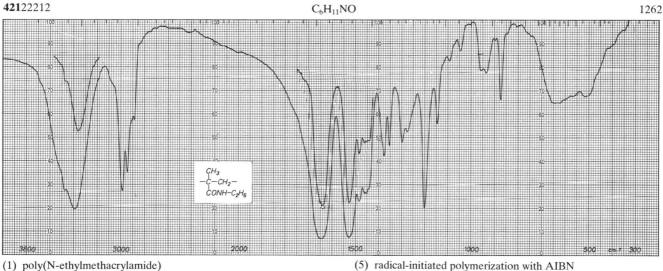

(1) poly(N-ethylmethacrylamide)
(2) white powder
(3) J. Kopeček, Institute of Macromolecular Chemistry, Czechoslovak Academy of Sciences, Praha

(5) radical-initiated polymerization with AIBN
(6) J. Strohalm, K. Ulbrich, J. Exner, J. Kopeček, Angew. Makromol. Chem. 49 (1976) 83...92
(7) KBr (2/350)

42122212   C₈H₁₅NO   1263

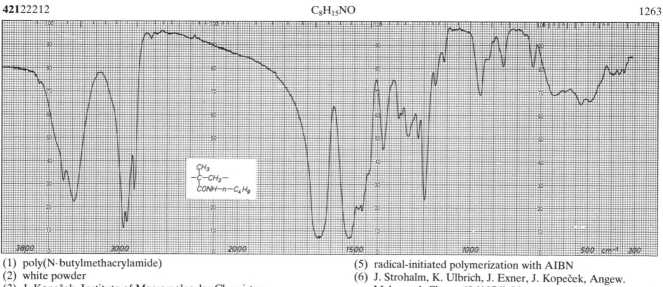

(1) poly(N-butylmethacrylamide)
(2) white powder
(3) J. Kopeček, Institute of Macromolecular Chemistry, Czechoslovak Akademy of Sciences, Praha

(5) radical-initiated polymerization with AIBN
(6) J. Strohalm, K. Ulbrich, J. Exner, J. Kopeček, Angew. Makromol. Chem. 49 (1976) 83...92
(7) KBr (2/350)

42122222 $C_{10}H_{11}NO$ 1264

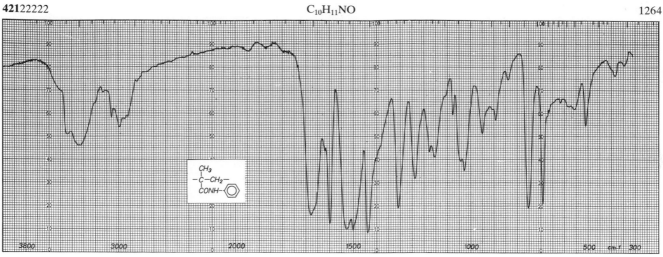

(1) poly(N-phenylmethacrylamide)
(2) white powder
(3) J. Kopeček, Institute of Macromolecular Chemistry, Czechoslovak Academy of Sciences, Praha
(5) radical-initiated polymerization with AIBN
(6) J. Strohalm, K. Ulbrich, J. Exner, J. Kopeček, Angew. Makromol. Chem. *49* (1976) 83...92
(7) KBr (2/350)

4212231 $C_7H_{13}NO$ 1265

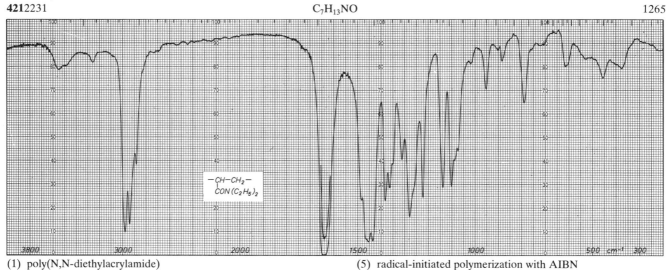

(1) poly(N,N-diethylacrylamide)
(2) white material
(3) J. Kopeček, Institute of Macromolecular Chemistry, Czechoslovak Academy of Sciences, Praha
(5) radical-initiated polymerization with AIBN
(6) J. Strohalm, K. Ulbrich, J. Exner, J. Kopeček, Angew. Makromol. Chem. *49* (1976) 83...92
(7) film from $CHCl_3$ on CsI

4212231 $C_9H_{15}NO_2$ 1266

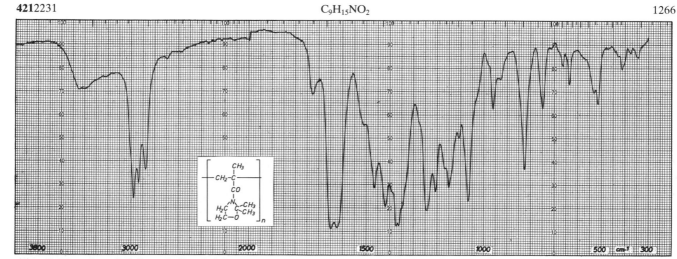

422

(1) poly(N-methacryloyl-1-aza-2-dimethyl-3-oxa-cyclopentane)
(2) white powder
(3) W. de Winter, Agfa Gevaert, N.V., Mortsel
(6) W. de Winter, IUPAC Macro, Aberdeen 1973; private communication
(7) film from $CHCl_3$ on CsI

4212231–33731121 C$_{10}$H$_{17}$NO$_2$–C$_5$H$_8$O$_2$ 1267

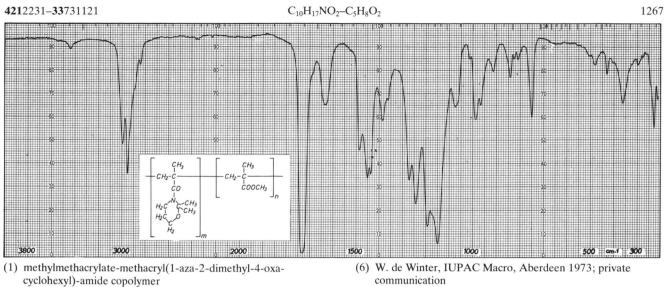

(1) methylmethacrylate-methacryl(1-aza-2-dimethyl-4-oxa-
cyclohexyl)-amide copolymer
(2) white powder
(3) W. de Winter, Agfa Gevaert, N.V., Mortsel

(6) W. de Winter, IUPAC Macro, Aberdeen 1973; private
communication
(7) film from CHCl$_3$ on CsI

4212232 C$_{20}$H$_{16}$N$_2$O$_2$ 1268

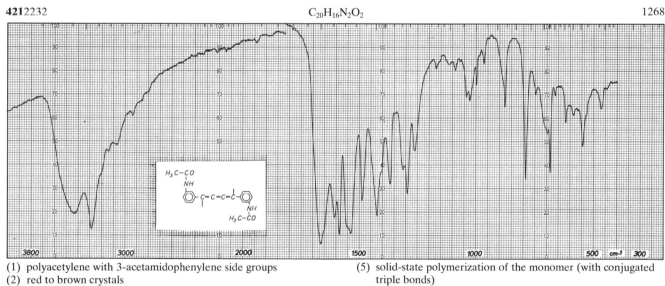

(1) polyacetylene with 3-acetamidophenylene side groups
(2) red to brown crystals
(3) G. Wegner, Universität Mainz/Universität Freiburg, Institut
für Organische Chemie

(5) solid-state polymerization of the monomer (with conjugated
triple bonds)
(6) G. Wegner, Makromol. Chem. *154* (1972) 35...48
(7) KBr

421224 C$_8$H$_{13}$NO 1269

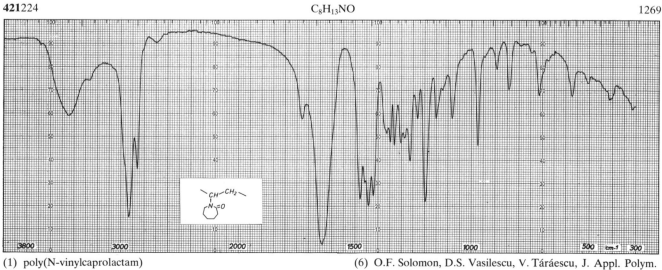

(1) poly(N-vinylcaprolactam)
(2) white substance
(3) O.F. Solomon, Laboratory of Macromolecular Chemistry,
Polytechnic Institute of Bucharest
(5) polymerization of N-vinylcaprolactam in chlorobenzene with
AIBN as an initiator at 60...80 °C

(6) O.F. Solomon, D.S. Vasilescu, V. Táráescu, J. Appl. Polym.
Sci. *13* (1969) 1
(7) KBr (2/350)

421224 $C_8H_{13}NO$ 1270

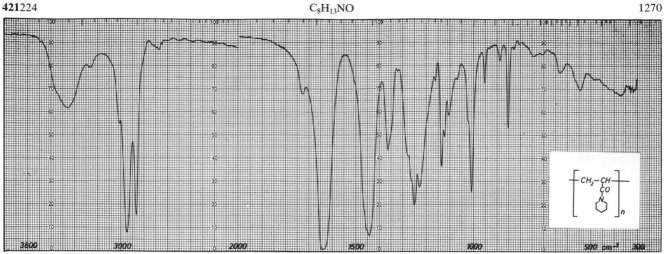

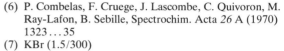

(1) poly(acrylopiperidide)
(2) white powder
(3) Ph. Combelas, Domaine Universitaire, Bordeaux
(5) radical polymerization with azo-bis-isobutyronitrile

(6) P. Combelas, F. Cruege, J. Lascombe, C. Quivoron, M. Ray-Lafon, B. Sebille, Spectrochim. Acta *26* A (1970) 1323...35
(7) KBr (1.5/300)

421225 $C_8H_6N_2O_2$ 1271

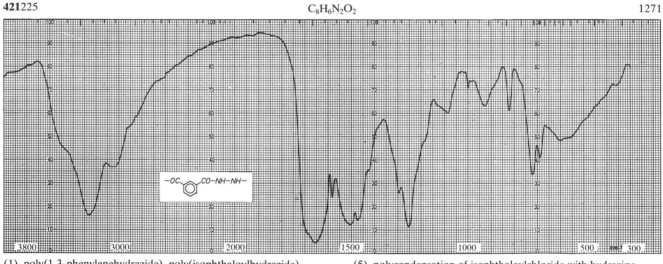

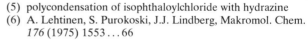

(1) poly(1,3-phenylenehydrazide), poly(isophthaloylhydrazide)
(2) white powder
(3) J.J. Lindberg, Department of Wood and Polymer Chemistry, University of Helsinki

(5) polycondensation of isophthaloylchloride with hydrazine
(6) A. Lehtinen, S. Purokoski, J.J. Lindberg, Makromol. Chem. *176* (1975) 1553...66

421225 $C_{15}H_{11}N_3O_4$ 1272

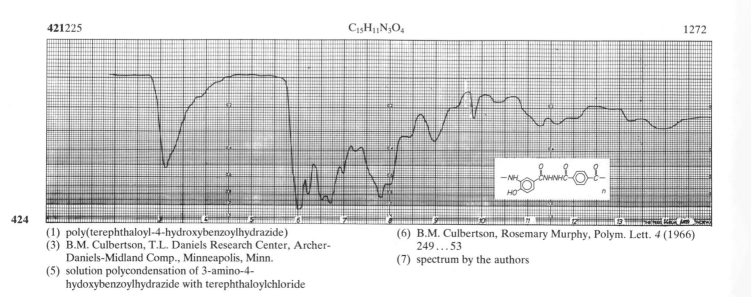

(1) poly(terephthaloyl-4-hydroxybenzoylhydrazide)
(3) B.M. Culbertson, T.L. Daniels Research Center, Archer-Daniels-Midland Comp., Minneapolis, Minn.
(5) solution polycondensation of 3-amino-4-hydoxybenzoylhydrazide with terephthaloylchloride

(6) B.M. Culbertson, Rosemary Murphy, Polym. Lett. *4* (1966) 249...53
(7) spectrum by the authors

421225 $C_{21}H_{16}N_4O_3$ 1273

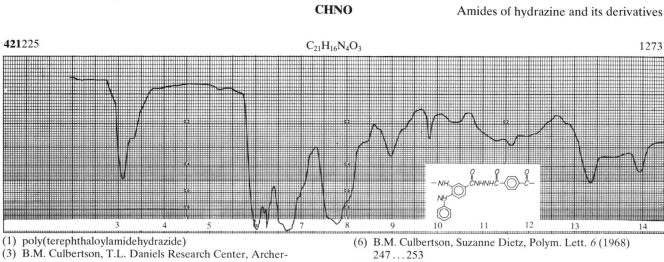

(1) poly(terephthaloylamidehydrazide)
(3) B.M. Culbertson, T.L. Daniels Research Center, Archer-Daniels-Midland Comp., Minneapolis, Minn.
(5) low temperature solution polycondensation of 3-amino-4-anilinobenzoylhydrazide with terephthaloylchloride

(6) B.M. Culbertson, Suzanne Dietz, Polym. Lett. *6* (1968) 247...253
(7) spectrum by the authors

421225 $C_{23}H_{20}N_6O_4$ 1274

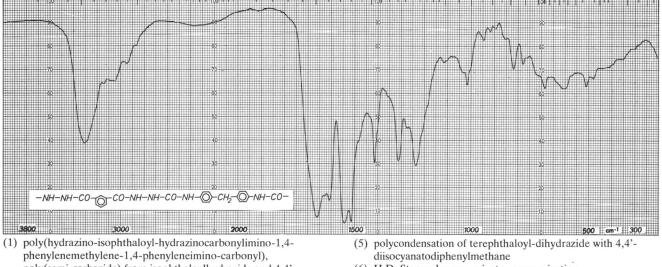

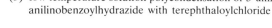

(1) poly(hydrazino-isophthaloyl-hydrazinocarbonylimino-1,4-phenylenemethylene-1,4-phenyleneimino-carbonyl), poly(semi-carbazide) from isophthaloylhydrazide and 4,4'-diisocyanatodiphenylmethane
(2) white, fibrous material
(3) H.D. Stenzenberger, Technochemie GmbH – Verfahrenstechnik, Dossenheim bei Heidelberg

(5) polycondensation of terephthaloyl-dihydrazide with 4,4'-diisocyanatodiphenylmethane
(6) H.D. Stenzenberger, private communication
(7) transparent film (10 μm) from dimethylacetamide
(8) ordinate expanded between 2000 and 200 cm^{-1}

421225 $C_{13}H_{14}N_8O_2$ 1275

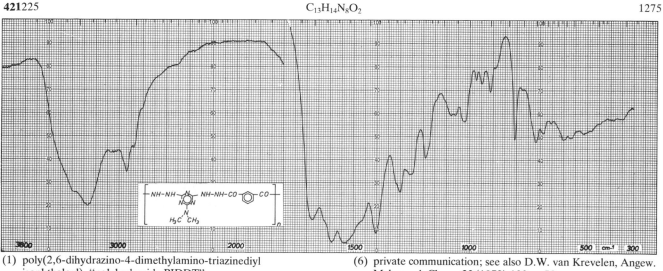

(1) poly(2,6-dihydrazino-4-dimethylamino-triazinediyl isophthaloyl), "polyhydrazide PIDDT"
(2) white powder
(3) Akzo Research Laboratories Obernburg/D.W. van Krevelen, Akzo Research and Engineering N.V., Arnhem

(6) private communication; see also D.W. van Krevelen, Angew. Makromol. Chem. *22* (1972) 133...58
(7) ground with KBr (2/350) and dimethylacetamide, dried and pressed

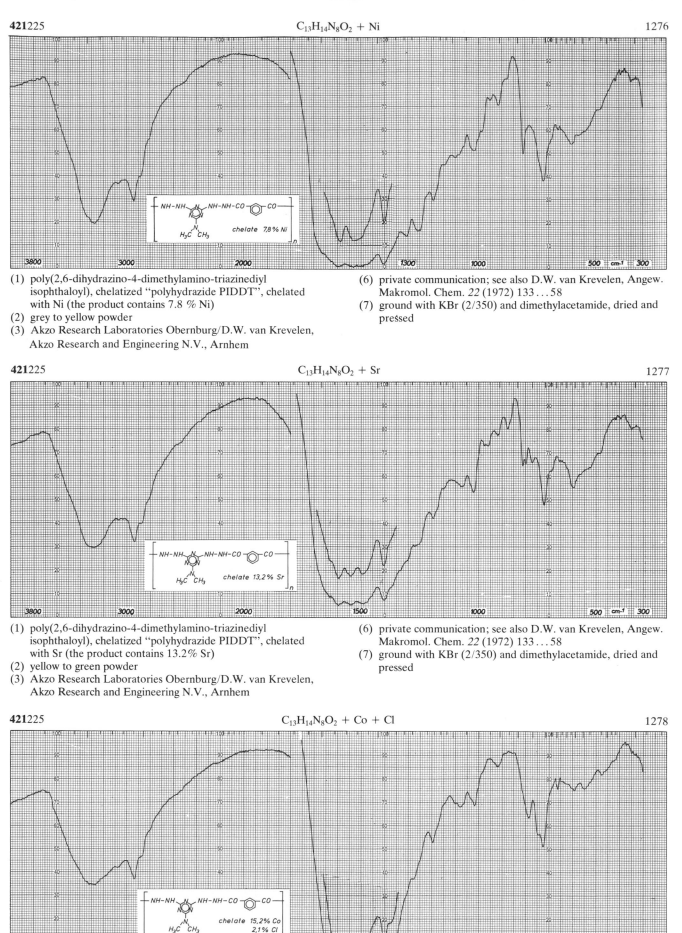

(1) poly(2,6-dihydrazino-4-dimethylamino-triazinediyl isophthaloyl), chelatized "polyhydrazide PIDDT", chelated with Ni (the product contains 7.8 % Ni)
(2) grey to yellow powder
(3) Akzo Research Laboratories Obernburg/D.W. van Krevelen, Akzo Research and Engineering N.V., Arnhem

(6) private communication; see also D.W. van Krevelen, Angew. Makromol. Chem. *22* (1972) 133...58
(7) ground with KBr (2/350) and dimethylacetamide, dried and pressed

(1) poly(2,6-dihydrazino-4-dimethylamino-triazinediyl isophthaloyl), chelatized "polyhydrazide PIDDT", chelated with Sr (the product contains 13.2% Sr)
(2) yellow to green powder
(3) Akzo Research Laboratories Obernburg/D.W. van Krevelen, Akzo Research and Engineering N.V., Arnhem

(6) private communication; see also D.W. van Krevelen, Angew. Makromol. Chem. *22* (1972) 133...58
(7) ground with KBr (2/350) and dimethylacetamide, dried and pressed

(1) poly(2,6-dihydrazino-4-dimethylamino-triazinediyl isophthaloyl), chelatized "polyhydrazide PIDDT", chelated with Co (the product contains 15.2% Co and 2.1% Cl)
(2) dark grey powder
(3) Akzo Research Laboratories Obernburg/D.W. van Krevelen, Akzo Research and Engineering N.V., Arnhem

(6) private communication; see also D.W. van Krevelen, Angew. Makromol. Chem. *22* (1972) 133...58
(7) ground with KBr (2/350) and dimethylacetamide, dried and pressed

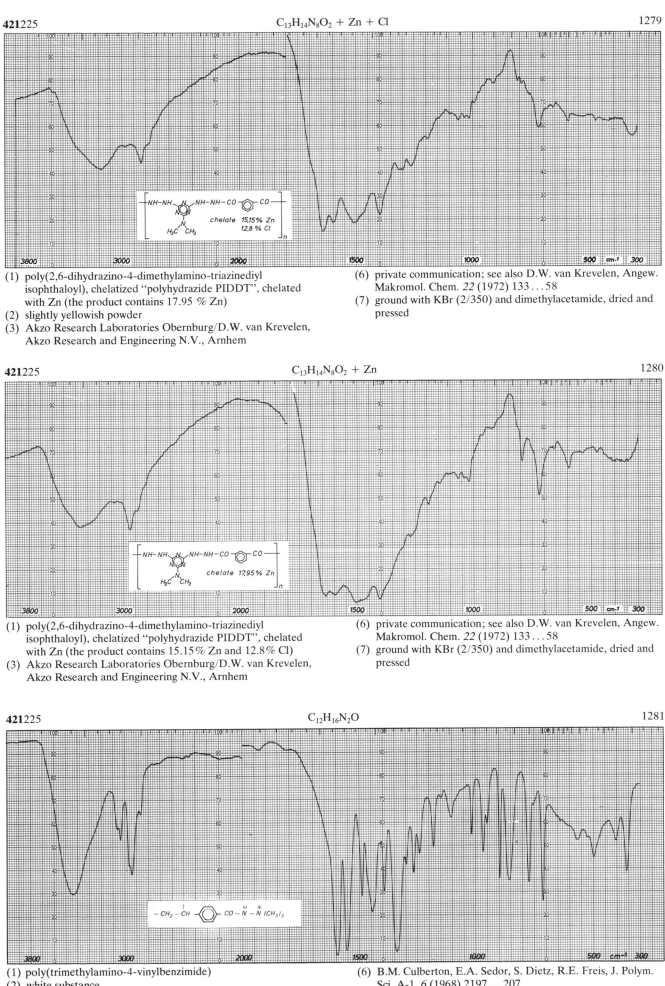

421225 $C_{13}H_{14}N_8O_2 + Zn + Cl$ 1279

(1) poly(2,6-dihydrazino-4-dimethylamino-triazinediyl isophthaloyl), chelatized "polyhydrazide PIDDT", chelated with Zn (the product contains 17.95 % Zn)
(2) slightly yellowish powder
(3) Akzo Research Laboratories Obernburg/D.W. van Krevelen, Akzo Research and Engineering N.V., Arnhem
(6) private communication; see also D.W. van Krevelen, Angew. Makromol. Chem. 22 (1972) 133...58
(7) ground with KBr (2/350) and dimethylacetamide, dried and pressed

421225 $C_{13}H_{14}N_8O_2 + Zn$ 1280

(1) poly(2,6-dihydrazino-4-dimethylamino-triazinediyl isophthaloyl), chelatized "polyhydrazide PIDDT", chelated with Zn (the product contains 15.15% Zn and 12.8% Cl)
(3) Akzo Research Laboratories Obernburg/D.W. van Krevelen, Akzo Research and Engineering N.V., Arnhem
(6) private communication; see also D.W. van Krevelen, Angew. Makromol. Chem. 22 (1972) 133...58
(7) ground with KBr (2/350) and dimethylacetamide, dried and pressed

421225 $C_{12}H_{16}N_2O$ 1281

(1) poly(trimethylamino-4-vinylbenzimide)
(2) white substance
(3) B.M. Culbertson, South Minneapolis, Minn.
(5) $H_2C=CH-\emptyset-CONH-N(CH_3)_2 + H_3C-\emptyset-SO_3CH_3 \rightarrow H_2C=CH-\emptyset-CONH-\overset{\oplus}{N}(CH_3)_3 \overset{\ominus}{OTS} \xrightarrow{KOH}$
$H_2C=CH-\emptyset=C-\overset{\ominus}{N}-\overset{\oplus}{N}(CH_3)_3 \rightarrow radic\ pol.$
$\overset{\parallel}{O}$
(6) B.M. Culberton, E.A. Sedor, S. Dietz, R.E. Freis, J. Polym. Sci. A-1, 6 (1968) 2197...207
(7) KBr (2/300)

427

421226   C₁₁H₁₃NO   1282

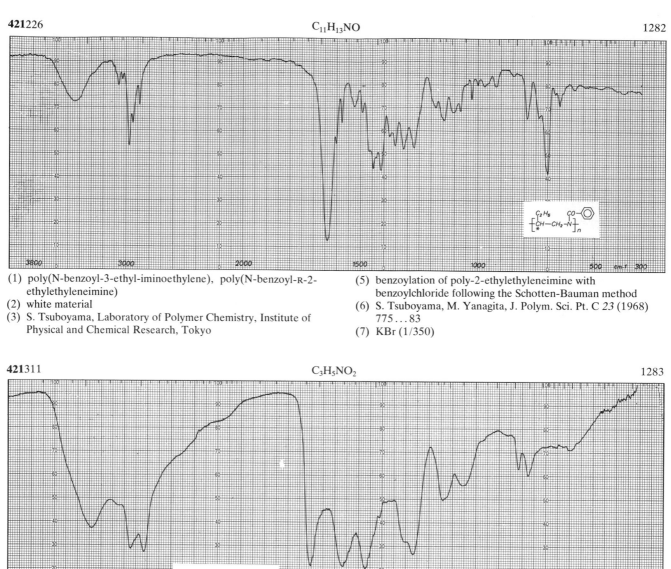

(1) poly(N-benzoyl-3-ethyl-iminoethylene), poly(N-benzoyl-R-2-ethylethyleneimine)
(2) white material
(3) S. Tsuboyama, Laboratory of Polymer Chemistry, Institute of Physical and Chemical Research, Tokyo
(5) benzoylation of poly-2-ethylethyleneimine with benzoylchloride following the Schotten-Bauman method
(6) S. Tsuboyama, M. Yanagita, J. Polym. Sci. Pt. C *23* (1968) 775...83
(7) KBr (1/350)

421311   C₃H₅NO₂   1283

— CH₂–CH₂–NH–COO —

(1) polyurethane-3, poly(oxycarbonyliminoethylene)
(2) yellowish, transparent, tough material
(3) K. Soga, Research Laboratory of Recources Utilization, Tokyo Institute of Technology, Tokyo
(5) copolymerization of carbondioxide with ethyleneimine in bulk at high pressure without catalyst
(6) K. Soga, S. Hosoda, S. Ikeda, Makromol. Chem. *175* (1974) 3309...13
(7) film on CsI

421311   C₁₀H₁₈N₂O₄   1284

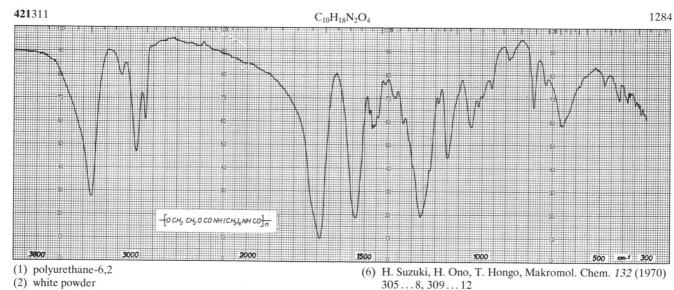

–[O CH₂ CH₂ O CO NH (CH₂)₆ NH CO]ₙ–

(1) polyurethane-6,2
(2) white powder
(3) H. Suzuki, Katata Research Institute, Toyobo Co., Otsu, Shiga
(5) polyaddition of ethyleneglycol and hexamethylene diisocyanate
(6) H. Suzuki, H. Ono, T. Hongo, Makromol. Chem. *132* (1970) 305...8, 309...12
(7) KBr (1/350)

421311 $C_{10}H_{18}N_2O_4$ 1285

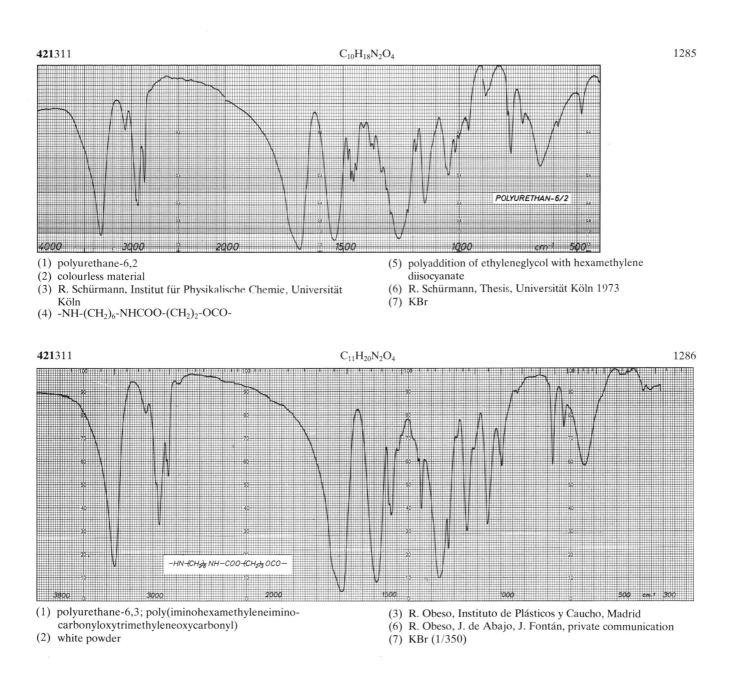

POLYURETHAN-6/2

(1) polyurethane-6,2
(2) colourless material
(3) R. Schürmann, Institut für Physikalische Chemie, Universität Köln
(4) -NH-$(CH_2)_6$-NHCOO-$(CH_2)_2$-OCO-

(5) polyaddition of ethyleneglycol with hexamethylene diisocyanate
(6) R. Schürmann, Thesis, Universität Köln 1973
(7) KBr

421311 $C_{11}H_{20}N_2O_4$ 1286

-HN-$(CH_2)_6$ NH-COO-$(CH_2)_3$ OCO-

(1) polyurethane-6,3; poly(iminohexamethyleneimino-carbonyloxytrimethyleneoxycarbonyl)
(2) white powder

(3) R. Obeso, Instituto de Plásticos y Caucho, Madrid
(6) R. Obeso, J. de Abajo, J. Fontán, private communication
(7) KBr (1/350)

421311 $C_{12}H_{22}N_2O_4$ 1287

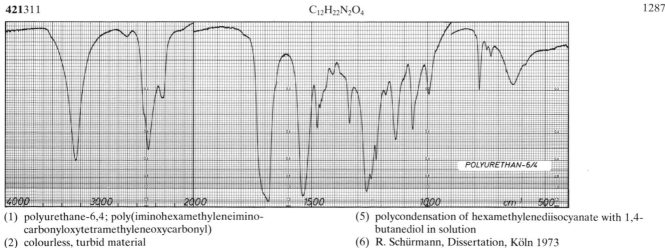

POLYURETHAN-6/4

(1) polyurethane-6,4; poly(iminohexamethyleneimino-carbonyloxytetramethyleneoxycarbonyl)
(2) colourless, turbid material
(3) R. Schürmann, Institut für Physikalische Chemie, Universität Köln

(5) polycondensation of hexamethylenediisocyanate with 1,4-butanediol in solution
(6) R. Schürmann, Dissertation, Köln 1973
(7) film from HCOOH, extracted several times with H_2O

421311 $C_{14}H_{26}N_2O_4$ 1288

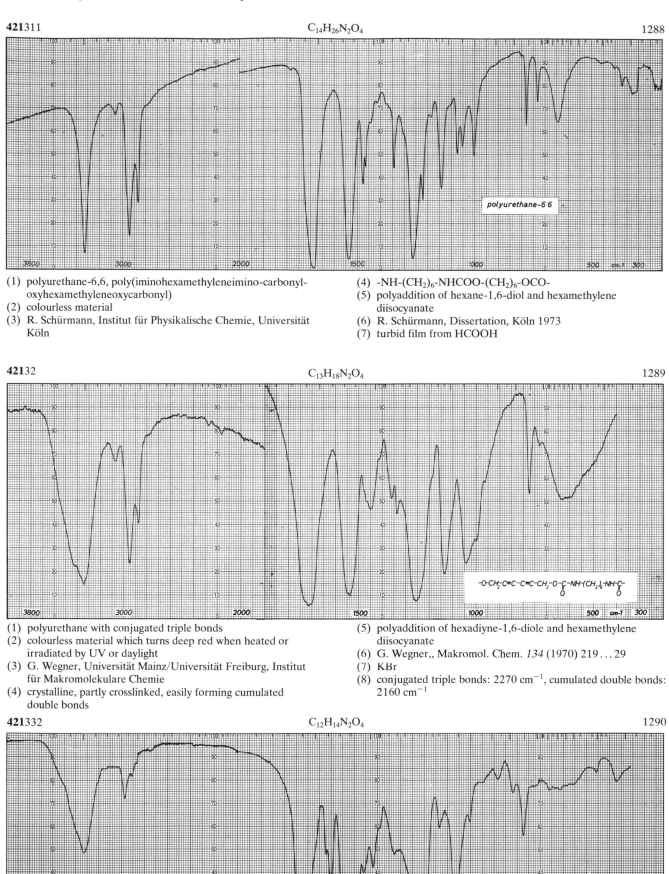

polyurethane-6 6

(1) polyurethane-6,6, poly(iminohexamethyleneimino-carbonyl-oxyhexamethyleneoxycarbonyl)
(2) colourless material
(3) R. Schürmann, Institut für Physikalische Chemie, Universität Köln

(4) -NH-$(CH_2)_6$-NHCOO-$(CH_2)_6$-OCO-
(5) polyaddition of hexane-1,6-diol and hexamethylene diisocyanate
(6) R. Schürmann, Dissertation, Köln 1973
(7) turbid film from HCOOH

42132 $C_{13}H_{18}N_2O_4$ 1289

-O-CH₂-C≡C-C≡C-CH₂-O-C-NH-(CH₂)₆-NH-C-
              O   O

(1) polyurethane with conjugated triple bonds
(2) colourless material which turns deep red when heated or irradiated by UV or daylight
(3) G. Wegner, Universität Mainz/Universität Freiburg, Institut für Makromolekulare Chemie
(4) crystalline, partly crosslinked, easily forming cumulated double bonds

(5) polyaddition of hexadiyne-1,6-diole and hexamethylene diisocyanate
(6) G. Wegner,, Makromol. Chem. *134* (1970) 219...29
(7) KBr
(8) conjugated triple bonds: 2270 cm⁻¹, cumulated double bonds: 2160 cm⁻¹

421332 $C_{12}H_{14}N_2O_4$ 1290

CH₃
-HN—◯—NH-COO-(CH₂)₃-OCO-

(1) polyurethane-TDI,3; poly(iminotoluyleneimino-carbonyltrimethyleneoxycarbonyl)
(2) white powder
(3) R. Obeso, Instituto de Plásticos y Caucho, Madrid

(5) polycondensation of toluylenediisocyanate ("Desmodur T 65") with 1,3-propanediol
(6) R. Obeso, J. de Abajo, J. Fontán, private communication
(7) KBr (0.9/350)

421332 $C_{12}H_{14}N_2O_4$ 1291

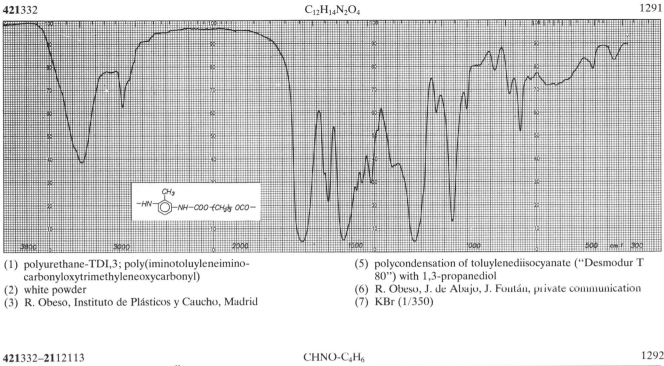

(1) polyurethane-TDI,3; poly(iminotoluyleneimino-carbonyloxytrimethyleneoxycarbonyl)
(2) white powder
(3) R. Obeso, Instituto de Plásticos y Caucho, Madrid

(5) polycondensation of toluylenediisocyanate ("Desmodur T 80") with 1,3-propanediol
(6) R. Obeso, J. de Abajo, J. Fontán, private communication
(7) KBr (1/350)

421332–2112113 $CHNO-C_4H_6$ 1292

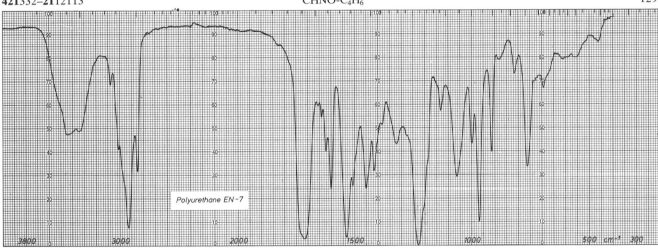

Polyurethane EN-7

(1) polyurethane-polybutadiene block copolymer, crosslinked
(2) light-yellow elastomer
(3) Conap Comp. (by R.A. Assink, Sandia Lab., Albuquerque, N.M.)
(4) the polymer contains polybutadiene soft segments, 2,4-toluene-diisocyanate based hard segments, and 2-ethyl-1,3-

hexanediol and bis(2-hydroxypropyl) aniline curing agents
(5) C. Arnold, National SAMPE, Technical Conference Series 7 (1975) 418
(6) R.A. Assink, ACS Polymer Prepr. *17*/2 (1976) 570...5
(7) ground with KBr (2/350) and CHCl₃, dried and pressed
(8) commercial product "polyurethane EN-7"

421332 $C_{18}H_{18}N_2O_4$ 1293

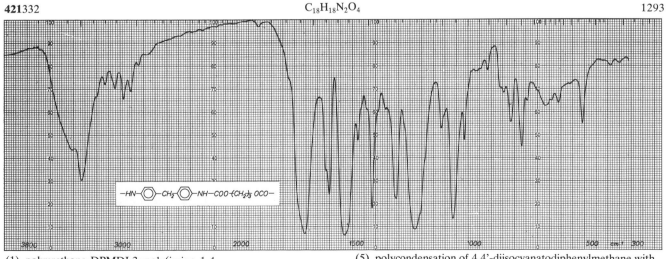

(1) polyurethane-DPMDI,3; poly(imino-1,4-phenylenemethylene-1,4-phenyleneimino-carbonlyoxytrimethyleneoxycarbonyl)
(2) eggshell-coloured powder
(3) R. Obeso, Instituto de Plásticos y Caucho, Madrid

(5) polycondensation of 4,4'-diisocyanatodiphenylmethane with 1,3-propanediol
(6) R. Obeso, J. de Abajo, J. Fontán, private communication
(7) KBr (1.3/350)

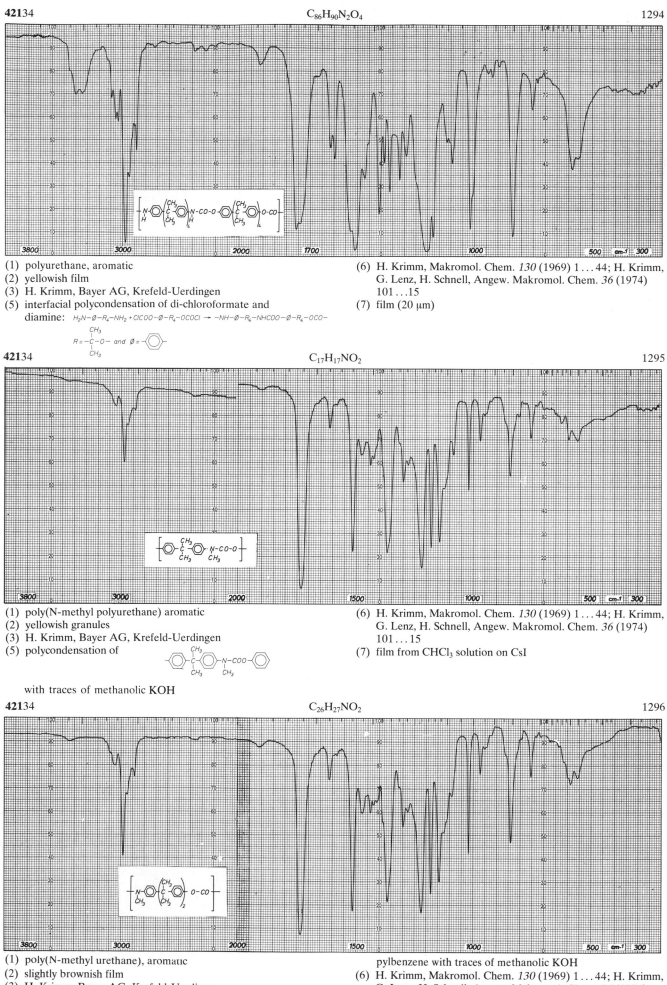

42134 $C_{86}H_{90}N_2O_4$ 1294

(1) polyurethane, aromatic
(2) yellowish film
(3) H. Krimm, Bayer AG, Krefeld-Uerdingen
(5) interfacial polycondensation of di-chloroformate and
     diamine: $H_2N-\emptyset-R_4-NH_2 + ClCOO-\emptyset-R_4-OCOCl \rightarrow -NH-\emptyset-R_4-NHCOO-\emptyset-R_4-OCO-$

$R = -\overset{CH_3}{\underset{CH_3}{C}}-O-$ and $\emptyset = $

(6) H. Krimm, Makromol. Chem. *130* (1969) 1...44; H. Krimm,
     G. Lenz, H. Schnell, Angew. Makromol. Chem. *36* (1974)
     101...15
(7) film (20 μm)

42134 $C_{17}H_{17}NO_2$ 1295

(1) poly(N-methyl polyurethane) aromatic
(2) yellowish granules
(3) H. Krimm, Bayer AG, Krefeld-Uerdingen
(5) polycondensation of

with traces of methanolic KOH

(6) H. Krimm, Makromol. Chem. *130* (1969) 1...44; H. Krimm,
     G. Lenz, H. Schnell, Angew. Makromol. Chem. *36* (1974)
     101...15
(7) film from CHCl₃ solution on CsI

42134 $C_{26}H_{27}NO_2$ 1296

432

(1) poly(N-methyl urethane), aromatic
(2) slightly brownish film
(3) H. Krimm, Bayer AG, Krefeld-Uerdingen
(5) polycondensation of the phenylurethane of α-(p-
     hydroxyphenyl)-α'-(p-methylaminophenyl)-p-diisopro-

pylbenzene with traces of methanolic KOH
(6) H. Krimm, Makromol. Chem. *130* (1969) 1...44; H. Krimm,
     G. Lenz, H. Schnell, Angew. Makromol. Chem. *36* (1974)
     101...15
(7) film from CHCl₃ solution on CsI

42134   C₄₃H₄₄N₂O₄   1297

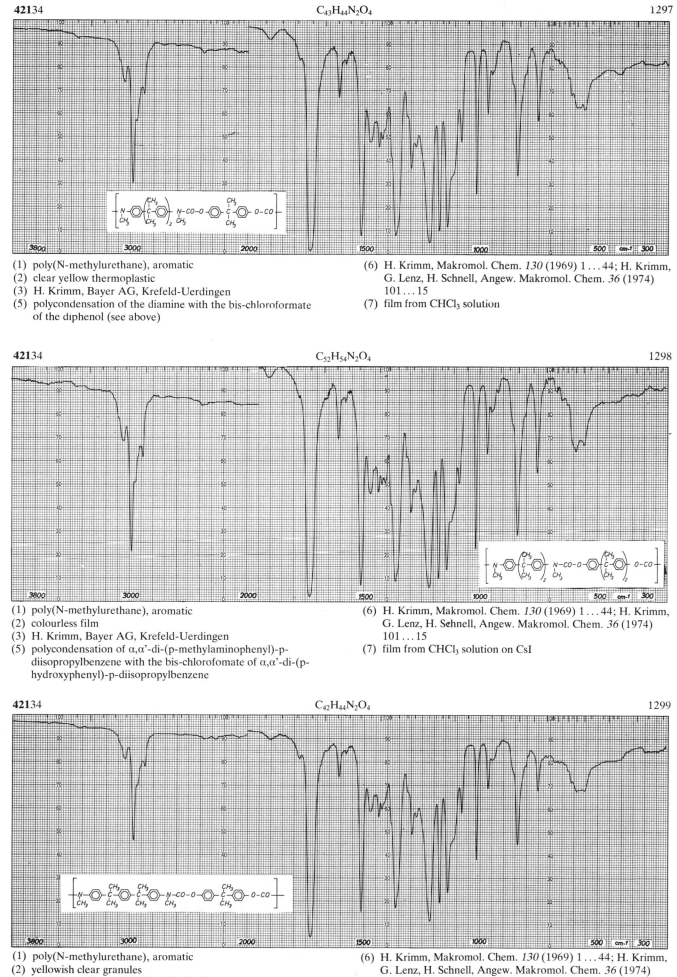

(1) poly(N-methylurethane), aromatic
(2) clear yellow thermoplastic
(3) H. Krimm, Bayer AG, Krefeld-Uerdingen
(5) polycondensation of the diamine with the bis-chloroformate
   of the diphenol (see above)

(6) H. Krimm, Makromol. Chem. *130* (1969) 1...44; H. Krimm,
   G. Lenz, H. Schnell, Angew. Makromol. Chem. *36* (1974)
   101...15
(7) film from CHCl₃ solution

42134   C₅₂H₅₄N₂O₄   1298

(1) poly(N-methylurethane), aromatic
(2) colourless film
(3) H. Krimm, Bayer AG, Krefeld-Uerdingen
(5) polycondensation of α,α'-di-(p-methylaminophenyl)-p-
   diisopropylbenzene with the bis-chlorofomate of α,α'-di-(p-
   hydroxyphenyl)-p-diisopropylbenzene

(6) H. Krimm, Makromol. Chem. *130* (1969) 1...44; H. Krimm,
   G. Lenz, H. Schnell, Angew. Makromol. Chem. *36* (1974)
   101...15
(7) film from CHCl₃ solution on CsI

42134   C₄₂H₄₄N₂O₄   1299

(1) poly(N-methylurethane), aromatic
(2) yellowish clear granules
(3) H. Krimm, Bayer AG, Krefeld-Uerdingen
(5) polycondensation of the diamine with the bis-chloroformate
   of the diphenol (see above)

(6) H. Krimm, Makromol. Chem. *130* (1969) 1...44; H. Krimm,
   G. Lenz, H. Schnell, Angew. Makromol. Chem. *36* (1974)
   101...15
(7) film from CHCl₃ solution on CsI

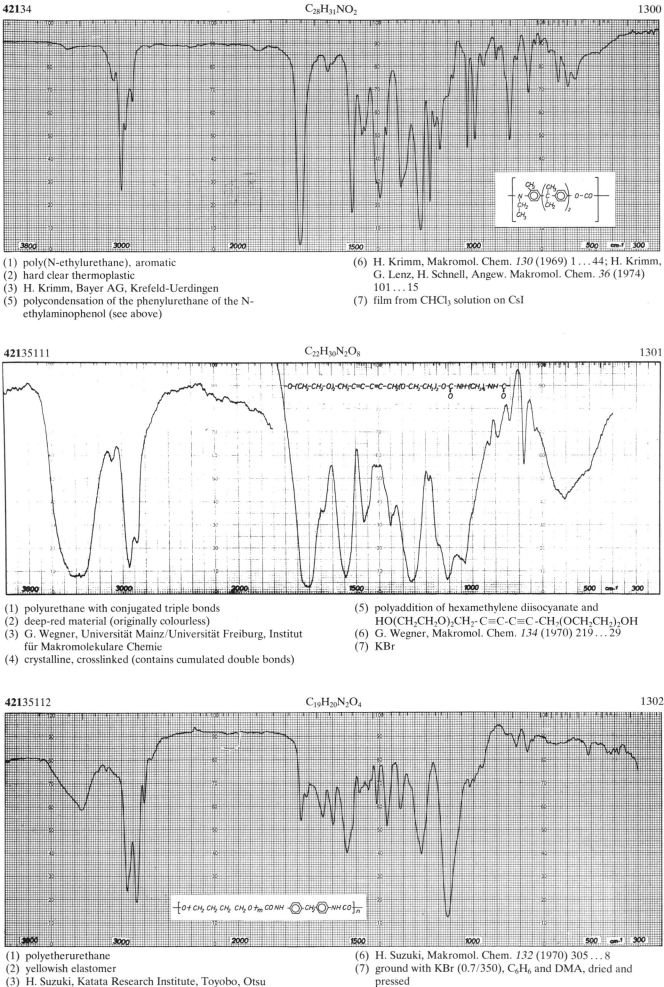

42134   C$_{28}$H$_{31}$NO$_2$ 1300

(1) poly(N-ethylurethane), aromatic
(2) hard clear thermoplastic
(3) H. Krimm, Bayer AG, Krefeld-Uerdingen
(5) polycondensation of the phenylurethane of the N-ethylaminophenol (see above)

(6) H. Krimm, Makromol. Chem. *130* (1969) 1...44; H. Krimm, G. Lenz, H. Schnell, Angew. Makromol. Chem. *36* (1974) 101...15
(7) film from CHCl$_3$ solution on CsI

42135111   C$_{22}$H$_{30}$N$_2$O$_8$ 1301

(1) polyurethane with conjugated triple bonds
(2) deep-red material (originally colourless)
(3) G. Wegner, Universität Mainz/Universität Freiburg, Institut für Makromolekulare Chemie
(4) crystalline, crosslinked (contains cumulated double bonds)

(5) polyaddition of hexamethylene diisocyanate and HO(CH$_2$CH$_2$O)$_2$CH$_2$-C≡C-C≡C-CH$_2$(OCH$_2$CH$_2$)$_2$OH
(6) G. Wegner, Makromol. Chem. *134* (1970) 219...29
(7) KBr

42135112   C$_{19}$H$_{20}$N$_2$O$_4$ 1302

(1) polyetherurethane
(2) yellowish elastomer
(3) H. Suzuki, Katata Research Institute, Toyobo, Otsu
(5) polyaddition of polyether-4 (with OH-endgroups) with 4,4'-diisocyanato-diphenylmethane

(6) H. Suzuki, Makromol. Chem. *132* (1970) 305...8
(7) ground with KBr (0.7/350), C$_6$H$_6$ and DMA, dried and pressed

42135112   C$_{19}$H$_{20}$N$_2$O$_4$ 1303

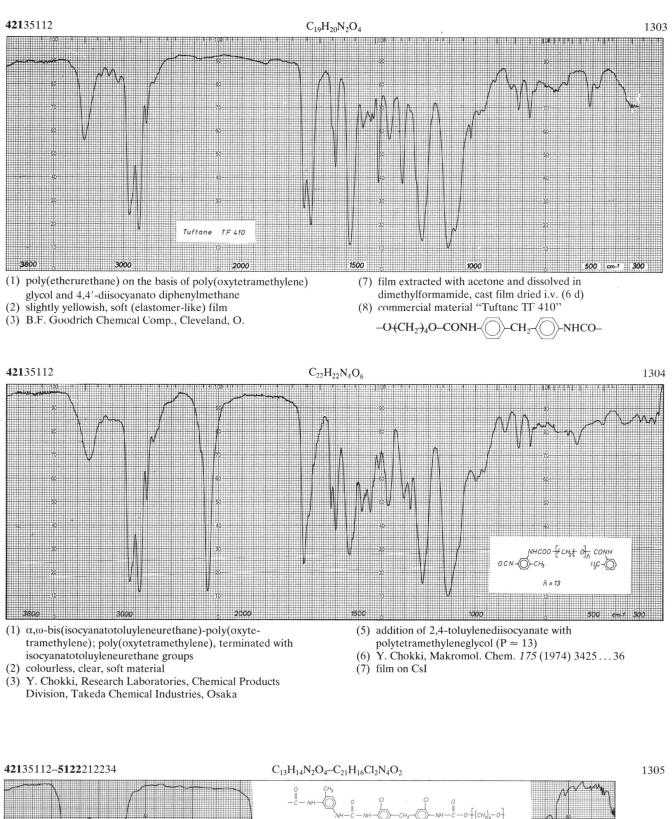

(1) poly(etherurethane) on the basis of poly(oxytetramethylene) glycol and 4,4′-diisocyanato diphenylmethane
(2) slightly yellowish, soft (elastomer-like) film
(3) B.F. Goodrich Chemical Comp., Cleveland, O.

(7) film extracted with acetone and dissolved in dimethylformamide, cast film dried i.v. (6 d)
(8) commercial material "Tuftanc TF 410"

$$-O(CH_2)_4O-CONH-\bigcirc-CH_2-\bigcirc-NHCO-$$

42135112   C$_{22}$H$_{22}$N$_4$O$_6$ 1304

(1) α,ω-bis(isocyanatotoluyleneurethane)-poly(oxyte- tramethylene); poly(oxytetramethylene), terminated with isocyanatotoluyleneurethane groups
(2) colourless, clear, soft material
(3) Y. Chokki, Research Laboratories, Chemical Products Division, Takeda Chemical Industries, Osaka

(5) addition of 2,4-toluylenediisocyanate with polytetramethyleneglycol (P ≈ 13)
(6) Y. Chokki, Makromol. Chem. *175* (1974) 3425...36
(7) film on CsI

42135112–**51**22212234   C$_{13}$H$_{14}$N$_2$O$_4$–C$_{21}$H$_{16}$Cl$_2$N$_4$O$_2$ 1305

(1) poly(urethane urea)segment copolymer on the basis of poly(oxytetramethylene), methylene-bis(o-chloroaniline) and 2,4-toluylenediisocyanate
(2) yellow elastomer, crosslinked
(3) A.R. Cain, The Firestone Comp., Central Research Laboratories, Akron, O.

(5) polycondensation of a commercial 2,4-toluylenediisocyanate- poly(oxytetramethylene) prepolymer with methylene-bis(p- chloroaniline)
(6) A.R. Cain, ACS Polym. Prepr. *17/2* (1976) 580
(7) free film

42135121 $C_{11}H_{18}N_2O_5$ 1306

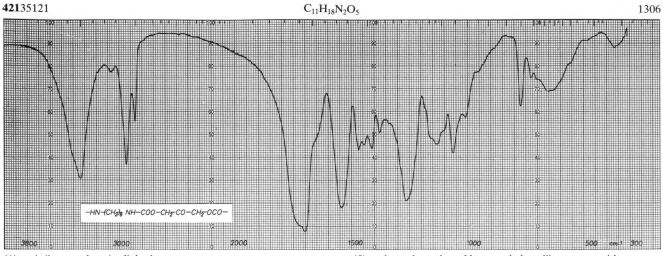

$-HN-(CH_2)_6-NH-COO-CH_2-CO-CH_2-OCO-$

(1) poly(ketourethane), aliphatic;
poly(iminohexamethyleneimino-carbonyloxymethylene-car-
bonyl-methyleneoxycarbonyl)
(2) yellowish-red powder
(3) R. Obeso, Instituto de Plásticos y Caucho, Madrid

(5) polycondensation of hexamethylenediisocyanate with
dihydroxymethylketone
(6) R. Obeso, J. de Abajo, J. Fontán, private communication
(7) KBr (1.5/350)

42135122 $C_{12}H_{12}N_2O_5$ 1307

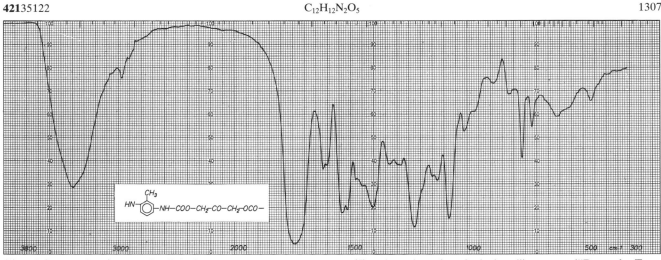

$HN-\langle\bigcirc\rangle^{CH_3}-NH-COO-CH_2-CO-CH_2-OCO-$

(1) poly(ketourethane), aromatic-aliphatic;
poly(iminotoluyleneimino-carbonyloxymethylenecarbonyl-
methyleneoxycarbonyl)
(2) yellowish-red powder
(3) R. Obeso, Instituto de Plásticos y Caucho, Madrid

(5) polycondensation of toluylenediisocyanate ("Desmodur T
80") with dihydroxymethylketone
(6) R. Obeso, J. de Abajo, J. Fontán, private communication
(7) KBr (1.5/350)

42135122 $C_{11}H_{12}N_2O_5$ 1308

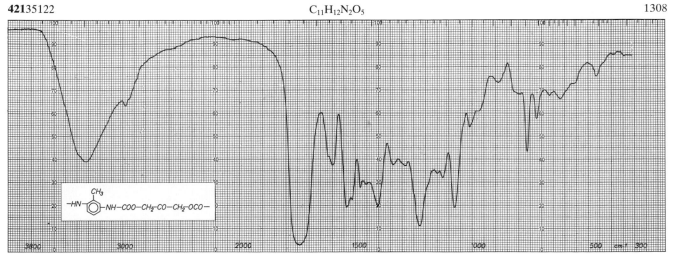

$-HN-\langle\bigcirc\rangle^{CH_3}-NH-COO-CH_2-CO-CH_2-OCO-$

(1) poly(ketourethane), aromatic-aliphatic;
poly(iminotoluyleneimino-carbonyloxymethylenecarbonyl-
methyleneoxycarbonyl)
(2) yellowish-red powder
(3) R. Obeso, Instituto de Plásticos y Caucho, Madrid

(5) polycondensation of toluylenediisocyanate („Desmodur T
65") with dihydroxymethylketone
(6) R. Obeso, J. de Abajo, J. Fontán, private communication
(7) ground with KBr (1/350) and HCOOH, dried and pressed

42135122   C$_{18}$H$_{16}$N$_2$O$_5$ 1309

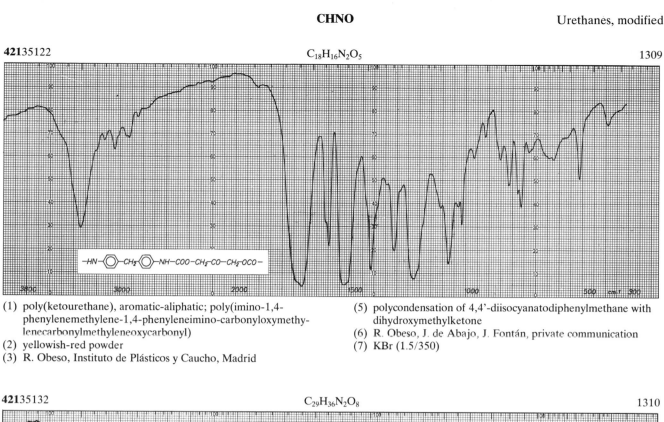

(1) poly(ketourethane), aromatic-aliphatic; poly(imino-1,4-phenylenemethylene-1,4-phenyleneimino-carbonyloxymethylenecarbonylmethyleneoxycarbonyl)
(2) yellowish-red powder
(3) R. Obeso, Instituto de Plásticos y Caucho, Madrid

(5) polycondensation of 4,4'-diisocyanatodiphenylmethane with dihydroxymethylketone
(6) R. Obeso, J. de Abajo, J. Fontán, private communication
(7) KBr (1.5/350)

42135132   C$_{29}$H$_{36}$N$_2$O$_8$ 1310

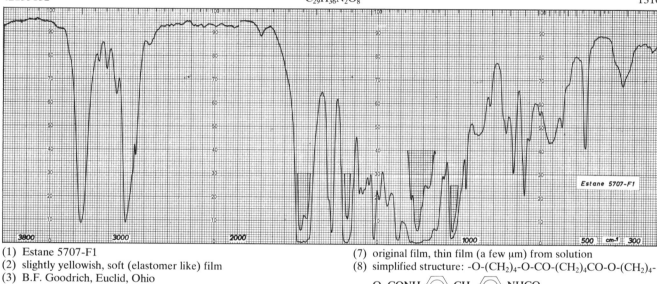

(1) Estane 5707-F1
(2) slightly yellowish, soft (elastomer like) film
(3) B.F. Goodrich, Euclid, Ohio
(4) polyesterurethane on the basis of poly(tetramethyleneadipate) and 4,4'-diisocyanato-diphenylmethane

(7) original film, thin film (a few μm) from solution
(8) simplified structure: -O-(CH$_2$)$_4$-O-CO-(CH$_2$)$_4$CO-O-(CH$_2$)$_4$-
–O–CONH–◯–CH$_2$–◯–NHCO–

42135132   C$_{29}$H$_{36}$N$_2$O$_8$ 1311

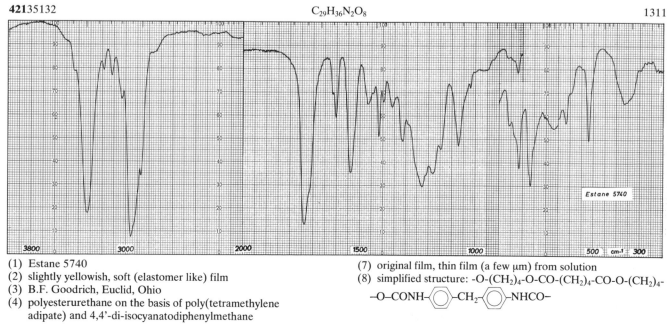

(1) Estane 5740
(2) slightly yellowish, soft (elastomer like) film
(3) B.F. Goodrich, Euclid, Ohio
(4) polyesterurethane on the basis of poly(tetramethylene adipate) and 4,4'-di-isocyanatodiphenylmethane

(7) original film, thin film (a few μm) from solution
(8) simplified structure: -O-(CH$_2$)$_4$-O-CO-(CH$_2$)$_4$-CO-O-(CH$_2$)$_4$-
–O–CONH–◯–CH$_2$–◯–NHCO–

42135132   1312

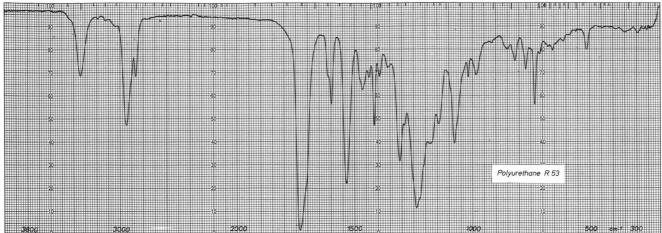

Polyurethane R 53

(1) poly(esterurethane) on the base of 4,4'-diphenylmethane diisocyanate
(2) colourless elastomer
(3) Hooker Chemical Comp. (by R.A. Assink, Sandia Laboratories, Albuquerque, N.M.)

(6) R.A. Assink, ACS Polymer Prepr. *17*/2 (1976) 570...5
(7) film from CHCl₃, ordinate expanded
(8) commercial product "polyurethane R 53"

42135132 $C_{20}H_{26}N_2O_8$ 1313

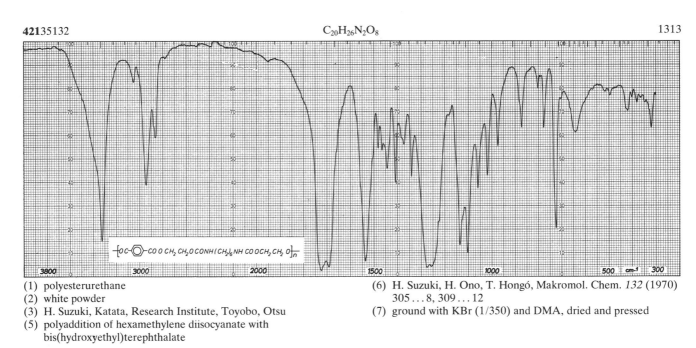

$\left[OC\text{-}\bigcirc\text{-}CO\,O\,CH_2\,CH_2\,O\,CONH(CH_2)_6\,NH\,CO\,OCH_2\,CH_2\,O \right]_n$

(1) polyesterurethane
(2) white powder
(3) H. Suzuki, Katata, Research Institute, Toyobo, Otsu
(5) polyaddition of hexamethylene diisocyanate with bis(hydroxyethyl)terephthalate

(6) H. Suzuki, H. Ono, T. Hongó, Makromol. Chem. *132* (1970) 305...8, 309...12
(7) ground with KBr (1/350) and DMA, dried and pressed

42135222 $C_{17}H_{19}N_3O_6$ 1314

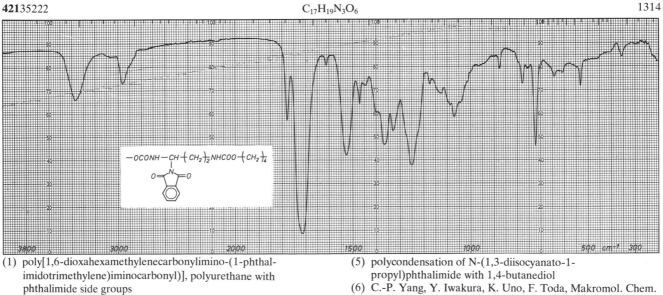

(1) poly[1,6-dioxahexamethylenecarbonylimino-(1-phthal-imidotrimethylene)iminocarbonyl)], polyurethane with phthalimide side groups
(2) white powder
(3) C.-P. Yang, Department of Chemical Engineering, Tatung Institute of Technology, Taipei, Taiwan

(5) polycondensation of N-(1,3-diisocyanato-1-propyl)phthalimide with 1,4-butanediol
(6) C.-P. Yang, Y. Iwakura, K. Uno, F. Toda, Makromol. Chem. *177* (1976) 3495...3514
(7) film from CHCl₃ on CsI

42135222 $C_{19}H_{23}N_3O_6$ 1315

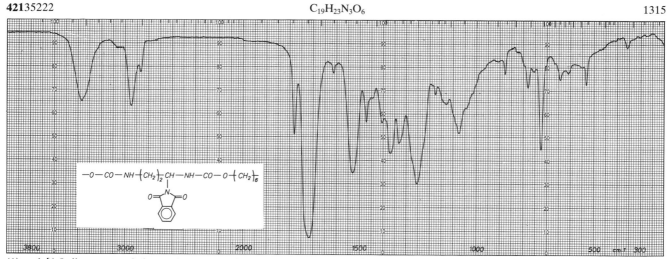

(1) poly[1,8-dioxaoctamethylenecarbonylimino-(1-phthal-imidotrimethylene)iminocarbonyl], polyurethane with phthalimide side groups
(2) white powder
(3) C.-P. Yang, Department of Chemical Engineering, Tatung Institute of Technology, Taipei, Taiwan

(5) polycondensation of N-(1,3-diisocyanato-1-propyl)phthalimide with 1,6-hexanediol
(6) C.-P. Yang, Y. Iwakura, K. Uno, F. Toda, Makromol. Chem. *177* (1976) 3495...514
(7) film from $CHCl_3$ on CsI

42135321 $C_{34}H_{58}N_6O_6$ 1316

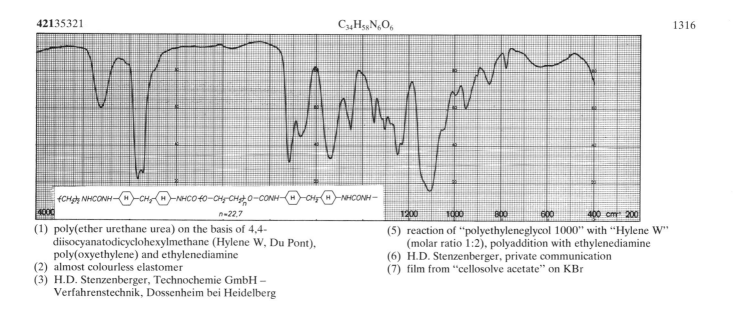

(1) poly(ether urethane urea) on the basis of 4,4-diisocyanatodicyclohexylmethane (Hylene W, Du Pont), poly(oxyethylene) and ethylenediamine
(2) almost colourless elastomer
(3) H.D. Stenzenberger, Technochemie GmbH – Verfahrenstechnik, Dossenheim bei Heidelberg

(5) reaction of "polyethyleneglycol 1000" with "Hylene W" (molar ratio 1:2), polyaddition with ethylenediamine
(6) H.D. Stenzenberger, private communication
(7) film from "cellosolve acetate" on KBr

42135321 $C_{34}H_{58}N_6O_6$ 1317

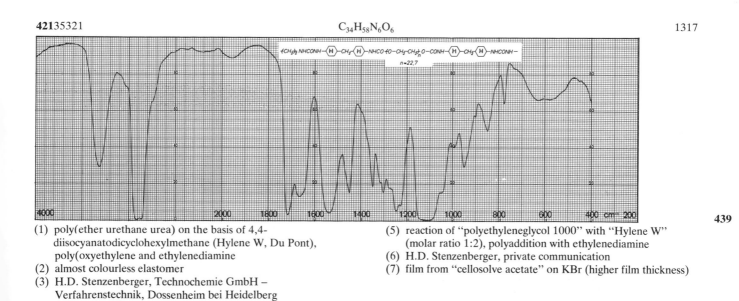

(1) poly(ether urethane urea) on the basis of 4,4-diisocyanatodicyclohexylmethane (Hylene W, Du Pont), poly(oxyethylene and ethylenediamine
(2) almost colourless elastomer
(3) H.D. Stenzenberger, Technochemie GmbH – Verfahrenstechnik, Dossenheim bei Heidelberg

(5) reaction of "polyethyleneglycol 1000" with "Hylene W" (molar ratio 1:2), polyaddition with ethylenediamine
(6) H.D. Stenzenberger, private communication
(7) film from "cellosolve acetate" on KBr (higher film thickness)

42135321 $C_{36}H_{62}N_6O_6$ 1318

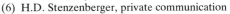

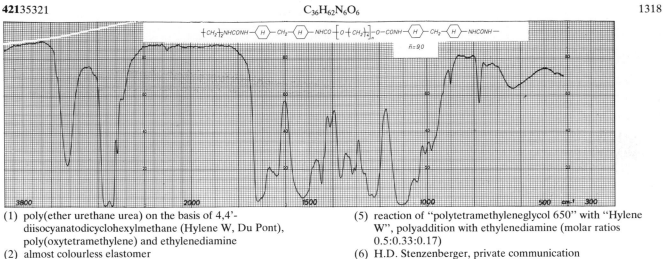

(1) poly(ether urethane urea) on the basis of 4,4'-
    diisocyanatodicyclohexylmethane (Hylene W, Du Pont),
    poly(oxytetramethylene) and ethylenediamine
(2) almost colourless elastomer
(3) H.D. Stenzenberger, Technochemie GmbH –
    Verfahrenstechnik, Dossenheim bei Heidelberg

(5) reaction of "polytetramethyleneglycol 650" with "Hylene
    W", polyaddition with ethylenediamine (molar ratios
    0.5:0.33:0.17)
(6) H.D. Stenzenberger, private communication
(7) film from CHCl₃ on KBr

42135321 $C_{36}H_{62}N_6O_6$ 1319

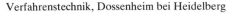

(1) poly(ether urethane urea) on the basis of 4,4'-
    diisocyanatodicyclohexylmethane (Hylene W, Du Pont),
    poly(oxytetramethylene) and ethylenediamine
(2) almost colourless elastomer
(3) H.D. Stenzenberger, Technochemie GmbH –
    Verfahrenstechnik, Dossenheim bei Heidelberg

(5) reaction of "polytetramethyleneglycol 1000" with "Hylene
    W", polyaddition with ethylenediamine (molar ratios
    0.5:0.33:0.17)
(6) H.D. Stenzenberger, private communication
(7) film from tetrahydrofuran on CsI

42135321 $C_{36}H_{62}N_6O_6$ 1320

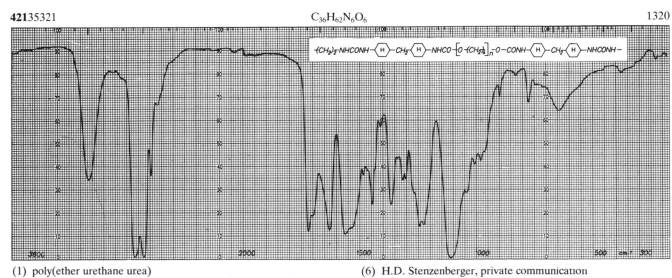

(1) poly(ether urethane urea)
(2) white material
(3) H.D. Stenzenberger, Technochemie GmbH –
    Verfahrenstechnik, Dossenheim bei Heidelberg
(5) reaction of "polytetramethyleneglycol 1000" with "Hylene
    W" (molar ratio 1.03:2), polyaddition with ethylenediamine

(6) H.D. Stenzenberger, private communication
(7) film from dimethylacetamide
(8) band at 1630 cm⁻¹ predominantly due to residual DMA

42135321 $C_{35}H_{60}N_6O_6$ 1321

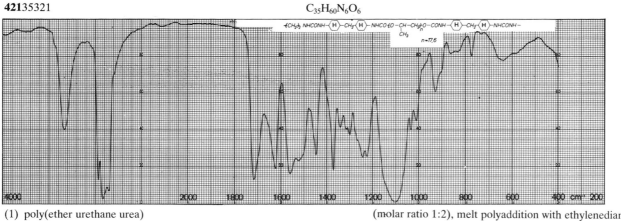

(1) poly(ether urethane urea)
(2) colourless elastomer
(3) H.D. Stenzenberger, Technochemie GmbH –
     Verfahrenstechnik, Dossenheim bei Heidelberg
(5) reaction of "polypropyleneglycol 1020" with "Hylene W"

(molar ratio 1:2), melt polyaddition with ethylenediamine
(catalyst: Sn-octoate)
(6) H.D. Stenzenberger, private communication
(7) film from dimethylacetamide (11μm)
(8) band at 1630 cm^{-1} partly due to residual DMA

42135322 $C_{23}H_{26}N_4O_6$ 1322

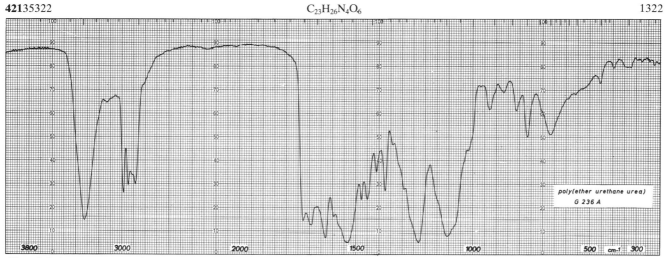

poly(ether urethane urea)
G 236 A

(1) poly(ether urethane urea)
(2) yellowish granules
(3) H.D. Stenzenberger, Technochemie GmbH –
     Verfahrenstechnik, Dossenheim bei Heidelberg
(5) reaction of "polypropyleneglycol 425" with 2,4-

toluylenediisocyanate, polyaddition with ethylenediamine
(molar ratios: 2:4:1.8)
(6) H.D. Stenzenberger, private communication
(7) film from dimethylformamide

42135322 $C_{71}H_{124}N_6O_{22}$ 1323

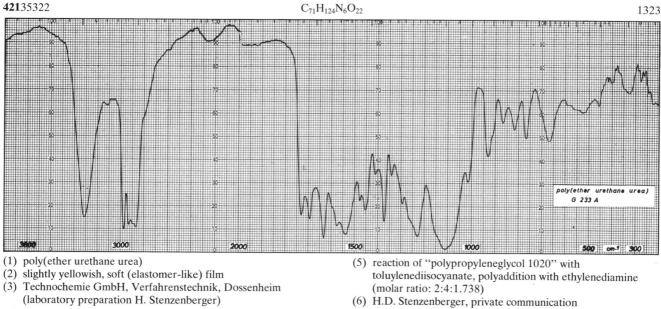

poly(ether urethane urea)
G 233 A

(1) poly(ether urethane urea)
(2) slightly yellowish, soft (elastomer-like) film
(3) Technochemie GmbH, Verfahrenstechnik, Dossenheim
     (laboratory preparation H. Stenzenberger)
(4) —CONH–Ar–NHCOO$\left(\text{CH–CH}_2\text{–O}\right)_{\overline{m}}$ CONH–Ar–NHCONH$\left(\text{CH}_2\right)_n$ NH– with Ar $\widehat{=}$

$\overline{m} = 17$ and $n = 2$

(5) reaction of "polypropyleneglycol 1020" with
toluylenediisocyanate, polyaddition with ethylenediamine
(molar ratio: 2:4:1.738)
(6) H.D. Stenzenberger, private communication
(7) film

42135322 $C_{73}H_{128}N_6O_{22}$ 1324

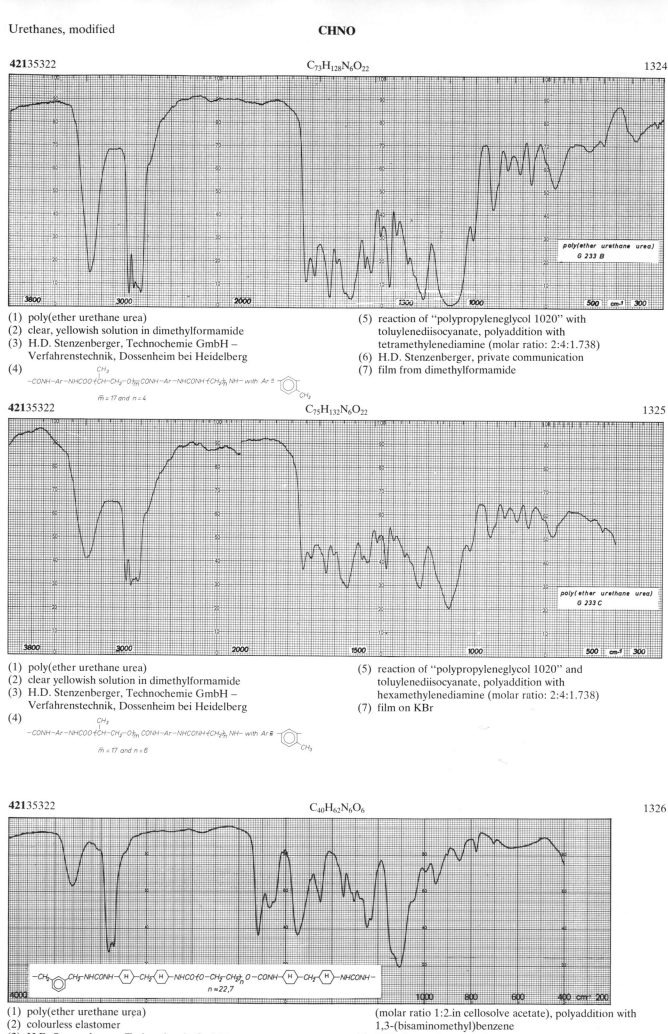

poly(ether urethane urea)
G 233 B

(1) poly(ether urethane urea)
(2) clear, yellowish solution in dimethylformamide
(3) H.D. Stenzenberger, Technochemie GmbH –
    Verfahrenstechnik, Dossenheim bei Heidelberg
(4)
    $-CONH-Ar-NHCOO\left(CH-CH_2-O\right)_{\overline{m}}CONH-Ar-NHCONH\left(CH_2\right)_{\overline{n}}NH-$ with $Ar \triangleq$ (ring) CH_3
                        CH_3
    $\overline{m} = 17$ and $n = 4$

(5) reaction of "polypropyleneglycol 1020" with
    toluylenediisocyanate, polyaddition with
    tetramethylenediamine (molar ratio: 2:4:1.738)
(6) H.D. Stenzenberger, private communication
(7) film from dimethylformamide

42135322 $C_{75}H_{132}N_6O_{22}$ 1325

poly(ether urethane urea)
G 233 C

(1) poly(ether urethane urea)
(2) clear yellowish solution in dimethylformamide
(3) H.D. Stenzenberger, Technochemie GmbH –
    Verfahrenstechnik, Dossenheim bei Heidelberg
(4)
    $-CONH-Ar-NHCOO\left(CH-CH_2-O\right)_{\overline{m}}CONH-Ar-NHCONH\left(CH_2\right)_{\overline{n}}NH-$ with $Ar \triangleq$ (ring) CH_3
                 CH_3
    $\overline{m} = 17$ and $n = 6$

(5) reaction of "polypropyleneglycol 1020" and
    toluylenediisocyanate, polyaddition with
    hexamethylenediamine (molar ratio: 2:4:1.738)
(7) film on KBr

42135322 $C_{40}H_{62}N_6O_6$ 1326

$-CH_2-$(ring)$-CH_2-NHCONH-$(H)$-CH_2-$(H)$-NHCO\left(O-CH_2-CH_2\right)_n O-CONH-(H)-CH_2-(H)-NHCONH-$
$n \approx 22,7$

(1) poly(ether urethane urea)
(2) colourless elastomer
(3) H.D. Stenzenberger, Technochemie GmbH –
    Verfahrenstechnik, Dossenheim bei Heidelberg
(5) reaction of "polyethyleneglycol 1000" with "Hylene W"

(molar ratio 1:2 in cellosolve acetate), polyaddition with
1,3-(bisaminomethyl)benzene
(6) H.D. Stenzenberger, private communication
(7) film from cellosolve acetate

42135322 $C_{40}H_{62}N_6O_6$ 1327

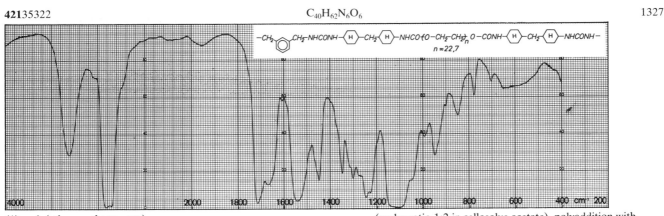

(1) poly(ether urethane urea)
(2) colourless elastomer
(3) H.D. Stenzenberger, Technochemie GmbH –
    Verfahrenstechnik, Dossenheim bei Heidelberg
(5) reaction of "polyethyleneglycol 1000" with "Hylene W"

(molar ratio 1:2 in cellosolve acetate), polyaddition with
1,3-(bisaminomethyl)benzene
(6) H.D. Stenzenberger, private communication
(7) film from cellosolve acetate (higher thickness)

42135322 $C_{42}H_{66}N_6O_6$ 1328

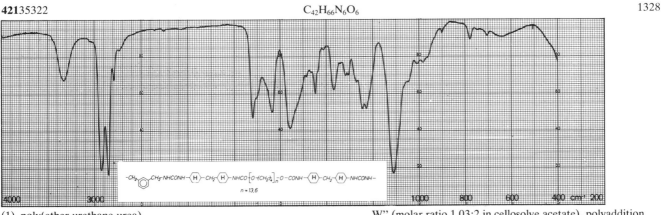

(1) poly(ether urethane urea)
(2) colourless elastomer
(3) H.D. Stenzenberger, Technochemie GmbH –
    Verfahrenstechnik, Dossenheim bei Heidelberg
(5) reaction of "polytetramethyleneglycol 1000" with "Hylene

W" (molar ratio 1.03:2 in cellosolve acetate), polyaddition
with 1,3-(bisaminomethyl)benzene
(6) H.D. Stenzenberger, private communication
(7) film from cellosolve acetate on KBr

42135322 $C_{42}H_{66}N_6O_6$ 1329

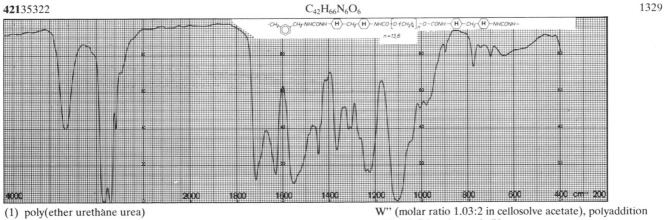

(1) poly(ether urethane urea)
(2) colourless elastomer
(3) H.D. Stenzenberger, Technochemie GmbH –
    Verfahrenstechnik, Dossenheim bei Heidelberg
(5) reaction of "polytetramethyleneglycol 1000" with "Hylene

W" (molar ratio 1.03:2 in cellosolve acetate), polyaddition
with 1,3-(bisaminomethyl)benzene
(6) H.D. Stenzenberger, private communication
(7) film from dimethylacetamide (14 μm)

42135322 $C_{41}H_{64}N_6O_6$ 1330

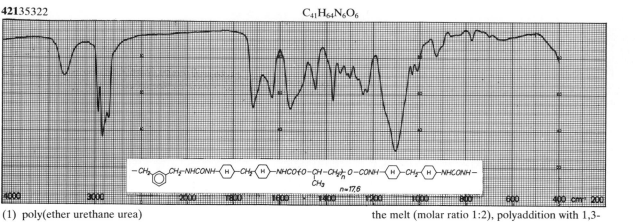

(1) poly(ether urethane urea)
(2) colourless elastomer
(3) H.D. Stenzenberger, Technochemie GmbH –
    Verfahrenstechnik, Dossenheim bei Heidelberg
(5) reaction of "polypropyleneglycol 1020" with "Hylene W" in

the melt (molar ratio 1:2), polyaddition with 1,3-
(bisaminomethyl)benzene (catalyst: Sn-octoate)
(6) H.D. Stenzenberger, private communication
(7) melting film on KBr

42135322 $C_{41}H_{64}N_6O_6$ 1331

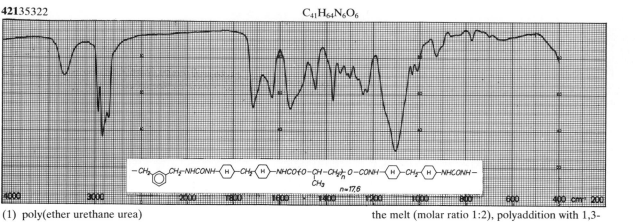

(1) poly(ether urethane urea)
(2) colourless elastomer
(3) H.D. Stenzenberger, Technochemie GmbH –
    Verfahrenstechnik, Dossenheim bei Heidelberg
(5) reaction of "polypropyleneglycol 1020" with "Hylene W" in

the melt (molar ratio 1:2), polyaddition with 1,3-
(bisaminomethyl)benzene (catalyst: Sn-octoate)
(6) H.D. Stenzenberger, private communication
(7) melting film on KBr (higher thickness)

42135322 $C_{45}H_{64}N_6O_6$ 1332

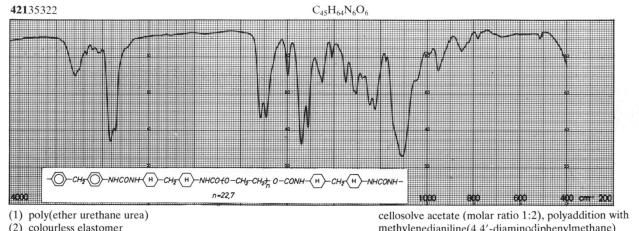

(1) poly(ether urethane urea)
(2) colourless elastomer
(3) H.D. Stenzenberger, Technochemie GmbH –
    Verfahrenstechnik, Dossenheim bei Heidelberg
(5) reaction of "polyethyleneglycol 1000" with "Hylene W" in

cellosolve acetate (molar ratio 1:2), polyaddition with
methylenedianiline(4,4'-diaminodiphenylmethane)
(6) H.D. Stenzenberger, private communication
(7) film from collosolve acetate on KBr

42135322 $C_{45}H_{64}N_6O_6$ 1333

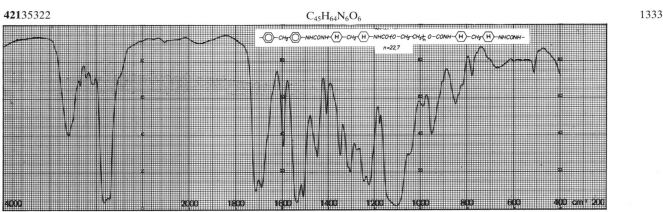

(1) poly(ether urethane urea)
(2) colourless elastomer
(3) H.D. Stenzenberger, Technochemie GmbH –
     Verfahrenstechnik, Dossenheim bei Heidelberg
(5) reaction of "polyethyleneglycol 1000" with "Hylene W" in

cellosolve acetate (molar ratio 1:2), polyaddition with
methylenedianiline(4,4'-diaminodiphenylmethane)
(6) H.D. Stenzenberger, private communication
(7) film from collosolve acetate on KBr (higher thickness)

42135322 $C_{79}H_{132}N_6O_{14}$ 1334

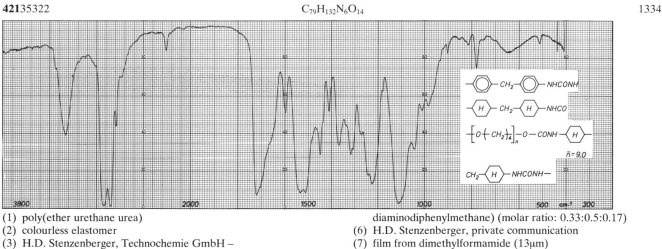

(1) poly(ether urethane urea)
(2) colourless elastomer
(3) H.D. Stenzenberger, Technochemie GmbH –
     Verfahrenstechnik, Dossenheim bei Heidelberg
(5) reaction of "polytetramethyleneglycol 650" with "Hylene W"
     in the melt, polyaddition with methylenedianiline (4,4-

diaminodiphenylmethane) (molar ratio: 0.33:0.5:0.17)
(6) H.D. Stenzenberger, private communication
(7) film from dimethylformamide (13μm)
(8) read the structure from top

42135322 $C_{47}H_{68}N_6O_6$ 1335

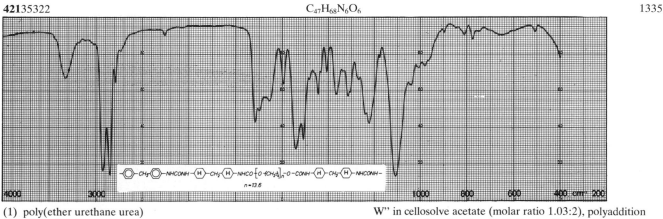

(1) poly(ether urethane urea)
(2) white elastomer
(3) H.D. Stenzenberger, Technochemie GmbH –
     Verfahrenstechnik, Dossenheim bei Heidelberg
(5) reaction of "polytetramethyleneglycol 1000" with "Hylene

W" in cellosolve acetate (molar ratio 1.03:2), polyaddition
with methylenedianiline (4,4'-diaminodiphenylmethane)
(6) H.D. Stenzenberger, private communication
(7) film from cellosolve acetate

42135322 $C_{47}H_{68}N_6O_6$ 1336

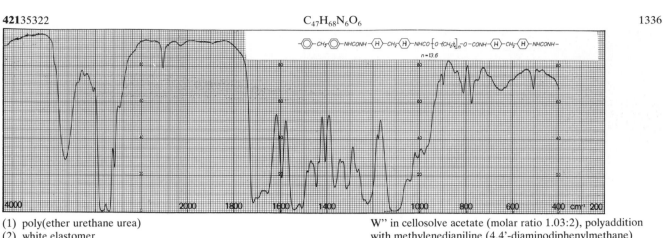

(1) poly(ether urethane urea)
(2) white elastomer
(3) H.D. Stenzenberger, Technochemie GmbH –
      Verfahrenstechnik, Dossenheim bei Heidelberg
(5) reaction of "polytetramethyleneglycol 1000" with "Hylene

W" in cellosolve acetate (molar ratio 1.03:2), polyaddition
with methylenedianiline (4,4'-diaminodiphenylmethane)
(6) H.D. Stenzenberger, private communication
(7) film from cellosolve acetate (higher thickness)

42135322 $C_{46}H_{66}N_6O_6$ 1337

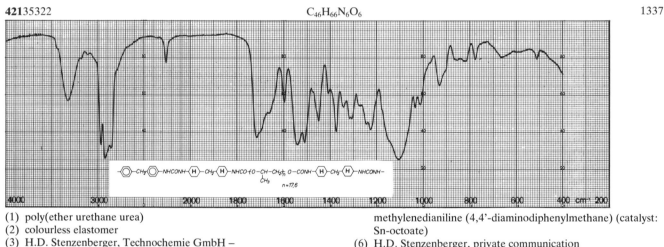

(1) poly(ether urethane urea)
(2) colourless elastomer
(3) H.D. Stenzenberger, Technochemie GmbH –
      Verfahrenstechnik, Dossenheim bei Heidelberg
(5) reaction of "polypropyleneglycol 1020" with "Hylene W" in
      the melt (molar ratio 1:2) polyaddition with

methylenedianiline (4,4'-diaminodiphenylmethane) (catalyst:
Sn-octoate)
(6) H.D. Stenzenberger, private communication
(7) melting film on KBr

42135322 $C_{46}H_{66}N_6O_6$ 1338

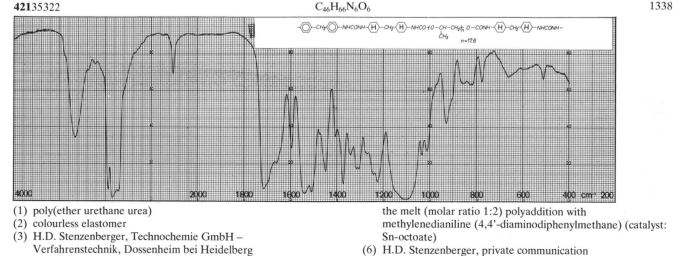

(1) poly(ether urethane urea)
(2) colourless elastomer
(3) H.D. Stenzenberger, Technochemie GmbH –
      Verfahrenstechnik, Dossenheim bei Heidelberg
(5) reaction of "polypropyleneglycol 1020" with "Hylene W" in

the melt (molar ratio 1:2) polyaddition with
methylenedianiline (4,4'-diaminodiphenylmethane) (catalyst:
Sn-octoate)
(6) H.D. Stenzenberger, private communication
(7) melting film on KBr (thicker film)

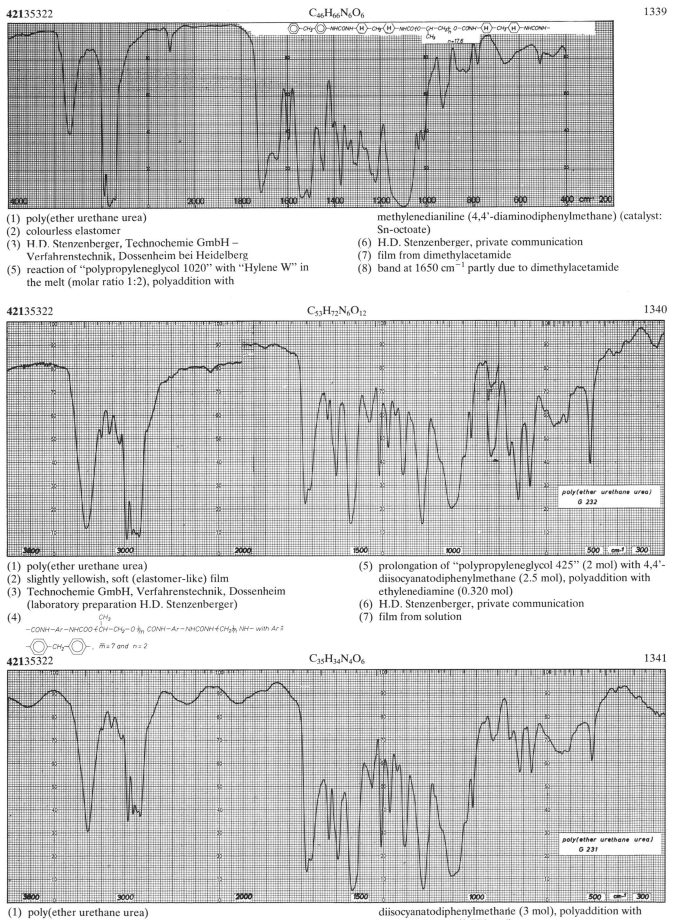

42135322 $C_{46}H_{66}N_6O_6$ 1339

(1) poly(ether urethane urea)
(2) colourless elastomer
(3) H.D. Stenzenberger, Technochemie GmbH –
Verfahrenstechnik, Dossenheim bei Heidelberg
(5) reaction of "polypropyleneglycol 1020" with "Hylene W" in
the melt (molar ratio 1:2), polyaddition with

methylenedianiline (4,4'-diaminodiphenylmethane) (catalyst:
Sn-octoate)
(6) H.D. Stenzenberger, private communication
(7) film from dimethylacetamide
(8) band at 1650 cm^{-1} partly due to dimethylacetamide

42135322 $C_{53}H_{72}N_6O_{12}$ 1340

(1) poly(ether urethane urea)
(2) slightly yellowish, soft (elastomer-like) film
(3) Technochemie GmbH, Verfahrenstechnik, Dossenheim
(laboratory preparation H.D. Stenzenberger)
(4)

$-CONH-Ar-NHCOO(CH-CH_2-O)_{\overline{m}}\ CONH-Ar-NHCONH(CH_2)_{\overline{n}}\ NH-$ with $Ar =$
with CH_3 on the CH. $-\bigcirc-CH_2-\bigcirc-$, $\overline{m} = 7$ and $n = 2$

(5) prolongation of "polypropyleneglycol 425" (2 mol) with 4,4'-
diisocyanatodiphenylmethane (2.5 mol), polyaddition with
ethylenediamine (0.320 mol)
(6) H.D. Stenzenberger, private communication
(7) film from solution

42135322 $C_{35}H_{34}N_4O_6$ 1341

(1) poly(ether urethane urea)
(2) slightly yellowish elastomer
(3) H.D. Stenzenberger, Technochemie GmbH –
Verfahrenstechnik, Dossenheim bei Heidelberg
(5) reaction of "polypropyleneglycol 425" (2 mol) with 4,4'-

diisocyanatodiphenylmethane (3 mol), polyaddition with
ethylenediamine (0.778 mol)
(6) H.D. Stenzenberger, private communication
(7) film from dimethylformamide (20 μm)

42135322   C$_{35}$H$_{34}$N$_4$O$_6$ 1342

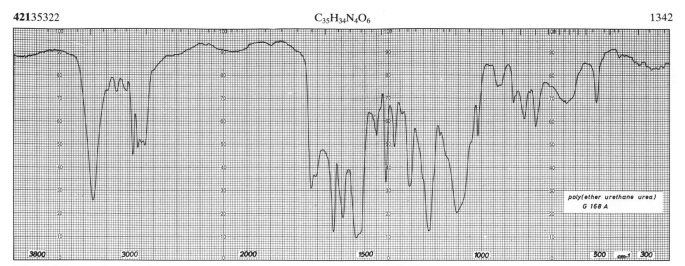

poly(ether urethane urea)
G 168 A

(1) poly(ether urethane urea)
(2) clear, yellowish solution in dimethylacetamide
(3) H.D. Stenzenberger, Technochemie GmbH –
Verfahrenstechnik, Dossenheim bei Heidelberg
(5) reaction of "polypropyleneglycol 425" (2 mol) with

4,4'-diisocyanatodiphenylmethane (4 mol), polyaddition with
ethylenediamine (1,793 mol)
(6) H.D. Stenzenberger, private communication
(7) film

42135322   C$_{35}$H$_{34}$N$_4$O$_6$ 1343

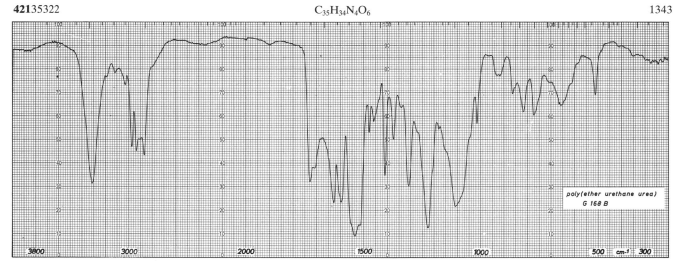

poly(ether urethane urea)
G 168 B

(1) poly(ether urethane urea)
(2) clear, yellowish solution in dimethylacetamide
(3) H.D. Stenzenberger, Technochemie GmbH –
Verfahrenstechnik, Dossenheim bei Heidelberg
(5) reaction of "polypropyleneglycol 425" (2 mol) with 4,4'-

diisocyanatodiphenylmethane (4 mol), polyaddition with
tetramethylenediamine (1.793 mol)
(6) H.D. Stenzenberger, private communication
(7) film

42135322   C$_{57}$H$_{80}$N$_6$O$_{12}$ 1344

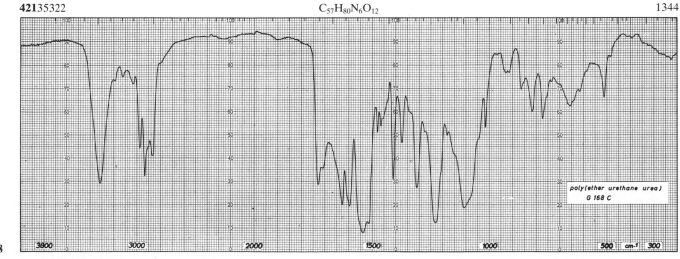

poly(ether urethane urea)
G 168 C

(1) poly(ether urethane urea)
(2) slightly yellowish, soft (elastomer-like) film
(3) Technochemie GmbH, Verfahrenstechnik, Dossenheim
(4)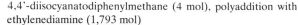
$-CONH-Ar-NHCOO\{CH-CH_2-O\}_{\overline{m}}CONH-Ar-NHCONH\{CH_2\}_{\overline{n}}NH-$ with Ar ≙

—⟨O⟩—CH$_2$—⟨O⟩— , $\overline{m}$ = 7 and n = 6

(5) prolongation of polypropyleneglycol 425 (2 mol) with 4,4'-
diisocyanatodiphenylmethane (4 mol), polyaddition with
hexamethylenediamine (1.739 mol)
(6) H.D. Stenzenberger, private communication
(7) film from solution

42135322 $C_{35}H_{34}N_4O_6$ 1345

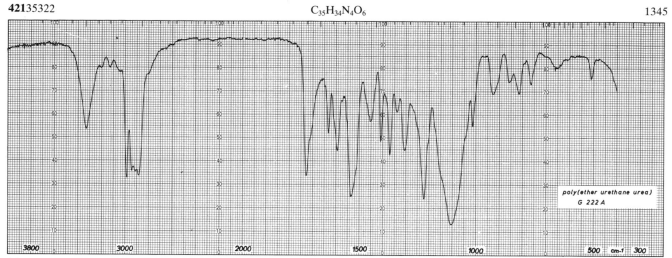

(1) poly(ether urethane urea)
(2) clear, yellowish solution in dimethylformamide
(3) H.D. Stenzenberger, Technochemic GmbII – Verfahrenstechnik, Dossenheim bci Heidelberg
(5) reaction of "polypropyleneglycol 1025" (2 mol) with 4,4'- diisocyanatodiphenylmethane (3 mol), polyaddition with ethylenediamine (0.7027 mol)
(6) H.D. Stenzenberger, private communication
(7) film in KBr

42135322 $C_{35}H_{34}N_4O_6$ 1346

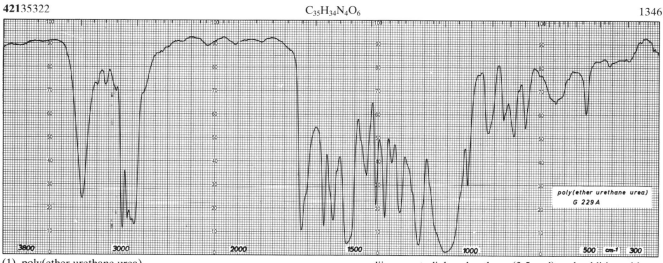

(1) poly(ether urethane urea)
(2) yellowish solution in dimethylformamide
(3) H.D. Stenzenberger, Technochemie GmbH – Verfahrenstechnik, Dossenheim bei Heidelberg
(5) reaction of "polypropyleneglycol 1025" (2 mol) with 4,4'- diisocyanatodiphenylmethane (3.5 mol), polyaddition with ethylenediamine (1.0736 mol)
(6) H.D. Stenzenberger, private communication
(7) film from dimethylformamide

42135322 $C_{41}H_{63}N_6O_{12}$ 1347

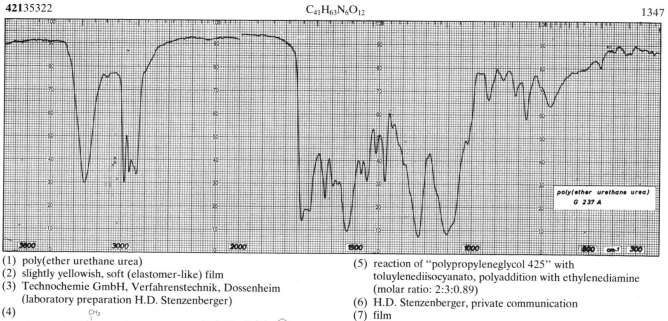

(1) poly(ether urethane urea)
(2) slightly yellowish, soft (elastomer-like) film
(3) Technochemie GmbH, Verfahrenstechnik, Dossenheim (laboratory preparation H.D. Stenzenberger)
(4) $-CONH-Ar-NHCOO+CH-CH_2-O+_m CONH-Ar-NHCONH+CH_2+_n NH-$ with Ar ≘
m = 7 and n = 2
(5) reaction of "polypropyleneglycol 425" with toluylenediisocyanato, polyaddition with ethylenediamine (molar ratio: 2:3:0.89)
(6) H.D. Stenzenberger, private communication
(7) film

449

42135322 $C_{83}H_{132}N_6O_{22}$ 1348

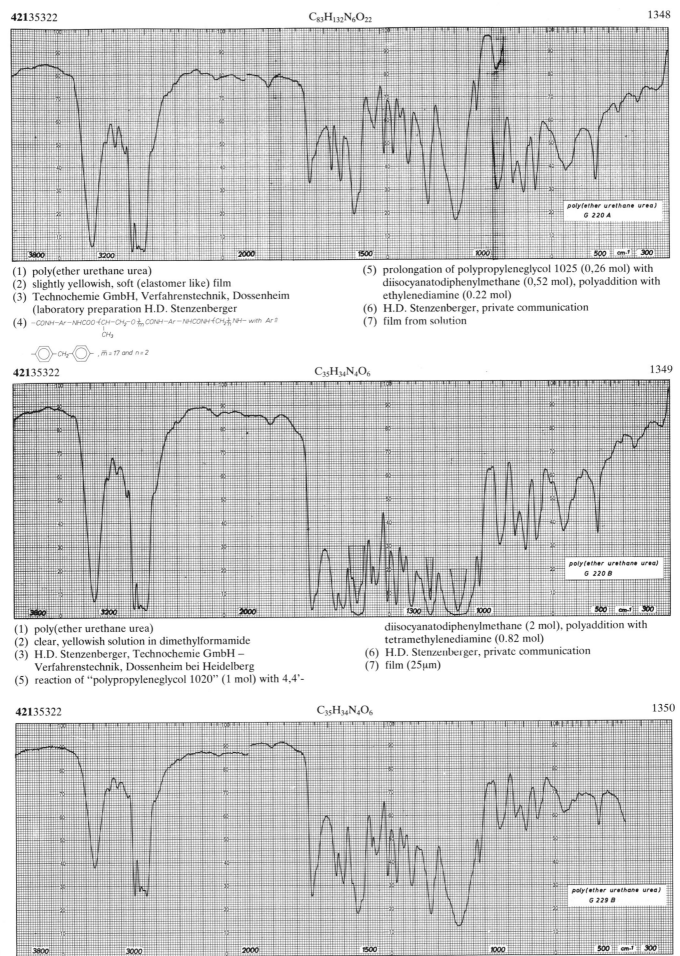

poly(ether urethane urea)
G 220 A

(1) poly(ether urethane urea)
(2) slightly yellowish, soft (elastomer like) film
(3) Technochemie GmbH, Verfahrenstechnik, Dossenheim
(laboratory preparation H.D. Stenzenberger

(4) $-CONH-Ar-NHCOO+CH-CH_2-O\frac{1}{m}CONH-Ar-NHCONH+CH_2\frac{1}{n}NH-$ with Ar =
    CH_3

    -⬡-CH_2-⬡- , $\overline{m} = 17$ and $n = 2$

(5) prolongation of polypropyleneglycol 1025 (0,26 mol) with
diisocyanatodiphenylmethane (0,52 mol), polyaddition with
ethylenediamine (0.22 mol)
(6) H.D. Stenzenberger, private communication
(7) film from solution

42135322 $C_{35}H_{34}N_4O_6$ 1349

poly(ether urethane urea)
G 220 B

(1) poly(ether urethane urea)
(2) clear, yellowish solution in dimethylformamide
(3) H.D. Stenzenberger, Technochemie GmbH –
Verfahrenstechnik, Dossenheim bei Heidelberg
(5) reaction of "polypropyleneglycol 1020" (1 mol) with 4,4'-

diisocyanatodiphenylmethane (2 mol), polyaddition with
tetramethylenediamine (0.82 mol)
(6) H.D. Stenzenberger, private communication
(7) film (25μm)

42135322 $C_{35}H_{34}N_4O_6$ 1350

poly(ether urethane urea)
G 229 B

(1) poly(ether urethane urea)
(2) clear yellowish solution in dimethylformamide
(3) H.D. Stenzenberger, Technochemie GmbH –
Verfahrenstechnik, Dossenheim bei Heidelberg
(5) reaction of "polypropyleneglycol 1025" (2 mol) with 4,4'-

diisocyanatodiphenylmethane (3.5 mol), polyaddition with
tetramethylenediamine (1.0736 mol)
(6) H.D. Stenzenberger, private communication
(7) film on KBr

42135322   C$_{35}$H$_{34}$N$_4$O$_6$ 1351

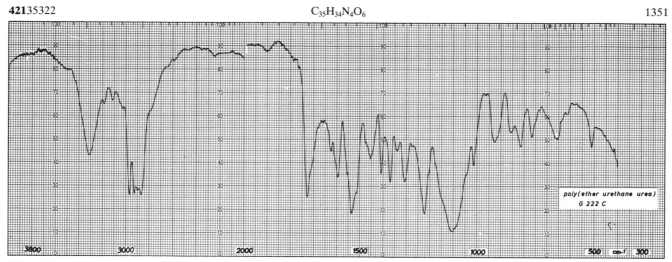

poly(ether urethane urea)
G 222 C

(1) poly(ether urethane urea)
(2) clear yellowish solution in dimethylformamide
(3) H.D. Stenzenberger, Technochemie GmbH –
Verfahrenstechnik, Dossenheim bei Heidelberg
(5) reaction of "polypropyleneglycol 1025" (2 mol) with 4,4'-

diisocyanatodiphenylmethane (3 mol), polyaddition with
hexamethylenediamine (0.7027 mol)
(6) H.D. Stenzenberger, private communication
(7) film on KBr

42135322   C$_{37}$H$_{40}$N$_6$O$_6$ 1352

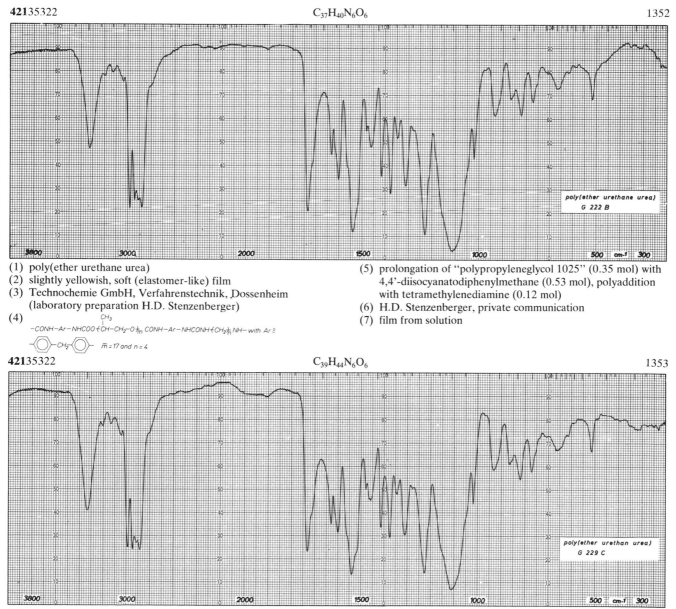

poly(ether urethane urea)
G 222 B

(1) poly(ether urethane urea)
(2) slightly yellowish, soft (elastomer-like) film
(3) Technochemie GmbH, Verfahrenstechnik, Dossenheim
(laboratory preparation H.D. Stenzenberger)
(4)

$$-CONH-Ar-NHCOO \{CH-CH_2-O\}_{\overline{m}} \underset{CH_3}{} CONH-Ar-NHCONH \{CH_2\}_{\overline{n}} NH- \text{ with } Ar \; \vdots$$

$-\langle\!\!\bigcirc\!\!\rangle\!-CH_2\!-\!\langle\!\!\bigcirc\!\!\rangle-$ $\overline{m} = 17$ and $n = 4$

(5) prolongation of "polypropyleneglycol 1025" (0.35 mol) with
4,4'-diisocyanatodiphenylmethane (0.53 mol), polyaddition
with tetramethylenediamine (0.12 mol)
(6) H.D. Stenzenberger, private communication
(7) film from solution

42135322   C$_{39}$H$_{44}$N$_6$O$_6$ 1353

poly(ether urethan urea)
G 229 C

(1) poly(ether urethane urea)
(2) clear, yellowish solution in dimethylformamide
(3) H.D. Stenzenberger, Technochemie GmbH –
Verfahrenstechnik, Dossenheim bei Heidelberg
(5) reaction of "polypropyleneglycol 1025" (2 mol) with 4,4'-

diisocyanatodiphenylmethane (3.5 mol), polyaddition with
hexamethylene diamine (1.0736 mol)
(6) H.D. Stenzenberger, private communication
(7) film

42135322   C$_{39}$H$_{44}$N$_6$O$_6$ 1354

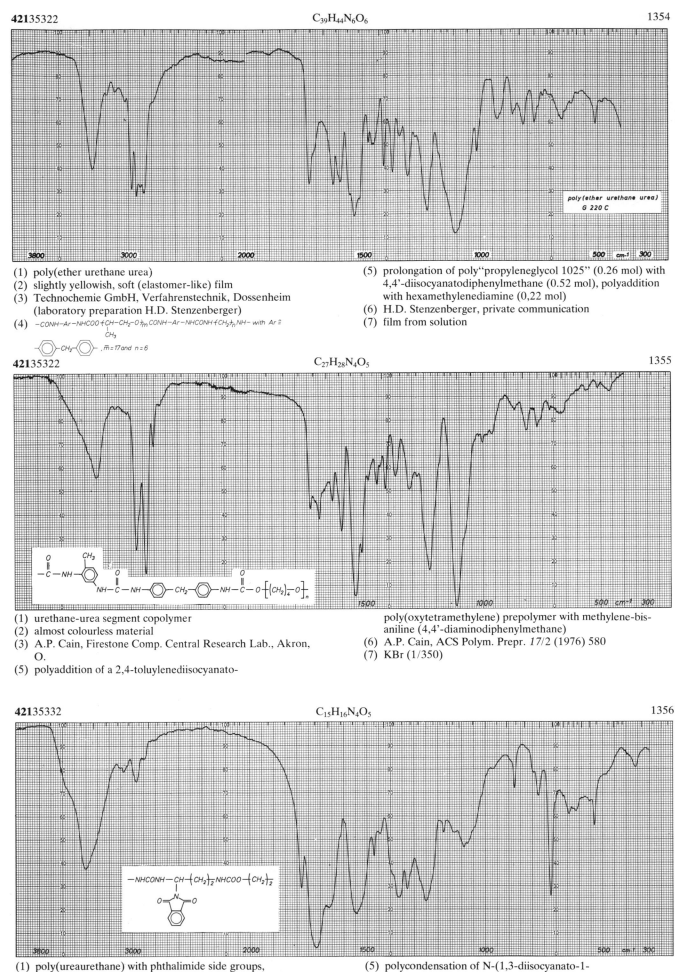

(1) poly(ether urethane urea)
(2) slightly yellowish, soft (elastomer-like) film
(3) Technochemie GmbH, Verfahrenstechnik, Dossenheim
(laboratory preparation H.D. Stenzenberger)
(4) $-$CONH$-$Ar$-$NHCOO$\{$CH$-$CH$_2-$O$\}_{\overline{m}}$CONH$-$Ar$-$NHCONH$\{$CH$_2\}_n$NH$-$ with Ar $\cong$
    $|$
    CH$_3$
$\bigcirc-$CH$_2-\bigcirc-$, $\overline{m}=17$ and $n=6$

(5) prolongation of poly"propyleneglycol 1025" (0.26 mol) with
4,4'-diisocyanatodiphenylmethane (0.52 mol), polyaddition
with hexamethylenediamine (0,22 mol)
(6) H.D. Stenzenberger, private communication
(7) film from solution

42135322   C$_{27}$H$_{28}$N$_4$O$_5$ 1355

(1) urethane-urea segment copolymer
(2) almost colourless material
(3) A.P. Cain, Firestone Comp. Central Research Lab., Akron,
O.
(5) polyaddition of a 2,4-toluylenediisocyanato-

poly(oxytetramethylene) prepolymer with methylene-bis-
aniline (4,4'-diaminodiphenylmethane)
(6) A.P. Cain, ACS Polym. Prepr. *17*/2 (1976) 580
(7) KBr (1/350)

42135332   C$_{15}$H$_{16}$N$_4$O$_5$ 1356

(1) poly(ureaurethane) with phthalimide side groups,
poly[oxycarbonylimino-(3-phthalimidotrimethylene)ureyle-
neethylene]
(2) yellowish powder
(3) C.-P. Yang, Department of Chemical Engineering, Tatung
Institute of Technology, Taipei, Taiwan

(5) polycondensation of N-(1,3-diisocyanato-1-
propyl)phthalimide with ethanolamine in dimethylsulfoxide in
the presence of Sn-catalyst
(6) C.-P. Yang, Y. Iwakura, K. Uno, F. Toda, Makromol. Chem.
177 (1976) 3495...514
(7) KBr (1.5/350)

421361   C$_3$H$_7$NO$_2$ 1357

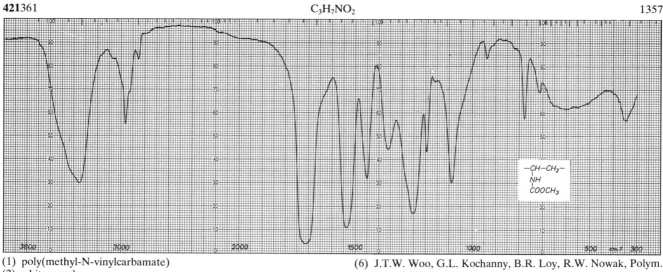

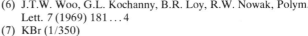

(1) poly(methyl-N-vinylcarbamate)
(2) white powder
(3) J.T.K. Woo, Dow Chemical Comp., Midland, Mich.
(5) γ-radiation-induced solid-state polymerization of methyl-N-vinyl-carbamate

(6) J.T.W. Woo, G.L. Kochanny, B.R. Loy, R.W. Nowak, Polym. Lett. 7 (1969) 181...4
(7) KBr (1/350)

421362   C$_{20}$H$_{16}$N$_2$O$_4$ 1358

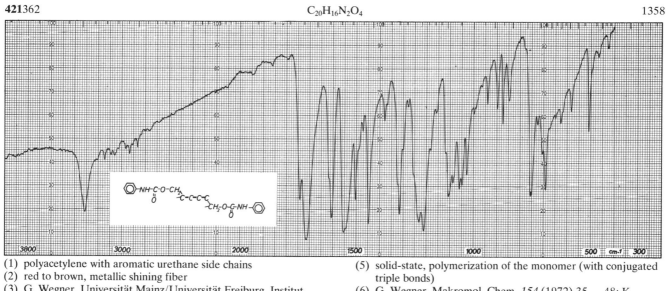

(1) polyacetylene with aromatic urethane side chains
(2) red to brown, metallic shining fiber
(3) G. Wegner, Universität Mainz/Universität Freiburg, Institut für Makromolekulare Chemie
(4) crystalline

(5) solid-state, polymerization of the monomer (with conjugated triple bonds)
(6) G. Wegner, Makromol. Chem. 154 (1972) 35...48; K. Takeda, G. Wegner, Makromol. Chem. 160 (1972) 349...53
(7) KBr (2/400)

421362   C$_{21}$H$_{18}$N$_2$O$_4$ 1359

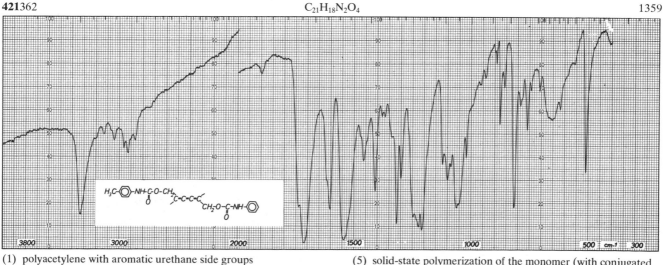

(1) polyacetylene with aromatic urethane side groups
(2) gold-brown, metallic shining fibers
(3) G. Wegner, Universität Mainz/Universität Freiburg, Institut für Makromolekulare Chemie
(4) crystalline

(5) solid-state polymerization of the monomer (with conjugated triple bonds)
(6) G. Wegner, Makromol. Chem. 154 (1972) 35...48; K. Takeda, G. Wegner, Makromol. Chem. 160 (1972) 349...53
(7) KBr (2/400)

421411 $C_7H_{14}N_2O$ 1360

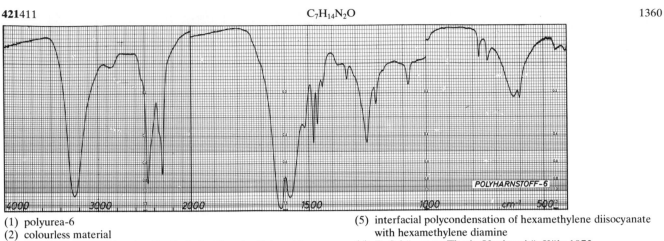

(1) polyurea-6
(2) colourless material
(3) R. Schürmann, Institut für Physikalische Chemie, Universität Köln
(4) -NH-CO-NH-$(CH_2)_6$-

(5) interfacial polycondensation of hexamethylene diisocyanate with hexamethylene diamine
(6) R. Schürmann, Thesis, Unviversität Köln 1973
(7) film

421411 $C_{10}H_{20}N_4O_2$ 1361

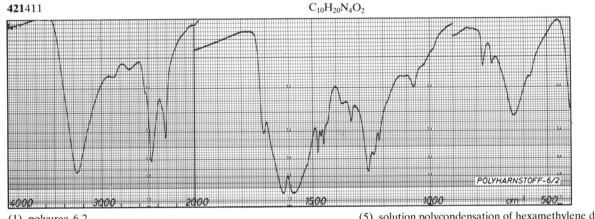

(1) polyurea-6,2
(2) colourless material
(3) R. Schürmann, Institut für Physikalische Chemie, Universität Köln
(4) -NHCONH-$(CH_2)_6$-NHCONH-$(CH_2)_2$-

(5) solution polycondensation of hexamethylene diisocyanate with ethylene diamine
(6) R. Schürmann, Thesis, Universität Köln 1973
(7) film from HCOOH solution

421411 $C_{12}H_{24}N_4O_2$ 1362

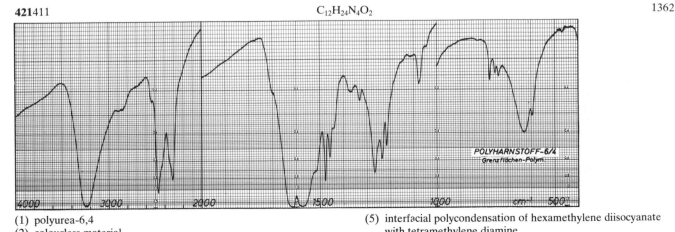

(1) polyurea-6,4
(2) colourless material
(3) R. Schürmann, Institut für Physikalische Chemie, Universität Köln
(4) -NHCONH-$(CH_2)_6$-NHCONH-$(CH_2)_4$-

(5) interfacial polycondensation of hexamethylene diisocyanate with tetramethylene diamine
(6) R. Schürmann, Thesis, Universität Köln 1973
(7) film

421411 $C_{12}H_{24}N_4O_2$ 1363

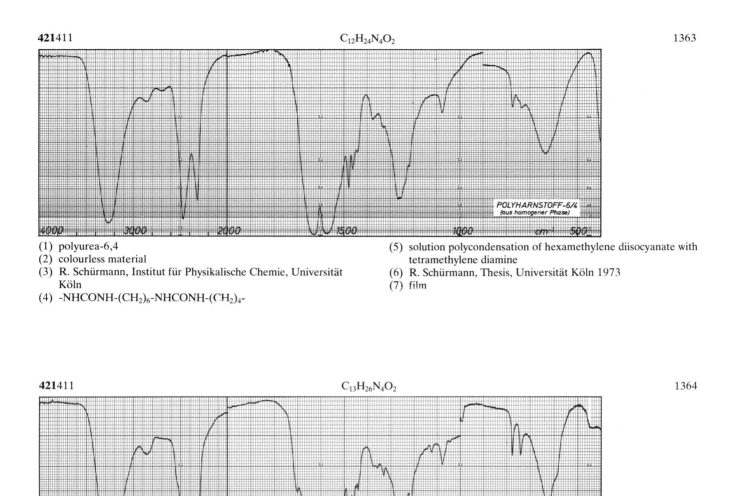

POLYHARNSTOFF-6/4
(aus homogener Phase)

(1) polyurea-6,4
(2) colourless material
(3) R. Schürmann, Institut für Physikalische Chemie, Universität Köln
(4) -NHCONH-(CH$_2$)$_6$-NHCONH-(CH$_2$)$_4$-
(5) solution polycondensation of hexamethylene diisocyanate with tetramethylene diamine
(6) R. Schürmann, Thesis, Universität Köln 1973
(7) film

421411 $C_{13}H_{26}N_4O_2$ 1364

POLYHARNSTOFF-6/5

(1) polyurea-6,5
(2) colourless material
(3) R. Schürmann, Institut für Physikalische Chemie, Universität Köln
(4) -NHCONH-(CH$_2$)$_6$-NHCONH-(CH$_2$)$_5$-
(5) interfacial polycondensation of hexamethylene diisocyanate with pentamethylene diamine
(6) R. Schürmann, Thesis, Universität Köln 1973
(7) film

421412 $C_8H_{16}N_2O$ 1365

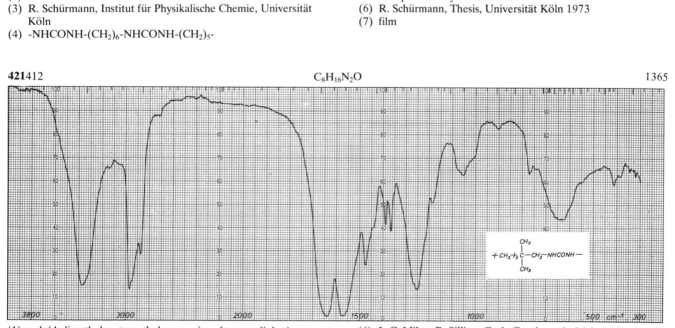

(1) poly(4-dimethylpentamethyleneurea); polyurea, aliphatic
(2) white material
(3) J.-C. Mileo, Department de Recherche de l'Institut Français de Pétrol, Centre d'Etudes Nucléaires de Grenoble, Grenoble
(5) polycondensation of 1,5-diamino-2-dimethyl-pentamethylene with urea
(6) J.-C. Mileo, B. Sillion, G. de Gaudemaris, Makromol. Chem. *127* (1969) 296...300
(7) ground with KBr (1.2/350) and dimethylacetamide, dried and pressed

421412–421411 $C_{15}H_{30}N_4O_2$ 1366

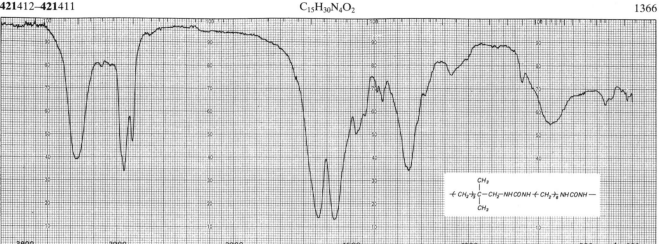

(1) poly(ureylenehexamethyleneureylene-2-dimethyl-penta-
    methylene); copolyurea, aliphatic
(2) ivory-coloured powder
(3) J.-C. Mileo, Department de Recherche de l'Institut Français
    de Pétrol, Centre d'Etudes Nucléaires de Grenoble, Grenoble
(5) polycondensation of 1,5-diamino-2-dimethylpentamethylene
    with hexamethylenediisocyanate

(6) J.-C. Mileo, B. Sillion, G. de Gaudemaris, Makromol. Chem.
    127 (1969) 296…300
(7) ground with KBr (2/350) and dimethylacetamide, dried and
    pressed

1367

421412–42143 $C_{22}H_{28}N_4O_2$

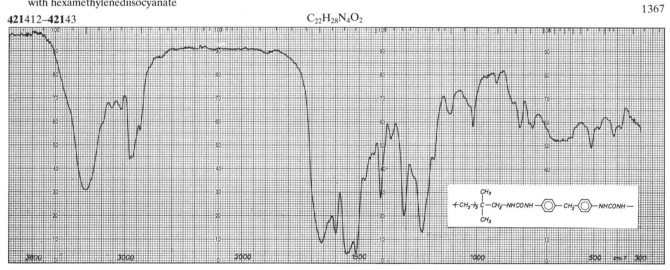

(1) poly(ureylene-2-dimethylpentamethyleneureylene-1,4-
    phenylenemethylene-1,4-phenylene); copolyurea, aliphatic-
    aromatic
(2) ivory coloured material
(3) J.-C. Mileo, Department de Recherche de l'Institut Français
    de Pétrol, Centre d'Etudes Nucléaires de Grenoble, Grenoble

(5) polycondensation of 1,5-diamino-2-dimethylpentamethylene
    with 4,4'-diisocyanatodiphenylmethane
(6) J.-C. Mileo, B. Sillion, G. de Gaudemaris, Makromol. Chem.
    127 (1969) 296…300
(7) ground with KBr (1/350) and dimethylacetamide, dried and
    pressed

421412–42144 $C_{16}H_{25}N_4O_2$ 1368

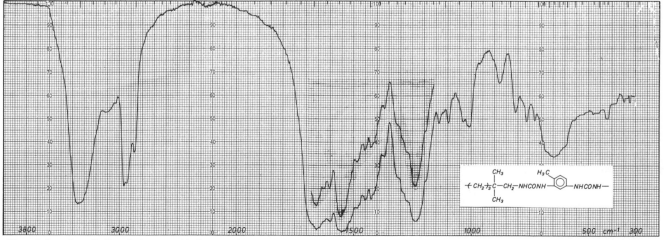

(1) poly(ureylene-2-dimethylpentamethyleneureylene-1,3-
    toluylene); copolyurea, aliphatic-aromatic
(2) white to yellowish material
(3) J.-C. Mileo, Department de Recherche de l'Institut Français
    de Pétrol, Centre d'Etudes Nucléaires de Grenoble, Grenoble

(5) polycondensation of 1,5-diamino-2-dimethylpentamethylene
    with 1,3-toluylenediisocyanate
(6) J.-C. Mileo, B. Sillion, G. De Gaudemaris, Makromol. Chem.
    127 (1969) 296…300
(7) KBr (2/300)

421412–**42144**   C$_{23}$H$_{30}$N$_4$O$_2$ 1369

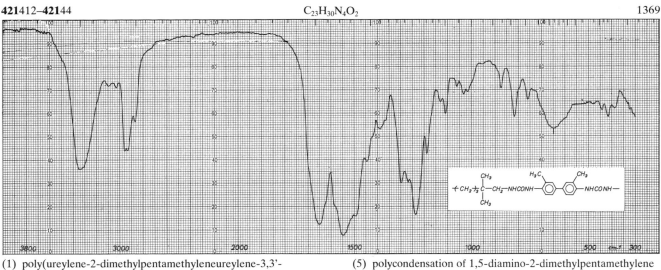

(1) poly(ureylene-2-dimethylpentamethyleneureylene-3,3'-
    dimethyl-1,4-diphenylene); copolyurea, aliphatic-aromatic
(2) ivory-coloured material
(3) J.-C. Mileo, Department de Recherche de l'Institut Français
    de Pétrol, Centre d'Etudes Nucléaires de Grenoble, Grenoble

(5) polycondensation of 1,5-diamino-2-dimethylpentamethylene
    with 4,4'-diisocyanato-3,3'-dimethyl-diphenyl
(6) J.-C. Mileo, B. Sillion, G. de Gaudemaris, Makromol. Chem.
    127 (1969) 296...300
(7) KBr (1/350)

421412–**42144**   C$_{19}$H$_{24}$N$_4$O$_2$ 1370

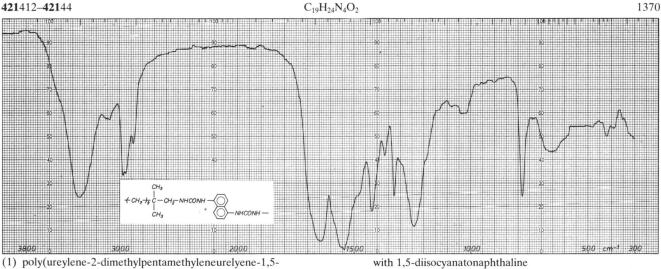

(1) poly(ureylene-2-dimethylpentamethyleneurelyene-1,5-
    naphthylene); copolyurea, aliphatic-aromatic
(2) white to yellowish material
(3) J.-C. Mileo, Department de Recherche de l'Institut Français
    de Pétrol, Centre d'Etudes Nucléaires de Grenoble, Grenoble
(5) polycondensation of 1,5-diamino-2-dimethylpentamethylene

with 1,5-diisocyanatonaphthaline
(6) J.-C. Mileo, B. Sillion, G. de Gaudemaris, Makromol. Chem.
    127 (1969) 296...300
(7) ground with KBr (1/350) and dimethylacetamide, dried and
    pressed

421412–**421452**   C$_{21}$H$_{26}$N$_4$O$_3$ 1371

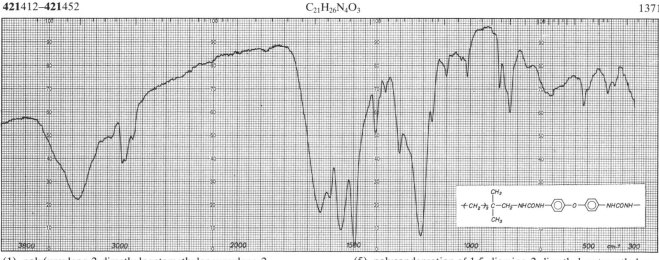

(1) poly(ureylene-2-dimethylpentamethyleneureylene-2-
    dimethylpentamethyleneurelyene-1,4-phenyleneoxy-1,4-
    phenylene); copolyurea-ether, aliphatic-aromatic
(2) white powder
(3) J.-C. Mileo, Department de Recherche de l'Institut Français
    de Pétrol, Centre d'Etudes Nucléaires de Grenoble, Grenoble

(5) polycondensation of 1,5-diamino-2-dimethylpentamethylene
    with 4,4'-diisocyanatodiphenylether
(6) J.-C. Mileo, B. Sillion, G. de Gaudemaris, Makromol. Chem.
    127 (1969) 296...300
(7) KBr (1/350)

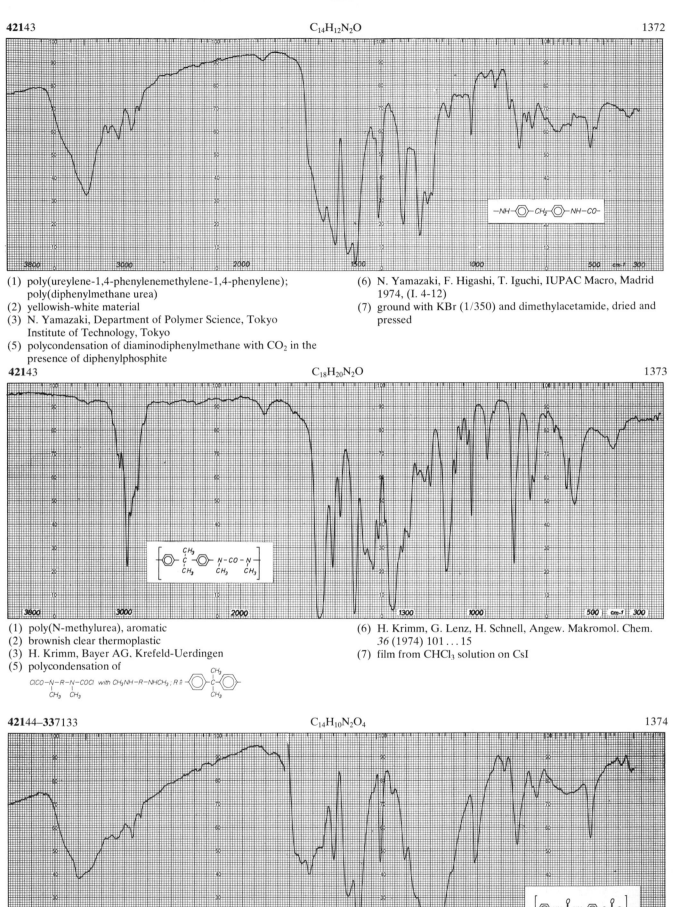

42143   C$_{14}$H$_{12}$N$_2$O   1372

(1) poly(ureylene-1,4-phenylenemethylene-1,4-phenylene); poly(diphenylmethane urea)
(2) yellowish-white material
(3) N. Yamazaki, Department of Polymer Science, Tokyo Institute of Technology, Tokyo
(5) polycondensation of diaminodiphenylmethane with CO$_2$ in the presence of diphenylphosphite
(6) N. Yamazaki, F. Higashi, T. Iguchi, IUPAC Macro, Madrid 1974, (I. 4-12)
(7) ground with KBr (1/350) and dimethylacetamide, dried and pressed

42143   C$_{18}$H$_{20}$N$_2$O   1373

(1) poly(N-methylurea), aromatic
(2) brownish clear thermoplastic
(3) H. Krimm, Bayer AG, Krefeld-Uerdingen
(5) polycondensation of

ClCO—N—R—N—COCl with CH$_3$NH—R—NHCH$_3$; R ≙
(with CH$_3$ groups)

(6) H. Krimm, G. Lenz, H. Schnell, Angew. Makromol. Chem. *36* (1974) 101…15
(7) film from CHCl$_3$ solution on CsI

42144–337133   C$_{14}$H$_{10}$N$_2$O$_4$ 1374

(1) poly(carbonate urea), aromatic
(2) red-brown material
(3) C. Giori, IIT Research Institute, Chicago, Ill.
(5) polycondensation of p-aminophenol with phosgene
(6) C. Giori, Polym. Prepr. *11* (1970) 326…31
(7) KBr (1/350)

421452 $C_{28}H_{24}N_2O_3$ 1375

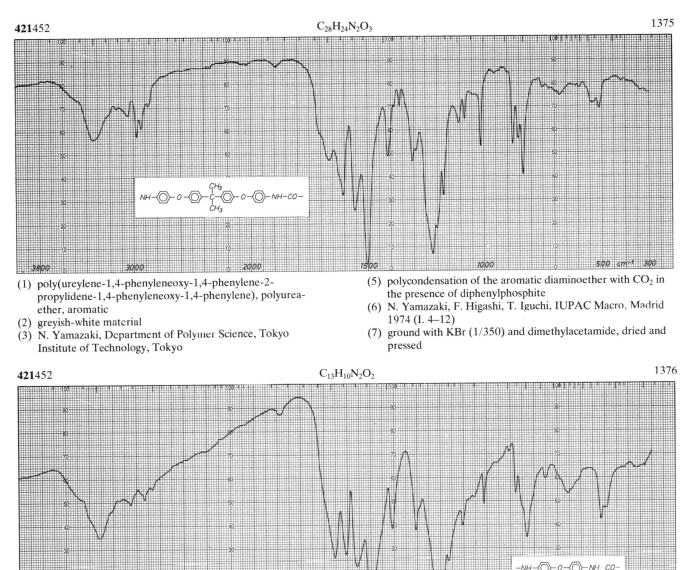

(1) poly(ureylene-1,4-phenyleneoxy-1,4-phenylene-2-propylidene-1,4-phenyleneoxy-1,4-phenylene), polyurea-ether, aromatic
(2) greyish-white material
(3) N. Yamazaki, Department of Polymer Science, Tokyo Institute of Technology, Tokyo
(5) polycondensation of the aromatic diaminoether with CO_2 in the presence of diphenylphosphite
(6) N. Yamazaki, F. Higashi, T. Iguchi, IUPAC Macro, Madrid 1974 (I. 4–12)
(7) ground with KBr (1/350) and dimethylacetamide, dried and pressed

421452 $C_{13}H_{10}N_2O_2$ 1376

(1) poly(ureylene-1,4-phenyleneoxy-1,4-phenylene); polyurea-ether, aromatic
(2) sand-coloured powder
(3) N. Yamazaki, Department of Polymer Science, Tokyo Institute of Technology, Tokyo
(5) polycondensation of diaminodiphenylether with CO_2 in the presence of diphenylphosphite
(6) N. Yamazaki, F. Higashi, T. Iguchi, IUPAC Macro, Madrid 1974 (I. 4–12)
(7) KBr (1/350)

421453 $C_{17}H_{21}N_5O_4$ 1377

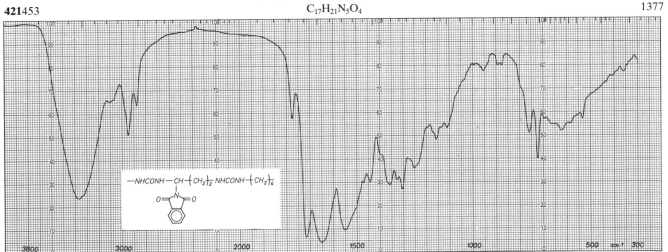

(1) poly[ureylene-(1-phthalimidotrimethylene)ureylene-tetramethylene]; polyurea with phthalimide side groups
(2) sand-coloured powder
(3) C.-P. Yang, Department of Chemical Engineering, Tatung Institute of Technology, Taipei, Taiwan
(5) polycondensation of N-(1,3-diisocyanato-1-propyl)phthalimide with 1,4-diaminobutane
(6) C.-P. Yang, Y. Iwakura, K. Uno, F. Toda, Makromol. Chem. 177 (1976) 3495...514
(7) KBr (1/350)

421453 $C_{21}H_{21}N_5O_4$ 1378

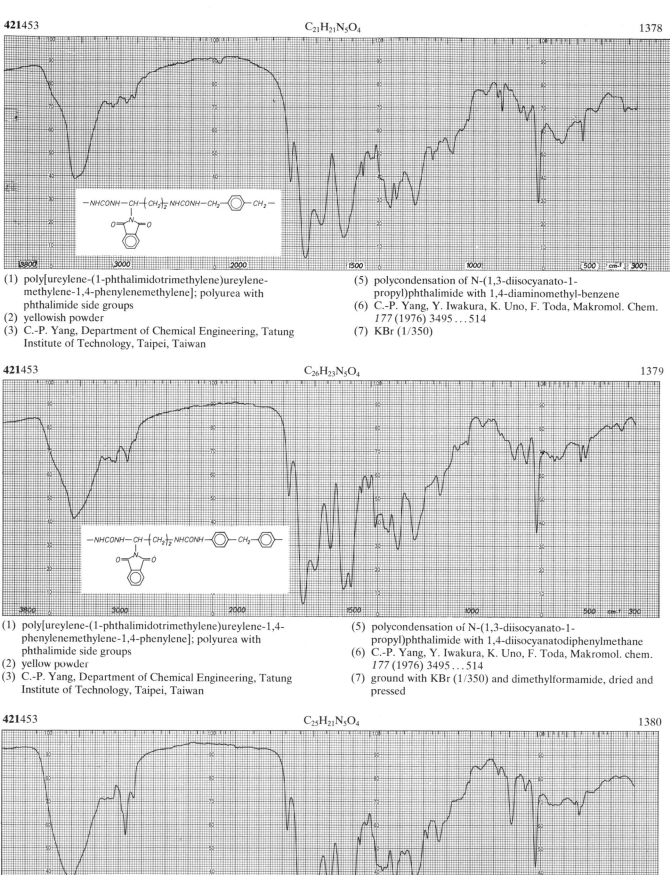

(1) poly[ureylene-(1-phthalimidotrimethylene)ureylene-methylene-1,4-phenylenemethylene]; polyurea with phthalimide side groups
(2) yellowish powder
(3) C.-P. Yang, Department of Chemical Engineering, Tatung Institute of Technology, Taipei, Taiwan
(5) polycondensation of N-(1,3-diisocyanato-1-propyl)phthalimide with 1,4-diaminomethyl-benzene
(6) C.-P. Yang, Y. Iwakura, K. Uno, F. Toda, Makromol. Chem. *177* (1976) 3495...514
(7) KBr (1/350)

421453 $C_{26}H_{23}N_5O_4$ 1379

(1) poly[ureylene-(1-phthalimidotrimethylene)ureylene-1,4-phenylenemethylene-1,4-phenylene]; polyurea with phthalimide side groups
(2) yellow powder
(3) C.-P. Yang, Department of Chemical Engineering, Tatung Institute of Technology, Taipei, Taiwan
(5) polycondensation of N-(1,3-diisocyanato-1-propyl)phthalimide with 1,4-diisocyanatodiphenylmethane
(6) C.-P. Yang, Y. Iwakura, K. Uno, F. Toda, Makromol. chem. *177* (1976) 3495...514
(7) ground with KBr (1/350) and dimethylformamide, dried and pressed

421453 $C_{25}H_{21}N_5O_4$ 1380

(1) poly[ureylene-(1-phthalimidotrimethylene)ureylene-4,4'-biphenylene]; polyurea with phthalimide side groups
(2) yellowish powder
(3) C.-P. Yang, Department of Chemical Engineering, Tatung Institute of Technology, Taipei, Taiwan
(5) polycondensation of N-(1,3-diisocyanato-1-propyl)phthalimide with benzidine
(6) C.-P. Yang, Y. Iwakura, K. Uno, F. Toda, Makromol. Chem. *177* (1976) 3495...514
(7) ground with KBr (1/350) and dimethylformamide, dried and pressed

4215111 $C_4H_3NO_2$ 1381

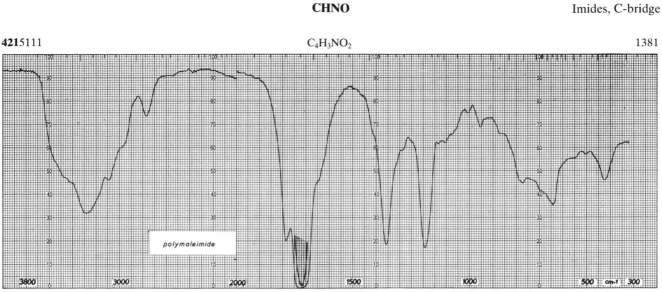

(1) polymaleimide
(2) orange to pink powder
(3) D. Decker, Centre de Recherche sur les Macromolecules, Strasbourg
(5) pyridine catalyzed polymerization in aqueous solution
(6) D. Decker, Makromol. Chem. *168* (1973) 51...8
(7) KBr (1/350) and 0,3/350)

42151111 $C_{15}H_{20}N_2O_4$ 1382

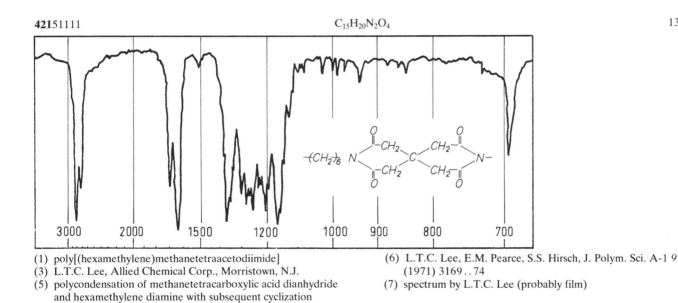

(1) poly[(hexamethylene)methanetetraacetodiimide]
(3) L.T.C. Lee, Allied Chemical Corp., Morristown, N.J.
(5) polycondensation of methanetetracarboxylic acid dianhydride and hexamethylene diamine with subsequent cyclization
(6) L.T.C. Lee, E.M. Pearce, S.S. Hirsch, J. Polym. Sci. A-1 *9* (1971) 3169..74
(7) spectrum by L.T.C. Lee (probably film)

42151113 $C_{34}H_{30}N_2O_4$ 1383

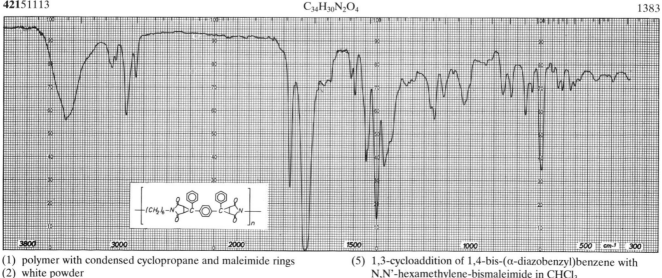

461

(1) polymer with condensed cyclopropane and maleimide rings
(2) white powder
(3) Y. Gilliams, Laboratory of Macromolecular Chemistry, University of Louvain
(5) 1,3-cycloaddition of 1,4-bis-(α-diazobenzyl)benzene with N,N'-hexamethylene-bismaleimide in $CHCl_3$
(6) Y. Gilliams, G. Smets, Makromol. Chem. *117* (1968) 1...11
(7) KBr (0.8/350)

42151113   C$_{34}$H$_{22}$N$_2$O$_4$ 1384

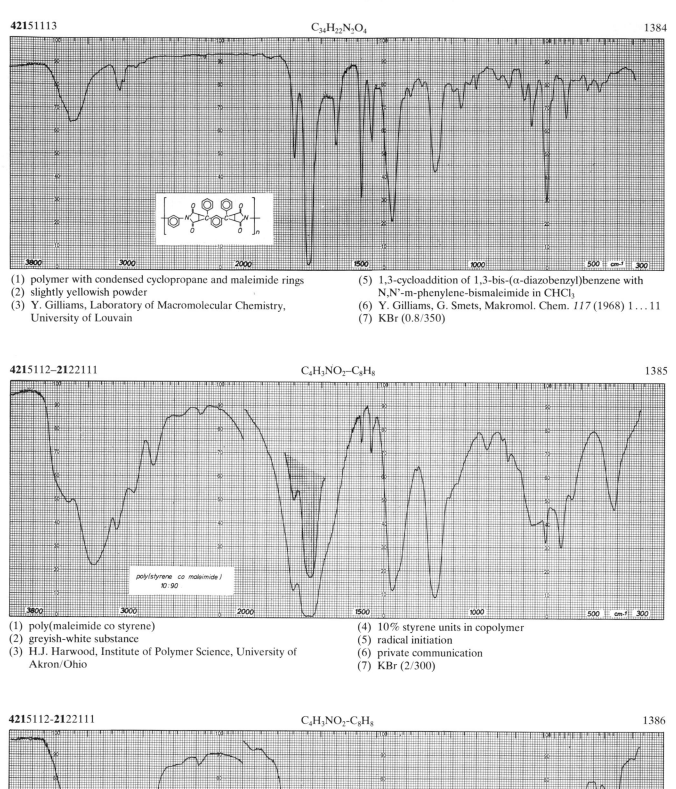

(1) polymer with condensed cyclopropane and maleimide rings
(2) slightly yellowish powder
(3) Y. Gilliams, Laboratory of Macromolecular Chemistry, University of Louvain

(5) 1,3-cycloaddition of 1,3-bis-(α-diazobenzyl)benzene with N,N'-m-phenylene-bismaleimide in CHCl$_3$
(6) Y. Gilliams, G. Smets, Makromol. Chem. *117* (1968) 1...11
(7) KBr (0.8/350)

4215112–**2122**111   C$_4$H$_3$NO$_2$–C$_8$H$_8$ 1385

poly(styrene co maleimide)
10:90

(1) poly(maleimide co styrene)
(2) greyish-white substance
(3) H.J. Harwood, Institute of Polymer Science, University of Akron/Ohio

(4) 10% styrene units in copolymer
(5) radical initiation
(6) private communication
(7) KBr (2/300)

4215112-**2122**111   C$_4$H$_3$NO$_2$-C$_8$H$_8$ 1386

poly(styrene co maleimide)
40:60

(1) poly(maleimide co styrene)
(2) greyish-white substance
(3) H.J. Harwood, Institute of Polymer Science, University of Akron/Ohio

(4) 40% styrene units in copolymer
(5) radical initiation
(6) private communication
(7) KBr (2/300)

C₄H₃NO₂–C₁₂H₈ — $C_4H_3NO_2$–$C_{12}H_8$

1387

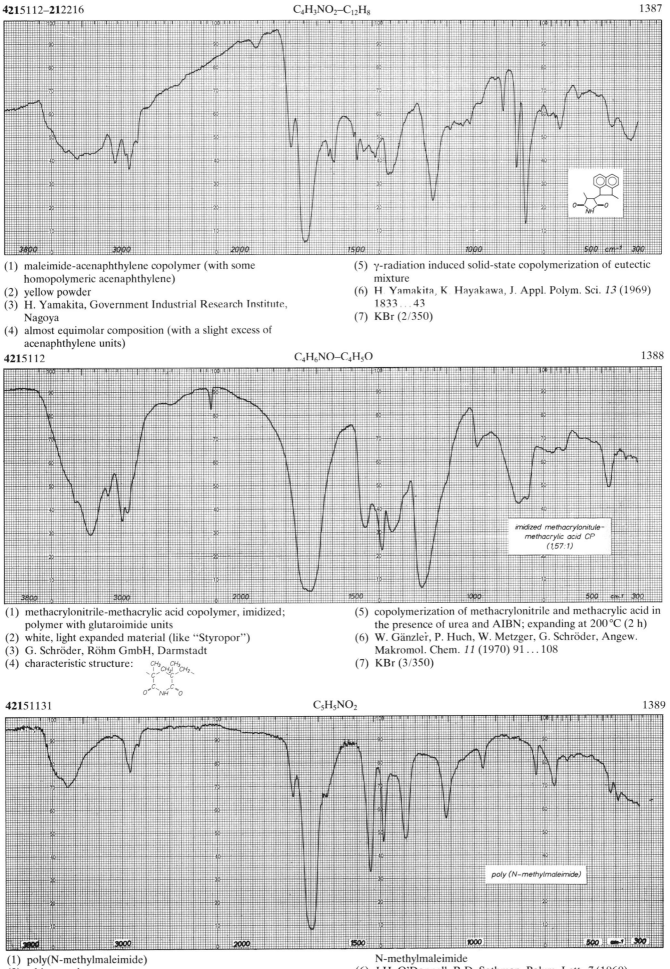

(1) maleimide-acenaphthylene copolymer (with some homopolymeric acenaphthylene)
(2) yellow powder
(3) H. Yamakita, Government Industrial Research Institute, Nagoya
(4) almost equimolar composition (with a slight excess of acenaphthylene units)

(5) γ-radiation induced solid-state copolymerization of eutectic mixture
(6) H. Yamakita, K. Hayakawa, J. Appl. Polym. Sci. *13* (1969) 1833...43
(7) KBr (2/350)

4215112

C_4H_6NO–C_4H_5O

1388

imidized methacrylonitule-methacrylic acid CP (1,57:1)

(1) methacrylonitrile-methacrylic acid copolymer, imidized; polymer with glutaroimide units
(2) white, light expanded material (like "Styropor")
(3) G. Schröder, Röhm GmbH, Darmstadt
(4) characteristic structure:

(5) copolymerization of methacrylonitrile and methacrylic acid in the presence of urea and AIBN; expanding at 200 °C (2 h)
(6) W. Gänzler, P. Huch, W. Metzger, G. Schröder, Angew. Makromol. Chem. *11* (1970) 91...108
(7) KBr (3/350)

42151131

$C_5H_5NO_2$

1389

poly (N–methylmaleimide)

(1) poly(N-methylmaleimide)
(2) white powder
(3) J.H. O'Donnell, Chemistry Department, University of Queensland, Brisbane
(5) γ-radiation induced solid-state polymerization of N-methylmaleimide

(6) J.H. O'Donnell, R.D. Sothman, Polym. Lett. *7* (1969) 129...34
(7) ground with KBr (1.7/350) and HCOOH, dried and pressed

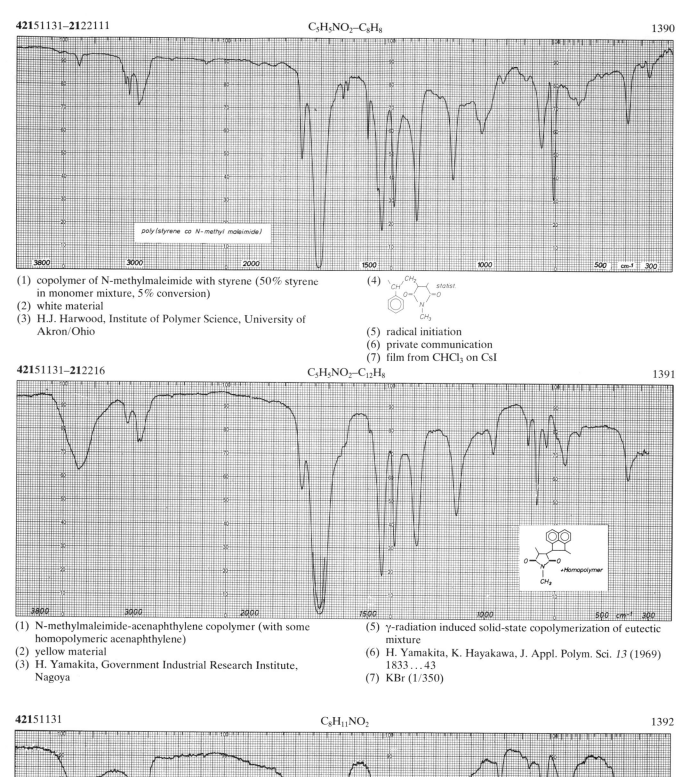

42151131–**21**22111 $C_5H_5NO_2$–C_8H_8 1390

poly (styrene co N-methyl maleimide)

(1) copolymer of N-methylmaleimide with styrene (50% styrene in monomer mixture, 5% conversion)
(2) white material
(3) H.J. Harwood, Institute of Polymer Science, University of Akron/Ohio
(4) CH CH₂ ... statist. ... O= ... =O ... N ... CH₃
(5) radical initiation
(6) private communication
(7) film from $CHCl_3$ on CsI

42151131–**21**2216 $C_5H_5NO_2$–$C_{12}H_8$ 1391

+Homopolymer
CH₃

(1) N-methylmaleimide-acenaphthylene copolymer (with some homopolymeric acenaphthylene)
(2) yellow material
(3) H. Yamakita, Government Industrial Research Institute, Nagoya
(5) γ-radiation induced solid-state copolymerization of eutectic mixture
(6) H. Yamakita, K. Hayakawa, J. Appl. Polym. Sci. *13* (1969) 1833...43
(7) KBr (1/350)

42151131 $C_8H_{11}NO_2$ 1392

poly(N-n-butyl maleimide)

(1) poly(N-n-butylmaleimide)
(2) white powder
(3) J.H. O'Donnell, Chemistry Department, University of Queensland, Brisbane
(5) γ-radiation induced solid-state polymerization of N-n-butylmaleimide
(6) J.H. O'Donnell, R.D. Sothman, Polym. Lett. 7 (1969) 129...34
(7) ground with KBr (1/350) and HCOOH, dried and pressed

42151131 $C_{12}H_{19}NO_2$ 1393

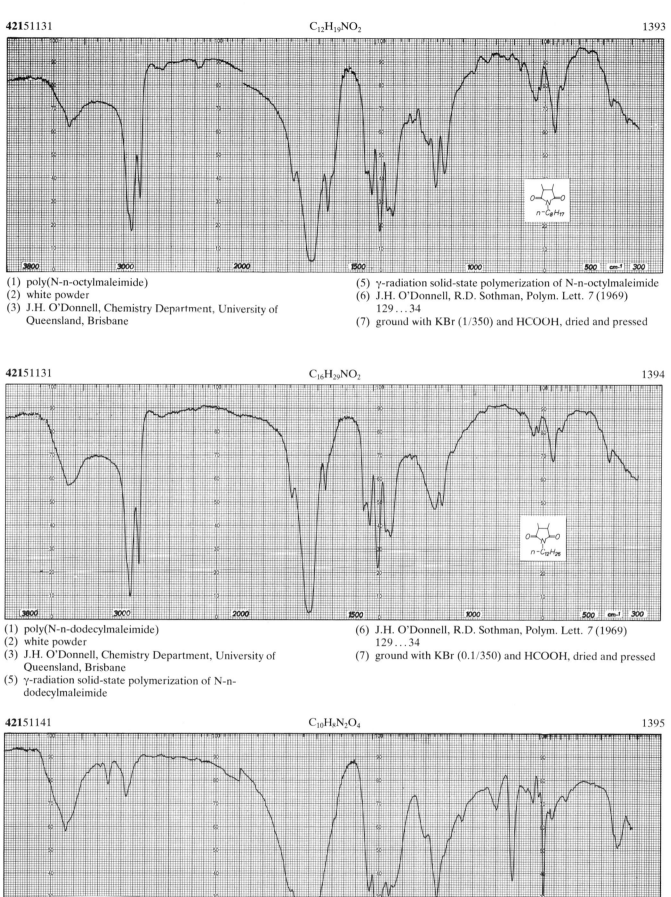

(1) poly(N-n-octylmaleimide)
(2) white powder
(3) J.H. O'Donnell, Chemistry Department, University of
    Queensland, Brisbane

(5) γ-radiation solid-state polymerization of N-n-octylmaleimide
(6) J.H. O'Donnell, R.D. Sothman, Polym. Lett. 7 (1969)
    129...34
(7) ground with KBr (1/350) and HCOOH, dried and pressed

42151131 $C_{16}H_{29}NO_2$ 1394

(1) poly(N-n-dodecylmaleimide)
(2) white powder
(3) J.H. O'Donnell, Chemistry Department, University of
    Queensland, Brisbane
(5) γ-radiation solid-state polymerization of N-n-
    dodecylmaleimide

(6) J.H. O'Donnell, R.D. Sothman, Polym. Lett. 7 (1969)
    129...34
(7) ground with KBr (0.1/350) and HCOOH, dried and pressed

42151141 $C_{10}H_8N_2O_4$ 1395

(1) poly(1,2-ethylenebismaleimide)
(2) brown, resinous, hard material
(3) H.D. Stenzenberger, Technochemie GmbH –
    Verfahrenstechnik, Dossenheim
(5) thermal polymerization at 200 °C
(6) H.D. Stenzenberger, private communication; see also H.D.

Stenzenberger, High Temperature Composites from
Bismaleimide Resins: A Binder Concept; Conference Fiber
Science, 1976, Arad and H.D. Stenzenberger, Appl. Polym.
Symp. 22 (1973) 77...88
(7) KBr (3/350)

42151141 $C_{14}H_{16}N_2O_4$ 1396

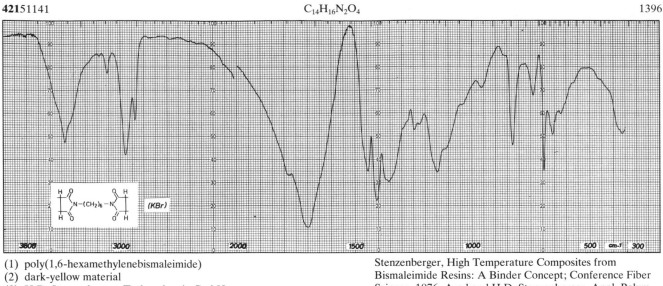

(1) poly(1,6-hexamethylenebismaleimide)
(2) dark-yellow material
(3) H.D. Stenzenberger, Technochemie GmbH –
    Verfahrenstechnik, Dossenheim
(5) thermal polymerization at 200 °C
(6) H.D. Stenzenberger, private communication; see also H.D.

Stenzenberger, High Temperature Composites from
Bismaleimide Resins: A Binder Concept; Conference Fiber
Science, 1976, Arad and H.D. Stenzenberger, Appl. Polym.
Symp. *22* (1973) 77 ... 88
(7) KBr (3/350)

42151141 $C_{16}H_{12}N_2O_4$ 1397

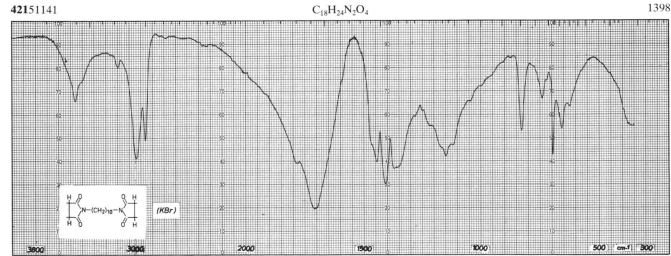

(1) poly(1,8-octamethylene-bismaleimide)
(2) dark-yellow powder
(3) H.D. Stenzenberger, Technochemie GmbH –
    Verfahrenstechnik, Dossenheim
(5) thermal polymerization at 200 °C
(6) H.D. Stenzenberger, private communication; see also H.D.

Stenzenberger, High Temperature Composites from
Bismaleimide Resins: A Binder Concept; Conference Fiber
Science, 1976, Arad and H.D. Stenzenberger, Appl. Polym.
Symp. *22* (1973) 77 ... 88
(7) KBr (3.5/350)

42151141 $C_{18}H_{24}N_2O_4$ 1398

(1) poly(1,10-decamethylenebismaleimide)
(2) dark-yellow, coarse powder
(3) H.D. Stenzenberger, Technochemie GmbH –
    Verfahrenstechnik, Dossenheim
(5) thermal polymerization at 200 °C
(6) H.D. Stenzenberger, private communication; see also H.D.

Stenzenberger, High Temperature Composites from
Bismaleimide Resins: A Binder Concept; Conference Fiber
Science, 1976, Arad and H.D. Stenzenberger, Appl. Polym.
Symp. *22* (1973) 77 ... 88
(7) KBr (3.5/350)

42151141 $C_{20}H_{28}N_2O_4$ 1399

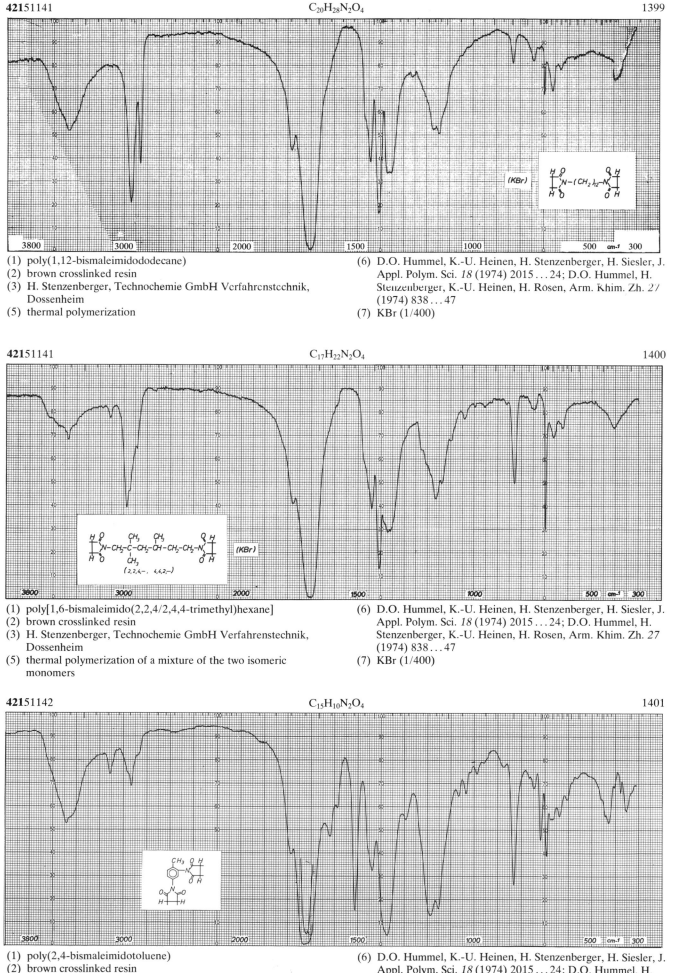

(1) poly(1,12-bismaleimidododecane)
(2) brown crosslinked resin
(3) H. Stenzenberger, Technochemie GmbH Verfahrenstechnik, Dossenheim
(5) thermal polymerization

(6) D.O. Hummel, K.-U. Heinen, H. Stenzenberger, H. Siesler, J. Appl. Polym. Sci. *18* (1974) 2015...24; D.O. Hummel, H. Stenzenberger, K.-U. Heinen, H. Rosen, Arm. Khim. Zh. *27* (1974) 838...47
(7) KBr (1/400)

42151141 $C_{17}H_{22}N_2O_4$ 1400

(1) poly[1,6-bismaleimido(2,2,4/2,4,4-trimethyl)hexane]
(2) brown crosslinked resin
(3) H. Stenzenberger, Technochemie GmbH Verfahrenstechnik, Dossenheim
(5) thermal polymerization of a mixture of the two isomeric monomers

(6) D.O. Hummel, K.-U. Heinen, H. Stenzenberger, H. Siesler, J. Appl. Polym. Sci. *18* (1974) 2015...24; D.O. Hummel, H. Stenzenberger, K.-U. Heinen, H. Rosen, Arm. Khim. Zh. *27* (1974) 838...47
(7) KBr (1/400)

42151142 $C_{15}H_{10}N_2O_4$ 1401

(1) poly(2,4-bismaleimidotoluene)
(2) brown crosslinked resin
(3) H. Stenzenberger, Technochemie GmbH – Verfahrenstechnik, Dossenheim
(5) thermal polymerization

(6) D.O. Hummel, K.-U. Heinen, H. Stenzenberger, H. Siesler, J. Appl. Polym. Sci. *18* (1974) 2015...24; D.O. Hummel, H. Stenzenberger, K.-U. Heinen, H. Rosen, Arm. Khim. Zh. *27* (1974) 838...47
(7) KBr (1/400)

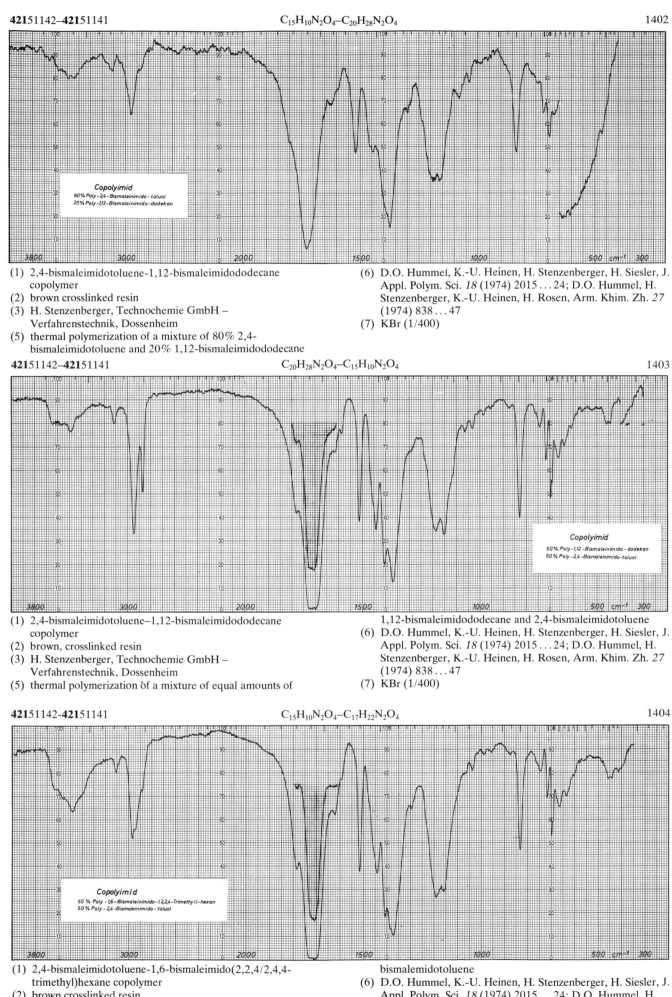

Copolyimid
80% Poly-2,4-Bismaleinimido-toluol
20% Poly-1,12-Bismaleinimido-dodekan

(1) 2,4-bismaleimidotoluene-1,12-bismaleimidododecane
   copolymer
(2) brown crosslinked resin
(3) H. Stenzenberger, Technochemie GmbH –
   Verfahrenstechnik, Dossenheim
(5) thermal polymerization of a mixture of 80% 2,4-
   bismaleimidotoluene and 20% 1,12-bismaleimidododecane

(6) D.O. Hummel, K.-U. Heinen, H. Stenzenberger, H. Siesler, J.
   Appl. Polym. Sci. *18* (1974) 2015...24; D.O. Hummel, H.
   Stenzenberger, K.-U. Heinen, H. Rosen, Arm. Khim. Zh. *27*
   (1974) 838...47
(7) KBr (1/400)

Copolyimid
50% Poly-1,12-Bismaleinimido-dodekan
50% Poly-2,4-Bismaleinimido-toluol

(1) 2,4-bismaleimidotoluene–1,12-bismaleimidododecane
   copolymer
(2) brown, crosslinked resin
(3) H. Stenzenberger, Technochemie GmbH –
   Verfahrenstechnik, Dossenheim
(5) thermal polymerization of a mixture of equal amounts of

1,12-bismaleimidododecane and 2,4-bismaleimidotoluene
(6) D.O. Hummel, K.-U. Heinen, H. Stenzenberger, H. Siesler, J.
   Appl. Polym. Sci. *18* (1974) 2015...24; D.O. Hummel, H.
   Stenzenberger, K.-U. Heinen, H. Rosen, Arm. Khim. Zh. *27*
   (1974) 838...47
(7) KBr (1/400)

Copolyimid
50% Poly-1,6-Bismaleinimido-(2,2,4-Trimethyl)-hexan
50% Poly-2,4-Bismaleinimido-toluol

(1) 2,4-bismaleimidotoluene-1,6-bismaleimido(2,2,4/2,4,4-
   trimethyl)hexane copolymer
(2) brown crosslinked resin
(3) H. Stenzenberger, Technochemie GmbH –
   Verfahrenstechnik, Dossenheim
(5) thermal polymerization of a mixture of equal amounts of
   1,6-bismaleimido (2,2,4/2,4,4-trimethyl)hexane and 2,4-

bismalemidotoluene
(6) D.O. Hummel, K.-U. Heinen, H. Stenzenberger, H. Siesler, J.
   Appl. Polym. Sci. *18* (1974) 2015...24; D.O. Hummel, H.
   Stenzenberger, K.-U. Heinen, H. Rosen, Arm. Khim. Zh *27*
   (1974) 838...47
(7) KBr (1/400)

42151142 $C_{21}H_{14}N_2O_4$ 1405

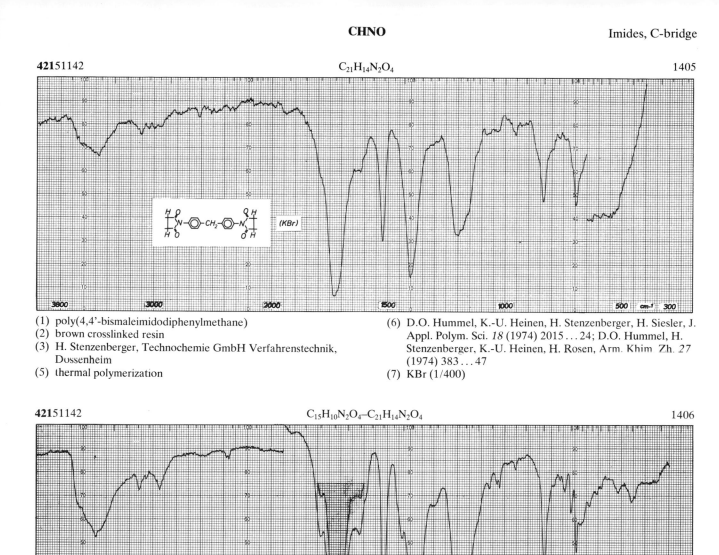

(1) poly(4,4'-bismaleimidodiphenylmethane)
(2) brown crosslinked resin
(3) H. Stenzenberger, Technochemie GmbH Verfahrenstechnik,
    Dossenheim
(5) thermal polymerization

(6) D.O. Hummel, K.-U. Heinen, H. Stenzenberger, H. Siesler, J.
    Appl. Polym. Sci. *18* (1974) 2015...24; D.O. Hummel, H.
    Stenzenberger, K.-U. Heinen, H. Rosen, Arm. Khim Zh. *27*
    (1974) 383...47
(7) KBr (1/400)

42151142 $C_{15}H_{10}N_2O_4$–$C_{21}H_{14}N_2O_4$ 1406

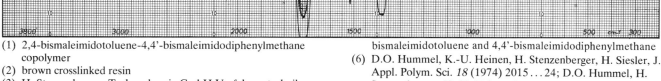

Copolyimid
50% Poly-2,4-Bismaleinimido-toluol
50% Poly-4,4'-Bismaleinimido-diphenylmethan

(1) 2,4-bismaleimidotoluene-4,4'-bismaleimidodiphenylmethane
    copolymer
(2) brown crosslinked resin
(3) H. Stenzenberger, Technochemie GmbH Verfahrenstechnik,
    Dossenheim
(5) thermal polymerization of equal amounts of 2,4-

bismaleimidotoluene and 4,4'-bismaleimidodiphenylmethane
(6) D.O. Hummel, K.-U. Heinen, H. Stenzenberger, H. Siesler, J.
    Appl. Polym. Sci. *18* (1974) 2015...24; D.O. Hummel, H.
    Stenzenberger, K.-U. Heinen, H. Rosen, Arm. Khim. Zh. *27*
    (1974) 838...47
(7) KBr (1/400)

42151142–**421**51141 $C_{15}H_{10}N_2O_4$–$C_{21}H_{14}N_2O_4$–$C_{20}H_{28}N_2O_4$ 1407

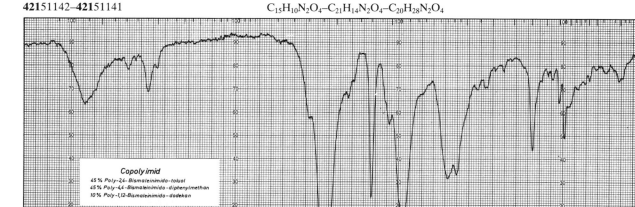

Copolyimid
45% Poly-2,4-Bismaleinimido-toluol
45% Poly-4,4'-Bismaleinimido-diphenylmethan
10% Poly-1,12-Bismaleinimido-dodekan

(1) terpolymer from bismaleimides
(2) brown crosslinked resin
(3) H. Stenzenberger, Technochemie GmbH Verfahrenstechnik,
    Dossenheim
(5) thermal polymerization of a mixture of 45% 2,4-
    bismaleimidotoluene, 45% 4,4'-
    bismaleimidodiphenylmethane and 10% 1,12-

bismaleimidododecane
(6) D.O. Hummel, K.-U. Heinen, H. Stenzenberger, H. Siesler, J.
    Appl. Polym. Sci. *18* (1974) 2015...24; D.O. Hummel, H.
    Stenzenberger, K.-U. Heinen, H. Rosen, Arm. Khim. Zh. *27*
    (1974) 838...47
(7) KBr (1/400)

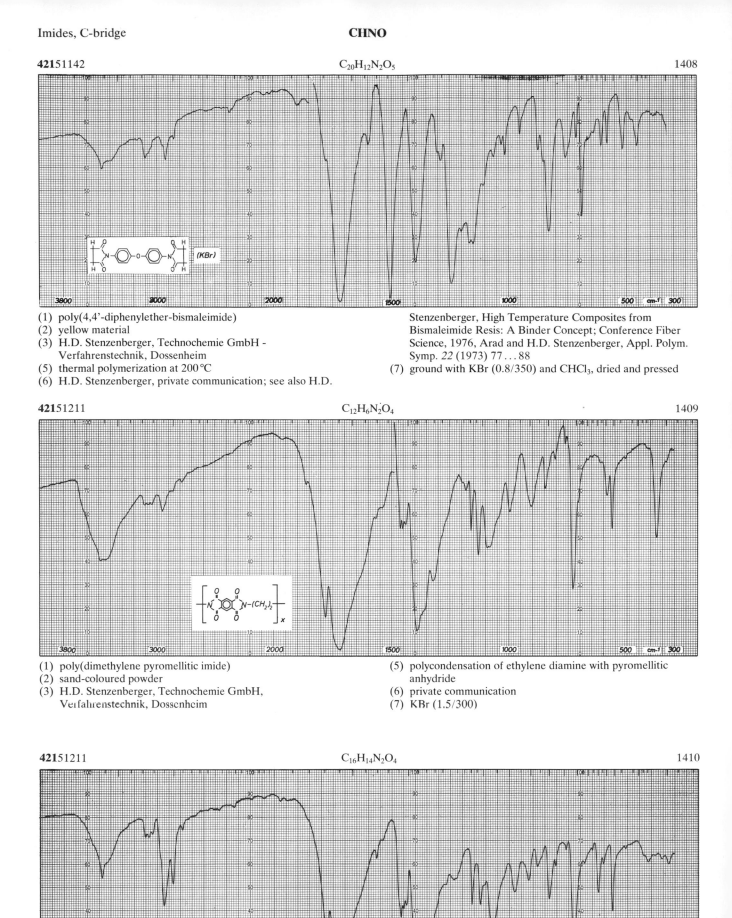

42151142 $C_{20}H_{12}N_2O_5$ 1408

(1) poly(4,4'-diphenylether-bismaleimide)
(2) yellow material
(3) H.D. Stenzenberger, Technochemie GmbH -
     Verfahrenstechnik, Dossenheim
(5) thermal polymerization at 200 °C
(6) H.D. Stenzenberger, private communication; see also H.D.

Stenzenberger, High Temperature Composites from
Bismaleimide Resis: A Binder Concept; Conference Fiber
Science, 1976, Arad and H.D. Stenzenberger, Appl. Polym.
Symp. *22* (1973) 77 ... 88
(7) ground with KBr (0.8/350) and CHCl₃, dried and pressed

42151211 $C_{12}H_6N_2O_4$ 1409

(1) poly(dimethylene pyromellitic imide)
(2) sand-coloured powder
(3) H.D. Stenzenberger, Technochemie GmbH,
     Verfahrenstechnik, Dossenheim

(5) polycondensation of ethylene diamine with pyromellitic
     anhydride
(6) private communication
(7) KBr (1.5/300)

42151211 $C_{16}H_{14}N_2O_4$ 1410

(1) poly(1,6-hexamethylenepyromelliticimide)
(2) white powder
(3) H.D. Stenzenberger, Technochemie GmbH -
     Verfahrenstechnik, Dossenheim

(5) polycondensation of 1,6-hexamethylenediamine with
     pyromellitic anhydride
(6) H.D. Stenzenberger, private communication
(7) KBr (2/300)

42151211 $C_{22}H_{26}N_2O_4$ 1411

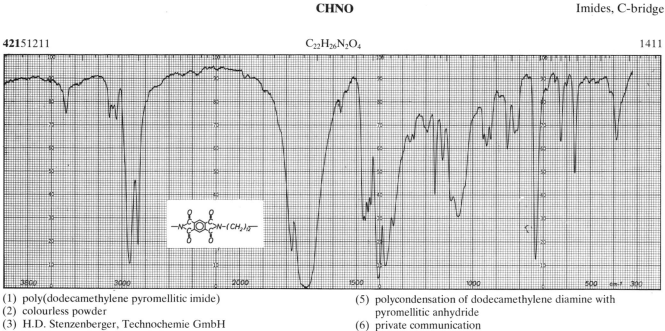

(1) poly(dodecamethylene pyromellitic imide)
(2) colourless powder
(3) H.D. Stenzenberger, Technochemie GmbH
     Verfahrenstechnik, Dossenheim

(5) polycondensation of dodecamethylene diamine with
     pyromellitic anhydride
(6) private communication
(7) KBr (2/300)

42151211 $C_{19}H_{20}N_2O_4$ 1412

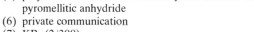

(1) poly(2,2,4-/2,4,4-trimethyl hexamethylene pyromellitic
     imide)
(2) grey powder
(3) H.D. Stenzenberger, Technochemie GmbH
     Verfahrenstechnik, Dossenheim

(5) polycondensation of 2,2,4-/2,4,4-hexamethylene diamine with
     pyromellitic anhydride
(6) private communication
(7) KBr (6/300)
(8) about equimolar mixture of isomers

42151212 $C_{27}H_{23}N_2O_5$ 1413

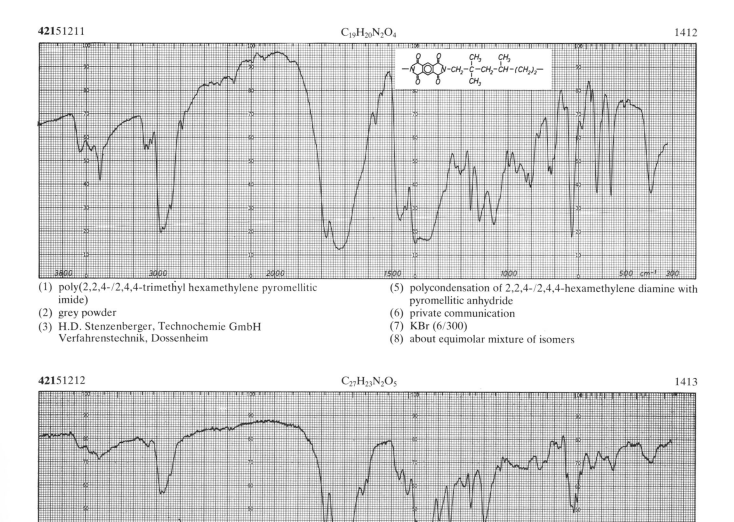

(1) poly(isophorone benzophenone tetracarboxylic imide)
(2) black casting
(3) H.D. Stenzenberger, Technochemie GmbH
     Verfahrenstechnik, Dossenheim

(5) polyaddition of benzophenone tetracarboxylic anhydride and
     isophorone diamine
(6) private communication
(7) KBr (1/400)

42151215   C$_{23}$H$_{12}$N$_2$O$_4$ 1414

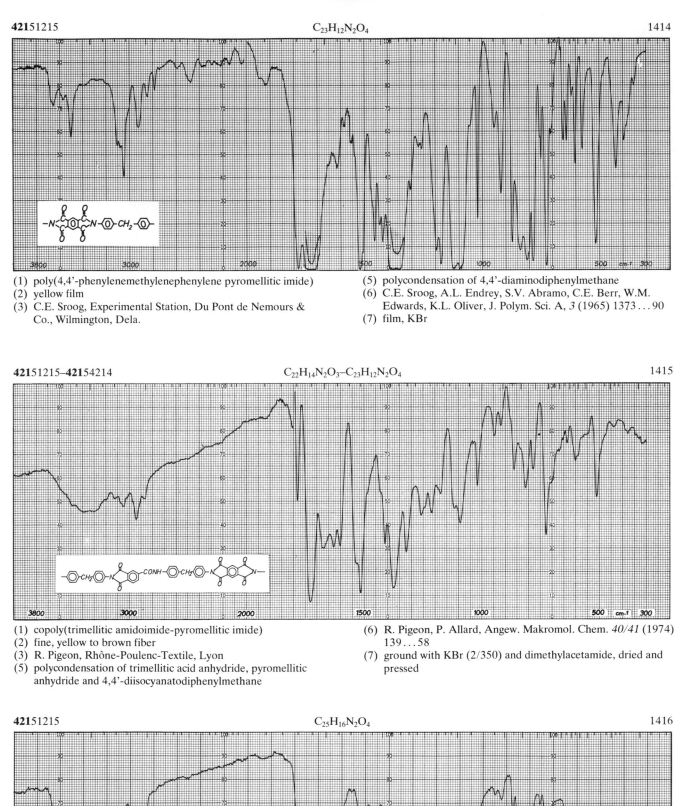

(1) poly(4,4'-phenylenemethylenephenylene pyromellitic imide)
(2) yellow film
(3) C.E. Sroog, Experimental Station, Du Pont de Nemours & Co., Wilmington, Dela.
(5) polycondensation of 4,4'-diaminodiphenylmethane
(6) C.E. Sroog, A.L. Endrey, S.V. Abramo, C.E. Berr, W.M. Edwards, K.L. Oliver, J. Polym. Sci. A, *3* (1965) 1373...90
(7) film, KBr

42151215–**42**154214   C$_{22}$H$_{14}$N$_2$O$_3$–C$_{23}$H$_{12}$N$_2$O$_4$ 1415

(1) copoly(trimellitic amidoimide-pyromellitic imide)
(2) fine, yellow to brown fiber
(3) R. Pigeon, Rhône-Poulenc-Textile, Lyon
(5) polycondensation of trimellitic acid anhydride, pyromellitic anhydride and 4,4'-diisocyanatodiphenylmethane
(6) R. Pigeon, P. Allard, Angew. Makromol. Chem. *40/41* (1974) 139...58
(7) ground with KBr (2/350) and dimethylacetamide, dried and pressed

42151215   C$_{25}$H$_{16}$N$_2$O$_4$ 1416

(1) poly[bis-(4,4'-phenylene)2-propyl pyromellitic imide]
(2) yellow film
(3) C.E. Sroog, Experimental Station, Du Pont de Nemours & Co., Wilmington, Dela.
(5) polycondensation of 2,2-bis(4-aminophenyl)propane and pyromellitic anhydride
(6) C.E. Sroog, A.L. Endrey, S.V. Abramo, C.E. Berr, W.M. Edwards, K.L. Oliver, J. Polym. Sci. A, *3* (1965) 1373...90
(7) KBr

42151216 C₁₆H₆N₂O₄ 1417

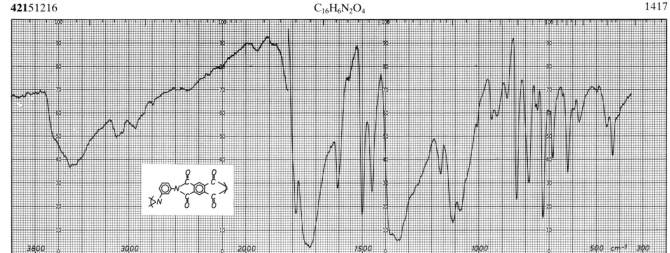

(1) poly(m-phenylene pyromellitic imide)
(2) yellow film
(3) C.E. Sroog, Experimental Station, Du Pont de Nemours & Co., Wilmington, Dela.
(5) polyaddition of m-phenylene diamine with pyromellitic anhydride

(6) C.E. Sroog, A.L. Endrey, S.V. Abramo, C.E. Berr, W.M. Edwards, K.L. Oliver, J. Polym. Sci. A, *3* (1965) 1373...90
(7) KBr (3.5/300)

42151216 C₂₂H₁₀N₂O₄ 1418

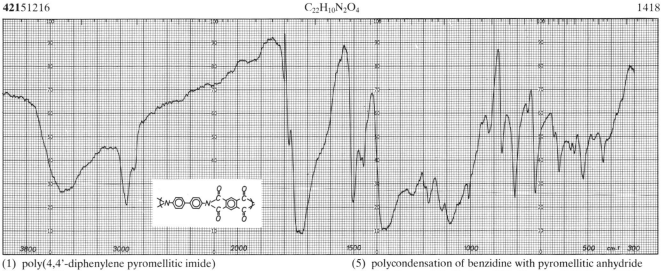

(1) poly(4,4'-diphenylene pyromellitic imide)
(2) brown film
(3) C.E. Sroog, Experimental Station, Du Pont de Nemours & Co., Wilmington, Dela.

(5) polycondensation of benzidine with pyromellitic anhydride
(6) C.E. Sroog, A.L. Endrey, S.V. Abramo, D.E. Berr, W.M. Edwards, K.L. Olivier, J. Polym. Sci. A, *3* (1965) 1373...90
(7) KBr (2.5/300)

421513 C₅H₇NO₂ 1419

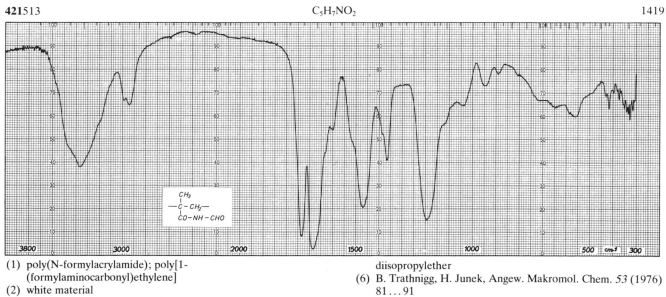

(1) poly(N-formylacrylamide); poly[1-(formylaminocarbonyl)ethylene]
(2) white material
(3) B. Trathnigg, Abteilung für Organische Chemie I der Universität Graz, Graz
(5) polymerization of N-formylacrylamide with AIBN in diisopropylether

(6) B. Trathnigg, H. Junek, Angew. Makromol. Chem. *53* (1976) 81...91
(7) KBr (1/350)
(8) sharp bands below 400 cm⁻¹ due to H₂O absorptions

421513 $C_4H_5NO_2$ 1420

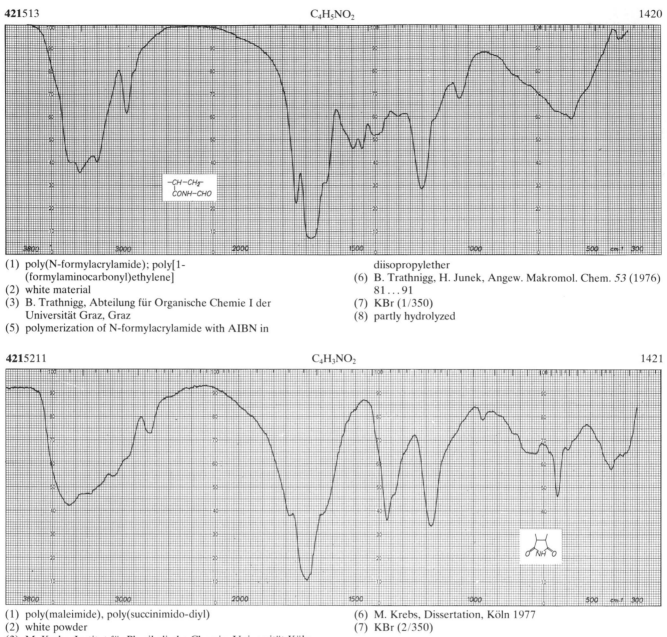

(1) poly(N-formylacrylamide); poly[1-
     (formylaminocarbonyl)ethylene]
(2) white material
(3) B. Trathnigg, Abteilung für Organische Chemie I der
     Universität Graz, Graz
(5) polymerization of N-formylacrylamide with AIBN in

diisopropylether
(6) B. Trathnigg, H. Junek, Angew. Makromol. Chem. *53* (1976)
     81...91
(7) KBr (1/350)
(8) partly hydrolyzed

4215211 $C_4H_3NO_2$ 1421

(1) poly(maleimide), poly(succinimido-diyl)
(2) white powder
(3) M. Krebs, Institut für Physikalische Chemie, Universität Köln
(5) γ-radiation induced polymerization of maleimide in dioxane
     solution at 72 °C

(6) M. Krebs, Dissertation, Köln 1977
(7) KBr (2/350)

42152111 $C_{20}H_{20}N_4O_4$ 1422

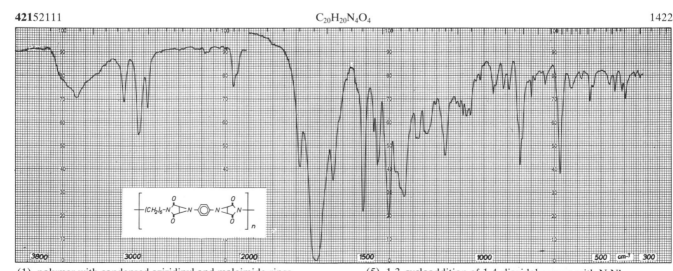

(1) polymer with condensed aziridinyl and maleimide rings
(2) ochre-coloured powder
(3) Y. Gilliams, Laboratory of Macromolecular Chemistry,
     University of Louvain

(5) 1,3-cycloaddition of 1,4-diazidobenzene with N,N'-
     hexamethylene-bismaleimide in toluene
(6) Y. Gilliams, G. Smets, Makromol. Chem. *117* (1968) 1...11
(7) KBr (1.5/350)

42152112 $C_{34}H_{26}N_4O_4$ 1423

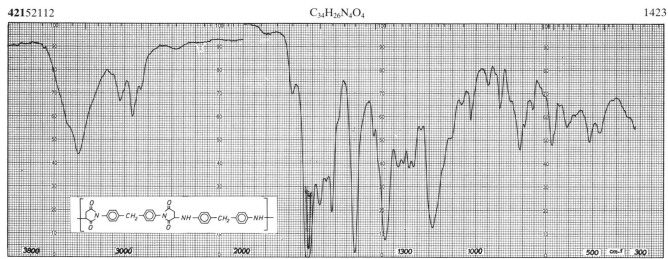

(1) poly(aspartimide)
(2) light-yellow powder
(3) J.V. Crivello, General Electric Company, Schenectady, N.Y.
(5) polyaddition of N,N'-bismaleimido-4,4'-diphenylmethane and 4,4'-diaminodiphenylmethane in cresol

(6) J.V. Crivello, J. Polym. Sci. *11* (1973) 1185...1200
(7) ground with KBr (1.3/350) and DMF, dried and pressed

42152232122 $C_{57}H_{30}N_6O_5$ 1424

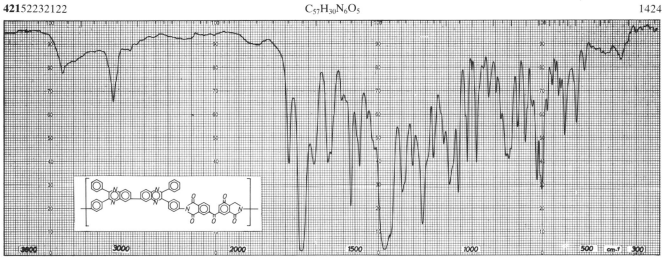

(1) polyimidoquinoxaline on the basis of benzophenonetetracarboxylic anhydride and a diamino bis-quinoxaline
(3) J.M. Augl, U.S. Naval Ordnance Laboratory, Silver Spring, Maryland

(5) J.M. Augl, J. Polym. Sci. A-1 *10* (1972) 2403, ibid. A-1 *8* (1970) 3145; J.M. Augl, J.V. Duffy, ibid. A-1 *9* (1971) 1343
(6) J.M. Augl, H.J. Booth, Polym. Prepr. *14*/1(1973) 612...7
(7) film (18 μm)

42153113 $C_{20}H_{14}N_2O_5$ 1425

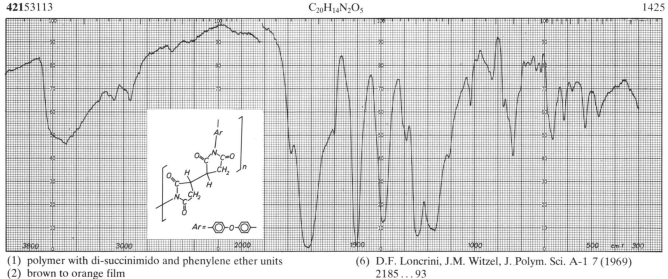

(1) polymer with di-succinimido and phenylene ether units
(2) brown to orange film
(3) D.F. Loncrini, The P.D. George Co., St. Lous, Mo.
(5) polycondensation of d,l-1,2,3,4-butanetetracarboxylic acid dianhydride and 4,4'-diaminodiphenyl ether

(6) D.F. Loncrini, J.M. Witzel, J. Polym. Sci. A-1 7 (1969) 2185...93
(7) KBr

42153113 $C_{20}H_{14}N_2O_5$ 1426

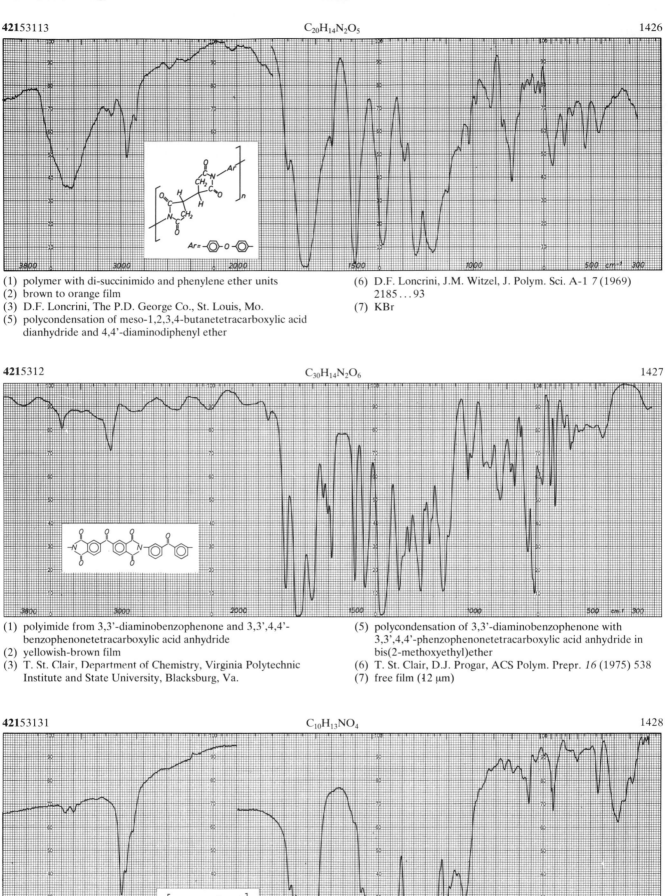

(1) polymer with di-succinimido and phenylene ether units
(2) brown to orange film
(3) D.F. Loncrini, The P.D. George Co., St. Louis, Mo.
(5) polycondensation of meso-1,2,3,4-butanetetracarboxylic acid
     dianhydride and 4,4'-diaminodiphenyl ether

(6) D.F. Loncrini, J.M. Witzel, J. Polym. Sci. A-1 7 (1969)
     2185...93
(7) KBr

4215312 $C_{30}H_{14}N_2O_6$ 1427

(1) polyimide from 3,3'-diaminobenzophenone and 3,3',4,4'-
     benzophenonetetracarboxylic acid anhydride
(2) yellowish-brown film
(3) T. St. Clair, Department of Chemistry, Virginia Polytechnic
     Institute and State University, Blacksburg, Va.

(5) polycondensation of 3,3'-diaminobenzophenone with
     3,3',4,4'-phenzophenonetetracarboxylic acid anhydride in
     bis(2-methoxyethyl)ether
(6) T. St. Clair, D.J. Progar, ACS Polym. Prepr. 16 (1975) 538
(7) free film (12 µm)

42153131 $C_{10}H_{13}NO_4$ 1428

(1) poly[N-(2-hydroxyethyl)-α,α-dimethyltricarballyl-(α,γ-
     imide)ate]
(2) colourless film
(3) R. Nehring, Forschungslaboratorien der Chemische Werke
     Hüls AG, Marl
(5) thermal polymerization of 11,11-dimethyl-2,10-dioxa-5-

azatricyclo[6.2.1.0^{1,5}]undecane-6,9-dione at 180...200°C; the
monomer was obtained by addition of 2-isopropyl-2-
oxazoline to maleic anhydride
(6) R. Nehring, W. Seeliger, Angew. Chem. 82 (1970) 448...9
(7) film from dimethylformamide on CsI

42153213   C$_{22}$H$_{10}$N$_2$O$_5$ 1429

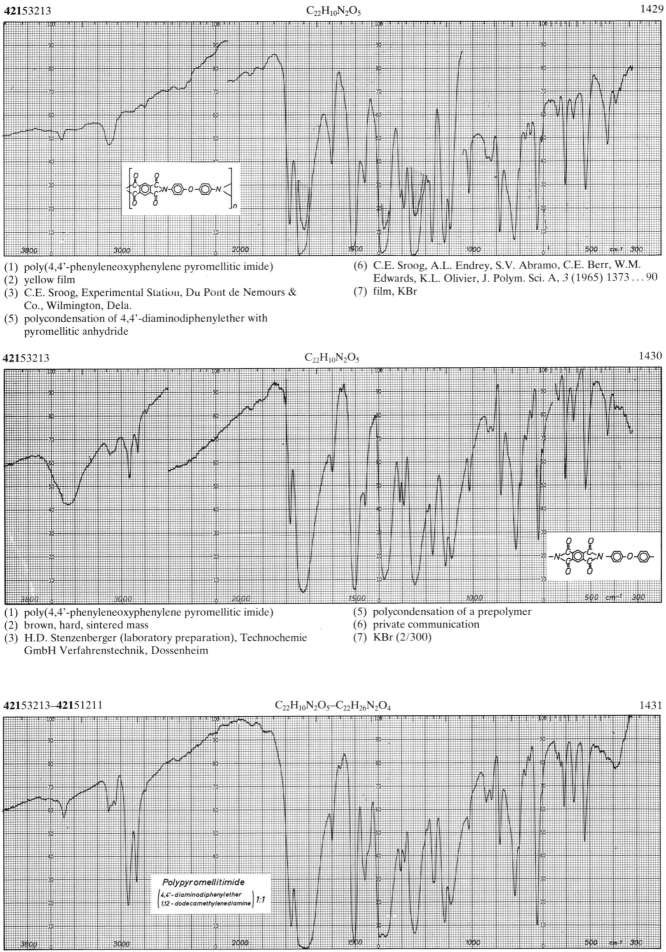

(1) poly(4,4'-phenyleneoxyphenylene pyromellitic imide)
(2) yellow film
(3) C.E. Sroog, Experimental Station, Du Pont de Nemours & Co., Wilmington, Dela.
(5) polycondensation of 4,4'-diaminodiphenylether with pyromellitic anhydride

(6) C.E. Sroog, A.L. Endrey, S.V. Abramo, C.E. Berr, W.M. Edwards, K.L. Olivier, J. Polym. Sci. A, *3* (1965) 1373 ... 90
(7) film, KBr

42153213   C$_{22}$H$_{10}$N$_2$O$_5$ 1430

(1) poly(4,4'-phenyleneoxyphenylene pyromellitic imide)
(2) brown, hard, sintered mass
(3) H.D. Stenzenberger (laboratory preparation), Technochemie GmbH Verfahrenstechnik, Dossenheim

(5) polycondensation of a prepolymer
(6) private communication
(7) KBr (2/300)

42153213–**42**151211   C$_{22}$H$_{10}$N$_2$O$_5$–C$_{22}$H$_{26}$N$_2$O$_4$ 1431

Polypyromellitimide

| 4,4'-diaminodiphenylether | | 1:1 |
| 1,12-dodecamethylenediamine | | |

(1) poly(pyromellitic imide)
(2) yellow powder for sintering processes
(3) H.D. Stenzenberger, Technochemie GmbH Verfahrenstechnik, Dossenheim
(5) polycondensation of about equal amounts of 4,4'-

diaminodiphenylether and 1,12-dodecamethylene diamine with pyromellitic anhydride
(6) private communication
(7) KBr (2/300)

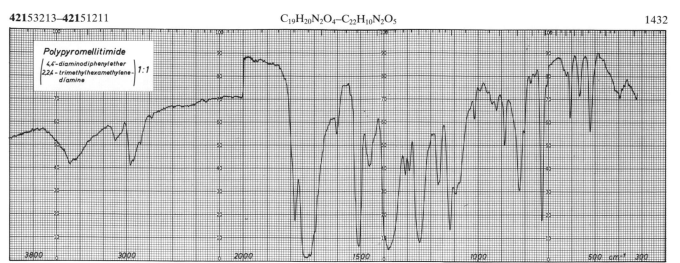

Polypyromellitimide
4,4'-diaminodiphenylether
2,2,4-trimethylhexamethylene-
diamine } 1:1

(1) poly(pyromellitic imide)
(2) yellow powder for sintering processes
(3) H.D. Stenzenberger, Technochemie GmbH
Verfahrenstechnik, Dossenheim
(5) polycondensation of about equal amounts of 4,4'-
diaminodiphenylether and 2,2,4/2,4,4-
trimethylhexamethylene diamine with pyromellitic anhydride
(6) private communication
(7) KBr (1.5/300)

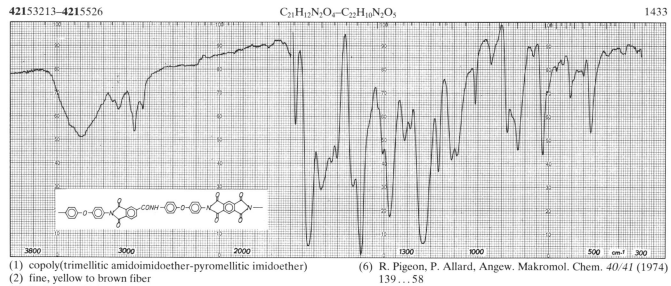

(1) copoly(trimellitic amidoimidoether-pyromellitic imidoether)
(2) fine, yellow to brown fiber
(3) R. Pigeon, Rhône-Poulenc-Textile, Lyon
(5) polycondensation of trimellitic acid anhydride, pyromellitic
anhydride and 4,4'-diisocyanatodiphenylether
(6) R. Pigeon, P. Allard, Angew. Makromol. Chem. *40/41* (1974)
139...58
(7) ground with KBr (2/350) and dimethylacetamide, dried and
pressed

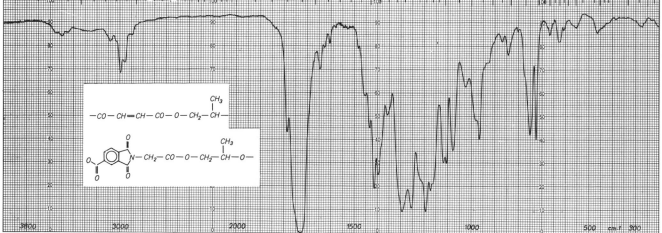

(1) polyesterimide, unsaturated; poly(trimellitic esterimide)
(2) white powder
(3) J. de Abajo, Instituto de Plásticos y Caucho, Madrid
(5) condensation of aminoacetic acid with trimellitic acid
anhydride, polycondensation with 1,2-propyleneglycol and
maleic anhydride in a two-step process
(6) Catherina L. Maros, J. de Abajo, Angew. Makromol. Chem.
55 (1976) 73...83
(7) film from CHCl₃ on CsI

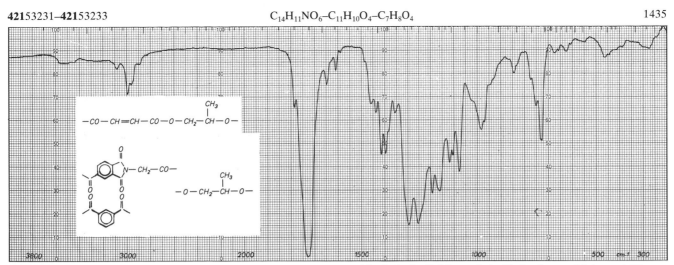

(1) copoly(trimellitic esterimide), unsaturated
(2) white powder
(3) J. de Abajo, Instituto de Plásticos y Caucho, Madrid
(5) condensation of aminoacetic acid with trimellitic acid anhydride, polycondensation with 1,2-propanediol, isophthalic acid and maleic anhydride in a two-step process

(6) Catherina L. Maros, J. de Abajo, Angew. Makromol. Chem. *55* (1976) 73 ... 83
(7) film from CHCl₃ on CsI

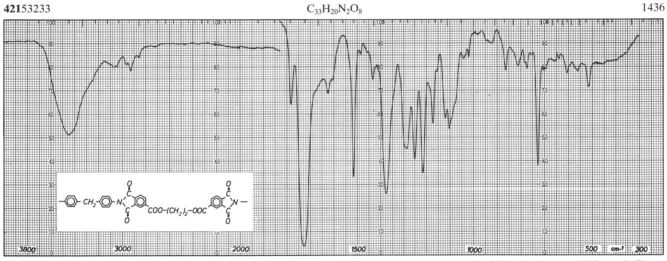

(1) poly(ester imide)
(2) yellow powder
(3) S.G. Babé, Instituto de Plásticos y Caucho, Madrid
(5) polycondensation of ethylene-bis-(trimellitate imide) with 4,4'-diaminodiphenylmethane

(6) S.G. Babé, J. de Abajo, J. Fontán, Angew. Makromol. Chem. *21* (1972) 65 ... 77
(7) KBr (0.6/300)

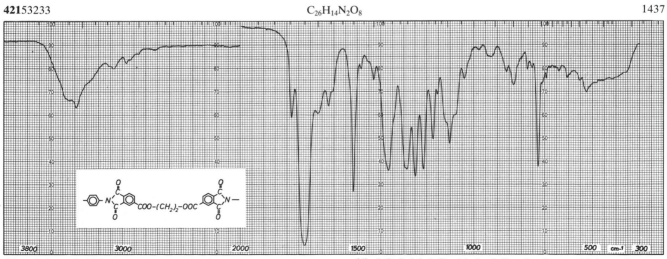

(1) poly(ester imide)
(2) ochre-coloured powder
(3) S.G. Babé, Instituto de Plásticos y Caucho, Madrid
(5) polycondensation of ethylene-bis(trimellitate imide) with p-phenylenediamine

(6) S.G. Babé, J. De Abajo, J. Fontán, Angew. Makromol. Chem. *21* (1972) 65 ... 77
(7) KBr (1/300)

42153234 $C_{30}H_{22}N_2O_8$ 1438

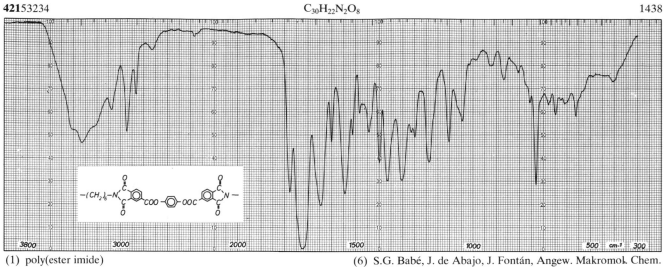

(1) poly(ester imide)
(2) white powder
(3) S.G. Babé, Instituto de Plásticos y Caucho, Madrid
(5) polycondensation of p-phenylene-bis(trimellitate imide) with hexamethylenediamine

(6) S.G. Babé, J. de Abajo, J. Fontán, Angew. Makromol. Chem. *21* (1972) 65...77
(7) KBr (0,75/300)

42153234 $C_{37}H_{20}N_2O_8$ 1439

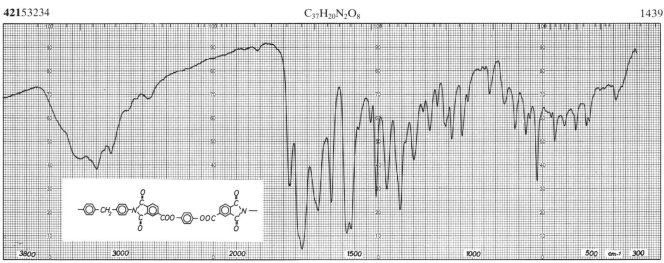

(1) poly(ester imide)
(2) yellow powder
(3) S.G. Babé, Instituto de Plásticos y Caucho, Madrid
(5) polycondensation of p-phenylene-bis(trimellitate imide) with 4,4'-diaminodiphenylmethane

(6) S.G. Babé, J. de Abajo, J. Fontán, Angew. Makromol. Chem. *21* (1972) 65...77
(7) KBr (1/300)

42153234 $C_{45}H_{28}N_2O_9$ 1440

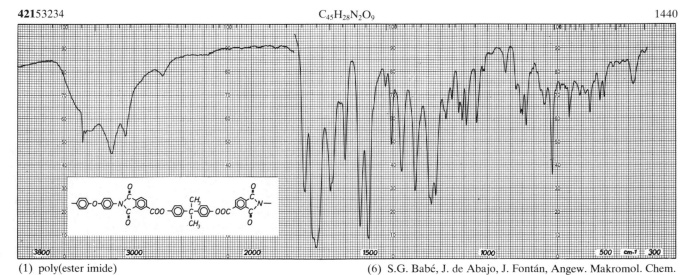

(1) poly(ester imide)
(2) ochre-coloured powder
(3) S.G. Babé, Instituto de Plásticos y Caucho, Madrid
(5) polycondensation of 2,2-bis(trimellitate imide)diphenyl propane with 4,4'-diaminodiphenylether

(6) S.G. Babé, J. de Abajo, J. Fontán, Angew. Makromol. Chem. *21* (1972) 65...77
(7) KBr (1/300)

42154211   C_{24}H_{25}N_3O_4   1441

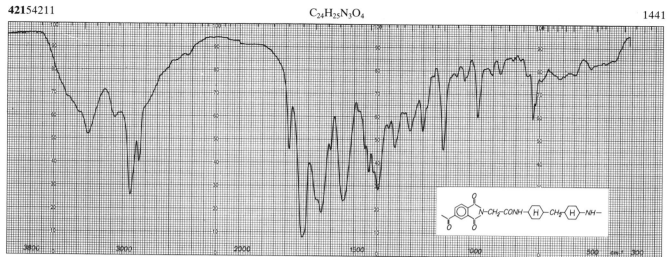

(1) poly(trimellitic amidoimide)
(2) greyisch-white powder
(3) J. de Abajo, Instituto de Plásticos y Caucho, Madrid
(5) condensation of aminoacetic acid with trimellitic acid

anhydride, polycondensation with 4,4'-diaminodicyclohexylmethane
(6) J.P. Gabarda, J. de Abajo, J. Fontán, private communication
(7) KBr (1.4/350)

42154211   C_{33}H_{43}N_3O_4   1442

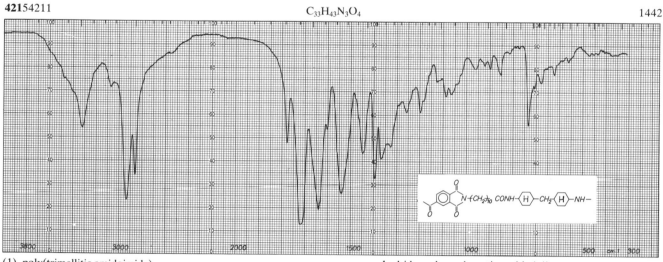

(1) poly(trimellitic amidoimide)
(2) white material
(3) J. de Abajo, Instituto de Plásticos y Caucho, Madrid
(5) condensation of 11-aminoundecanoic acid with trimellitic acid

anhydride, polycondensation with 4,4'-diaminodicyclohexylmethane
(6) J.P. Gabarda, J. de Abajo, J. Fontán, private communication
(7) KBr (1.5/350)

42154212   C_{17}H_{11}N_3O_4   1443

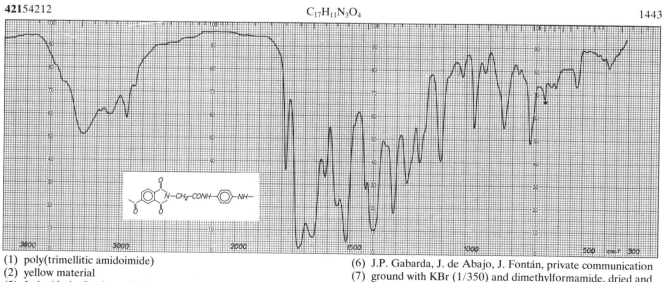

(1) poly(trimellitic amidoimide)
(2) yellow material
(3) J. de Abajo, Instituto de Plásticos y Caucho, Madrid
(5) condensation of aminoacetic acid with trimellitic acid anhydride, polycondensation with p-phenylenediamine

(6) J.P. Gabarda, J. de Abajo, J. Fontán, private communication
(7) ground with KBr (1/350) and dimethylformamide, dried and pressed
(8) * residual dimethylformamide

42154212   C$_{26}$H$_{29}$N$_3$O$_4$ 1444

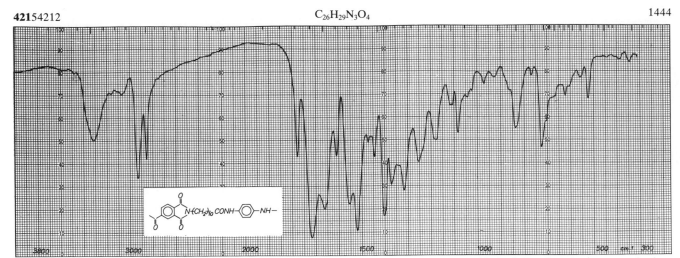

(1) poly(trimellitic amidoimide)
(2) light-yellow material
(3) J. de Abajo, Instituto de Plásticos y Caucho, Madrid
(5) condensation of 11-amioundecanoic acid with trimellitic acid
anhydride, polycondensation with p-phenylenediamine

(6) J.P. Gabarda, J. de Abajo, J. Fontán, private communication
(7) KBr (1.5/350)

42154212   C$_{24}$H$_{17}$N$_3$O$_4$ 1445

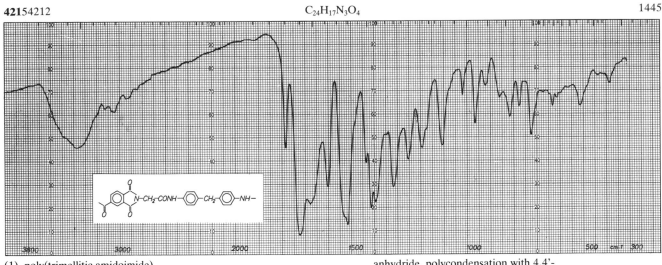

(1) poly(trimellitic amidoimide)
(2) light-yellow material
(3) J. de Abajo, Instituto de Plásticos y Caucho, Madrid
(5) condensation of aminoacetic acid with trimellitic acid

anhydride, polycondensation with 4,4'-
diaminodiphenylmethane
(6) J.P. Gabarda, J. de Abajo, J. Fontán, private communication
(7) KBr (1.2/350)

42154212   C$_{33}$H$_{35}$N$_3$O$_4$ 1446

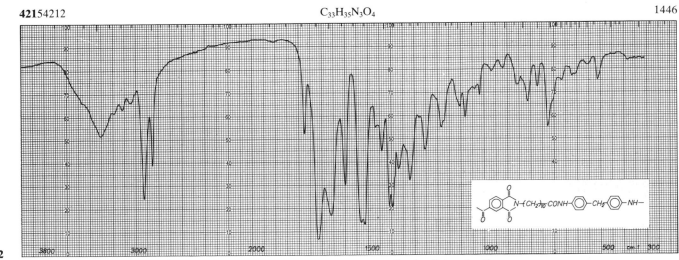

(1) poly(trimellitic amidoimide)
(2) yellowish fibrous material
(3) J. de Abajo, Instituto de Plásticos y Caucho, Madrid
(5) condensation of 11-aminoundecanoic acid with trimellitic acid
anhydride, polycondensation with 4,4'-

diaminodiphenylmethane
(6) J.P. Gabarda, J. de Abajo, J. Fontán, private communication
(7) ground with KBr (1.2/350) and dimethylacetamide, dried and
pressed

42154212   C_{23}H_{15}N_3O_4   1447

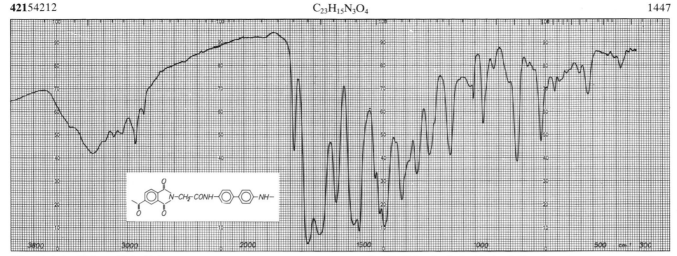

(1) poly(trimellitic amidoimide)
(2) yellow material
(3) J. de Abajo, Instituto de Plásticos y Caucho, Madrid
(5) condensation of aminoacetic acid with trimellitic acid anhydride, polycondensation with 4,4'-diaminobiphenyl
(6) J.P. Gabarda, J. de Abajo, J. Fontán, private communication
(7) ground with KBr (1/350) and dimethylformamide, dried and pressed

42154212   C_{32}H_{33}N_3O_4   1448

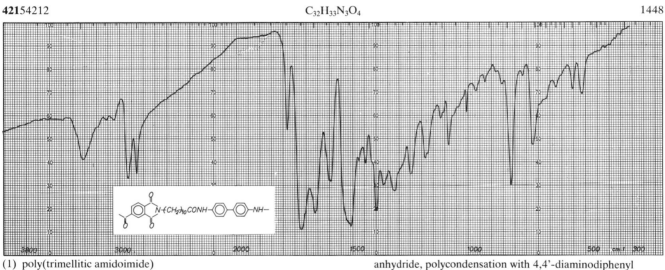

(1) poly(trimellitic amidoimide)
(2) ochre-coloured powder
(3) J. de Abajo, Instituto de Plásticos y Caucho, Madrid
(5) condensation of 11-aminoundecanoic acid with trimellitic acid anhydride, polycondensation with 4,4'-diaminodiphenyl
(6) J.P. Gabarda, J. de Abajo, J. Fontán, private communication
(7) KBr (1.5/350)

42154214   C_{22}H_{14}N_2O_3   1449

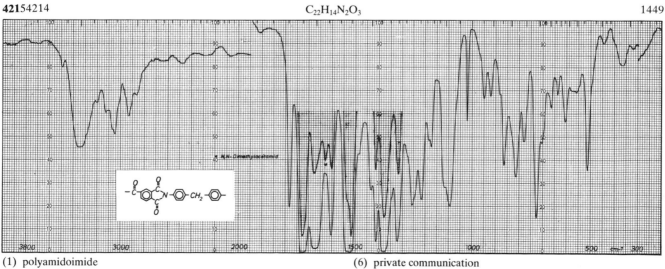

(1) polyamidoimide
(2) yellow film
(3) R. Mücke, Hoechst AG, Werk Gendorf (laboratory preparation)
(5) polyaddition of trimellitic anhydride and 4,4'-diaminodiphenylethane, subsequent cyclization
(6) private communication
(7) film (12 μm), KBr (1/400), ground with DMA, dried and pressed
(8) structure like „Amoco AI 10"

42154214   C_{22}H_{14}N_{2}O_{3}   1450

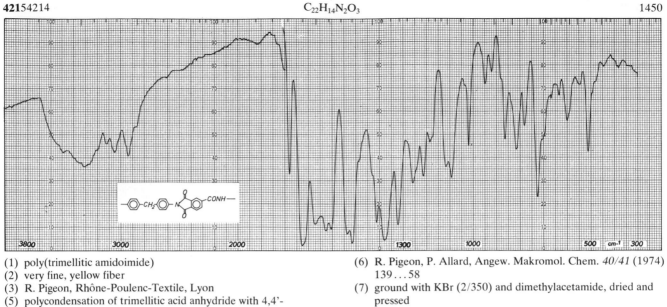

(1) poly(trimellitic amidoimide)
(2) very fine, yellow fiber
(3) R. Pigeon, Rhône-Poulenc-Textile, Lyon
(5) polycondensation of trimellitic acid anhydride with 4,4'-diisocyanatodiphenylmethane

(6) R. Pigeon, P. Allard, Angew. Makromol. Chem. *40/41* (1974) 139...58
(7) ground with KBr (2/350) and dimethylacetamide, dried and pressed

42154214   C_{23}H_{11}N_{3}O_{5}   1451

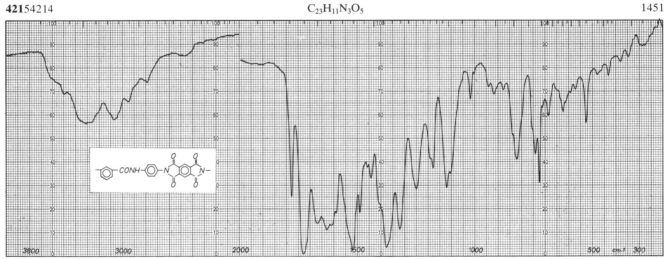

(1) poly(pyromellitic amidoimide)
(2) solution of (15...18% solids) the brown prepolymer with carboxylic groups
(3) L.C. Scala, Research and Development Center, Westinghouse Electric Corp., Pittsburgh, Pa.

(6) L.C. Scala, G.W.M. Hickman, J. Marschik, J. Polym. Sci. *12* (1968) 2339...57
(7) film on CsI, cured at 200 °C i.v. (24 h)
(8) Westinghouse Experimental Polyimide AI-8 Resin (solution)

42154214   C_{23}H_{11}N_{3}O_{5}   1452

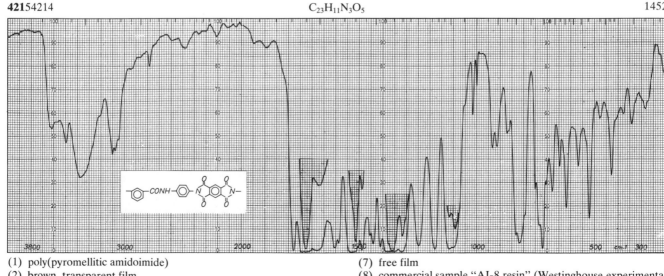

(1) poly(pyromellitic amidoimide)
(2) brown, transparent film
(3) L.C. Scala, Research and Development Center, Westinghouse Electric Corp., Pittsburgh, Pa.
(6) L.C. Scala, G.W.M. Hickman, J. Marschik, J. Polym. Sci. *12* (1968) 2339...57

(7) free film
(8) commercial sample "AI-8 resin" (Westinghouse experimental polyimide)

4215425411 $C_{37}H_{16}N_4O_7$ 1453

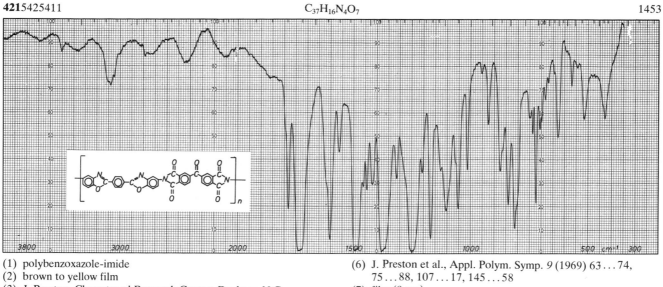

(1) polybenzoxazole-imide
(2) brown to yellow film
(3) J. Preston, Chemstrand Research Center, Durham, N.C.
(5) J. Preston, W.B. Black, J. Polym. Sci. B, *4* (1966) 267

(6) J. Preston et al., Appl. Polym. Symp. *9* (1969) 63...74, 75...88, 107...17, 145...58
(7) film (8 μm)

4215425411 $C_{36}H_{16}N_4O_7$ 1454

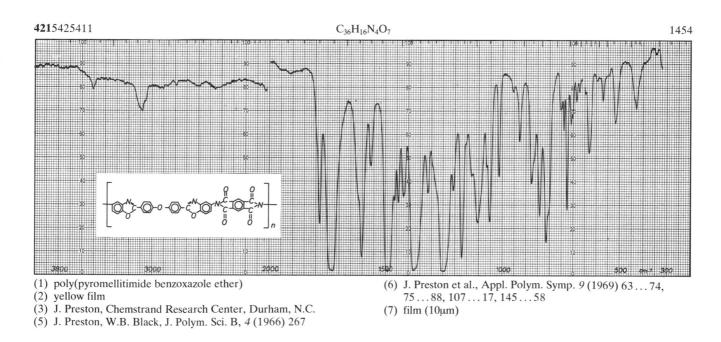

(1) poly(pyromellitimide benzoxazole ether)
(2) yellow film
(3) J. Preston, Chemstrand Research Center, Durham, N.C.
(5) J. Preston, W.B. Black, J. Polym. Sci. B, *4* (1966) 267

(6) J. Preston et al., Appl. Polym. Symp. *9* (1969) 63...74, 75...88, 107...17, 145...58
(7) film (10μm)

4215425412 $C_{24}H_{10}N_4O_5$ 1455

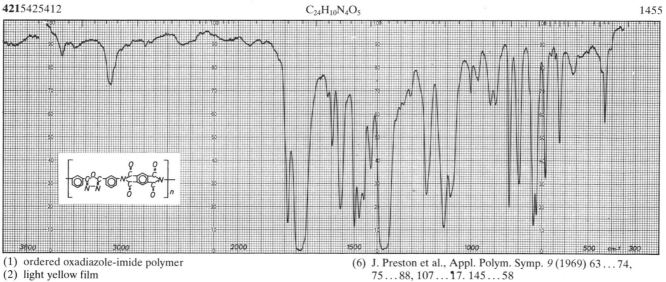

(1) ordered oxadiazole-imide polymer
(2) light yellow film
(3) J. Preston, Chemstrand Research Center, Durham, N.C.
(5) J. Preston, W.B. Black, J. Polym. Sci. B, *4* (1966) 267

(6) J. Preston et al., Appl. Polym. Symp. *9* (1969) 63...74, 75...88, 107...17. 145...58
(7) film (8 μm)

4215425412 $C_{24}H_{10}N_4O_5$ 1456

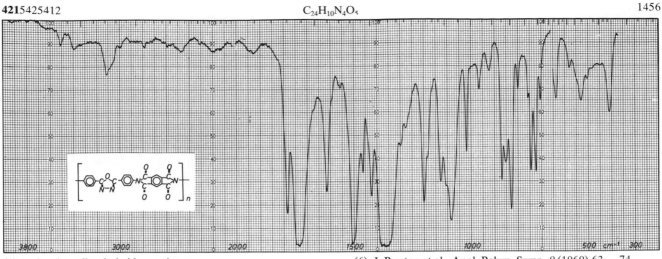

(1) ordered oxadiazole-imide copolymer
(2) brown to yellow film
(3) J. Preston, Chemstrand Research Center, Durham, N.C.
(5) J. Preston, W.B. Black, J. Polym. Sci. N, *4* (1966) 267

(6) J. Preston et al., Appl. Polym. Symp. *9* (1969) 63...74, 75...88, 107...17, 145...58
(7) film (8 μm)

4215425412 $C_{31}H_{14}N_4O_6$ 1457

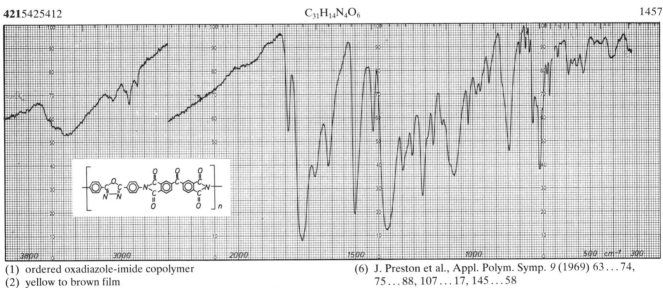

(1) ordered oxadiazole-imide copolymer
(2) yellow to brown film
(3) J. Preston, Chemstrand Research Center, Durham, N.C.
(5) J. Preston, W.B. Black, J. Polym. Sci. B, *4* (1966) 267

(6) J. Preston et al., Appl. Polym. Symp. *9* (1969) 63...74, 75...88, 107...17, 145...58
(7) film (25 μm), KBr

4215522 $C_{32}H_{18}N_2O_9$ 1458

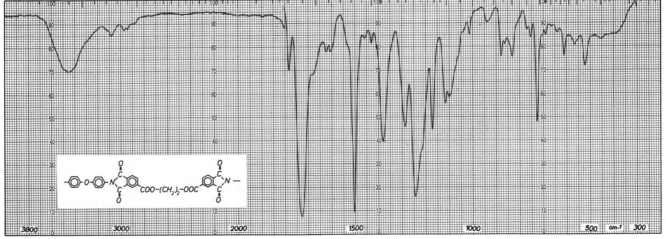

(1) poly(trimellitc imidoesterether)
(2) slightly greyish-green powder
(3) S.G. Babé, Instituto de Plásticos y Caucho, Madrid
(5) polycondensation of ethylene-bis(trimellitate imide) with 4,4'-diaminodiphenylether (development of ammonia)

(6) S.G. Babé, J. de Abajo, J. Fontán, Angew. Makromol. Chem. *21* (1972) 65...77
(7) KBr (0.75/300)

4215526 C$_{21}$H$_{12}$N$_2$O$_4$ 1459

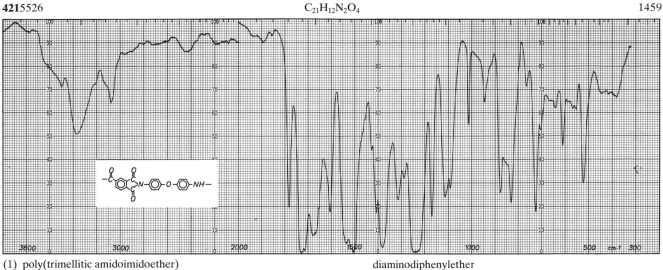

(1) poly(trimellitic amidoimidoether)
(2) yellowish film
(3) W. Wrasidlo, U.S. Naval Ordnance Laboratory, Silver Spring, Maryland
(5) polycondensation of trimellitic anhydride with 4,4'-

diaminodiphenylether
(6) W. Wrasidlo, J.M. Augl, J. Polym. Sci. A-1, 7 (1969) 321...32
(7) film (10 µm)

4215526 C$_{21}$H$_{12}$N$_2$O$_4$ 1460

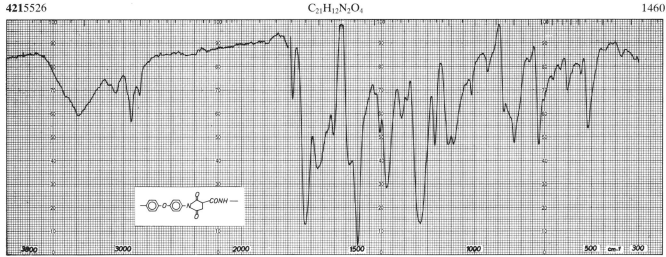

(1) poly(trimellitic amidoimidoether)
(2) fine yellow fiber
(3) R. Pigeon, Rhône-Poulenc Textile, Lyon
(5) polycondensation of trimellitic acid anhydride with 4,4'-diisocyanatodiphenylether

(6) R. Pigeon, P. Allard, Angew. Makromol. Chem. 40/41 (1974) 139...58
(7) ground with KBr (2/350) and dimethylacetamide, dried and pressed

4215526 C$_{23}$H$_{15}$N$_3$O$_5$ 1461

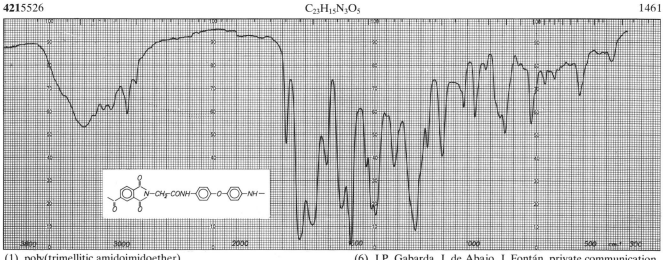

(1) poly(trimellitic amidoimidoether)
(2) light-yellow material
(3) J. de Abajo, Instituto de Plásticos y Caucho, Madrid
(5) condensation of amioacetic acid with trimellitic acid anhydride, polycondensation with 4,4'-diaminodiphenylether

(6) J.P. Gabarda, J. de Abajo, J. Fontán, private communication
(7) ground with KBr (1/350) and dimethylformamide, dried and pressed

4215526 $C_{32}H_{33}N_3O_5$ 1462

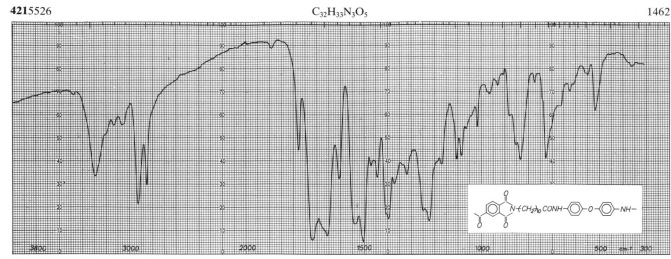

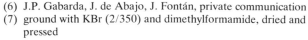

(1) poly(trimellitic amidoimidoether)
(2) yellowish granules
(3) J. de Abajo, Instituto de Plásticos y Caucho, Madrid
(5) condensation of 11-aminoundecanoic acid with trimellitic acid anhydride, polycondensation with 4,4'-diaminodiphenylether

(6) J.P. Gabarda, J. de Abajo, J. Fontán, private communication
(7) ground with KBr (2/350) and dimethylformamide, dried and pressed

4215526 $C_{42}H_{24}N_4O_8$ 1463

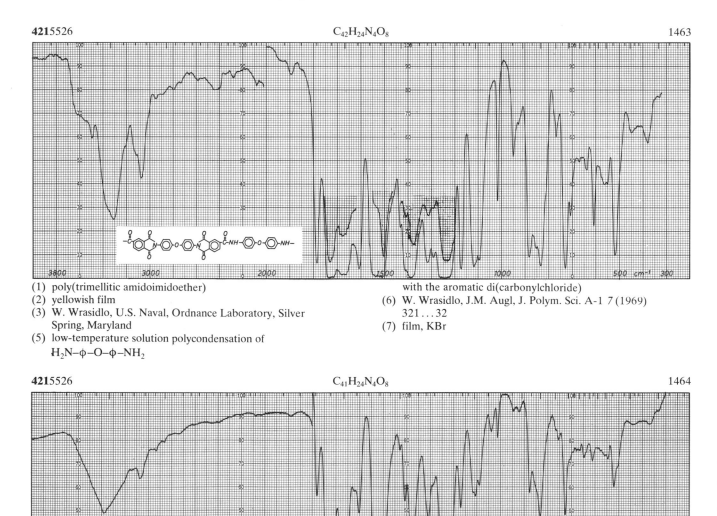

(1) poly(trimellitic amidoimidoether)
(2) yellowish film
(3) W. Wrasidlo, U.S. Naval, Ordnance Laboratory, Silver Spring, Maryland
(5) low-temperature solution polycondensation of $H_2N-\phi-O-\phi-NH_2$

with the aromatic di(carbonylchloride)
(6) W. Wrasidlo, J.M. Augl, J. Polym. Sci. A-1 7 (1969) 321...32
(7) film, KBr

4215526 $C_{41}H_{24}N_4O_8$ 1464

(1) poly(trimellitic amidoimidoether)
(2) yellow powder
(3) S.G. Babé, Instituto de Plásticos y Caucho, Madrid
(5) polycondensation of 4,4'-bis-(3,4-dicarboxyimide benzamide)diphenylether and diaminodiphenylether

(6) S.G. Babé, J. de Abajo, J. Fontán, Angew. Makromol. Chem. *21* (1972) 65...77
(7) KBr (1/300)

4215526 $C_{30}H_{24}N_4O_9$ 1465

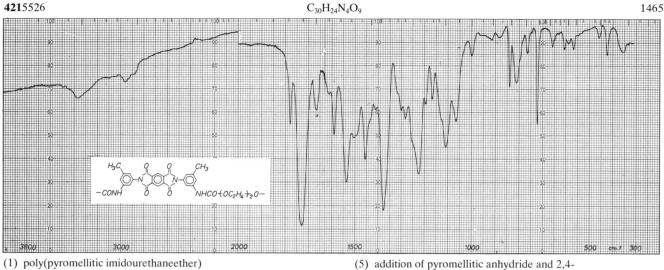

(1) poly(pyromellitic imidourethaneether)
(2) yellow powder
(3) H. Matsuda, Research Laboratory, Okura Industrial Co., 1515 Nakatsu-cho

(5) addition of pyromellitic anhydride and 2,4-toluylenediisocyanate, polyaddition with diethyleneglycol
(6) H. Matsuda, Makromol. Chem. *176* (1975) 573...85
(7) film from dimethylformamide on CsI

4215526 $C_{28}H_{20}N_4O_8$ 1466

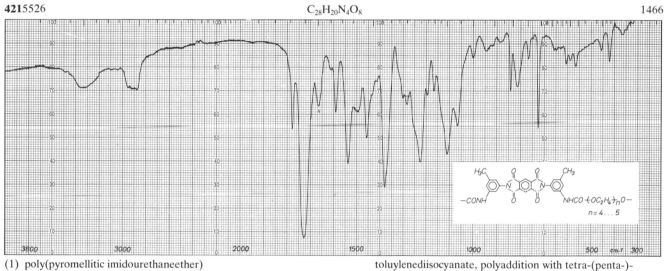

(1) poly(pyromellitic imidourethaneether)
(2) yellow powder
(3) H. Matsuda, Research Laboratory, Okura Industrial Co., 1515 Nakatsu-cho
(5) addition of pyromellitic anhydride and 2,4-

toluylenediisocyanate, polyaddition with tetra-(penta-)-ethyleneglycol
(6) H. Matsuda, Makromol. Chem. *176* (1975) 573...85
(7) film from dimethylformamide on CsI

4215526 $C_{44}H_{52}N_4O_{16}$ 1467

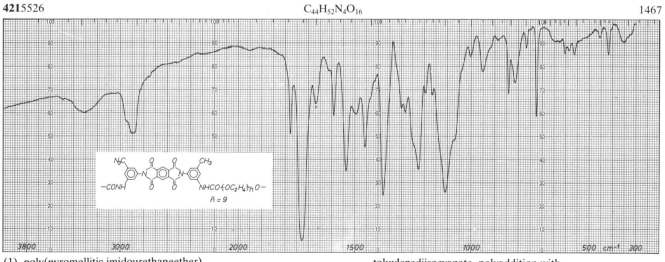

(1) poly(pyromellitic imidourethaneether)
(2) orange-coloured powder
(3) H. Matsuda, Research Laboratory, Okura Industrial Co., 1515 Nakatsu-cho
(5) addition of pyromellitic anhydride and 2,4-

toluylenediisocyanate, polyaddition with poly(oxyethylene)glycol (nonameric)
(6) H. Matsuda, Makromol. Chem. *176* (1975) 573...85
(7) film from dimethylformamide on CsI

42156 $C_{20}H_{18}N_6O_4$ 1468

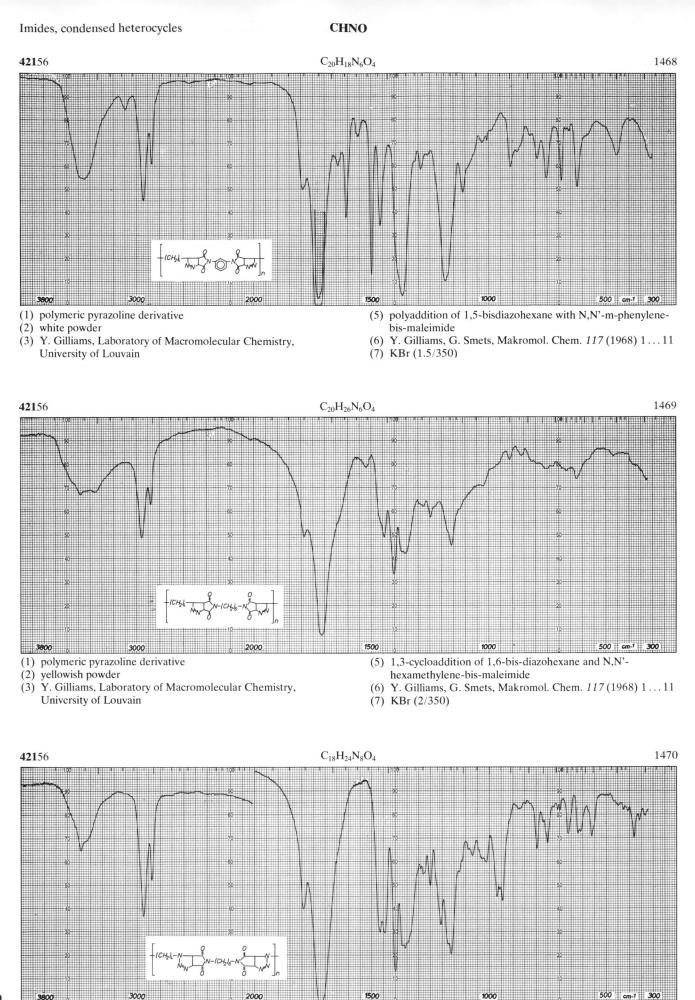

(1) polymeric pyrazoline derivative
(2) white powder
(3) Y. Gilliams, Laboratory of Macromolecular Chemistry,
     University of Louvain
(5) polyaddition of 1,5-bisdiazohexane with N,N'-m-phenylene-
     bis-maleimide
(6) Y. Gilliams, G. Smets, Makromol. Chem. *117* (1968) 1...11
(7) KBr (1.5/350)

42156 $C_{20}H_{26}N_6O_4$ 1469

(1) polymeric pyrazoline derivative
(2) yellowish powder
(3) Y. Gilliams, Laboratory of Macromolecular Chemistry,
     University of Louvain
(5) 1,3-cycloaddition of 1,6-bis-diazohexane and N,N'-
     hexamethylene-bis-maleimide
(6) Y. Gilliams, G. Smets, Makromol. Chem. *117* (1968) 1...11
(7) KBr (2/350)

42156 $C_{18}H_{24}N_8O_4$ 1470

(1) polymeric triazole derivative
(2) yellowish powder
(3) Y. Gilliams, Laboratory of Macromolecular Chemistry,
     University of Louvain
(5) polyaddition of 1,6-hexamethylene diazide with N,N'-
     hexamethylene-bis-maleimide
(6) Y. Gilliams, G. Smets, Makromol. Chem. *117* (1968) 1...11
(7) KBr (1.5/350)

42161131   C₁₂H₉N₃O   1471

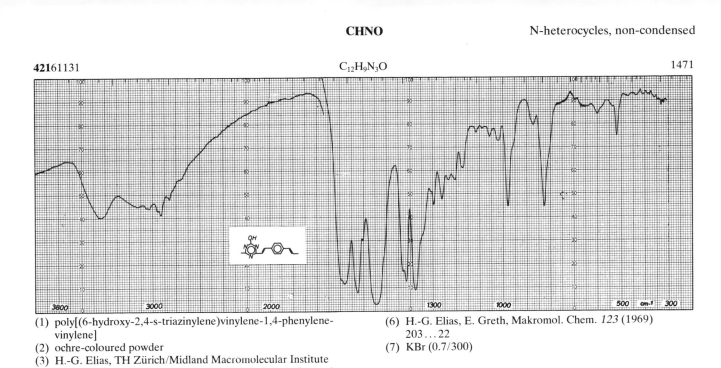

(1) poly[(6-hydroxy-2,4-s-triazinylene)vinylene-1,4-phenylene-vinylene]
(2) ochre-coloured powder
(3) H.-G. Elias, TH Zürich/Midland Macromolecular Institute
(5) polycondensation of 6-methoxy-2,4-dimethyl-s-triazine and terephthalic aldehyde in H₂SO₄ (60 °C)
(6) H.-G. Elias, E. Greth, Makromol. Chem. *123* (1969) 203...22
(7) KBr (0.7/300)

42161131   C₈H₅N₃O   1472

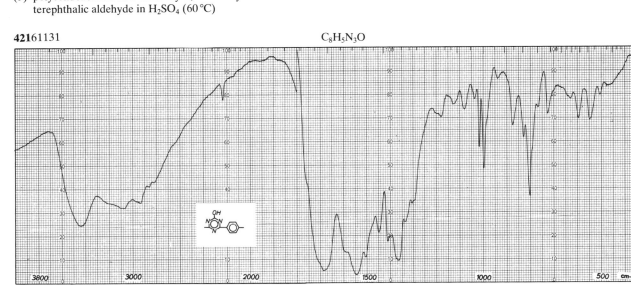

(1) poly[(6-hydroxy-2,4-s-triazinylene)1,4-phenylene]
(2) light-yellow powder
(3) H.-G. Elias, TH Zürich/Midland Macromolecular Institute
(6) private communication, see also H.-G. Elias, E. Greth, Makromol. Chem. *123* (1969) 203...22
(7) KBr (1,1/350)

42161132   C₃₄H₂₂N₆O   1473

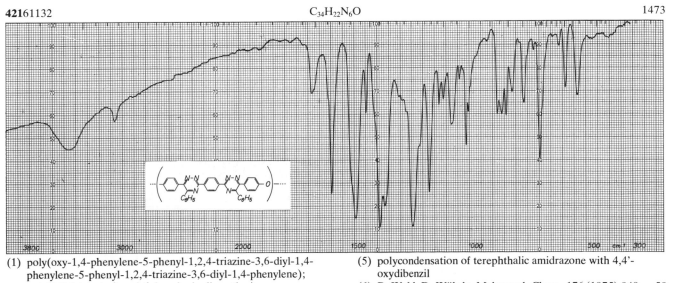

(1) poly(oxy-1,4-phenylene-5-phenyl-1,2,4-triazine-3,6-diyl-1,4-phenylene-5-phenyl-1,2,4-triazine-3,6-diyl-1,4-phenylene); poly(1,2,4-triazine); poly(phenylquinoline ether)
(2) light-yellow powder
(3) D. Wöhrle, Freie Universität, Berlin/Universität Bremen
(5) polycondensation of terephthalic amidrazone with 4,4'-oxydibenzil
(6) B. Wahl, D. Wöhrle, Makromol. Chem. *176* (1975) 849...58
(7) KBr (1.5/350)

42161132   1474

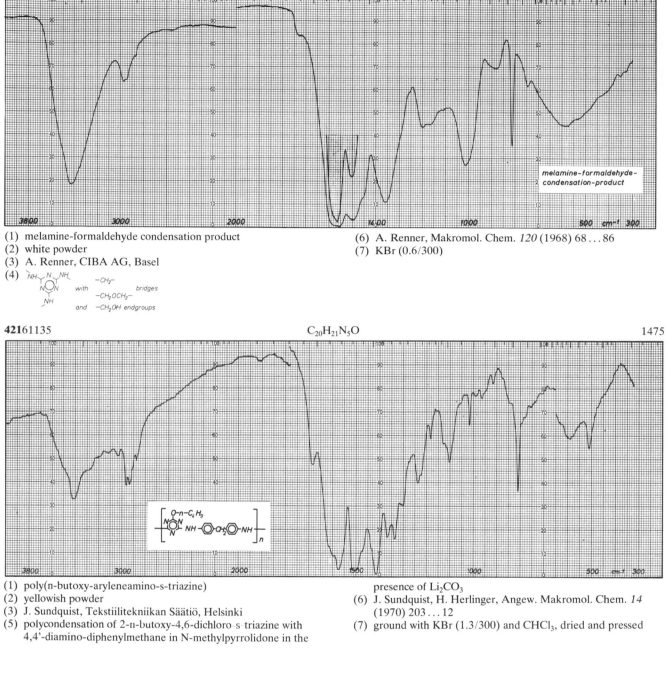

melamine-formaldehyde-condensation-product

(1) melamine-formaldehyde condensation product
(2) white powder
(3) A. Renner, CIBA AG, Basel
(4)

(6) A. Renner, Makromol. Chem. *120* (1968) 68...86
(7) KBr (0.6/300)

42161135 $C_{20}H_{21}N_5O$ 1475

(1) poly(n-butoxy-aryleneamino-s-triazine)
(2) yellowish powder
(3) J. Sundquist, Tekstiilitekniikan Säätiö, Helsinki
(5) polycondensation of 2-n-butoxy-4,6-dichloro-s-triazine with
4,4'-diamino-diphenylmethane in N-methylpyrrolidone in the

presence of Li_2CO_3
(6) J. Sundquist, H. Herlinger, Angew. Makromol. Chem. *14*
(1970) 203...12
(7) ground with KBr (1.3/300) and $CHCl_3$, dried and pressed

---

42161135 $C_{19}H_{19}N_5O$ 1476

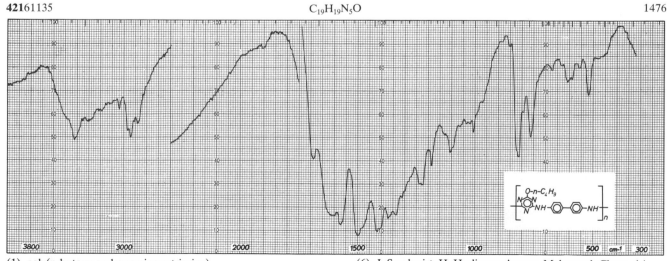

(1) poly(n-butoxy-aryleneamino-s-triazine)
(2) yellowish powder
(3) S. Sundquist, Tekstiilitekniikan Säätiö, Helsinki
(5) polycondensation of 2-n-butoxy-4,6-dichloro-s-triazine with
benzidine in N-methylpyrrolidone in the presence of Li_2CO_3

(6) J. Sundquist, H. Herlinger, Angew. Makromol. Chem. *14*
(1970) 203...12
(7) ground with KBr (1.2/350) and $CHCl_3$, dried and pressed

42161135 $C_{19}H_{19}N_5O_2$ 1477

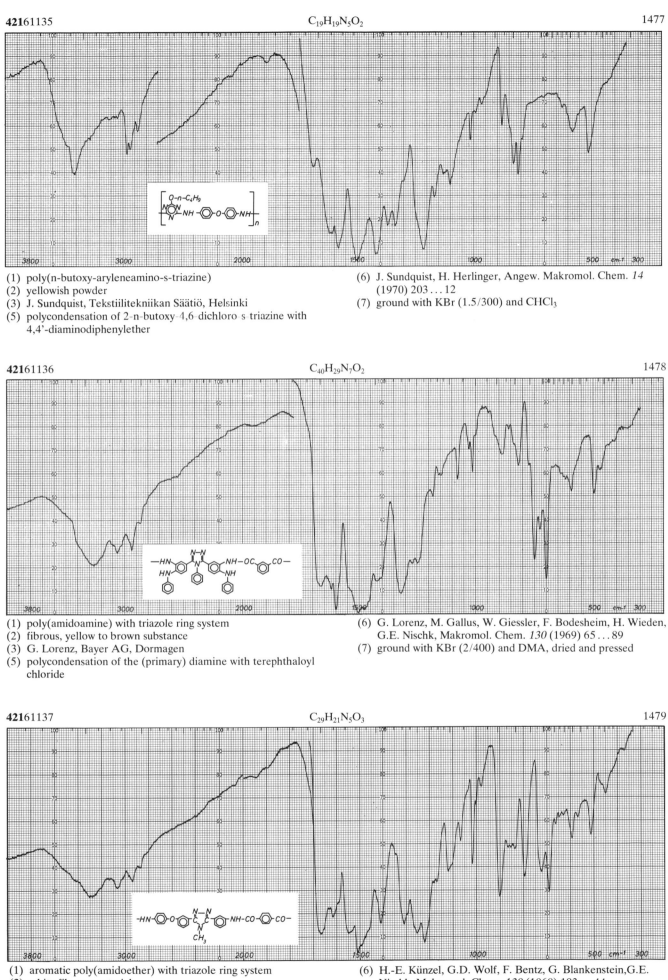

(1) poly(n-butoxy-aryleneamino-s-triazine)
(2) yellowish powder
(3) J. Sundquist, Tekstiilitekniikan Säätiö, Helsinki
(5) polycondensation of 2-n-butoxy-4,6-dichloro-s-triazine with 4,4'-diaminodiphenylether

(6) J. Sundquist, H. Herlinger, Angew. Makromol. Chem. *14* (1970) 203...12
(7) ground with KBr (1.5/300) and CHCl₃

42161136 $C_{40}H_{29}N_7O_2$ 1478

(1) poly(amidoamine) with triazole ring system
(2) fibrous, yellow to brown substance
(3) G. Lorenz, Bayer AG, Dormagen
(5) polycondensation of the (primary) diamine with terephthaloyl chloride

(6) G. Lorenz, M. Gallus, W. Giessler, F. Bodesheim, H. Wieden, G.E. Nischk, Makromol. Chem. *130* (1969) 65...89
(7) ground with KBr (2/400) and DMA, dried and pressed

42161137 $C_{29}H_{21}N_5O_3$ 1479

(1) aromatic poly(amidoether) with triazole ring system
(2) white fibrous material
(3) H.-E. Künzel, Bayer AG, Dormagen
(5) polycondensation of the heterocyclic diamine with terephthaloyl chloride

(6) H.-E. Künzel, G.D. Wolf, F. Bentz, G. Blankenstein, G.E. Nischk, Makromol. Chem. *130* (1969) 103...44
(7) ground with KBr (3.5/300) and DMA, dried and pressed

421611327 $C_{40}H_{27}N_5O_4$ 1480

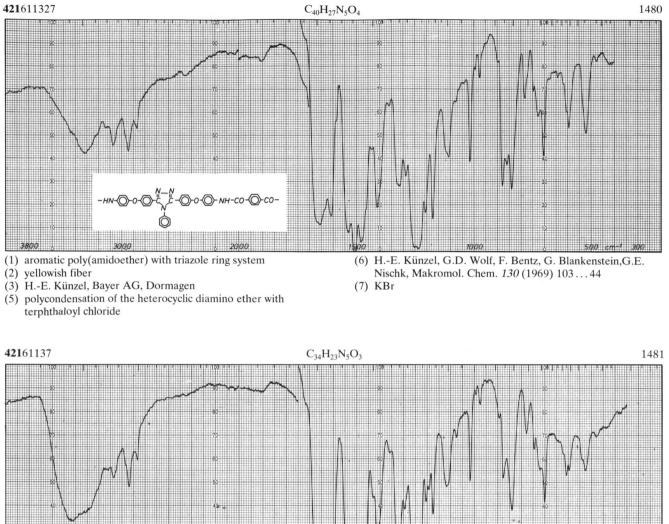

(1) aromatic poly(amidoether) with triazole ring system
(2) yellowish fiber
(3) H.-E. Künzel, Bayer AG, Dormagen
(5) polycondensation of the heterocyclic diamino ether with terphthaloyl chloride

(6) H.-E. Künzel, G.D. Wolf, F. Bentz, G. Blankenstein,G.E. Nischk, Makromol. Chem. *130* (1969) 103...44
(7) KBr

42161137 $C_{34}H_{23}N_5O_3$ 1481

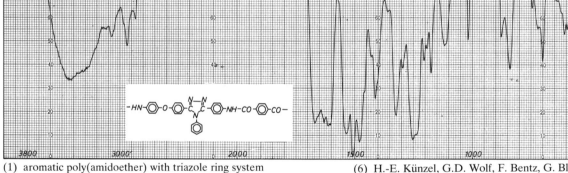

(1) aromatic poly(amidoether) with triazole ring system
(2) yellow fiber
(3) H.-E. Künzel, Bayer AG, Dormagen
(5) polycondensation of the heterocyclic diamine with terephthaloyl chloride

(6) H.-E. Künzel, G.D. Wolf, F. Bentz, G. Blankenstein,G.E. Nischk, Makromol. Chem. *130* (1969) 103...44
(7) KBr (1.5/300)

42161139 $C_{58}H_{41}N_7O_5$ 1482

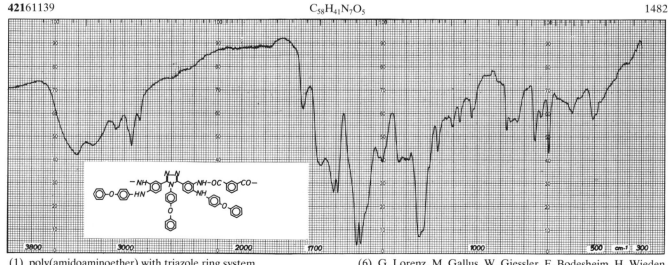
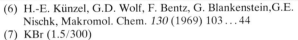

(1) poly(amidoaminoether) with triazole ring system
(2) yellow to brown material
(3) G. Lorenz, Bayer AG, Dormagen
(5) polycondensation of the aromatic (primary) diamine with isophthaloyl chloride

(6) G. Lorenz, M. Gallus, W. Giessler, F. Bodesheim, H. Wieden, G.E. Nischk, Makromol. Chem. *130* (1969) 65...89
(7) ground with KBr (1.5/400) and DMA, dried and pressed

42161213 $C_9H_9NO_2$ 1483

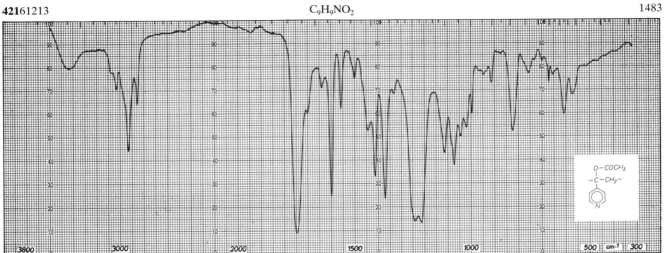

(1) poly(α-acetoxy-4-vinylpyridine)
(2) ochre-coloured powder
(3) T. Furuyama, Asahi Chemical Ind., Tokyo
(5) γ-induced polymerization of the monomer, see H.C. Haas, H.S. Kolesinski, N.W. Schuler, J. Polym. Sci. B, *3* (1965) 879,

H.S. Aaron, O.O. Owens, P.D. Rosenstock, S. Leonard, S. Elkin, J.I. Miller, J. Org. Chem., *30* (1965) 1331
(6) T. Furuyama, K. Mori, R. Wakas, J. Polym. Sci. A-1, *9* (1971) 3411
(7) ground with KBr (2/350) and CHCl₃, dried and pressed

42161213 $C_9H_9NO_2$ 1484

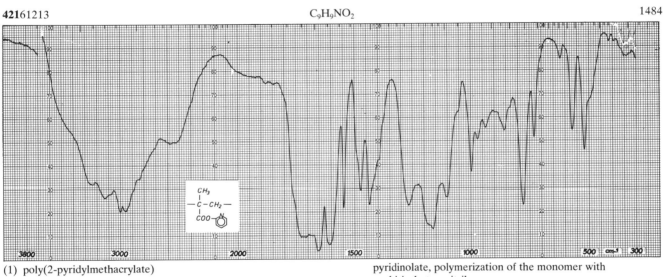

(1) poly(2-pyridylmethacrylate)
(2) greyish-white material
(3) K. Yokota, Department of Synthetic Chemistry, Nagoya University
(5) condensation of methacryloylchloride and sodium-2-

pyridinolate, polymerization of the monomer with azobisisobutyronitrile
(6) K. Yokota, M. Sasaki, Y. Ishi, J. Polym. Sci. A-1 *6* (1968) 2935...8
(7) KBr (2/350)

421621122 $C_{42}H_{26}N_2O_2$ 1485

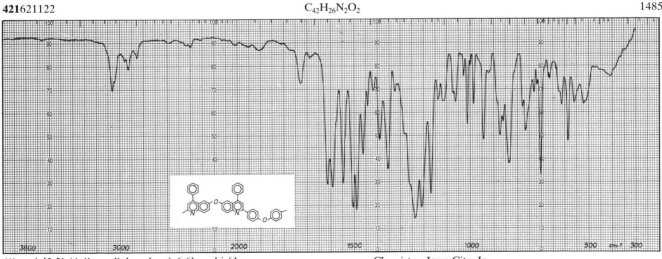

(1) poly[2,2'-(4,4'-oxydiphenylene)-6,6'-oxybis(4-phenylquinoline)]
(2) white fibrous material
(3) J.F. Wolfe, St. O. Norris, University of Iowa, Department of

Chemistry, Iowa City, Io.
(6) J.K. Stille, International Conference on Thermostable Polymers, Baranóv, 1975
(7) film from CHCl₃ on CsI

421621122 $C_{42}H_{26}N_2O_2$ 1486

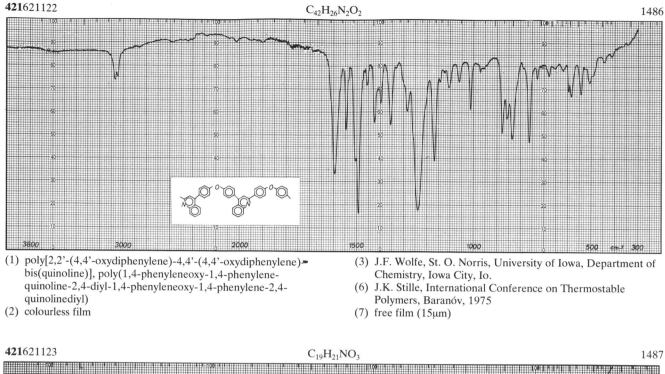

(1) poly[2,2'-(4,4'-oxydiphenylene)-4,4'-(4,4'-oxydiphenylene)-bis(quinoline)], poly(1,4-phenyleneoxy-1,4-phenylene-quinoline-2,4-diyl-1,4-phenyleneoxy-1,4-phenylene-2,4-quinolinediyl)
(2) colourless film

(3) J.F. Wolfe, St. O. Norris, University of Iowa, Department of Chemistry, Iowa City, Io.
(6) J.K. Stille, International Conference on Thermostable Polymers, Baranóv, 1975
(7) free film (15μm)

421621123 $C_{19}H_{21}NO_3$ 1487

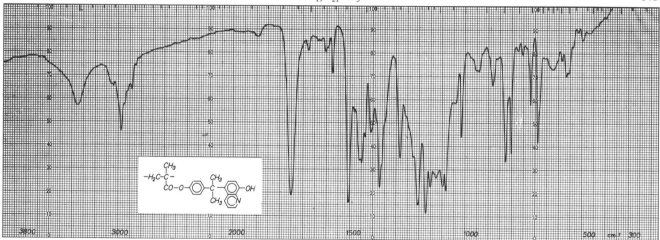

(1) poly[1-methyl-1-(8-hydroxyquinoline-5-yl-2-propylidene-1,4-phenyleneoxycarbonyl)ethylene]; poly[4-{ (8-hydroxyquinoline-5-yl)-2-propyl}phenylmethacrylate]
(2) greyish white powder
(3) K. Idel, Zentralbereich Zentrale Forschung, Wissenschaftliches Hauptlaboratorium, Bayer AG, Krefeld-Uerdingen

(5) condensation of 5-[2-(4-hydroxyphenyl)-2-propyl]-8-quinolinol with methacryloylchloride in CH_2Cl_2 (with triethylamine and Na_2CO_3 in an aqueous phase), polymerization
(6) K. Idel, D. Freitag, H. Vernaleken, Makromol. Chem. *177* (1976) 2927...43
(7) KBr (1.5/350)

421621211 $C_{22}H_{25}N_4O_2$ 1488

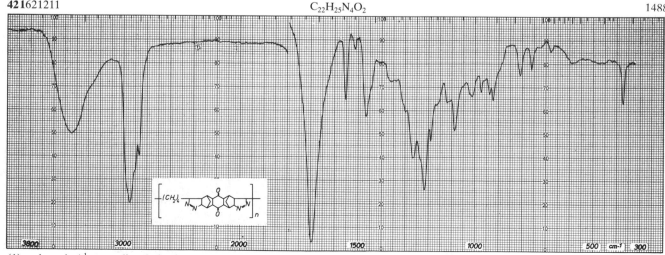

(1) polymeric Δ^1-pyrazoline derivative
(2) light-yellow powder
(3) Y. Gilliams, Laboratory of Macromolecular Chemistry, University of Louvain

(5) 1,3-cycloaddition of 1,5-bisdiazohexane to bis-cyclopentadiene-quinone
(6) Y. Gilliams, G. Smets, Makromol. Chem. *117* (1968) 1...11
(7) KBr (2/350)

421621211   C_{12}H_{10}N_4O_2   1489

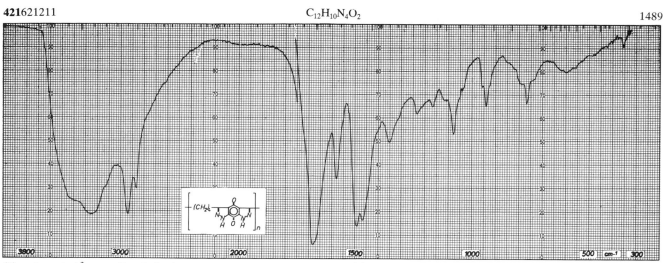

(1) polymeric Δ²-pyrazoline derivative
(2) yellowish material
(3) Y. Gilliams, Laboratory of Macromolecular Chemistry, University of Louvain

(5) 1,3-cycloaddition of 1,6-bisdiazohexane to p-benzoquinone
(6) Y. Gilliams, G. Smets, Makromol. Chem. *117* (1968) 1...11
(7) KBr (1.5/350)

421621221–**421**64112   C_{24}H_{13}N_5O_5   1490

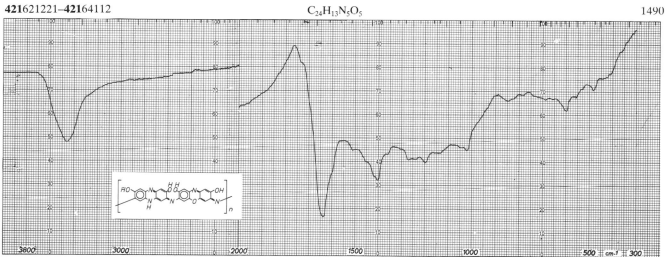

(1) polymer from 2,5-diaminohydroquinone dihydrochloride and 2,5-diamino-p-benzoquinonediimide
(2) black powder
(3) C.S. Marvel, Department of Chemistry, University of Arizona, Tucson, Ariz.
(5) polycondensation of 2,5-diamino-p-benzoquinonediimide

with 2,5-diamino-p-hydroquinone-dihydrochloride in methanesulfonic acid at 110...150 °C
(6) J. Szita, C.S. Marvel, J. Polym. Sci. A-1 7 (1969) 3203...17
(7) ground with KBr (2/350) and dimethylacetamide, dried and pressed

421621222   C_{22}H_{12}N_4O   1491

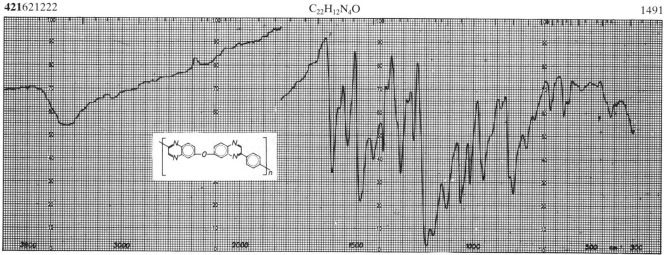

(1) poly(1,4-phenylene-2,7-quinoxaline-diyl-oxy-7,2-quinoxaline-diyl)
(2) black, coarse material
(3) H. Rosen, Institut für Physikalische Chemie, Universität Köln
(5) polycondensation of 3,3'-,4,4'-tetraaminodiphenylether and

1,4-phenylenediglyoxal in dioxane, cyclization at 250 °C (2 h, N_2) and at 375 °C (2 h, i.v.)
(6) H. Rosen, Dissertation, Köln 1977
(7) KBr (1/350), ordinate expanded

421621222 $C_{34}H_{20}N_4O$ 1482

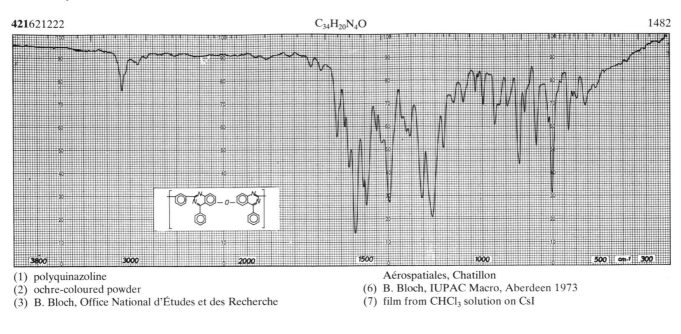

(1) polyquinazoline

(2) ochre-coloured powder

(3) B. Bloch, Office National d'Études et des Recherche

Aérospatiales, Chatillon

(6) B. Bloch, IUPAC Macro, Aberdeen 1973

(7) film from $CHCl_3$ solution on CsI

421621222 $C_{40}H_{24}N_2O_2$ 1493

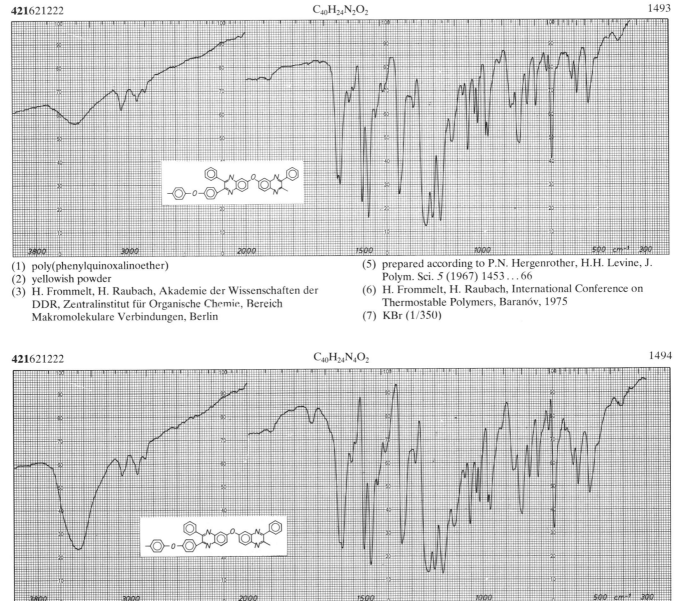

(1) poly(phenylquinoxalinoether)

(2) yellowish powder

(3) H. Frommelt, H. Raubach, Akademie der Wissenschaften der DDR, Zentralinstitut für Organische Chemie, Bereich Makromolekulare Verbindungen, Berlin

(5) prepared according to P.N. Hergenrother, H.H. Levine, J. Polym. Sci. *5* (1967) 1453...66

(6) H. Frommelt, H. Raubach, International Conference on Thermostable Polymers, Baranóv, 1975

(7) KBr (1/350)

421621222 $C_{40}H_{24}N_4O_2$ 1494

498

(1) poly(phenylquinoxalinoether)

(2) yellow film

(3) H. Frommelt, H. Raubach, Akademie der Wissenschaften der DDR, Zentralinstitut für Organische Chemie, Bereich Makromolekulare Verbindungen, Berlin

(5) polycondensation of 4,4'-bis(phenylglyoxalyl)-diphenylether

and 3,3',4,4'-tetraaminodiphenylether; see P.N. Hergenrother, H.H. Levine, J. Polym. Sci. *5* (1967) 1453...66

(6) H. Frommelt, H. Raubach, International Conference on Thermostable Polymers, Baranóv, 1975

(7) KBr (2/350)

421621222   C$_{34}$H$_{20}$N$_4$O$_2$ 1495

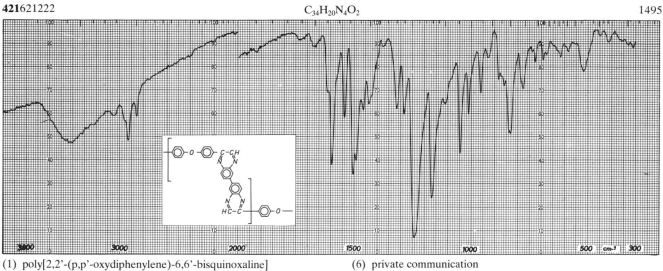

(1) poly[2,2'-(p,p'-oxydiphenylene)-6,6'-bisquinoxaline]
(2) yellowish-brown film
(3) F.D. Trischler, Whittaker Corp., San Diego, Calif.

(6) private communication
(7) KBr, ordinate expanded

421621222–**421**61132   C$_{58}$H$_{37}$N$_7$O$_3$ 1496

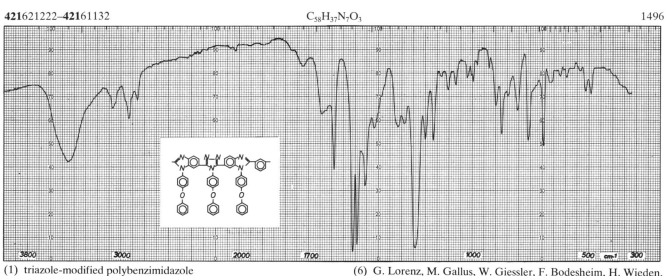

(1) triazole-modified polybenzimidazole
(2) colourless material
(3) G. Lorenz, Bayer AG, Dormagen
(5) thermal polycyclocondensation of the N-arylsubstituted polyamido-amine

(6) G. Lorenz, M. Gallus, W. Giessler, F. Bodesheim, H. Wieden, G.E. Nischk, Makromol. Chem. *130* (1969) 65 ... 89
(7) ground with KBr (1.5/350) and THF, dried and pressed

42162123   C$_{28}$H$_{14}$N$_4$O$_2$ 1497

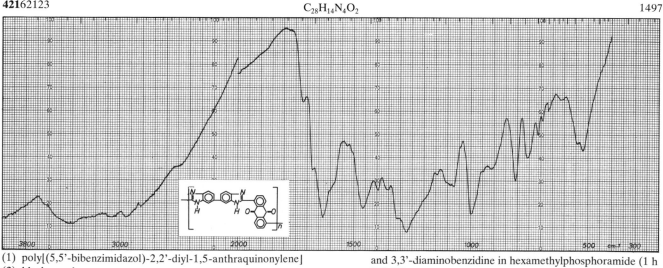

(1) poly[(5,5'-bibenzimidazol)-2,2'-diyl-1,5-anthraquinonylene]
(2) black powder
(3) C.S. Marvel, University of Arizona, Tucson, Ariz.
(4) the polymer probably contains Schiff base links
(5) polycondensation of diphenyl-1,5-anthraquinonedicarboxylate

and 3,3'-diaminobenzidine in hexamethylphosphoramide (1 h 240 °C)
(6) H. Kokelenberg, C.S. Marvel, J. Polym. Sci. A-1, *8* (1970) 3199 ... 209
(7) KBr (3/300)

42162123 $C_{28}H_{14}N_4O_2$ 1498

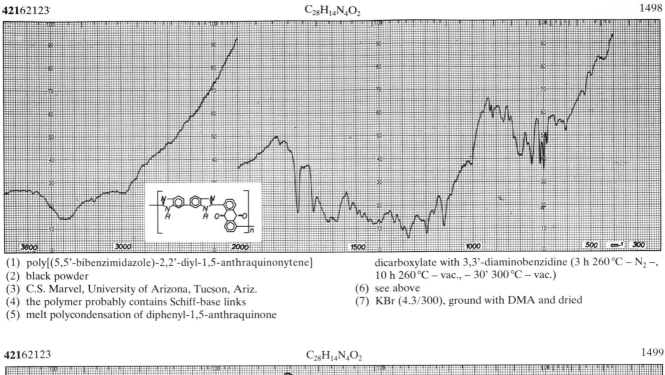

(1) poly[(5,5'-bibenzimidazole)-2,2'-diyl-1,5-anthraquinonytene]
(2) black powder
(3) C.S. Marvel, University of Arizona, Tucson, Ariz.
(4) the polymer probably contains Schiff-base links
(5) melt polycondensation of diphenyl-1,5-anthraquinone

dicarboxylate with 3,3'-diaminobenzidine (3 h 260 °C – N$_2$ –, 10 h 260 °C – vac., – 30' 300 °C – vac.)
(6) see above
(7) KBr (4.3/300), ground with DMA and dried

42162123 $C_{28}H_{14}N_4O_2$ 1499

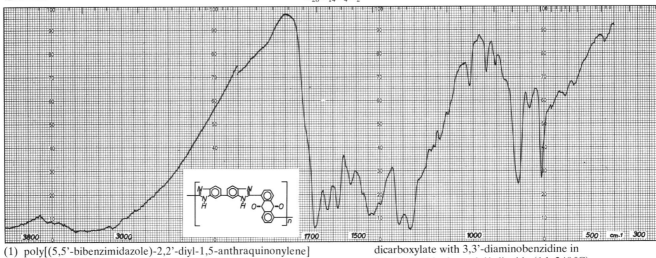

(1) poly[(5,5'-bibenzimidazole)-2,2'-diyl-1,5-anthraquinonylene]
(2) black powder
(3) C.S. Marvel, University of Arizona, Tucson, Ariz.
(4) the polymer probably contains Schiff base links
(5) polycondensation of diphenyl-1,5-anthraquinone

dicarboxylate with 3,3'-diaminobenzidine in tetrahydrothiophene-1,1'-dioxide (1 h 240 °C)
(6) see above
(7) KBr (3/300)

42163121 $C_8H_4N_2O$ 1500

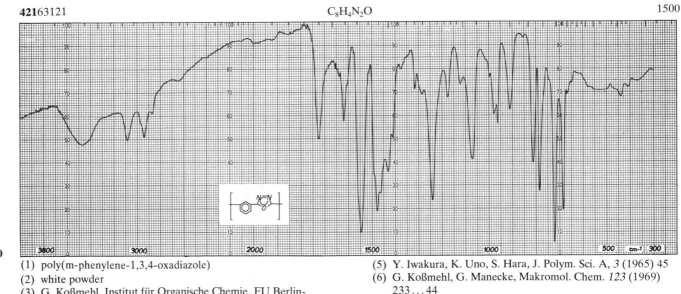

(1) poly(m-phenylene-1,3,4-oxadiazole)
(2) white powder
(3) G. Koßmehl, Institut für Organische Chemie, FU Berlin-Dahlem

(5) Y. Iwakura, K. Uno, S. Hara, J. Polym. Sci. A, *3* (1965) 45
(6) G. Koßmehl, G. Manecke, Makromol. Chem. *123* (1969) 233…44
(7) KBr (2/300)

42163121 $C_8H_4N_2O$ 1501

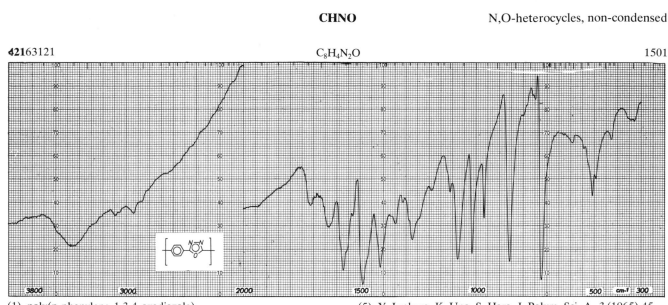

(1) poly(p-phenylene-1,3,4-oxadiazole)
(2) yellow powder
(3) G. Koßmehl, Institut für Organische Chemie, FU Berlin-Dahlem

(5) Y. Iwakura, K. Uno, S. Hara, J. Polym. Sci. A, *3* (1965) 45
(6) G. Koßmehl, G. Manecke, Makromol. Chem. *123* (1969) 233...44
(7) ground with KBr (2/300) and DMA, dried and pressed

42163121 $C_{16}H_8N_4O_2$ 1502

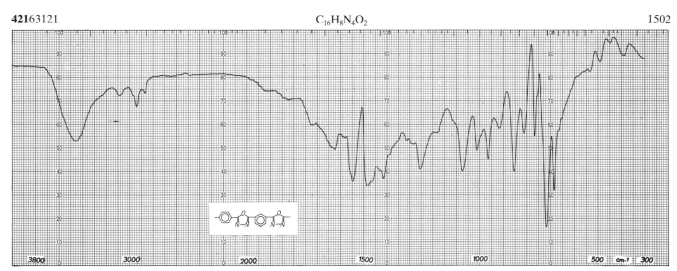

(1) poly(1,4-phenylene-1,3,4-oxadiazole-2,5-diyl-1,3-phenylene-1,3,4-oxadiazole-2,5-diyl)
(2) yellowish fiber
(3) A.H. Frazer, Textile Fibers Dept., Pioneering Research Division, E.I. Du Pont de Nemours & Comp., Wilmington, Dela.

(5) cyclodehydration of the copolyhydrazide fiber derived from terephthaloylchloride and isophthaloylhydrazide
(6) A.H. Frazer, D.R. Wilson, Appl. Polym. Symp. *9* (1969) 89...106
(7) KBr (2/350); ordinate expanded between 2000 cm^{-1} and 200 cm^{-1}

42163121–**42**164111 $C_{15}H_7N_3O_2$ 1503

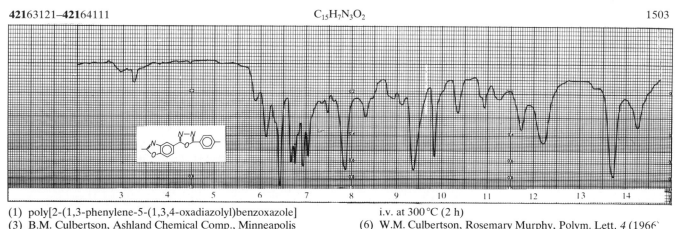

(1) poly[2-(1,3-phenylene-5-(1,3,4-oxadiazolyl)benzoxazole]
(3) B.M. Culbertson, Ashland Chemical Comp., Minneapolis Research Center, Minneapolis, Minn.
(5) polycondensation of 4-amino-3-hydroxybenzoyl hydrazide with terephthaloyl chloride, cyclization of the polyhydrazide

i.v. at 300 °C (2 h)
(6) W.M. Culbertson, Rosemary Murphy, Polym. Lett. *4* (1966) 249...53
(7) spectrum by B.M. Culbertson

42165121   C$_{25}$H$_{10}$N$_4$O$_4$ 1504

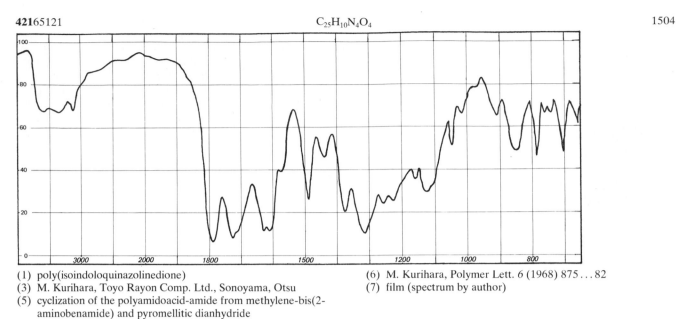

(1) poly(isoindoloquinazolinedione)
(3) M. Kurihara, Toyo Rayon Comp. Ltd., Sonoyama, Otsu
(5) cyclization of the polyamidoacid-amide from methylene-bis(2-aminobenamide) and pyromellitic dianhydride

(6) M. Kurihara, Polymer Lett. 6 (1968) 875...82
(7) film (spectrum by author)

42165121   C$_{37}$H$_{46}$N$_6$O$_2$ 1505

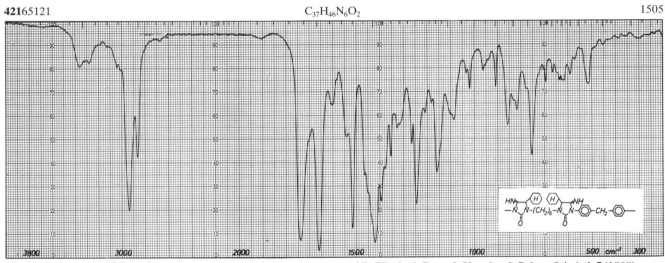

(1) poly(iminoimidazolidinone)
(2) white powder
(3) Elizabeth Dyer, University of Delaware, Newark, Dela.
(5) polycondensation of N,N'-bis(1-cyanocycloalkyl)diamine with methylene-bis(4-phenyl isocyanate) and subsequent cyclization

(6) Elizabeth Dyer, J. Hartzler, J. Polym. Sci. A-1 7 (1969) 833...49
(7) film from CHCl$_3$ solution on CsI

42165121   C$_{39}$H$_{42}$N$_6$O$_2$ 1506

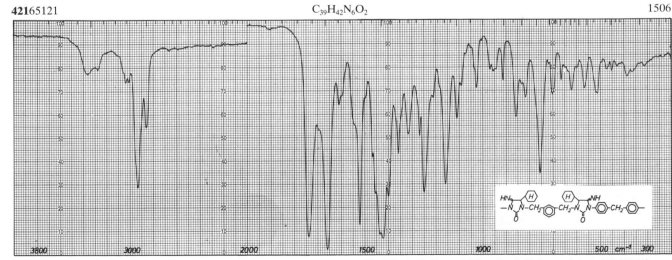

(1) poly(iminoimidazolidinone)
(2) white powder
(3) Elizabeth Dyer, University of Delaware, Newark, Dela.
(5) polycondensation of N,N'-bis(1-cyanocycloalkyl)diamine with methylene-bis(4-phenylisocyanate) and subsequent cyclization

(6) Elizabeth Dyer, J. Hartzler, J. Polymer Sci. A-1 7 (1969) 833...49
(7) film from CHCl$_3$ solution on CsI

42165131   C$_{27}$H$_{30}$N$_4$O$_4$ 1507

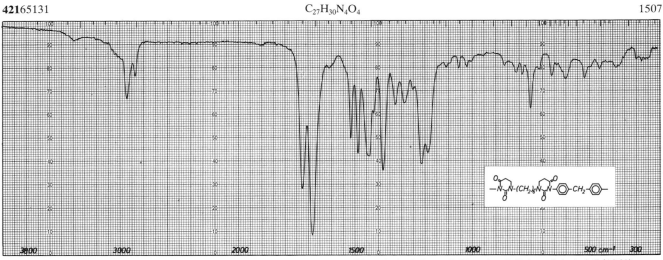

(1) poly(hydrouracil)
(2) white powder
(3) Elizabeth Dyer, University of Delaware, Newark, Dela.
(5) cyclization of 2-carbomethyl-substituted polyurea in polyphosphoric acid

(6) Elizabeth Dyer, J. Hartzler, J. Polym. Sci. A-1 7 (1969) 833...49
(7) film from CHCl$_3$ solution on CsI

42165131   C$_{29}$H$_{32}$N$_4$O$_4$ 1508

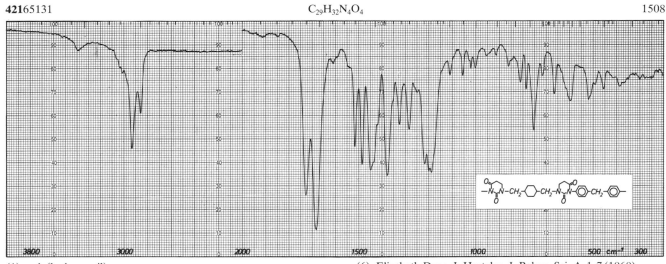

(1) poly(hydrouracil)
(2) white powder
(3) Elizabeth Dyer, University of Delaware, Newark, Dela.
(5) cyclization of 2-carbomethoxyethyl-substituted polyurea in polyphosphoric acid

(6) Elizabeth Dyer, J. Hartzler, J. Polym. Sci. A-1 7 (1969) 833...49
(7) film from CHCl$_3$ solution on CsI

42165133   C$_{17}$H$_{14}$N$_2$O$_3$ 1509

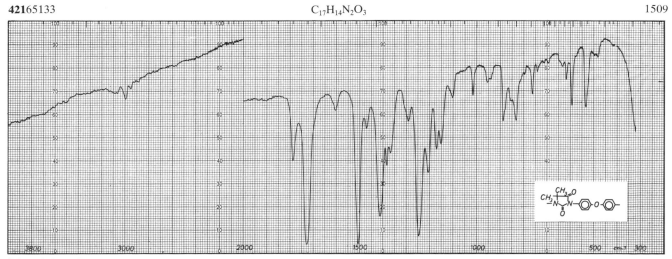

(1) poly(1,4-phenyleneoxy-1,4-phenylene-1,3-hydrantoin-diyl)
(2) turbid, light-brown film
(3) R. Merten, Bayer AG, ATA-Kunststoffe, Dormagen

(6) R. Merten, Angew. Chem. 83 (1971) 339...48
(7) film from dimethylacetamide

42165135 $C_{25}H_{20}N_4O_4$ 1510

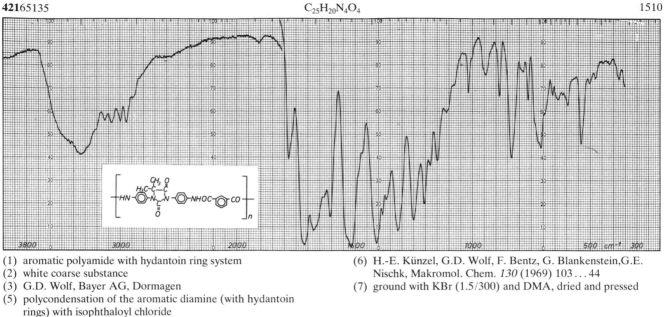

(1) aromatic polyamide with hydantoin ring system
(2) white coarse substance
(3) G.D. Wolf, Bayer AG, Dormagen
(5) polycondensation of the aromatic diamine (with hydantoin rings) with isophthaloyl chloride

(6) H.-E. Künzel, G.D. Wolf, F. Bentz, G. Blankenstein,G.E. Nischk, Makromol. Chem. *130* (1969) 103...44
(7) ground with KBr (1.5/300) and DMA, dried and pressed

42165138 $C_{48}H_{38}N_6O_8$ 1511

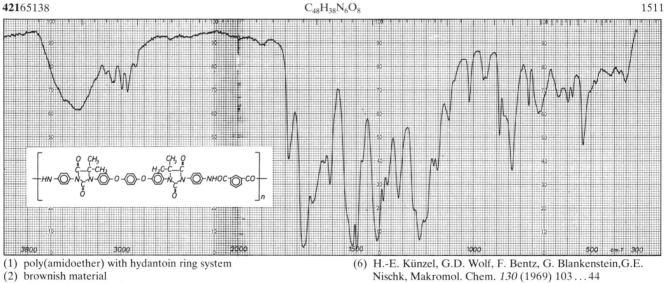

(1) poly(amidoether) with hydantoin ring system
(2) brownish material
(3) G.D. Wolf, Bayer AG, Dormagen
(5) polycondensation of the aromatic diamine (with hydantoin rings) with isophthaloyl chloride

(6) H.-E. Künzel, G.D. Wolf, F. Bentz, G. Blankenstein,G.E. Nischk, Makromol. Chem. *130* (1969) 103...44
(7) ground with KBr (2/300) and DMA, dried and pressed

42165138 $C_{42}H_{34}N_6O_7$ 1512

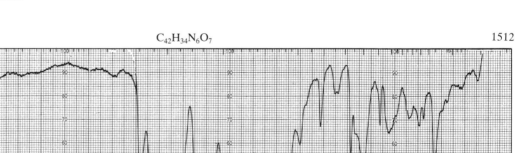

(1) poly(amidoether) with hydantoin ring system
(2) brownish coarse powder
(3) D.G. Wolf, Bayer AG, Dormagen
(5) polycondensation of the aromatic diamine (with hydantoin rings) with isophthaloyl chloride

(6) H.-E. Künzel, G.D. Wolf, F. Bentz, G. Blankenstein,G.E. Nischk, Makromol. Chem. *130* (1969) 103...44
(7) ground with KBr (1.5/300) and DMA, dried and pressed

42165135   C$_{22}$H$_{12}$N$_4$O$_4$ 1513

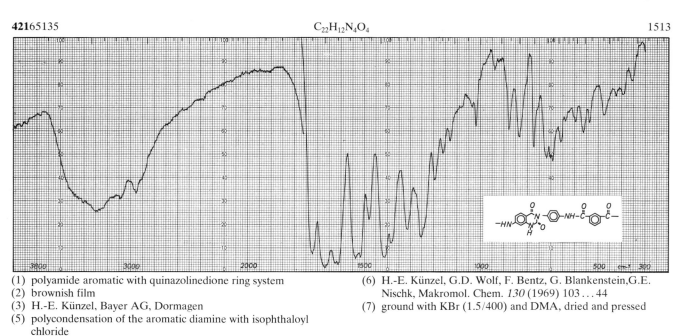

(1) polyamide aromatic with quinazolinedione ring system
(2) brownish film
(3) H.-E. Künzel, Bayer AG, Dormagen
(5) polycondensation of the aromatic diamine with isophthaloyl
     chloride

(6) H.-E. Künzel, G.D. Wolf, F. Bentz, G. Blankenstein,G.E.
     Nischk, Makromol. Chem. *130* (1969) 103...44
(7) ground with KBr (1.5/400) and DMA, dried and pressed

42165142   C$_{16}$H$_{13}$N$_5$O   1514

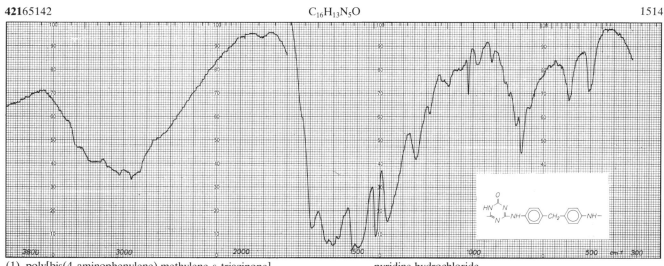

(1) poly[bis(4-aminophenylene) methylene-s-triazinone]
(2) yellowish powder
(3) J. Sundquist, Tekstiilitekniikan, Säätiö, SF Helsinki 18
(5) polycondensation of 2-n-butoxy-4,6-dichloro-s-triazine with
     4,4-diaminodiphenylmethane in N-methylpyrrolidone in the
     presence of Li$_2$CO$_3$, treatment of the s-triazine derivative with

pyridine hydrochloride
(6) Jorma Sundquist and H. Herlinger, Angew. Makromol.
     Chem. *14* (1970) 203...12
(7) KBr (0.8/350), ground with CHCl$_3$, dried and pressed

42165146   C$_{15}$H$_{11}$N$_5$O$_2$ 1515

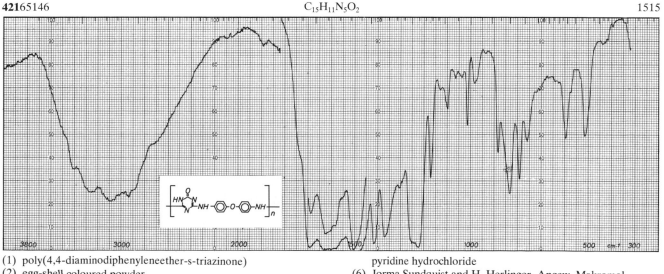

(1) poly(4,4-diaminodiphenyleneether-s-triazinone)
(2) egg-shell coloured powder
(3) J. Sundquist, Tekstiilitekniikan, Säätiö, SF Helsinki 18
(5) polycondensation of 2-n-butoxy-4,6-dichloro-s-triazine with
     4,4-diaminodiphenylene ether in N-methylpyrrolidone in the
     presence of Li$_2$CO$_3$, treatment of the s-triazine derivative with

pyridine hydrochloride
(6) Jorma Sundquist and H. Herlinger, Angew. Makromol.
     Chem. *14* (1970) 203...12
(7) KBr (1.2/350, 0.6/350), ground with CHCl$_3$, dried and
     pressed

42165142 $C_{15}H_{11}N_5O$ 1516

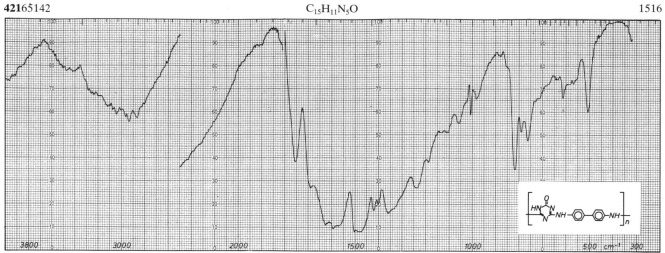

(1) poly(4,4'-diaminodiphenylene-s-triazinone)   hydrochloride
(2) greyish-yellow powder
(3) J. Sundquist, Tekstiilitekniikan, Säätiö, SF Helsinki 18
(5) polycondensation of 2-n-butoxy-4,6-dichloro-s-triazine with benzidine, in N-methylpyrrolidone in the presence of Li_2CO_3, treatment of the s-triazine derivative with pyridine

(6) Jorma Sundquist and H. Herlinger, Angew. Makromol. Chem. *14* (1970) 203...12
(7) KBr (1.2/350) ground with $CHCl_3$, dried and pressed

42166113 $C_{21}H_{20}N_2O_6$ 1517

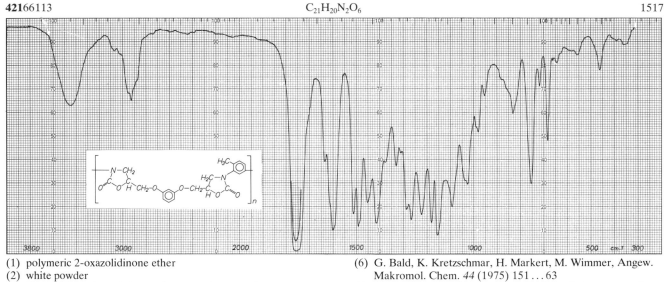

(1) polymeric 2-oxazolidinone ether
(2) white powder
(3) G. Bald, Forschungslaboratorium der Siemens AG, Erlangen
(5) polyaddition of resorcylbisglycidyl ether with 2,4-toluylene diisocyanate

(6) G. Bald, K. Kretzschmar, H. Markert, M. Wimmer, Angew. Makromol. Chem. *44* (1975) 151...63
(7) ground with KBr (1.5/350) and $CHCl_3$, dried and pressed

42166121 $C_{29}H_{16}N_2O_6$ 1518

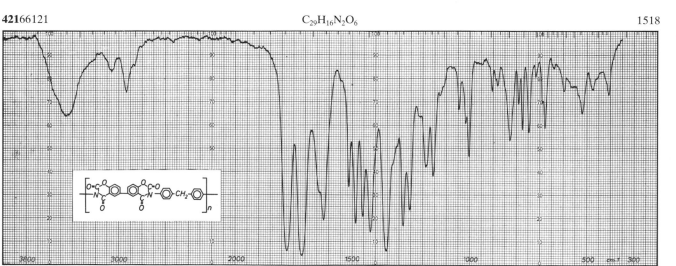

(1) poly(benzoxazinedione)
(2) colourless film
(3) L. Bottenbruch, Bayer AG, Krefeld-Uerdingen
(5) polyaddition and simultaneous polycyclization of o,o'-dihydroxyaryldicarbonic diphenylester and diphenylether-4,4'-diisocyanate

(6) L. Bottenbruch, Angew. Makromol. Chem. *13* (1970) 109...25
(7) dissolved in DMA, ground with KBr, dried and pressed

42166121 C$_{31}$H$_{20}$N$_2$O$_6$ 1519

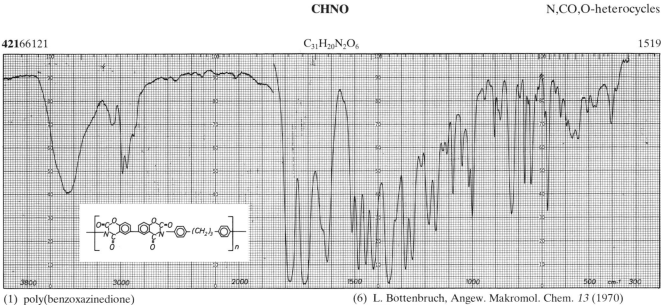

(1) poly(benzoxazinedione)
(2) colourless film
(3) L. Bottenbruch, Bayer AG, Krefeld-Uerdingen
(5) polyaddition and simultaneous polycyclization of
o,o'dihydroxyaryldicarbonic phenylester and aromatic
diisocyanate

(6) L. Bottenbruch, Angew. Makromol. Chem. *13* (1970)
109...25
(7) dissolved in DMA, ground with KBr, dried and pressed

42166121 C$_{23}$H$_9$N$_2$O$_6$ 1520

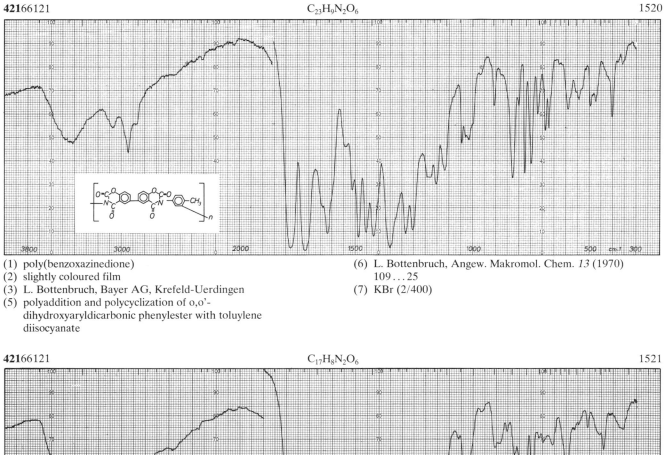

(1) poly(benzoxazinedione)
(2) slightly coloured film
(3) L. Bottenbruch, Bayer AG, Krefeld-Uerdingen
(5) polyaddition and polycyclization of o,o'-
dihydroxyaryldicarbonic phenylester with toluylene
diisocyanate

(6) L. Bottenbruch, Angew. Makromol. Chem. *13* (1970)
109...25
(7) KBr (2/400)

42166121 C$_{17}$H$_8$N$_2$O$_6$ 1521

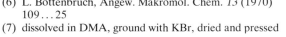

(1) poly(benzoxazinedione)
(2) yellow film
(3) L. Bottenbruch, Bayer AG, Krefeld-Uerdingen
(5) polyaddition and polycyclization of o,o'-
dihydroxyaryldicarbonic phenylester with toluylene
diisocyanate

(6) L. Bottenbruch, Angew. Makromol. Chem. *13* (1970)
109...25
(7) 1 mg dissolved in DMA, ground with 400 mg KBr, dried and
pressed

42166121   C₂₃H₁₂N₂O₆   1522

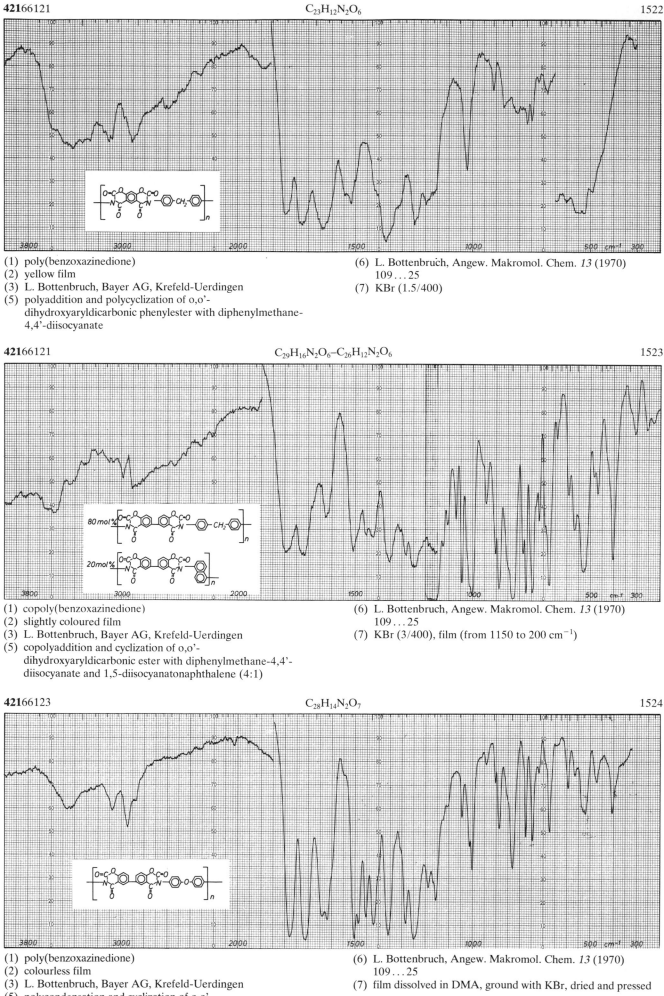

(1) poly(benzoxazinedione)
(2) yellow film
(3) L. Bottenbruch, Bayer AG, Krefeld-Uerdingen
(5) polyaddition and polycyclization of o,o'-dihydroxyaryldicarbonic phenylester with diphenylmethane-4,4'-diisocyanate

(6) L. Bottenbruch, Angew. Makromol. Chem. *13* (1970) 109...25
(7) KBr (1.5/400)

42166121   C₂₉H₁₆N₂O₆–C₂₆H₁₂N₂O₆   1523

(1) copoly(benzoxazinedione)
(2) slightly coloured film
(3) L. Bottenbruch, Bayer AG, Krefeld-Uerdingen
(5) copolyaddition and cyclization of o,o'-dihydroxyaryldicarbonic ester with diphenylmethane-4,4'-diisocyanate and 1,5-diisocyanatonaphthalene (4:1)

(6) L. Bottenbruch, Angew. Makromol. Chem. *13* (1970) 109...25
(7) KBr (3/400), film (from 1150 to 200 cm⁻¹)

42166123   C₂₈H₁₄N₂O₇   1524

(1) poly(benzoxazinedione)
(2) colourless film
(3) L. Bottenbruch, Bayer AG, Krefeld-Uerdingen
(5) polycondensation and cyclization of o,o'-dihydroxyaryldicarbonic ester and diphenylether-4,4'-diisocyanate

(6) L. Bottenbruch, Angew. Makromol. Chem. *13* (1970) 109...25
(7) film dissolved in DMA, ground with KBr, dried and pressed

4216621 $C_{11}H_{15}NO_2$ 1525

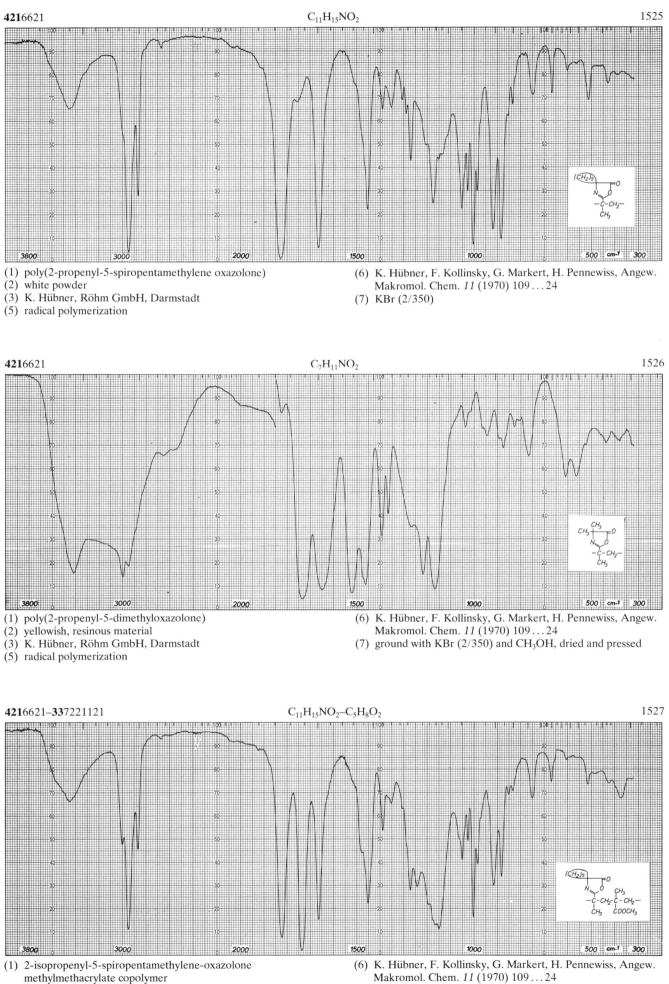

(1) poly(2-propenyl-5-spiropentamethylene oxazolone)
(2) white powder
(3) K. Hübner, Röhm GmbH, Darmstadt
(5) radical polymerization

(6) K. Hübner, F. Kollinsky, G. Markert, H. Pennewiss, Angew. Makromol. Chem. *11* (1970) 109...24
(7) KBr (2/350)

4216621 $C_7H_{11}NO_2$ 1526

(1) poly(2-propenyl-5-dimethyloxazolone)
(2) yellowish, resinous material
(3) K. Hübner, Röhm GmbH, Darmstadt
(5) radical polymerization

(6) K. Hübner, F. Kollinsky, G. Markert, H. Pennewiss, Angew. Makromol. Chem. *11* (1970) 109...24
(7) ground with KBr (2/350) and CH_3OH, dried and pressed

4216621–337221121 $C_{11}H_{15}NO_2$–$C_5H_8O_2$ 1527

(1) 2-isopropenyl-5-spiropentamethylene-oxazolone
   methylmethacrylate copolymer
(2) white powder
(3) K. Hübner, Röhm GmbH, Darmstadt
(5) radical copolymerization

(6) K. Hübner, F. Kollinsky, G. Markert, H. Pennewiss, Angew. Makromol. Chem. *11* (1970) 109...24
(7) KBr (2/350)

4216811 $C_{25}H_{10}N_4O_4$ 1528

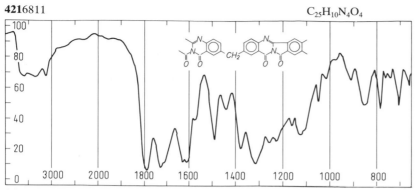

(1) poly(isoindoloquinazolinedione)
(3) M. Kurihara, Basic Research Laboratories, Toyo Rayon Comp., Kamakura
(5) polycondensation of methylene-bis(2-aminobenzamide) with pyromellitic dianhydride, cyclopolycondensation of the polyamidocarboxylic acid

(6) M. Kurihara, N. Yoda, J. Polym. Sci., Polym. Letters Ed. 6 (1968) 875...82
(7) spectrum by M. Kurihara

4216812 $C_{22}H_8N_4O_2$ 1529

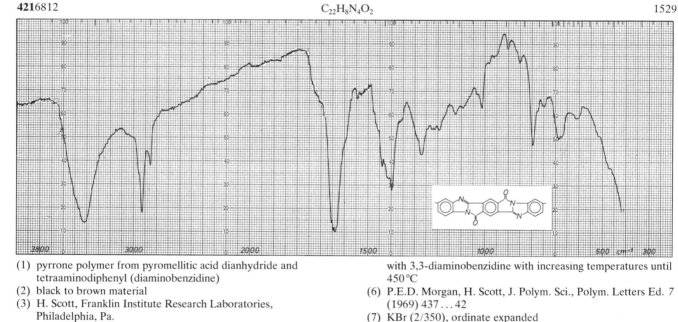

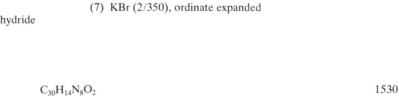

(1) pyrrone polymer from pyromellitic acid dianhydride and tetraaminodiphenyl (diaminobenzidine)
(2) black to brown material
(3) H. Scott, Franklin Institute Research Laboratories, Philadelphia, Pa.
(5) high-pressure polycondensation of pyromellitic dianhydride

with 3,3-diaminobenzidine with increasing temperatures until 450°C
(6) P.E.D. Morgan, H. Scott, J. Polym. Sci., Polym. Letters Ed. 7 (1969) 437...42
(7) KBr (2/350), ordinate expanded

4216812 $C_{30}H_{14}N_8O_2$ 1530

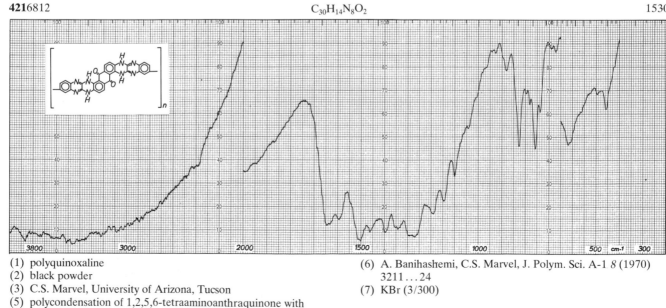

(1) polyquinoxaline
(2) black powder
(3) C.S. Marvel, University of Arizona, Tucson
(5) polycondensation of 1,2,5,6-tetraaminoanthraquinone with 2,2',3,3'-tetrachloro-6,6'-diquinoxaline in pyridine

(6) A. Banihashemi, C.S. Marvel, J. Polym. Sci. A-1 8 (1970) 3211...24
(7) KBr (3/300)

4216814　　　　　　　　　　　　　　　$C_{24}H_{11}N_5O_4$　　　　　　　　　　　　　　　1531

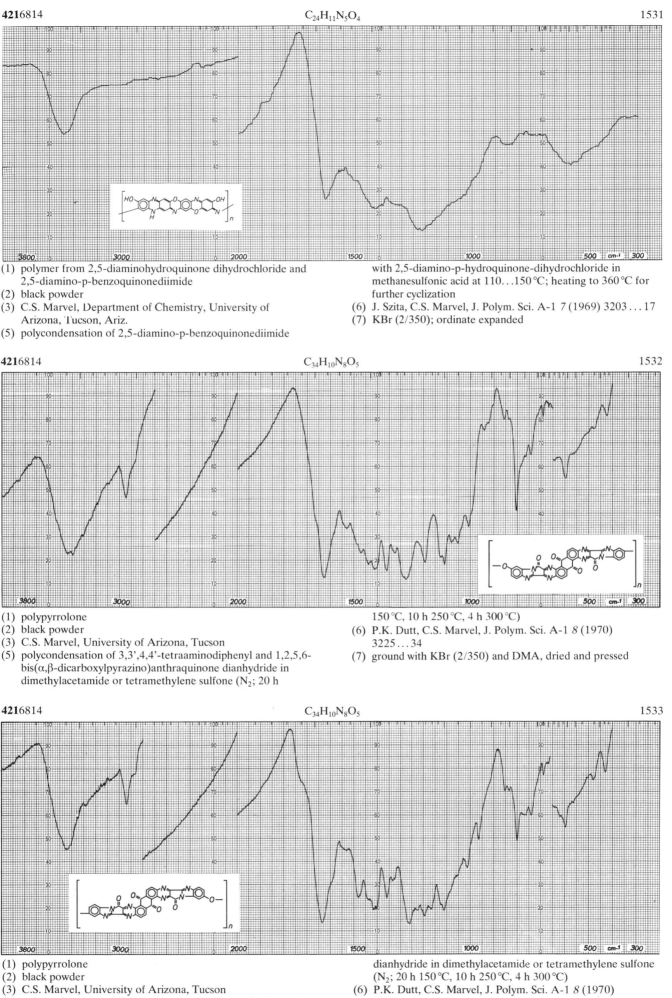

(1) polymer from 2,5-diaminohydroquinone dihydrochloride and
     2,5-diamino-p-benzoquinonediimide
(2) black powder
(3) C.S. Marvel, Department of Chemistry, University of
     Arizona, Tucson, Ariz.
(5) polycondensation of 2,5-diamino-p-benzoquinonediimide

with 2,5-diamino-p-hydroquinone-dihydrochloride in
methanesulfonic acid at 110...150 °C; heating to 360 °C for
further cyclization
(6) J. Szita, C.S. Marvel, J. Polym. Sci. A-1 7 (1969) 3203...17
(7) KBr (2/350); ordinate expanded

4216814　　　　　　　　　　　　　　　$C_{34}H_{10}N_8O_5$　　　　　　　　　　　　　　　1532

(1) polypyrrolone
(2) black powder
(3) C.S. Marvel, University of Arizona, Tucson
(5) polycondensation of 3,3',4,4'-tetraaminodiphenyl and 1,2,5,6-
     bis(α,β-dicarboxylpyrazino)anthraquinone dianhydride in
     dimethylacetamide or tetramethylene sulfone (N$_2$; 20 h

150 °C, 10 h 250 °C, 4 h 300 °C)
(6) P.K. Dutt, C.S. Marvel, J. Polym. Sci. A-1 8 (1970)
     3225...34
(7) ground with KBr (2/350) and DMA, dried and pressed

4216814　　　　　　　　　　　　　　　$C_{34}H_{10}N_8O_5$　　　　　　　　　　　　　　　1533

(1) polypyrrolone
(2) black powder
(3) C.S. Marvel, University of Arizona, Tucson
(5) polycondensation of 3,3',4,4'-tetraaminodiphenyl ether and
     1,2,5,6-bis(α,β-dicarboxylpyrazino)anthraquinone

dianhydride in dimethylacetamide or tetramethylene sulfone
(N$_2$; 20 h 150 °C, 10 h 250 °C, 4 h 300 °C)
(6) P.K. Dutt, C.S. Marvel, J. Polym. Sci. A-1 8 (1970)
     3225...34
(7) ground with KBr (2,5/300) and DMA, dried and pressed

4216821 $C_{14}H_9N_3O_3$ 1534

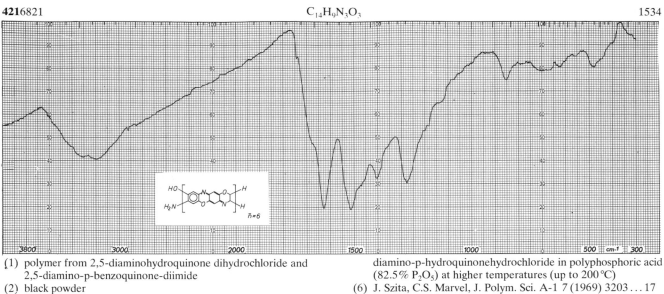
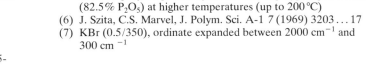

(1) polymer from 2,5-diaminohydroquinone dihydrochloride and 2,5-diamino-p-benzoquinone-diimide

(2) black powder

(3) C.S. Marvel, Department of Chemistry, University of Arizona, Tucson, Ariz.

(5) polycondensation of 2,5-diamino-p-benzoquinone with 2,5-diamino-p-hydroquinonehydrochloride in polyphosphoric acid (82.5% P_2O_5) at higher temperatures (up to 200 °C)

(6) J. Szita, C.S. Marvel, J. Polym. Sci. A-1 7 (1969) 3203 . . . 17

(7) KBr (0.5/350), ordinate expanded between 2000 cm^{-1} and 300 cm^{-1}

4216821 $C_{22}H_{16}N_4O_2$ 1535

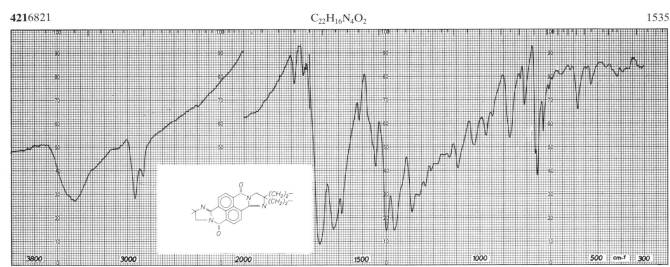

(1) spiropolymer, aromatic

(2) dark-green to black material

(3) J. Heller, Stanford Research Institute, Menlo Park, Calif.

(5) polycondensation and simultanous cyclization of trans-1,4-bis(aminomethyl)1,4-diaminocyclohexane and 1,4,5,8-naphthalenetetracarboxylic dianhydride

(6) J.H. Hodkin, J. Heller, J. Macromol. Sci.-Chem. A3(6) (1969) 1067 . . . 86

(7) KBr (2/300)

4216821 $C_{14}H_9N_2O_3$ 1536

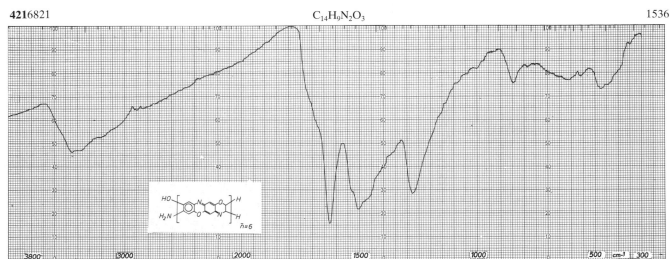

(1) polymer from 2,5-diaminohydroquinone dihydrochloride and 2,5-diamino-p-benzoquinone-diimde

(2) black powder

(3) C.S. Marvel, Department of Chemistry, University of Arizona, Tucson, Ariz.

(5) polycondensation of 2,5-diamino-p-benzoquinone with 2,5-diamino-p-hydroquinonehydrochloride in polyphosphoric acid (82.5% P_2O_5) at higher temperatures (up to 200 °C); isolated product heated to 360 °C for further cyclization

(6) J. Szita, C.S. Marvel, J. Polym. Sci. A-1 7 (1969) 3203 . . . 17

(7) KBr (0.5/350), ordinate expanded between 2000 cm^{-1} and 300 cm^{-1}

4216821 $C_{14}H_8N_2O_2$ 1537

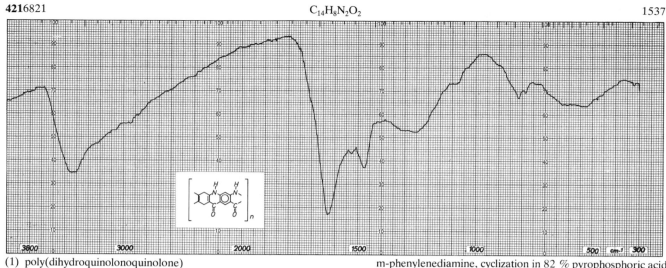

(1) poly(dihydroquinolonoquinolone)
(2) black powder
(3) S. Kimura, Research Laboratories, Meiji Sugar Co., Kawasaki
(5) polycondensation of diethylsuccinosuccinate with

m-phenylenediamine, cyclization in 82 % pyrophosphoric acid at 393 ... 400 K (3 h) under nitrogen
(6) S. Kimura, Makromol. Chem. *117* (1968) 203 ... 9
(7) KBr (0.6/350)

4216821 $C_{28}H_6N_8O_4$ 1538

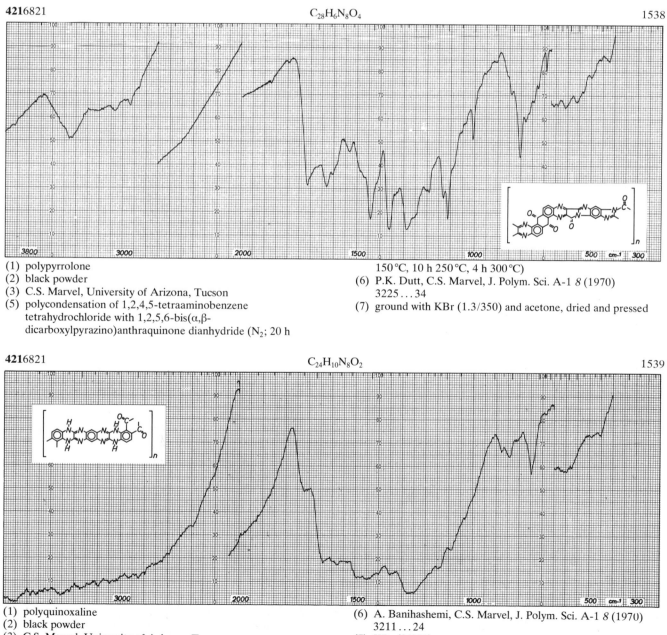

(1) polypyrrolone
(2) black powder
(3) C.S. Marvel, University of Arizona, Tucson
(5) polycondensation of 1,2,4,5-tetraaminobenzene tetrahydrochloride with 1,2,5,6-bis(α,β-dicarboxylpyrazino)anthraquinone dianhydride (N₂; 20 h

150 °C, 10 h 250 °C, 4 h 300 °C)
(6) P.K. Dutt, C.S. Marvel, J. Polym. Sci. A-1 *8* (1970) 3225 ... 34
(7) ground with KBr (1.3/350) and acetone, dried and pressed

4216821 $C_{24}H_{10}N_8O_2$ 1539

(1) polyquinoxaline
(2) black powder
(3) C.S. Marvel, University of Arizona, Tucson
(5) polycondensation of 1,2,5,6-tetraaminoanthraquinone with 2,3-dichloroquinoxaline in pyridine or tetramethylene sulfone

(6) A. Banihashemi, C.S. Marvel, J. Polym. Sci. A-1 *8* (1970) 3211 ... 24
(7) KBr (2/300)

421745   C$_6$H$_{11}$NO$_2$ 1540

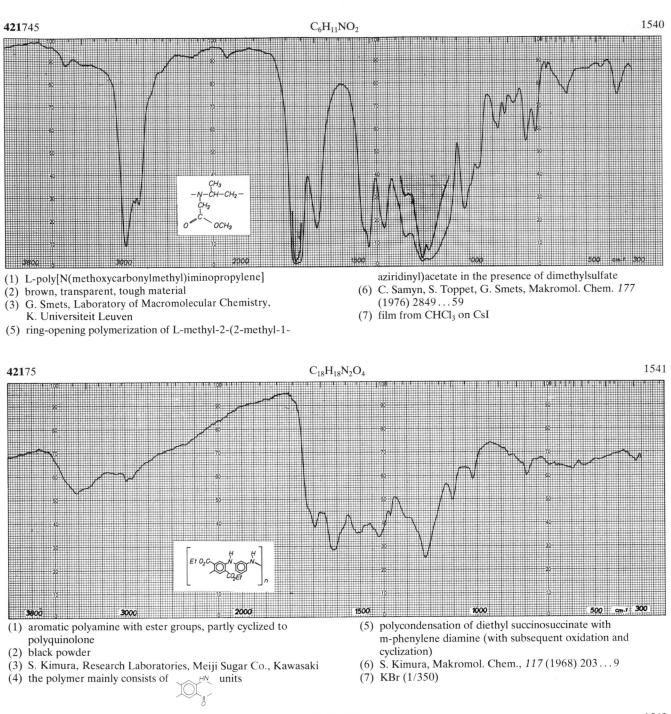

(1) L-poly[N(methoxycarbonylmethyl)iminopropylene]
(2) brown, transparent, tough material
(3) G. Smets, Laboratory of Macromolecular Chemistry,
    K. Universiteit Leuven
(5) ring-opening polymerization of L-methyl-2-(2-methyl-1-

aziridinyl)acetate in the presence of dimethylsulfate
(6) C. Samyn, S. Toppet, G. Smets, Makromol. Chem. *177*
    (1976) 2849...59
(7) film from CHCl$_3$ on CsI

42175   C$_{18}$H$_{18}$N$_2$O$_4$ 1541

(1) aromatic polyamine with ester groups, partly cyclized to
    polyquinolone
(2) black powder
(3) S. Kimura, Research Laboratories, Meiji Sugar Co., Kawasaki
(4) the polymer mainly consists of   units

(5) polycondensation of diethyl succinosuccinate with
    m-phenylene diamine (with subsequent oxidation and
    cyclization)
(6) S. Kimura, Makromol. Chem., *117* (1968) 203...9
(7) KBr (1/350)

42175   C$_{18}$H$_{20}$N$_2$O   1542

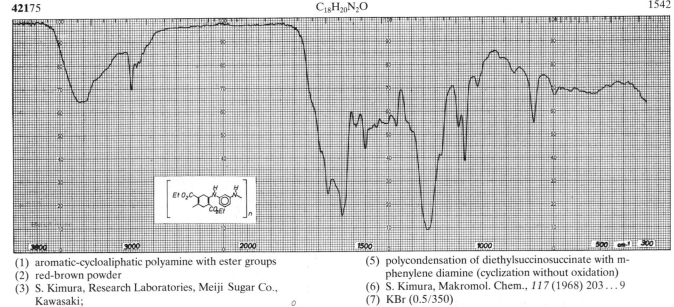

(1) aromatic-cycloaliphatic polyamine with ester groups
(2) red-brown powder
(3) S. Kimura, Research Laboratories, Meiji Sugar Co.,
    Kawasaki;
(4) partly cyclized, the polymer contains quinolone units:

(5) polycondensation of diethylsuccinosuccinate with m-
    phenylene diamine (cyclization without oxidation)
(6) S. Kimura, Makromol. Chem., *117* (1968) 203...9
(7) KBr (0.5/350)

4219111   C₄H₅NO   1543

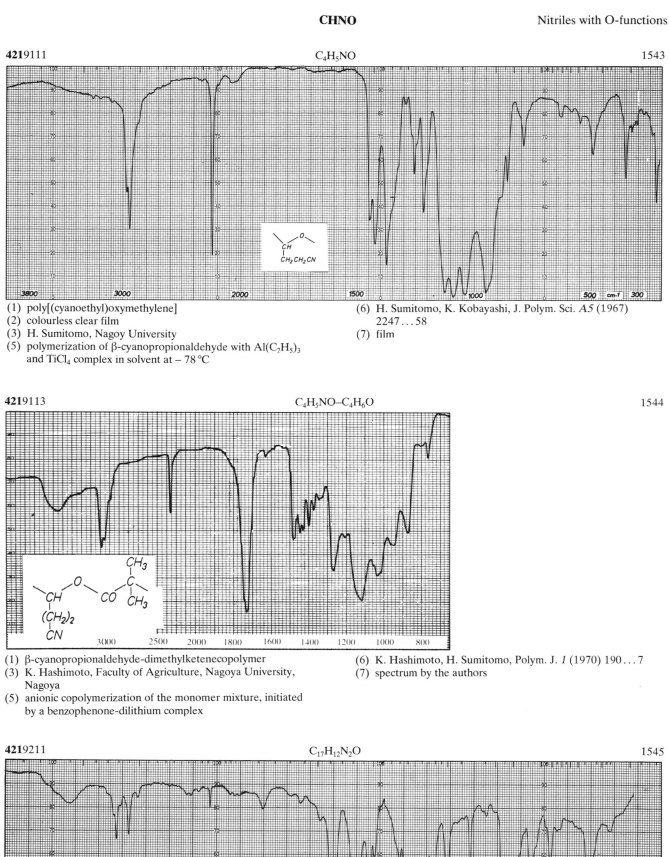

(1) poly[(cyanoethyl)oxymethylene]
(2) colourless clear film
(3) H. Sumitomo, Nagoy University
(5) polymerization of β-cyanopropionaldehyde with Al(C₂H₅)₃
   and TiCl₄ complex in solvent at − 78 °C

(6) H. Sumitomo, K. Kobayashi, J. Polym. Sci. *A5* (1967)
   2247…58
(7) film

4219113   C₄H₅NO–C₄H₆O   1544

(1) β-cyanopropionaldehyde-dimethylketenecopolymer
(3) K. Hashimoto, Faculty of Agriculture, Nagoya University,
   Nagoya
(5) anionic copolymerization of the monomer mixture, initiated
   by a benzophenone-dilithium complex

(6) K. Hashimoto, H. Sumitomo, Polym. J. *1* (1970) 190…7
(7) spectrum by the authors

4219211   C₁₇H₁₂N₂O   1545

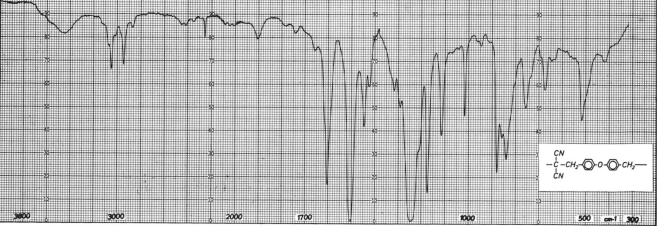

(1) poly(dicyanomethine-4,4'-dimethylene-diphenylether)
(2) white material
(3) D. Brown, Imperial Chemical Industries, The Heath, Runcon,
   Cheshire
(5) polycondensation of malonitrile and bis(p-chloro-
   -methylphenyl)ether

(6) D. Brown, M.E.B. Jones, W.R. Maltman, J. Polym. Sci.,
   Polym. Letters Ed. *6* (1968) 635…7
(7) KBr (6/1000)

4219222 $C_{10}H_9NO$ 1546

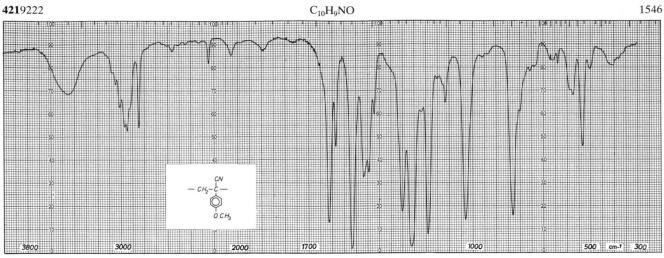

(1) poly[α-(4-methoxyphenyl)acrylonitrile]
(2) white powder
(3) W. Funke, Forschungsinstitut für Pigmente und Lacke, Stuttgart
(5) radical polymerization
(6) W. Funke, Makromol. Chem. *137* (1970) 23...8
(7) KBr (2/350)

4221341111 $C_5H_{10}N_2S_2$ 1547

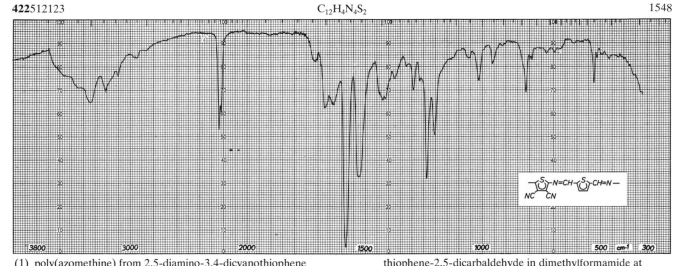

(1) poly[(N-dithiocarboxylato)iminoethylenehydrogenimino-ethylene]
(2) light-yellow powder
(3) J.H. Barnes, Department of Chemistry, University of Reading, Whiteknights, Reading, Berks.
(5) reaction of poly(iminoethylene) with CS_2 in aqueous ethanol under mild conditions
(6) J.H. Barnes, G.F. Esslemont, Makromol. Chem. *177* (1976) 307...10
(7) KBr (2/350)

422512123 $C_{12}H_4N_4S_2$ 1548

(1) poly(azomethine) from 2,5-diamino-3,4-dicyanothiophene and thiophene-2,5-dicarbaldehyde
(2) deep-brown powder
(3) G. Koßmehl, Institut für Organische Chemie, FU Berlin
(5) polycondensation of 2,5-diamino-3,4-dicyanothiophene with
thiophene-2,5-dicarbaldehyde in dimethylformamide at 150°C
(6) D. Wöhrle, G. Kossmehl, G. Manecke, Makromol. Chem. *154* (1972) 111...20
(7) KBr (0.5/350), ordinate expanded

42281123   C$_{28}$H$_{14}$N$_2$S$_2$ 1549

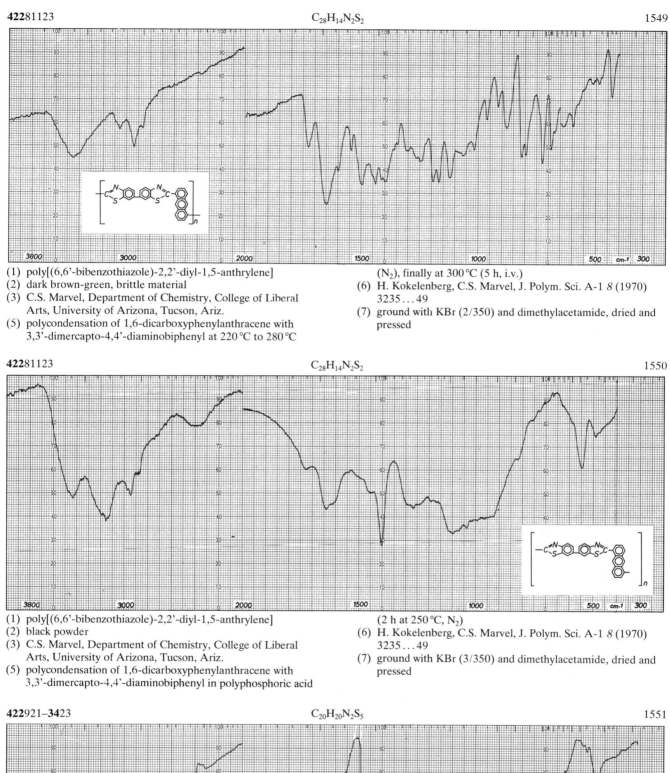

(1) poly[(6,6'-bibenzothiazole)-2,2'-diyl-1,5-anthrylene]
(2) dark brown-green, brittle material
(3) C.S. Marvel, Department of Chemistry, College of Liberal Arts, University of Arizona, Tucson, Ariz.
(5) polycondensation of 1,6-dicarboxyphenylanthracene with 3,3'-dimercapto-4,4'-diaminobiphenyl at 220 °C to 280 °C

(N$_2$), finally at 300 °C (5 h, i.v.)
(6) H. Kokelenberg, C.S. Marvel, J. Polym. Sci. A-1 *8* (1970) 3235...49
(7) ground with KBr (2/350) and dimethylacetamide, dried and pressed

42281123   C$_{28}$H$_{14}$N$_2$S$_2$ 1550

(1) poly[(6,6'-bibenzothiazole)-2,2'-diyl-1,5-anthrylene]
(2) black powder
(3) C.S. Marvel, Department of Chemistry, College of Liberal Arts, University of Arizona, Tucson, Ariz.
(5) polycondensation of 1,6-dicarboxyphenylanthracene with 3,3'-dimercapto-4,4'-diaminobiphenyl in polyphosphoric acid

(2 h at 250 °C, N$_2$)
(6) H. Kokelenberg, C.S. Marvel, J. Polym. Sci. A-1 *8* (1970) 3235...49
(7) ground with KBr (3/350) and dimethylacetamide, dried and pressed

422921–3423   C$_{20}$H$_{20}$N$_2$S$_5$ 1551

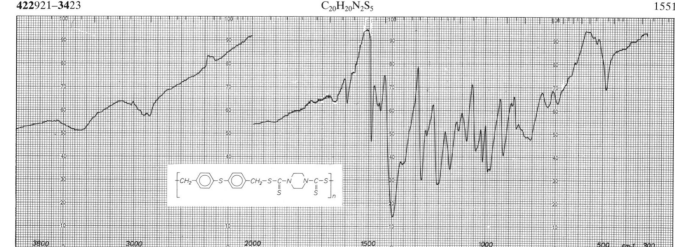

(1) poly(thiourethane-thioether)
(2) ivory-coloured powder
(3) Z. Szymik, Institut für Chemische Technologie der Schlesischen Universität, Katowice
(5) polycondensation of 4,4'-bis-chloromethylated

diphenylthioether with the Na-salt of piperazine-N,N'-bis-thiolthionic acid in methanol or dioxane solution
(6) Z. Szymik, W. Podkoscielny, W. Rudz, Angew. Makromol. Chem. *45* (1975) 185...9
(7) KBr (3/350)

422932 $C_{14}H_{10}N_2S$ 1552

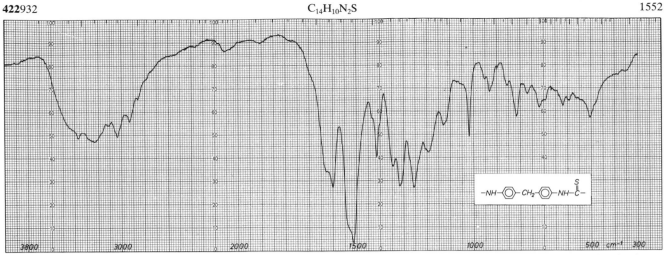

(1) poly(iminothiocarbonylimino-1,4-phenylenemethylene-1,4-phenylene); poly(thiourea) from 4,4'-diaminodiphenylmethane
(2) ochre-coloured powder
(3) N. Yamazaki, Department of Polymer Science, Tokyo Institute of Technology, Tokyo
(5) polycondensation of 4,4'-diaminodiphenylmethane with CS_2

in pyridine at 40°C in the presence of the N-phosphonium salt of pyridine
(6) N. Yamazaki, F. Higashi, T. Iguchi, IUPAC Macro, Madrid 1974 (I. 4–12)
(7) ground with KBr (2/350) and dimethylacetamide, dried and pressed

43111212 $C_5H_{10}OS_2$ 1553

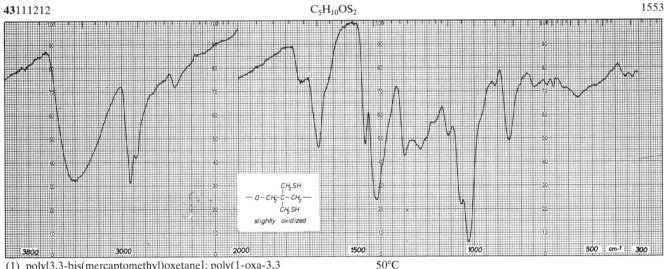

(1) poly[3,3-bis(mercaptomethyl)oxetane]; poly(1-oxa-3,3 dimercaptomethyl-tetramethylene)
(2) slightly yellowish powder
(3) E.J. Goethals, Laboratory of Organic Chemistry, University of Ghent, Gent
(5) polymerization of, e.g., the diacetate of 3,3-bis(mercaptomethyl)oxetane with BF_3-etherate at $-30\,°C$, hydrolysis of the polymer with NaOH in ethanol/H_2O (2:1) at

50°C
(6) E. du Prez, E.J. Goethals, Makromol. Chem. *146* (1971) 145...58
(7) ground with KBr (2/350) and dimethylformamide, dried and pressed
(8) the material is easily oxidizable and hygroscopic; the bands at 1660 and 3400 cm^{-1} are partly due to absorbed water

431212131211 C_4H_8OS 1554

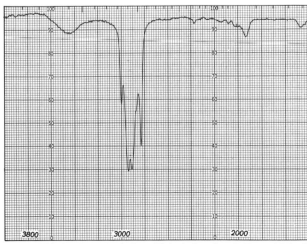

(1) poly[1-(methoxymethylenethio)ethylene], poly(formaldehyde-S-vinyl-O-methyl-monothioacetal)
(2) colourless material
(3) H. Ringsdorf, Institut für Polymere, Universität Marburg/Institut für Organische Chemie, Universität Mainz

(5) radical polymerization of vinyl-methoxymethyl-thioether
(6) R. Kroker, H. Ringsdorf, Makromol. Chem. *121* (1969) 240...57
(7) film from CHCl$_3$ on KBr

431212331121–3331111 C_5H_7O_3S NA-C_3H_6O_3 1555

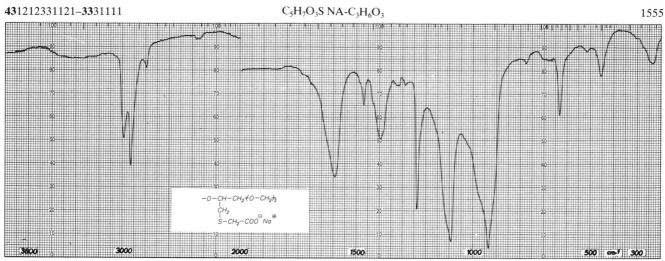

(1) oxy-1-(carboxylatomethylenethiomethylene)ethylene-tri(oxymethylene) copolymer, Na⁺ salt
(2) slightly yellowish, transparent film
(3) K.-F. Wissbrun, Celanese Research Comp., Summit, N. J.
(5) bulk-copolymerization of trioxane with epichlorohydrin in the

presence of BF_3-di-n-butyletherate at 65 °C; reaction of the copolymer with disodiumthioglycolate
(6) K.-F. Wissbrun, Makromol. Chem. _118_ (1968) 211...29
(7) film from CH_3OH/H_2O on KRS-5

431432232 C_8H_8O_2S_4 1556

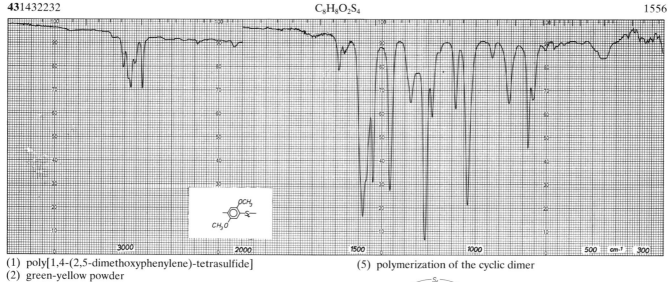

(1) poly[1,4-(2,5-dimethoxyphenylene)-tetrasulfide]
(2) green-yellow powder
(3) N.A. Hiatt, Uniroyal Chemical, Div. of Unitoyal, Naugatuck, Conn.

(5) polymerization of the cyclic dimer

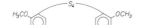

(6) N.A. Hiatt, ACS Polym. Prepr. _13_/1 (1972) 594
(7) film from CHCl_3 on CsI

431432232 C_10H_12O_2S_4 1557

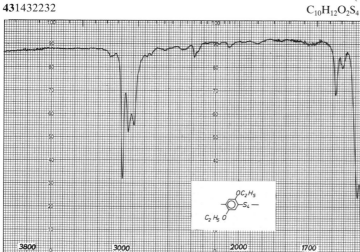

(1) poly[1,4-(2,5-diethoxyphenylene)-tetrasulfide]
(2) lemon-yellow powder
(3) N.A. Hiatt, Uniroyal Chemical, Div. of Uniroyal, Naugatuck, Conn.

(5) polymerization of the cyclic dimer in bulk at 195 °C

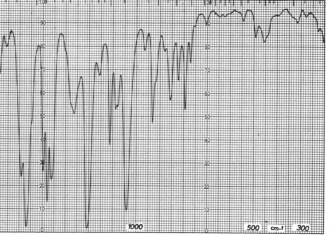

(6) N.A. Hiatt, ACS Polym. Prepr. _13_/1 (1972) 594

432111 C_2H_2OS 1558

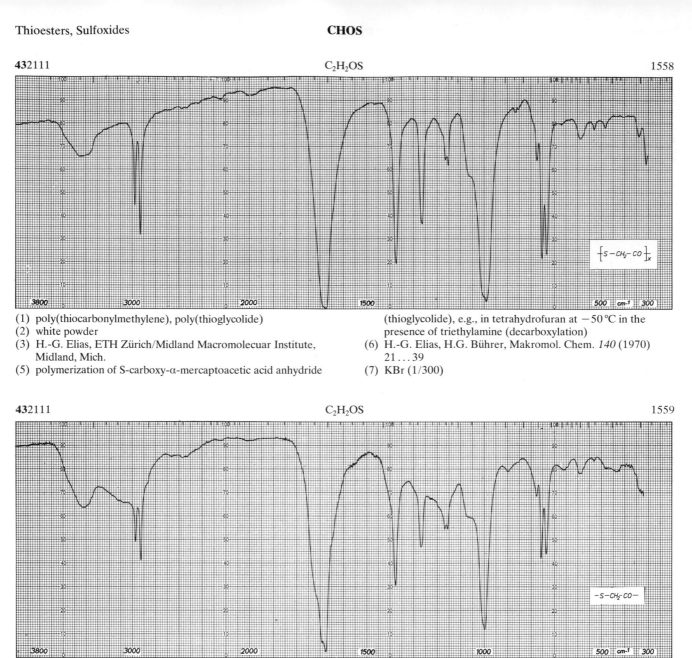

(1) poly(thiocarbonylmethylene), poly(thioglycolide)
(2) white powder
(3) H.-G. Elias, ETH Zürich/Midland Macromolecuar Institute, Midland, Mich.
(5) polymerization of S-carboxy-α-mercaptoacetic acid anhydride

(thioglycolide), e.g., in tetrahydrofuran at −50 °C in the presence of triethylamine (decarboxylation)
(6) H.-G. Elias, H.G. Bührer, Makromol. Chem. *140* (1970) 21...39
(7) KBr (1/300)

432111 C_2H_2OS 1559

(1) poly(thiocarbonylmethylene), poly(thioglycolide)
(2) white powder
(3) H.-G. Elias, ETH Zürich, Midland Macromolecular Institute, Midland, Mich.
(4) low-molecular product ($\bar{M}_w = 5500$)

(5) polymerization of S-carboxy-α-mercaptoacetic acid anhydride in the presence of NaBH₄
(6) H.-G. Elias, H.G. Bührer, Makromol. Chem. *140* (1970) 21...39
(7) KBr (0.8/350)

432112 C_3H_4OS 1560

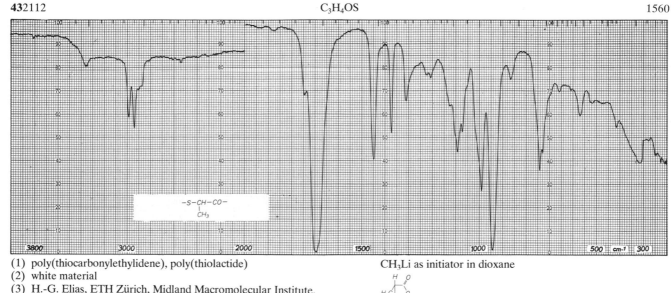

(1) poly(thiocarbonylethylidene), poly(thiolactide)
(2) white material
(3) H.-G. Elias, ETH Zürich, Midland Macromolecular Institute, Midland, Mich.
(4) 20% D, 71% L units
(5) polymerization of 4-methyl-1,3-oxathiolane-2,5-dione, with

CH₃Li as initiator in dioxane

(6) H.G. Bührer, H.-G. Elias, Makromol. Chem. *140* (1970) 41...54
(7) film from CHCl₃ on CsI

432112 C_3H_4OS 1561

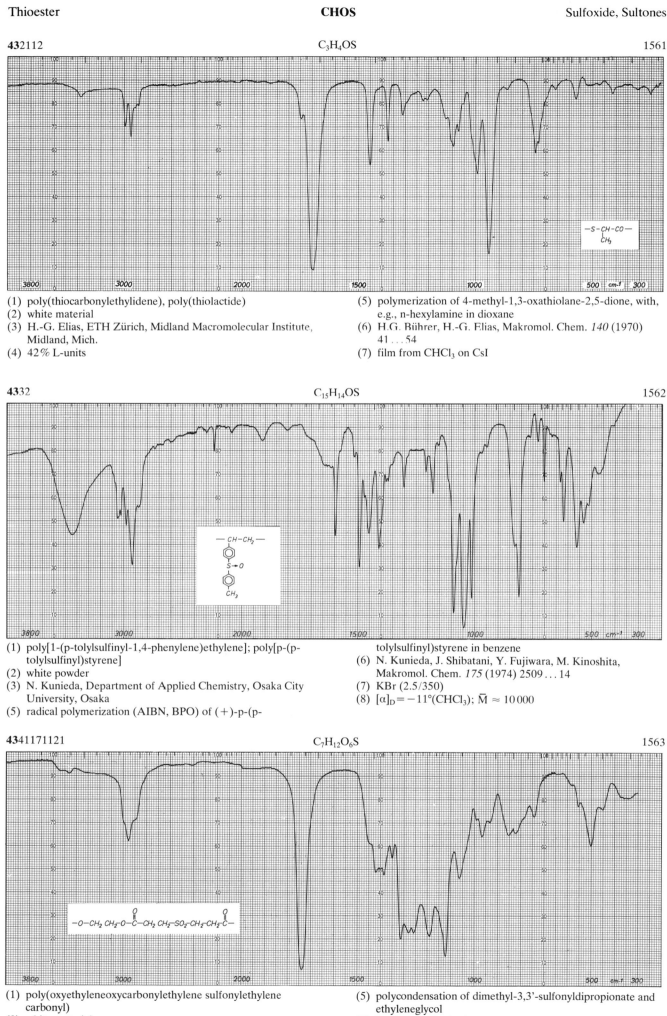

(1) poly(thiocarbonylethylidene), poly(thiolactide)
(2) white material
(3) H.-G. Elias, ETH Zürich, Midland Macromolecular Institute, Midland, Mich.
(4) 42% L-units

(5) polymerization of 4-methyl-1,3-oxathiolane-2,5-dione, with, e.g., n-hexylamine in dioxane
(6) H.G. Bührer, H.-G. Elias, Makromol. Chem. *140* (1970) 41...54
(7) film from $CHCl_3$ on CsI

4332 $C_{15}H_{14}OS$ 1562

(1) poly[1-(p-tolylsulfinyl-1,4-phenylene)ethylene]; poly[p-(p-tolylsulfinyl)styrene]
(2) white powder
(3) N. Kunieda, Department of Applied Chemistry, Osaka City University, Osaka
(5) radical polymerization (AIBN, BPO) of (+)-p-(p-

tolylsulfinyl)styrene in benzene
(6) N. Kunieda, J. Shibatani, Y. Fujiwara, M. Kinoshita, Makromol. Chem. *175* (1974) 2509...14
(7) KBr (2.5/350)
(8) $[\alpha]_D = -11°(CHCl_3)$; $\bar{M} \approx 10\,000$

4341171121 $C_7H_{12}O_6S$ 1563

(1) poly(oxyethyleneoxycarbonylethylene sulfonylethylene carbonyl)
(2) white material
(3) R. Kerber, Lehrstuhl für Makromolekulare Stoffe, Technische Universität München, München

(5) polycondensation of dimethyl-3,3'-sulfonyldipropionate and ethyleneglycol
(6) R. Kerber, O. Nuyken, E. Pöschl, Makromol. Chem. *177* (1976) 2285...93
(7) film from $CHCl_3$ on KBr

521

434121 $C_3H_6O_2S$ 1564

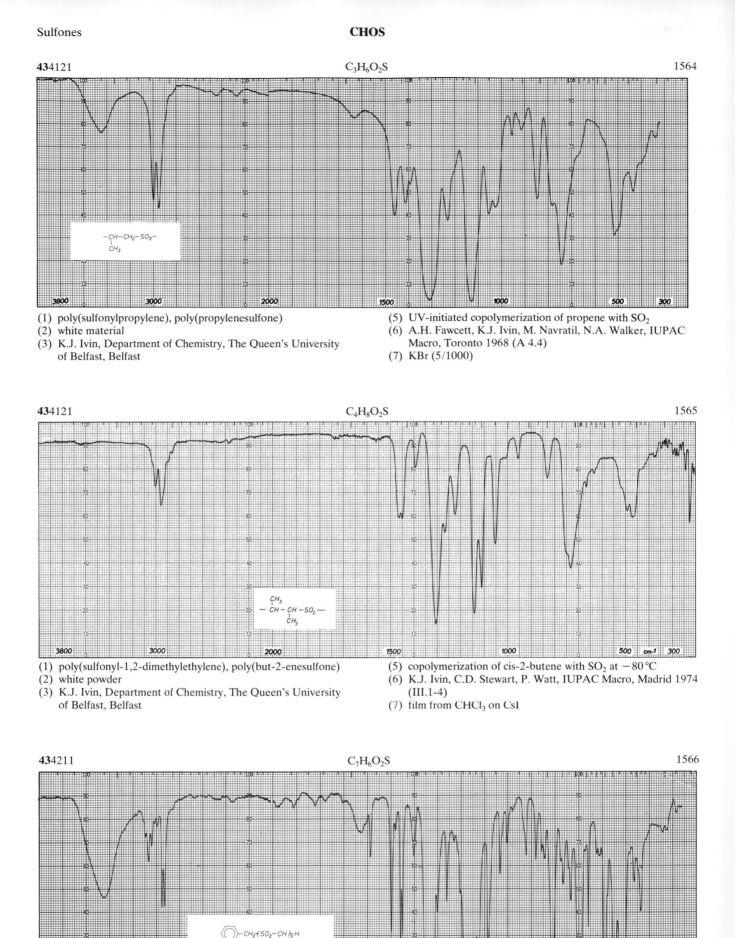

(1) poly(sulfonylpropylene), poly(propylenesulfone)
(2) white material
(3) K.J. Ivin, Department of Chemistry, The Queen's University of Belfast, Belfast
(5) UV-initiated copolymerization of propene with SO_2
(6) A.H. Fawcett, K.J. Ivin, M. Navratil, N.A. Walker, IUPAC Macro, Toronto 1968 (A 4.4)
(7) KBr (5/1000)

434121 $C_4H_8O_2S$ 1565

(1) poly(sulfonyl-1,2-dimethylethylene), poly(but-2-enesulfone)
(2) white powder
(3) K.J. Ivin, Department of Chemistry, The Queen's University of Belfast, Belfast
(5) copolymerization of cis-2-butene with SO_2 at $-80\,°C$
(6) K.J. Ivin, C.D. Stewart, P. Watt, IUPAC Macro, Madrid 1974 (III.1-4)
(7) film from $CHCl_3$ on CsI

434211 $C_7H_6O_2S$ 1566

(1) phenylmethylenetrisulfone
(2) white powder
(3) N. Tokura, Department of Applied Chemistry, Faculty of Engineering, Osaka University, Osaka
(5) reaction of benzylsulfonylfluoride with phenyllithium in ether at $-70\,°C$, fractionation with tetrahydrofuran
(6) N. Tokura, T. Nagai, Y. Shirota, J. Polym. Sci. *C 23* (1968) 793...802 see also N. Tokura, Olefin-Sulfur Dioxide Copolymers, Encyclopedia of Polymer Science and Technology, Vol. 9, John Wiley, New York 1968
(7) KBr (2/350)

434211   C$_7$H$_6$O$_2$S   1567

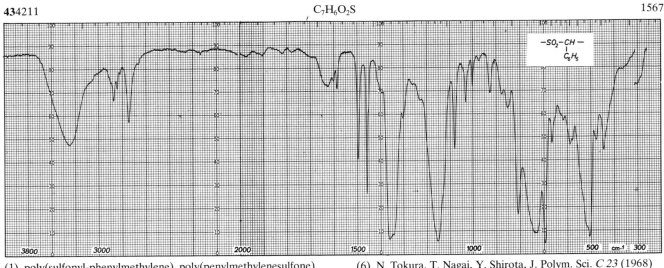

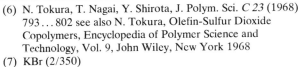

(1) poly(sulfonyl-phenylmethylene), poly(penylmethylenesulfone)
(2) white powder
(3) N. Tokura, Department of Applied Chemistry, Faculty of Engineering, Osaka University, Osaka
(5) reaction of benzylsulfonylfluoride with phenyllithium in ether at −70 °C, fractionation with tetrahydrofuran

(6) N. Tokura, T. Nagai, Y. Shirota, J. Polym. Sci. *C 23* (1968) 793…802 see also N. Tokura, Olefin-Sulfur Dioxide Copolymers, Encyclopedia of Polymer Science and Technology, Vol. 9, John Wiley, New York 1968
(7) KBr (2/350)

4342133213   C$_{27}$H$_{22}$O$_4$S   1568

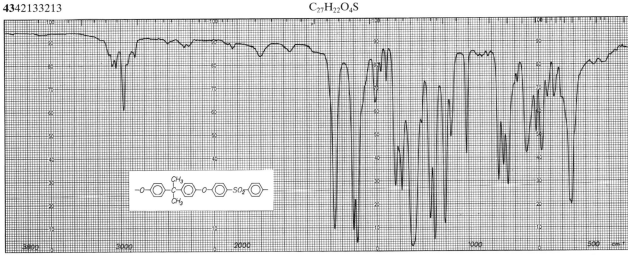

(1) poly(oxy-1,4-phenylene-2-propylidene-1,4-phenyleneoxy-1,4-phenylenesulfonyl); poly(bisphenol A-diphenylsulfone ether)
(2) colourless, clear film
(3) R.K. Walton, Plastics Research and Development Department, Union Carbide Corp., Bound Brook, N.J.

(5) polycondensation of the sodium salt of 2,2-bis(4-hydroxyphenyl)propane and 4,4'-dichlorodiphenylsulfone
(6) R.K. Walton, Modern Plastics Encyclopedia *46* (Oct. 1969) 198
(7) film from CHCl$_3$ on CsI
(8) commercial material "Bakelite Polysulfone"

4342133213   C$_{27}$H$_{22}$O$_4$S   1569

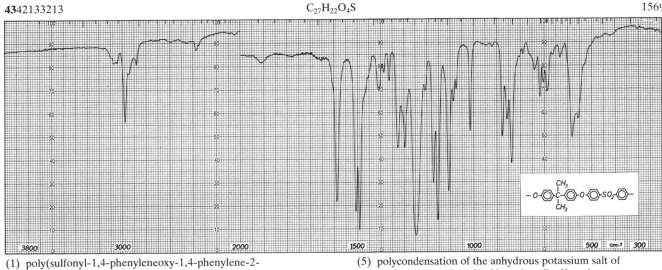

(1) poly(sulfonyl-1,4-phenyleneoxy-1,4-phenylene-2-propylidene-1,4-phenyleneoxy-1,4-phenylene); poly(arylenesulfone ether)
(2) white, flocky material
(3) R.J. Cornell, Uniroyal Chemical, Div. of Uniroyal, Naugatuck, Conn.

(5) polycondensation of the anhydrous potassium salt of bisphenol A with bis(4-chlorophenyl)sulfone in tetrahydrothiophene-1,1-dioxide ("sulfolane")
(6) R.J. Cornell, ACS Polym. Prepr. *13*/1 (1972) 607…10
(7) film from CHCl$_3$ on CsI

4342133213 $C_{36}H_{32}O_4S$ 1570

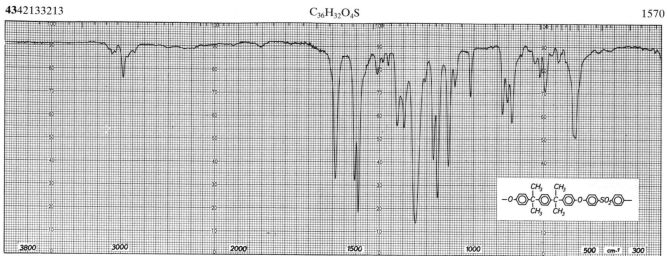

(1) poly(sulfonyl-1,4-phenyleneoxy-1,4-phenylene-2-propylidene-1,4-phenylene-2-propylidene-1,4-phenyleneoxy-1,4-phenylene); poly(arylenesulfone ether)

(2) amber-coloured, clear thermoplastic

(3) R.J. Cornell, Uniroyal Chemical, Div. of Uniroyal, Naugatuck, Conn.

(5) condensation of p-diisopropenylbenzene with phenol in toluene, polycondensation of the potassium salt of the resulting α,α'-bis(4-hydroxyphenyl)-p-diisopropylbenzene with bis(4-chlorophenyl)sulfone

(6) R.J. Cornell, ACS Polym. Prepr. *13*/1 (1972) 607. . . 10

(7) film from CHCl₃ on CsI

434222 $C_9H_{10}O_4S_2$ 1571

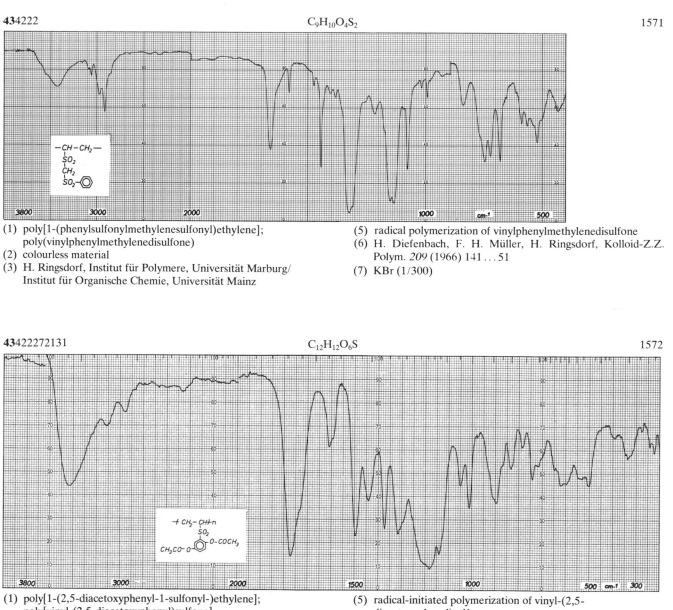

(1) poly[1-(phenylsulfonylmethylenesulfonyl)ethylene]; poly(vinylphenylmethylenedisulfone)

(2) colourless material

(3) H. Ringsdorf, Institut für Polymere, Universität Marburg/ Institut für Organische Chemie, Universität Mainz

(5) radical polymerization of vinylphenylmethylenedisulfone

(6) H. Diefenbach, F. H. Müller, H. Ringsdorf, Kolloid-Z.Z. Polym. *209* (1966) 141 . . . 51

(7) KBr (1/300)

43422272131 $C_{12}H_{12}O_6S$ 1572

(1) poly[1-(2,5-diacetoxyphenyl-1-sulfonyl-)ethylene]; poly[vinyl-(2,5-diacetoxyphenyl)sulfone]

(2) brittle, brown material

(3) G. Manecke, Fritz-Haber-Institut, Max-Planck-Gesellschaft, Berlin-Dahlem

(5) radical-initiated polymerization of vinyl-(2,5-diacetoxyphenyl)sulfone

(6) G. Manecke, H.-J. Beyer, Makromol. Chem. *123* (1969) 223 . . . 32

(7) melting film on CsI

43423 $C_9H_{10}O_4S_2$ 1573

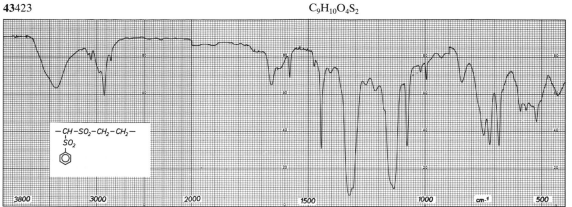

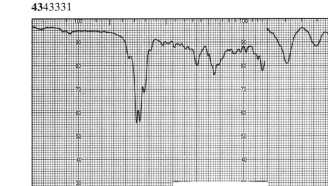

(1) poly(sulfonyl-1-phenylsulfonyl-trimethylene)
(2) colourless material
(3) R. Kroker, H. Ringsdorf, Institut für Polymere, Universität Marburg/Institut für Organische Chemie, Universität Mainz

(5) anionic polymerization of vinylphenylmethylenedisulfon
(6) H. Diefenbach, F. H. Müller, H. Ringsdorf, Kolloid-Z.Z. Polym. *209* (1966) 141...51
(7) KBr (1/300)

4343331 $C_{12}H_8O_3S$ 1574

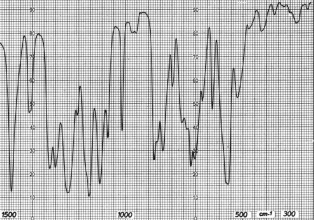
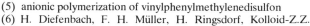

(1) poly(sulfonyl-1,4-phenyleneoxy-1,4-phenylene), poly(phenylenesulfone ether)
(2) white material
(3) J.B. Rose, ICI, Welwyn Garden City, Herts.
(5) melt polycondensation of the 4-chlorophenyl-4'-

hydroxyphenylsulfone or, alternatively, polysulfonylation of diphenylether-4-sulfonyl chloride in the presence of $FeCl_3$
(6) J.B. Rose, Polymer *15* (1974) 456...65
(7) film from $CHCl_3$ on CsI

4343331 $C_{24}H_{16}O_5S_2$ 1575

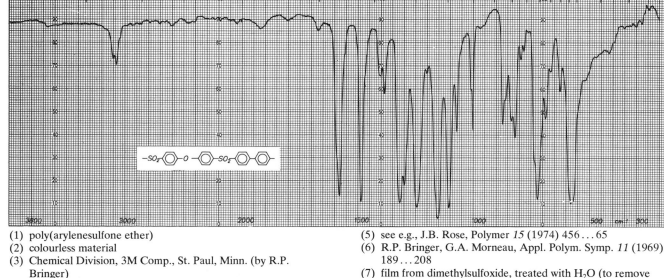

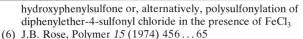

(1) poly(arylenesulfone ether)
(2) colourless material
(3) Chemical Division, 3M Comp., St. Paul, Minn. (by R.P. Bringer)
(4) copolyether sulfone with the following units:
(formula in the spectrum is idealized)

(5) see e.g., J.B. Rose, Polymer *15* (1974) 456...65
(6) R.P. Bringer, G.A. Morneau, Appl. Polym. Symp. *11* (1969) 189...208
(7) film from dimethylsulfoxide, treated with H_2O (to remove DMSO)
(8) commercial material "Astrel 360"

43437132 $C_{20}H_{12}O_6S$ 1576

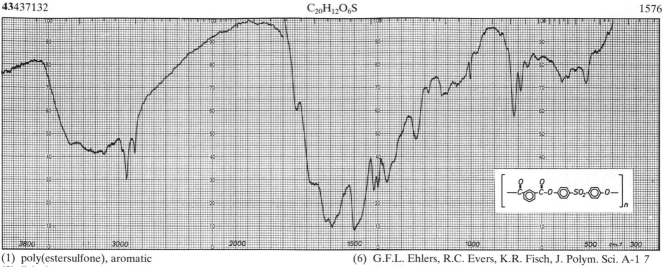

(1) poly(estersulfone), aromatic
(2) light-brown powder
(3) G.F.L. Ehlers, Wright Patterson AFB, O.
(5) interfacial polycondensation of 4,4'-dihydroxydiphenylsulfone
     with isophthaloylchloride

(6) G.F.L. Ehlers, R.C. Evers, K.R. Fisch, J. Polym. Sci. A-1 7
     (1969) 3413...5
(7) ground with KBr (0.5/300) and acetone, dried and pressed
(8) the sample was partly hydrolyzed

434374132 $C_{25}H_{22}O_7S$ 1577

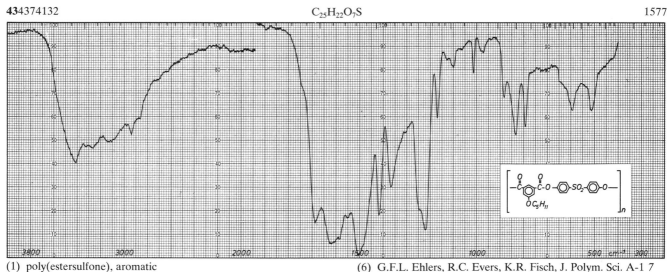

(1) poly(estersulfone), aromatic
(2) eggshell-coloured powder
(3) G.F.L. Ehlers, Wright-Patterson AFB, O.
(5) interfacial polycondensation of 4,4'-dihydroxyphenylsulfone
     with 5-(amyloxy)isophthaloylchloride

(6) G.F.L. Ehlers, R.C. Evers, K.R. Fisch, J. Polym. Sci. A-1 7
     (1969) 3413...5
(7) KBr (0.7/350)
(8) the material was partly hydrolyzed

43536112 $C_{20}H_{22}O_8S_2$ 1578

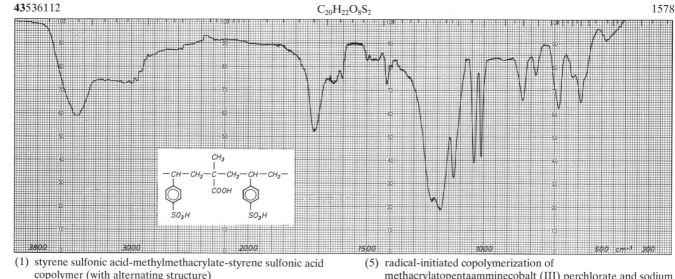

(1) styrene sulfonic acid-methylmethacrylate-styrene sulfonic acid
     copolymer (with alternating structure)
(2) white powder
(3) Y. Osada, Department of Chemistry, University of Lowell/
     College of General Education, Ibaraki University, Mito
(4) the copolymer contains alternating ABA sequences

(5) radical-initiated copolymerization of
     methacrylatopentaamminecobalt (III) perchlorate and sodium
     styrene-4-sulfonate, dialysis of the polymeric complex
(6) Y. Osada, K. Ishida, Makromol. Chem. *177* (1976)
     2209...13
(7) KBr

43613411

1579

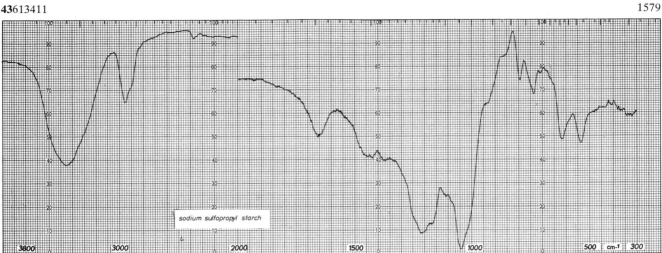

sodium sulfopropyl starch

(1) starch, sulfopropylated, sodium salt; sulfopropyl starch, sodium salt
(2) fine white powder
(3) E.J. Goethals, Laboratory of Organic Chemistry, State University of Ghent, Gent
(4) degree of substitution: 0.98

(5) reaction of alkali starch with propane sultone in isopropanol or acetone at 45 °C
(6) G. Natus, E.J. Goethals, J. Macromol. Sci.-Chem. *A2* (3) (1968) 489...99
(7) KBr (2/350), ordinate expanded

43613411

1580

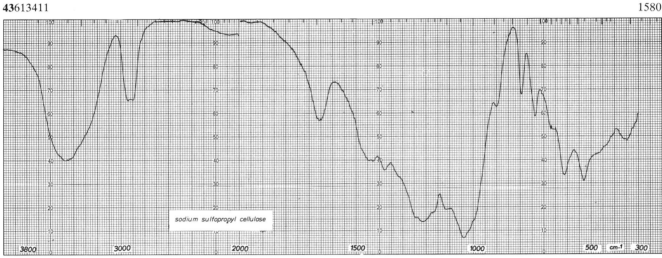

sodium sulfopropyl cellulose

(1) cellulose, sulfopropylated, sodium salt; sulfopropyl cellulose, sodium salt
(2) slightly greyish powder
(3) E.J. Goethals, Laboratory of Organic Chemistry, State University of Ghent, Gent
(4) degree of substitution: 0.65

(5) reaction of alkali cellulose with propenesulfone in isopropanol or acetone at 45 °C
(6) G. Natus, E.J. Goethals, J. Macromol. Sci.-Chem. *A2* (3) (1968) 489...99
(7) KBr (3/350), ordinate expanded

43622–336212

$C_8H_7O_3S/Na-C_4H_5O_2/Co(NH_3)_5(ClO_4)_2$

1581

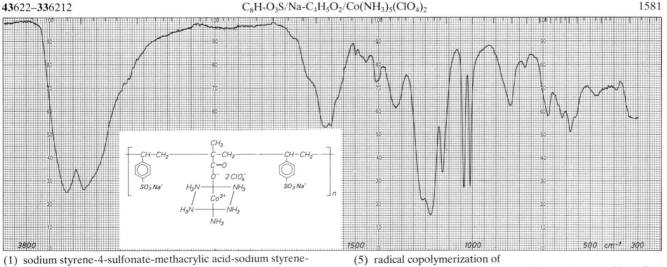

(1) sodium styrene-4-sulfonate-methacrylic acid-sodium styrene-4-sulfonate alternating (ABA) copolymer, coordinated to a Co(III)complex
(2) pink powder
(3) Y. Osada, Department of Chemistry, College of General Education, Ibaraki University, Mito

(5) radical copolymerization of methacrylatopentaamminecobalt(III) perchlorate with sodium styrene-4-sulfonate in an aqueous medium
(6) Y. Osada, K. Ishida, Makromol. Chem. *177* (1976) 2209...13
(7) KBr (0.6/350)

437131 $C_6H_4O_3S$ 1582

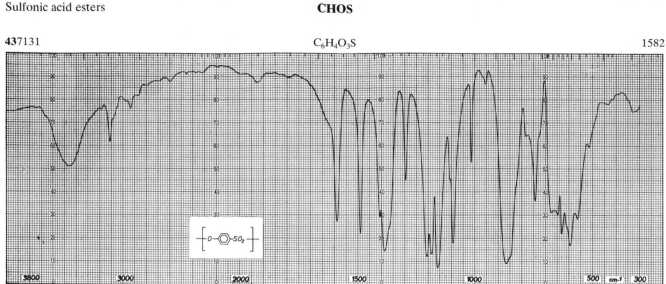

(1) poly(sulfonyloxy-1,4-phenylene), poly(1,4-phenylenesulfonate)
(2) white powder
(3) R.W. Campbell, Phillips Petroleum Comp., Bartlesville, Okla.
(5) polycondensation of 4-hydroxybenzenesulfonylchloride by treatment with tertiary amines in polar amide solvents (e.g.,

triethylamine and hexamethylphosphoramide)
(6) R.W. Campbell, H.Wayne Hill, Macromolecules 6 (1973) 492...5
(7) KBr (1.5/350)

437132 $C_{21}H_{18}O_6S_2$ 1583

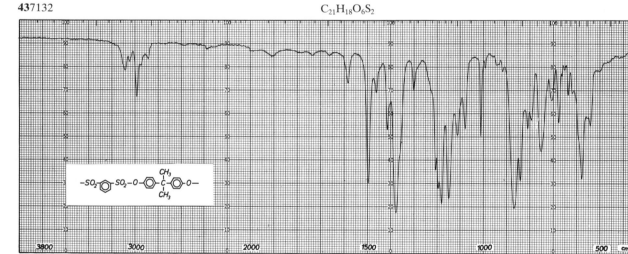

(1) poly(m-phenylenedisulfonyloxy-1,4-phenylene-2-propylidene-1,4-phenylene), poly(bisphenol A-1,3-phenylenesulfonate)
(2) white fibrous material
(3) J.E. Herweh, Armstrong Cork Comp., Lancaster
(5) interfacial polycondensation of 1,3-

phenylenedisulfonylchloride with the potassium salt of bisphenol A
(6) J.L. Work, J.E. Herweh, J. Polym. Sci. A1 6 (1968)2022...30
(7) film from $CHCl_3$ on CsI

437132 $C_{24}H_{16}O_7S_2$ 1584

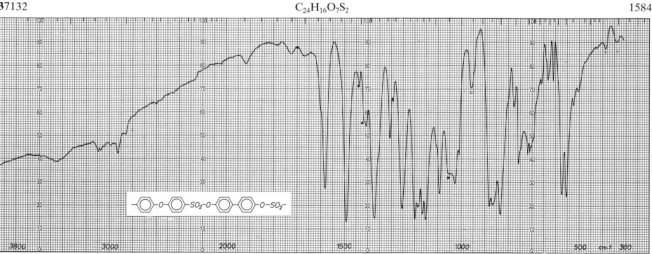

(1) poly(sulfonate) on the basis of diphenylether-4,4'-disulfonic acid and 4,4'-dihydroxybiphenyl
(2) white material
(3) G.F.L. Ehlers, Wright-Patterson AFB, O.
(5) interfacial polycondensation (benzene-water) of diphenylether-4,4'-disulfonylchloride with 4,4'-

dihydroxydiphenyl in the presence of Na_2CO_3
(6) G.F.L. Ehlers, K.R. Fisch, W.R. Powell, J. Polym. Sci. A-1 7 (1969) 2955
(7) ground with KBr (2/350) and dimethylsulfoxide, dried and pressed
(8) *: absorptions of dimethylsulfoxide

437132   C$_{24}$H$_{16}$O$_7$S$_2$ 1585

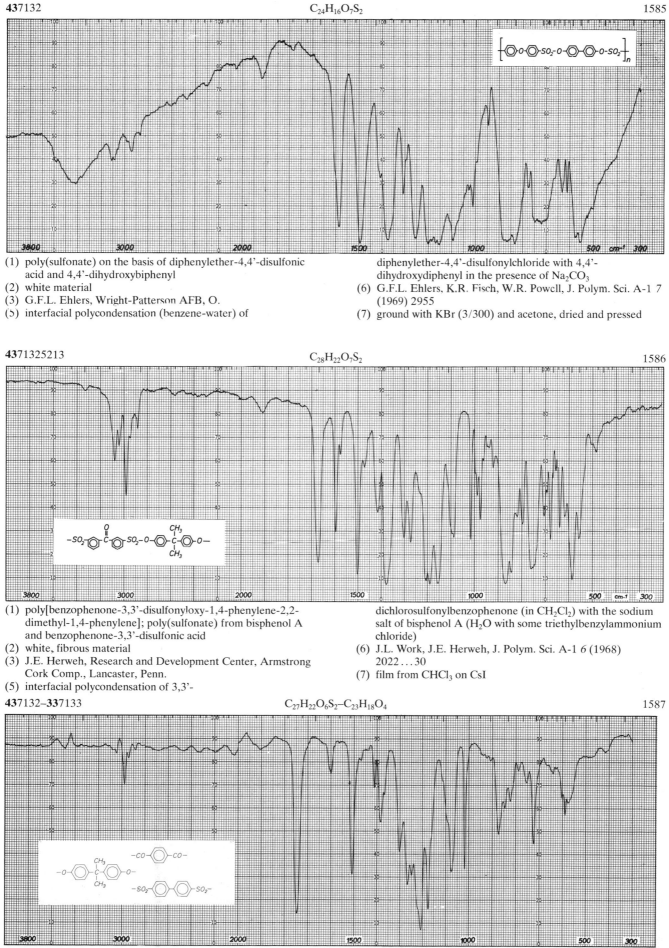

(1) poly(sulfonate) on the basis of diphenylether-4,4'-disulfonic acid and 4,4'-dihydroxybiphenyl

(2) white material

(3) G.F.L. Ehlers, Wright-Patterson AFB, O.

(5) interfacial polycondensation (benzene-water) of

diphenylether-4,4'-disulfonylchloride with 4,4'-dihydroxydiphenyl in the presence of Na$_2$CO$_3$

(6) G.F.L. Ehlers, K.R. Fisch, W.R. Powell, J. Polym. Sci. A-1 7 (1969) 2955

(7) ground with KBr (3/300) and acetone, dried and pressed

4371325213   C$_{28}$H$_{22}$O$_7$S$_2$ 1586

(1) poly[benzophenone-3,3'-disulfonyloxy-1,4-phenylene-2,2-dimethyl-1,4-phenylene]; poly(sulfonate) from bisphenol A and benzophenone-3,3'-disulfonic acid

(2) white, fibrous material

(3) J.E. Herweh, Research and Development Center, Armstrong Cork Comp., Lancaster, Penn.

(5) interfacial polycondensation of 3,3'-

dichlorosulfonylbenzophenone (in CH$_2$Cl$_2$) with the sodium salt of bisphenol A (H$_2$O with some triethylbenzylammonium chloride)

(6) J.L. Work, J.E. Herweh, J. Polym. Sci. A-1 6 (1968) 2022...30

(7) film from CHCl$_3$ on CsI

437132–337133   C$_{27}$H$_{22}$O$_6$S$_2$–C$_{23}$H$_{18}$O$_4$ 1587

(1) copoly(bisphenol-A-terephthalate 4,4'-biphenylsulfonate)

(3) J.E. Forrette, Roy C. Ingersoll Research Center, Borg-Warner Corp., Des Plaines, Ill./Velsicol Chemical Corp.. Chicago, Ill.

(5) interfacial polycondensation of the sodium salt of bisphenol A with terephthaloyl chloride and 4,4'-biphenyldisulfonyl

chloride; see E.P. Goldberg, F. Scardiglia, US Pat. 3262914 (1966)

(6) J.E. Forrette, J. Burroughs, Christine Booker, J. Appl. Polym. Sci. 12 (1968) 2039...45

(7) film from CHCl$_3$ on KBr

437213   C$_{20}$H$_{18}$O$_6$S$_2$ 1588

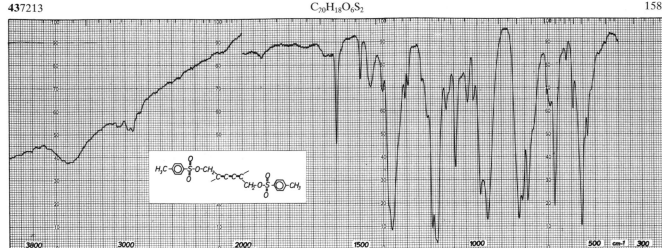

(1) poly(1,4-ditosyloxy-tetradiyne)
(2) G. Wegner, Institut für Physikalische Chemie, Universität Mainz/Institut für Makromolekulare Chemie, Universität Freiburg
(5) photochemically initiated polymerization of the monomer in the solid state

(6) G. Wegner, private communication; see also G. Wegner, Makromol. Chem. *134* (1970) 219...29, ibid. *154* (1972) 35...48, Houben-Weyl, *Methoden der Organischen Chemie*, 4–5b, Teilband II, *Photopolymerisation* (1499...1518)
(7) KBr (1/400)

4374–**437231**   C$_5$H$_8$O$_3$S   1589

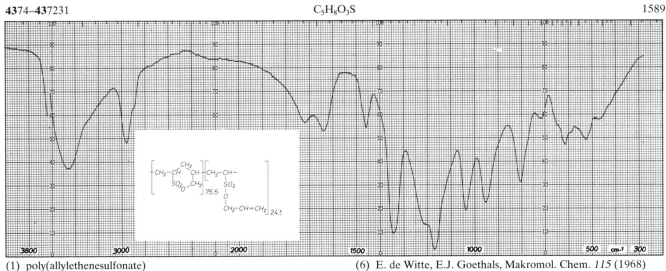

(1) poly(allylethenesulfonate)
(2) eggshell-coloured material
(3) E.J. Goethals, Laboratory of Organic Chemistry, University of Ghent, Gent
(5) radical-initiated polymerization of allylethenesulfonate in benzene with AIBN as intiator

(6) E. de Witte, E.J. Goethals, Makromol. Chem. *115* (1968) 234...44
(7) KBr (4/1000)
(8) the figures in the structural formula denote mol-%

4374–**437231**–**33721111**   C$_5$H$_8$O$_3$S–C$_4$H$_6$O$_2$ 1590

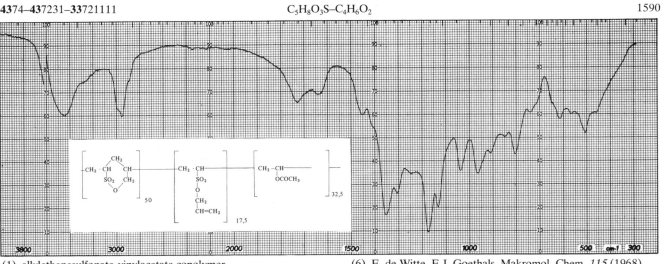

(1) allylethenesulfonate-vinylacetate copolymer
(2) yellowish material
(3) E.J. Goethals, Laboratory of Organic Chemistry, University of Ghent, Gent
(5) radical-initiated copolymerization of the monomers in benzene at 60 °C

(6) E. de Witte, E.J. Goethals, Makromol. Chem. *115* (1968) 234...44
(7) KBr (4/1000)
(8) the figures in the structural formula denote mol-%

4374–437231–437211   C₆H₁₀O₃S   1591

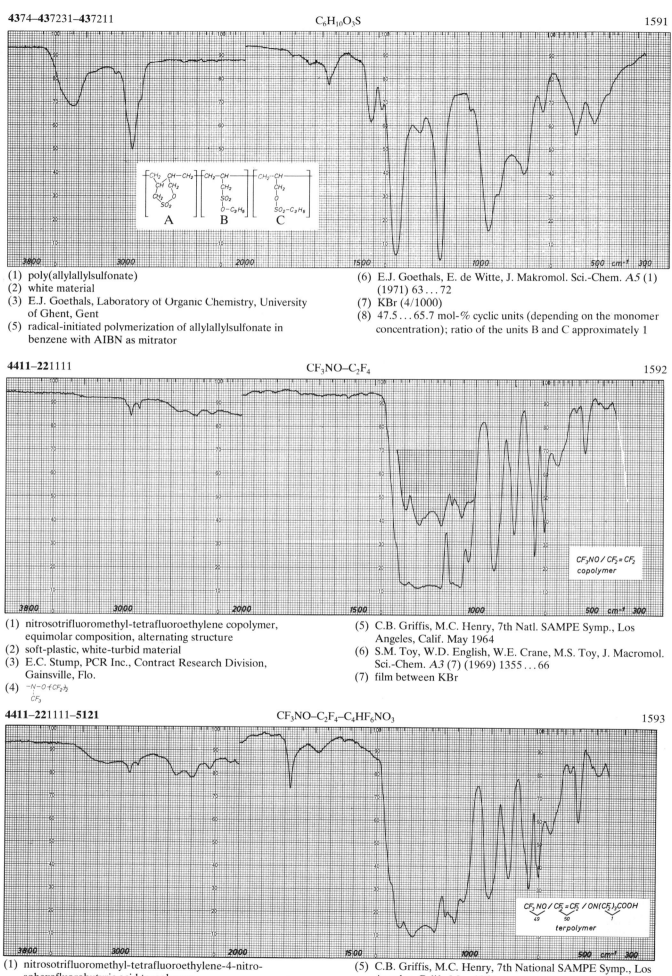

(1) poly(allylallylsulfonate)
(2) white material
(3) E.J. Goethals, Laboratory of Organic Chemistry, University of Ghent, Gent
(5) radical-initiated polymerization of allylallylsulfonate in benzene with AIBN as mitrator

(6) E.J. Goethals, E. de Witte, J. Makromol. Sci.-Chem. *A5* (1) (1971) 63 . . . 72
(7) KBr (4/1000)
(8) 47.5 . . . 65.7 mol-% cyclic units (depending on the monomer concentration); ratio of the units B and C approximately 1

4411–221111   CF₃NO–C₂F₄   1592

(1) nitrosotrifluoromethyl-tetrafluoroethylene copolymer, equimolar composition, alternating structure
(2) soft-plastic, white-turbid material
(3) E.C. Stump, PCR Inc., Contract Research Division, Gainsville, Flo.
(4) –N–O–(CF₂)₂–
     |
     CF₃

(5) C.B. Griffis, M.C. Henry, 7th Natl. SAMPE Symp., Los Angeles, Calif. May 1964
(6) S.M. Toy, W.D. English, W.E. Crane, M.S. Toy, J. Macromol. Sci.-Chem. *A3* (7) (1969) 1355 . . . 66
(7) film between KBr

4411–221111–5121   CF₃NO–C₂F₄–C₄HF₆NO₃   1593

(1) nitrosotrifluoromethyl-tetrafluoroethylene-4-nitrosohexafluorobutyric acid terpolymer
(2) soft-plastic, brownish, slightly turbid material
(3) E.C. Stump, PCR Contract Research Division, Gainesville, Flo.
(4) the nitrosotrifluoromethyl-tetrafluoroethylene units are alternating

(5) C.B. Griffis, M.C. Henry, 7th National SAMPE Symp., Los Angeles, Calif., May 1964
(6) S.M. Toy, W.D. English, W.E. Crane, M.S. Toy, J. Macromol. Sci.-Chem. *A3* (7) (1969) 1355 . . . 66
(7) film between KBr

4411–5121 CF₃NO–C₂F₄–C₄HF₆NO₃ 1594

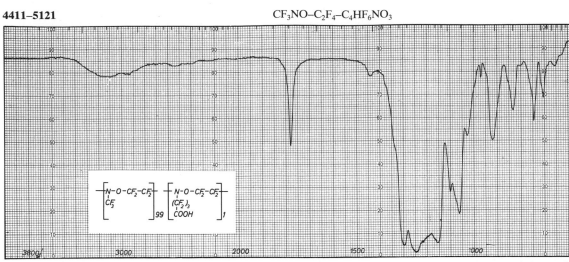

(1) nitrosotrifluoromethyl-tetrafluoroethylene-perfluorobutyric acid terpolymer
(2) viscous material
(3) N.B. Levine, Reaction Motors Div., Thiokol Chemical Corp., Denville, N.J.

(5) alternating copolymerization of nitrosotrifluoromethyl and tetrafluoroethylene in the presence of a small amount of nitrosoperfluorobutyric acid at low temperatures
(6) N.B. Levine, Appl. Polym. Symp. *11* (1969) 135...56
(7) film on KBr

5121110510 C₁₆H₂₀F₆N₂O₄ 1595

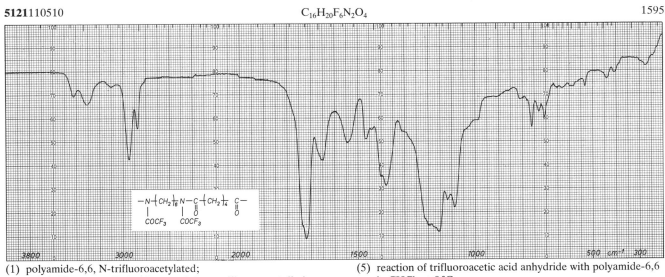

(1) polyamide-6,6, N-trifluoroacetylated; poly(trifluoroacetylimino-hexamethylene-trifluoro-acetylimino-adipoyl)
(2) colourless material
(3) R.C. Schulz, Institut für Organische Chemie, Universität Mainz

(5) reaction of trifluoroacetic acid anhydride with polyamide-6,6 in CHCl₃ at 0 °C
(6) H. Schuttenberg, R.C. Schulz, Angew. Chem. *88* (1976) 848...9
(7) film from CH₂Cl₂ on CsI
(8) slightly hydrolyzed

5122111211 C₆H₉Cl₂NO 1596

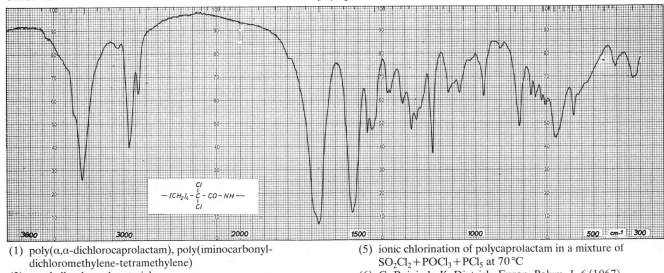

(1) poly(α,α-dichlorocaprolactam), poly(iminocarbonyl-dichloromethylene-tetramethylene)
(2) eggshell-coloured material
(3) G. Reinisch, Institut für Faserstoff-Forschung, Deutsche Akademie der Wissenschaften zu Berlin, Berlin-Teltow

(5) ionic chlorination of polycaprolactam in a mixture of SO₂Cl₂+POCl₃+PCl₅ at 70 °C
(6) G. Reinisch, K. Dietrich, Europ. Polym. J. *6* (1967) 1269...76
(7) KBr (2/350)

5122310211   C₁₃H₈ClNO₂   1597

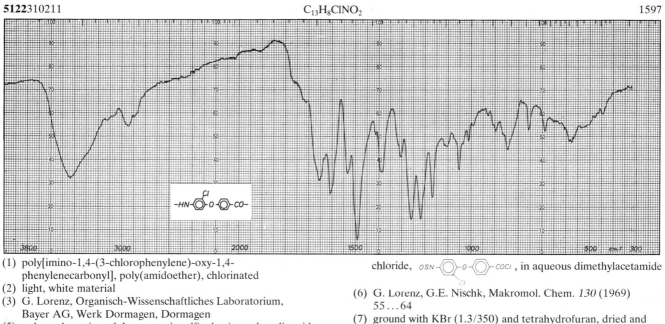

(1) poly[imino-1,4-(3-chlorophenylene)-oxy-1,4-
    phenylenecarbonyl], poly(amidoether), chlorinated
(2) light, white material
(3) G. Lorenz, Organisch-Wissenschaftliches Laboratorium,
    Bayer AG, Werk Dormagen, Dormagen
(5) polycondensation of the aromatic sulfinylaminocarboxylic acid

chloride, , in aqueous dimethylacetamide

(6) G. Lorenz, G.E. Nischk, Makromol. Chem. *130* (1969)
    55...64
(7) ground with KBr (1.3/350) and tetrahydrofuran, dried and
    pressed

5122310682   C₂₄H₁₁ClN₈O₂   1598

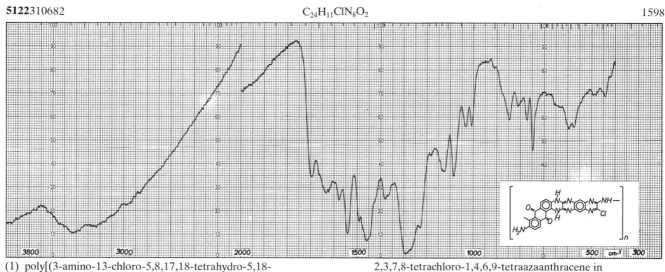

(1) poly[(3-amino-13-chloro-5,8,17,18-tetrahydro-5,18-
    dioxonaphtho[2,3-f]pyrazino[2,3-b:5,6-g']diquinoxaline-4,12-
    diyl)imino]
(2) black powder
(3) C.S. Marvel, Department of Chemistry, University of
    Arizona, Tucson, Ariz.
(5) polycondensation of 1,2,5,6-tetraaminoanthraquinone with

2,3,7,8-tetrachloro-1,4,6,9-tetraazaanthracene in
tetramethylenesulfone, isolation of the precipitate, heating at
330...350°C from several hours under reduced pressure

(6) A. Banihashemi, C.S. Marvel, J. Polym. Sci. A-1 *8* (1970)
    3211...24
(7) KBr (2/300)

5122320651   C₁₉H₁₂Cl₄N₂O₅   1599

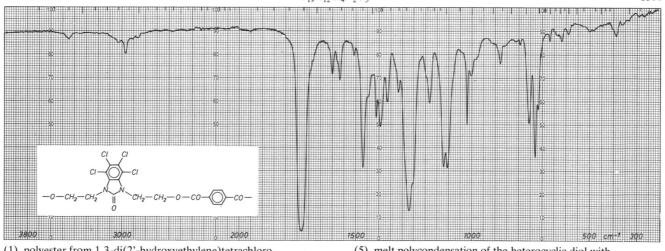

(1) polyester from 1,3-di(2'-hydroxyethylene)tetrachloro-
    benzimidazolone-2², 1,4-dihydroxybutylene, and terephthalic
    acid
(2) brown, clear piece
(3) H. Batzer, J. Habermeier, Ciba-Geigy AG, Basel

(5) melt polycondensation of the heterocyclic diol with
    dimethylterephthalate
(6) J. Habermeier, L. Buxbaum, Ursula T. Kreibich, H. Batzer,
    Angew. Makromol. Chem. *55* (1976) 155...73
(7) film from CHCl₃ on CsI

5122320651–**337**1221 $C_{19}H_{12}Cl_4N_2O_5$–$C_{10}H_8O_4$ 1600

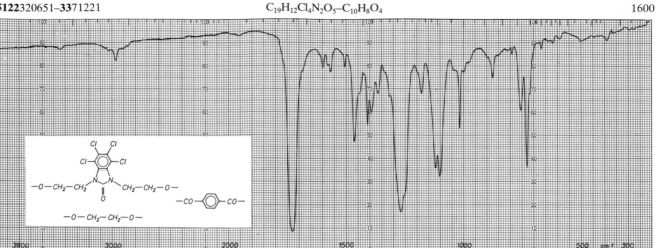

(1) copolyester from 1,3-di(2'-hydroxyethylene)tetrachloro-benzimidazolone-2², ethyleneglycol, and terephthalic acid
(2) brown, clear piece
(3) H. Batzer, J. Habermeier, Ciba-Geigy AG, Basel
(4) 50 mol-% of the heterocyclic diol
(5) melt polycondensation (transesterification) of

dimethylterephthalate, ethyleneglycol and the heterocyclic diol
(6) J. Habermeier, L. Buxbaum, Ursula T. Kreibich, H. Batzer, Angew. Makromol. Chem. *55* (1976) 155...73
(7) film from CHCl₃ on CsI

5122320651–**337**1221 $C_{19}H_{12}Cl_4N_2O_5$–$C_{10}H_8O_4$ 1601

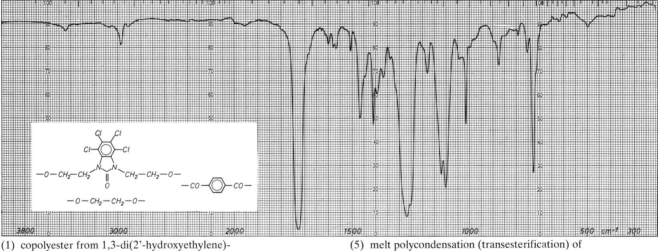

(1) copolyester from 1,3-di(2'-hydroxyethylene)-tetrachlorobenzimidazolone-2²-ethyleneglycol, and terephthalic acid
(2) light-brown, clear piece
(3) H. Batzer, J. Habermeier, Ciba-Geigy AG, Basel
(4) 33,3 mol-% of the heterocyclic diol

(5) melt polycondensation (transesterification) of dimethylterephthalate, ethyleneglycol and heterocyclic diol in the presence of tetraisopropyl-orthotitanate
(6) J. Habermeier, L. Buxbaum, Ursula T. Kreibich, H. Batzer, Angew. Makromol. Chem. *55* (1976) 155...73
(7) film from CHCl₃ on CsI

5122320651–**337**1221 $C_{19}H_{12}Cl_4N_2O_5$–$C_{12}H_{12}O_4$ 1602

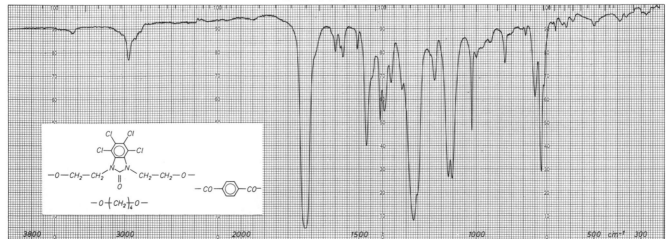

(1) copolyester from 1,3-di(2'-hydroxyethylene)-tetrachlorobenzimidazolone-2², 1,4-dihydroxybutylene, and terephthalic acid
(2) slight brownish, clear pieces
(3) H. Batzer, J. Habermeier, Ciba-Geigy AG, Basel
(4) 50 mol-% of the heterocyclic diol in the polyester

(5) melt polycondensation of dimethylterephthalate with the diols at 160...220 °C in the presence of tetraisopropyl-orthotitanate
(6) J. Habermeier, L. Buxbaum, Ursula T. Kreibich, H. Batzer, Angew. Makromol. Chem. *55* (1976) 155...73
(7) film from CHCl₃ on CsI

5123320651–3371221   C₁₉H1₂Br₄N₂O₅–C₁₀H₈O₄   1603

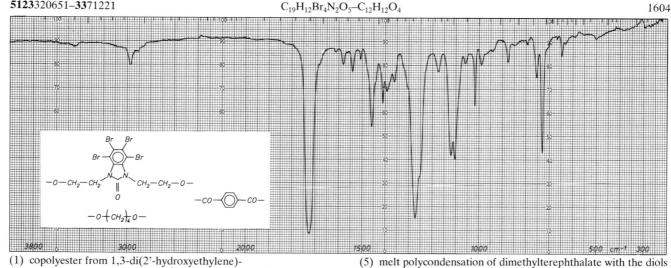

(1) copolyester from 1,3-di(2'-hydroxyethylene)tetrabromo-
    benzimidazolone-2², ethyleneglycol, and terephthalic acid
(2) brown, clear material
(3) H. Batzer, J. Habermeier, Ciba-Geigy AG, Basel
(4) 50 mol % of the heterocyclic diol in the polyester

(5) melt polycondensation of dimethylterephthalate with the diols
    at 160...200°C in the presence of tetraisopropyl-orthotitanate
(6) J. Habermeier, L. Buxbaum, Ursula T. Kreibich, H. Batzer,
    Angew. Makromol. Chem. 55 (1976) 155...73
(7) film from CHCl₃ on CsI

5123320651–3371221   C₁₉H₁₂Br₄N₂O₅–C₁₂H₁₂O₄   1604

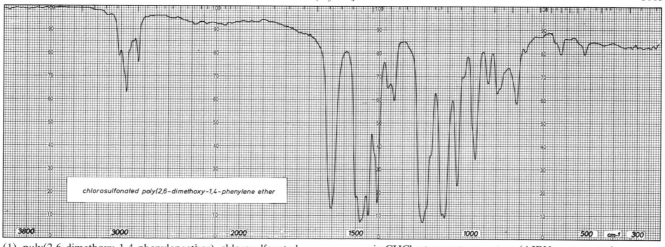

(1) copolyester from 1,3-di(2'-hydroxyethylene)-
    tetrabromobenzimidazolone-2², 1,4-dihydroxybutylene, and
    terephthalic acid
(2) slightly yellow to brown, clear piece
(3) H. Batzer, J. Habermeier, Ciby-Geigy AG, Basel
(4) 50 mol-% of the heterocyclic diol in the polyester

(5) melt polycondensation of dimethylterephthalate with the diols
    at 160...220 °C in the presence of tetraisopropyl-
    orthotitanate
(6) J. Habermeier, L. Buxbaum, Ursula T. Kreibich, H. Batzer,
    Angew. Makromol. Chem. 55 (1976) 155...73
(7) film from CHCL₃ on CSi

5132000323   C₇H₅ClO₄S   1605

chlorosulfonated poly(2,6-dimethoxy-1,4-phenylene ether)

(1) poly(2,6-dimethoxy-1,4-phenyleneether), chlorosulfonated
(2) brownish-white material
(3) J.J. Lindberg, Department of Wood and Polymer Chemistry,
    University of Helsinki, Helsinki
(4) the product contains 15.4% Cl
(5) oxidative polycondensation of 2,6-dimethoxyphenol (Ag₂O/
    triethylamine), reaction of the polymer with sulfonyl chloride

in CHCl₃ at room temperature (AIBN as promotor)
(6) J.J. Lindberg, E.Priha, V. Erä, Angew. Makromol. Chem. 37
    (1974) 161...6
(7) film from CHCl₃ on CsI
(8) the chlorosulfonation is accompanied by demethoxylation and
    chlorination

5132111000421 $C_{14}H_{18}Cl_2O_4S_2$ 1606

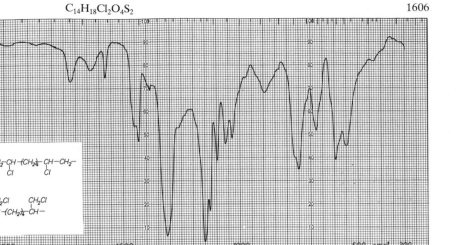

(1) poly(1,2-phenylenesulfone) with chlorinated alkyl bridge
(2) white powder
(3) G.G. Cameron, University of Aberdeen, Dept. of Chemistry, Old Aberdeen
(5) polyaddition of benzene-1,2-disulfenylchloride and 1,7-

octadiene, controlled oxidation of the polythioether with m-chloroperbenzoic acid in $CHCl_3$
(6) private communication; see also G.G. Cameron, D.R. Hogg, S.A. Stachowiak, Makromol. Chem. *176* (1975) 9 . . . 21
(7) KBr (2/350)

5132111000421 $C_{20}H_{22}Cl_2O_4S_2$ 1607

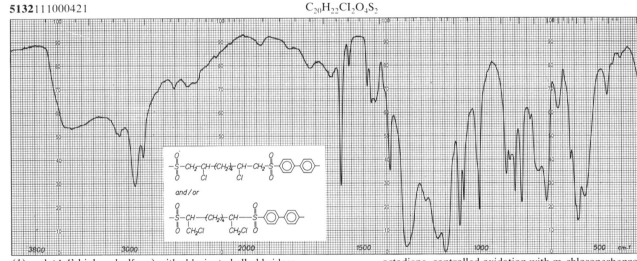

(1) poly(4,4'-biphenylsulfone) with chlorinated alkyl bridges
(2) white powder
(3) G.G. Cameron, University of Aberdeen, Dept. of Chemistry, Old Aberdeen
(5) polyaddition of 4,4'-biphenyl-disulfenylchloride and 1,7-

octadiene, controlled oxidation with m-chloroperbenzoic acid in $CHCl_3$
(6) G.G. Cameron, D.R. Hogg, S.A. Stachowiak, Makromol. Chem. *176* (1975) 9 . . . 21
(7) KBr (3/350)

5132111000421 $C_{21}H_{22}Cl_2O_4S_2$ 1608

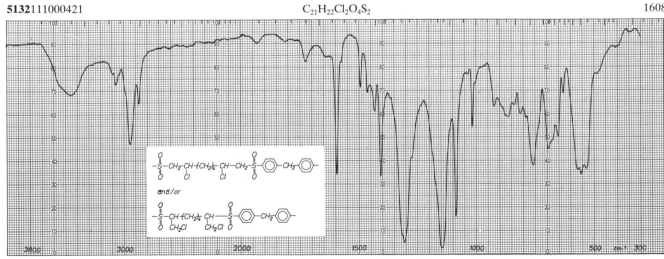

(1) polysulfone, aromatic, with chlorinated alkyl bridges
(2) white powder
(3) G.G. Cameron, University of Aberdeen, Dept. of Chemistry, Old Aberdeen
(5) polyaddition of 4,4'-diphenylmethanedisulfenylchloride and

1,7 octadiene, controlled oxidation with m-chloroperbenzoic acid in $CHCl_3$
(6) G.G. Cameron, D.R. Hogg, S.A. Stachowiak, Makromol. Chem. *176* (1975) 9 . . . 21
(7) KBr (3/350)

5132112000421 $C_{20}H_{22}Cl_2O_4S_2$ 1609

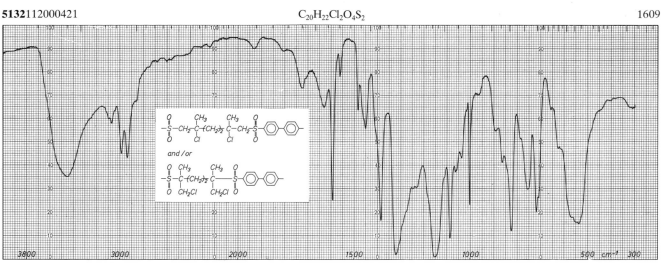

(1) polysulfone, aromatic, with chlorinated alkyl bridges
(2) white powder
(3) G.G. Cameron, University of Aberdeen, Dept. of Chemistry, Old Aberdeen
(5) polyaddition of 4,4'-biphenyldisulfenylchloride and

2,5-dimethyl-1,5-hexadiene, controlled oxidation with m-chloroperbenzoic acid in $CHCl_3$
(6) G.G. Cameron, D.R. Hogg, S.A. Stachowiak, Makromol. Chem. *176* (1975) 9...21
(7) KBr (3/350)

5132121000411 $C_4H_5ClO_2S$ 1610

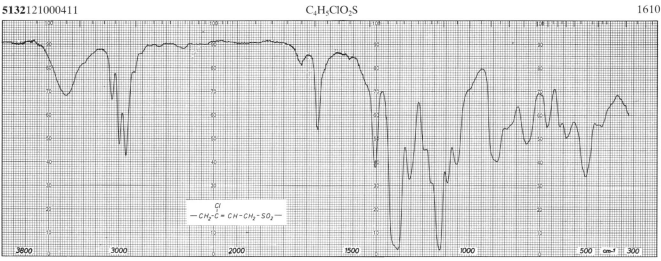

(1) poly(sulfonyl-2-chloro-2-butenylene), 2-chlorobutadiene-SO_2 copolymer
(2) white powder
(3) F. Hrabák, Institut für Makromolekulare Chemie der Tschechoslowakischen Akademie der Wissenschaften, Praha

(5) copolymerization of the monomer mixture at $-20\,°C$ in polar solvent, e.g., dimethylformamide with perbenzoic acid as initiator
(6) J. Likaj, F. Hrabák, Makromol. Chem. *136* (1970) 281...90
(7) KBr (2/350)

5132310322430 $C_7H_5ClOS_4$ 1611

(1) poly(tetrasulfo-2-chloro-5-methoxy-1,4-phenylene), poly(2-chloro-5-methoxy-1,4-phenylene-tetrasulfide)
(2) yellow powder
(3) N.A. Hiatt, Uniroyal Chemical, Div. of Uniroyal, Naugatuck, Conn.

(5) thermal polymerization of the cyclic dimer
(6) N.A. Hiatt, ACS Polym. Prepr. *13*/1 (1972) 594

(7) film from $CHCl_3$ on CsI

5221233 $C_8H_9N_2O_4S_2$ 1612

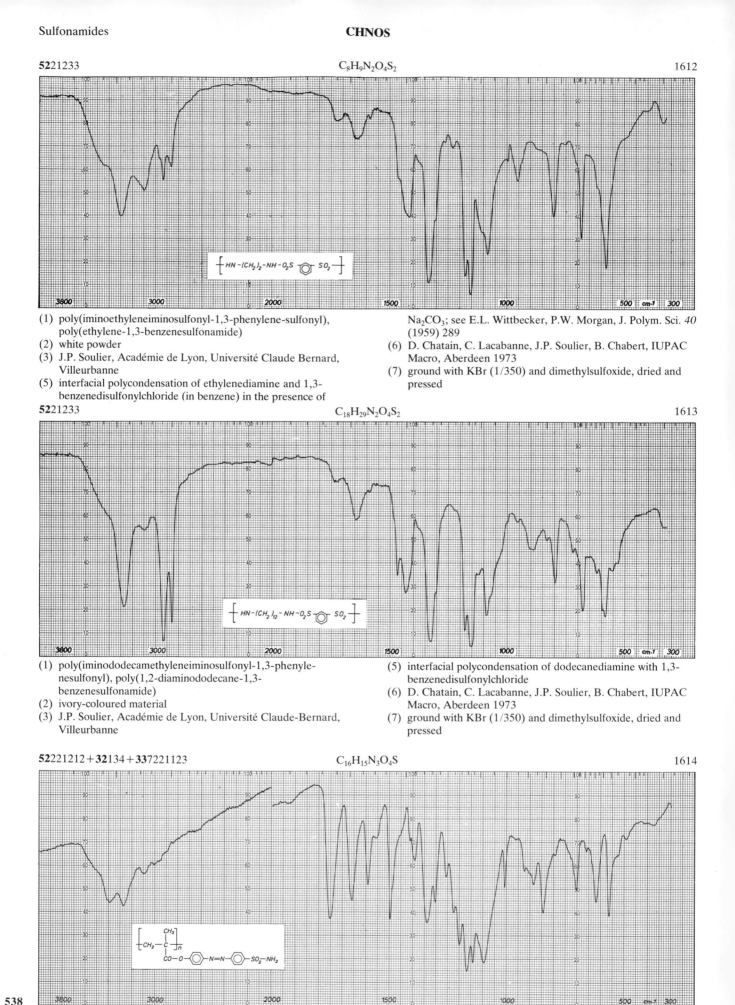

(1) poly(iminoethyleneiminosulfonyl-1,3-phenylene-sulfonyl), poly(ethylene-1,3-benzenesulfonamide)
(2) white powder
(3) J.P. Soulier, Académie de Lyon, Université Claude Bernard, Villeurbanne
(5) interfacial polycondensation of ethylenediamine and 1,3-benzenedisulfonylchloride (in benzene) in the presence of

Na_2CO_3; see E.L. Wittbecker, P.W. Morgan, J. Polym. Sci. *40* (1959) 289
(6) D. Chatain, C. Lacabanne, J.P. Soulier, B. Chabert, IUPAC Macro, Aberdeen 1973
(7) ground with KBr (1/350) and dimethylsulfoxide, dried and pressed

5221233 $C_{18}H_{29}N_2O_4S_2$ 1613

(1) poly(iminododecamethyleneiminosulfonyl-1,3-phenyle-nesulfonyl), poly(1,2-diaminododecane-1,3-benzenesulfonamide)
(2) ivory-coloured material
(3) J.P. Soulier, Académie de Lyon, Université Claude-Bernard, Villeurbanne

(5) interfacial polycondensation of dodecanediamine with 1,3-benzenedisulfonylchloride
(6) D. Chatain, C. Lacabanne, J.P. Soulier, B. Chabert, IUPAC Macro, Aberdeen 1973
(7) ground with KBr (1/350) and dimethylsulfoxide, dried and pressed

52221212 + **32**134 + **337**221123 $C_{16}H_{15}N_3O_4S$ 1614

538

(1) poly[p-(4-sulfamoylphenylazo)phenylmethacrylate]
(2) salmon-red powder
(3) M. Przybylski, Institut für Organische Chemie, Universität Mainz

(6) private communication; see also V. Hofmann, M. Przybylski, H. Ringsdorf, H. Ritter, Makromol. Chem. *177* (1976) 1791...1813
(7) KBr (1/350)

52221212 + 32134 + 4212122211   C$_{16}$H$_{16}$N$_4$O$_3$S   1615

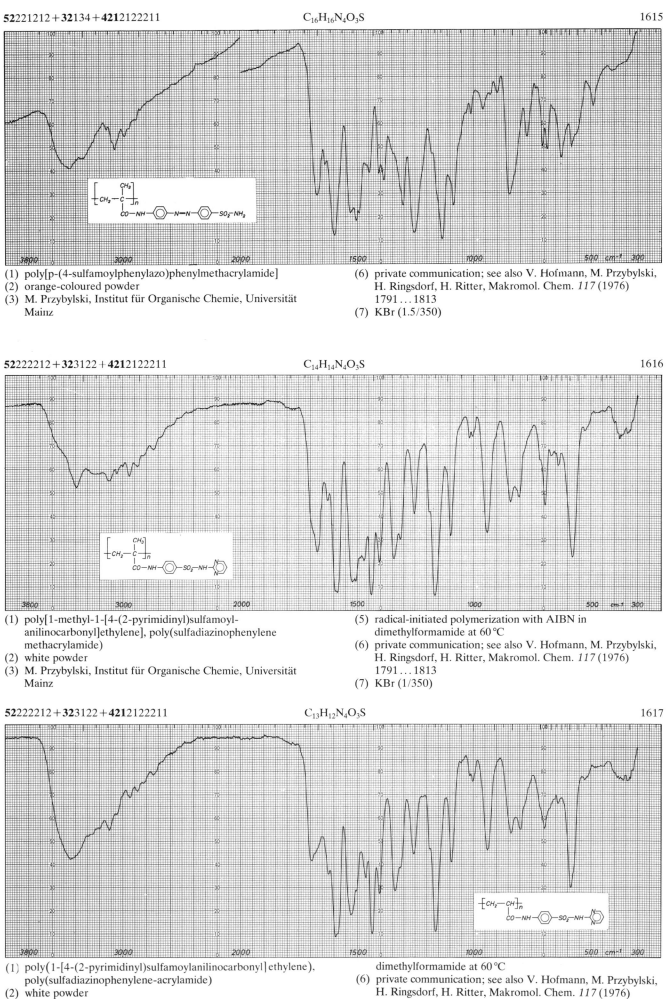

(1) poly[p-(4-sulfamoylphenylazo)phenylmethacrylamide]
(2) orange-coloured powder
(3) M. Przybylski, Institut für Organische Chemie, Universität Mainz

(6) private communication; see also V. Hofmann, M. Przybylski, H. Ringsdorf, H. Ritter, Makromol. Chem. *117* (1976) 1791...1813
(7) KBr (1.5/350)

52222212 + 323122 + 4212122211   C$_{14}$H$_{14}$N$_4$O$_3$S   1616

(1) poly[1-methyl-1-[4-(2-pyrimidinyl)sulfamoyl-anilinocarbonyl]ethylene], poly(sulfadiazinophenylene methacrylamide)
(2) white powder
(3) M. Przybylski, Institut für Organische Chemie, Universität Mainz

(5) radical-initiated polymerization with AIBN in dimethylformamide at 60 °C
(6) private communication; see also V. Hofmann, M. Przybylski, H. Ringsdorf, H. Ritter, Makromol. Chem. *117* (1976) 1791...1813
(7) KBr (1/350)

52222212 + 323122 + 4212122211   C$_{13}$H$_{12}$N$_4$O$_3$S   1617

(1) poly(1-[4-(2-pyrimidinyl)sulfamoylanilinocarbonyl]ethylene), poly(sulfadiazinophenylene-acrylamide)
(2) white powder
(3) M. Przybylski, Institut für Organische Chemie, Universität Mainz
(5) radical-initiated polymerization with AIBN in

dimethylformamide at 60 °C
(6) private communication; see also V. Hofmann, M. Przybylski, H. Ringsdorf, H. Ritter, Makromol. Chem. *117* (1976) 1791...1813
(7) KBr (0.75/350)

52221212+**421**2122211   C₉H₁₀N₂O₃S   1618

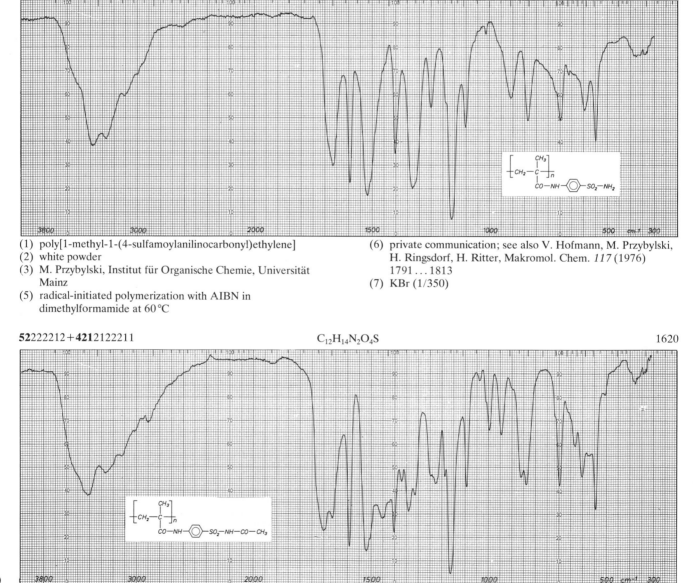

(1) poly[1-(4-sulfamoylanilinocarbonyl)ethylene]
(2) white powder
(3) M. Przybylski, Institut für Organische Chemie, Universität Mainz
(5) radical-initiated polymerization with AIBN in dimethylformamide at 60°C

(6) private communication; see also V. Hofmann, M. Przybylski, H. Ringsdorf, H. Ritter, Makromol. Chem. *117* (1976) 1791...1813
(7) KBr (1/350)

52221212+**421**2122211   C₁₀H₁₂N₂O₃S   1619

(1) poly[1-methyl-1-(4-sulfamoylanilinocarbonyl)ethylene]
(2) white powder
(3) M. Przybylski, Institut für Organische Chemie, Universität Mainz
(5) radical-initiated polymerization with AIBN in dimethylformamide at 60°C

(6) private communication; see also V. Hofmann, M. Przybylski, H. Ringsdorf, H. Ritter, Makromol. Chem. *117* (1976) 1791...1813
(7) KBr (1/350)

52222212+**421**2122211   C₁₂H₁₄N₂O₄S   1620

(1) poly(1-methyl-1-[4-(acetyl)sulfamoylanilinocarbonyl]ethylene)
(2) white powder
(3) M. Przybylski, Institut für Organische Chemie, Universität Mainz
(5) radical-initiated polymerization with AIBN in dimethylformamide at 60°C

(6) private communication; see also V. Hofmann, M. Przybylski, H. Ringsdorf, H. Ritter, Makromol. Chem. *117* (1976) 1791...1813
(7) KBr (1/350)

52222212 + **42**12122211   C₁₁H₁₃N₃O₄S   1621

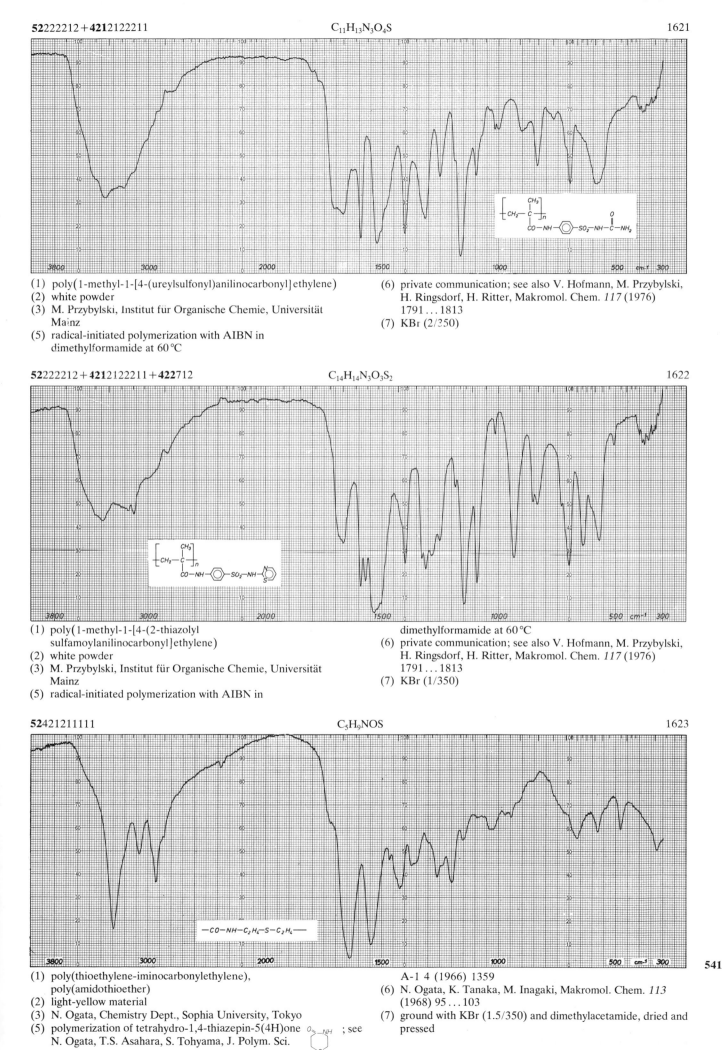

(1) poly(1-methyl-1-[4-(ureylsulfonyl)anilinocarbonyl]ethylene)
(2) white powder
(3) M. Przybylski, Institut für Organische Chemie, Universität Mainz
(5) radical-initiated polymerization with AIBN in dimethylformamide at 60 °C

(6) private communication; see also V. Hofmann, M. Przybylski, H. Ringsdorf, H. Ritter, Makromol. Chem. *117* (1976) 1791...1813
(7) KBr (2/350)

52222212 + **42**12122211 + **42**2712   C₁₄H₁₄N₃O₃S₂   1622

(1) poly(1-methyl-1-[4-(2-thiazolyl sulfamoylanilinocarbonyl]ethylene)
(2) white powder
(3) M. Przybylski, Institut für Organische Chemie, Universität Mainz
(5) radical-initiated polymerization with AIBN in

dimethylformamide at 60 °C
(6) private communication; see also V. Hofmann, M. Przybylski, H. Ringsdorf, H. Ritter, Makromol. Chem. *117* (1976) 1791...1813
(7) KBr (1/350)

52421211111   C₅H₉NOS   1623

(1) poly(thioethylene-iminocarbonylethylene), poly(amidothioether)
(2) light-yellow material
(3) N. Ogata, Chemistry Dept., Sophia University, Tokyo
(5) polymerization of tetrahydro-1,4-thiazepin-5(4H)one ; see N. Ogata, T.S. Asahara, S. Tohyama, J. Polym. Sci.

A-1 4 (1966) 1359
(6) N. Ogata, K. Tanaka, M. Inagaki, Makromol. Chem. *113* (1968) 95...103
(7) ground with KBr (1.5/350) and dimethylacetamide, dried and pressed

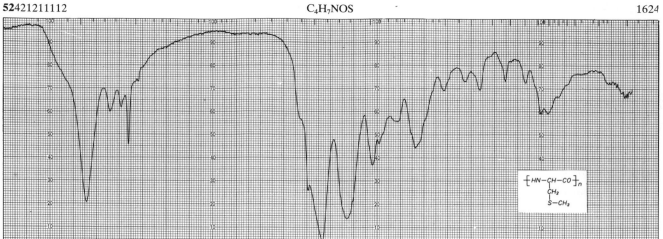

(1) poly(S-methyl-L-cystein)
(2) white powder
(3) G. Ebert, Fachbereich Physikalische Chemie, Philipps-
      Universität, Marburg

(6) G. Ebert, Makromolekulares Kolloquium, Freiburg/Br. 1975
(7) KBr (1.2/300)

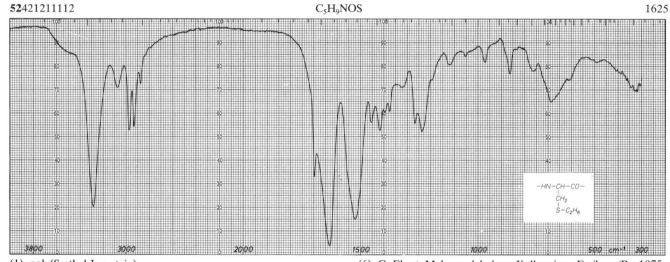

(1) poly(S-ethyl-L-cystein)
(2) white material
(3) G. Ebert, Fachbereich Physikalische Chemie, Philipps-
      Universität, Marburg

(6) G. Ebert, Makromolekulares Kolloquium, Freiburg/Br. 1975
(7) KBr (1/300)

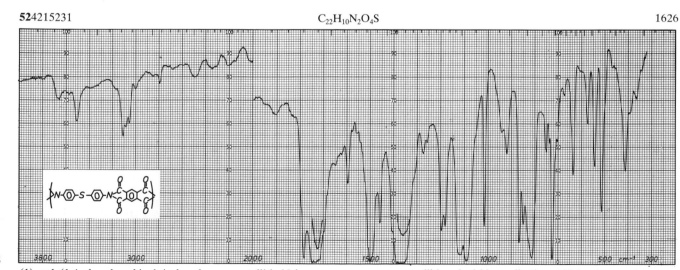

(1) poly(1,4-phenylenethio-1,4-phenylene pyromellitimide)
(2) orange-coloured film
(3) C.E. Sroog, Experimental Station, Du Pont de Nemours &
      Comp., Wilmington, Dela.
(5) polycondensation of 4,4'-diaminodiphenylthioether with

pyromellitic anhydride, cyclization at higher temperatures
(6) C.E. Sroog, A.L. Endrey, S.V. Abramo, C.E. Berr, W.M.
      Edwards, K.L. Oliver, J. Polym. Sci. *A3* (1965) 1373 . . . 90
(7) original film (approx. 20 µm); KBr

524215232 $C_{21}H_{16}N_2O_4S$ 1627

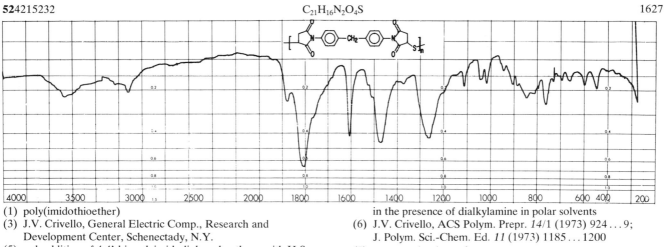

(1) poly(imidothioether)

(3) J.V. Crivello, General Electric Comp., Research and Development Center, Schenectady, N.Y.

(5) polyaddition of 4,4'-bismaleimidodiphenylmethane with H_2S

in the presence of dialkylamine in polar solvents

(6) J.V. Crivello, ACS Polym. Prepr. *14/1* (1973) 924...9; J. Polym. Sci.-Chem. Ed. *11* (1973) 1185...1200

(7) spectrum by the author

5243221241 $C_{21}H_{13}N_3O_4S$ 1628

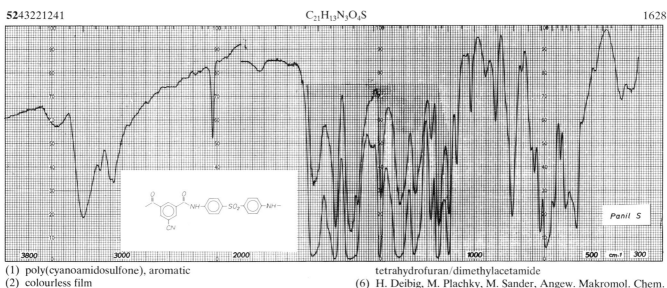

(1) poly(cyanoamidosulfone), aromatic

(2) colourless film

(3) Battelle Institut, Frankfurt/M. (by H. Deibig)

(5) polycondensation (at $-20\,°C$) of dicyanophthaloylchloride with 4,4'-diamino-4,4'-diphenylenesulfone in

tetrahydrofuran/dimethylacetamide

(6) H. Deibig, M. Plachky, M. Sander, Angew. Makromol. Chem. *32* (1973) 131...36

(7) film, KBr

(8) commercial material „Panil S"

5243221111 C_5H_9NOS 1229

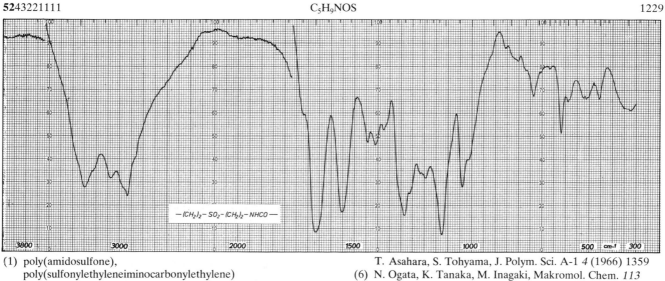

(1) poly(amidosulfone), poly(sulfonylethyleneiminocarbonylethylene)

(2) ochre-coloured material

(3) N. Ogata, Chemistry Department, Sophia University, Tokyo

(5) polymerization of the lactamsulfone, ; see N. Ogata,

T. Asahara, S. Tohyama, J. Polym. Sci. A-1 *4* (1966) 1359

(6) N. Ogata, K. Tanaka, M. Inagaki, Makromol. Chem. *113* (1968) 95...103

(7) ground with KBr (2.2/350) and dimethylacetamide, dried and pressed

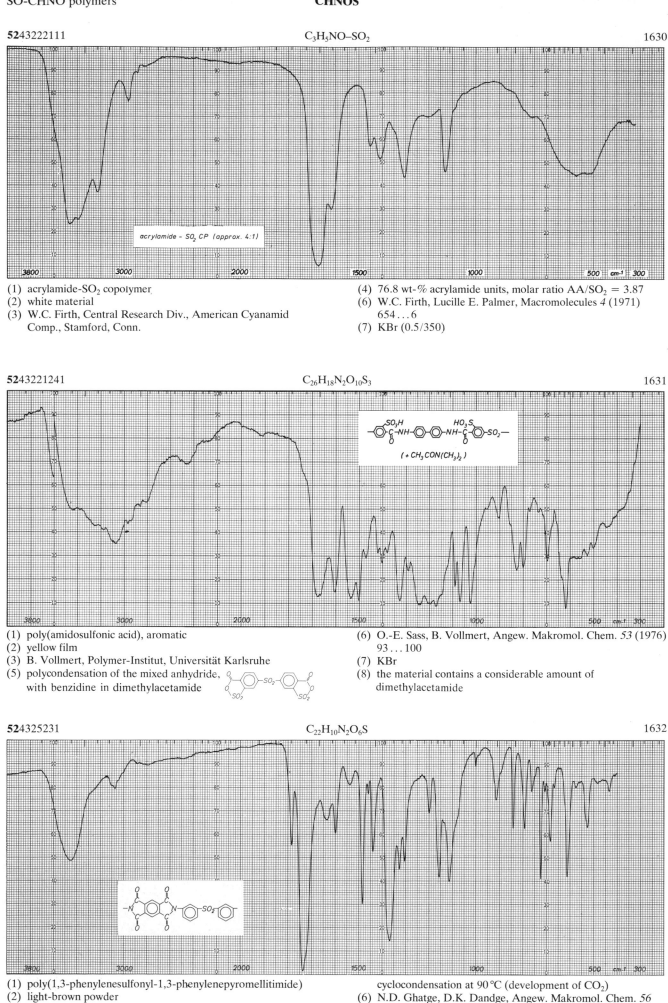

(1) acrylamide-SO$_2$ copolymer
(2) white material
(3) W.C. Firth, Central Research Div., American Cyanamid
    Comp., Stamford, Conn.

(4) 76.8 wt-% acrylamide units, molar ratio AA/SO$_2$ = 3.87
(6) W.C. Firth, Lucille E. Palmer, Macromolecules *4* (1971)
    654...6
(7) KBr (0.5/350)

(1) poly(amidosulfonic acid), aromatic
(2) yellow film
(3) B. Vollmert, Polymer-Institut, Universität Karlsruhe
(5) polycondensation of the mixed anhydride,
    with benzidine in dimethylacetamide

(6) O.-E. Sass, B. Vollmert, Angew. Makromol. Chem. *53* (1976)
    93...100
(7) KBr
(8) the material contains a considerable amount of
    dimethylacetamide

(1) poly(1,3-phenylenesulfonyl-1,3-phenylenepyromellitimide)
(2) light-brown powder
(3) N.D. Ghatge, National Chemical Laboratory, Poona
(5) polyaddition of 3,3'-sulfonyl-bis(phenylisocyanate) with
    pyromellitic anhydride (in, e.g., dimethylformamide, 40 °C),

cyclocondensation at 90 °C (development of CO$_2$)
(6) N.D. Ghatge, D.K. Dandge, Angew. Makromol. Chem. *56*
    (1976) 163...71
(7) KBr

524325211 $C_{13}H_{14}N_2O_6S$ 1633

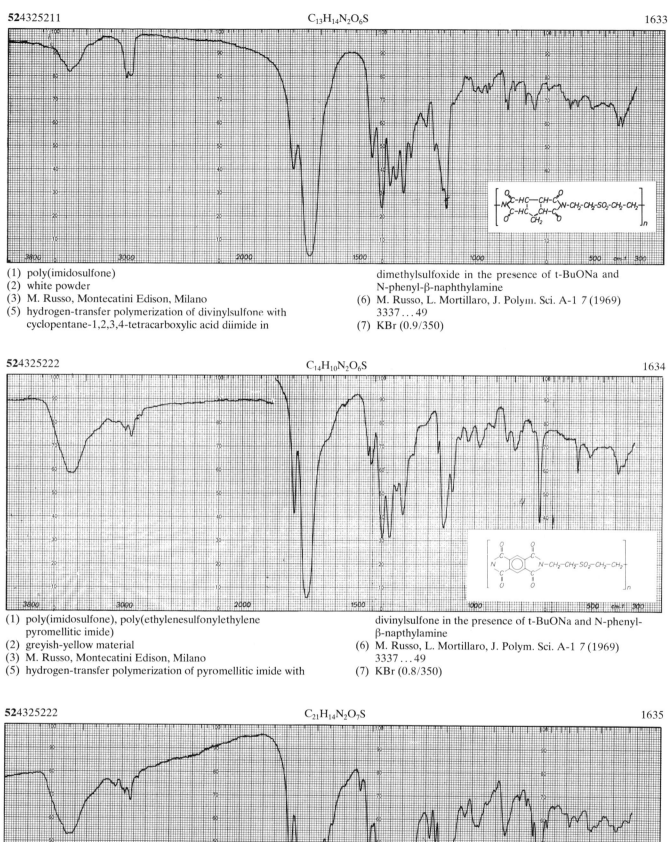

(1) poly(imidosulfone)
(2) white powder
(3) M. Russo, Montecatini Edison, Milano
(5) hydrogen-transfer polymerization of divinylsulfone with cyclopentane-1,2,3,4-tetracarboxylic acid diimide in

dimethylsulfoxide in the presence of t-BuONa and N-phenyl-β-naphthylamine
(6) M. Russo, L. Mortillaro, J. Polym. Sci. A-1 7 (1969) 3337...49
(7) KBr (0.9/350)

524325222 $C_{14}H_{10}N_2O_6S$ 1634

(1) poly(imidosulfone), poly(ethylenesulfonylethylene pyromellitic imide)
(2) greyish-yellow material
(3) M. Russo, Montecatini Edison, Milano
(5) hydrogen-transfer polymerization of pyromellitic imide with

divinylsulfone in the presence of t-BuONa and N-phenyl-β-napthylamine
(6) M. Russo, L. Mortillaro, J. Polym. Sci. A-1 7 (1969) 3337...49
(7) KBr (0.8/350)

524325222 $C_{21}H_{14}N_2O_7S$ 1635

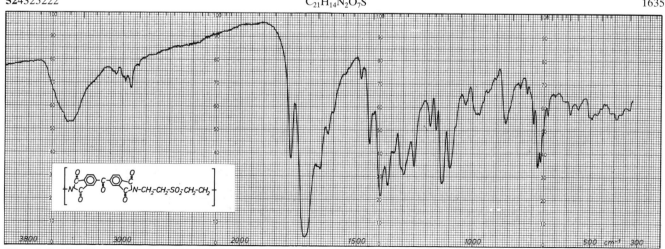

(1) poly(imidosulfone) on the basis of benzophenonetetracarboxylic acid imide and divinylsulfone
(2) yellowish-brown powder
(3) M. Russo, Montecatini Edison, Milano
(5) hydrogen-transfer polymerization of 3,3'-,4,4'-tetracarboxylic

acid imide with divinylsulfone in the presence of t-BuONa and N-phenyl-β-naphthylamine
(6) M. Russo, L. Mortillaro, J. Polym. Sci. A-1 7 (1969) 3337...49
(7) KBr (0.9/350)

524325231   C$_{22}$H$_{10}$N$_2$O$_6$S   1636

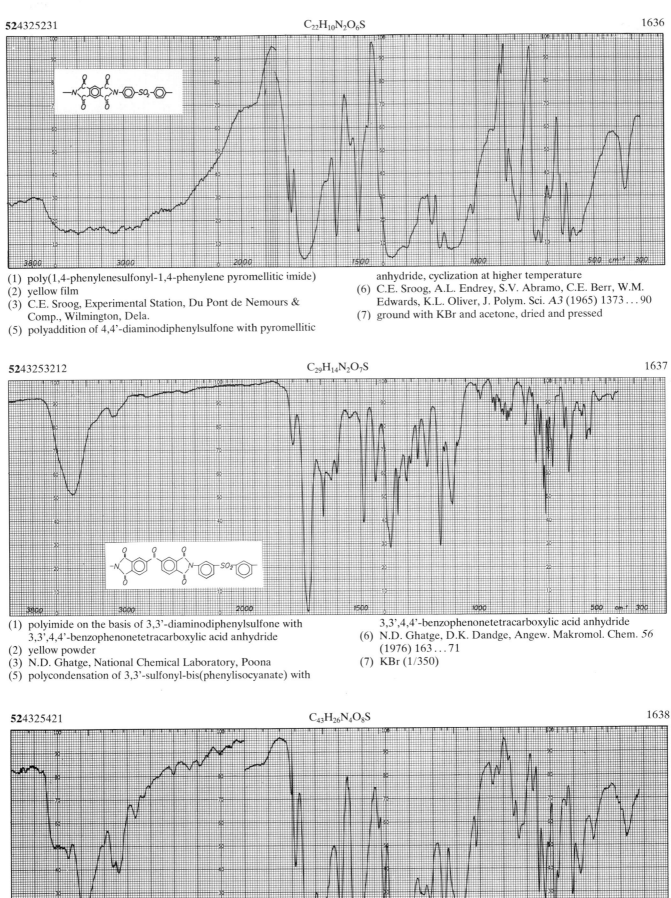

(1) poly(1,4-phenylenesulfonyl-1,4-phenylene pyromellitic imide)
(2) yellow film
(3) C.E. Sroog, Experimental Station, Du Pont de Nemours & Comp., Wilmington, Dela.
(5) polyaddition of 4,4'-diaminodiphenylsulfone with pyromellitic

anhydride, cyclization at higher temperature
(6) C.E. Sroog, A.L. Endrey, S.V. Abramo, C.E. Berr, W.M. Edwards, K.L. Oliver, J. Polym. Sci. *A3* (1965) 1373...90
(7) ground with KBr and acetone, dried and pressed

5243253212   C$_{29}$H$_{14}$N$_2$O$_7$S   1637

(1) polyimide on the basis of 3,3'-diaminodiphenylsulfone with 3,3',4,4'-benzophenonetetracarboxylic acid anhydride
(2) yellow powder
(3) N.D. Ghatge, National Chemical Laboratory, Poona
(5) polycondensation of 3,3'-sulfonyl-bis(phenylisocyanate) with

3,3',4,4'-benzophenonetetracarboxylic acid anhydride
(6) N.D. Ghatge, D.K. Dandge, Angew. Makromol. Chem. *56* (1976) 163...71
(7) KBr (1/350)

524325421   C$_{43}$H$_{26}$N$_4$O$_8$S   1638

(1) poly(amidoimidosulfone), aromatic
(2) yellow-brown film
(3) W. Wrasidlo, U.S. Naval Ordnance Laboratory, White Oak, Silverspring, Maryl.
(5) low temperature solution condensation of 4,4'-diaminodiphenylmethane with sulfuryl-bis[N-(4-

phenylene)-4'-chloroformyl) phthalimide]
(6) W. Wrasidlo, J.M. Augl, J. Polym. Sci. A-1 *7* (1969) 321...32
(7) KBr (2000...300 cm^{-1}); original film (approx. 25 µm, 4000...2000 cm^{-1})

5243254214   C$_{36}$H$_{20}$N$_4$O$_8$S   1639

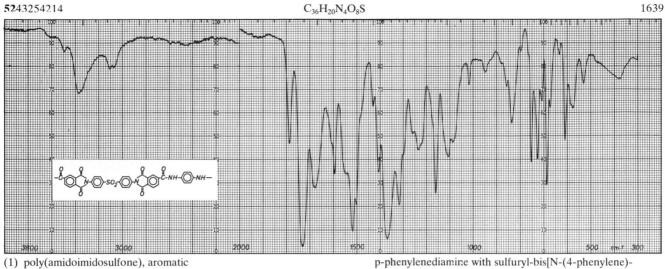

(1) poly(amidoimidosulfone), aromatic
(2) yellow film
(3) W. Wrasidlo, U.S. Naval Ordnance Laboratory, White Oak, Silverspring, Maryl.
(5) low-temperature solution polycondensation of

p-phenylenediamine with sulfuryl-bis[N-(4-phenylene)-4'-(chloroformyl)phthalimide]
(6) W. Wrasidlo, J.M. Augl, J. Polym. Sci. A-1 7 (1969) 321...32
(7) film (20μm and 10 μm)

5243254214   C$_{42}$H$_{24}$N$_4$O$_{10}$S$_2$ 1640

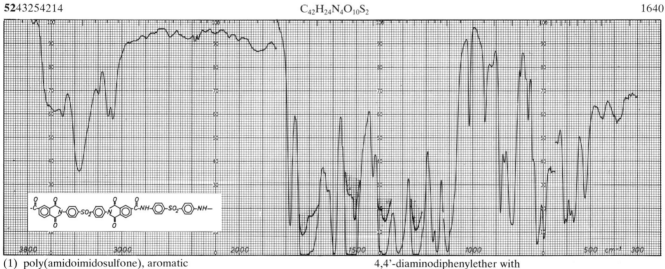

(1) poly(amidoimidosulfone), aromatic
(2) yellow-brown film
(3) W. Wrasidlo, U.S. Naval Ordnance Laboratory, White Oak, Silverspring, Maryl.
(5) low-temperature solution polycondensation of

4,4'-diaminodiphenylether with sulfuryl-bis[N-(4-phenylene)-4'-(chloroformyl)phthalimide]
(6) W. Wrasidlo, J.M. Augl, J. Polym. Sci. A-1 7 (1969) 321...32
(7) film (20 μm and 8 μm)

5243254214   C$_{36}$H$_{20}$N$_4$O$_8$S   1641

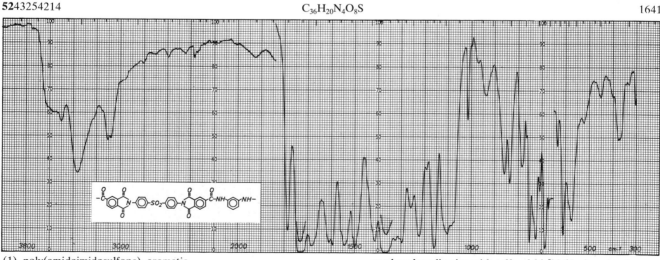

(1) poly(amidoimidosulfone), aromatic
(2) yellow-brown film
(3) W. Wrasidlo, U.S. Naval Ordnance Laboratory, White Oak, Silverspring, Maryl.
(5) low-temperature solution polycondensation of

m-phenylenediamine with sulfuryl-bis[N-(4-phenylene)-4'-(chloroformyl)phthalimide]
(6) W. Wrasidlo, J.M. Augl, J. Polym. Sci. A-1 7 (1969) 321...32
(7) KBr, original film

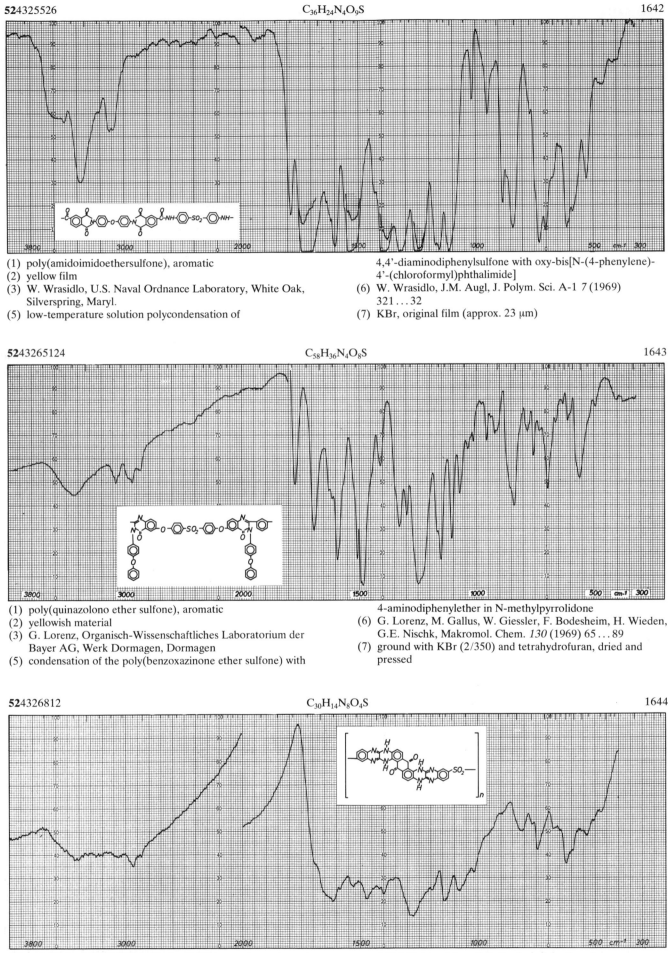

524325526 $C_{36}H_{24}N_4O_9S$ 1642

(1) poly(amidoimidoethersulfone), aromatic
(2) yellow film
(3) W. Wrasidlo, U.S. Naval Ordnance Laboratory, White Oak, Silverspring, Maryl.
(5) low-temperature solution polycondensation of

4,4'-diaminodiphenylsulfone with oxy-bis[N-(4-phenylene)-4'-(chloroformyl)phthalimide]
(6) W. Wrasidlo, J.M. Augl, J. Polym. Sci. A-1 7 (1969) 321 ... 32
(7) KBr, original film (approx. 23 μm)

524326512 $C_{58}H_{36}N_4O_8S$ 1643

(1) poly(quinazolono ether sulfone), aromatic
(2) yellowish material
(3) G. Lorenz, Organisch-Wissenschaftliches Laboratorium der Bayer AG, Werk Dormagen, Dormagen
(5) condensation of the poly(benzoxazinone ether sulfone) with

4-aminodiphenylether in N-methylpyrrolidone
(6) G. Lorenz, M. Gallus, W. Giessler, F. Bodesheim, H. Wieden, G.E. Nischk, Makromol. Chem. *130* (1969) 65 ... 89
(7) ground with KBr (2/350) and tetrahydrofuran, dried and pressed

524326812 $C_{30}H_{14}N_8O_4S$ 1644

(1) poly[(6,7,10,17,18,21-hexahydro-7,18-dioxodiquinoxalino[2,3-b:2',3'-b-]-benzo[1,2-f:4,5-f'] diquinoxaline-2,14-diyl)sulfone]; poly(quinoxalinosulfone)
(2) black powder
(3) C.S. Marvel, Department of Chemistry, University of Arizona, Tucson, Ariz.
(5) polycondensation of 1,2,5,6-tetraaminoanthraquinone with

2,2',3,3'-tetrachloro-6,6'-diquinoxalylsulfone in dimethylacetamide and dimethylaniline, cyclization of the black prepolymer at 350 °C i.v.
(6) A. Banishashemi, C.S. Marvel, J. Polym. Sci. A-1 *8* (1970) 3211 ... 24
(7) ground with KBr (5/300) and dimethylacetamide, dried and pressed

5262211151116   C$_{20}$H$_{22}$N$_2$O$_4$S$_2$ 1645

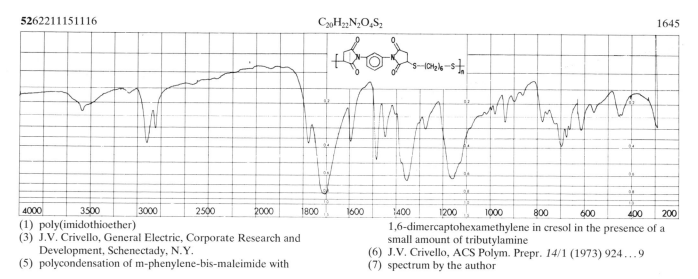

(1) poly(imidothioether)
(3) J.V. Crivello, General Electric, Corporate Research and
    Development, Schenectady, N.Y.
(5) polycondensation of m-phenylene-bis-maleimide with

1,6-dimercaptohexamethylene in cresol in the presence of a
small amount of tributylamine
(6) J.V. Crivello, ACS Polym. Prepr. *14*/1 (1973) 924...9
(7) spectrum by the author

52628112225   C$_6$H$_4$N$_2$O$_2$S   1646

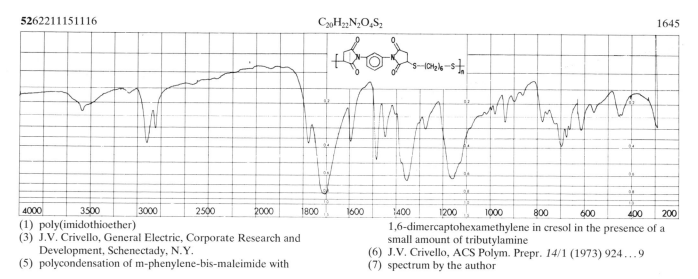

(1) poly(thiophene-2,5-dicarboxylic hydrazide)
(2) ivory-coloured powder
(3) G. Kossmehl, Institut für Organische Chemie, FU Berlin,
    Berlin-Dahlem
(5) reaction of thiophene-2,5-bicarbonylchloride with thiophene-

2,5-dicarboxylic dihydrazide
(6) G. Kossmehl, G. Manecke, Makromol. Chem. *123* (1969)
    233...44
(7) ground with KBr (1.6/300) and dimethylacetamide, dried and
    pressed

526281126515   C$_{17}$H$_8$N$_2$O$_2$S$_2$ 1647

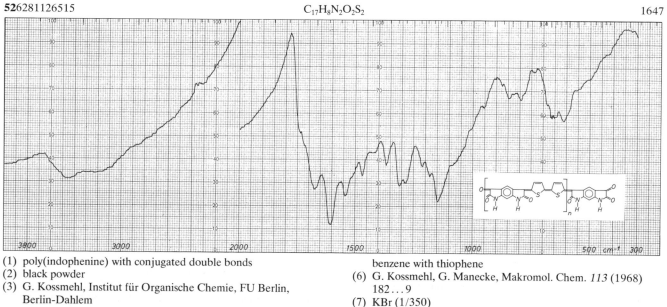

(1) poly(indophenine) with conjugated double bonds
(2) black powder
(3) G. Kossmehl, Institut für Organische Chemie, FU Berlin,
    Berlin-Dahlem
(5) polycondensation of bis-[dioxapyrrolino(2',3':1,2; 2'',3'':5,4)]

benzene with thiophene
(6) G. Kossmehl, G. Manecke, Makromol. Chem. *113* (1968)
    182...9
(7) KBr (1/350)

52722121241 $C_{14}H_6N_4O_2S$ 1648

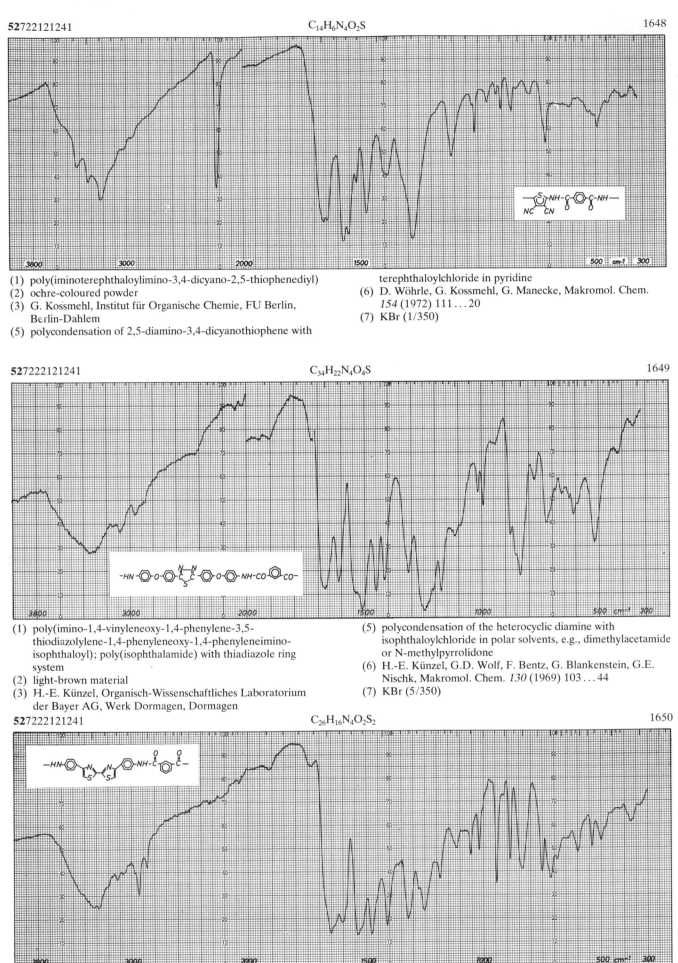

(1) poly(iminoterephthaloylimino-3,4-dicyano-2,5-thiophenediyl)
(2) ochre-coloured powder
(3) G. Kossmehl, Institut für Organische Chemie, FU Berlin, Berlin-Dahlem
(5) polycondensation of 2,5-diamino-3,4-dicyanothiophene with

terephthaloylchloride in pyridine
(6) D. Wöhrle, G. Kossmehl, G. Manecke, Makromol. Chem. *154* (1972) 111...20
(7) KBr (1/350)

527222121241 $C_{34}H_{22}N_4O_4S$ 1649

(1) poly[imino-1,4-vinyleneoxy-1,4-phenylene-3,5-thiodiazolylene-1,4-phenyleneoxy-1,4-phenyleneimino-isophthaloyl]; poly(isophthalamide) with thiadiazole ring system
(2) light-brown material
(3) H.-E. Künzel, Organisch-Wissenschaftliches Laboratorium der Bayer AG, Werk Dormagen, Dormagen

(5) polycondensation of the heterocyclic diamine with isophthaloylchloride in polar solvents, e.g., dimethylacetamide or N-methylpyrrolidone
(6) H.-E. Künzel, G.D. Wolf, F. Bentz, G. Blankenstein, G.E. Nischk, Makromol. Chem. *130* (1969) 103...44
(7) KBr (5/350)

527222121241 $C_{26}H_{16}N_4O_2S_2$ 1650

(1) poly[imino-1,4-phenylene-4,4'-(2,2'-bithiazolediyl)-1,4-phenyleneiminoisophthaloyl]; poly[4,4'-bis-(4-aminophenyl)2,2'-bithiazole isophthalamide]
(2) yellow material
(3) J. Preston, Chemstrand Research Center, Durham, N.C.

(5) low-temperature solution polycondensation of the bis(aminophenyl)bithiazole with isophthaloylchloride
(6) J. Preston, W.B. Black, J. Polym. Sci. *C 23* (1968) 441...8
(7) ground with KBr and dimethylacetamide, dried and pressed

5281813542　　　　　　　　　　　　$C_{28}H_{12}N_2O_2S_2$　　　　　　　　　　　　1651

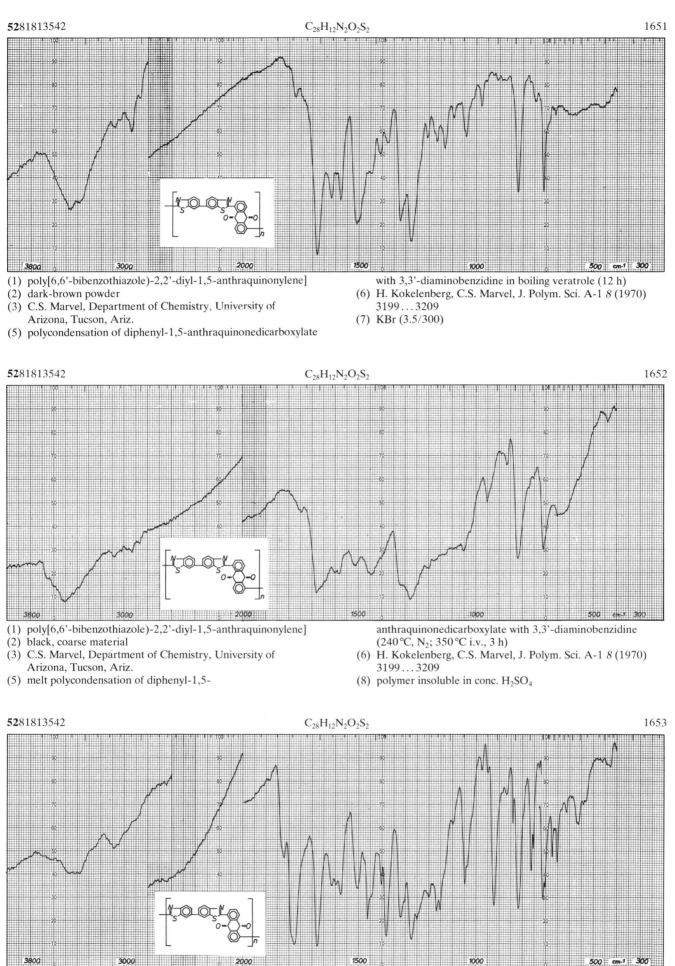

(1) poly[6,6'-bibenzothiazole)-2,2'-diyl-1,5-anthraquinonylene]
(2) dark-brown powder
(3) C.S. Marvel, Department of Chemistry, University of
　　Arizona, Tucson, Ariz.
(5) polycondensation of diphenyl-1,5-anthraquinonedicarboxylate

with 3,3'-diaminobenzidine in boiling veratrole (12 h)
(6) H. Kokelenberg, C.S. Marvel, J. Polym. Sci. A-1 *8* (1970)
　　3199...3209
(7) KBr (3.5/300)

5281813542　　　　　　　　　　　　$C_{28}H_{12}N_2O_2S_2$　　　　　　　　　　　　1652

(1) poly[6,6'-bibenzothiazole)-2,2'-diyl-1,5-anthraquinonylene]
(2) black, coarse material
(3) C.S. Marvel, Department of Chemistry, University of
　　Arizona, Tucson, Ariz.
(5) melt polycondensation of diphenyl-1,5-

anthraquinonedicarboxylate with 3,3'-diaminobenzidine
(240 °C, N_2; 350 °C i.v., 3 h)
(6) H. Kokelenberg, C.S. Marvel, J. Polym. Sci. A-1 *8* (1970)
　　3199...3209
(8) polymer insoluble in conc. H_2SO_4

5281813542　　　　　　　　　　　　$C_{28}H_{12}N_2O_2S_2$　　　　　　　　　　　　1653

(1) poly[6,6'-bibenzothiazole)-2,2'-diyl-1,5-anthraquinonylene]
(2) dark-brown powder
(3) C.S. Marvel, Department of Chemistry, University of
　　Arizona, Tucson, Ariz.
(5) polycondensation of diphenyl-1,5-anthraquinonedicarboxylate

with 3,3'-diaminobenzidine in boiling diethylaniline (20 min)
(6) H. Kokelenberg, C.S. Marvel, J. Polym. Sci. A-1 *8* (1970)
　　3199...3209
(7) KBr (3.1/300)

5281813542 $C_{28}H_{12}N_2O_2S_2$ 1654

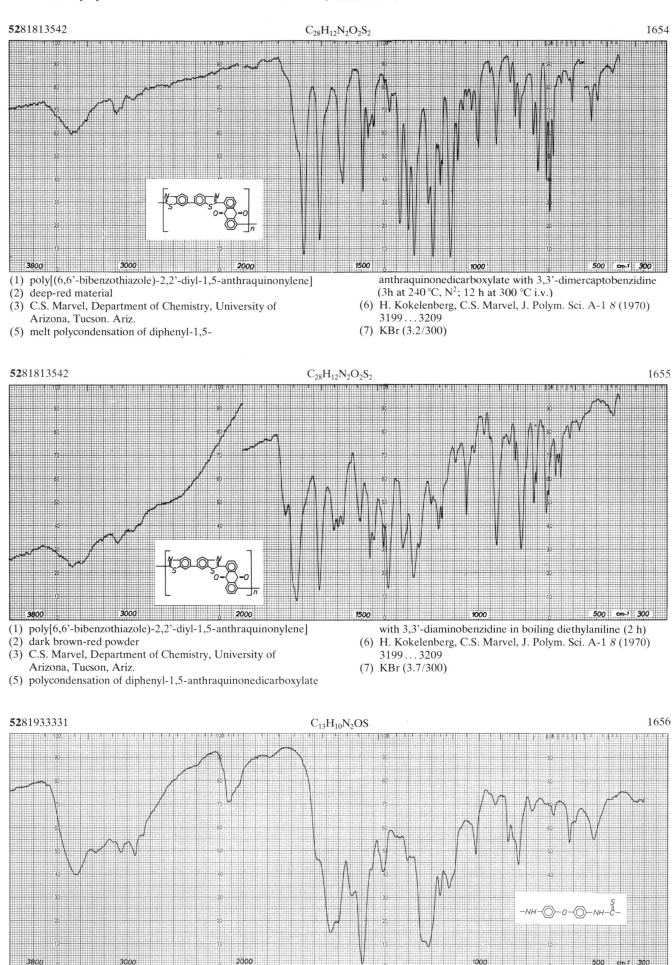

(1) poly[(6,6'-bibenzothiazole)-2,2'-diyl-1,5-anthraquinonylene]
(2) deep-red material
(3) C.S. Marvel, Department of Chemistry, University of Arizona, Tucson. Ariz.
(5) melt polycondensation of diphenyl-1,5-

anthraquinonedicarboxylate with 3,3'-dimercaptobenzidine (3h at 240 °C, N²; 12 h at 300 °C i.v.)
(6) H. Kokelenberg, C.S. Marvel, J. Polym. Sci. A-1 *8* (1970) 3199...3209
(7) KBr (3.2/300)

5281813542 $C_{28}H_{12}N_2O_2S_2$ 1655

(1) poly[6,6'-bibenzothiazole)-2,2'-diyl-1,5-anthraquinonylene]
(2) dark brown-red powder
(3) C.S. Marvel, Department of Chemistry, University of Arizona, Tucson, Ariz.
(5) polycondensation of diphenyl-1,5-anthraquinonedicarboxylate

with 3,3'-diaminobenzidine in boiling diethylaniline (2 h)
(6) H. Kokelenberg, C.S. Marvel, J. Polym. Sci. A-1 *8* (1970) 3199...3209
(7) KBr (3.7/300)

5281933331 $C_{13}H_{10}N_2OS$ 1656

552

(1) poly(imino-1,4-phenyleneoxy-1,4-phenylene-iminothiocarbonyl); poly(thiourea ether), aromatic
(2) sand-coloured powder
(3) N. Yamazaki, Department of Polymer Science, Tokyo Institute of Technology, Tokyo
(5) polycondensation of 4,4'-diaminodiphenylether with CS_2
(6) private communication; see also N. Yamazaki, F. Higashi, T.Iguchi, IUPAC Macro, Madrid 1974 (I.4-12)
(7) ground with KBr (1/350) and dimethylacetamide, dried and pressed

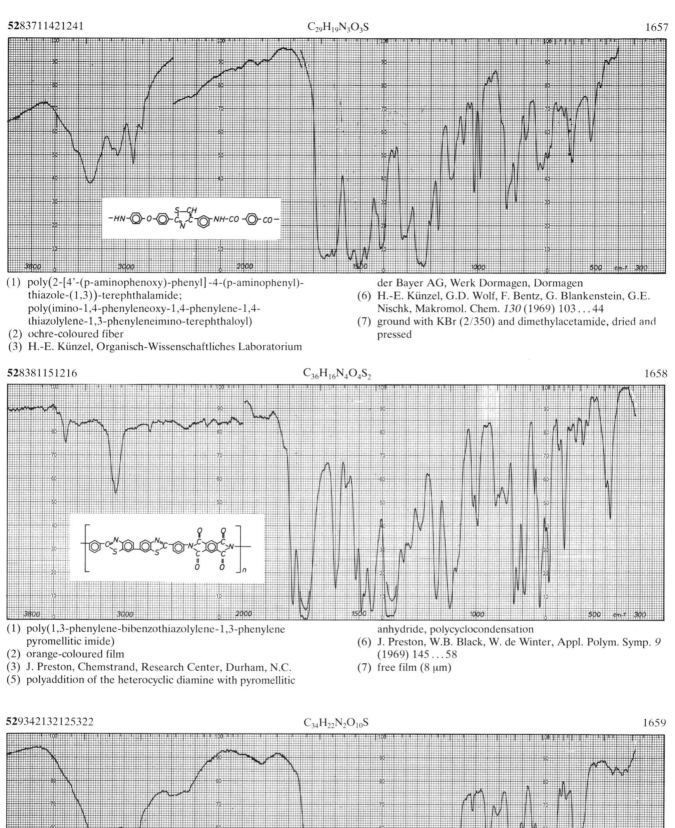

5283711421241 $C_{29}H_{19}N_3O_3S$ 1657

(1) poly(2-[4'-(p-aminophenoxy)-phenyl]-4-(p-aminophenyl)-thiazole-(1,3))-terephthalamide; poly(imino-1,4-phenyleneoxy-1,4-phenylene-1,4-thiazolylene-1,3-phenyleneimino-terephthaloyl))
(2) ochre-coloured fiber
(3) H.-E. Künzel, Organisch-Wissenschaftliches Laboratorium der Bayer AG, Werk Dormagen, Dormagen
(6) H.-E. Künzel, G.D. Wolf, F. Bentz, G. Blankenstein, G.E. Nischk, Makromol. Chem. *130* (1969) 103...44
(7) ground with KBr (2/350) and dimethylacetamide, dried and pressed

528381151216 $C_{36}H_{16}N_4O_4S_2$ 1658

(1) poly(1,3-phenylene-bibenzothiazolylene-1,3-phenylene pyromellitic imide)
(2) orange-coloured film
(3) J. Preston, Chemstrand, Research Center, Durham, N.C.
(5) polyaddition of the heterocyclic diamine with pyromellitic anhydride, polycyclocondensation
(6) J. Preston, W.B. Black, W. de Winter, Appl. Polym. Symp. *9* (1969) 145...58
(7) free film (8 µm)

529342132125322 $C_{34}H_{22}N_2O_{10}S$ 1659

(1) poly(amidocarboxylic acid) with ether and sulfo bridges
(2) white, very light material
(3) G. Lorenz, Organisch-Wissenschaftliches Laboratorium der Bayer AG, Werk Dormagen, Dormagen
(5) polycondensation of 4,4'-bis(4-carboxy-3-aminophenoxy)-diphenylsulfone with isophthaloyl chloride
(6) G. Lorenz, M. Gallus, W. Giessler, F. Bodesheim, H. Wieden, G.E. Nischk, Makromol. Chem. *130* (1969) 65...89
(7) ground with KBr (2/350) and tetrahydrofuran, dried and pressed
(8) precursor for the polybenzoxazinone

529342132125322   C$_{34}$H$_{24}$N$_2$O$_{10}$S   1660

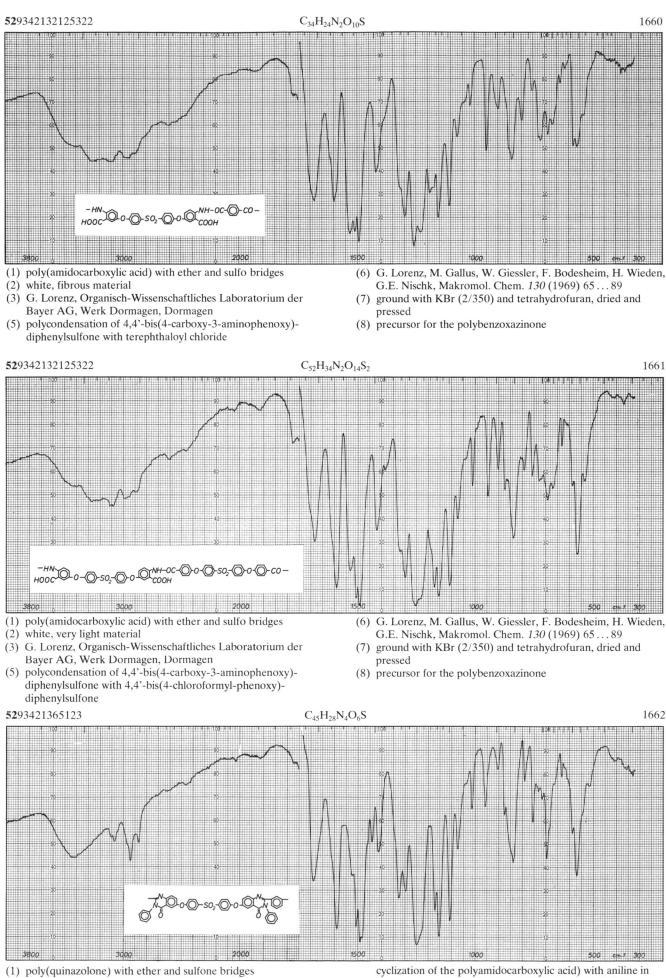

(1) poly(amidocarboxylic acid) with ether and sulfo bridges
(2) white, fibrous material
(3) G. Lorenz, Organisch-Wissenschaftliches Laboratorium der Bayer AG, Werk Dormagen, Dormagen
(5) polycondensation of 4,4'-bis(4-carboxy-3-aminophenoxy)-diphenylsulfone with terephthaloyl chloride

(6) G. Lorenz, M. Gallus, W. Giessler, F. Bodesheim, H. Wieden, G.E. Nischk, Makromol. Chem. *130* (1969) 65...89
(7) ground with KBr (2/350) and tetrahydrofuran, dried and pressed
(8) precursor for the polybenzoxazinone

529342132125322   C$_{52}$H$_{34}$N$_2$O$_{14}$S$_2$ 1661

(1) poly(amidocarboxylic acid) with ether and sulfo bridges
(2) white, very light material
(3) G. Lorenz, Organisch-Wissenschaftliches Laboratorium der Bayer AG, Werk Dormagen, Dormagen
(5) polycondensation of 4,4'-bis(4-carboxy-3-aminophenoxy)-diphenylsulfone with 4,4'-bis(4-chloroformyl-phenoxy)-diphenylsulfone

(6) G. Lorenz, M. Gallus, W. Giessler, F. Bodesheim, H. Wieden, G.E. Nischk, Makromol. Chem. *130* (1969) 65...89
(7) ground with KBr (2/350) and tetrahydrofuran, dried and pressed
(8) precursor for the polybenzoxazinone

5293421365123   C$_{45}$H$_{28}$N$_4$O$_6$S   1662

(1) poly(quinazolone) with ether and sulfone bridges
(2) eggshell-coloured material
(3) G. Lorenz, Organisch-Wissenschaftliches Laboratorium der Bayer AG, Werk Dormagen, Dormagen
(5) condensation of the analogous polybenzoxazinone (by

cyclization of the polyamidocarboxylic acid) with aniline in N-methylpyrrolidone (15 h at 160°C, 2 h at 180°C)
(6) G. Lorenz, M. Gallus, W. Giessler, F. Bodesheim, H. Wieden, G.E. Nischk, Makromol. Chem. *130* (1969) 65...89
(7) KBr (1.3/350)

5293421365123 $C_{64}H_{40}N_4O_{10}S$ 1663

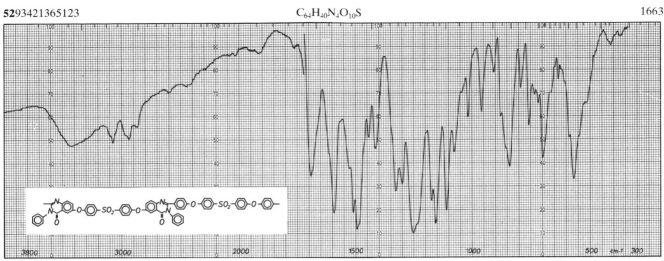

(1) poly(quinazolone) with ether and sulfone bridges
(2) eggshell-coloured material
(3) G. Lorenz, Organisch-Wissenschaftliches Laboratorium der
    Bayer AG, Werk Dormagen, Dormagen
(5) condensation of the analogous polybenzoxazinone (by
    cyclization of the polyamidocarboxylic acid) with aniline in

N-methylpyrrolidone (16 h at 160 °C, 2 h at 180 °C)
(6) G. Lorenz, M. Gallus, W. Giessler, F. Bodesheim, H. Wieden,
    G.E. Nischk, Makromol. Chem. *130* (1969) 65 ... 89
(7) ground with KBr (2/350) and tetrahydrofuran, dried and
    pressed

5293421366113 $C_{32}H_{18}N_2O_8S$ 1664

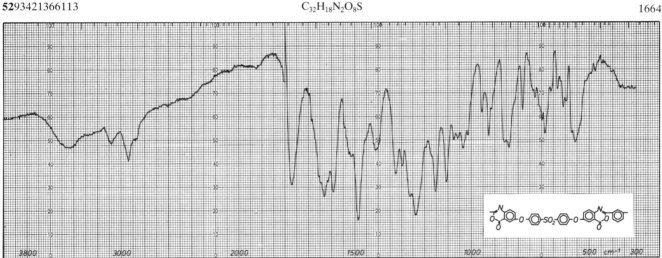

(1) poly(benzoxazinone) with ether and sulfone bridges
(2) ivory-coloured, fibrous material
(3) G. Lorenz, Organisch-Wissenschaftliches Laboratorium der
    Bayer AG, Werk Dormagen, Dormagen
(5) polycondensation of 4,4'-bis(4-carboxy-3-aminophenoxy)-
    diphenylsulfone with isophthaloyl-chloride, cyclocondensation

of the dissolved polymer (in N-methylpyrrolidone) in the
presence of POCl₃ (1 h at 100 °C)
(6) G. Lorenz, M. Gallus, W. Giessler, F. Bodesheim, H. Wieden,
    G.E. Nischk, Makromol. Chem. *130* (1969) 65 ... 89
(7) ground with KBr (2/400) and dimethylacetamide, dried and
    pressed

5293421366113 $C_{32}H_{18}N_2O_8S$ 1665

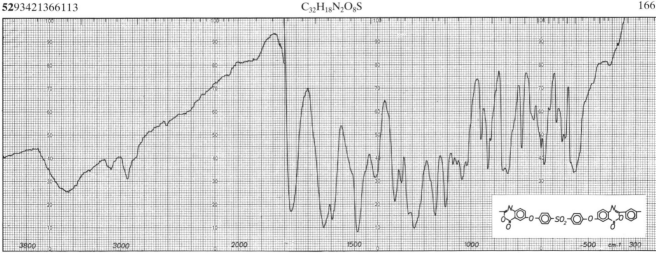

(1) poly(benzoxazinone) with ether and sulfone bridges
(2) white, fibrous material
(3) G. Lorenz, Organisch-Wissenschaftliches Laboratorium der
    Bayer AG, Werk Dormagen, Dormagen
(5) polycondensation of 4,4'-bis(4-carboxy-3-aminophenoxy)-
    diphenylsulfone with isophthaloyl-chloride, cyclocondensation

of the dissolved polymer (in N-methylpyrrolidone) in the
presence of P₂O₅ (4 h at 130 °C)
(6) G. Lorenz, M. Gallus, W. Giessler, F. Bodesheim, H. Wieden,
    G.E. Nischk, Makromol. Chem. *130* (1969) 65 ... 89
(7) ground with KBr (2.5/400) and dimethylacetamide, dried and
    pressed

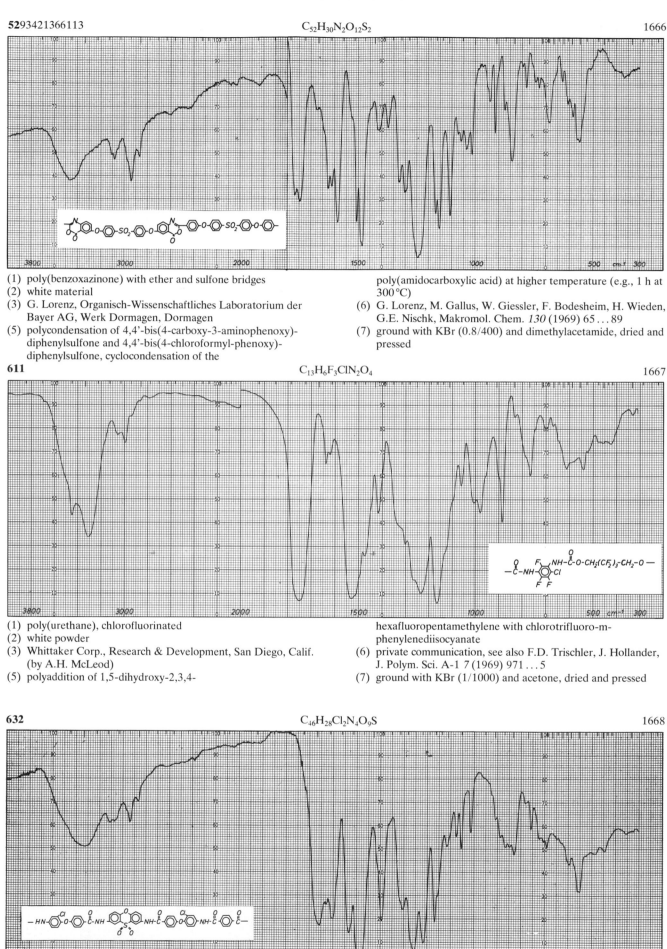

5293421366113 $C_{52}H_{30}N_2O_{12}S_2$ 1666

(1) poly(benzoxazinone) with ether and sulfone bridges
(2) white material
(3) G. Lorenz, Organisch-Wissenschaftliches Laboratorium der Bayer AG, Werk Dormagen, Dormagen
(5) polycondensation of 4,4'-bis(4-carboxy-3-aminophenoxy)-diphenylsulfone and 4,4'-bis(4-chloroformyl-phenoxy)-diphenylsulfone, cyclocondensation of the

poly(amidocarboxylic acid) at higher temperature (e.g., 1 h at 300 °C)
(6) G. Lorenz, M. Gallus, W. Giessler, F. Bodesheim, H. Wieden, G.E. Nischk, Makromol. Chem. *130* (1969) 65...89
(7) ground with KBr (0.8/400) and dimethylacetamide, dried and pressed

611 $C_{13}H_6F_3ClN_2O_4$ 1667

(1) poly(urethane), chlorofluorinated
(2) white powder
(3) Whittaker Corp., Research & Development, San Diego, Calif. (by A.H. McLeod)
(5) polyaddition of 1,5-dihydroxy-2,3,4-

hexafluoropentamethylene with chlorotrifluoro-m-phenylenediisocyanate
(6) private communication, see also F.D. Trischler, J. Hollander, J. Polym. Sci. A-1 7 (1969) 971...5
(7) ground with KBr (1/1000) and acetone, dried and pressed

632 $C_{46}H_{28}Cl_2N_4O_9S$ 1668

(1) polyamide with phenoxthine-S-dioxide ring system
(2) greyish-white, coarse fiber
(3) H.-E. Künzel, Organisch-Wissenschaftliches Laboratorium der Bayer AG, Werk Dormagen, Dormagen
(5) polycondensation of 3,6-bis-[4'-(p-amino-o-chlorophenoxy)-benzoylamino]-phenoxthine with terephthaloylchloride in

N-methylpyrrolidone
(6) H.-E. Künzel, F. Bentz, G.D. Wolf, G. Blankenstein, G. Nischk, Makromol. Chem. *138* (1970) 223...50
(7) ground with KBr (1/300) and dimethylacetamide, dried and pressed

711111   D$_4$C$_2$ 1669

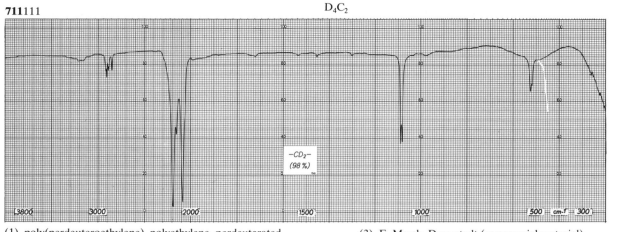

(1) poly(perdeuteroethylene), polyethylene, perdeuterated
(2) white, fibrous material

(3) E. Merck, Darmstadt (commercial material)
(7) pressed and tempered film

71111211   D$_6$C$_3$ 1670

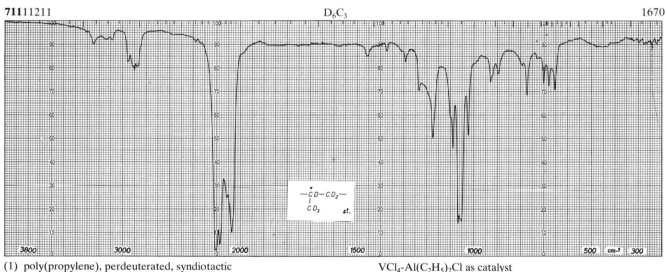

(1) poly(propylene), perdeuterated, syndiotactic
(2) colourless, turbid material
(3) A. Zambelli, Istituto di Chimica Industriale del Polytechnico,
     Milano
(5) low-temperature polymerization of propene-d$_6$ with

VCl$_4$-Al(C$_2$H$_5$)$_2$Cl as catalyst
(6) A. Zambelli, G. Natta, I. Pasquon, J. Polym. Sci. *C 4* (1968)
     411...26
(7) recrystallized melting film between CsI

71122111   D$_8$C$_8$ 1671

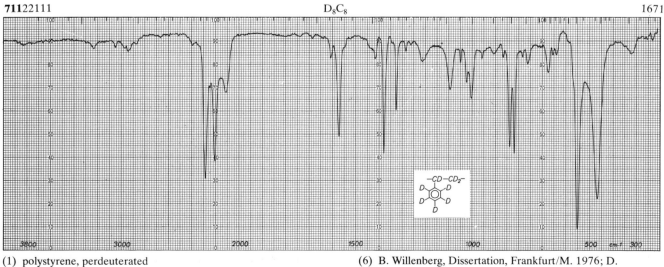

(1) polystyrene, perdeuterated
(2) white fibrous material
(3) H. Sillescu, Institut für Physikalische Chemie, Universität
     Mainz
(5) thermal polymerization of styrene-d$_8$ in bulk (from Aldrich
     Chemicals)

(6) B. Willenberg, Dissertation, Frankfurt/M. 1976; D.
     Hentschel, H. Sillescu, H.W. Spiess, R. Voelkel, B.
     Willenberg, Magnet. Reson. Relat. Phenom., Proc. Congr.
     Ampère 19th 1976, p. 381
(7) film from CHCl$_3$ on CsI

71237221121 $D_8C_5O_2$ 1672

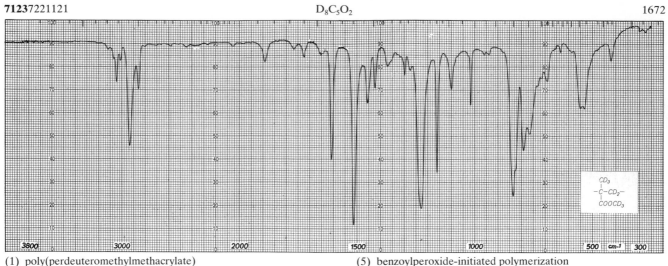

(1) poly(perdeuteromethylmethacrylate)
(2) white material
(3) R. Kirste, Institut für Physikalische Chemie, Universität Mainz
(4) 0,6% protons
(5) benzoylperoxide-initiated polymerization
(6) private communication; R.G. Kirste, W.A. Kruse, K. Ibel, Polymer *16* (1975) 120
(7) film from CHCl₃ on CsI

71237221121–**337**221121 $D_8C_5O_2/C_5H_8O_2$ 1673

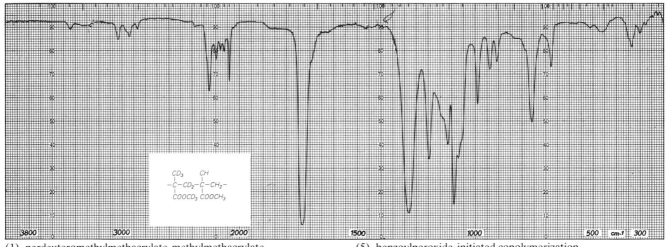

(1) perdeuteromethylmethacrylate-methylmethacrylate copolymer
(2) white material
(3) R. Kirste, Institut für Physikalische Chemie, Universität Mainz
(4) 1.2% H-MMA
(5) benzoylperoxide-initiated copolymerization, dodecylmercaptan as a regulator
(6) private communication; R.G. Kirste, W.A. Kruse, K. Ibel, Polymer *16* (1975) 120
(7) film from CHCl₃ on CsI

72111211 $D_3C_3H_3$ 1674

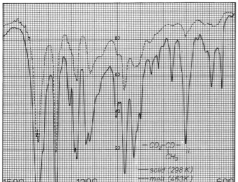

(1) poly(propylene-1,1,2-d₃), isotactic; poly(1-methyl-ethylene-d₃), isotactic
(3) C. Tosi, Centro Ricerche Milano, Montecatini Edison SpA, Milano
(5) Ziegler-Natta catalyst
(6) C. Wolfsgruber, F. Cawassi, C. Tosi, Makromol. Chem. *165* (1973) 281...95
(7) spectrum by the authors
(8) solid line: solid material (298 K), dashed line: melt (463 K)

72111211 D_5C_3H 1675

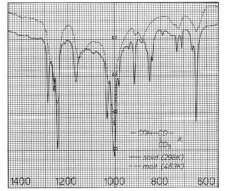

(1) poly(propylene-1,2,3,3,3-d_5), threo-diisotactic; poly(1-trideuteromethyl-ethylene-1,2-d_2), threo-diisotactic
(3) C. Tosi, Centro Ricerche Milano, Montecatini Edison SpA, Milano
(5) polymerization of trans-propene-1,2,3,3,3-d_5 with-

TiCl$_3$/Al(C$_2$H$_5$)$_2$Cl in toluene at 288 K
(6) C. Wolfsgruber, F. Cawassi, C. Tosi, Makromol. Chem. *165* (1973) 281 ... 95
(7) spectrum by the authors
(8) solid line: solid material (298 K), dashed line: melt (463 K)

72111211 D_5C_3H 1676

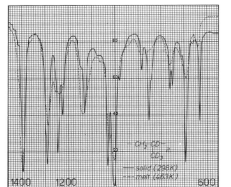

(1) poly(propylene-1,2,3,3,3-d_5), erythro-diisotactic; poly(1-trideuteromethyl-ethylene-1,2-d_2), erythro-diisotactic
(3) C. Tosi, Centro Ricerche Milano, Montecatini Edison SpA, Milano
(5) polymerization of cis-propene-1,2,3,3,3-d_5 with

VCl$_3$/Al (C$_2$H$_5$)$_2$Cl in toluene at 288 K
(6) C. Wolfsgruber, F. Cawassi, C. Tosi, Makromol. Chem. *165* (1973) 281 ... 95
(7) spectrum by the authors
(8) solid line: solid material (298 K), dashed line: melt (463 K)

72111211 $D_4C_3H_2$ 1677

(1) poly(propylene-2,3,3,3-d_4), isotactic; poly(1-trideuteromethyl-ethylene-1-d_1), isotactic
(3) C. Tosi, Centro Ricerche Milano, Montecatini Edison SpA, Milano
(5) polymerization with TiCl$_3$/Al(C$_2$H$_5$)$_2$I in n-heptane at 273 K

(6) C. Wolfsgruber, F. Cawassi, C. Tosi, Makromol. Chem. *165* (1973) 281 ... 95
(7) spectrum by the authors
(8) solid line: solid material (198 K), dashed line: melt (463 K)

72111211 $D_4C_3H_2$ 1678

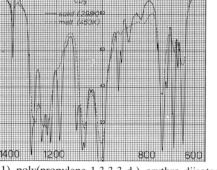

(1) poly(propylene-1,3,3,3-d_4), erythro-diisotactic; poly(1-trideuteromethyl-ethylene-2-d_1), erythro-diisotactic
(3) C. Tosi, Centro Ricerche Milano, Montecatini Edison SpA, Milano
(5) polymerization of cis-propene-1,3,3,3-d_4 with

TiCl$_3$/Al(C$_2$H$_5$)$_2$I in heptane at 273 K
(6) C. Wolfsgruber, F. Cawassi, C. Tosi, Makromol. Chem. *165* (1973) 281...95
(7) spectrum by the authors
(8) solid line: solid material (298 K), dashed line: melt (463 K)

72111211 $D_4C_3H_2$ 1679

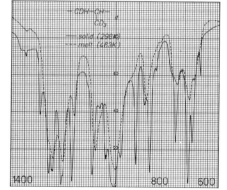

(1) poly(propylene-1,3,3,3-d_4), threo-diisotactic; poly(1-trideuteromethyl-ethylene-2-d_1), threo-diisotactic
(3) C. Tosi, Centro Ricerche Milano, Montecatini Edison SpA, Milano
(5) polymerization of trans-propene-1,3,3,3,-d_4 with

TiCl$_3$/Al (C$_2$H$_5$)$_2$I in heptane at 273 K
(6) C. Wolfsgruber, F. Cawassi, C. Tosi, Makromol. Chem. *165* (1973) 281...95
(7) spectrum by the authors
(8) solid line: solid material (298 K), dashed line: melt (463 K)

72111211 D_5C_3H 1680

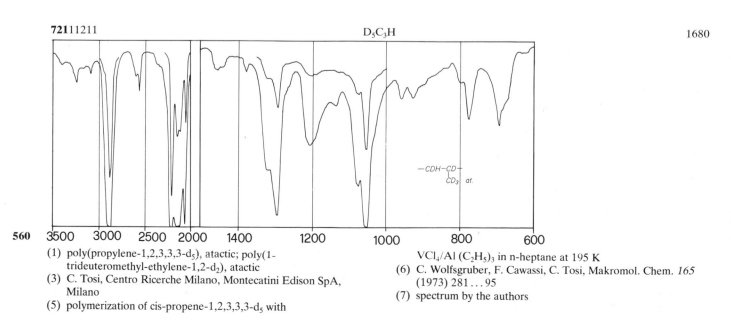

(1) poly(propylene-1,2,3,3,3-d_5), atactic; poly(1-trideuteromethyl-ethylene-1,2-d_2), atactic
(3) C. Tosi, Centro Ricerche Milano, Montecatini Edison SpA, Milano
(5) polymerization of cis-propene-1,2,3,3,3-d_5 with

VCl$_4$/Al (C$_2$H$_5$)$_3$ in n-heptane at 195 K
(6) C. Wolfsgruber, F. Cawassi, C. Tosi, Makromol. Chem. *165* (1973) 281...95
(7) spectrum by the authors

72111211 D$_4$C$_3$H$_2$ 1681

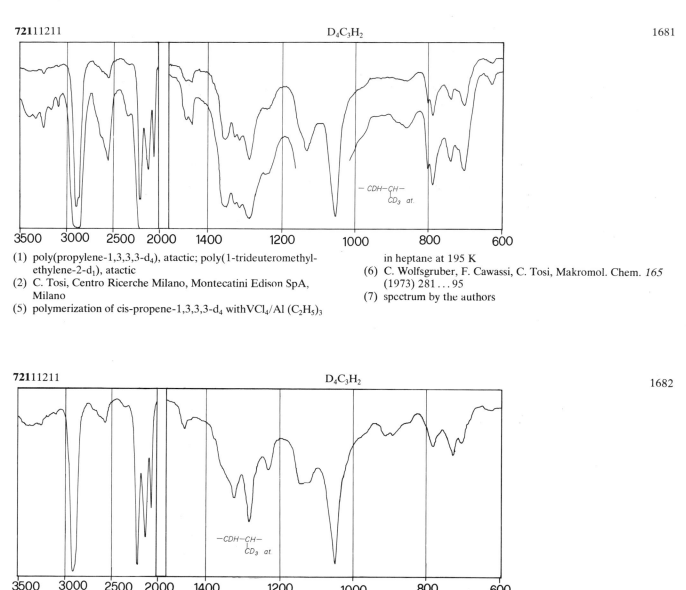

— CDH—CH—
|
CD$_3$ at.

3500 3000 2500 2000 1400 1200 1000 800 600

(1) poly(propylene-1,3,3,3-d$_4$), atactic; poly(1-trideuteromethyl-
   ethylene-2-d$_1$), atactic
(2) C. Tosi, Centro Ricerche Milano, Montecatini Edison SpA,
   Milano
(5) polymerization of cis-propene-1,3,3,3-d$_4$ with VCl$_4$/Al (C$_2$H$_5$)$_3$

in heptane at 195 K
(6) C. Wolfsgruber, F. Cawassi, C. Tosi, Makromol. Chem. *165*
   (1973) 281...95
(7) spectrum by the authors

72111211 D$_4$C$_3$H$_2$ 1682

— CDH—CH—
|
CD$_3$ at.

3500 3000 2500 2000 1400 1200 1000 800 600

(1) poly(propylene-1,3,3,3-d$_4$), atactic; poly(1-trideuteromethyl-
   ethylene-2-d$_1$), atactic
(3) C. Tosi, Centro Ricerche Milano, Montecatini Edison SpA,
   Milano
(5) polymerization of trans-propene-1,3,3,3-d$_4$ with

VCl$_4$/Al (C$_2$H$_5$)$_3$ in heptane at 195 K
(6) C. Wolfsgruber, F. Cawassi, C. Tosi, Makromol. Chem. *165*
   (1973) 281...95
(7) spectrum by the authors

72111211 D$_3$C$_3$H$_3$ 1683

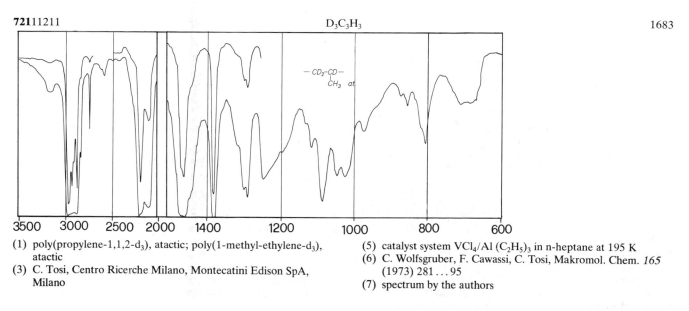

— CD$_2$–CD—
|
CH$_3$ at

3500 3000 2500 2000 1400 1200 1000 800 600

(1) poly(propylene-1,1,2-d$_3$), atactic; poly(1-methyl-ethylene-d$_3$),
   atactic
(3) C. Tosi, Centro Ricerche Milano, Montecatini Edison SpA,
   Milano

(5) catalyst system VCl$_4$/Al (C$_2$H$_5$)$_3$ in n-heptane at 195 K
(6) C. Wolfsgruber, F. Cawassi, C. Tosi, Makromol. Chem. *165*
   (1973) 281...95
(7) spectrum by the authors

72111211 D$_2$C$_3$H$_4$ 1684

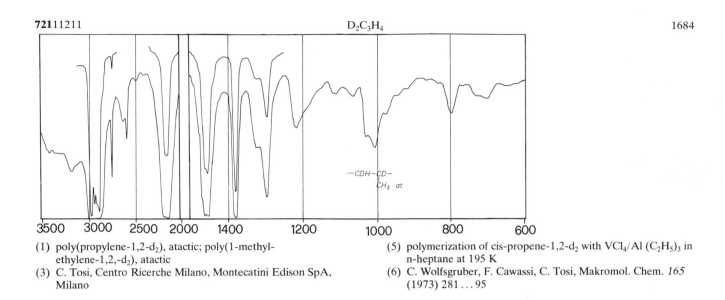

$-CDH-CD-$
CH_3 at.

(1) poly(propylene-1,2-d$_2$), atactic; poly(1-methyl-
ethylene-1,2,-d$_2$), atactic
(3) C. Tosi, Centro Ricerche Milano, Montecatini Edison SpA,
Milano

(5) polymerization of cis-propene-1,2-d$_2$ with VCl$_4$/Al (C$_2$H$_5$)$_3$ in
n-heptane at 195 K
(6) C. Wolfsgruber, F. Cawassi, C. Tosi, Makromol. Chem. *165*
(1973) 281...95

72111211 DC$_3$H$_5$ 1685

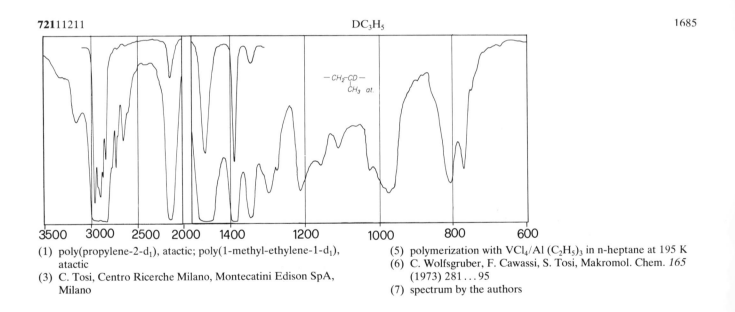

$-CH_2-CD-$
CH_3 at.

(1) poly(propylene-2-d$_1$), atactic; poly(1-methyl-ethylene-1-d$_1$),
atactic
(3) C. Tosi, Centro Ricerche Milano, Montecatini Edison SpA,
Milano

(5) polymerization with VCl$_4$/Al (C$_2$H$_5$)$_3$ in n-heptane at 195 K
(6) C. Wolfsgruber, F. Cawassi, S. Tosi, Makromol. Chem. *165*
(1973) 281...95
(7) spectrum by the authors

72111213 D$_2$C$_5$H$_8$ 1686

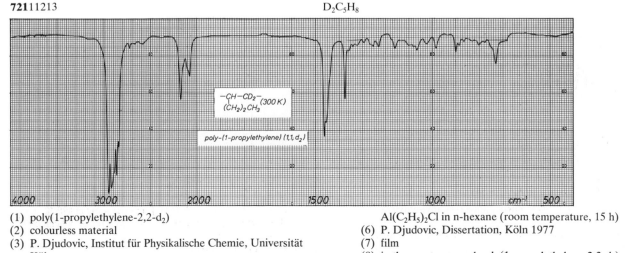

$-CH-CD_2-$ (300 K)
$(CH_2)_2CH_3$

poly-(1-propylethylene) (1,1,d$_2$)

562

(1) poly(1-propylethylene-2,2-d$_2$)
(2) colourless material
(3) P. Djudovic, Institut für Physikalische Chemie, Universität
Köln
(5) polymerization with TiCl$_3$ (suspension in n-hexane) and

Al(C$_2$H$_5$)$_2$Cl in n-hexane (room temperature, 15 h)
(6) P. Djudovic, Dissertation, Köln 1977
(7) film
(8) in the spectrum read poly(1-propylethylene-2,2-d$_2$)

72111213 $D_2C_5H_8$ 1687

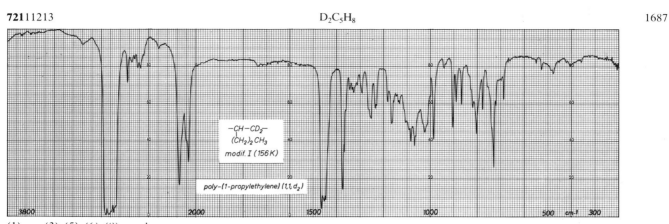

–CH–CD$_2$–
(CH$_2$)$_2$CH$_3$
modif. I (156 K)

poly-(1-propylethylene) (1,1,d$_2$)

(1) . . . (3), (5), (6), (8) see above
(4) crystalline, modification I
(7) 156 K

72111213 $D_3C_5H_7$ 1688

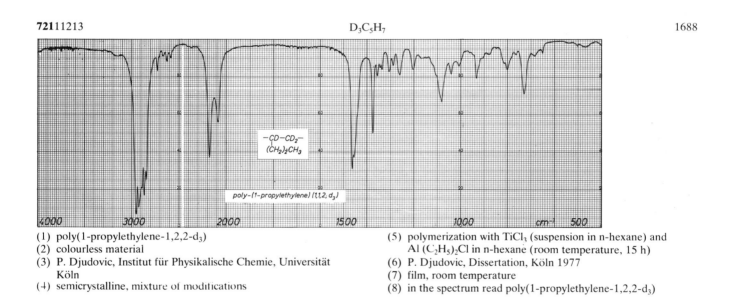

–CD–CD$_2$–
(CH$_2$)$_2$CH$_3$

poly-(1-propylethylene) (1,1,2; d$_3$)

(1) poly(1-propylethylene-1,2,2-d$_3$)
(2) colourless material
(3) P. Djudovic, Institut für Physikalische Chemie, Universität Köln
(4) semicrystalline, mixture of modifications

(5) polymerization with TiCl$_3$ (suspension in n-hexane) and Al (C$_2$H$_5$)$_2$Cl in n-hexane (room temperature, 15 h)
(6) P. Djudovic, Dissertation, Köln 1977
(7) film, room temperature
(8) in the spectrum read poly(1-propylethylene-1,2,2-d$_3$)

72111213 $D_3C_5H_7$ 1689

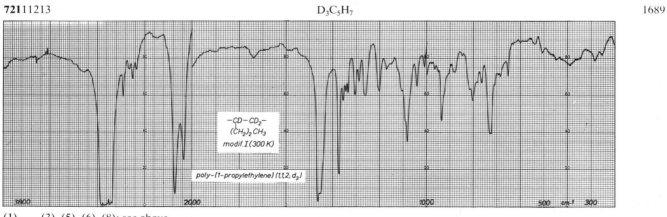

–CD–CD$_2$–
(CH$_2$)$_2$CH$_3$
modif. I (300 K)

poly-(1-propylethylene) (1,1,2; d$_3$)

(1) . . . (3), (5), (6), (8): see above
(4) crystalline, modification I
(7) film (300 K)

72111213 $D_3C_5H_7$ 1690

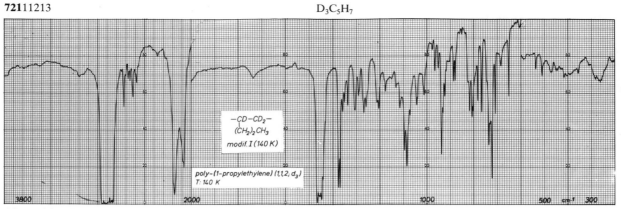

$$-CD-CD_2-$$
$$(CH_2)_2CH_3$$
modif. I (140 K)

poly-(1-propylethylene) (1,1,2; d_3)
T: 140 K

(1) ... (6), (8): see above
(7) film (140 K)

72111214 $D_2C_{12}H_{22}$ 1691

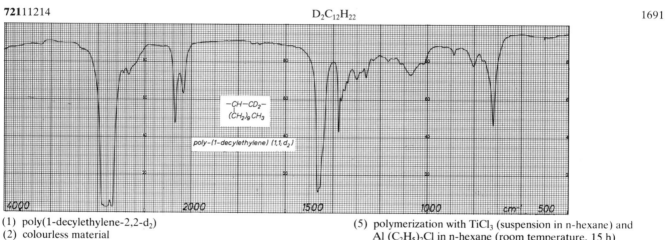

$$-CH-CD_2-$$
$$(CH_2)_9CH_3$$

poly-(1-decylethylene) (1,1, d_2)

(1) poly(1-decylethylene-2,2-d_2)
(2) colourless material
(3) P. Djudovic, Institut für Physikalische Chemie, Universität Köln
(4) semi-crystalline

(5) polymerization with $TiCl_3$ (suspension in n-hexane) and $Al(C_2H_5)_2Cl$ in n-hexane (room temperature, 15 h)
(6) P. Djudovic, Disseration, Köln 1977
(7) film (room temperature)
(8) in the spectrum read poly(1-decylethylene-2,2-d_2)

72112113 $D_2C_4H_4$ 1692

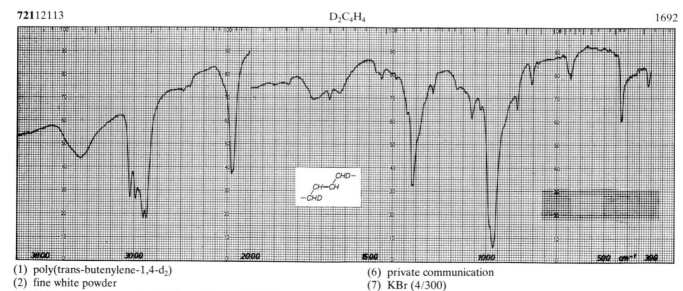

$$CHD-$$
$$CH=CH$$
$$-CHD$$

(1) poly(trans-butenylene-1,4-d_2)
(2) fine white powder
(3) C. Tosi, Centro Ricerche di Milano, Montecatini Edison S.p.A., Milano

(6) private communication
(7) KBr (4/300)

72122111 $D_3C_8H_5$ 1693

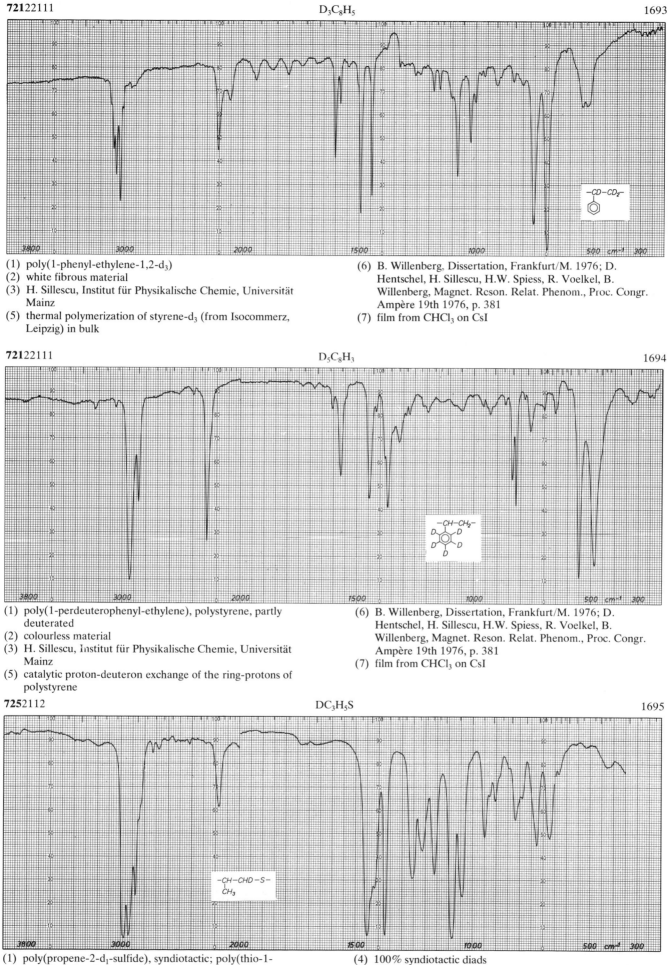

(1) poly(1-phenyl-ethylene-1,2-d$_3$)
(2) white fibrous material
(3) H. Sillescu, Institut für Physikalische Chemie, Universität Mainz
(5) thermal polymerization of styrene-d$_3$ (from Isocommerz, Leipzig) in bulk

(6) B. Willenberg, Dissertation, Frankfurt/M. 1976; D. Hentschel, H. Sillescu, H.W. Spiess, R. Voelkel, B. Willenberg, Magnet. Rcson. Relat. Phenom., Proc. Congr. Ampère 19th 1976, p. 381
(7) film from CHCl$_3$ on CsI

72122111 $D_5C_8H_3$ 1694

(1) poly(1-perdeuterophenyl-ethylene), polystyrene, partly deuterated
(2) colourless material
(3) H. Sillescu, Institut für Physikalische Chemie, Universität Mainz
(5) catalytic proton-deuteron exchange of the ring-protons of polystyrene

(6) B. Willenberg, Dissertation, Frankfurt/M. 1976; D. Hentschel, H. Sillescu, H.W. Spiess, R. Voelkel, B. Willenberg, Magnet. Reson. Relat. Phenom., Proc. Congr. Ampère 19th 1976, p. 381
(7) film from CHCl$_3$ on CsI

7252112 DC_3H_5S 1695

(1) poly(propene-2-d$_1$-sulfide), syndiotactic; poly(thio-1-methylethylene), deuterated
(2) greyish-white, hard-elastomeric material
(3) K.J. Ivin, Department of Chemistry, The Queen's University of Belfast

(4) 100% syndiotactic diads
(5) polymerization of propene-2-d$_1$-sulfide with Cd-tartrate
(6) K.J. Ivin, E.D. Lillie, P. Sigwalt, N. Spassky, Macromolecules 4 (1971) 345...7
(7) film from CHCl$_3$ on KBr

7252112 DC_3H_5S 1696

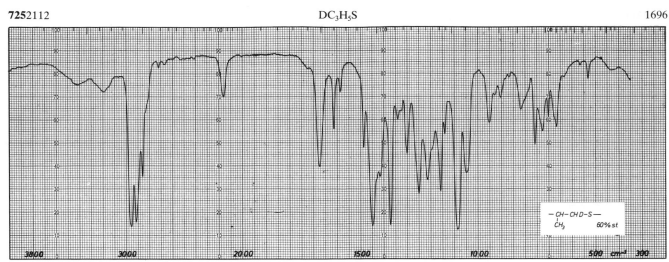

$-CH-CHD-S-$
$\quad\;\; CH_3 \qquad 60\% st$

(1) poly(propene-2-d_1-sulfide), poly(thio-1-methylethylene), deuterated
(2) clear viscous substance
(3) K.J. Ivin, Department of Chemistry, The Queen's University of Belfast

(4) 60 % syndiotactic dyads
(5) polymerization of propene-2-d_1-sulfide with Cd-tartrate
(6) K.J. Ivin, E.D. Lillie, P. Sigwalt, N. Spassky, Macromolecules *4* (1971) 345...7
(7) film on KBr from $CHCl_3$

7281212131211 $D_3C_4H_5OS$ 1697

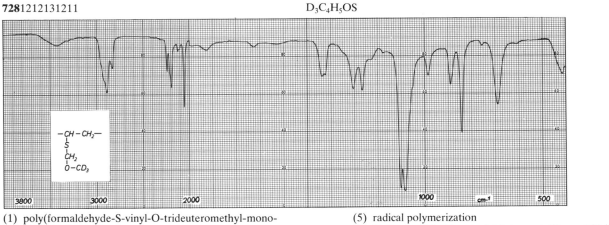

$-CH-CH_2-$
$\quad\; S$
$\quad\; CH_2$
$\quad\; O-CD_3$

(1) poly(formaldehyde-S-vinyl-O-trideuteromethyl-mono-thioacetal)
(2) colourless material
(3) R. Kroker, H. Ringsdorf, Institut für Polymere, Universität Marburg/Institut für Organische Chemie, Universität Mainz

(5) radical polymerization
(6) R. Kroker, H. Ringsdorf, Makromol. Chem. *121* (1969) 240...57
(7) film from $CHCl_3$ on KBr

7284121 $D_2C_3H_4O_2S$ 1698

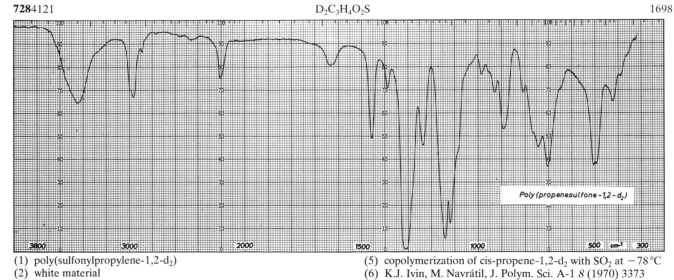

Poly (propenesulfone-1,2-d_2)

(1) poly(sulfonylpropylene-1,2-d_2)
(2) white material
(3) K.J. Ivin, Department of Chemistry, The Queen's University of Belfast, N. Ireland
(4) $-SO_2-CD-CHD-$
$\qquad\qquad\;\; CH_3$

(5) copolymerization of cis-propene-1,2-d_2 with SO_2 at $-78\,°C$
(6) K.J. Ivin, M. Navrátil, J. Polym. Sci. A-1 *8* (1970) 3373
(7) KBr (2.5/1000)

7312   D$_6$SiCO   1699

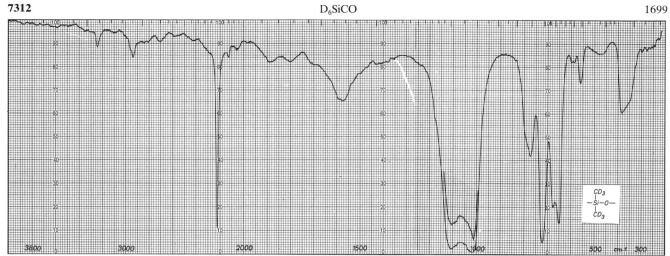

(1) poly(perdeutero-dimethylsiloxane)
(2) colourless, viscous liquid
(3) R. Kirste, Institut für Physikalische Chemie, Universität Mainz
(5) anionic polymerization of hexamethyl-d$_3$-cyclotrisiloxane, see

H.J. Hölle, B.R. Lehnen, Europ. Polym. J. *11* (1975) 663...7
(6) R.G. Kirste, B.R. Lehnen, Makromol. Chem. *177* (1976) 1137
(7) film between CsI

811233211   BC$_{14}$H$_{11}$O$_3$ 1700

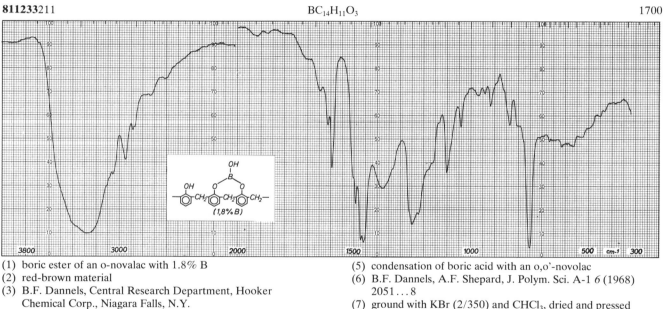

(1) boric ester of an o-novalac with 1.8% B
(2) red-brown material
(3) B.F. Dannels, Central Research Department, Hooker Chemical Corp., Niagara Falls, N.Y.

(5) condensation of boric acid with an o,o'-novolac
(6) B.F. Dannels, A.F. Shepard, J. Polym. Sci. A-1 *6* (1968) 2051...8
(7) ground with KBr (2/350) and CHCl$_3$, dried and pressed

813113374131   B$_{10}$C$_{30}$H$_{30}$O$_5$ 1701

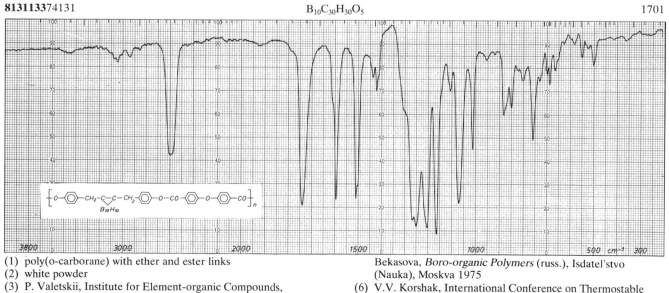

(1) poly(o-carborane) with ether and ester links
(2) white powder
(3) P. Valetskii, Institute for Element-organic Compounds, Academy of Sciences, USSR, Moskva
(5) see, e.g., H.A. Schroeder, Inorganic Macromolecules Reviews *1* (1970) 45...73; V. V. Korshak, V. A. Samjatina, I.N.

Bekasova, *Boro-organic Polymers* (russ.), Isdatel'stvo (Nauka), Moskva 1975
(6) V.V. Korshak, International Conference on Thermostable Polymers, Baranów, Poland, 1975
(7) film from CHCl$_3$ on CsI

813113374131 B$_{10}$C$_{28}$H$_{26}$O$_5$ 1702

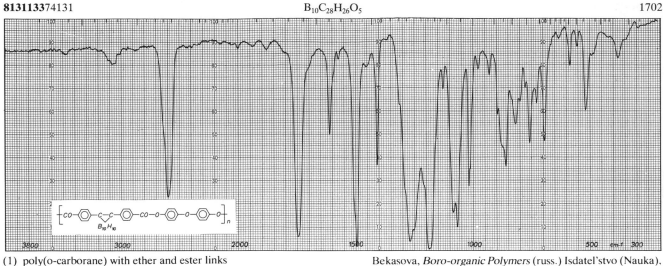

(1) poly(o-carborane) with ether and ester links
(2) white material
(3) P. Valetskii, Institute for Element-organic Compounds, Academy of Sciences, USSR, Moskva
(5) see, e.g., H. A. Schroeder, Inorganic Macromolecules Reviews *1* (1970) 45...73; V. V. Korshak, V. A. Samjatina, I. N.

Bekasova, *Boro-organic Polymers* (russ.) Isdatel'stvo (Nauka), Moskva 1975
(6) V.V. Korshak, International Conference on Thermostable Polymers, Baranów, Poland, 1975
(7) film from CHCl$_3$ on CsI

813113374131 B$_{10}$C$_{28}$H$_{26}$O$_5$ 1703

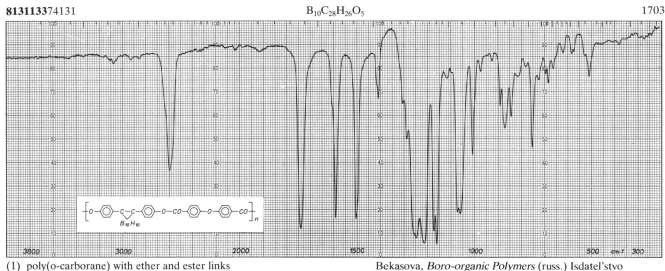

(1) poly(o-carborane) with ether and ester links
(2) white powder
(3) P. Valetskii, Institute for Element-organic Compounds, Academy of Sciences, USSR, Moskva
(5) see, e.g., H.A. Schroeder, Inorganic Macromolecules Reviews *1* (1970) 45...73; V.V. Korshak, V.A. Samjatina, I.N.

Bekasova, *Boro-organic Polymers* (russ.) Isdatel'stvo (Nauka), Moskva 1975
(6) V.V. Korshak, International Conference on Thermostable Polymers, Baranów, Poland, 1975
(7) film from CHCl$_3$ on CsI

813133374131 B$_{10}$C$_{28}$H$_{26}$O$_5$ 1704

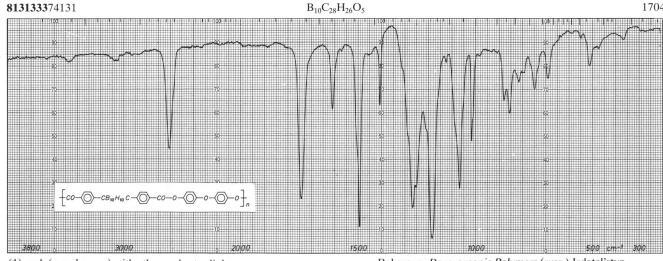

(1) poly(p-carborane) with ether and ester links
(2) white material
(3) P. Valetskii, Institute for Element-organic Compounds, Academy of sciences, USSR, Moskva
(5) see e.g., H.A. Schroeder, Inorganic Macromolecules Reviews *1* (1970) 45...73; V.V. Korshak, V.A. Samjatina, I.N.

Bekasova, *Boro-organic Polymers* (russ.) Isdatel'stvo (Nauka), Moskva 1975
(6) V.V. Korshak, International Conference on Thermostable Polymers, Baranów, Poland 1975
(7) film from CHCl$_3$ on CsI

81311142153213 $B_{10}C_{30}H_{24}N_2O_5$ 1705

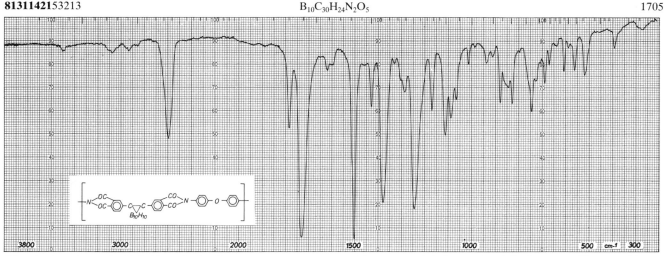

(1) polyy(o-carborane) with imido and ether links
(2) greyish-white powder
(3) P. Valetskii, Institute for Element-organic Compounds, Acad. of Sciences, USSR, Moscow

(6) V.V. Korshak, International Conference on Thermostable Polymers, Baranów, Poland, 1975
(7) film from CHCl₃ on CsI

81311342153213 $B_{10}C_{30}H_{24}N_2O_5$ 1706

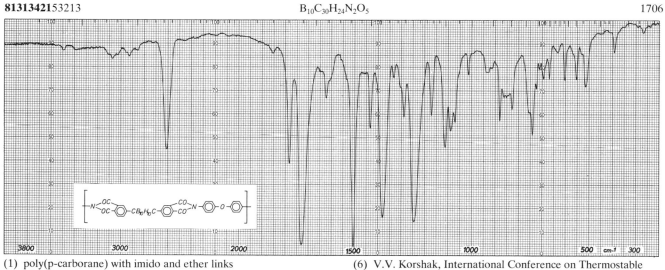

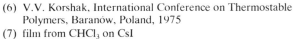

(1) poly(p-carborane) with imido and ether links
(2) greyish-white powder
(3) P. Valetskii, Institute for Element-organic Compounds, Acad. of Sciences, USSR, Moscow

(6) V.V. Korshak, International Conference on Thermostable Polymers, Baranów, Poland, 1975
(7) film from CHCl₃ on CsI

82113331121 $SiC_7H_{16}O$ 1707

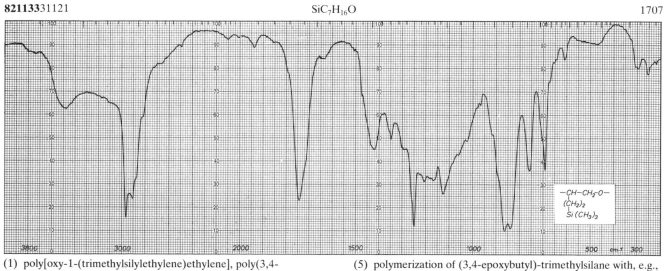

(1) poly[oxy-1-(trimethylsilylethylene)ethylene], poly(3,4-epoxybutyltrimethylsilane)
(2) colourless, soft, waxy material
(3) T. Tsuruta, Department of Synthetic Chemistry, University of Tokyo, Tokyo

(5) polymerization of (3,4-epoxybutyl)-trimethylsilane with, e.g., ZnEt₂-H₂O (1:1) at 80 °C in benzene
(6) T. Tsuruta, S. Inoue, H. Koenuma, Makromol. Chem. *112* (1968) 58…65
(7) film between CsI

82123122211   SiC₁₁H₁₅Cl   1708

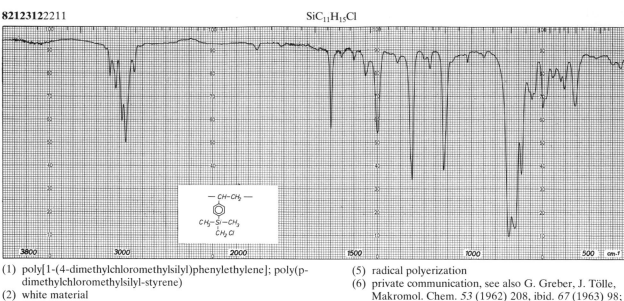

(1) poly[1-(4-dimethylchloromethylsilyl)phenylethylene]; poly(p-dimethylchloromethylsilyl-styrene)
(2) white material
(3) G. Greber, Institut für Makromolekulare Chemie, Universität Freiburg/Ciba-Geigy AG, Basel
(5) radical polyerization
(6) private communication, see also G. Greber, J. Tölle, Makromol. Chem. *53* (1962) 208, ibid. *67* (1963) 98; Angew. Makromol. Chem. *2* (1968) 133...45
(7) film from CHCl₃ on CsI

821233721112   SiC₁₂H₁₆O₂   1709

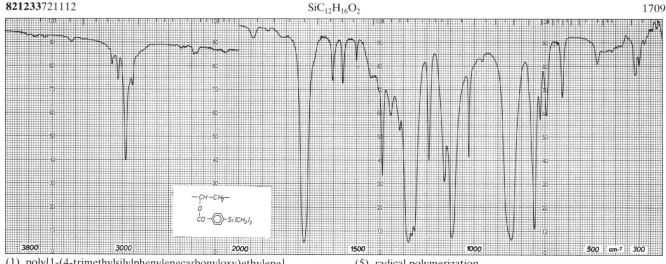

(1) poly[1-(4-trimethylsilylphenylenecarbonyloxy)ethylene] poly(vinyl-p-trimethylsilylbenzoate)
(2) white material
(3) H. Hopff, Technisch-chemisches Laboratorium, ETH, Zürich
(5) radical polymerization
(6) private communication; H. Hopff, Makromolekulares Kolloquium, Freiburg 1969
(7) film from CHCl₃ on CsI

82153241121   SiC₃₈H₂₆N₄   1710

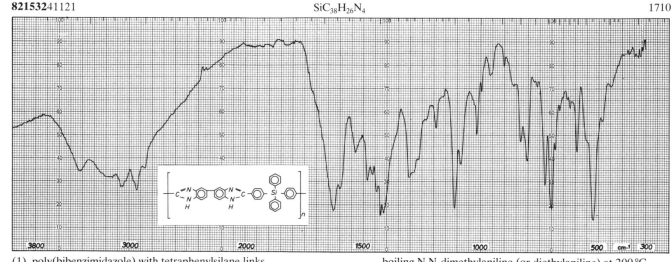

(1) poly(bibenzimidazole) with tetraphenylsilane links
(2) light-brown powder
(3) T.T. McGillicuddy, US Naval Applied Science Laboratory, Brooklyn, N.Y.
(5) polycondensation of dipentachlorophenylester of bis(p-carboxyphenyl)diphenylsilane and 3,3'-diaminobenzidine in
boiling N,N-dimethylaniline (or diethylaniline) at 200 °C (3...11 h)
(6) Hanna Nagy Kovacs, A.D. Delman, B.B. Simms, J. Polym. Sci. A-1 *6* (1968) 2103...15
(7) ground with KBr (3/350) and dimethylacetamide, dried and pressed

821536   SiC$_{26}$H$_{18}$N$_2$O   1711

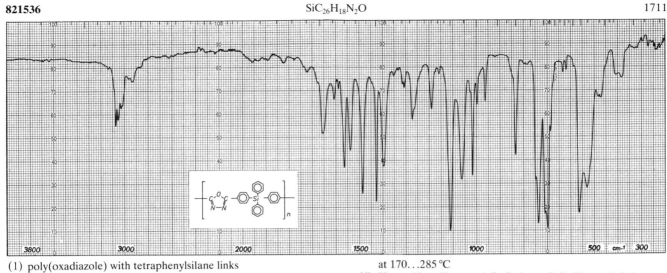

(1) poly(oxadiazole) with tetraphenylsilane links
(2) brittle, resinous material
(3) T.T. McGillicuddy, US Naval Applied Science Laboratory, Brooklyn, N.Y.
(5) polycyclocondensation of the polyhydrazide (see above), i.v.

at 170...285 °C
(6) Hanna Nagy Kovacs, A.D. Delman, B.B. Simms, J. Polym. Sci. A-1 6 (1968) 2103...15
(7) film from CHCl$_3$ on CsI

821542121241   SiC$_{32}$H$_{24}$N$_2$O$_2$ 1712

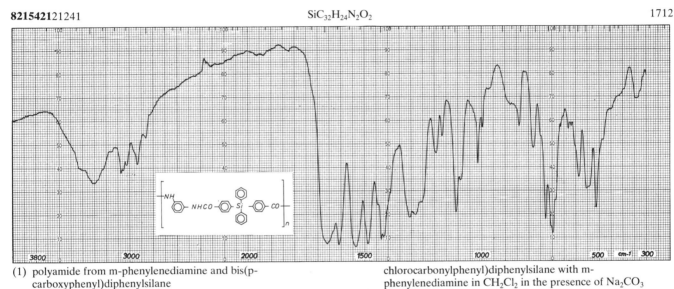

(1) polyamide from m-phenylenediamine and bis(p-carboxyphenyl)diphenylsilane
(2) eggshell-coloured powder
(3) T.T. McGillicuddy, US Naval Applied Science Laboratory, Brooklyn, N.Y.
(5) interfacial (or solution) polycondensation of bis(p-

chlorocarbonylphenyl)diphenylsilane with m-phenylenediamine in CH$_2$Cl$_2$ in the presence of Na$_2$CO$_3$
(6) Hanna Nagy Kovacs, A.D. Delman, B.B. Simms, J. Polym. Sci. A-1 6 (1968) 2103...15
(7) ground with KBr (2.5/350) and dimethylacetamide, dried and pressed

821542121241   SiC$_{32}$H$_{24}$N$_2$O$_2$ 1713

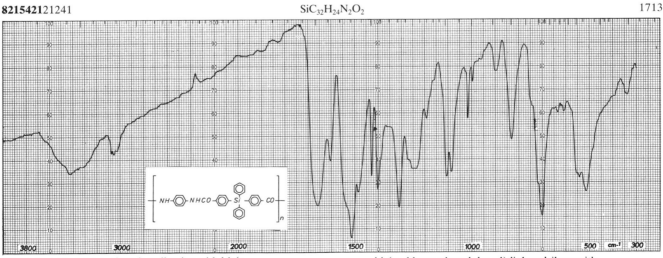

(1) polyamide from p-phenylenediamine with bis(p-carboxyphenyl)diphenylsilane
(2) white powder
(3) T.T. McGillicuddy, US Naval Applied Science Laboratory, Brooklyn, N.Y.
(5) interfacial (or solution) polycondensation of

bis(p-chlorocarbonylphenyl)diphenylsilane with p-phenylenediamine in CH$_2$Cl$_2$ in the presence of Na$_2$CO$_3$
(6) Hanna Nagy Kovacs, A.D. Delman, B.B. Simms, J. Polym. Sci. A-1 6 (1968) 2103...15
(7) KBr (2/350)

82154211241   SiC$_{38}$H$_{28}$N$_2$O$_2$ 1714

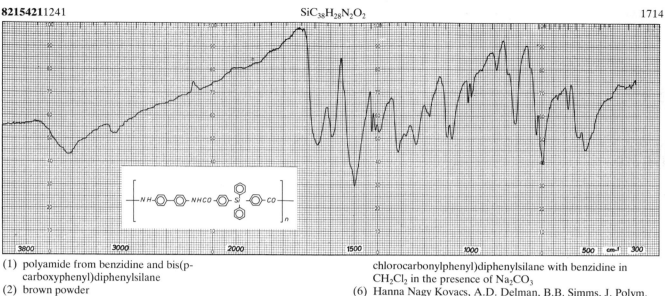

(1) polyamide from benzidine and bis(p-carboxyphenyl)diphenylsilane
(2) brown powder
(3) T.T. McGillicuddy, US Naval Applied Science Laboratory, Brooklyn, N.Y.
(5) interfacial (or solution) polycondensation of bis(p-chlorocarbonylphenyl)diphenylsilane with benzidine in CH$_2$Cl$_2$ in the presence of Na$_2$CO$_3$
(6) Hanna Nagy Kovacs, A.D. Delman, B.B. Simms, J. Polym. Sci. A-1 *6* (1968) 2103 ... 15
(7) KBr (1.5/350)

821542121441   SiC$_{26}$H$_{20}$N$_2$O$_2$ 1715

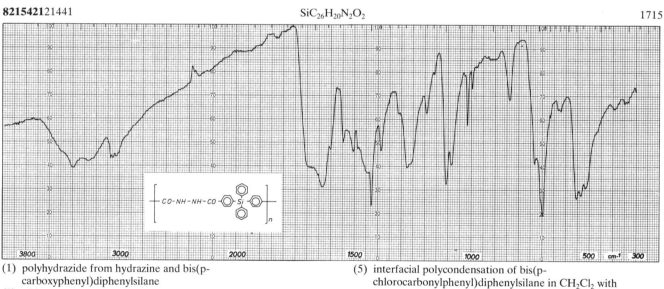

(1) polyhydrazide from hydrazine and bis(p-carboxyphenyl)diphenylsilane
(2) white powder
(3) T.T. McGillicuddy, US Naval Applied Science Laboratory, Brooklyn, N.Y.
(5) interfacial polycondensation of bis(p-chlorocarbonylphenyl)diphenylsilane in CH$_2$Cl$_2$ with hydrazinesulfate in the presence of KOH
(6) Hanna Nagy Kovacs, A.D. Delman, B.B. Simms, J. Polym. Sci. A-1 *6* (1968) 2103 ... 15

822323213   SiC$_7$H$_7$NO$_2$ 1716

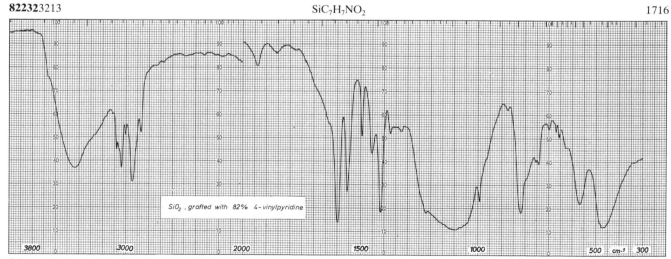

(1) poly(4-vinylpyridine), grafted on to SiO$_2$
(2) yellow, coarse material
(3) N. Fery, Forschungsinstitut für Pigmente und Lacke, Stuttgart
(4) the material contained 82 mol-% 4-vinylpyridine units
     polymerization with vinylpyridine
(6) N. Fery, R. Hoene, K. Hamann, Makromolekulares Kolloquium, Freiburg 1972; private communication
(7) KBr (5/300)
(8) the amorphous SiO$_2$ was „Aerosil 200"

8241232121   SiC₂₅H₂₀N₂   1717

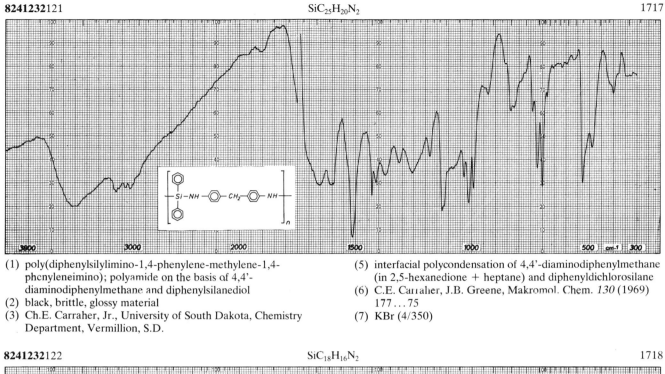

(1) poly(diphenylsilylimino-1,4-phenylene-methylene-1,4-phenyleneimino); polyamide on the basis of 4,4'-diaminodiphenylmethane and diphenylsilanediol
(2) black, brittle, glossy material
(3) Ch.E. Carraher, Jr., University of South Dakota, Chemistry Department, Vermillion, S.D.

(5) interfacial polycondensation of 4,4'-diaminodiphenylmethane (in 2,5-hexanedione + heptane) and diphenyldichlorosilane
(6) C.E. Carraher, J.B. Greene, Makromol. Chem. *130* (1969) 177...75
(7) KBr (4/350)

8241232122   SiC₁₈H₁₆N₂   1718

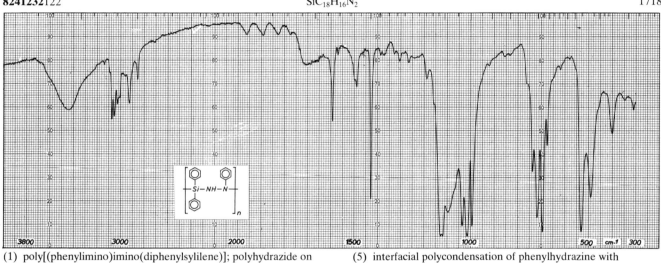

(1) poly[(phenylimino)imino(diphenylsylilene)]; polyhydrazide on the basis of phenylhydrazine and diphenylsilanediol
(2) dark-brown, brittle, glossy material
(3) Ch.E. Carraher, Jr., University of South Dakota, Chemistry Department, Vermillion, S.D.

(5) interfacial polycondensation of phenylhydrazine with diphenyldichlorosilane
(6) C.E. Carraher, Macromolecules *2* (1969) 306...8

82413   SiC₆H₅O₂   1719

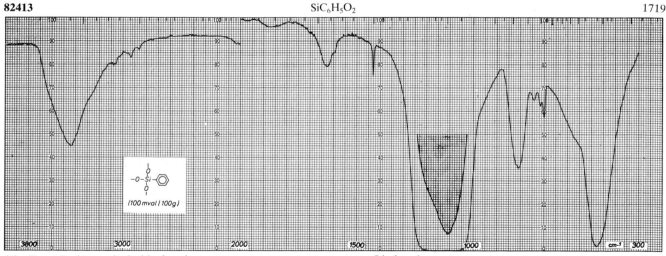

(1) silicon dioxide, grafted with phenyl groups
(2) white, light powder
(3) N. Fery, II. Institut für Technische Chemie, Universität Stuttgart, Stuttgart
(4) 100 mval phenylgroups by 100 g material
(5) reaction of amorphous SiO₂ with SOCl₂, conversion with

Li-phenyl
(6) N. Fery, R. Hoene, K. Hamann, Makromolekulares Kolloquium, Freiburg/Br. 1972
(7) KBr (1/300)
(8) the amorphous SiO₂ was Aerosil 200

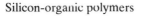

824133331122   SiC$_2$H$_6$O   1720

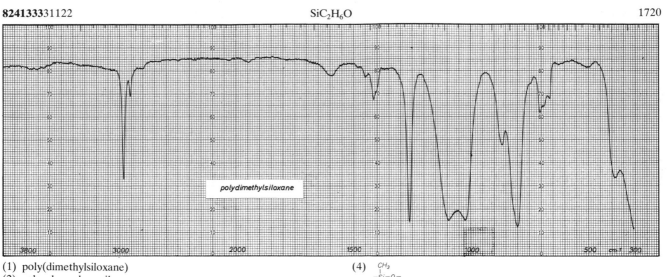

(1) poly(dimethylsiloxane)
(2) colourless, clear oil
(3) Bayer AG, Leverkusen (by W. Noll)

(4)
$$\begin{array}{c} CH_3 \\ | \\ -Si-O- \\ | \\ CH_3 \end{array}$$

(7) film between KBr

824133331122–211212   SiC$_2$H$_6$O–C$_5$H$_8$ 1721

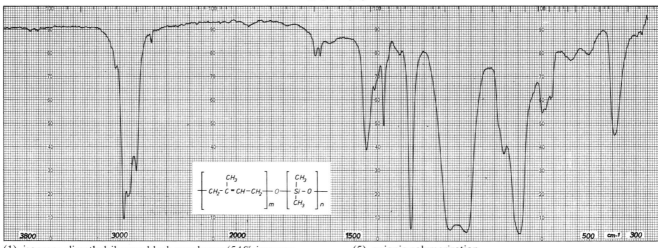

(1) isoprene-dimethylsiloxane block copolymer (54% isoprene units)
(2) colourless, tough material
(3) Y. Gallot, C.N.R.S.-C.R.M., Strasbourg

(5) anionic polymerization
(6) Y. Gallot, A. Marsiat, IUPAC Macro, Madrid 1974 (II.3–8)
(7) film on CsI

824133331122–2122111   SiC$_2$H$_6$O–C$_8$H$_8$ 1722

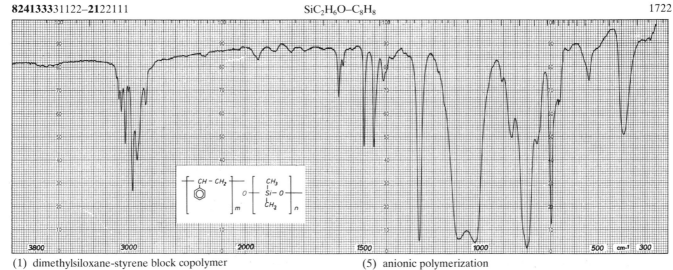

574

(1) dimethylsiloxane-styrene block copolymer
(2) white, waxy material
(3) Y. Gallot, C.N.R.S.-C.R.M., Strasbourg

(5) anionic polymerization
(6) Y. Gallot, A. Marsiat, IUPAC Macro, Madrid 1974 (II.3-8)
(7) film from CHCl$_3$ on CsI

824133331122–**2122111**–**824133**312212   SiC₂H₆O-C₈H₈-SiC₁₀H₁₃O   1723

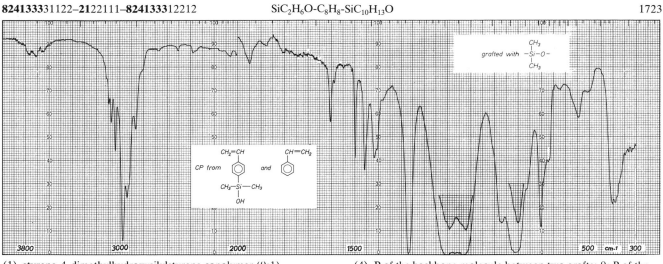

(1) styrene-4-dimethylhydroxysilylstyrene copolymer (9:1), grafted with poly(dimethylsiloxane)
(2) colourless material
(3) G. Greber, Institut für Makromolekulare Chemie, Universität Freiburg, Br./Ciba-Geigy AG, Basel

(4) P of the backbone molecule between two grafts: 9; P of the grafts: 38
(6) G. Greber, Makromolekulares Kolloquium, Freiburg/Br. 1969; private communication
(7) film from benzene on KBr

824133331122–**2122131**   SiC₂H₆O-C₉H₁₀   1724

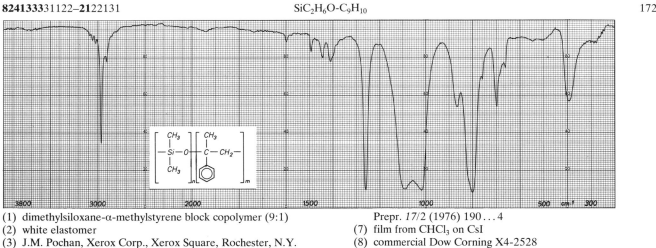

(1) dimethylsiloxane-α-methylstyrene block copolymer (9:1)
(2) white elastomer
(3) J.M. Pochan, Xerox Corp., Xerox Square, Rochester, N.Y.
(6) J.M. Pochan, T.J. Pacansky, D.F. Hinman, ACS Polym.

Prepr. *17/2* (1976) 190...4
(7) film from CHCl₃ on CsI
(8) commercial Dow Corning X4-2528

824133331122–**2122131**   SiC₂H₆O-C₉H₁₀   1725

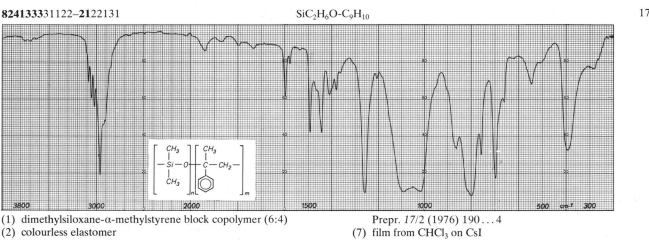

(1) dimethylsiloxane-α-methylstyrene block copolymer (6:4)
(2) colourless elastomer
(3) J.M. Pochan, Xerox Corp., Xerox Square, Rochester, N.Y.
(6) J.M. Pochan, T.J. Pacansky, D.F. Hinman, ACS Polym.

Prepr. *17/2* (1976) 190...4
(7) film from CHCl₃ on CsI
(8) commercial Dow Corning X4-2528

824133331122–33711211   SiC₂H₆O-C₁₄H₂₄O₄   1726

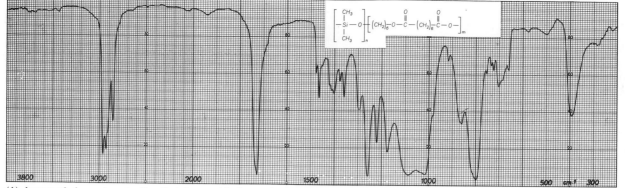

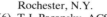

(1) hexamethylenesebacate-dimethylsiloxane block copolymer (60:40)

(2) white, waxy material

(3) T.J. Pacansky, Xerox Corp., Webster Research Center,

Rochester, N.Y.

(6) T.J. Pacansky, ACS Polym. Prepr. *17/2* (1976) 564...9

(7) film from toluene on CsI

824133331122–33711211   SiC₂H₆O-C₁₄H₂₄O₄   1727

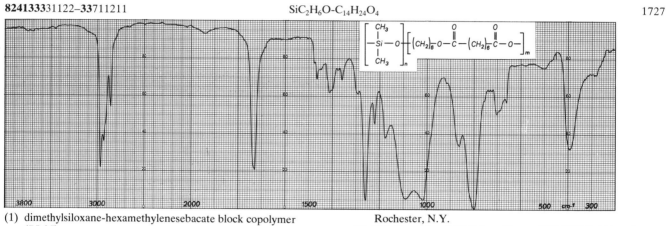

(1) dimethylsiloxane-hexamethylenesebacate block copolymer (75:25)

(2) white waxy material

(3) T.J. Pacansky, Xerox Corp., Webster Research Center,

Rochester, N.Y.

(6) T.J. Pacansky, ACS Polym. Prepr. *17/2* (1976) 564...9

(7) film from toluene on CsI

824133331122–337133   SiC₂H₆O-C₁₆H₁₄O₃   1728

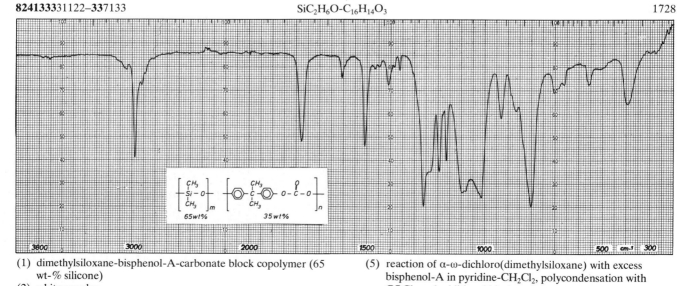

576

(1) dimethylsiloxane-bisphenol-A-carbonate block copolymer (65 wt-% silicone)

(2) white powder

(3) R.P. Kambour, General Electric Research and Development Center, Schenectady, N.Y.

(4) alternating, random block polymer of the -ABABA-type (polydisperse blocks)

(5) reaction of α-ω-dichloro(dimethylsiloxane) with excess bisphenol-A in pyridine-CH₂Cl₂, polycondensation with COCl₂ and additional bisphenol-A

(6) R.P. Kambour, ACS Polym. Prepr. *10/2* (1969) 995...92; Block Polymers, Plenum Press, New York 1970

(7) film from CHCl₃ on CsI

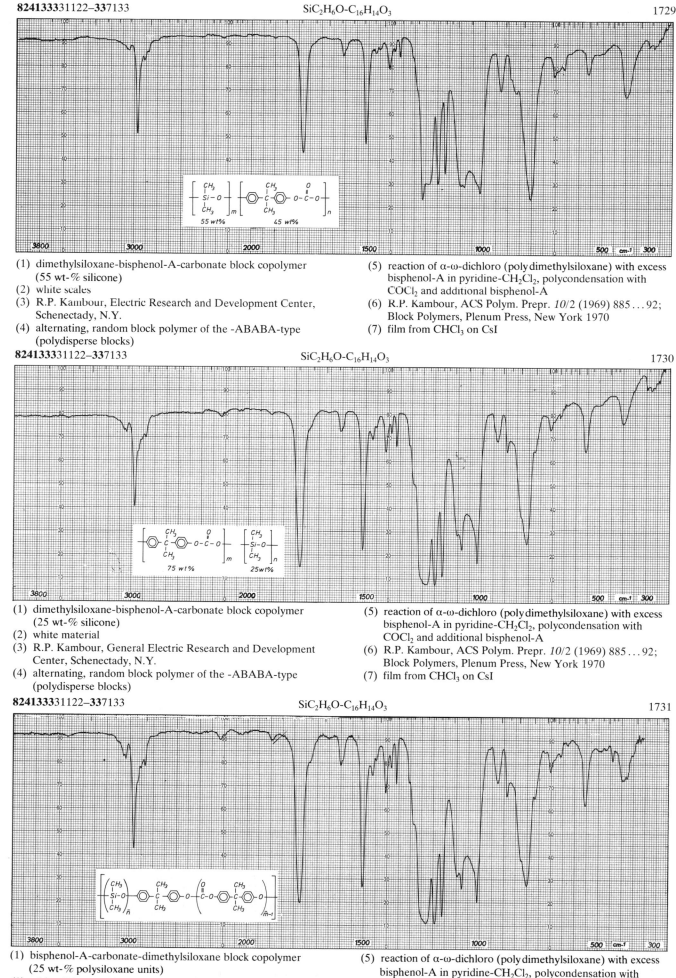

(1) dimethylsiloxane-bisphenol-A-carbonate block copolymer (55 wt-% silicone)
(2) white scales
(3) R.P. Kambour, Electric Research and Development Center, Schenectady, N.Y.
(4) alternating, random block polymer of the -ABABA-type (polydisperse blocks)

(5) reaction of α-ω-dichloro (polydimethylsiloxane) with excess bisphenol-A in pyridine-CH$_2$Cl$_2$, polycondensation with COCl$_2$ and additional bisphenol-A
(6) R.P. Kambour, ACS Polym. Prepr. *10*/2 (1969) 885...92; Block Polymers, Plenum Press, New York 1970
(7) film from CHCl$_3$ on CsI

(1) dimethylsiloxane-bisphenol-A-carbonate block copolymer (25 wt-% silicone)
(2) white material
(3) R.P. Kambour, General Electric Research and Development Center, Schenectady, N.Y.
(4) alternating, random block polymer of the -ABABA-type (polydisperse blocks)

(5) reaction of α-ω-dichloro (polydimethylsiloxane) with excess bisphenol-A in pyridine-CH$_2$Cl$_2$, polycondensation with COCl$_2$ and additional bisphenol-A
(6) R.P. Kambour, ACS Polym. Prepr. *10*/2 (1969) 885...92; Block Polymers, Plenum Press, New York 1970
(7) film from CHCl$_3$ on CsI

(1) bisphenol-A-carbonate-dimethylsiloxane block copolymer (25 wt-% polysiloxane units)
(2) white, light powder
(3) H.A. Vaughn, Silicon Products Department, General Electric Co., Waterford, N.Y.
(4) alternating, random block polymer of the -ABABA-type (polydisperse blocks)

(5) reaction of α-ω-dichloro (polydimethylsiloxane) with excess bisphenol-A in pyridine-CH$_2$Cl$_2$, polycondensation with COCl$_2$ and additional bisphenol-A
(6) H.A. Vaughn, J. Polym. Sci., Polym. Letters Ed. *7* (1969) 569...72
(7) film from CHCl$_3$ on CsI

82433331122–337133   SiC$_2$H$_6$O-C$_{16}$H$_{14}$O$_3$ 1732

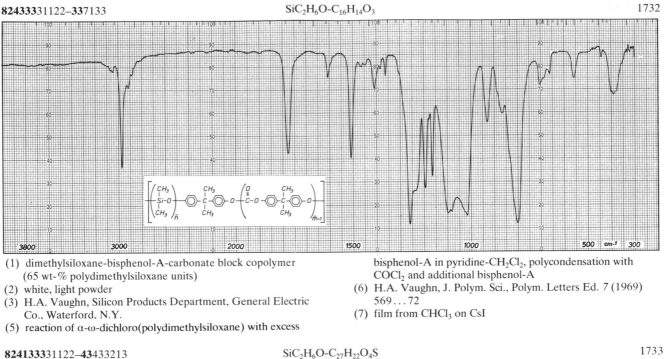

(1) dimethylsiloxane-bisphenol-A-carbonate block copolymer
     (65 wt-% polydimethylsiloxane units)
(2) white, light powder
(3) H.A. Vaughn, Silicon Products Department, General Electric
     Co., Waterford, N.Y.
(5) reaction of α-ω-dichloro(polydimethylsiloxane) with excess

bisphenol-A in pyridine-CH$_2$Cl$_2$, polycondensation with
COCl$_2$ and additional bisphenol-A
(6) H.A. Vaughn, J. Polym. Sci., Polym. Letters Ed. 7 (1969)
     569...72
(7) film from CHCl$_3$ on CsI

824133331122–**43**433213   SiC$_2$H$_6$O-C$_{27}$H$_{22}$O$_4$S   1733

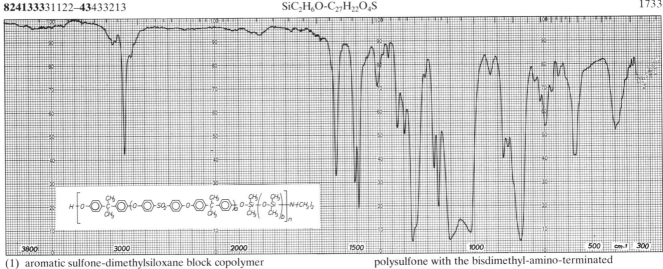

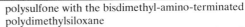

(1) aromatic sulfone-dimethylsiloxane block copolymer
(2) white, fibrous material
(3) A. Noshay, Chemicals and Plastics, Union Carbide Corp.,
     Bound Brook, N.J.
(4) alternating block structure, two-microphase system
(5) polycondensation of the preformed dihydroxy-terminated

polysulfone with the bisdimethyl-amino-terminated
polydimethylsiloxane
(6) A. Noshay, M. Matzner, C.N. Merriam, J. Polym. Sci. A-1 9
     (1971) 3147...59
(7) film from CHCl$_3$ on CsI

824133331122   SiC$_2$H$_6$O-SiC$_4$H$_6$O   1734

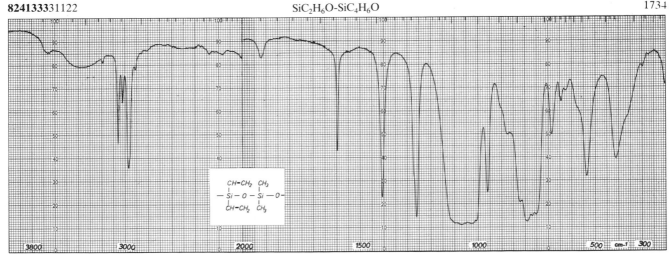

(1) poly(dimethylsiloxy-divinylsiloxane)
(2) clear, colourless liquid
(3) G. Greber, Institut für Makromolekulare Chemie, Universität

Freiburg, Br./Ciba-Geigy AG, Basel
(6) private communication
(7) film between CsI

2111211–824133331122 C_3H_6-SiC_3H_5O 1735

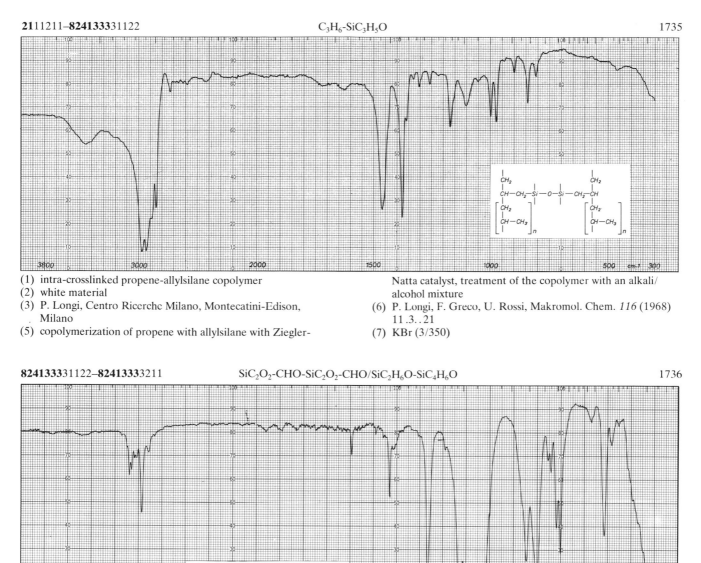

(1) intra-crosslinked propene-allylsilane copolymer
(2) white material
(3) P. Longi, Centro Ricerche Milano, Montecatini-Edison, Milano
(5) copolymerization of propene with allylsilane with Ziegler-

Natta catalyst, treatment of the copolymer with an alkali/alcohol mixture
(6) P. Longi, F. Greco, U. Rossi, Makromol. Chem. *116* (1968) 11.3..21
(7) KBr (3/350)

824133331122–82413333211 SiC_2O_2-CHO-SiC_2O_2-CHO/SiC_2H_6O-SiC_4H_6O 1736

poly(dimethylsiloxa diphenylsiloxane)

(1) poly(dimethylsiloxy-diphenylsiloxane)
(2) clear, colourless liquid
(3) Bayer AG, Leverkusen (by W. Noll)
(4) statistical copolycondensate, approx. 1:1, trimethylsiloxy end

groups
(6) private communication
(7) film between KBr

824133331122–82413333211 SiC_2O_2-CHO-SiC_2O_2-CHO/SiC_2H_6O-$SiC_7H_{10}O$ 1737

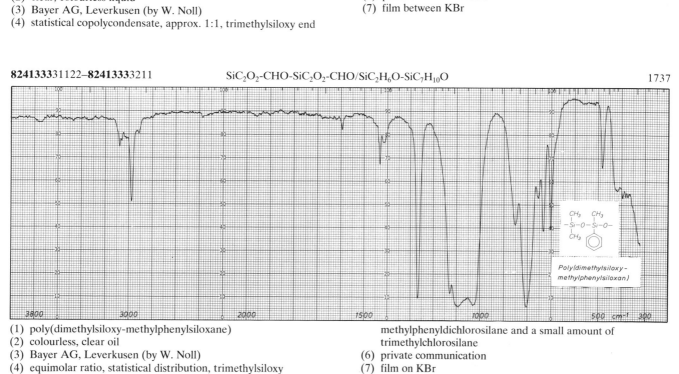

Poly(dimethylsiloxy-methylphenylsiloxan)

(1) poly(dimethylsiloxy-methylphenylsiloxane)
(2) colourless, clear oil
(3) Bayer AG, Leverkusen (by W. Noll)
(4) equimolar ratio, statistical distribution, trimethylsiloxy endgroups
(5) polycondensation of dimethyldichlorosilane with

methylphenyldichlorosilane and a small amount of trimethylchlorosilane
(6) private communication
(7) film on KBr
(8) the absorption increase beyond 450 cm⁻¹ is due to KBr

824133331211   SiC₁₄H₃₀O₃   1738

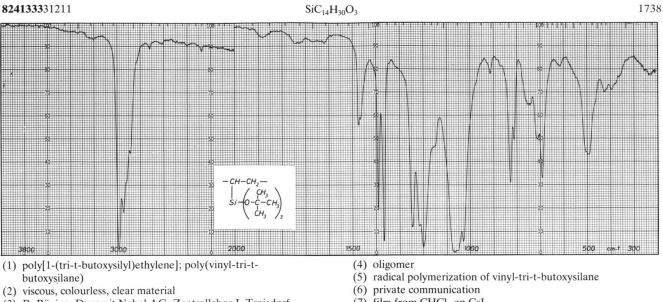

(1) poly[1-(tri-t-butoxysilyl)ethylene]; poly(vinyl-tri-t-butoxysilane)
(2) viscous, colourless, clear material
(3) R. Büning, Dynamit Nobel AG, Zentrallabor I, Troisdorf

(4) oligomer
(5) radical polymerization of vinyl-tri-t-butoxysilane
(6) private communication
(7) film from CHCl₃ on CsI

3121111–824133331211   SiC₅H₁₂O₃-C₂H₃Cl   1739

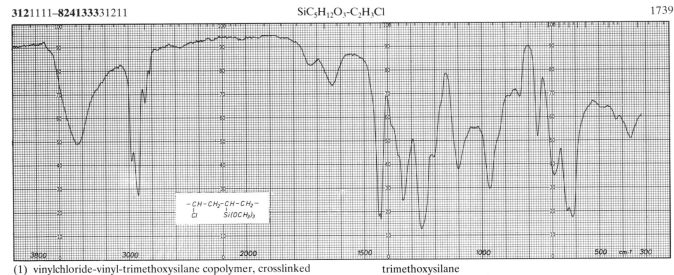

(1) vinylchloride-vinyl-trimethoxysilane copolymer, crosslinked
(2) white, coarse material
(3) R. Büning, Dynamit Nobel AG, Zentrallabor I, Troisdorf
(5) radical copolymerization of vinylchloride with vinyl-

trimethoxysilane
(6) private communication
(7) ground with KBr (5/350) and CHCl₃, dried and pressed

3121111–824133331211   SiC₁₄H₃₀O₃-C₂H₃Cl   1740

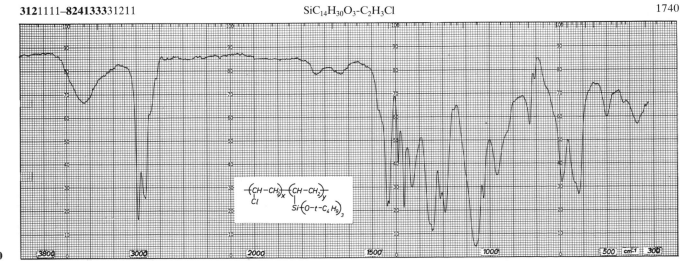

(1) vinylchloride-vinyl-tri-t-butoxysilane copolymer
(2) white, coarse material
(3) R. Büning, Dynamit Nobel AG, Zentrallabor I, Troisdorf
(5) radical copolymerization of vinylchlorde with vinyl-tri-t-

butoxysilane
(6) private communication
(7) ground with KBr (5/350) and CHCl₃, dried and pressed

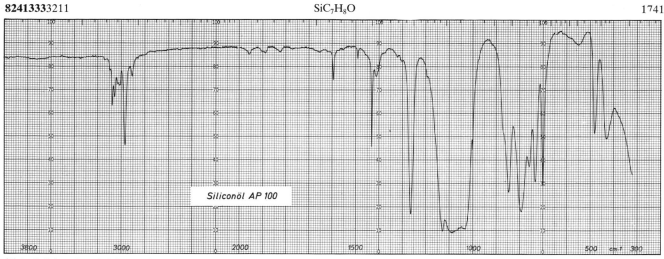

Siliconöl AP 100

(1) poly(phenylmethylsiloxane), probably with dimethylsiloxy
     groups
(2) colourless liquid
(3) Wacker-Chemie GmbH, München (commercial material

     "Siliconöl AP 100")
(4) higher phenyl content than "Siliconöl AP 100"
(8) absorption increase beyond 450 cm⁻¹ due to KBr

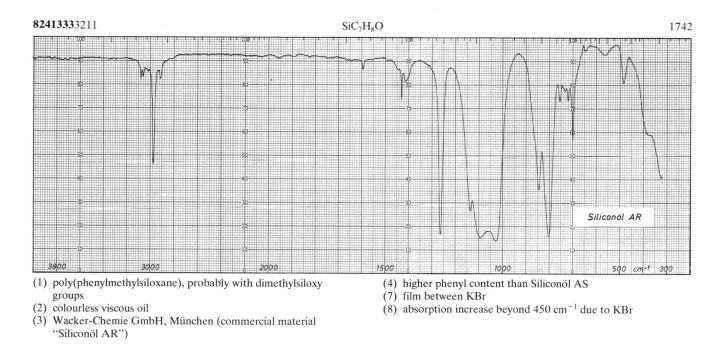

Siliconöl AR

(1) poly(phenylmethylsiloxane), probably with dimethylsiloxy
     groups
(2) colourless viscous oil
(3) Wacker-Chemie GmbH, München (commercial material
     "Siliconöl AR")
(4) higher phenyl content than Siliconöl AS
(7) film between KBr
(8) absorption increase beyond 450 cm⁻¹ due to KBr

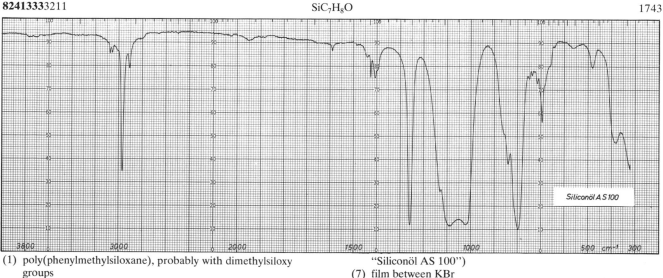

Siliconöl A S 100

(1) poly(phenylmethylsiloxane), probably with dimethylsiloxy
     groups
(2) colourless viscous oil
(3) Wacker-Chemie GmbH, München (commercial material

     "Siliconöl AS 100")
(7) film between KBr
(8) absorption increase beyond 450 cm⁻¹ due to KBr

82413333211 SiC₁₀H₁₆O 1744

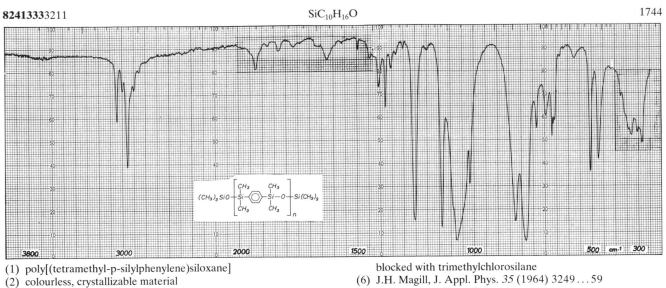

(1) poly[(tetramethyl-p-silylphenylene)siloxane]
(2) colourless, crystallizable material
(3) J.H. Magill, Mellon Institute, Pittsburgh, Pa.
(5) R.L. Merker, M.J. Scott, J. Polym. Sci. *A2* (1964) 15; and

blocked with trimethylchlorosilane
(6) J.H. Magill, J. Appl. Phys. *35* (1964) 3249...59
(7) film from CHCl₃ on CsI

82413333211–333113 SiC₂₀H₂₄O₂ 1745

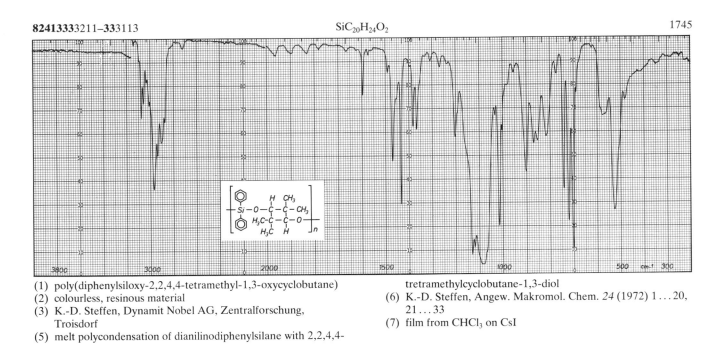

(1) poly(diphenylsiloxy-2,2,4,4-tetramethyl-1,3-oxycyclobutane)
(2) colourless, resinous material
(3) K.-D. Steffen, Dynamit Nobel AG, Zentralforschung, Troisdorf
(5) melt polycondensation of dianilinodiphenylsilane with 2,2,4,4-

tetramethylcyclobutane-1,3-diol
(6) K.-D. Steffen, Angew. Makromol. Chem. *24* (1972) 1...20, 21...33
(7) film from CHCl₃ on CsI

82413333211–333113 SiC₂₀H₂₆O₂ 1746

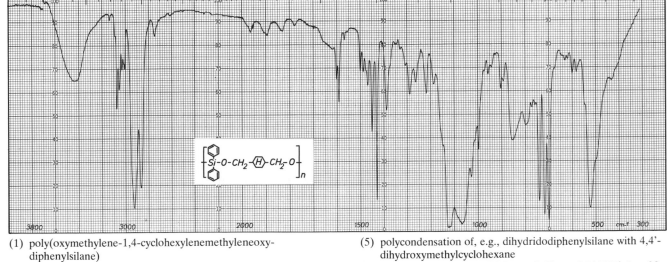

(1) poly(oxymethylene-1,4-cyclohexylenemethyleneoxy-diphenylsilane)
(2) colourless, resinous material
(3) K.-D. Steffen, Zentralforschung der Dynamit Nobel AG, Troisdorf

(5) polycondensation of, e.g., dihydridodiphenylsilane with 4,4'-dihydroxymethylcyclohexane
(6) K.-D. Steffen, Angew. Makromol. Chem. *24* (1972) 1...20, 21...33
(7) film from CHCl₃ on CsI

82413333211–3371223 $SiC_{13}H_{16}O_4$ 1747

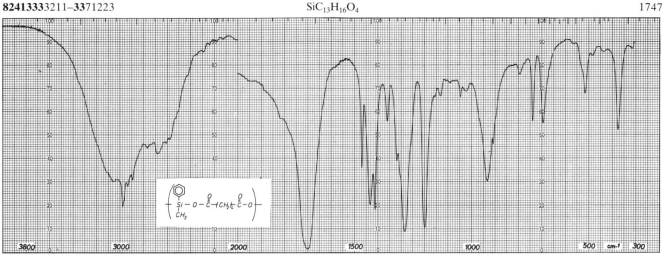

(1) poly(oxyadipoyloxy-methylphenylsilane)
(2) white material
(3) C.E. Carraher, Jr., Chemistry Department, University of South Dakota, Vermillion, S.D.
(5) polycondensation of phenylmethyldichlorosilane with adipic acid (alkaline medium)
(6) C. Carraher, R. Dammeier, ACS Polym. Prepr. *11/2* (1970) 606; J. Polym. Sci. *8* (1970) 973 ... 8
(7) KBr (1/300)

82413333212–33121 $SiC_{26}H_{20}O_2$ 1748

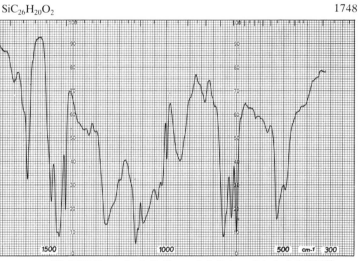

(5% Si)

(1) diphenylsilicic acid ester of an o,o'-novolac
(3) B.F. Dannels, Central Research Department, Hooker Chemical Corporation, Niagara Falls, N.Y.
(5) condensation of diphenyldichlorosilane with an o,o'-novolac
(6) W.F. Dannels, A.F. Shepard, J. Polym. Sci. A-1 *6* (1968) 2051 ... 8
(7) ground with KBr (2/350) and CHCl₃, dried and pressed

82413333212–333212 $SiC_{18}H_{14}O_2$ 1749

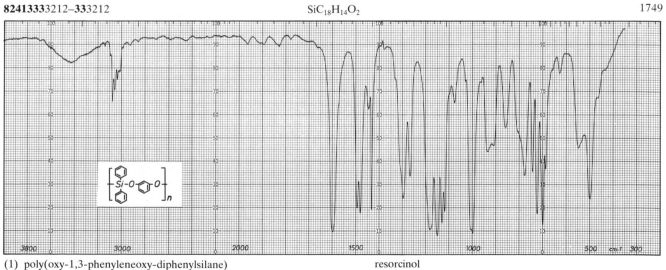

(1) poly(oxy-1,3-phenyleneoxy-diphenylsilane)
(2) colourless, resinous material
(3) K.-D. Steffen, Zentralforschung der Dynamit Nobel AG, Troisdorf
(5) polycondensation of, e.g., dihydridodiphenylsilane with resorcinol
(6) K.-D. Steffen, Angew. Makromol. Chem. *24* (1972) 1 ... 20, 21 ... 33
(7) film from CHCl₃ on CsI

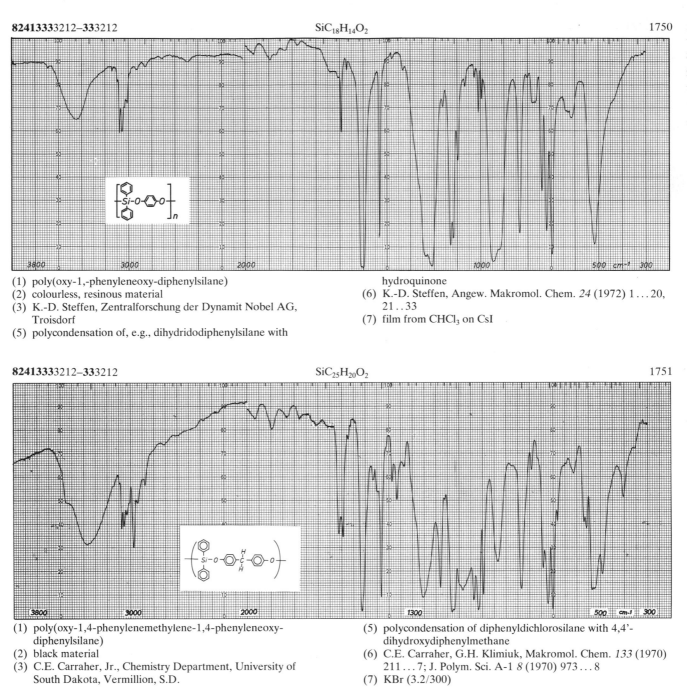

(1) poly(oxy-1,-phenyleneoxy-diphenylsilane)
(2) colourless, resinous material
(3) K.-D. Steffen, Zentralforschung der Dynamit Nobel AG,
     Troisdorf
(5) polycondensation of, e.g., dihydridodiphenylsilane with

hydroquinone
(6) K.-D. Steffen, Angew. Makromol. Chem. *24* (1972) 1...20,
     21..33
(7) film from CHCl₃ on CsI

(1) poly(oxy-1,4-phenylenemethylene-1,4-phenyleneoxy-
     diphenylsilane)
(2) black material
(3) C.E. Carraher, Jr., Chemistry Department, University of
     South Dakota, Vermillion, S.D.
(5) polycondensation of diphenyldichlorosilane with 4,4'-
     dihydroxydiphenylmethane
(6) C.E. Carraher, G.H. Klimiuk, Makromol. Chem. *133* (1970)
     211...7; J. Polym. Sci. A-1 *8* (1970) 973...8
(7) KBr (3.2/300)

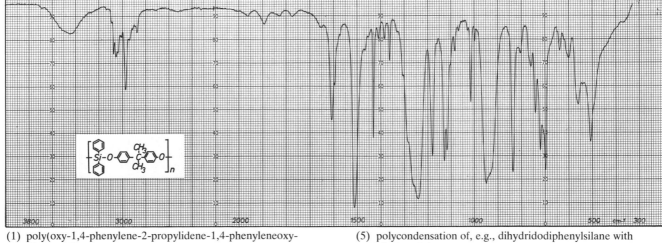

(1) poly(oxy-1,4-phenylene-2-propylidene-1,4-phenyleneoxy-
     diphenylsilane)
(2) colourless, resinous material
(3) K.-D. Steffen, Zentralforschung der Dynamit Nobel AG,
     Troisdorf
(5) polycondensation of, e.g., dihydridodiphenylsilane with
     bisphenol A
(6) K.-D. Steffen, Angew. Makromol. Chem. *24* (1972) 1...20,
     21..33
(7) film from CHCl₃ on CsI

82413333212–333212 $SiC_{37}H_{28}O_2$ 1753

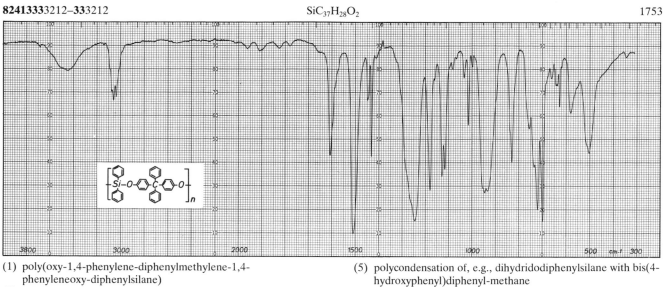

(1) poly(oxy-1,4-phenylene-diphenylmethylene-1,4-phenyleneoxy-diphenylsilane)

(2) colourless, resinous material

(3) K.-D. Steffen, Zentralforschung der Dynamit Nobel AG, Troisdorf

(5) polycondensation of, e.g., dihydridodiphenylsilane with bis(4-hydroxyphenyl)diphenyl-methane

(6) K.-D. Steffen, Angew. Makromol. Chem. *24* (1972) 1 . . . 20, 21 . . . 33

(7) film from CHCl₃ on CsI

82413333212–333212 $SiC_{24}H_{18}O_2$ 1754

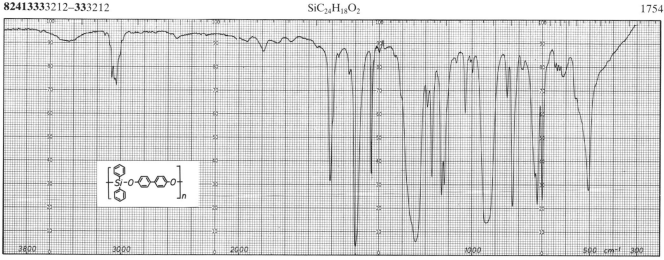

(1) poly(4,4'-dioxybiphenyl-diphenylsilane)

(2) colourless, resinous material

(3) K.-D. Steffen, Zentralforschung der Dynamit Nobel AG, Troisdorf

(5) polycondensation of, e.g., dihydridodiphenylsilane with 4,4'-dihydroxydiphenyl

(6) K.-D. Steffen, Angew. Makromol. Chem. *24* (1972) 1 . . . 20, 21 . . . 33

(7) film from CHCl₃ on CsI

82413333212–337722 $SiC_{32}H_{22}O_4$ 1755

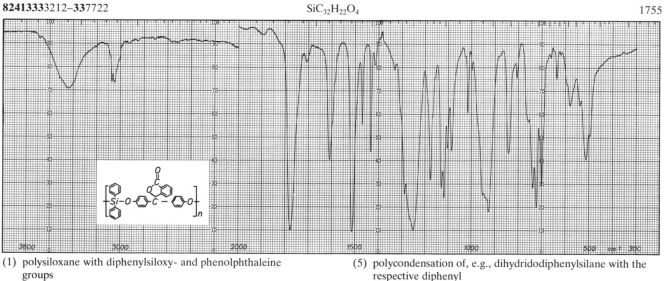

(1) polysiloxane with diphenylsiloxy- and phenolphthaleine groups

(2) colourless, resinous material

(3) K.-D. Steffen, Zentralforschung der Dynamit Nobel AG, Troisdorf

(5) polycondensation of, e.g., dihydridodiphenylsilane with the respective diphenyl

(6) K.-D. Steffen, Angew. Makromol. Chem. *24* (1972) 1 . . . 20, 21 . . . 33

(7) film from CHCl₃ on CsI

82413333212**–41323212**   SiC$_{24}$H$_{14}$Cl$_4$O$_2$ 1756

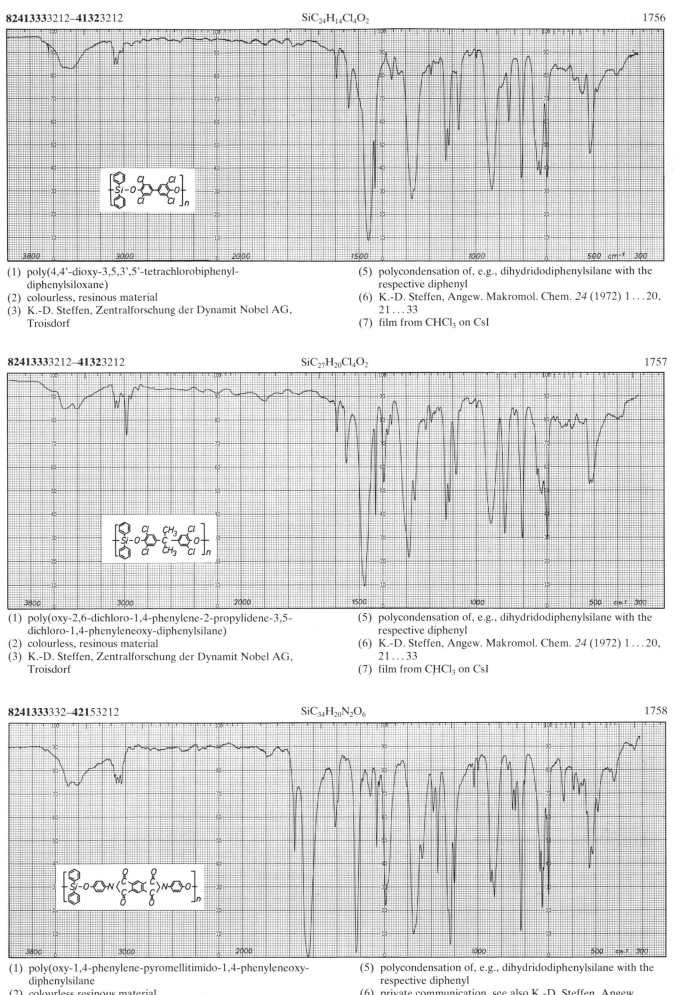

(1) poly(4,4'-dioxy-3,5,3',5'-tetrachlorobiphenyl-
    diphenylsiloxane)
(2) colourless, resinous material
(3) K.-D. Steffen, Zentralforschung der Dynamit Nobel AG,
    Troisdorf

(5) polycondensation of, e.g., dihydridodiphenylsilane with the
    respective diphenyl
(6) K.-D. Steffen, Angew. Makromol. Chem. *24* (1972) 1...20,
    21...33
(7) film from CHCl$_3$ on CsI

82413333212**–41323212**   SiC$_{27}$H$_{20}$Cl$_4$O$_2$ 1757

(1) poly(oxy-2,6-dichloro-1,4-phenylene-2-propylidene-3,5-
    dichloro-1,4-phenyleneoxy-diphenylsilane)
(2) colourless, resinous material
(3) K.-D. Steffen, Zentralforschung der Dynamit Nobel AG,
    Troisdorf

(5) polycondensation of, e.g., dihydridodiphenylsilane with the
    respective diphenyl
(6) K.-D. Steffen, Angew. Makromol. Chem. *24* (1972) 1...20,
    21...33
(7) film from CHCl$_3$ on CsI

8241333332**–42153212**   SiC$_{34}$H$_{20}$N$_2$O$_6$ 1758

(1) poly(oxy-1,4-phenylene-pyromellitimido-1,4-phenyleneoxy-
    diphenylsilane
(2) colourless resinous material
(3) K.-D. Steffen, Zentralforschung der Dynamit Nobel AG,
    Troisdorf

(5) polycondensation of, e.g., dihydridodiphenylsilane with the
    respective diphenyl
(6) private communication, see also K.-D. Steffen, Angew.
    Makromol. Chem. *24* (1972) 1...20, 21...33
(7) film from CHCl$_3$ on CsI

82413413131121   SiC₄H₇F₃O   1759

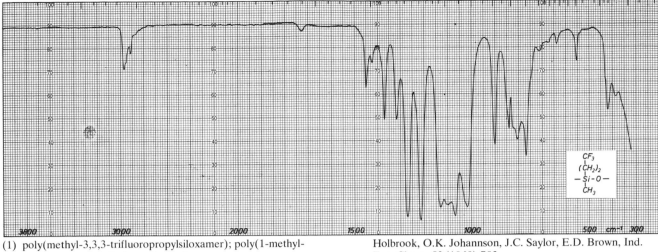

(1) poly(methyl-3,3,3-trifluoropropylsiloxamer); poly(1-methyl-
1-trifluoromethylethylene-siloxane)

(2) colourless, viscous oil

(3) R.R. Buch, Dow Corning Corp., Midland, Mich.

(5) polymerization of the cyclic trimer with trimethylsilanol
sodium salt, [(CH₃)₃SiONa]; see also O.R. Pierce, G.W.

Holbrook, O.K. Johannson, J.C. Saylor, E.D. Brown, Ind.
Eng. Chem. *52* (1960) 783

(6) R.R. Buch, Helen M. Klimisch, O.K. Johannson, J. Polym.
Sci. A-2 *7* (1969) 563...74

(7) film between KBr

82413413133211   SiC₇H₇FO   1760

(1) poly[(p-fluorophenyl)-methylsiloxane]; poly[1-methyl-1-(4-
fluorophenyl)siloxane]

(2) colourless, viscous liquid

(3) H. Deibig, Battelle-Institut, Frankfurt/Main

(5) polycondensation of p-fluorophenyl-methyldiethoxysilane

(6) H. Deibig, H. Lukas, private communication

(7) film between CsI

82413413133211–**8241331**121   SiC₇H₇FO-SiC₃H₆O   1761

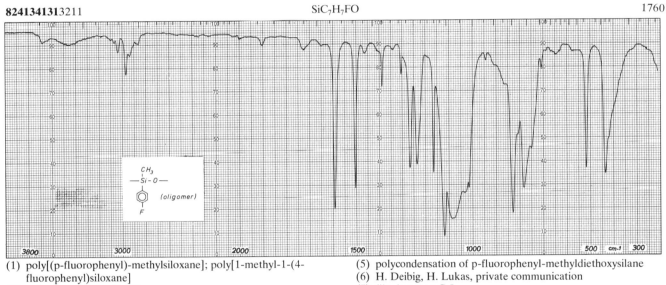

(1) p-fluorophenylmethylsilicone-vinylmethylsilicone copolymer
(oligomer)

(2) colourless, viscous liquid

(3) H. Deibig, Battelle-Institut, Frankfurt/Main

(4) 5% vinylmethylsilicone

(5) copolycondensation of p-fluorophenyl-methyldiethoxysilane
with vinylmethyldiethoxysilane

(6) H. Deibig, H. Lukas, private communication

(7) film between CsI

8241341313211–8241331121   SiC₇H₇FO-SiC₃H₆O   1762

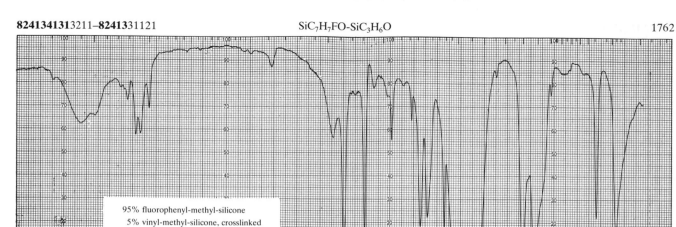

95% fluorophenyl-methyl-silicone
5% vinyl-methyl-silicone, crosslinked

(1) p-fluorophenylmethylsilicone-vinylmethylsilicone copolymer,
    crosslinked
(2) slightly greyish-brown, soft film
(3) H. Deibig, Battelle-Institut, Frankfurt/Main

(5) radical-initiated crosslinking of the copolycondensate
(6) H. Deibig, H. Lukas, private communication
(7) ground with KBr (1.2/350) and CHCl₃, dried and pressed

8241342153212   Si₃C₂₈H₂₈N₂O₈   1763

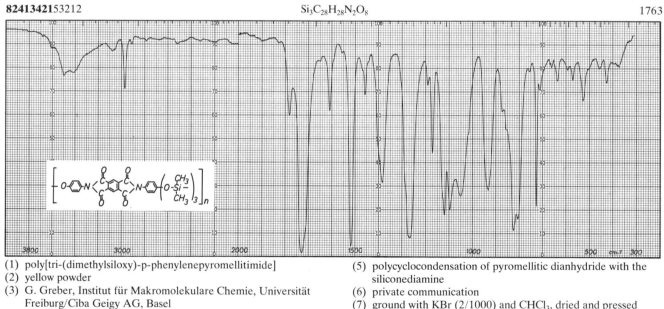

(1) poly[tri-(dimethylsiloxy)-p-phenylenepyromellitimide]
(2) yellow powder
(3) G. Greber, Institut für Makromolekulare Chemie, Universität
    Freiburg/Ciba Geigy AG, Basel

(5) polycyclocondensation of pyromellitic dianhydride with the
    siliconediamine
(6) private communication
(7) ground with KBr (2/1000) and CHCl₃, dried and pressed

82413421831   SiC₂₄H₁₈N₂O₂   1764

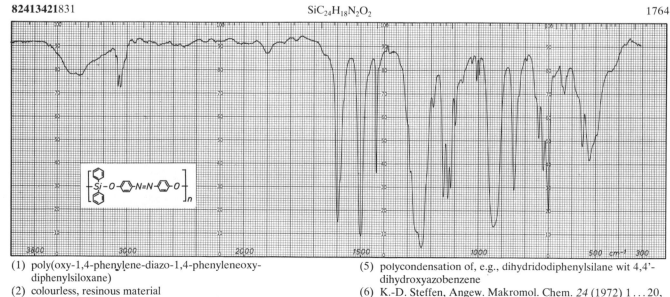

(1) poly(oxy-1,4-phenylene-diazo-1,4-phenyleneoxy-
    diphenylsiloxane)
(2) colourless, resinous material
(3) K.-D. Steffen, Zentralforschung der Dynamit Nobel AG,
    Troisdorf

(5) polycondensation of, e.g., dihydridodiphenylsilane wit 4,4'-
    dihydroxyazobenzene
(6) K.-D. Steffen, Angew. Makromol. Chem. *24* (1972) 1…20,
    21…33
(7) film from CHCl₃ on CsI

8241342163123   SiC$_{26}$H$_{18}$N$_2$O$_3$ 1765

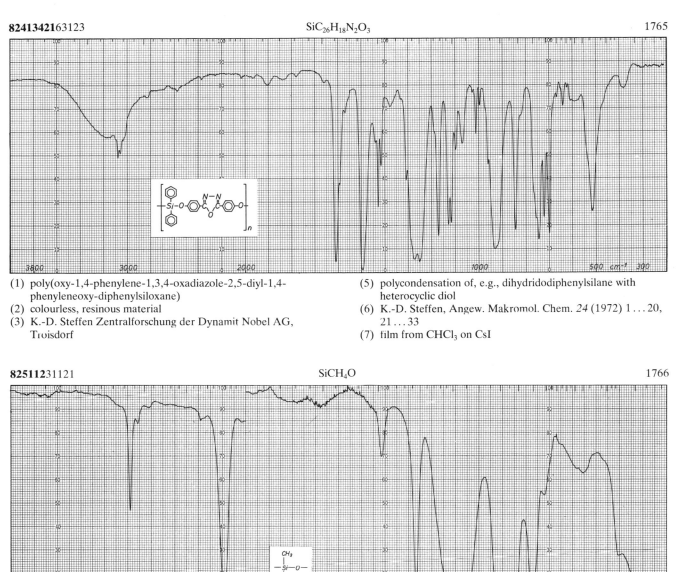

(1) poly(oxy-1,4-phenylene-1,3,4-oxadiazole-2,5-diyl-1,4-phenyleneoxy-diphenylsiloxane)
(2) colourless, resinous material
(3) K.-D. Steffen Zentralforschung der Dynamit Nobel AG, Troisdorf

(5) polycondensation of, e.g., dihydridodiphenylsilane with heterocyclic diol
(6) K.-D. Steffen, Angew. Makromol. Chem. *24* (1972) 1...20, 21...33
(7) film from CHCl$_3$ on CsI

82511231121   SiCH$_4$O   1766

(1) poly(methylhydrogensiloxane)
(2) colourless, clear liquid
(3) Aldirch-Europe Janssen Pharmaceutica

(7) film between KBr
(8) commercial material

82511231121   SiCH$_4$O   1767

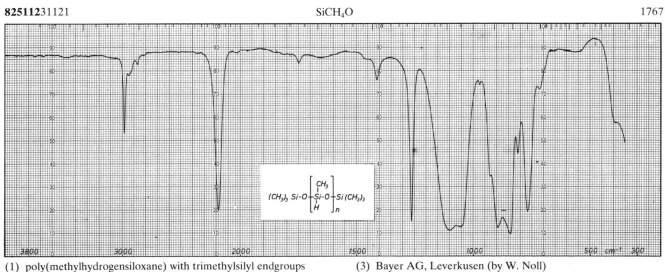

(1) poly(methylhydrogensiloxane) with trimethylsilyl endgroups
(2) colourless, clear, viscous liquid

(3) Bayer AG, Leverkusen (by W. Noll)
(7) film on KBr

827   SiC$_{32}$H$_{16}$N$_8$O   1768

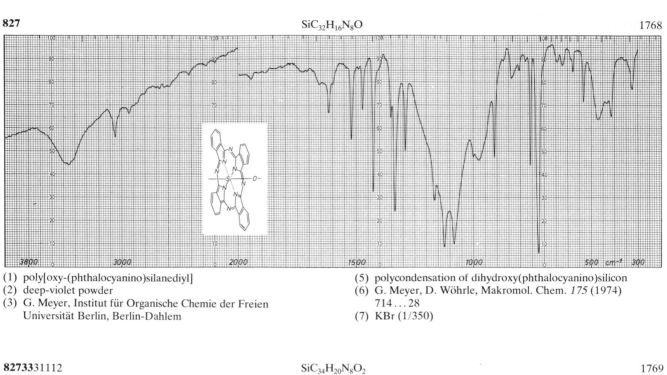

(1) poly[oxy-(phthalocyanino)silanediyl]
(2) deep-violet powder
(3) G. Meyer, Institut für Organische Chemie der Freien
    Universität Berlin, Berlin-Dahlem

(5) polycondensation of dihydroxy(phthalocyanino)silicon
(6) G. Meyer, D. Wöhrle, Makromol. Chem. *175* (1974)
    714...28
(7) KBr (1/350)

8273331112   SiC$_{34}$H$_{20}$N$_8$O$_2$ 1769

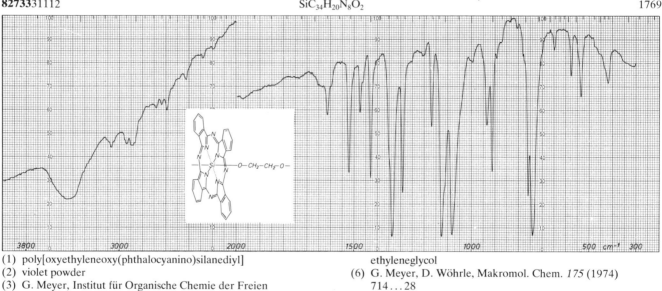

(1) poly[oxyethyleneoxy(phthalocyanino)silanediyl]
(2) violet powder
(3) G. Meyer, Institut für Organische Chemie der Freien
    Universität Berlin, Berlin-Dahlem
(5) polycondensation of dihydroxy(phthalocyanino)silicon with

ethyleneglycol
(6) G. Meyer, D. Wöhrle, Makromol. Chem. *175* (1974)
    714...28
(7) KBr (1/350)

82733331   SiC$_{38}$H$_{20}$N$_8$O$_2$ 1770

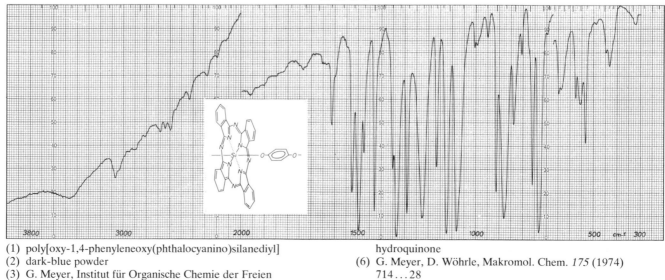

(1) poly[oxy-1,4-phenyleneoxy(phthalocyanino)silanediyl]
(2) dark-blue powder
(3) G. Meyer, Institut für Organische Chemie der Freien
    Universität Berlin, Berlin-Dahlem
(5) polycondensation of dichloro(phthalocyanino)silicon with

hydroquinone
(6) G. Meyer, D. Wöhrle, Makromol. Chem. *175* (1974)
    714...28
(7) KBr (1/350)

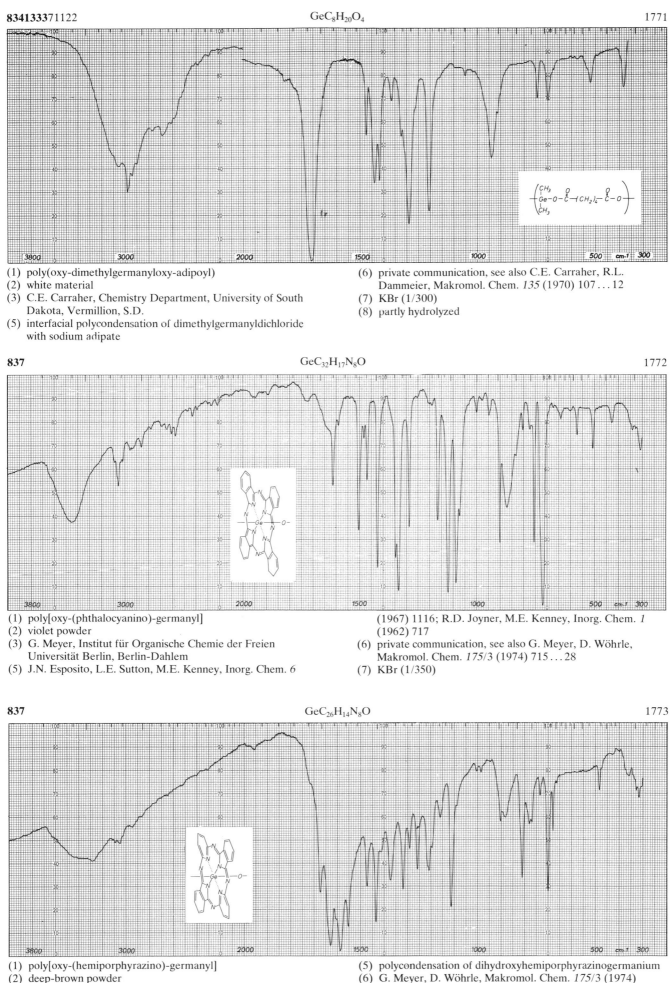

834133371122   GeC$_8$H$_{20}$O$_4$ 1771

(1) poly(oxy-dimethylgermanyloxy-adipoyl)
(2) white material
(3) C.E. Carraher, Chemistry Department, University of South Dakota, Vermillion, S.D.
(5) interfacial polycondensation of dimethylgermanyldichloride with sodium adipate

(6) private communication, see also C.E. Carraher, R.L. Dammeier, Makromol. Chem. *135* (1970) 107...12
(7) KBr (1/300)
(8) partly hydrolyzed

837   GeC$_{32}$H$_{17}$N$_8$O   1772

(1) poly[oxy-(phthalocyanino)-germanyl]
(2) violet powder
(3) G. Meyer, Institut für Organische Chemie der Freien Universität Berlin, Berlin-Dahlem
(5) J.N. Esposito, L.E. Sutton, M.E. Kenney, Inorg. Chem. *6*

(1967) 1116; R.D. Joyner, M.E. Kenney, Inorg. Chem. *1* (1962) 717
(6) private communication, see also G. Meyer, D. Wöhrle, Makromol. Chem. *175*/3 (1974) 715...28
(7) KBr (1/350)

837   GeC$_{26}$H$_{14}$N$_8$O   1773

(1) poly[oxy-(hemiporphyrazino)-germanyl]
(2) deep-brown powder
(3) G. Meyer, Institut für Organische Chemie der Freien Universität Berlin, Berlin-Dahlem

(5) polycondensation of dihydroxyhemiporphyrazinogermanium
(6) G. Meyer, D. Wöhrle, Makromol. Chem. *175*/3 (1974) 715...28
(7) KBr (1/350)

591

84111332131　　　　　　　　　　$P_3C_{21}H_{35}N_9$　　　　　　　　　　1774

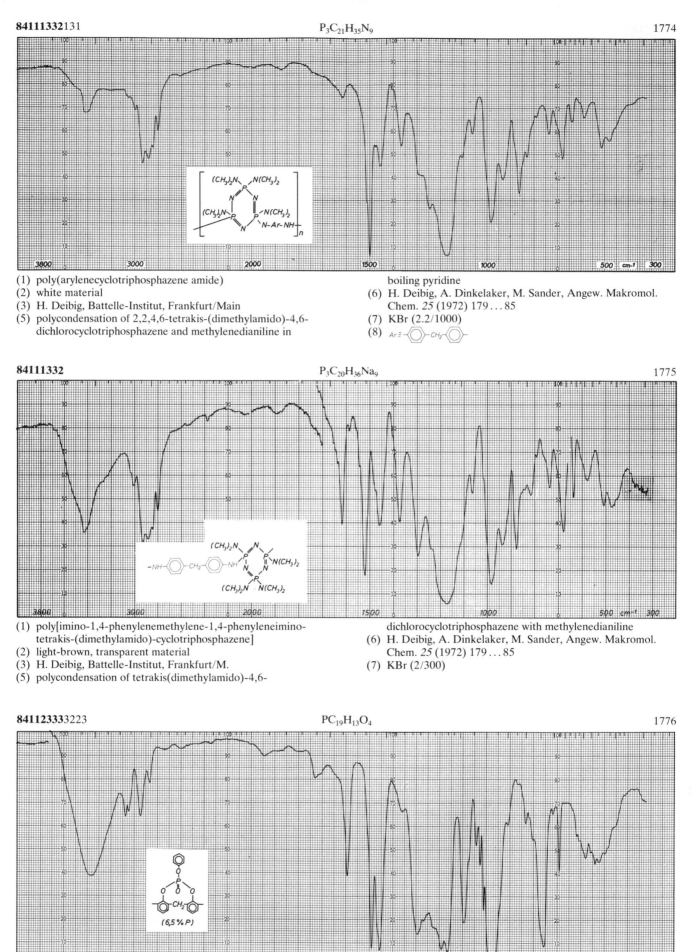

(1) poly(arylenecyclotriphosphazene amide)
(2) white material
(3) H. Deibig, Battelle-Institut, Frankfurt/Main
(5) polycondensation of 2,2,4,6-tetrakis-(dimethylamido)-4,6-dichlorocyclotriphosphazene and methylenedianiline in

boiling pyridine
(6) H. Deibig, A. Dinkelaker, M. Sander, Angew. Makromol. Chem. *25* (1972) 179...85
(7) KBr (2.2/1000)
(8) Ar = ⬡–CH₂–⬡–

84111332　　　　　　　　　　$P_3C_{20}H_{36}Na_9$　　　　　　　　　　1775

(1) poly[imino-1,4-phenylenemethylene-1,4-phenyleneimino-tetrakis-(dimethylamido)-cyclotriphosphazene]
(2) light-brown, transparent material
(3) H. Deibig, Battelle-Institut, Frankfurt/M.
(5) polycondensation of tetrakis(dimethylamido)-4,6-

dichlorocyclotriphosphazene with methylenedianiline
(6) H. Deibig, A. Dinkelaker, M. Sander, Angew. Makromol. Chem. *25* (1972) 179...85
(7) KBr (2/300)

841123333223　　　　　　　　　　$PC_{19}H_{13}O_4$　　　　　　　　　　1776

(1) phosphoric ester of an o-novolac
(2) white powder with 6.5% P
(3) B.F. Dannels, Central Research Department, Hooker Chemical Corp., Niagara Falls, N.Y.
(5) polycondensation (esterfication) of o,o'-novolac with

$C_6H_5OPOCl_2$; see also W.E. Cass, U.S. Pat. 2616873 (1952)
(6) B.F. Dannels, A.F. Shepard, J. Polym. Sci. A-1 *6* (1968) 2051...8
(7) ground with KBr (2/350) and CHCl₃, dried and pressed

842112   PC₁₂H₁₀N   1777

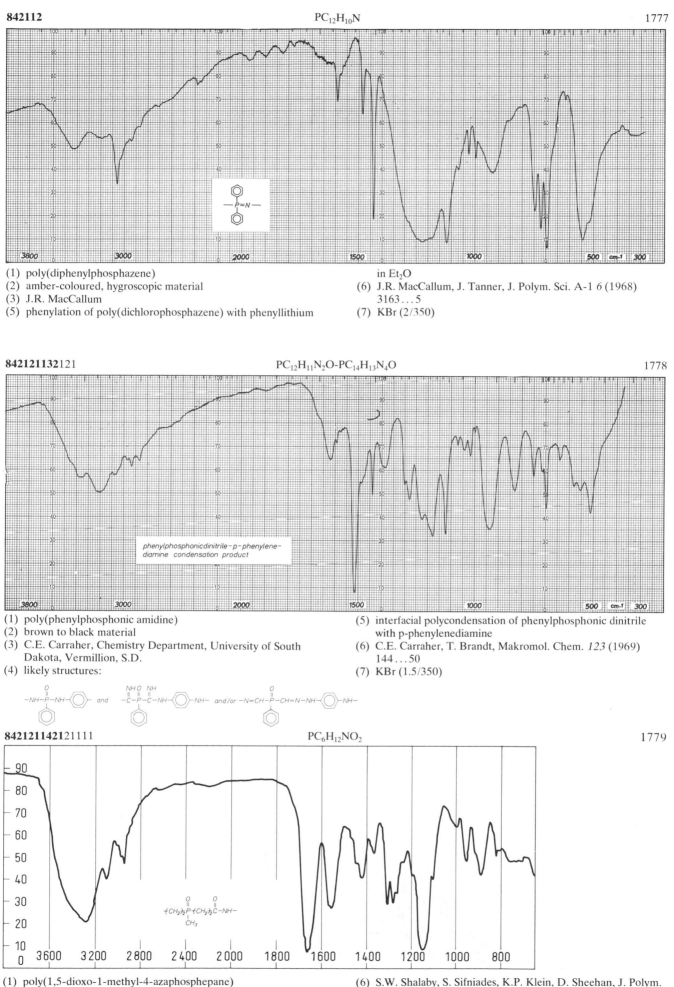

(1) poly(diphenylphosphazene)
(2) amber-coloured, hygroscopic material
(3) J.R. MacCallum
(5) phenylation of poly(dichlorophosphazene) with phenyllithium

in Et₂O
(6) J.R. MacCallum, J. Tanner, J. Polym. Sci. A-1 *6* (1968)
3163...5
(7) KBr (2/350)

842121132121   PC₁₂H₁₁N₂O-PC₁₄H₁₃N₄O   1778

phenylphosphonicdinitrile-p-phenylene-diamine condensation product

(1) poly(phenylphosphonic amidine)
(2) brown to black material
(3) C.E. Carraher, Chemistry Department, University of South Dakota, Vermillion, S.D.
(4) likely structures:

(5) interfacial polycondensation of phenylphosphonic dinitrile with p-phenylenediamine
(6) C.E. Carraher, T. Brandt, Makromol. Chem. *123* (1969) 144...50
(7) KBr (1.5/350)

842121142121111   PC₆H₁₂NO₂   1779

(1) poly(1,5-dioxo-1-methyl-4-azaphosphepane)
(5) polymerization of 1,5-dioxo-1-methyl-4-azaphosphepane in the presence of H₂O, SnCl₂ or phosphoric acid at temperatures above 200°C

(6) S.W. Shalaby, S. Sifniades, K.P. Klein, D. Sheehan, J. Polym. Sci.-Polym. Chem. Ed. *12* (1974) 2917...25
(7) film from trifluoroethanol solution
(8) spectrum by the authors

84212114371212 PC₂₈H₂₅O₇S₂ 1780

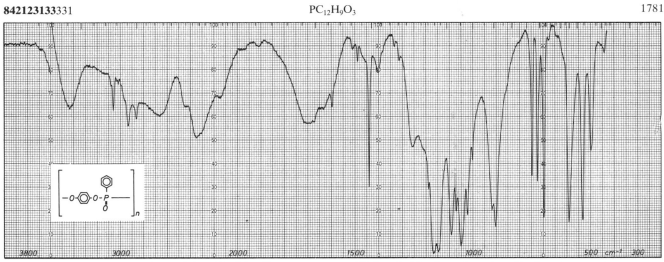

(1) polysulfonate from bisphenol A and bis(m-chlorosulfonylphenyl)methylphosphine oxide
(2) white powder
(3) J.E. Herweh, Research and Development Center, Armstrong Cork Comp., Lancaster, Penn.
(5) interfacial polycondensation of equimolar amounts of-

4,4'-isopropylidenediphenol and-bis(m-chlorosulfonylphenyl)methylphosphineoxide in-CH_2Cl_2/aqueous alkali
(6) J.L. Work, J.E. Herweh, J. Polym. Sci. A-1 *6* (1968) 2022...30
(7) film from $CHCl_3$ on CsI

842123133331 PC₁₂H₉O₃ 1781

(1) poly[oxy-1,4-phenyleneoxy)phenylphosphinylidene)]
(2) white powder
(3) F. Millich, Chemistry Department, Polymer Section, University of Missouri, Kansas City, Miss.

(5) interfacial polycondensation of hydroquinone and a phenylphosphonic dichloride in aqueous alkali/CCl_4
(6) F. Millich, C.E. Carraher, Macromolecules *3* (1970) 253...6
(7) KBr (1.5/300)

842123221112 PC₆H₁₃O₃ 1782

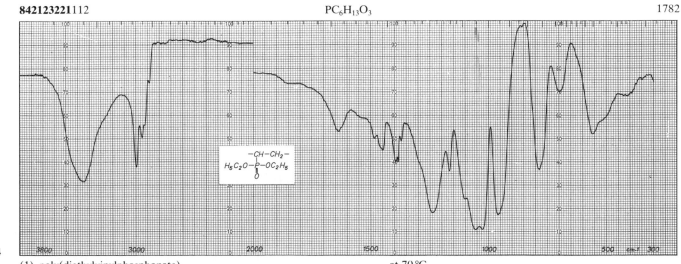

(1) poly(diethylvinylphosphonate)
(2) yellowish, light material
(3) N. Inagaki, Polymer Chemistry Section, Faculty of Engineering, Shizuoka University, Hamamatsu
(5) radical-initiated polymerization of the monomer with AIBN

at 70 °C
(6) N. Inagaki, K. Goto, K. Katsuura, Polymer *16* (1975) 641...4
(7) KBr (2/350)

842123221112   PC₁₀H₁₁O₃   1783

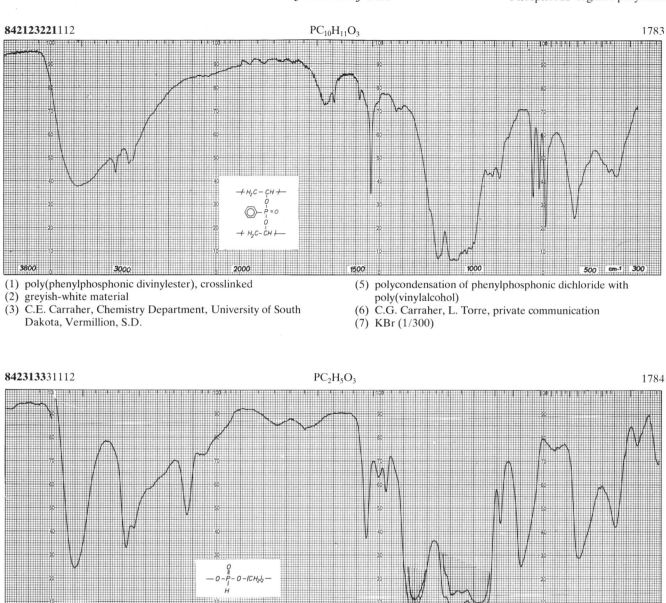

(1) poly(phenylphosphonic divinylester), crosslinked
(2) greyish-white material
(3) C.E. Carraher, Chemistry Department, University of South Dakota, Vermillion, S.D.

(5) polycondensation of phenylphosphonic dichloride with poly(vinylalcohol)
(6) C.G. Carraher, L. Torre, private communication
(7) KBr (1/300)

842313331112   PC₂H₅O₃   1784

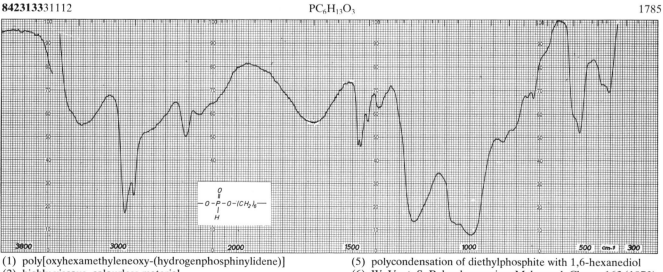

(1) poly[oxyethyleneoxy-(hydrogenphosphinylidene)]
(2) highyl viscous, colourless material
(3) W. Vogt, Organisch-Chemisches Institut der Universität Mainz, Mainz

(5) polycondensation of diethylphosphite with ethyleneglycol
(6) W. Vogt, S. Balasubramanian, Makromol. Chem. *163* (1973) 111...34
(7) film between CsI (25 μm)

842313331112   PC₆H₁₃O₃   1785

(1) poly[oxyhexamethyleneoxy-(hydrogenphosphinylidene)]
(2) highly viscous, colourless material
(3) W. Vogt, Organisch-Chemisches Institut der Universität Mainz, Mainz

(5) polycondensation of diethylphosphite with 1,6-hexanediol
(6) W. Vogt, S. Balasubramanian, Makromol. Chem. *163* (1973) 111...34
(7) film between CsI (25 μm)

842313331112   PC₈H₁₇O₃   1786

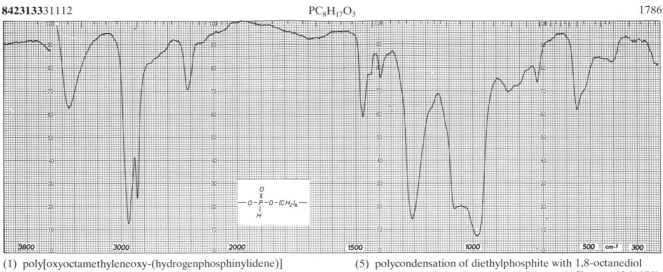

(1) poly[oxyoctamethyleneoxy-(hydrogenphosphinylidene)]
(2) highly viscous, colourless material
(3) W. Vogt, Organisch-Chemisches Institut der Universität Mainz, Mainz

(5) polycondensation of diethylphosphite with 1,8-octanediol
(6) W. Vogt, S. Balasubramanian, Makromol. Chem. *163* (1973) 111…34
(7) film between CsI (25 μm)

842411   PF₂N   1787

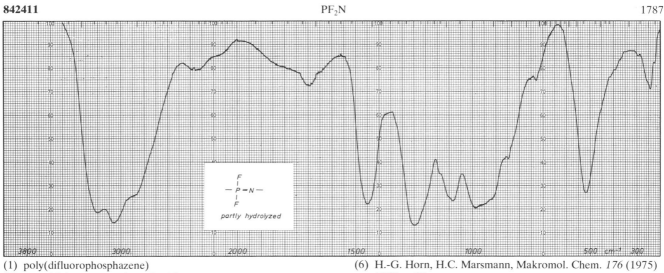

(1) poly(difluorophosphazene)
(2) greenish brown mass (not plastic)
(3) H.-G. Horn, Lehrstuhl für Anorganische Chemie II, Ruhr-Universität Bochum, Bochum
(5) thermal polymerization of hexafluorocyclotriphosphazene

(6) H.-G. Horn, H.C. Marsmann, Makromol. Chem. *176* (1975) 1359…67
(7) film from C₆F₆ on CsI
(8) the material was partly hydrolyzed

842421   PCl₂N   1788

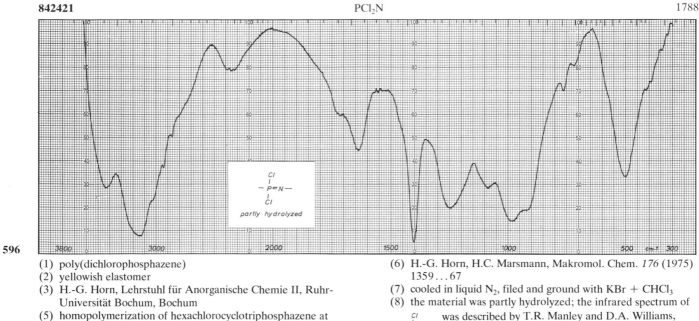

(1) poly(dichlorophosphazene)
(2) yellowish elastomer
(3) H.-G. Horn, Lehrstuhl für Anorganische Chemie II, Ruhr-Universität Bochum, Bochum
(5) homopolymerization of hexachlorocyclotriphosphazene at 300°C (12 h)

(6) H.-G. Horn, H.C. Marsmann, Makromol. Chem. *176* (1975) 1359…67
(7) cooled in liquid N₂, filed and ground with KBr + CHCl₃
(8) the material was partly hydrolyzed; the infrared spectrum of
    $-\overset{\underset{|}{Cl}}{\underset{|}{\underset{Cl}{P}}}=N-$ was described by T.R. Manley and D.A. Williams, Polymer *10* (1969) 307

84242332131   P₃C₁₈H₁₄Cl₂N₅   1789

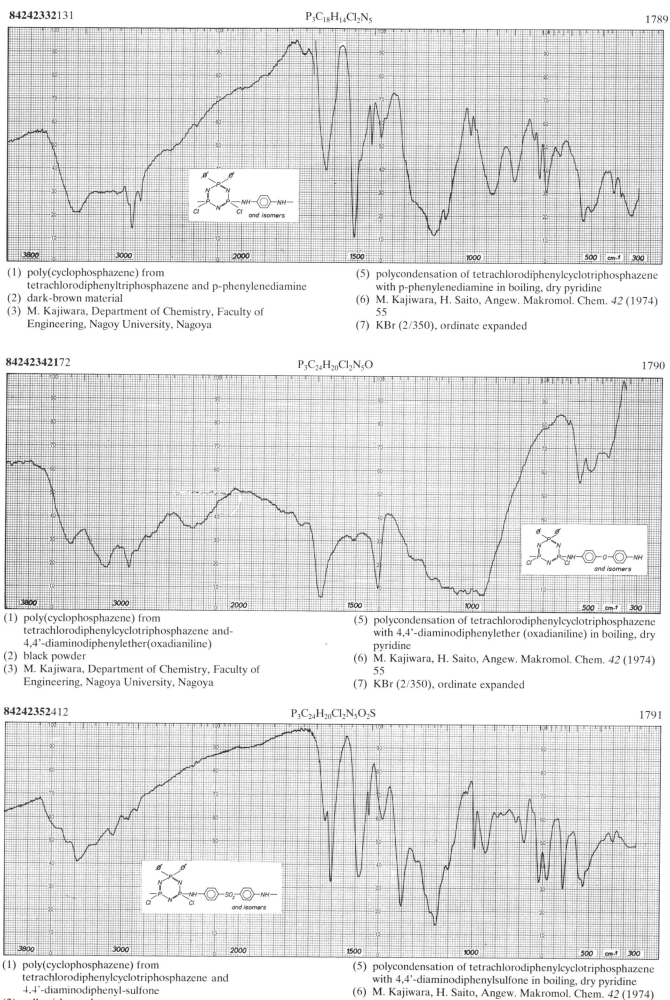

(1) poly(cyclophosphazene) from
     tetrachlorodiphenyltriphosphazene and p-phenylenediamine
(2) dark-brown material
(3) M. Kajiwara, Department of Chemistry, Faculty of
     Engineering, Nagoy University, Nagoya

(5) polycondensation of tetrachlorodiphenylcyclotriphosphazene
     with p-phenylenediamine in boiling, dry pyridine
(6) M. Kajiwara, H. Saito, Angew. Makromol. Chem. *42* (1974)
     55
(7) KBr (2/350), ordinate expanded

84242342172   P₃C₂₄H₂₀Cl₂N₅O   1790

(1) poly(cyclophosphazene) from
     tetrachlorodiphenylcyclotriphosphazene and-
     4,4'-diaminodiphenylether(oxadianiline)
(2) black powder
(3) M. Kajiwara, Department of Chemistry, Faculty of
     Engineering, Nagoya University, Nagoya

(5) polycondensation of tetrachlorodiphenylcyclotriphosphazene
     with 4,4'-diaminodiphenylether (oxadianiline) in boiling, dry
     pyridine
(6) M. Kajiwara, H. Saito, Angew. Makromol. Chem. *42* (1974)
     55
(7) KBr (2/350), ordinate expanded

84242352412   P₃C₂₄H₂₀Cl₂N₅O₂S   1791

(1) poly(cyclophosphazene) from
     tetrachlorodiphenylcyclotriphosphazene and
     4,4'-diaminodiphenyl-sulfone
(2) yellowish powder
(3) M. Kajiwara, Department of Chemistry, Faculty of
     Engineering, Nagoya University, Nagoya

(5) polycondensation of tetrachlorodiphenylcyclotriphosphazene
     with 4,4'-diaminodiphenylsulfone in boiling, dry pyridine
(6) M. Kajiwara, H. Saito, Angew. Makromol. Chem. *42* (1974)
     55
(7) KBr (1/350)

8425133 $PC_{24}H_{18}NO_2$ 1792

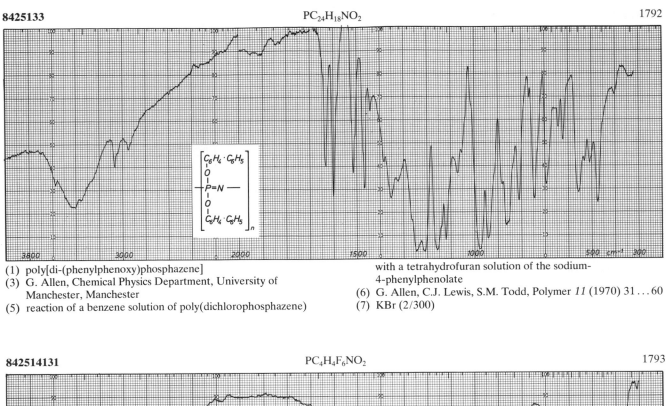

(1) poly[di-(phenylphenoxy)phosphazene]
(3) G. Allen, Chemical Physics Department, University of Manchester, Manchester
(5) reaction of a benzene solution of poly(dichlorophosphazene) with a tetrahydrofuran solution of the sodium-4-phenylphenolate
(6) G. Allen, C.J. Lewis, S.M. Todd, Polymer *11* (1970) 31...60
(7) KBr (2/300)

842514131 $PC_4H_4F_6NO_2$ 1793

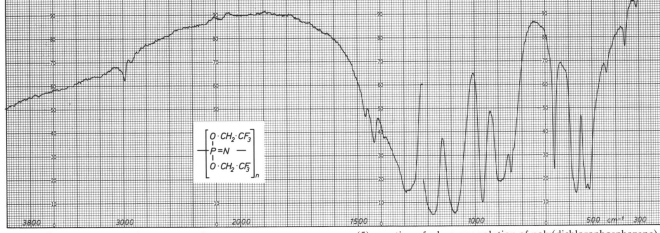

(1) poly[bis(trifluoroethoxy)phosphazene]
(2) white, fibrous material
(3) G. Allen, Chemical Physics Department, University of Manchester, Manchester
(5) reaction of a benzene solution of poly(dichlorophosphazene) with a tetrahydrofuran solution of 1,1,1-trifluoroethanol
(6) G. Allen, C.J. Lewis, S.M. Todd, Polymer *11* (1970) 31...60
(7) KBr (3/300)

842514131 $PC_7H_5F_{11}NO_2$ 1794

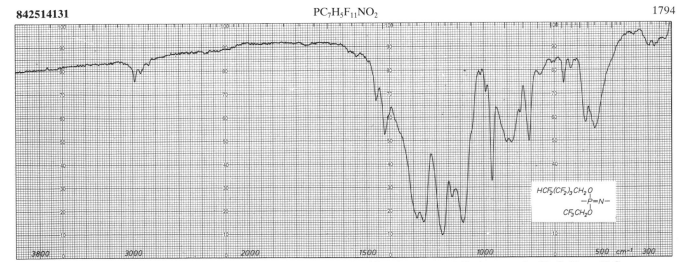

(1) poly(octafluoropentoxy-trifluoroethoxy-phosphazene)
(2) yellowish elastomer
(3) H.-G. Horn, Lehrstuhl für Anorganische Chemie II, Ruhr-Universität Bochum, Bochum
(6) private communication; see also H.-G. Horn, H.C. Marsmann, Makromol. Chem. *176* (1975) 1359...67
(7) swollen in benzene, spreaded on CsI and dried

842514132   PC₁₂H₁₀Cl₂NO₂   1795

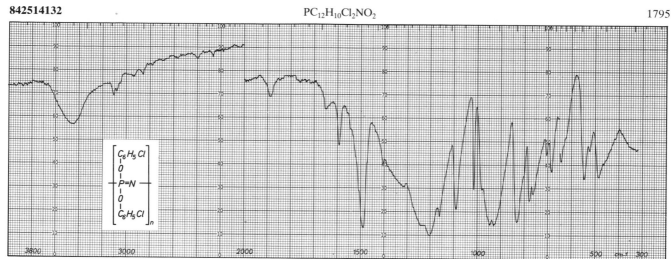

(1) poly[bis(p-chlorophenoxy)phosphazene]
(2) slightly brownish material
(3) G. Allen, Chemical Physics Department, University of Manchester, Manchester
(5) reaction of a benzene solution of poly(dichlorophosphazene)

with tetrahydrofuran solution of the sodium salt of-p-chlorophenol
(6) G. Allen, C.J. Lewis, S.M. Todd, Polymer *11* (1970) 31...60
(7) KBr (2/300)

8425141323212   P₃C₂₉H₄₈Cl₂N₇O₄   1796

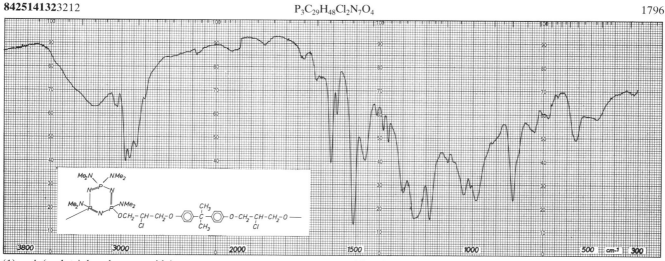

(1) poly(cyclotriphosphazeneamide)
(2) brown resin
(3) H. Deibig, Battelle-Institut, Frankfurt/Main
(5) polycondensation of 2,2,4,6-tetrakis-(dimethylamido)-4,6-dichlorocyclotriphosphazene with "Epikote 828"

(6) private communication; see also H. Deibig, A. Dinkelaker,M. Sander, Angew. Makromol. Chem. *25* (1972) 179...85
(7) KBr (4/300)

8425141323212   1797

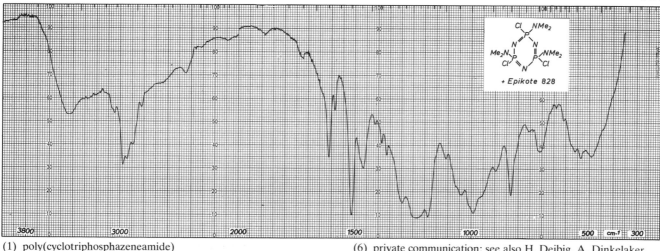

(1) poly(cyclotriphosphazeneamide)
(2) brown resin
(3) H. Deibig, Battelle-Institut, Frankfurt/Main
(5) polycondensation of 2,4,6–tris–(dimethylamido)-2,4,6-trichlorocyclotriphosphazene with "Epikote 828" (2:3)

(6) private communication; see also H. Deibig, A. Dinkelaker, M. Sander, Angew. Makromol. Chem. *25* (1972) 179...85
(7) KBr (3/300)

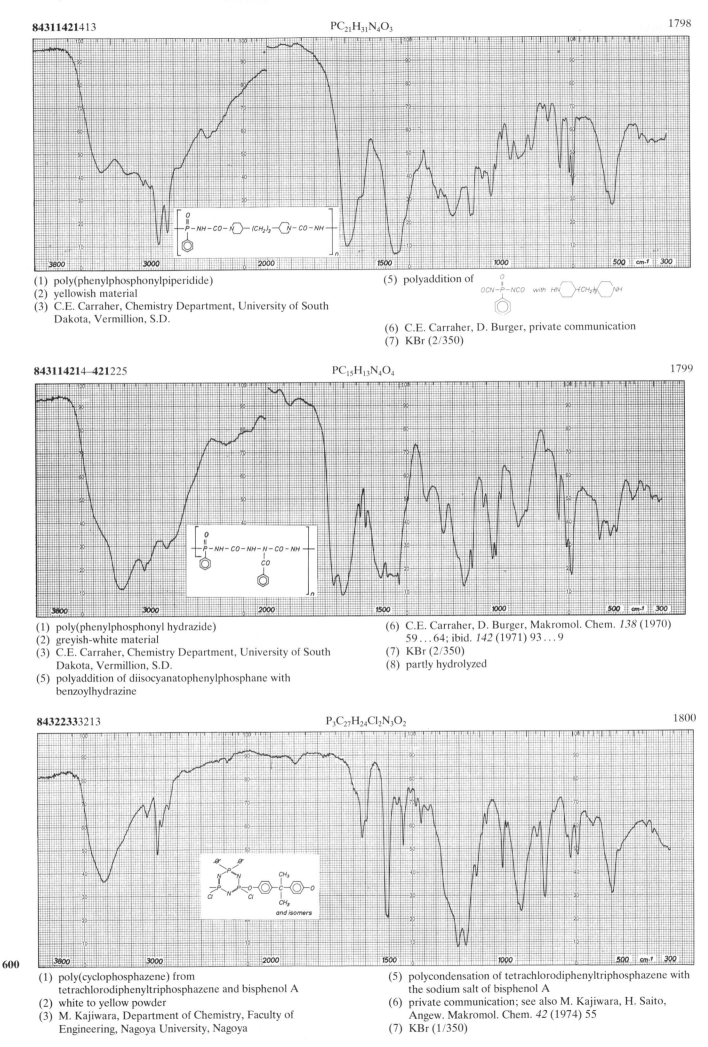

84311421413   PC₂₁H₃₁N₄O₃   1798

(1) poly(phenylphosphonylpiperidide)
(2) yellowish material
(3) C.E. Carraher, Chemistry Department, University of South
     Dakota, Vermillion, S.D.

(5) polyaddition of

(6) C.E. Carraher, D. Burger, private communication
(7) KBr (2/350)

843114214–421225   PC₁₅H₁₃N₄O₄   1799

(1) poly(phenylphosphonyl hydrazide)
(2) greyish-white material
(3) C.E. Carraher, Chemistry Department, University of South
     Dakota, Vermillion, S.D.
(5) polyaddition of diisocyanatophenylphosphane with
     benzoylhydrazine

(6) C.E. Carraher, D. Burger, Makromol. Chem. *138* (1970)
     59...64; ibid. *142* (1971) 93...9
(7) KBr (2/350)
(8) partly hydrolyzed

84322333213   P₃C₂₇H₂₄Cl₂N₃O₂   1800

(1) poly(cyclophosphazene) from
     tetrachlorodiphenyltriphosphazene and bisphenol A
(2) white to yellow powder
(3) M. Kajiwara, Department of Chemistry, Faculty of
     Engineering, Nagoya University, Nagoya

(5) polycondensation of tetrachlorodiphenyltriphosphazene with
     the sodium salt of bisphenol A
(6) private communication; see also M. Kajiwara, H. Saito,
     Angew. Makromol. Chem. *42* (1974) 55
(7) KBr (1/350)

8432233331   P₃C₁₈H₁₄Cl₂N₃O₂   1801

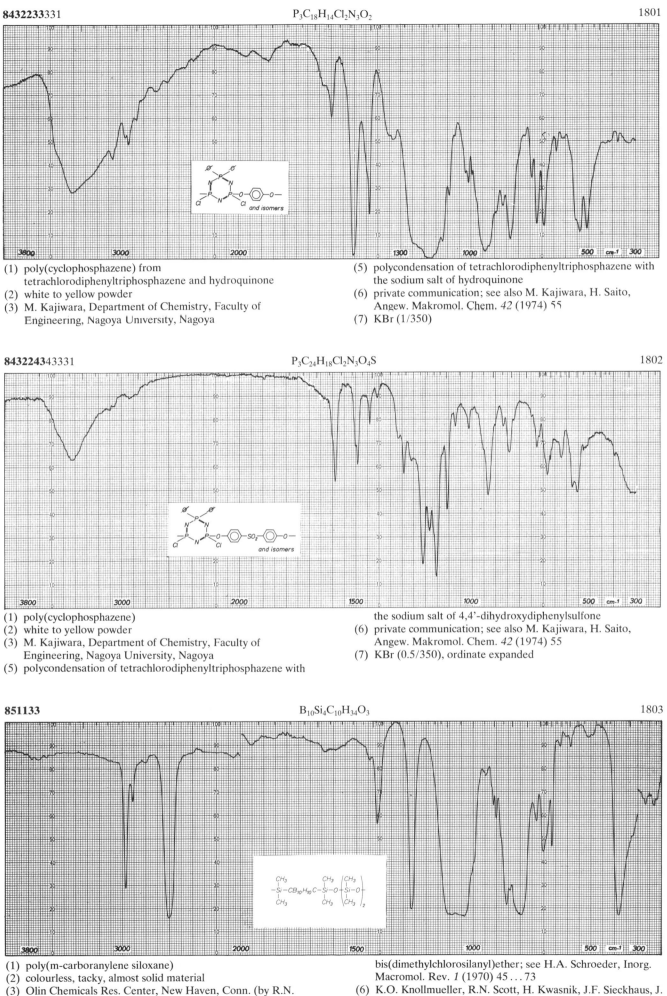

(1) poly(cyclophosphazene) from tetrachlorodiphenyltriphosphazene and hydroquinone
(2) white to yellow powder
(3) M. Kajiwara, Department of Chemistry, Faculty of Engineering, Nagoya University, Nagoya

(5) polycondensation of tetrachlorodiphenyltriphosphazene with the sodium salt of hydroquinone
(6) private communication; see also M. Kajiwara, H. Saito, Angew. Makromol. Chem. *42* (1974) 55
(7) KBr (1/350)

843224343331   P₃C₂₄H₁₈Cl₂N₃O₄S   1802

(1) poly(cyclophosphazene)
(2) white to yellow powder
(3) M. Kajiwara, Department of Chemistry, Faculty of Engineering, Nagoya University, Nagoya
(5) polycondensation of tetrachlorodiphenyltriphosphazene with

the sodium salt of 4,4'-dihydroxydiphenylsulfone
(6) private communication; see also M. Kajiwara, H. Saito, Angew. Makromol. Chem. *42* (1974) 55
(7) KBr (0.5/350), ordinate expanded

851133   B₁₀Si₄C₁₀H₃₄O₃   1803

(1) poly(m-carboranylene siloxane)
(2) colourless, tacky, almost solid material
(3) Olin Chemicals Res. Center, New Haven, Conn. (by R.N. Scott)
(5) condensation of bis(dimethylchlorosilanyl)-m-carborane with methanol(-HCl), polycondensation of the resulting bis(dimethylmethoxysilanyl)-m-carborane with

bis(dimethylchlorosilanyl)ether; see H.A. Schroeder, Inorg. Macromol. Rev. *1* (1970) 45...73
(6) K.O. Knollmueller, R.N. Scott, H. Kwasnik, J.F. Sieckhaus, J. Polym. Sci. A-1 *9* (1971) 1071...88; H.A. Schroeder, Inorg. Macromol. Rev. *1* (1970) 45...73
(7) film on CsI
(8) commercial "Dexsil 300"

851133 $B_{10}Si_5C_{17}H_{42}O_4$ 1804

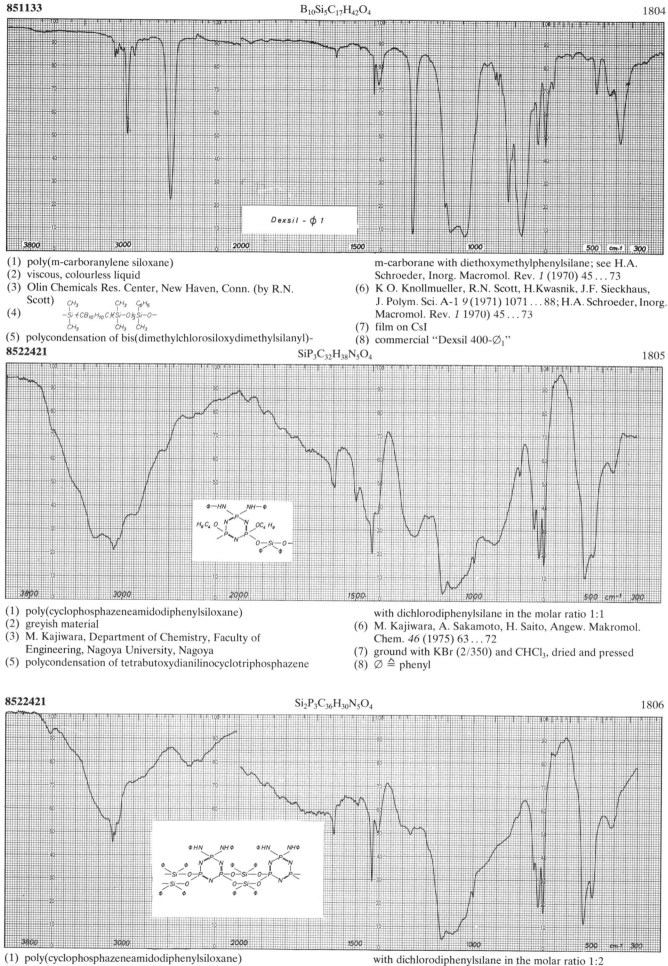

Dexsil - φ 1

(1) poly(m-carboranylene siloxane)
(2) viscous, colourless liquid
(3) Olin Chemicals Res. Center, New Haven, Conn. (by R.N. Scott)
(4)
(5) polycondensation of bis(dimethylchlorosiloxydimethylsilanyl)-

m-carborane with diethoxymethylphenylsilane; see H.A. Schroeder, Inorg. Macromol. Rev. *1* (1970) 45...73
(6) K.O. Knollmueller, R.N. Scott, H.Kwasnik, J.F. Sieckhaus, J. Polym. Sci. A-1 *9* (1971) 1071...88; H.A. Schroeder, Inorg. Macromol. Rev. *1* 1970) 45...73
(7) film on CsI
(8) commercial "Dexsil 400-$\varnothing_1$"

8522421 $SiP_3C_{32}H_{38}N_5O_4$ 1805

(1) poly(cyclophosphazeneamidodiphenylsiloxane)
(2) greyish material
(3) M. Kajiwara, Department of Chemistry, Faculty of Engineering, Nagoya University, Nagoya
(5) polycondensation of tetrabutoxydianilinocyclotriphosphazene

with dichlorodiphenylsilane in the molar ratio 1:1
(6) M. Kajiwara, A. Sakamoto, H. Saito, Angew. Makromol. Chem. *46* (1975) 63...72
(7) ground with KBr (2/350) and CHCl₃, dried and pressed
(8) $\varnothing \triangleq$ phenyl

8522421 $Si_2P_3C_{36}H_{30}N_5O_4$ 1806

(1) poly(cyclophosphazeneamidodiphenylsiloxane)
(2) brown material
(3) M. Kajiwara, Department of Chemistry, Faculty of Engineering, Nagoya University, Nagoya
(5) polycondensation of tetrabutoxydianilinocyclotriphosphazene

with dichlorodiphenylsilane in the molar ratio 1:2
(6) M. Kajiwara, A. Sakamoto, H. Saito, Angew. Makromol. Chem. *46* (1975) 63...72
(7) ground with KBr (2/350) and CHCl₃, dried and pressed
(8) $\varnothing \triangleq$ phenyl

8642133 $P_2BeC_{16}H_{36}O_4$ 1807

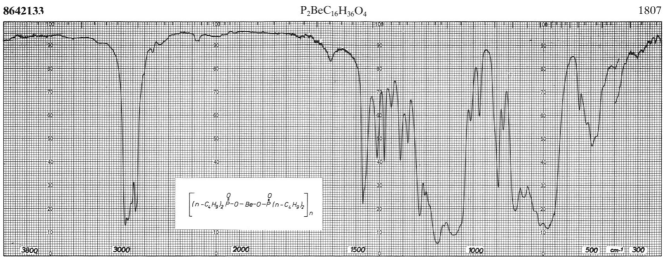

(1) poly(beryllium-di-n-butylphosphinate)
(2) colourless, plastic material
(3) V. Giancotti, Univ. degli Studi di Trieste, Trieste
(5) polyaddition of di-n-butylphosphinic acid (Na salt) and $Be(NO_3)_2 \cdot 4\,H_2O$

(6) V. Gomiti, V. Giancotti, A. Ripamonti, J. chem. Soc. (Lond.) (A) *1968*, 763; V. Giancotti, F. Giordano, A. Ripamonti, Makromol. Chem. *120* (1968) 96...102
(7) film from $CHCl_3$ on CsI

8614121 $B_{10}SnC_4H_{16}$ 1808

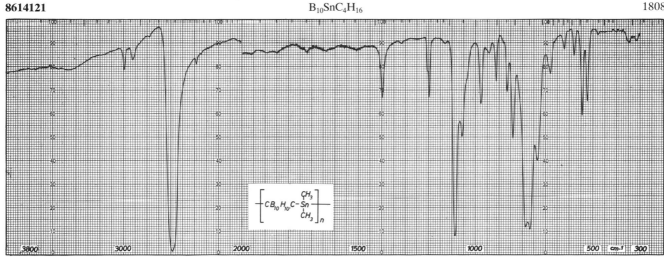

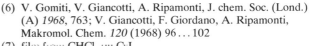

(1) poly(dimethyltin-p-carborane)
(2) white powder
(3) Olin Chemicals Research Center, New Haven, Conn. (by R.N. Scott)
(5) polycondensation of the di-lithium salt of p-carborane with dimethyltin dichloride

(6) H.A. Schroeder, S. Papetti, R.P. Alexander, J.F. Sieckhaus, T.L. Heying, Inorg. Chem. *8* (1969) 2444...9; H.A. Schroeder, Inorg. Makromol. Rev. *1* (1970) 45...73
(7) KBr (2/350)
(8) commercial sample TB-I

91237 $CuC_{24}N_8S_4$ 1809

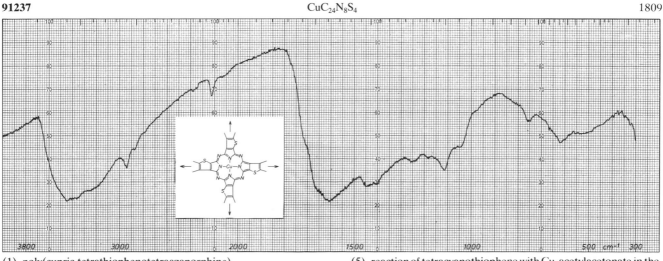

(1) poly(cupric tetrathiophenotetraazaporphine)
(2) black powder
(3) G. Manecke, Institut für Organische Chemie der freien Universität Berlin, Berlin-Dahlem

(5) reaction of tetracyanothiophene with Cu-acetylacetonate in the molar ratio 2:1 at 200 °C
(7) KBr (1/350)

912421 $CuC_8H_5N_2O_2/2Cl^-$ 1810

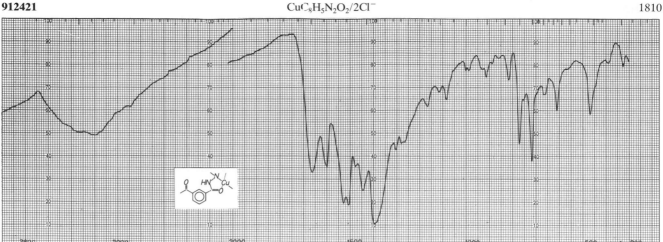

(1) poly(isophthaloylhydrazide), chelated with CuCl$_2$
(2) black powder
(3) J.J. Lindberg, Department of Wood and Polymer Chemistry, University of Helsinki, Helsinki
(5) reaction of poly(isophthaloylhydrazide) with CuCl$_2$

(6) private communication; see also A. Lehtinen, S. Purokoski, J.J. Lindberg, Makromol. Chem. *176* (1975) 1553...66
(7) KBr
(8) the 2 Cl$^-$ ions have been left out in the structural formula

912421 $CuC_8H_5N_2O_2/2Cl^- - C_6H_8N_2$ 1811

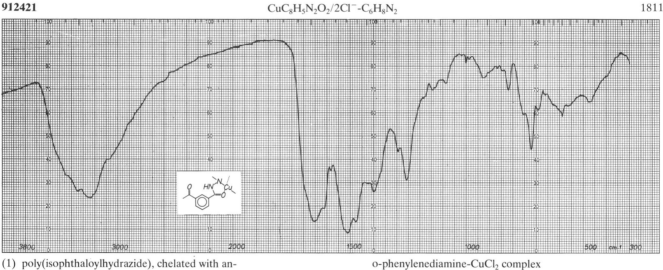

(1) poly(isophthaloylhydrazide), chelated with an-o-phenylenediamine-CuCl$_2$ complex
(2) dark-brown powder
(3) J.J. Lindberg, Department of Wood and Polymer Chemistry, University of Helsinki, Helsinki
(5) reaction of poly(isophthaloylhydrazide) with an-

o-phenylenediamine-CuCl$_2$ complex
(6) private communication; see also A. Lehtinen, S. Purokoski, J.J. Lindberg, Makromol. Chem. *176* (1975) 1553...66
(7) KBr (1/350)
(8) the o-phenylenediamine residue as well as the 2 Cl$^-$ have been left out of the structural formula

912421 $CuC_{16}H_{11}N_4O_4$ 1812

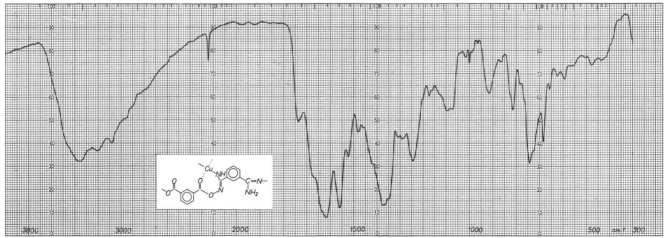

(1) poly(O-isophthaloylisophthalamide oxime), chelated with CuCl$_2$
(2) greyish-green powder
(3) J.J. Lindberg, Department of Wood and Polymer Chemistry, University of Helsinki, Helsinki
(5) addition of an aqueous solution of CuCl$_2$ to a solution of poly(O-isophthaloylisophthalamide oxime) in-

N-methylpyrrolidone, reaction at room temperature, precipitation with methanol or water
(6) A. Lehtinen, S. Purokoski, J.J. Lindberg, Makromol. Chem. *176* (1975) 1553...66
(7) KBr (1.5/350)
(8) the 2 Cl$^-$ ions have been left out of the structural formula

912421 $CuC_{21}H_{13}N_3O_4$ 1813

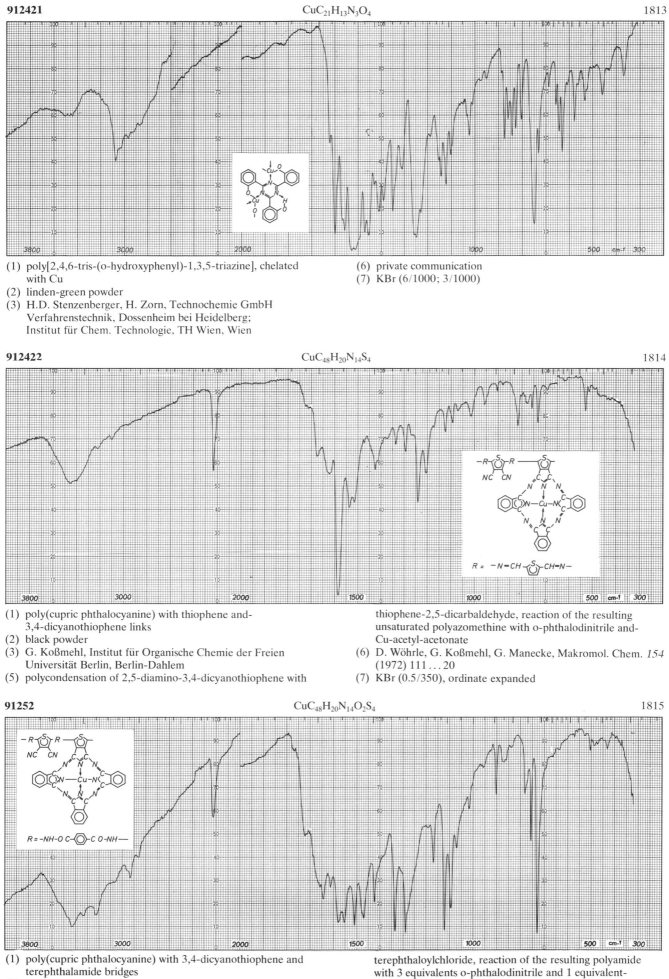

(1) poly[2,4,6-tris-(o-hydroxyphenyl)-1,3,5-triazine], chelated
with Cu
(2) linden-green powder
(3) H.D. Stenzenberger, H. Zorn, Technochemie GmbH
Verfahrenstechnik, Dossenheim bei Heidelberg;
Institut für Chem. Technologie, TH Wien, Wien

(6) private communication
(7) KBr (6/1000; 3/1000)

912422 $CuC_{48}H_{20}N_{14}S_4$ 1814

(1) poly(cupric phthalocyanine) with thiophene and-
3,4-dicyanothiophene links
(2) black powder
(3) G. Koßmehl, Institut für Organische Chemie der Freien
Universität Berlin, Berlin-Dahlem
(5) polycondensation of 2,5-diamino-3,4-dicyanothiophene with

thiophene-2,5-dicarbaldehyde, reaction of the resulting
unsaturated polyazomethine with o-phthalodinitrile and-
Cu-acetyl-acetonate
(6) D. Wöhrle, G. Koßmehl, G. Manecke, Makromol. Chem. *154*
(1972) 111...20
(7) KBr (0.5/350), ordinate expanded

91252 $CuC_{48}H_{20}N_{14}O_2S_4$ 1815

(1) poly(cupric phthalocyanine) with 3,4-dicyanothiophene and
terephthalamide bridges
(2) blue-black powder
(3) G. Koßmehl, Institut für Organische Chemie der Freien
Universität Berlin, Berlin-Dahlem
(5) polycondensation of 2,5-diamino-3,4-dicyanothiophene with

terephthaloylchloride, reaction of the resulting polyamide
with 3 equivalents o-phthalodinitrile and 1 equivalent-
Cu-acetyl-acetonate (200 °C, then 250 °C)
(6) D. Wöhrle, G. Koßmehl, G. Manecke, Makromol. Chem. *154*
(1972) 111...20
(7) KBr (0.5/350); ordinate expanded

922421 · ZnC$_{21}$H$_{13}$N$_3$O$_4$ · 1816

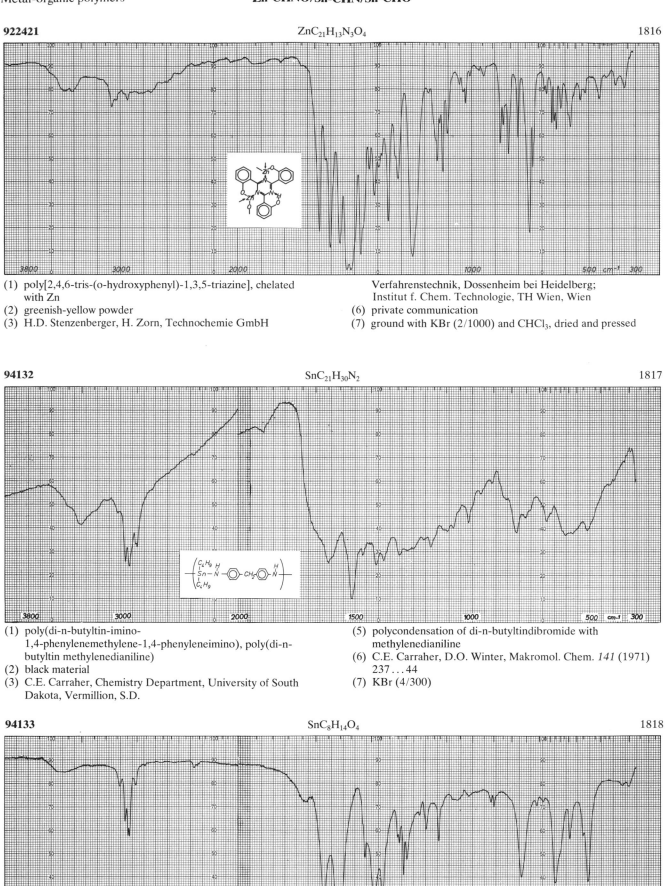

(1) poly[2,4,6-tris-(o-hydroxyphenyl)-1,3,5-triazine], chelated
with Zn
(2) greenish-yellow powder
(3) H.D. Stenzenberger, H. Zorn, Technochemie GmbH

Verfahrenstechnik, Dossenheim bei Heidelberg;
Institut f. Chem. Technologie, TH Wien, Wien
(6) private communication
(7) ground with KBr (2/1000) and CHCl$_3$, dried and pressed

94132 · SnC$_{21}$H$_{30}$N$_2$ · 1817

(1) poly(di-n-butyltin-imino-
1,4-phenylenemethylene-1,4-phenyleneimino), poly(di-n-
butyltin methylenedianiline)
(2) black material
(3) C.E. Carraher, Chemistry Department, University of South
Dakota, Vermillion, S.D.

(5) polycondensation of di-n-butyltindibromide with
methylenedianiline
(6) C.E. Carraher, D.O. Winter, Makromol. Chem. *141* (1971)
237...44
(7) KBr (4/300)

94133 · SnC$_8$H$_{14}$O$_4$ · 1818

(1) poly(dimethyltin adipate)
(2) colourless material
(3) C.E. Carraher, Dept. of Chemistry, Univ. of South Dakota,
Vermillion, S.D.
(5) interfacial polycondensation of dimethyltin dichloride and

sodium adipate
(6) C.E. Carraher, R.L. Dammeier, Makromol. Chem. *135*
(1970) 107...12
(7) KBr (1/300)

94133 SnC$_{14}$H$_{26}$O$_4$ 1819

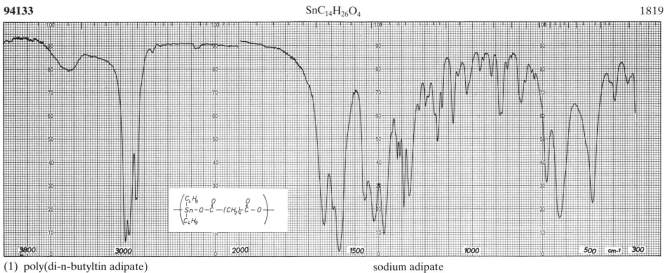

(1) poly(di-n-butyltin adipate)
(2) white material
(3) C.E. Carraher, Chemistry Department, University of South Dakota, Vermillion, S.D.
(5) interfacial polycondensation of di-n-butyltin dichloride with

sodium adipate
(6) C.E. Carraher, R.L. Dammeier, Makromol. Chem. *135* (1970) 107...12
(7) KBr (2.5/300)

94133 SnC$_{22}$H$_{42}$O$_4$ 1820

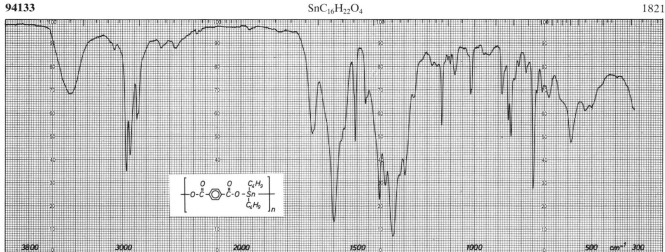

(1) poly(di-n-octyltin adipate)
(2) white material
(3) C.E. Carraher, Chemistry Department, University of South Dakota, Vermillion, S.D.
(5) interfacial polycondensation of di-n-octyltin dichloride with

sodium adipate
(6) C.E. Carraher, R.L. Dammeier, Makromol. Chem. *135* (1970) 107...12
(7) KBr (2/300)

94133 SnC$_{16}$H$_{22}$O$_4$ 1821

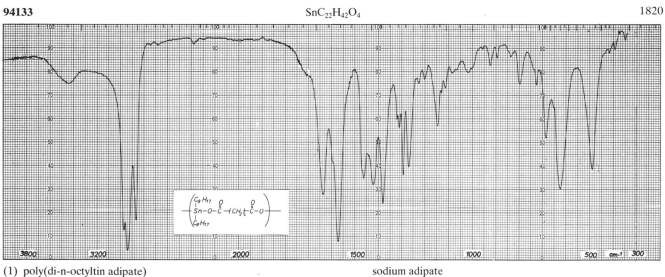

(1) poly(di-n-butyltin terephthalate)
(2) white material
(3) S. D. Bruck, Chem. Engng. Dept., The Catholic University of America, Washington, D.C.

(5) low-temperature polycondensation of alkali terephthalate and dialkyltin dihalide
(6) S.D. Bruck, J. Polymer Sci. A-1 *7* (1969) 781
(7) KBr (1/350)

941421 $SnC_{34}H_{16}N_8O_2$ 1822

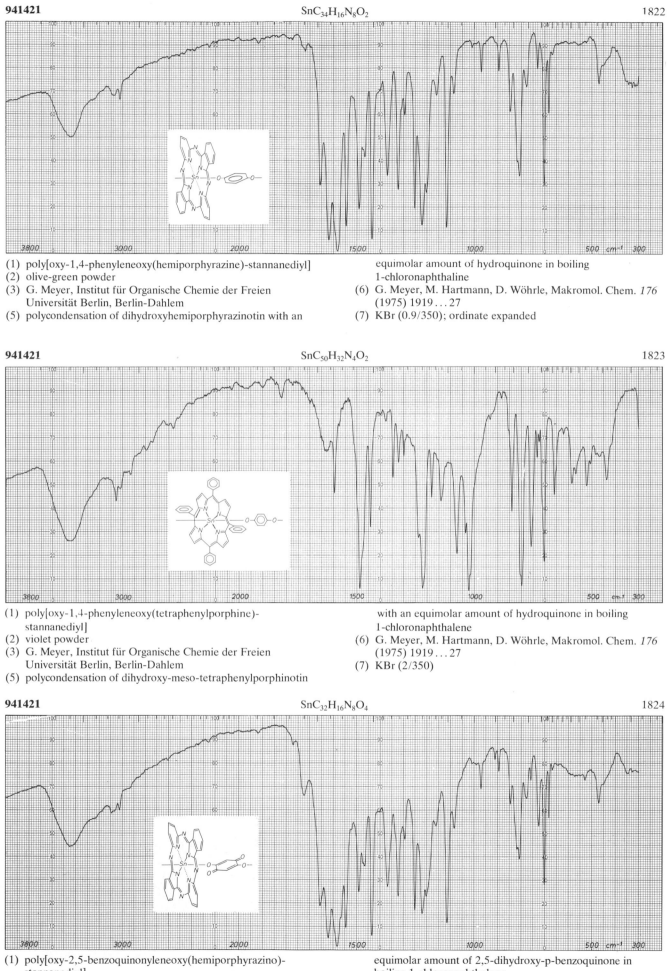

(1) poly[oxy-1,4-phenyleneoxy(hemiporphyrazine)-stannanediyl]
(2) olive-green powder
(3) G. Meyer, Institut für Organische Chemie der Freien
    Universität Berlin, Berlin-Dahlem
(5) polycondensation of dihydroxyhemiporphyrazinotin with an

equimolar amount of hydroquinone in boiling
1-chloronaphthaline
(6) G. Meyer, M. Hartmann, D. Wöhrle, Makromol. Chem. *176*
    (1975) 1919...27
(7) KBr (0.9/350); ordinate expanded

941421 $SnC_{50}H_{32}N_4O_2$ 1823

(1) poly[oxy-1,4-phenyleneoxy(tetraphenylporphine)-
    stannanediyl]
(2) violet powder
(3) G. Meyer, Institut für Organische Chemie der Freien
    Universität Berlin, Berlin-Dahlem
(5) polycondensation of dihydroxy-meso-tetraphenylporphinotin

with an equimolar amount of hydroquinone in boiling
1-chloronaphthalene
(6) G. Meyer, M. Hartmann, D. Wöhrle, Makromol. Chem. *176*
    (1975) 1919...27
(7) KBr (2/350)

941421 $SnC_{32}H_{16}N_8O_4$ 1824

(1) poly[oxy-2,5-benzoquinonyleneoxy(hemiporphyrazino)-
    stannanediyl]
(2) black powder
(3) G. Meyer, Institut für Organische Chemie der Freien
    Universität Berlin, Berlin-Dahlem
(5) polycondensation of dihydroxyhemiporphyrazinotin with an

equimolar amount of 2,5-dihydroxy-p-benzoquinone in
boiling 1-chloronaphthalene
(6) G. Meyer, M. Hartmann, D. Wöhrle, Makromol. Chem. *176*
    (1975) 1919...27
(7) KBr (1/350)

941421   SnC$_{50}$H$_{30}$N$_4$O$_4$ **1825**

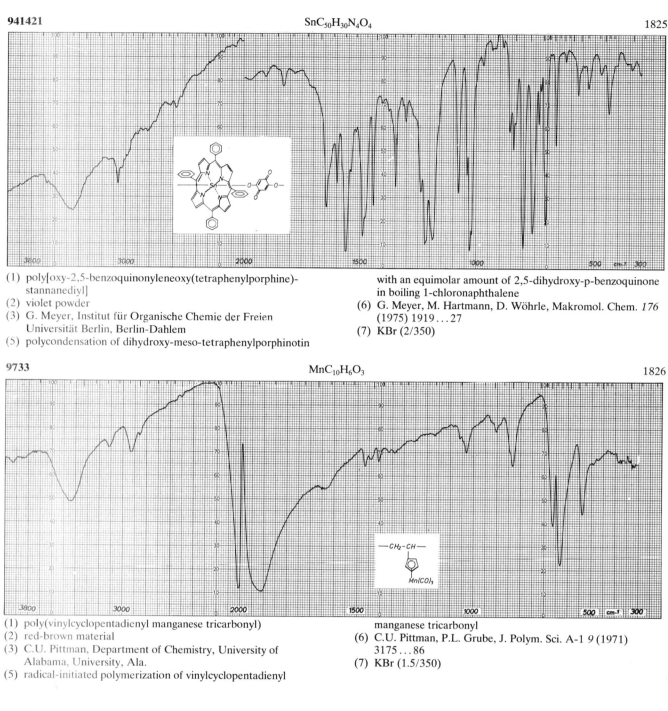

(1) poly[oxy-2,5-benzoquinonyleneoxy(tetraphenylporphine)-
    stannanediyl]
(2) violet powder
(3) G. Meyer, Institut für Organische Chemie der Freien
    Universität Berlin, Berlin-Dahlem
(5) polycondensation of dihydroxy-meso-tetraphenylporphinotin

with an equimolar amount of 2,5-dihydroxy-p-benzoquinone
in boiling 1-chloronaphthalene
(6) G. Meyer, M. Hartmann, D. Wöhrle, Makromol. Chem. *176*
    (1975) 1919...27
(7) KBr (2/350)

9733   MnC$_{10}$H$_6$O$_3$ **1826**

(1) poly(vinylcyclopentadienyl manganese tricarbonyl)
(2) red-brown material
(3) C.U. Pittman, Department of Chemistry, University of
    Alabama, University, Ala.
(5) radical-initiated polymerization of vinylcyclopentadienyl

manganese tricarbonyl
(6) C.U. Pittman, P.L. Grube, J. Polym. Sci. A-1 *9* (1971)
    3175...86
(7) KBr (1.5/350)

9733–2122111   MnC$_{10}$H$_6$O$_3$-C$_8$H$_8$ **1827**

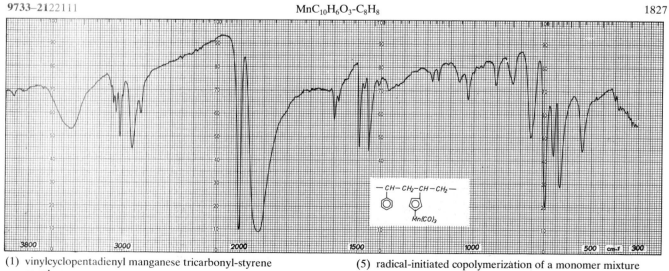

(1) vinylcyclopentadienyl manganese tricarbonyl-styrene
    copolymer
(2) light-brown material
(3) C.U. Pittman, Department of Chemistry, University of
    Alabama, University, Ala.

(5) radical-initiated copolymerization of a monomer mixture
(6) private communication; see also C.U. Pittman, P.L. Grube,
    J. Polym. Sci. A-1 *9* (1971) 3175...86
(7) KBr (1.5/350)

98121 $FeC_{12}H_{12}$ 1828

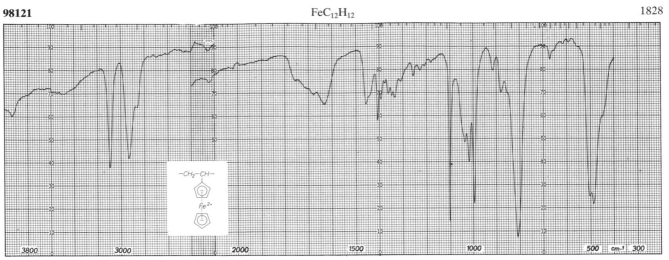

(1) poly(vinylferrocene)
(2) yellow-orange powder
(3) Ch. Aso, Department of Organic Synthesis, Faculty of Engineering, Kyushu University, Fukuoka

(5) cationic Friedel-Crafts polymerization of vinylferrocene
(6) Ch. Aso, T. Kunitake, T. Nakashima, Makromol. Chem. *124* (1969) 232...40
(7) KBr (3/300)

98121–3372211 $FeC_{12}H_{12}\text{-}C_4H_6O_2$ 1829

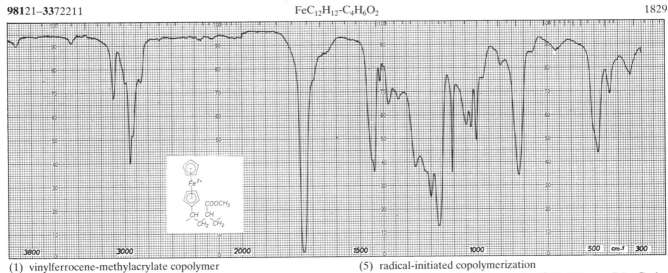

(1) vinylferrocene-methylacrylate copolymer
(2) orange-coloured powder
(3) C.U. Pittman, Department of Chemistry, University of Alabama, University, Ala.

(5) radical-initiated copolymerization
(6) private communication; see also C.U. Pittman, P.L. Grube, J. Polym. Sci. A-1 *9* (1971) 3175...86
(7) film from $CHCl_3$ on CsI

98121 $FeC_{14}H_{10}$ 1830

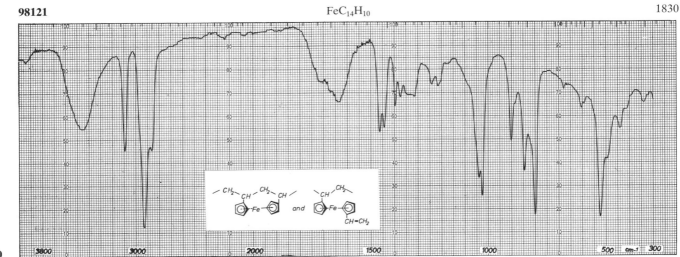

(1) poly(1,1'-divinylferrocene)
(2) yellow powder
(3) T. Kunitake, Department of Organic Synthesis, Faculty of Engineering, Kyushu University, Fukuoka
(5) cyclopolymerization of 1,1'-divinylferrocene with AIBN in

benzene at 80 °C
(6) T. Kunitake, T. Nakashima, Ch. Aso, J. Polym. Sci. A-1 *8* (1970) 2853; see also Makromol. Chem. *146* (1971) 79...90
(7) KBr (3/300)

98121   FeC₁₂H₁₀   1831

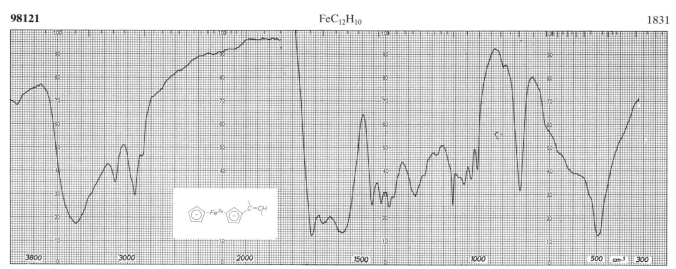

(1) poly(ferrocenylacetylene)
(2) brown powder
(3) G. Simionescu, Institutul Politehnic, Academia Republicii
    Socialiste România, Iasi
(5) radical-initiated polymerization of ferrocenylacetylene in the

presence of dibenzoylperoxide
(6) C. Simionescu, Tatiana Lixandru, I. Mazilu, Lucia Tătaru,
    Makromol. Chem. *147* (1971) 69 . . . 78
(7) ground with KBr (4/350) and acetone, dried and pressed

98121   FeC₁₄H₁₀   1832

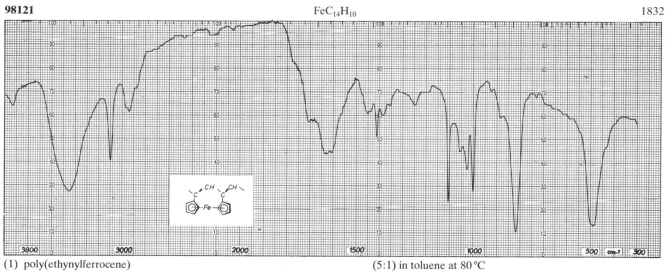

(1) poly(ethynylferrocene)
(2) dark-brown powder
(3) T. Kunitake, Department of Organic Synthesis, Faculty of
    Engineering, Kyushu University, Fukuoka
(5) polymerization of ethynylferrocene with Al(i-butyl)₃/Ti(OBu)₄

(5:1) in toluene at 80 °C
(6) T. Kunitake, T. Nakashima, Ch. Aso, Makromol. Chem. *146*
    (1871) 79 . . . 90; see also J. Polym. Sci. A-1 *8* (1970) 2853
(7) KBr (3/350)

211131–98121–81322   C₅H₈-FeC₁₀H₈-BC₆H₅   1833

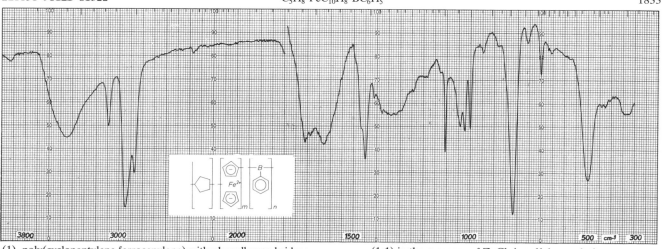

(1) poly(cyclopentylene ferrocenylene) with phenylboron bridges
(2) deep-brown powder
(3) E.W. Neuse, Polymer Laboratory, Missile & Space Systems
    Div., Douglas Aircraft Comp., Santa Monica, Calif.
(4) i:m:n: = 11:8:3
(5) copolycondensation of ferrocene and phenylborondichloride

(1:1) in the presence of ZnCl₂ in sulfolane solution
(6) E.W. Neuse, J. Macromol. Sci.-chem. *A2* (4) (1968) 751 . . . 9
(7) KBr (2/350); ordinate expanded between 1800 cm⁻¹ and
    300 cm⁻¹
(8) sample 3 in table 1 of the refered publication

98133 $FeC_{14}H_{14}O_2$ 1834

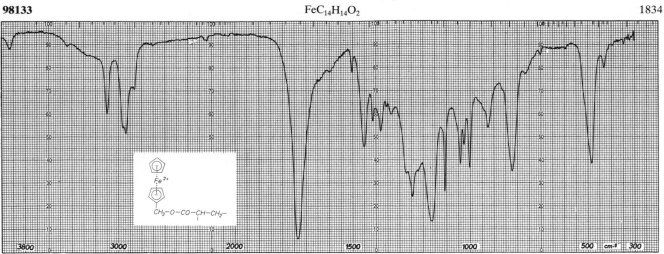

(1) poly(ferrocenyl methylacrylate)
(2) orange-brown material
(3) C.U. Pittman, Department of Chemistry, University of Alabama, University, Ala.
(5) radical-initiated polymerization
(6) private communication; see also C.U. Pittman, P.L. Grube, J. Polym. Sci. A-1 *9* (1971) 3175...86
(7) film from $CHCl_3$ on CsI

98133 $FeC_{15}H_{16}O_2$ 1835

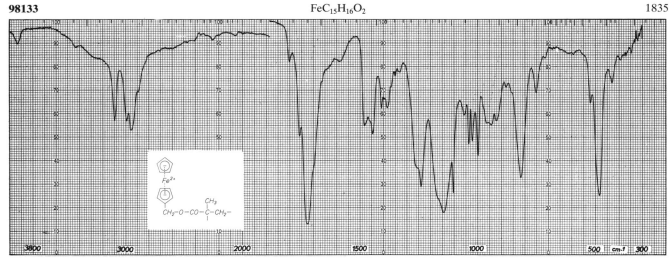

(1) poly(ferrocenyl methylmethacrylate)
(2) brown material
(3) C.U. Pittman, Department of Chemistry, University of Alabama, University, Ala.
(5) radical-initiated polymerization
(6) private communication; see also C. U. Pittmann, P. L. Grube, J. Polym. Sci. A-1 *9* (1971) 3175...86
(7) film from $CHCl_3$ on CsI

98221–81322 $RuC_{15}H_{16}\text{-}BC_6H_5$ 1836

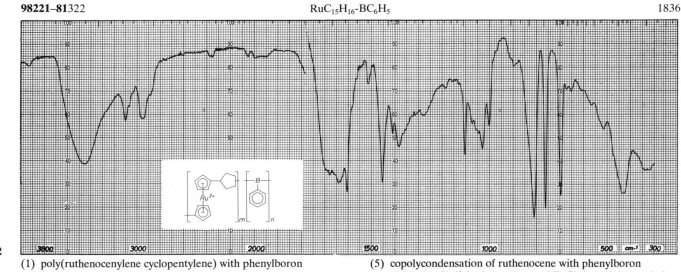

(1) poly(ruthenocenylene cyclopentylene) with phenylboron bridges
(2) deep-brown powder
(3) E.W. Neuse, Polymer Laboratory, Missile & Space Systems Div., Douglas Aircraft Comp., Santa Monica, Calif.
(4) m:n = 2
(5) copolycondensation of ruthenocene with phenylboron dichloride (1:1) in the presence of $ZnCl_2$ in sulfolane solution
(6) E.W. Neuse, J. Macromol. Sci.-Chem. *A2* (4) (1968) 751...9
(7) KBr (2/350); ordinate expanded between 1800 cm^{-1} and 300 cm
(8) sample 5 in table 1 of the refered publication

21212–32234 C_8H_6-$C_6H_4N_2$/$C_{14}H_{10}N_2$ 1837

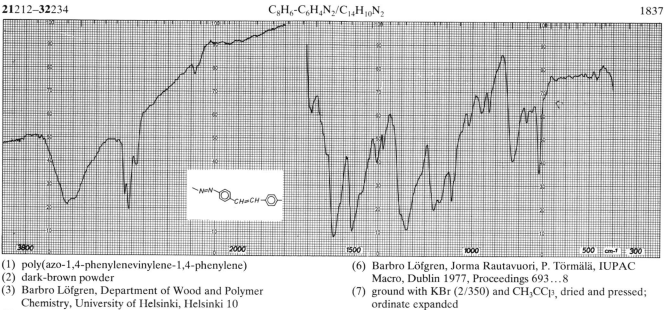

(1) poly(azo-1,4-phenylenevinylene-1,4-phenylene)
(2) dark-brown powder
(3) Barbro Löfgren, Department of Wood and Polymer Chemistry, University of Helsinki, Helsinki 10
(5) J. Heleskivi, Barbro Löfgren, J. Polym. Sci. A-2 *10* (1972) 747

(6) Barbro Löfgren, Jorma Rautavuori, P. Törmälä, IUPAC Macro, Dublin 1977, Proceedings 693…8
(7) ground with KBr (2/350) and CH_3CCl_3, dried and pressed; ordinate expanded

21**22111–3331112** C_8H_8-C_2H_4O 1838

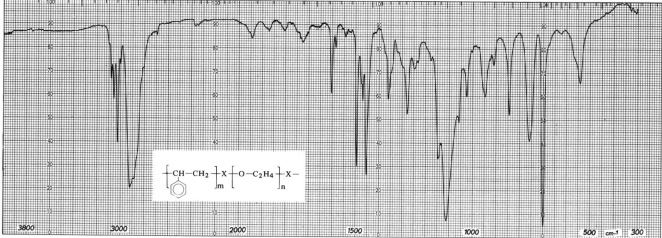

(1) styrene-oxyethylene block copolymer with urethane bridges
(2) white flocks
(3) B.M. Baysal, Department of Chemistry, Polymer Research Institute, Middle East Technical University, Ankara
(4)

(5) reaction of polyethyleneglycol 2000 with Hylene W, addition of 2,5-dimethyl-2,5-dihydroperoxyhexane (Luperox 2,5–2,5), reaction with styrene at 80°C under N_2
(6) B.M. Baysal, S. Kiliç, E.H. Orhan, I. Yilgör, IUPAC Macro, Dublin 1977, Proceedings 775…9
(7) film from $CHCl_3$ ond CsI

312221 C_9H_9Cl 1839

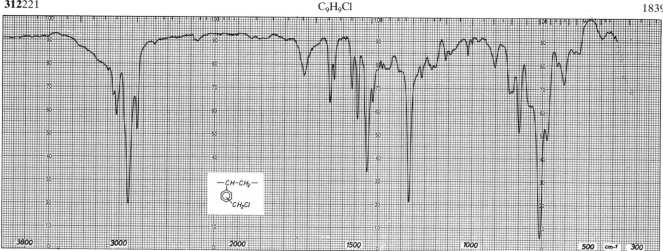

(1) poly(vinylbenzylchloride), poly[1-(chloromethylphenyl)-ethylene]
(2) white material
(3) H.W. Gibson, Webster Research Center, Xerox Corp., Webster, N.Y.
(4) substitution not defined

(5) chloromethylation of polystyrene; see H.W. Gibson, F.C. Bailey, J. Polym. Sci., Polym. Chem. Ed. *12* (1974) 2141
(6) F.C. Bailey, H.W. Gibson, IUPAC Macro Dublin 1977, Proceedings 427…31
(7) KBr (2/350)

322152–4211511 $C_4H_5N\text{-}C_8H_7NO_2$ 1840

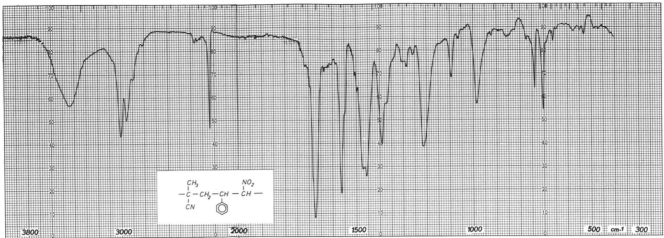

(1) methacrylonitrile-β-nitrostyrene copolymer
(2) white powder
(3) W. Schnabel, Hahn-Meitner-Institut für Kernforschung, Berlin GmbH, Bereich Strahlenchemie, Berlin
(4) 11 mol-% β-nitrostyrene in the copolymer
(5) anionic copolymerization of MAN with β-NS in hexamethyl-

phosphoric triamide
(6) B. Dinh-Ngoc, W. Schnabel, IUPAC Macro, Dublin 1977, Proceedings 101...7
(7) KBr (2/350)
(8) part of the nitrile groups are used during cp.; the resulting imine groups absorb at 1673 cm⁻¹

32224 $C_7H_6N_2$ 1841

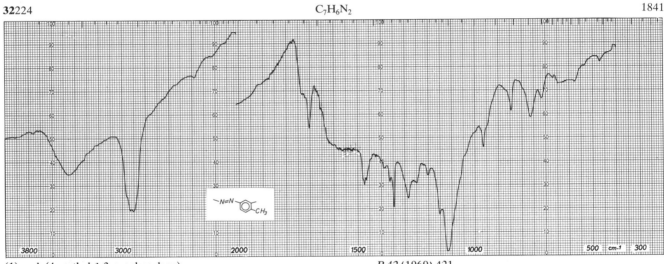

(1) poly(4-methyl-1,3-azophenylene)
(2) black powder
(3) Barbro Löfgren, Department of Wood and Polymer Chemistry, University of Helsinki, Helsinki 10
(5) oxidative coupling of 2,4-diaminotoluene, see B. Sandholm (Löfgren), J.-F. Selin, J.J. Lindberg, Suomen Kemistilehti

B 42 (1969) 421
(6) Barbro Löfgren, Jorma Rautavuori, P. Törmälä, IUPAC Macro, Dublin 1977, Proceedings 693...8
(7) ground with KBr (2/350) and CH_3CCl_3, dried and pressed; ordinate expanded

32224 $C_7H_6N_2$ 1842

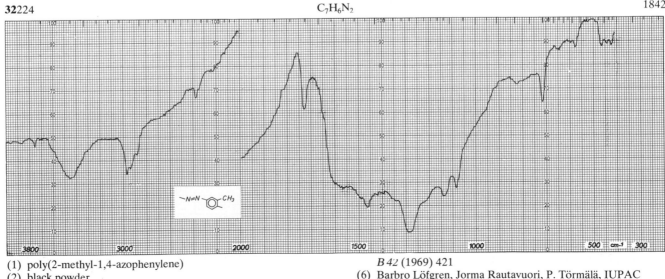

(1) poly(2-methyl-1,4-azophenylene)
(2) black powder
(3) Barbro Löfgren, Department of Wood and Polymer Chemistry, University of Helsinki, Helsinki 10
(5) oxidative coupling of 2,5-diaminotoluene, see B. Sandholm (Löfgren), J.-F. Selin, J.J. Lindberg, Suomen Kemistilehti

B 42 (1969) 421
(6) Barbro Löfgren, Jorma Rautavuori, P. Törmälä, IUPAC Macro, Dublin 1977, Proceedings 693...8
(7) ground with KBr (2/350) and CH_3CCl_3, dried and pressed; ordinate expanded

323213   C₇H₈N-Cl   1843

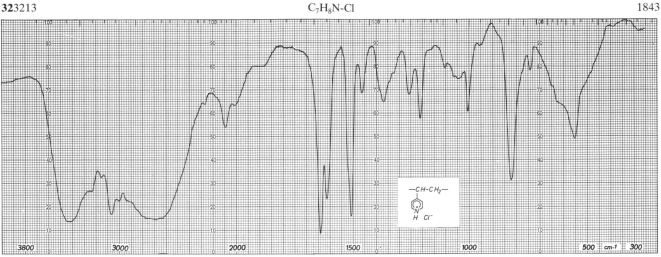

(1) poly(4-vinylpyridiniumchloride)
(2) yellowish, hard material
(3) H.-G. Biedermann, Anorganisch-Chemisches Laboratorium, TU München; Elsbeth Zoschke, Institut für Physikalische

Chemie, Universität Köln
(5) reaction of poly(4-vinylpyridine) in methanolic solution with HCl
(7) film from H₂O on KRS-5 (thallium bromide iodide)

323221   C₅H₆N₂   1844

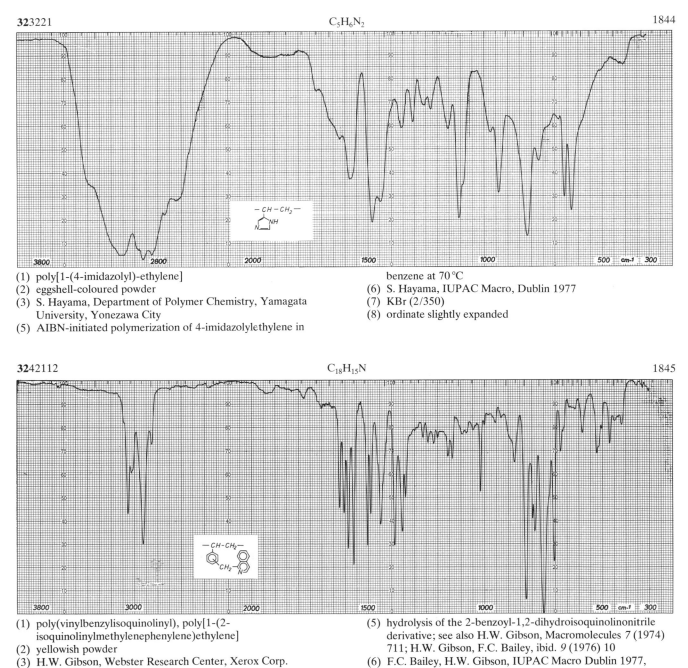

(1) poly[1-(4-imidazolyl)-ethylene]
(2) eggshell-coloured powder
(3) S. Hayama, Department of Polymer Chemistry, Yamagata University, Yonezawa City
(5) AIBN-initiated polymerization of 4-imidazolylethylene in

benzene at 70 °C
(6) S. Hayama, IUPAC Macro, Dublin 1977
(7) KBr (2/350)
(8) ordinate slightly expanded

3242112   C₁₈H₁₅N   1845

(1) poly(vinylbenzylisoquinolinyl), poly[1-(2-isoquinolinylmethylenephenylene)ethylene]
(2) yellowish powder
(3) H.W. Gibson, Webster Research Center, Xerox Corp. Webster, N.Y.
(4) substitution of the benzyl residue not defined

(5) hydrolysis of the 2-benzoyl-1,2-dihydroisoquinolinonitrile derivative; see also H.W. Gibson, Macromolecules 7 (1974) 711; H.W. Gibson, F.C. Bailey, ibid. 9 (1976) 10
(6) F.C. Bailey, H.W. Gibson, IUPAC Macro Dublin 1977, 427...31 (III/12)
(7) film from CHCl₃ ond CsI

615

3242211 $C_{21}H_{17}N$ 1846

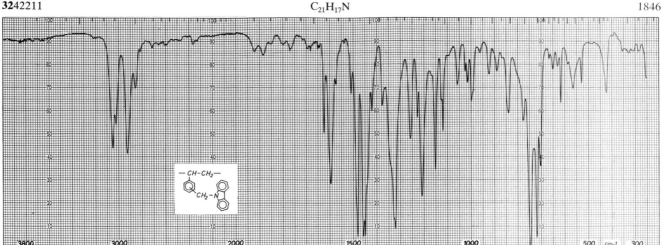

(1) poly(vinylbenzyl-N-carbazole), poly[1-(N-carbazolylmethylenephenylene)-ethylene]
(2) white powder
(3) H.W. Gibson, Webster Research Center, Xerox Corp. Webster, N.Y.
(4) substitution of the benzyl residue not defined

(5) reaction of poly(vinylbenzylchloride) with the N-anion of carbazole; see also H.W. Gibson, F.C. Bailey, Macromolecules 9 (1976) 688
(6) F.C. Bailey, H.W. Gibson, IUPAC Macro Dublin 1977, 427..31 (III/12)
(7) film from CHCl₃ on CsI

33212 $C_6H_4O_2$ 1847

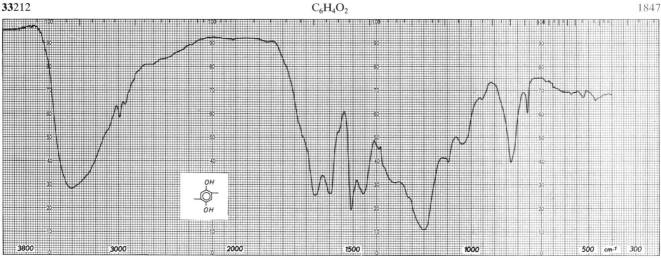

(1) poly(hydroquinone), poly(2,5-dihydroxy-1,4-phenylene)
(2) brown powder
(3) A.V. Ragimov, Sumgait Department of the Institute of Petrochemical Processes of the Academy of Sciences of the SSR Azerbaijan
(5) anionic polymerization of p-benzoquinone in the presence of

KOH in ethanol solution
(6) A.V. Ragimov, B.A. Mamedov, B.I. Liogonky, IUPAC Macro, Dublin 1977, Proceedings 109...12
(7) ground with KBr (1/350) and acetone, dried and pressed
(8) the material contains some residual quinoid rings

3331112 C_2H_4O 1848

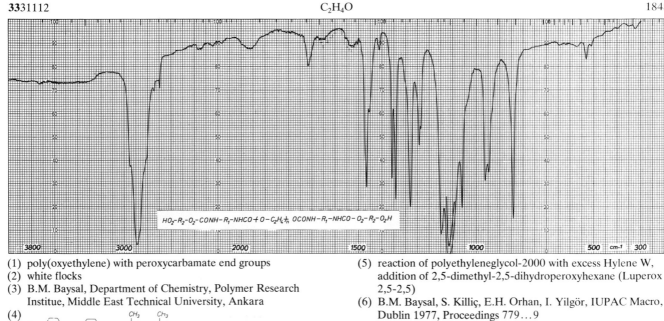

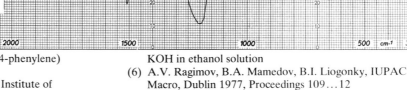

(1) poly(oxyethylene) with peroxycarbamate end groups
(2) white flocks
(3) B.M. Baysal, Department of Chemistry, Polymer Research Institue, Middle East Technical University, Ankara
(4)

(5) reaction of polyethyleneglycol-2000 with excess Hylene W, addition of 2,5-dimethyl-2,5-dihydroperoxyhexane (Luperox 2,5-2,5)
(6) B.M. Baysal, S. Killiç, E.H. Orhan, I. Yilgör, IUPAC Macro, Dublin 1977, Proceedings 779...9
(7) film from CHCl₃ on CsI

3332212 $C_{16}H_{16}O_2$ 1849

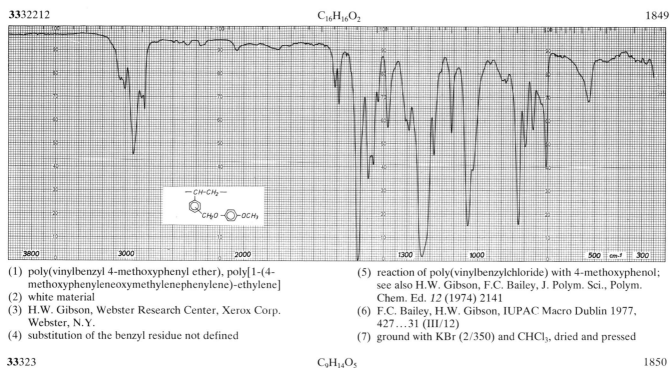

(1) poly(vinylbenzyl 4-methoxyphenyl ether), poly[1-(4-methoxyphenyleneoxymethylenephenylene)-ethylene]
(2) white material
(3) H.W. Gibson, Webster Research Center, Xerox Corp. Webster, N.Y.
(4) substitution of the benzyl residue not defined

(5) reaction of poly(vinylbenzylchloride) with 4-methoxyphenol; see also H.W. Gibson, F.C. Bailey, J. Polym. Sci., Polym. Chem. Ed. *12* (1974) 2141
(6) F.C. Bailey, H.W. Gibson, IUPAC Macro Dublin 1977, 427...31 (III/12)
(7) ground with KBr (2/350) and CHCl₃, dried and pressed

33323 $C_9H_{14}O_5$ 1850

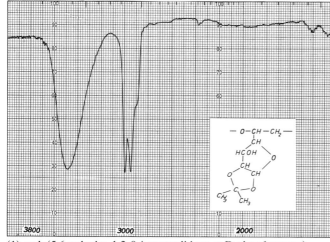
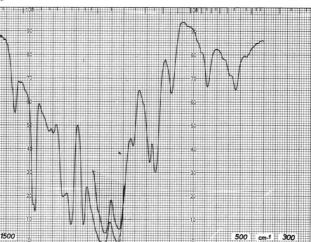

(1) poly(5,6-anhydro-1,2-0-isopropylidene-α-D-glucofuranose)
(2) white powder
(3) T. Uryu, Department of Industrial Chemistry, Faculty of Engineering, University of Tokyo, Hongo, Tokyo
(5) ring-opening polymerization of 5,6-anhydro-1,2-0-

isopropylidene-α-D-glucofuranose with PF₅ or BF₃-etherate in CH₂Cl₂ solution
(6) T. Uryu, K. Kitano, H. Tachikawa, K. Matsuzaki, IUPAC Macro, Dublin 1977, Proceedings 307...12
(7) KBr (2/350)

335122 C_9H_8O 1851

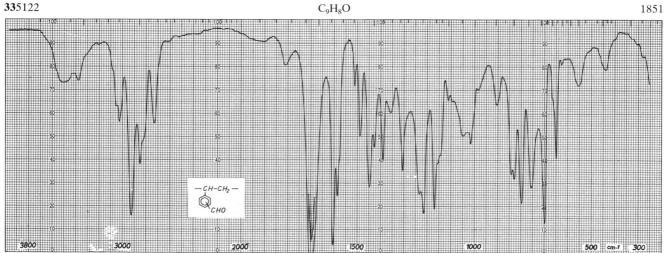

(1) poly(vinylbenzaldehyde)
(2) white powder
(3) H.W. Gibson, Webster Research Center, Xerox Corp. Webster, N.Y.
(4) substitution not defined
(5) oxidation of poly(vinylbenzylchloride) with dimethylsulfoxide;

see also H.W. Gibson, F.C. Bailey, J. Polm. Sci., Polym. Chem. Ed. *13* (1975) 1951
(6) F.C. Bailey, H.W. Gibson, IUPAC Macro Dublin 1977, 427...31 (III/12)
(7) film from CHCl₃ on CsI

     $C_{26}H_{16}O_6$

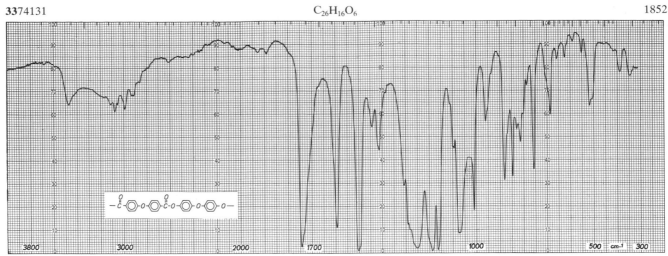

(1) poly(ester ether) aromatic; poly[bis(oxy-1,4-phenylene)-oxycarbonyl-1,4-phenyleneoxy-1,4-phenylenecarbonyl]
(2) white powder
(3) P. Valetskii, Institute for Organo-element Compounds, Academy of Sciences, USSR, Moscow

(5) polycondensation of diphenylether-4,4'-dicarbonylchloride with 4,4'-dihydroxy-diphenylether
(6) P. Valetskii, private communication
(7) ground with KBr (1/350) and dimethylsulfoxide, dried (15 h at 60 °C i.V.) and pressed

     $C_{28}H_{16}O_6$

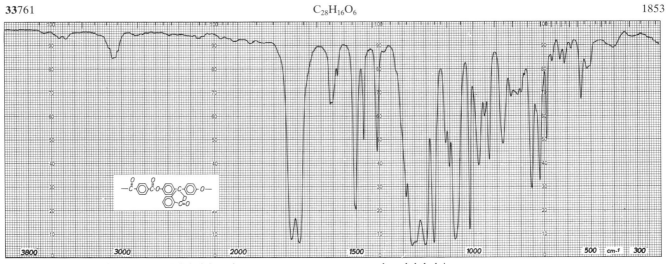

(1) polyester, aromatic, with phenolphthalein units
(2) white coarse material
(3) P.M. Valetzkii, Inst. for Element-Organic Compounds, Academy of Sciences, Moscow
(5) low-temperature polycondensation of terephthalic acid and phenolphthalein
(6) I.P. Storožuk, P.M. Valetzkii, S.V. Vinogradova, V.V. Korshak, Vysokomol. Soed. (Moscow), in print
(7) film from CHCl₃ on CsI

     $C_{28}H_{16}O_6$

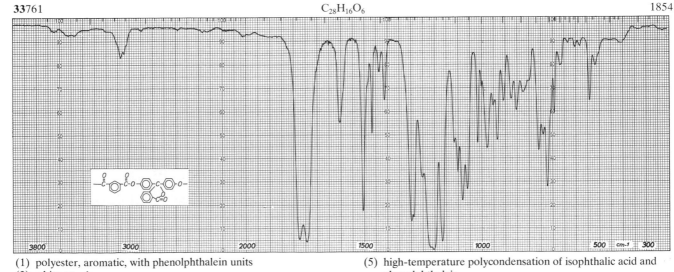

(1) polyester, aromatic, with phenolphthalein units
(2) white powder
(3) P.M. Valetzkii, Inst. for Element-Organic-Compounds, Academy of Sciences, Moscow

(5) high-temperature polycondensation of isophthalic acid and phenolphthalein
(6) I.P. Storožuk, P.M. Valetzkii, S.V. Vinogradova, V.V. Korshak. Vysokomol. Soed. (Moscow), in print
(7) film from CHCl₃ on CsI

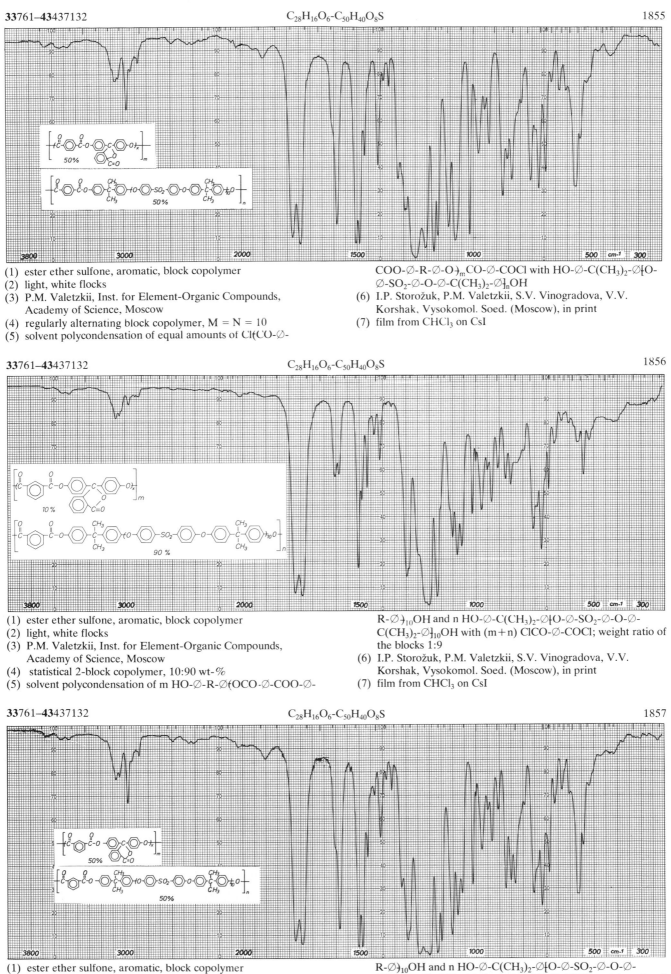

33761–43437132 $C_{28}H_{16}O_6-C_{50}H_{40}O_8S$ 1855

(1) ester ether sulfone, aromatic, block copolymer
(2) light, white flocks
(3) P.M. Valetzkii, Inst. for Element-Organic Compounds,
     Academy of Science, Moscow
(4) regularly alternating block copolymer, M = N = 10
(5) solvent polycondensation of equal amounts of Cl⁅CO-∅-

COO-∅-R-∅-O⁆ₘCO-∅-COCl with HO-∅-C(CH₃)₂-∅⁅O-
∅-SO₂-∅-O-∅-C(CH₃)₂-∅⁆ₙOH
(6) I.P. Storožuk, P.M. Valetzkii, S.V. Vinogradova, V.V.
     Korshak, Vysokomol. Soed. (Moscow), in print
(7) film from CHCl₃ on CsI

33761–43437132 $C_{28}H_{16}O_6-C_{50}H_{40}O_8S$ 1856

(1) ester ether sulfone, aromatic, block copolymer
(2) light, white flocks
(3) P.M. Valetzkii, Inst. for Element-Organic Compounds,
     Academy of Science, Moscow
(4) statistical 2-block copolymer, 10:90 wt-%
(5) solvent polycondensation of m HO-∅-R-∅⁅OCO-∅-COO-∅-

R-∅⁆₁₀OH and n HO-∅-C(CH₃)₂-∅⁅O-∅-SO₂-∅-O-∅-
C(CH₃)₂-∅⁆₁₀OH with (m+n) ClCO-∅-COCl; weight ratio of
the blocks 1:9
(6) I.P. Storožuk, P.M. Valetzkii, S.V. Vinogradova, V.V.
     Korshak, Vysokomol. Soed. (Moscow), in print
(7) film from CHCl₃ on CsI

33761–43437132 $C_{28}H_{16}O_6-C_{50}H_{40}O_8S$ 1857

(1) ester ether sulfone, aromatic, block copolymer
(2) light, white flocks
(3) P.M. Valetzkii, Inst. for Element-Organic Compounds,
     Academy of Science, Moscow
(4) statistical 2-block copolymer, 50:50 wt-%
(5) solvent polycondensation of m HO-∅-R-∅⁅OCO-∅-COO-∅-

R-∅⁆₁₀OH and n HO-∅-C(CH₃)₂-∅⁅O-∅-SO₂-∅-O-∅-
C(CH₃)₂-∅⁆₁₀OH with (m+n) ClCO-∅-COCl; weight ratio of
the blocks 5:5
(6) I.P. Storožuk, P.M. Valetzkii, S.V. Vinogradova, V.V.
     Korshak, Vysokomol. Soed. (Moscow), in print
(7) film from CHCl₃ on CsI

33761–**43**437132 $C_{28}H_{16}O_6$-$C_{50}H_{40}O_8S$ 1858

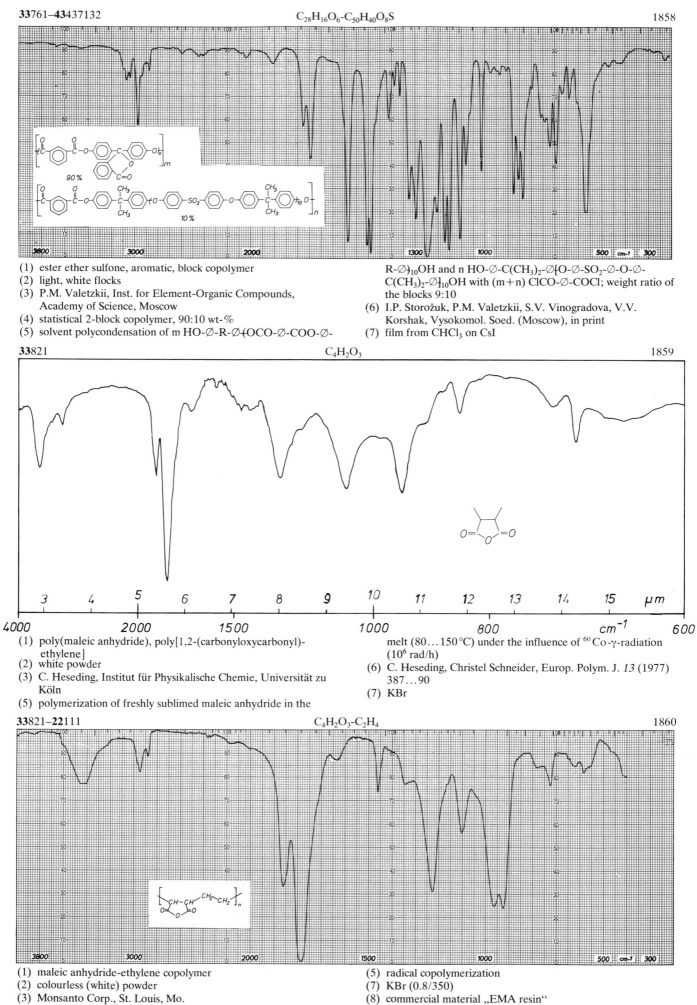

(1) ester ether sulfone, aromatic, block copolymer
(2) light, white flocks
(3) P.M. Valetzkii, Inst. for Element-Organic Compounds, Academy of Science, Moscow
(4) statistical 2-block copolymer, 90:10 wt-%
(5) solvent polycondensation of m HO-∅-R-∅-(OCO-∅-COO-∅-

R-∅)₁₀OH and n HO-∅-C(CH₃)₂-∅[O-∅-SO₂-∅-O-∅-C(CH₃)₂-∅]₁₀OH with (m+n) ClCO-∅-COCl; weight ratio of the blocks 9:10
(6) I.P. Storožuk, P.M. Valetzkii, S.V. Vinogradova, V.V. Korshak, Vysokomol. Soed. (Moscow), in print
(7) film from CHCl₃ on CsI

33821 $C_4H_2O_3$ 1859

(1) poly(maleic anhydride), poly[1,2-(carbonyloxycarbonyl)-ethylene]
(2) white powder
(3) C. Heseding, Institut für Physikalische Chemie, Universität zu Köln
(5) polymerization of freshly sublimed maleic anhydride in the

melt (80...150 °C) under the influence of ⁶⁰Co-γ-radiation (10⁶ rad/h)
(6) C. Heseding, Christel Schneider, Europ. Polym. J. *13* (1977) 387...90
(7) KBr

33821–**22**111 $C_4H_2O_3$-C_2H_4 1860

(1) maleic anhydride-ethylene copolymer
(2) colourless (white) powder
(3) Monsanto Corp., St. Louis, Mo.
(4) alternating 1:1 structure

(5) radical copolymerization
(7) KBr (0.8/350)
(8) commercial material „EMA resin"

33821–33613 $C_4H_2O_3/C_8H_4O_6$ 1861

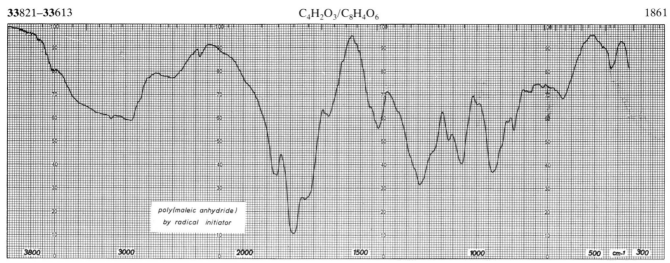

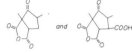

(1) poly(maleic anhydride)
(2) light-brown to pink powder
(4) the product contains free carboxyl and ketone groups; in addition to succinic anhydride structures, the following structures are discussed:

(5) polymerization of maleic anhydride in solution with high concentration of radical initiator; the polymerization is accompanied by d carboxylation
(6) D. Braun, I.A. Aziz el Sayed, J. Pomakis, Makromol. Chem. *124* (1969) 249…62
(7) KBr (2/350)

3423–32235 $C_{12}H_8S_2$-C_7H_3N 1862

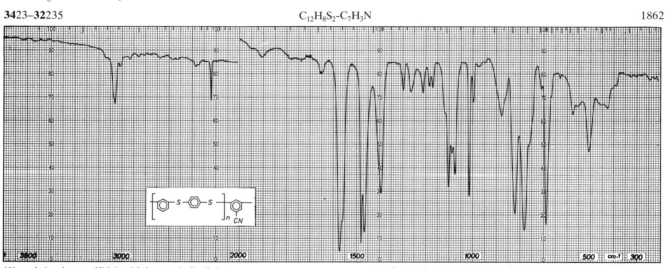

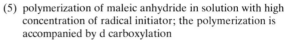

(1) poly(arylene sulfide) with benzonitrile links
(2) dark-grey, coarse material
(3) C.S. Marvel, Department of Chemistry, College of Liberal Arts, University of Arizna Tucson, Ariz.
(5) polycondensation of m-dimercaptobenzene (50 mol-%),-

p-dibromobenzene (40 mol-%) and 1,3-dichloro-5-cyanobenzene (10 mol-%)
(6) C.S. Marvel, IUPAC Macro, Aberdeen 1973; private communication
(7) film from $CHCl_3$ on CsI

413232212 $C_{15}H_{13}ClO$ 1863

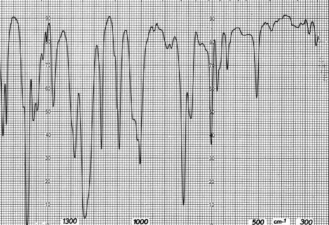

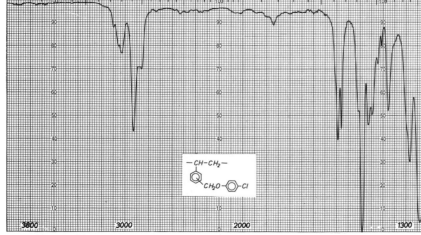

(1) poly(vinylbenzyl p-chlorophenyl ether), poly[1-(4-chlorophenyleneoxymethylene-phenylene)-ethylene]
(2) white, light material
(3) H.W. Gibson, Webster Research Center, Xerox Corp., Webster, N.Y.
(4) substitution of the benzyl residue not defined

(5) reaction of poly(vinylbenzylchloride) with 4-chlorophenol; see also H.W. Gibson, F.C. Bailey, J. Polym. Sci., Polym. Chem. Ed. *12* (1974) 2141
(6) F.C. Bailey, H.W. Gibson, IUPAC Macro Dublin 1977, 427…31 (III/12)
(7) film from $CHCl_3$ on CsI

41341 $C_{39}H_{22}I_2O_5$ 1864

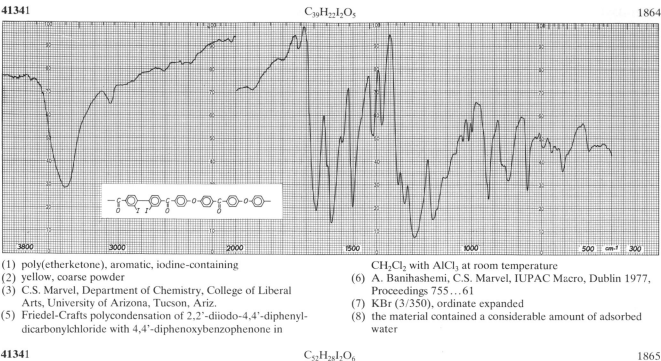

(1) poly(etherketone), aromatic, iodine-containing
(2) yellow, coarse powder
(3) C.S. Marvel, Department of Chemistry, College of Liberal Arts, University of Arizona, Tucson, Ariz.
(5) Friedel-Crafts polycondensation of 2,2'-diiodo-4,4'-diphenyl-dicarbonylchloride with 4,4'-diphenoxybenzophenone in

CH$_2$Cl$_2$ with AlCl$_3$ at room temperature
(6) A. Banihashemi, C.S. Marvel, IUPAC Macro, Dublin 1977, Proceedings 755...61
(7) KBr (3/350), ordinate expanded
(8) the material contained a considerable amount of adsorbed water

41341 $C_{52}H_{28}I_2O_6$ 1865

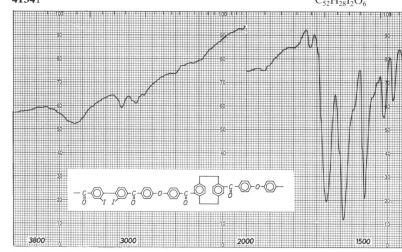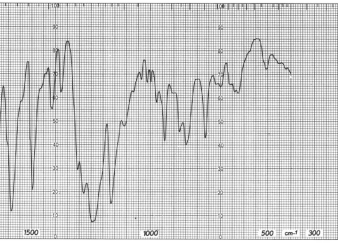

(1) poly(etherketone), aromatic, iodine-containing
(2) light-yellow, fine powder
(3) C.S. Marvel, Department of Chemistry, College of Liberal Arts, University of Tucson, Ariz.
(5) Friedel-Crafts polycondensation of 2,2'-diiodo-4,4'-diphenyl-

dicarbonylchloride with 3,9-bis(p-phenoxybenzoyl-[2,2]-p-cyclophane) in CH$_2$Cl$_2$ with AlCl$_3$ at room temperature
(6) A. Banihashemi, C.S. Marvel, IUPAC Macro, Dublin 1977, Proceedings 755...61
(7) KBr (2/350)

4211521 $C_8H_7NO_2$ 1866

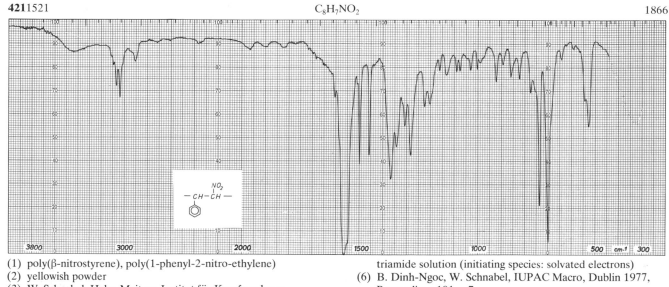

(1) poly(β-nitrostyrene), poly(1-phenyl-2-nitro-ethylene)
(2) yellowish powder
(3) W. Schnabel, Hahn-Meitner-Institut für Kernforschung, Berlin GmbH, Bereich Strahlenchemie, Berlin
(5) polymerization of β-nitrostyrene in hexamethylphosphoric

triamide solution (initiating species: solvated electrons)
(6) B. Dinh-Ngoc, W. Schnabel, IUPAC Macro, Dublin 1977, Proceedings 101...7
(7) KBr (1/350)

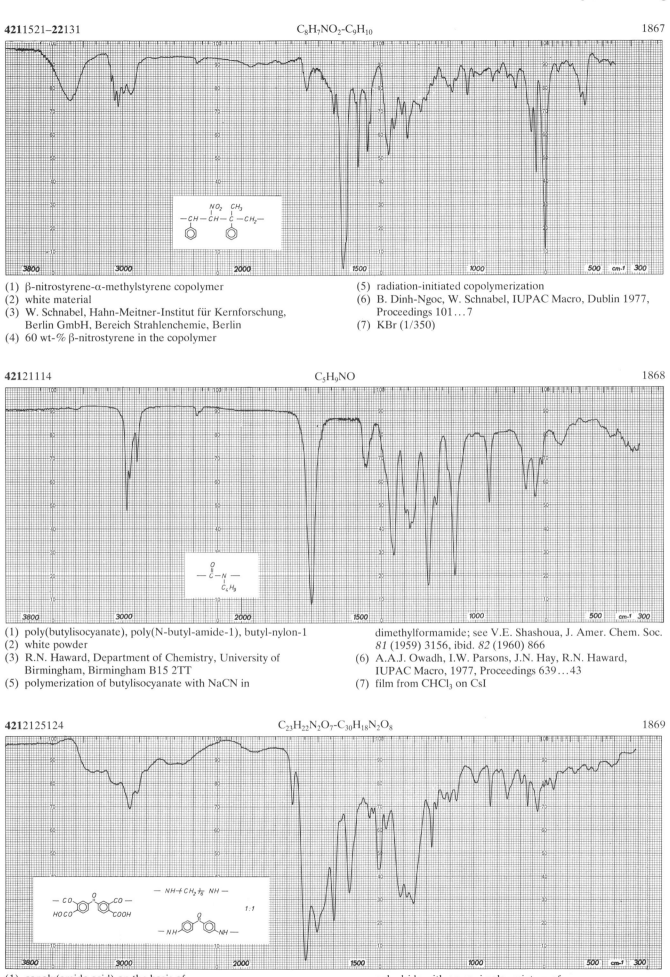

4211521–**22**131 $C_8H_7NO_2$-C_9H_{10} 1867

(1) β-nitrostyrene-α-methylstyrene copolymer
(2) white material
(3) W. Schnabel, Hahn-Meitner-Institut für Kernforschung, Berlin GmbH, Bereich Strahlenchemie, Berlin
(4) 60 wt-% β-nitrostyrene in the copolymer
(5) radiation-initiated copolymerization
(6) B. Dinh-Ngoc, W. Schnabel, IUPAC Macro, Dublin 1977, Proceedings 101...7
(7) KBr (1/350)

42121114 C_5H_9NO 1868

(1) poly(butylisocyanate), poly(N-butyl-amide-1), butyl-nylon-1
(2) white powder
(3) R.N. Haward, Department of Chemistry, University of Birmingham, Birmingham B15 2TT
(5) polymerization of butylisocyanate with NaCN in dimethylformamide; see V.E. Shashoua, J. Amer. Chem. Soc. *81* (1959) 3156, ibid. *82* (1960) 866
(6) A.A.J. Owadh, I.W. Parsons, J.N. Hay, R.N. Haward, IUPAC Macro, 1977, Proceedings 639...43
(7) film from $CHCl_3$ on CsI

4212125124 $C_{23}H_{22}N_2O_7$-$C_{30}H_{18}N_2O_8$ 1869

(1) copoly(amido acid) on the basis of benzophenonetetracarboxylic anhydride
(2) brownish-yellow solution (16%) in N-methylpyrrolidone
(3) J. Kovács, BASF AG, Ludwigshafen
(4) partly cyclized (imide rings)
(5) copolycondensate of benzophenone-3,3',4,4'-tetracarboxylic anhydride with an equimolar mixture of hexamethylenediamine and 4,4'-diaminobenzophenone in-N-methylpyrrolidone
(6) J. Kovács, Angew. Makromol. Chem. *45* (1975) 21...39
(7) film on CsI, dried at 40°C i.v.
(8) ordinate expanded

4212125124 $C_{30}H_{18}N_2O_8 - C_{23}H_{14}N_2O_7$ 1870

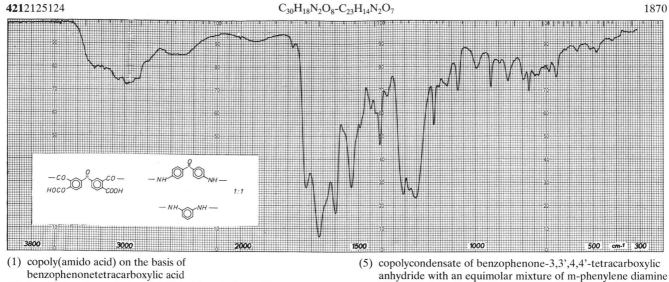

(1) copoly(amido acid) on the basis of benzophenonetetracarboxylic acid
(2) brownish-yellow solution (16%) in N-methylpyrrolidone
(3) J. Kovács, BASF, Ludwigshafen
(4) partly cyclized (imide rings)
(5) copolycondensate of benzophenone-3,3',4,4'-tetracarboxylic anhydride with an equimolar mixture of m-phenylene diamine and 4,4'-diaminobenzophenone
(6) J. Kovács, Angew. Makromol. Chem. 45 (1975) 21...39
(7) film on CsI, dried at 40 °C i.v.

4212125322 $C_{26}H_{18}N_2O_4$ 1871

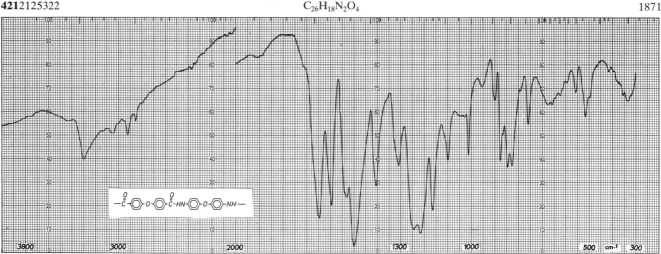

(1) poly(amidoether), aromatic; poly(imino-1,4-phenyleneoxy-1,4-phenyleneiminocarbonyl-1,4-phenyleneoxy-1,4-phenylenecarbonyl)
(2) white powder
(3) P. Valetskii, Institute for Organo-element Compounds, Academy of Sciences, USSR, Moscow
(5) polycondensation of diphenylether-4,4'-dicarbonylchloride with 4,4'-diaminodiphenylether
(6) P. Valetskii, private communication
(7) ground with KBr (1/350) and dimethylsulfoxide, dried (4 d at 60 °C i.v.) and pressed

4215 1141 $C_{14}H_{16}N_2O_4$ 1872

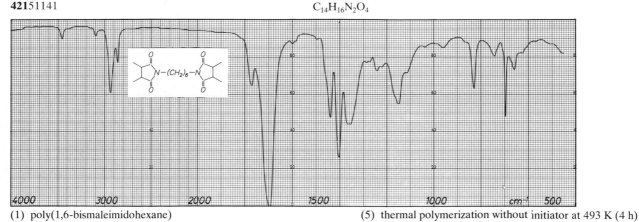

(1) poly(1,6-bismaleimidohexane)
(2) brown film
(3) K. Bohle, Institut für Physikalische Chemie, Universität zu Köln
(5) thermal polymerization without initiator at 493 K (4 h)
(6) K. Bohle, Dissertation, Köln 1978
(7) film (20 μm) between KBr wafers

42151142 $C_{21}H_{14}N_2O_4$ 1873

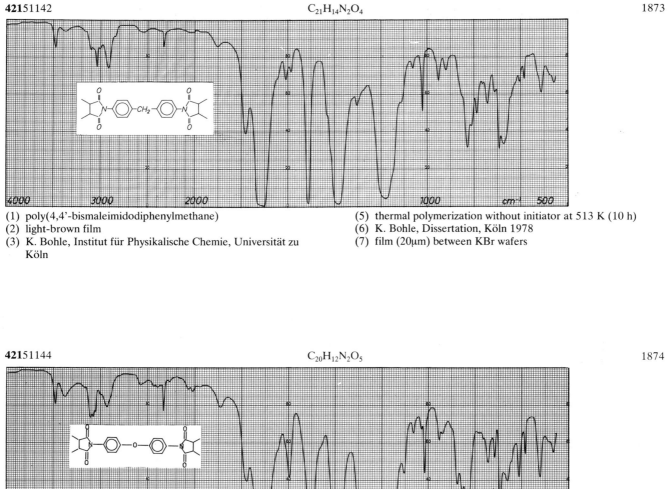

(1) poly(4,4'-bismaleimidodiphenylmethane)
(2) light-brown film
(3) K. Bohle, Institut für Physikalische Chemie, Universität zu Köln

(5) thermal polymerization without initiator at 513 K (10 h)
(6) K. Bohle, Dissertation, Köln 1978
(7) film (20μm) between KBr wafers

42151144 $C_{20}H_{12}N_2O_5$ 1874

(1) poly(4,4'-bismaleimidodiphenylether)
(2) light-brown film
(3) K. Bohle, Institut für Physikalische Chemie, Universität zu Köln

(5) thermal polymerization at 513 K without initiator (10 h)
(6) K. Bohle, Dissertation, Köln 1978
(7) film (20μm) between KBr wafers

42151211–**421**53223 $C_{23}H_{18}N_2O_5$-$C_{30}H_{10}N_2O_6$ 1875

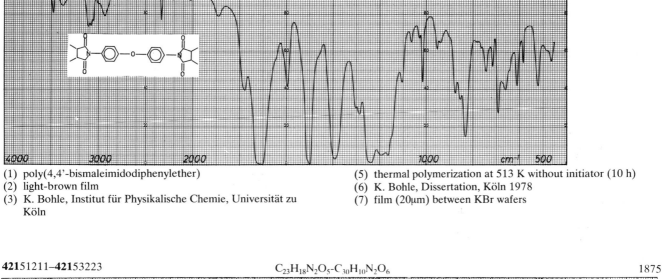

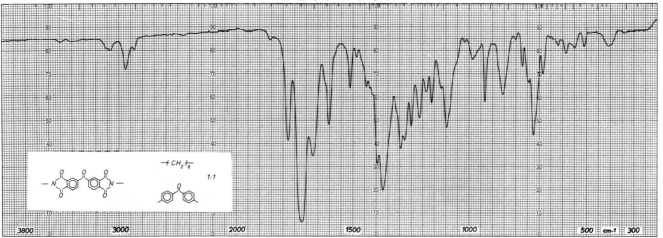

(1) copolyimide on the basis of benzophenonetetracarboxylic anhydride
(2) yellow film
(3) J. Kovács, BASF AG, Ludwigshafen
(5) copolycondensation of benzophenone-3,3',4,4'-tetracarboxylic anhydride with an equimolar mixture of

hexamethylene diamine and 4,4'-diaminobenzophenone in-N-methylpyrrolidone, cyclization at 200 °C
(6) J. Kovács, Angew. Makromol. Chem. *45* (1975) 21...39
(7) film on CsI
(8) the film probably still contains a small amount of the solvent

42151216–42153123 $C_{30}H_{10}N_2O_6$–$C_{23}H_{10}N_2O_5$ 1876

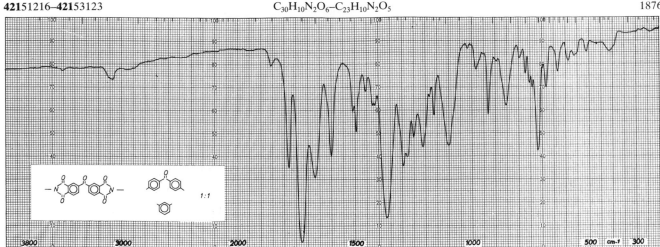

(1) copolyimide on the basis of benzophenonetetracarboxylic anhydride
(2) yellow film
(3) J. Kovács, BASF AG, Ludwigshafen
(5) copolycondensation of benzophenone-3,3',4,4'-tetracarboxylic anhydride with an equimolar mixture of

m-phenylene diamine and 4,4'-diaminobenzophenone, cyclization at 200 °C
(6) J. Kovács, Angew. Makromol. Chem. *45* (1975) 21...39
(7) film on CsI
(8) the film probably still contains a small amount of the solvent

4215123 $C_{17}H_{13}NO_2$ 1877

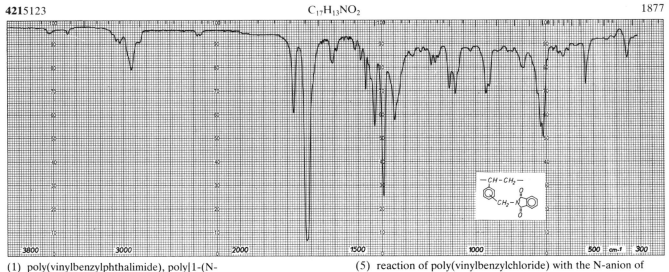

(1) poly(vinylbenzylphthalimide), poly[1-(N-phthalimidomethylenephenylene)-ethylene]
(2) light-yellow powder
(3) H.W. Gibson, Webster Research Center, Xerox Corp. Webster, N.Y.
(4) substitution of the benzyl residue not defined

(5) reaction of poly(vinylbenzylchloride) with the N-anion of phthalimide
(6) F.C. Bailey, H.W. Gibson, IUPAC Macro Dublin 1977, 427...31(III/12)
(7) film from $CHCl_3$ on CsI

42152112 $C_{34}H_{36}N_6O_8$ 1878

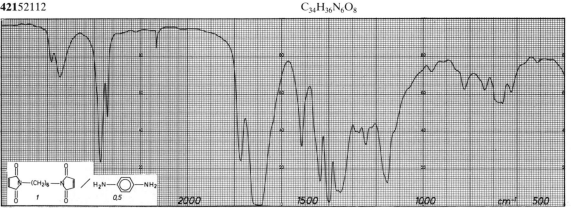

(1) copolymer from 1,6-bismaleimidohexane and p-phenylenediamine
(2) brown film
(3) K. Bohle, Institut für Physikalische Chemie, Universität zu Köln
(4)

(5) 1:0.5 molar mixture cured at 523 K (20 h)
(6) K. Bohle, Dissertation, Köln 1978
(7) film (20 µm) between KBr wafers

42152112 $C_{41}H_{42}N_6O_8$ 1879

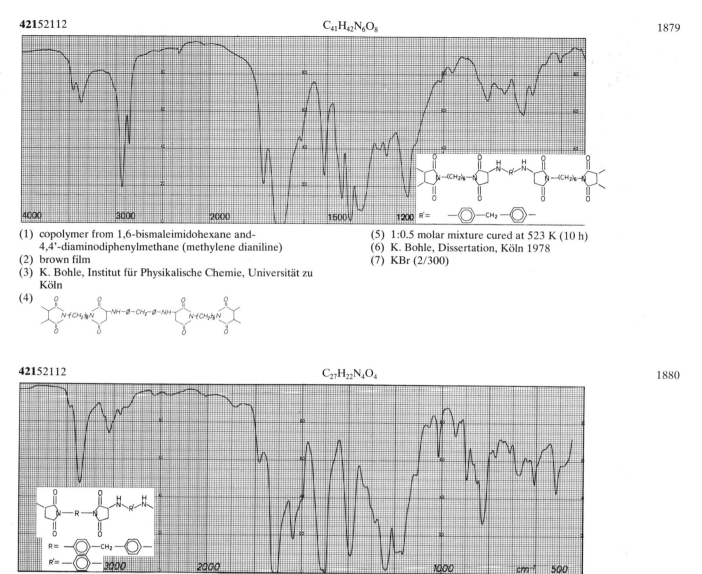

(1) copolymer from 1,6-bismaleimidohexane and-
    4,4'-diaminodiphenylmethane (methylene dianiline)
(2) brown film
(3) K. Bohle, Institut für Physikalische Chemie, Universität zu
    Köln
(4)

(5) 1:0.5 molar mixture cured at 523 K (10 h)
(6) K. Bohle, Dissertation, Köln 1978
(7) KBr (2/300)

42152112 $C_{27}H_{22}N_4O_4$ 1880

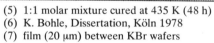

(1) copolymer from 4,4'-bismaleimidodiphenylmethane and-
    p-phenylenediamine
(2) light-brown film
(3) K. Bohle, Institut für Physikalische Chemie, Universität zu
    Köln

(5) 1:1 molar mixture cured at 435 K (48 h)
(6) K. Bohle, Dissertation, Köln 1978
(7) film (20 μm) between KBr wafers

42152112 $C_{46}H_{32}N_6O_{10}$ 1881

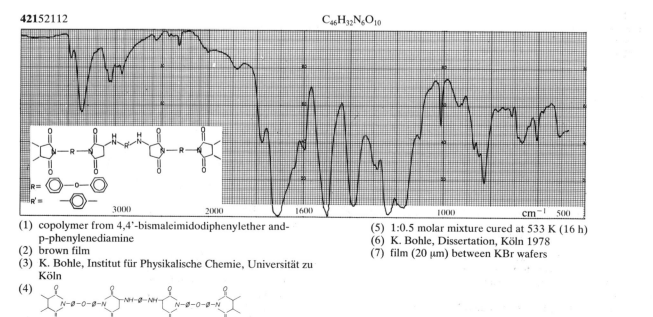

(1) copolymer from 4,4'-bismaleimidodiphenylether and-
    p-phenylenediamine
(2) brown film
(3) K. Bohle, Institut für Physikalische Chemie, Universität zu
    Köln
(4)

(5) 1:0.5 molar mixture cured at 533 K (16 h)
(6) K. Bohle, Dissertation, Köln 1978
(7) film (20 μm) between KBr wafers

42152112 $C_{53}H_{38}N_6O_{10}$ 1882

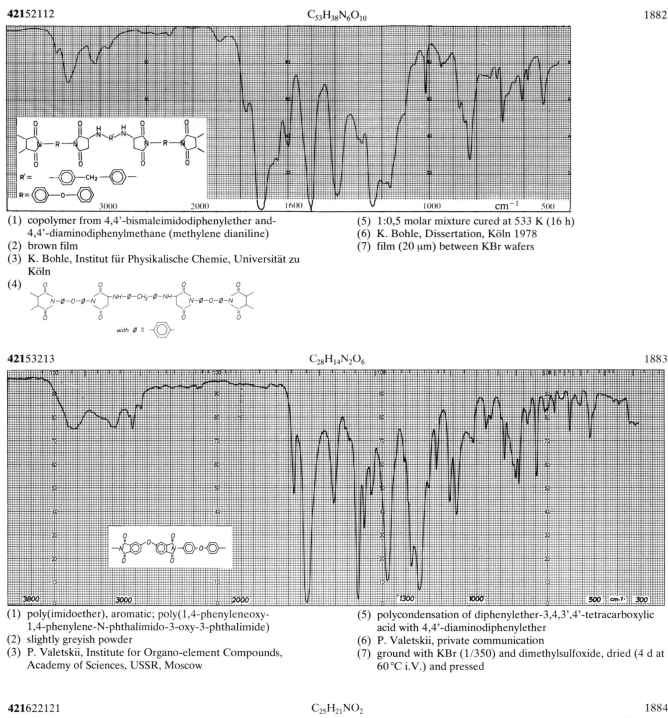

(1) copolymer from 4,4'-bismaleimidodiphenylether and-
    4,4'-diaminodiphenylmethane (methylene dianiline)

(2) brown film

(3) K. Bohle, Institut für Physikalische Chemie, Universität zu
    Köln

(4)

(5) 1:0,5 molar mixture cured at 533 K (16 h)

(6) K. Bohle, Dissertation, Köln 1978

(7) film (20 µm) between KBr wafers

42153213 $C_{28}H_{14}N_2O_6$ 1883

(1) poly(imidoether), aromatic; poly(1,4-phenyleneoxy-
    1,4-phenylene-N-phthalimido-3-oxy-3-phthalimide)

(2) slightly greyish powder

(3) P. Valetskii, Institute for Organo-element Compounds,
    Academy of Sciences, USSR, Moscow

(5) polycondensation of diphenylether-3,4,3',4'-tetracarboxylic
    acid with 4,4'-diaminodiphenylether

(6) P. Valetskii, private communication

(7) ground with KBr (1/350) and dimethylsulfoxide, dried (4 d at
    60°C i.V.) and pressed

421622121 $C_{25}H_{21}NO_2$ 1884

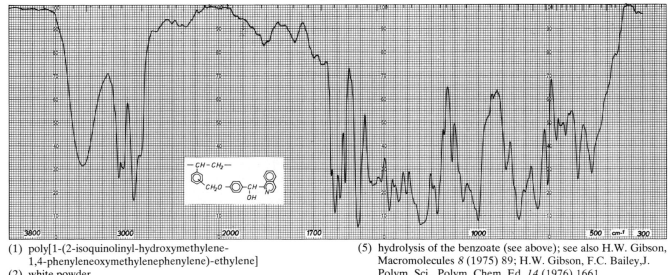

(1) poly[1-(2-isoquinolinyl-hydroxymethylene-
    1,4-phenyleneoxymethylenephenylene)-ethylene]

(2) white powder

(3) H.W. Gibson, Webster Research Center, Xerox Corp.
    Webster, N.Y.

(4) substitution of the benzyl residue not defined

(5) hydrolysis of the benzoate (see above); see also H.W. Gibson,
    Macromolecules 8 (1975) 89; H.W. Gibson, F.C. Bailey, J.
    Polym. Sci., Polym. Chem. Ed. 14 (1976) 1661

(6) F.C. Bailey, H.W. Gibson, IUPAC Macro Dublin 1977,
    427...31 (III/12)

(7) film from CHCl₃ on CsI, slight pink discolouration

421622123   C₃₂H₂₅NO₃   1885

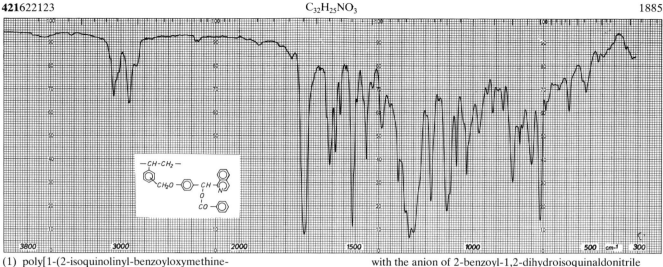

(1) poly[1-(2-isoquinolinyl-benzoyloxymethine-
 1,4-phenyleneoxymethylenephenylene)-ethylene]
(2) white powder
(3) H.W. Gibson, Webster Research Center, Xerox Corp.
 Webster, N.Y.
(4) substitution of the benzyl residue not defined
(5) reaction of poly(vinylbenzyl 4-methoxyphenyl ether), poly[1-
 (4-methoxyphenyleneoxy-methylenephenylene)-ethylene]

with the anion of 2-benzoyl-1,2-dihydroisoquinaldonitrile
(isoquinoline Reissert compound); see also H.W. Gibson,
Macromolecules **8** (1975) 89; H.W. Gibson, F.C. Bailey,J.
Polym. Sci., Polym. Chem. Ed. *14* (1976) 1661
(6) F.C. Bailey, H.W. Gibson, IUPAC Macro Dublin 1977,
 427...31 (III/12)
(7) film from CHCl₃ on CsI

421822   C₇H₆N₂O   1886

(1) poly(4-methoxy-1,3-azophenylene)
(2) black powder
(3) Barbro Löfgren, Department of Wood and Polymer
 Chemistry, University of Helsinki, Helsinki
(5) oxidative coupling of 2,4-diaminoanisole, see B. Sandholm
 (Löfgren), J.-F. Selin, J.J. Lindberg, Suomen Kemistileith

B 42 (1969) 421
(6) Barbro Löfgren, Jorma Rautavuori, P. Törmälä, IUPAC
 Macro, Dublin 1977, Proceedings 693...8
(7) ground with KBr (1/350) and CH₃CCl₃, dried and pressed;
 oridinate expanded

4219124   C₆H₇NO₂   1887

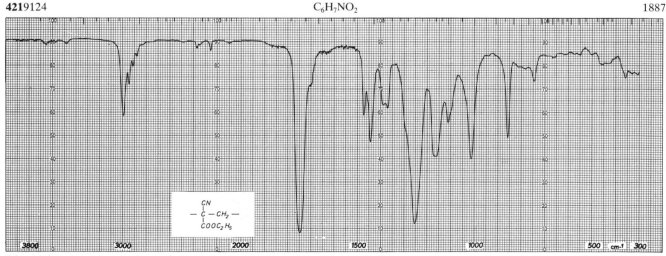

(1) poly(ethylcyanoacrylate), poly(1-cyano-1-ethoxycarbonyl-
 ethylene)
(2) white powder
(3) D.S. Johnston, Chemical Laboratory, Trinity College, Dublin
(5) zwitterionic polymerization of ethylcyanoacrylate with

triethylphosphine or pyridine in tetrahydrofuran
(6) D.S. Johnston, D.C. Pepper, IUPAC Macro, Dublin 1977,
 Proceedings 121...7
(7) film from CHCl₃ on CsI

4219124 $C_8H_{11}NO_2$ 1888

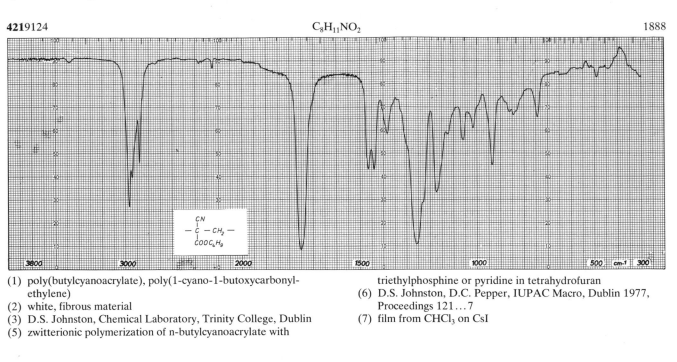

(1) poly(butylcyanoacrylate), poly(1-cyano-1-butoxycarbonyl-ethylene)
(2) white, fibrous material
(3) D.S. Johnston, Chemical Laboratory, Trinity College, Dublin
(5) zwitterionic polymerization of n-butylcyanoacrylate with triethylphosphine or pyridine in tetrahydrofuran
(6) D.S. Johnston, D.C. Pepper, IUPAC Macro, Dublin 1977, Proceedings 121...7
(7) film from $CHCl_3$ on CsI

5134 $C_{38}H_{30}I_2O_6S$ 1889

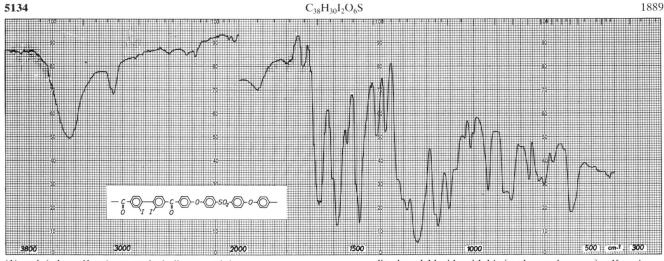

(1) poly(ethersulfone), aromatic, iodine-containing
(2) yellow-coarse powder
(3) C.S. Marvel, Department of Chemistry, College of Liberal Arts, University of Arizona, Tucson, Ariz.
(5) Friedel-Crafts polycondensation of 2,2'-diiodo-4,4'-diphenyl-dicarbonylchloride with bis (p-phenoxybenzene) sulfone in CH_2Cl_2 with $AlCl_3$ at room temperature
(6) A. Banihashemi, C.S. Marvel, IUPAC Macro, Dublin 1977, Proceedings 755...61
(7) KBr (3/350), ordinate expanded

5134 $C_{44}H_{26}I_2O_8S_2$ 1890

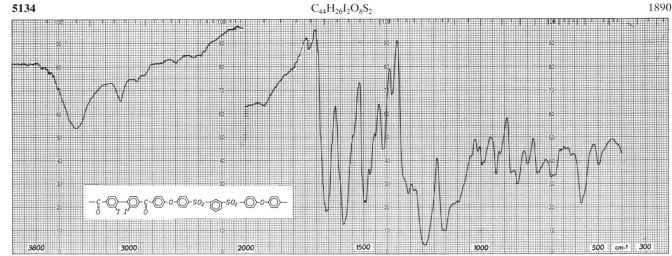

(1) poly(ethersulfone), aromatic, iodine-containing
(2) yellow-coarse powder
(3) C.S. Marvel, Department of Chemistry, College of Liberal Arts, University of Arizona, Tucson, Ariz.
(5) Friedel-Crafts polycondensation of 2,2'-diiodo-4,4'-diphenyl-dicarbonylchloride with 1,3-bis(diphenoxybenzenesulfonyl)-benzene in CH_2Cl_2 with $AlCl_3$ at room temperature
(6) A. Banihashemi, C.S. Marvel, IUPAC Macro, Dublin 1977, Proceedings 755...61
(7) KBr (3/350), ordinate expanded

5243252112 $C_{34}H_{32}N_6O_{10}S$ 1891

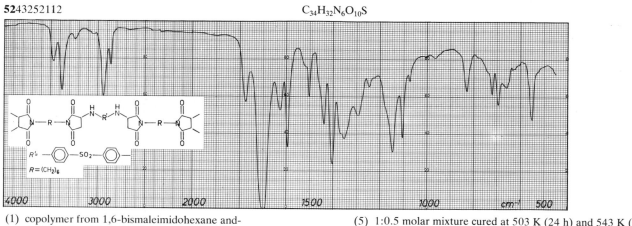

(1) copolymer from 1,6-bismaleimidohexane and-
     4,4'-diaminodiphenylsulfone
(2) brown film
(3) K. Bohle, Institut für Physikalische Chemie, Universität zu
     Köln

(5) 1:0.5 molar mixture cured at 503 K (24 h) and 543 K (1 h)
(6) K. Bohle, Dissertation, Köln 1978
(7) film between KBr wafers

72221111 DC_2H_2Cl 1892

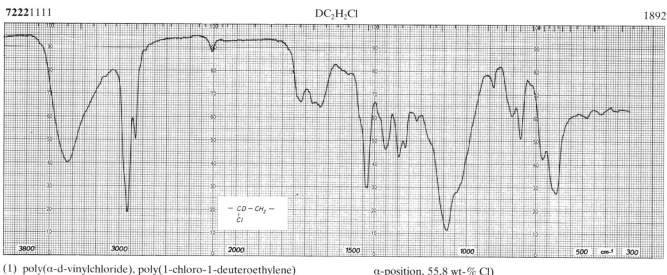

(1) poly(α-d-vinylchloride), poly(1-chloro-1-deuteroethylene)
(2) white powder
(3) M. Kolínský, Institute of Macromolecular Chemistry,
     Czechoslovac Academy of Sciences, Praha 616
(5) suspension polymerization of α-d-vinylchloride (96 wt-% D in

     α-position, 55,8 wt-% Cl)
(6) M. Kolínský, R. Lukas, IUPAC Macro, Dublin 1977 (II/27)
(7) ground with KBr (3/350) and $CHCl_3$, dried and pressed
(8) ordinate expanded

72221111 DC_2H_2Cl 1893

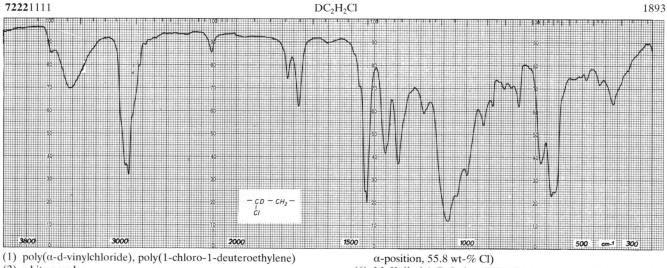

(1) poly(α-d-vinylchloride), poly(1-chloro-1-deuteroethylene)
(2) white powder
(3) M. Kolínský, Institute of Macromolecular Chemistry,
     Czechoslovac Academy of Sciences, Praha 616
(5) suspension polymerization of α-d-vinylchloride (96 wt-% D in

     α-position, 55.8 wt-% Cl)
(6) M. Kolínský, R. Lukas, IUPAC Macro, Dublin 1977 (II/27)
(7) film from tetrahydrofuran on CsI
(8) bands at 1777 and 1729 cm^{-1} due to an oxidation product
     (from the peroxides in THF)

72221111   DC$_2$H$_2$Cl   1894

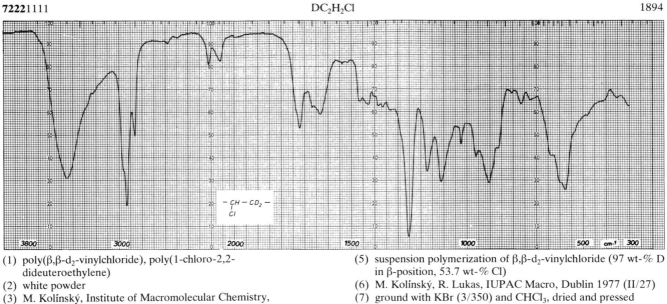

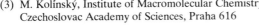

(1) poly(β,β-d$_2$-vinylchloride), poly(1-chloro-2,2-dideuteroethylene)
(2) white powder
(3) M. Kolínský, Institute of Macromolecular Chemistry, Czechoslovac Academy of Sciences, Praha 616
(5) suspension polymerization of β,β-d$_2$-vinylchloride (97 wt-% D in β-position, 53.7 wt-% Cl)
(6) M. Kolínský, R. Lukas, IUPAC Macro, Dublin 1977 (II/27)
(7) ground with KBr (3/350) and CHCl$_3$, dried and pressed

72221111   DC$_2$H$_2$Cl   1895

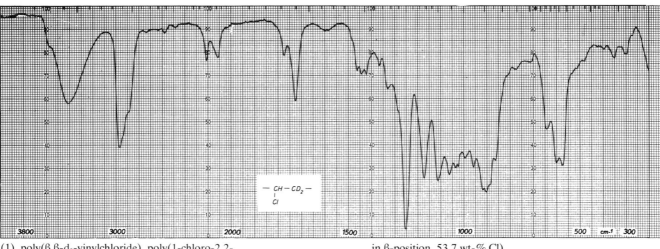

(1) poly(β,β-d$_2$-vinylchloride), poly(1-chloro-2,2-dideuteroethylene)
(2) white powder
(3) M. Kolínský, Institute of Macromolecular Chemistry, Czechoslovac Academy of Sciences, Praha 616
(5) suspension polymerization of β,β-d$_2$-vinylchloride (97 wt-% D in β-position, 53.7 wt-% Cl)
(6) M. Kolínský, R. Lukas, IUPAC Macro, Dublin 1977 (II/27)
(7) film from tetrahydrofuran on CsI
(8) bands at 1775 and 1726 cm^{-1} due to an oxidation product (from the peroxides in THF)

72221112   DC$_2$H$_2$Cl   1896

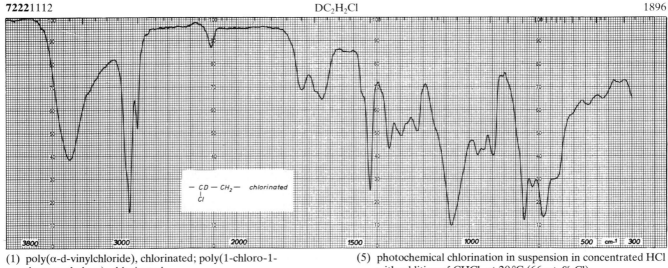

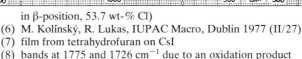

(1) poly(α-d-vinylchloride), chlorinated; poly(1-chloro-1-deuteroethylene), chlorinated
(2) white powder
(3) M. Kolínský, Institute of Macromolecular Chemistry, Czechoslovac Academy of Sciences, Praha 616
(5) photochemical chlorination in suspension in concentrated HCl with addition of CHCl$_3$ at 20 °C (66 wt-% Cl)
(6) M. Kolínský, R. Lukas, IUPAC Macro, Dublin 1977 (II/27)
(7) ground with KBr (3/350) and CHCl$_3$, dried and pressed
(8) ordinate expanded

72221112   DC$_2$H$_2$Cl

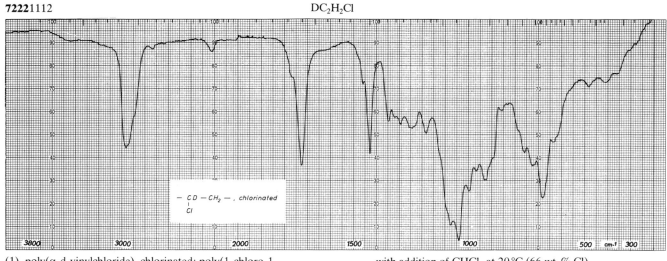

(1) poly(α-d-vinylchloride), chlorinated; poly(1-chloro-1-deuteroethylene), chlorinated

(2) white powder

(3) M. Kolínský, Institute of Macromolecular Chemistry, Czechoslovac Academy of Sciences, Praha 616

(5) photochemical chlorination in suspension in concentrated HCl

with addition of CHCl$_3$ at 20 °C (66 wt-% Cl)

(6) M. Kolínský, R. Lukas, IUPAC Macro, Dublin 1977 (II/27)

(7) film from tetrahydrofuran on CsI

(8) band at 1728 cm^{-1} due to an oxidation product (from the peroxides in THF), ordinate expanded

72221112   DC$_2$H$_2$Cl   1898

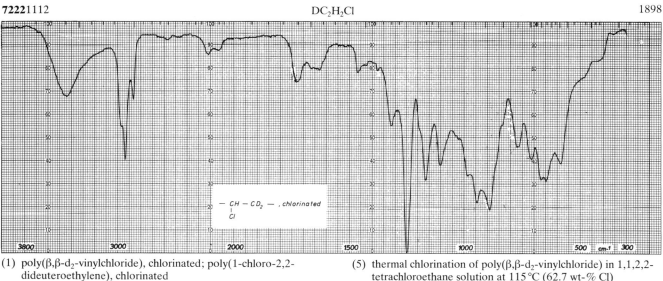

(1) poly(β,β-d$_2$-vinylchloride), chlorinated; poly(1-chloro-2,2-dideuteroethylene), chlorinated

(2) white powder

(3) M. Kolínský, Institute of Macromolecular Chemistry, Czechoslovac Academy of Sciences, Praha 616

(5) thermal chlorination of poly(β,β-d$_2$-vinylchloride) in 1,1,2,2-tetrachloroethane solution at 115 °C (62.7 wt-% Cl)

(6) M. Kolínský, R. Lukas, IUPAC Macro, Dublin 1977 (II/27)

(7) ground with KBr (3/350) and CHCl$_3$, dried and pressed

(8) ordinate expanded

72221112   DC$_2$H$_2$Cl   1899

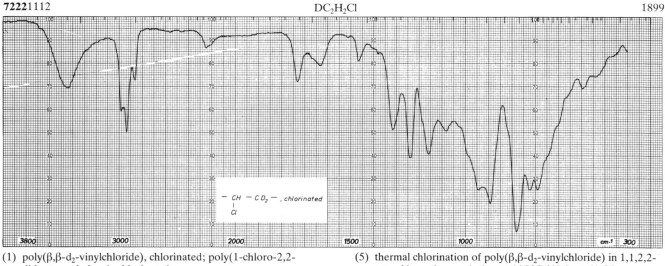

(1) poly(β,β-d$_2$-vinylchloride), chlorinated; poly(1-chloro-2,2-dideuteroethylene), chlorinated

(2) white powder

(3) M. Kolínský, Institute of Macromolecular Chemistry, Czechoslovac Academy of Sciences, Praha 616

(5) thermal chlorination of poly(β,β-d$_2$-vinylchloride) in 1,1,2,2-tetrachloroethane solution at 115 °C (69.2 wt-% Cl)

(6) M. Kolínský, R. Lukas, IUPAC Macro, Dublin 1977 (II/27)

(7) ground with KBr (3/350) and CHCl$_3$, dried and pressed

(8) ordinate expanded

72221112   DC₂H₂Cl   1900

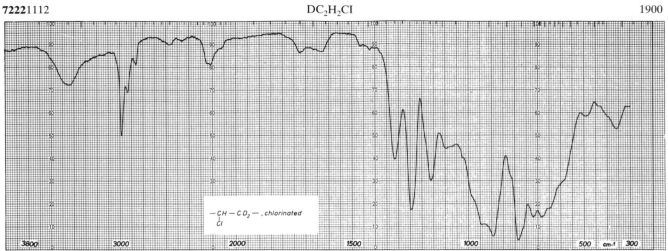

$-CH-CD_2-$, chlorinated
|
Cl

(1) poly(β,β-d₂-vinylchloride), chlorinated; poly(1-chloro-2,2-dideuteroethylene), chlorinated
(2) white powder
(3) M. Kolínský, Institute of Macromolecular Chemistry, Czechoslovac Academy of Sciences, Praha 616
(5) photochemical chlorination of poly(β,β-d₂-vinylchloride) in

suspension in concentrated HCl with addition of CHCl₃ at 20 °C (66.1 wt-% Cl)
(6) M. Kolínský, R. Lukas, IUPAC, Dublin 1977 (II/27)
(7) ground with KBr (3/350) and CHCl₃, dried and pressed
(8) ordinate expanded

72221112   DC₂H₂Cl   1901

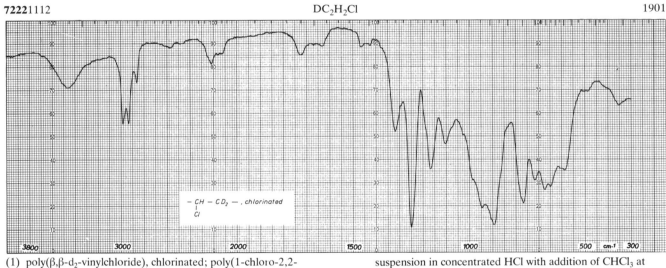

$-CH-CD_2-$, chlorinated
|
Cl

(1) poly(β,β-d₂-vinylchloride), chlorinated; poly(1-chloro-2,2-dideuteroethylene), chlorinated
(2) white powder
(3) M. Kolínský, Institute of Macromolecular Chemistry, Czechoslovac Academy of Sciences, Praha 661
(5) photochemical chlorination of poly(β,β-d₂-vinylchloride) in

suspension in concentrated HCl with addition of CHCl₃ at 20 °C (66.1 wt-% Cl)
(6) M. Kolínský, R. Lukas, IUPAC Macro, Dublin 1977 (II/27)
(7) ground with KBr (3/350) and CHCl₃, dried and pressed
(8) ordinate expanded

81311   B₁₀C₂₈H₂₈N₂O₃   1902

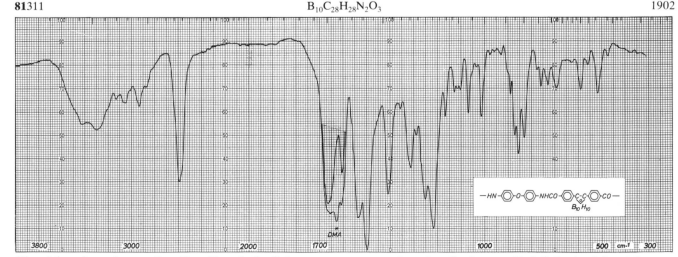

(1) poly(o-carborane), aromatic, with amido and ether links; poly(imino-1,4-phenyleneoxy-1,4-phenyleneiminocarbonyl-1,4-phenylene-o-carboranylene-1,4-phenylenecarbonyl
(2) white, fibrous material
(3) P. Valetskii, Institute for Organo-element Compounds, Academy of Sciences, USSR, Moscow
(5) polycondensation of the acid chloride of 1,2-bis(4-

carboxyphenyl)carborane with 4,4'-diaminodiphenylether
(6) V.V. Korshak, P.M. Valetskii, L.A. Glivka, S.V. Vinogradova, N.S. Titova, V.I. Stanko, Vysokomol. soyed. *A 14* (1972) 1034...47
(7) ground with KBr (1/350) and dimethylacetamide, dried (4 h at 40 °C i.V.) and pressed

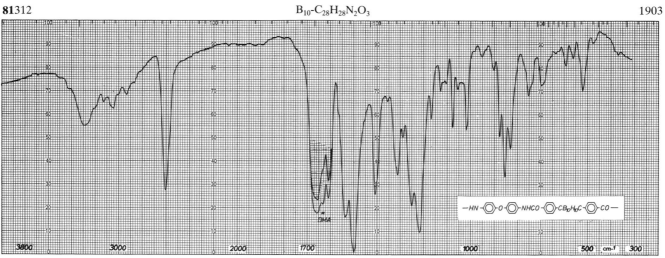

(1) poly(m-carborane), aromatic, with amido and ether links; poly(imino-1,4-phenylene-oxy-1,4-phenyleneiminocarbonyl-1,4-phenylene-m-carboranylene-1,4-phenylenecarbonyl)

(2) white, fibrous material

(3) P. Valetskii, Institute for Organo-element Compounds, Academy of Sciences, USSR, Moscow

(5) polycondensation of the acid chloride of 1,7-bis(p-carboxyphenyl)carborane with 4,4'-diaminodiphenylether

(6) P.M. Valetskii, L.A. Glivka, L.V. Dubrovina, S.A. Vinogradova, V.G. Danilov, V.I. Stanko, V.V. Korshak, Vysokomol. Soyed. *A 15* (1973) 1227...33

(7) ground with KBr (1/350) and dimethylacetamide, dried (4 h at 40 °C i.V.) and pressed

Index

Alphabetic Index of Compounds and Spectra
of Monomeric Units in Polymers and Copolymers*

639

*Note: *ethene, propene* denote the olefinic monomers, and *ethylene, propylene* the saturated units in polymers.

641

polyamide

from benzidine and 1,3-quadratic acid *415*

from 1,3-di-(4-piperidyl)-propylene and terephthalic acid *410*

from 1,10-diaminodecane and 1,2-quadratic acid *414*

from 1,10-diaminodecane and 1,3-quadratic acid *414*

from 4,4'-diaminodiphenylmethane and diphenylsilanediol *573*

from N,N'-dimethyl-1,6-diaminohexane and 1,2-quadratic acid *413*

from 2,4-diphenyl-1,3-dicarboxy-cyclobutane and 1,2-bis(methylamino)ethane *394*

from 4,4'-dipiperidyl and 4,4'-dicarboxydiphenylene *412*

from 4,4'-dipiperidyl and naphthalene-2,6-dicarbocylic acid *413*

from 1,3-di(piperidylpropane) and naphthalene-2,6-dicarboxylic acid *413*

from 1,3-di(4-piperidyl)propane and 4,4'-dicarboxydiphenylene *412*

from 1,2-ethylene-di(4,4'-piperidyl) and naphthaline-2,6-dicarboxylic acid *411*

with phenoxthine-S-dioxide ring system *556*

from m-phenylenediamine and bis(p-carboxyphenyl)diphenylsilane *571*

from p-phenylenediamine with bis(p-carboxyphenyl)diphenylsilane *571*

from piperazine and 2,4-diphenyl-1,3-dicarboxycyclobutane *410*

from 1,3-quadratic acid and piperazine *415*

from tetramethylenediamine and 2,4-diphenyl-1,3-dicarboxy-cyclobutane *394*

poly

amides with additional hetero groups *376 – 379, 400 – 410*

amides with cyclic imino groups *411 – 413*

amides of hydrazin and its derivatives *424 – 428*

amides of the quadratic acids *413 – 415*

amides type x
aliphatic *352 – 375*

aliphatic-aromatic *375 – 376, 394 – 397*

amides type xy
aliphatic *380 – 393*

amidoacid-amide *406*

amidoamine *493*

amidoaminoether with triazole ring system *494*

amidocarboxylic acid on the basis of pyromellitic anhydride and benzidine *406*

amidocarboxylic acid with ether and sulfo bridges *553, 554*

amidoether, aromatic *624*

amidoether, aromatic-aliphatic *401*

poly

amidoether, aromatic with triptycene units *404*

amidoether, chlorinated *533*

amidoether with hydantoin ring system *504*

amidoether with triazole ring system *493, 494*

amidoetherquinazolone *405*

amidoethertriazole *400, 404*

amidoimide *483*

amidoimidoethersulfone, aromatic *548*

amidoimidosulfone, aromatic *546, 547*

amidosulfone *543*

amidosulfonic acid, aromatic *544*

amidothioether *541*

amine, aromatic-cycloaliphatic quinolone *514*

amines
aliphatic *116 – 117*

aromatic-aliphatic *123 – 124, 397 – 393*

aminoamidocarboxylic acid, aromatic *377*

1-aminocarbonyl-ethylene *415*

1-(4-aminocarbonyl-phenylene)ethylene *416*

(3-amino-13-chloro-5,8,17,18-tetra-hydro-5,18-dioxonaphtho[2,3-f]pyrazino-[2,3-b:5,6-g']diquinoxaline-4,12-diyl)imino *533*

bis(4-aminocyclohexyl)methane-dodecanedioic amide *390*

1-aminoethylene *116*

1-aminoethylene hydrochloride *117*

1,2-bis(4-aminomethylcyclohexyl)-ethane-adipamide *390*

1,2-bis(4-aminomethylcyclohexyl)-ethane-adipamide *389*

(-)-s-β-aminopentanoic acid *372*

2-[4'-(p-aminophenoxy)-phenyl]-4-(p-aminophenyl)-thiazole-(1,3)-terephthalamide *553*

4,4'-bis(4-aminophenyl)-2,2'-bithiazole isophthalamide *550*

bis(4-aminophenylene)methylene-s-triazinone *505*

1-(m-aminophenyl)ethylene *123*

m-aminostyrene *123*

amylose, etherified with benzylchloride *174*

anhydrides *302 – 304*

5,6-anhydro-1,2-O-isopropylidene-α-D-glucofuranose *617*

anthracene *78*

arylene sulfide *621*

arylenecyclotriphosphazene amide *592*

arylenesulfone ether *524*

arylenesulfone ethers *523 – 525*

poly

aspartimide *475*

1-aza-2-methyl-4-oxo-tetramethylene *369*

azi-decazamer-alt-quadratyl(1,2)amer *414*

azi-diphenylene(4,4')azamer-alt-quadratyl(1,3)amer *415*

aziridinyl maleimide *474*

azo-1,4-phenylenevinylene-1,4-phenylene *613*

azomethine from 2,5-diamino-3,4-dicyanothiophene and thiophene-2,5-dicarbaldehyde *516*

benzimidazol *129, 137 – 140*

benzimidazol-triazol-benzimidazol *499*

benzophenone-3,3'-disulfonyloxy-1,4-phenylene-2,2-dimethyl-1,4-phenylene *529*

benzoxazinedione *506, 507, 508*

benzoxazinone with ether and sulfone bridges *555, 556*

benzoxazole-imide *485*

N-benzoyl-r-2-ethylethyleneimine *428*

N-benzoyl-3-ethyl-iminoethylene *428*

o-benzyl *49*

γ-benzyl-L-glutamate *375*

benzylacrylate *263*

benzylmethacrylate *284*

beryllium-di-n-butylphosphinate *603*

p-biphenylacrylate *266*

p-biphenylmethacrylate *286*

o-biphenylmethacrylate *286*

4,4'-biphenylsulfone with chlorinated alkyl bridges *536*

3,3-bischloromethyl-oxatetra-methylene, phenoxylated *334, 335*

bischloromethyloxacyclotetramethane *335*

bismaleimides *465 – 470*

1,12-bismaleimidododecane *467*

4,4'-bismaleimidodiphenylether *625*

4,4'-bismaleimidodiphenylmethane *469, 625*

1,6-bismaleimidohexane *624*

2,4-bismaleimidotoluene *467*

1,6-bismaleimido(2,2,4/2,4,4-trimethyl-hexane *467*

bisphenol A-diphenylsulfone ether *523*

bisphenol A-sebacate *235*

bisphenol A-1,3-phenylenesulfonate *528*

bromoesters *346 – 347*

bromoether *346*

bromohydrocarbons *110*

1-(o-bromophenyl)ethylene *110*

o-bromostyrene *110*

ω-bromoundecylacrylate *346*

ω-bromoundecylmethacrylate *346*

but-2-enesulfone *522*

cis-but-2-enylene-alt-trans-but-2-enylene *29*

643

645

649

Formula Index of Monomeric Units in Polymers and Copolymers*

657

*The formulae are arranged in alphabetic order with increasing number of C atoms, followed by increasing numbers of the other atoms. Within one formula CHHal (XYZ), the sequence of halogens is the chemical one. Deuterated polymers, hetero-atom polymers and metal-organic polymers are collected on p. 663

Author Index